D1360850

WITHDRAWN FROM
U MASS LOWELL
LIBRARIES

ITALIAN PHYSICAL SOCIETY

PROCEEDINGS

OF THE

INTERNATIONAL SCHOOL OF PHYSICS « ENRICO FERMI »

COURSE XXXVI

edited by C. BLOCH
Director of the Course

VARENNA ON LAKE COMO
VILLA MONASTERO
26th JULY - 14th AUGUST 1965

Many-Body Description of Nuclear Structure and Reactions

1966

ACADEMIC PRESS • NEW YORK AND LONDON

SOCIETÀ ITALIANA DI FISICA

RENDICONTI
DELLA
SCUOLA INTERNAZIONALE DI FISICA «ENRICO FERMI»

XXXVI CORSO

a cura di C. BLOCH
Direttore del Corso

VARENNA SUL LAGO DI COMO
VILLA MONASTERO
26 LUGLIO - 14 AGOSTO 1965

Struttura e reazioni nucleari nella teoria dei molti corpi

1966

53446

AP

ACADEMIC PRESS • NEW YORK AND LONDON

ACADEMIC PRESS INC.
111 Fifth Avenue
New York 3, N. Y.

United Kingdom Edition
Published by
ACADEMIC PRESS INC. (London) Ltd.
Berkeley Square House, London W. 1

Copyright © 1966, by Società Italiana di Fisica

ALL RIGHTS RESERVED

NO PART OF THIS BOOK MAY BE REPRODUCED IN ANY FORM,
BY PHOTOSTAT, MICROFILM, OR ANY OTHER MEANS,
WITHOUT WRITTEN PERMISSION FROM THE PUBLISHERS.

Library of Congress Catalog Card Number: 66-14729

PRINTED IN ITALY

INDICE

V. Gillet – Approximate methods in nuclear-structure calculations.

Foreword.

C. Bloch

Centre d'Etudes Nucléaires de Saclay
Service de Physique Théorique - Gif-sur-Yvette

The title of this Course may require some explanation. How could nuclear structure and reaction theory not be treated as a many-body problem? What is meant is actually a question of point of view and emphasis. In the study of nuclei many models have been devised to explain particular features. These models do not enter the full complexity of the nuclear many-body problem. Their remarkable property, on the contrary, is to emphasize only whichever aspect of nuclear structure is most relevant in a particular situation. In this fashion it has often been possible to obtain remarkable agreement with experiments by means of very simple models.

This, however, is only part of the game. The theory of nuclei should be able to explain all nuclear properties starting from the Schrödinger equation and the nucleon-nucleon interaction. This much more ambitious program was actually started long ago, really in the first days of nuclear physics. In the past few years, however, tremendous progress has been achieved in that direction. One actually gets the impression that we are now in possession of the proper tools but that we are still extremely far from having exploited them to their full possibilities. It is that particular point of view which is the object of this Course. Consequently there will be no discussion, for instance, of the fundamental Copenhagen model of collective motions, except to discuss its foundation from a many-body point of view, and many other extremely important aspects of nuclear structure or reactions will be totally omitted, simply because the many-body theory has not much to say about them, for the time being.

Of course, one should not conclude that simple models have completely lost their interest. In fact, in many respects, simple models are badly needed. This is because, although we may have a general scheme which in principle, with sufficient numerical work, should account for the observed experimental results, in practice the actual calculations are often too complicated to be carried out with their full complexity. Simple models may then serve as guide to a selection of the most important features of the problem. Simple models, however, should no longer be considered for their own sake, as in the early days, but essentially as complements to the more basic theory.

The basic concepts of the many-body theory will be recalled by Drs. GILLET and ELLIOTT. These lectures will also give a report on the situation of numerical results (V. GILLET) and analytically soluble models (J. P. ELLIOTT).

Dr. F. VILLARS will develop his recent work on one of the least satisfactory points in the basis of the theory, namely the systematic treatment of deformed nuclei from a many-body point of view.

When there are many nucleons off closed shells, pedestrian methods of calculation become useless; Dr. J. B. FRENCH will develop the more fancy techniques which become necessary in such cases.

The problem of clustering in nuclei dealt with by Dr. BRINK rests perhaps on less solid ground than the subjects of the previous lecturers. This question has been under discussion for a long time, and it has not been clear whether there is a cluster structure or not. Of course ^{8}Be certainly has a 2α-particle structure, but the question is how important is this aspect of the wave function in other nuclei.

Dr. MIGDAL will bring a rather new approach based on the application of Landau's theory of Fermi liquids to nuclei. It is somewhat opposite, or rather complementary to the point of view used by most western nuclear theoreticians, and the comparison of these approaches should bring about interesting discussions.

Finally I shall try to tell you about, perhaps the most recent direction taken by the many-body study of nuclei: the theory of nuclear reactions. There are still few actual results, and most workers are still in the process of defining the proper formalism. This explains the large number of formal work done on this line. I shall not attempt to discuss it all, but rather try to give you as simple and straightforward a presentation as I can.

I would like to express my thanks to the lecturers, particularly for their effort in making the courses understandable even by a nonspecialist in the field. I am also very grateful to the authors of seminars for complementing the lectures by reports on their current work. Last, but not least, I am particularly indebted to the Secretary of the School Dr. R. RICCI for his untiring and efficient help in the preparation as well as the running of the School.

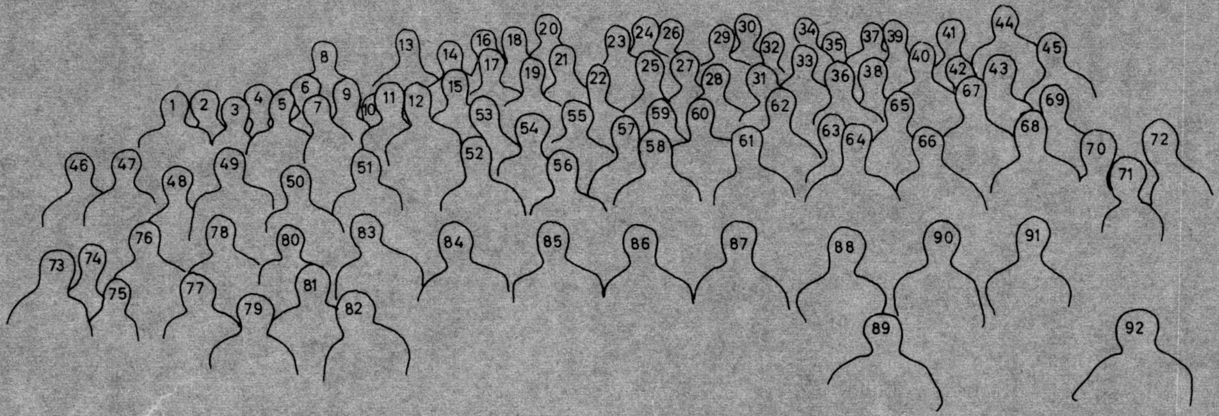

1. M. Grypeos
2. G. Berthier
3. L. Grünbaum
4. J.-C. Hocquenghem
5. N. K. Ganguly
6. J. Pradal
7. J.-C. Faivre
8. F. Miglietta
9. A. Ritcher
10. P. Van Leuven
11. H. Guttfreund
12. G. Schiffrer
13. P. R. Maurenzig
14. J. Revai
15. A. Sourriaux
16. P. Quarati
17. I. Da Providencia
18. G. Ponzano
19. G. Ciocchetti
20. M. Rosina
21. M. Vijicic
22. R. Lombard
23. J. Picard
24. E. Ostgaard
25. W. Hermans
26. M. Di Toro
27. F. Herbut
28. V. Lopac-Dugi
29. J. Krumlinde
30. C. J. Veje
31. C. Quesne
32. M. Marangoni
33. P. Camiz
34. G. Wiechers
35. A. M. Saruis
36. De Raedt
37. K. Johansson
38. S. C. K. Nair
39. E. Clementel
40. I. Brandus
41. D. Vautherin
42. P. Lipnik
43. F. Krmpotić
44. R. Leonardi
45. J. E. Blomqvist
46. Z. Pluhar
47. F. Zardi
48. M. R. Bhagavan
49. C. Mahaux
50. N. Van Sen
51. L. J. Wiegert
52. O. Kaalhus
53. R. Potenza
54. B. Koltary Gyarmati
55. N. Rosenzweig
56. L. Grenacs
57. M. A. Melkanoff
58. G. Pisent
59. A. Messiah
60. V. Ardente
61. M. Savoia
62. A. Sandulescu
63. N. Van Giai
64. E. Verondini
65. O. Bohigas
66. G. Ricco
67. E. Brezin
68. M. Bouten
69. H. G. Wahsweiler
70. K. Bleuler
71. E. Hayward
72. Schütte
73. G. Germanà
74. Brown
75. F. Saya
76. N. Auerbach
77. G. E. Fimov
78. J. Bar-Touv
79. G. Campagnoli
80. P. J. Feibelman
81. A. Molinari
82. M. Chemtob
83. S. Harar
84. J. B. French
85. F. Villars
86. A. B. Migdal
87. C. Bloch
88. R. Ricci
89. Oberlechner
90. J. P. Elliott
91. D. Brink
92. V. Gillet

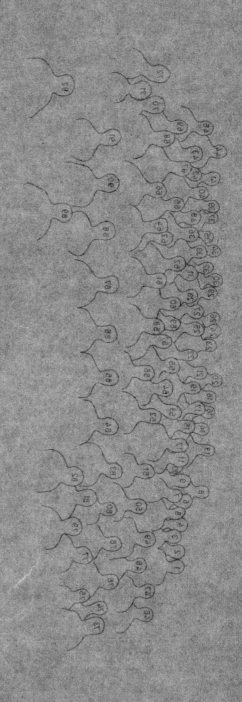

SOCIETÀ ITALIANA DI FISICA

SCUOLA INTERNAZIONALE DI FISICA « E. FERMI »

XXXVI CORSO - VARENNA SUL LAGO DI COMO - VILLA MONASTERO - 26 Luglio - 14 Agosto 1965

Introduction to the Hartree-Fock Formalism.

F. VILLARS
Massachusetts Institute of Technology - Cambridge, Mass.

Introduction.

The Hartree-Fock (H.F.) method, applied to systems of A identical fermions, is a variational principle destined to find the « best » wave functions of the form of an antisymmetrized product of one-particle wave functions.

It is therefore the basic tool to establish the independent-particle approximation in the description of nuclear states.

These lectures concern themselves with a brief derivation of the H.F. equations, and a discussion of the properties of its solutions.

1. – Notation.

The Hamiltonian of a system of A nucleons is

$$H = \sum_{i=1}^{A} T_i + \sum_{i<j}^{A} V_{ij}\,, \tag{1}$$

where $T = p^2/2m$ is the kinetic energy. Only two-body interactions V_{ij} are assumed here, but the method is easily extended to many-body forces.

Let $\varphi_\alpha(i)$ be a complete, orthonormal basis of one-particle wave functions. i stands for $\boldsymbol{x}_i$, s_i, t_i: position, spin and isospin; similarly we use

$$\int \mathrm{d}\tau_i \equiv \int \mathrm{d}\boldsymbol{x}_i \sum_{s_i} \sum_{t_i}$$

to indicate integration over space and summation over spin-isospin. The properties of $\varphi_\alpha(i)$ are then

$$\int d\tau_i \varphi^*_\alpha(i)\varphi_\beta(i) = \delta_{\alpha\beta}\,, \tag{2a}$$

$$\sum_\alpha \varphi_\alpha(i)\varphi^*_\alpha(j) = \delta(i, j)\,. \tag{2b}$$

Trial functions $\Phi(1, 2, ..., A)$ are constructed by means of A orthogonal one-particle functions $\psi_\lambda(i)$, $(\lambda = 1, ..., A;\ i = 1, ..., A)$, which are suitable linear combinations of the φ_α and have the form

$$\Phi(1, 2, ..., A) = (A\,!)^{-\frac{1}{2}} \sum_p \text{sign}\,(p)\,\psi_1(1p)\,\psi_2(2p) \ldots \psi_A(Ap)\,, \tag{3}$$

$$= (A\,!)^{-\frac{1}{2}} \det|\psi_\lambda(i)|\,. \tag{3d}$$

$(1p, 2p \ldots Ap)$ is a permutation of $1, 2, ..., A$, and sign $(p) = \pm 1$. Φ is normalized to 1, if the ψ_λ are.

2. – Statement of the problem.

Find a set of A functions $\psi_\lambda(i)$ with the property that

$$\langle H\rangle = \int \prod_{i=1}^{A} d\tau_i\, \Phi^* H \Phi \tag{4}$$

is *stationary* with respect to a variation of the individual ψ_λ. Since H contains only one- and two-body operators, $\langle H\rangle$ can be expressed in terms of the *density-matrices*:

$$\varrho(1; 1') = A\int d\tau_2 \ldots d\tau_A \Phi(1, 2, ..., A)\,\Phi^*(1', 2, ..., A) = \sum_{\lambda=1}^{A} \psi_\lambda(1)\,\psi^*_\lambda(1') \tag{5}$$

and

$$\begin{cases} \varrho(1\,2; 1'2') = A(A-1)\int d\tau_3 \ldots d\tau_A \Phi(1\,2\,3 \ldots A)\,\Phi^*(1'2'3 \ldots A) = \\ \qquad = \varrho(1; 1')\,\varrho(2; 2') - \varrho(1; 2')\,\varrho(2; 1')\,. \end{cases} \tag{6}$$

The second line of (6) expresses the structure of Φ as an antisymmetrized product wave function.

The one-body density matrix has the properties

$$\int d\tau''_1\, \varrho(1; 1'')\,\varrho(1''; 1') = \varrho(1; 1')\,, \qquad \text{in short } \varrho^2 = \varrho \tag{7}$$

and

(8) $$\int d\tau_1 \varrho(1;1) = A\,, \qquad \text{in short Tr } \varrho = A\,.$$

(In the future, ϱ will always refer to $\varrho(1;1')$.)

We shall also use the *transformed* density matrices

(9) $$\varrho_{\alpha\beta} = \int d\tau_1\, d\tau_{1'}\, \varphi^*_\alpha(1)\, \varrho(1;1')\, \varphi_\beta(1')\,,$$

(10) $$\begin{cases} \varrho_{\alpha\beta;\,\gamma\delta} = \int d\tau_1 \ldots d\tau_{2}\, \varphi^*_\alpha(1)\varphi^*_\beta(2)\varrho(12;1'2')\varphi_\gamma(1')\varphi_\delta(2') = \\ = \varrho_{\alpha\gamma}\varrho_{\beta\delta} - \varrho_{\alpha\delta}\varrho_{\beta\gamma}\,. \end{cases}$$

The properties (7), (8) are invariant under this transformation

(7*a*) $$\sum_\gamma \varrho_{\alpha\gamma}\varrho_{\gamma\beta} = \varrho_{\alpha\beta}\,,$$

(8*a*) $$\sum_\alpha \varrho_{\alpha\alpha} = A\,.$$

Representative terms T_1 and V_{12} in kinetic and potential energy are given by the matrices

(11) $$(1|t|1') = (1|p^2/2m|1') = -\frac{1}{2m}\nabla^2\delta(\boldsymbol{x}_1 - \boldsymbol{x}_{1'})\,\delta_{s_1 s_{1'}}\,\delta_{t_1 t_{1'}}$$

and $(12|v|1'2')$; this latter may represent a local or nonlocal interaction; we shall however assume both translation and Galilean invariance, implying that V_{12} commutes with both $\boldsymbol{x}_1 + \boldsymbol{x}_2$ and $\boldsymbol{p}_1 + \boldsymbol{p}_2$.

We shall also use the transformed of these matrices:

(12) $$t_{\alpha\beta} = \int d\tau_1\, d\tau_{1'}\, \varphi^*_\alpha(1)\,(1|t|1')\,\varphi_\beta(1')$$

and

(13) $$v_{\alpha\beta;\,\gamma\delta} = \int d\tau_1 \ldots d\tau_{2'}\, \varphi^*_\alpha(1)\varphi^*_\beta(2)\,(1\,2|v|1'2')\,\varphi_\gamma(1')\varphi_\delta(2')\,.$$

Of the latter, only the antisymmetrized combination

(14) $$v_{\alpha\beta,\,\gamma\delta} - v_{\alpha\beta,\,\delta\gamma} \equiv v^A_{\alpha\beta;\,\gamma\delta}$$

will actually occur.

The expectation value $\langle H\rangle$ of H with respect to Φ can now be written as

$$(15)\quad \begin{cases} \langle H\rangle = \int (1|t|1')\varrho(1';1) + \frac{1}{2}\int (1\,2|v|1'2')\big(\varrho(1',1)\varrho(2',2) - \varrho(1',2)\varrho(2',1)\big) = \\ \quad = \sum t_{\alpha\beta}\varrho_{\beta\alpha} + \frac{1}{2}\sum v^{A}_{\alpha\beta;\gamma\delta}\varrho_{\gamma\alpha}\varrho_{\delta\beta}\,. \end{cases}$$

A variation of $\langle H\rangle$ is then induced by a variation of ϱ, and the problem is to find a $\varrho^{(0)}$ such that $\delta\langle H\rangle = 0$ to first order in a variation $\varrho = \varrho^{(0)} + \delta\varrho$

3. – Variational principle and H.F. equations.

Let $\varrho^{(0)}$ be the density matrix which provides a stationary $\langle H\rangle$. A variation may thus be described by

$$(16)\qquad \varrho = \varrho^{(0)} + \lambda\varrho^{(1)} + \lambda^2\varrho^{(2)} + \dots,$$

λ being a small parameter. As $\varrho^{(0)}$ satisfies eqs. (7) and (8), one has

— to $O(\lambda)$:

$$(17)\qquad \operatorname{Tr}\,\varrho_1 = 0\,,\qquad \varrho_0\varrho_1 + \varrho_1\varrho_0 = \varrho_1\,,$$

— to $O(\lambda^2)$:

$$(18)\qquad \operatorname{Tr}\,\varrho_2 = 0\,,\qquad \varrho_0\varrho_2 + \varrho_2\varrho_0 + \varrho_1^2 = \varrho_2\,.$$

These equations are most easily exploited in a representation where $\varrho^{(0)}$ is *diagonal*. With eqs. (5) and (9) this means that the A functions ψ_λ are all linear combinations of A functions φ_α. Because of (7), (8), a diagonal $\varrho^{(0)}$ has the form

$$(19)\qquad \varrho^{(0)}_{\alpha\beta} = \delta_{\alpha\beta}\times\begin{cases} 1 & \alpha,\beta \leqslant A \quad \text{use } \lambda,\mu \text{ for such indices,} \\ 0 & \alpha,\beta > A \quad \text{use } \sigma,\tau \text{ for such indices.} \end{cases}$$

Equations (17) then indicate

$$(20a)\qquad \varrho^{(1)}_{\lambda\mu} = \varrho^{(1)}_{\sigma\tau} = 0 \qquad \left.\begin{matrix}\varrho^{(1)}_{\sigma\mu}\\ \varrho^{(1)}_{\mu\sigma}\end{matrix}\right\}\text{ arbitrary},$$

and eqs. (18) give

$$(20b)\qquad \begin{cases} \varrho^{(2)}_{\sigma\mu} = 0\,, & \varrho^{(2)}_{\lambda\mu} = -\sum_\sigma \varrho^{(1)}_{\lambda\sigma}\varrho^{(1)}_{\sigma\mu}\,, \\ \varrho^{(2)}_{\mu\sigma} = 0\,, & \varrho^{(2)}_{\sigma\tau} = +\sum_\lambda \varrho^{(1)}_{\sigma\lambda}\varrho^{(1)}_{\lambda\tau}\,. \end{cases}$$

We now impose that $\delta\langle H\rangle = 0 + O(\lambda^2)$. Now to order λ, one has

$$\delta\langle H\rangle = \sum_{\mu\sigma} \left(\mathscr{H}(\varrho^0)_{\mu\sigma}\,\varrho^{(1)}_{\sigma\mu} + \mathscr{H}(\varrho^0)_{\sigma\mu}\,\varrho^{(1)}_{\mu\sigma}\right) = 0 \tag{21}$$

where $\mathscr{H}(\varrho^0)$ is a new particle operator defined by

$$\begin{cases} \mathscr{H}(\varrho^0)_{\alpha\beta} = t_{\alpha\beta} + \sum\limits_{\gamma\delta} v^A_{\alpha\gamma;\,\beta\delta}\,\overset{0}{\varrho}_{\delta\gamma} = \\ \qquad = t_{\alpha\beta} + \sum\limits_{\mu=1} v^A_{\alpha\mu;\,\beta\mu}\,. \end{cases} \tag{22}$$

To derive (21), one has made use of an obvious symmetry property of V: $v^A_{\alpha\beta;\,\gamma\delta} = v^A_{\beta\alpha;\,\delta\gamma}$, and in the second line of (22) one has used the diagonal form of ϱ^0, eq. (19). Equation (21) now gives

$$\mathscr{H}(\varrho^0)_{\mu\sigma} = \mathscr{H}(\varrho^0)_{\sigma\mu} = 0\,. \tag{22a}$$

Let us represent this graphically

$$\left(\begin{array}{c|c} \mathscr{H}(\varrho^0)_{\mu\mu'} & \mathscr{H}_{\mu\sigma} = 0 \\ \hline \mathscr{H}_{\sigma'\mu'} = 0 & \mathscr{H}_{\sigma\sigma'} \end{array}\right) \qquad \left(\begin{array}{cccc|c} 1 & & & & \\ & 1 & & & 0 \\ & & 1 & & \\ & & & 1 & \\ \hline & & 0 & & 0 \end{array}\right)$$

Matrix $\mathscr{H}_{\alpha\beta}(\varrho^0)$ Matrix $\overset{0}{\varrho}_{\alpha\beta}$.

In this representation, the condition $\delta\langle H\rangle \sim O(\lambda^2)$ expresses itself in the property that $\mathscr{H}(\varrho^0)$ and ϱ^0 *commute*

$$[\mathscr{H}(\varrho^0), \varrho^0] = 0\,. \tag{23}$$

This condition does not uniquely specify the ψ_λ used in constructing the trial function Φ. Φ is in fact *invariant* under a unitary transformation of the $\mathscr{A}$ functions ψ_λ among themselves.

We can now specify a *complete set* of functions ψ_α (the first A of which determine Φ) such as to make both ϱ^0 and $\mathscr{H}(\varrho^0)$ diagonal:

$$\mathscr{H}(\varrho^0)_{\alpha\beta} = \varepsilon_\alpha \delta_{\alpha\beta}\,, \tag{24}$$

$$\varrho^{(0)}_{\alpha\beta} = \delta_{\alpha\beta} \times \begin{cases} 1 & \alpha, \beta \leqslant A\,, \\ 0 & \alpha, \beta > A\,. \end{cases} \tag{25}$$

Equation (24) gives

(26) $$t_{\alpha\beta}+\sum_{\mu=1}^{A} v^{A}_{\alpha\mu,\,\beta\mu}=\varepsilon_\alpha\delta_{\alpha\beta}\,.$$

These are the H.F. equations. They may be transformed into a co-ordinate representation

(26a) $$\int \mathrm{d}\tau_{1'}(1|\mathscr{H}|1')\,\psi_\alpha(1')=\varepsilon_\alpha\psi_\alpha(1)\,,$$

where

$$(1|\mathscr{H}|1')=(1|t|1')+\int \mathrm{d}\tau_2\,\mathrm{d}\tau_{2'}\big((1\,2|v|1'2')-(1\,2|v|2'1')\big)\,\varrho^{(0)}(2',2)$$

and

(27) $$\varrho^{(0)}(2',2)=\sum_{\mu=1}^{A}\psi_\mu(2')\,\psi^*_\mu(2)\,.$$

This last form emphasizes the nonlinearity of the problem; a self-consistent solution requires that the eigenfunctions of $\mathscr{H}$ contain the set of A functions ψ_μ which determine $\mathscr{H}$. We will discuss now some of the properties of the H.F. equation and of their solutions.

3·1. *Self-consistent potential well; constants of motion.* – The self-consistent operator $\mathscr{H}(\varrho^{(0)})$ is the sum of a kinetic and potential energy

(28) $$\mathscr{H}=p^2/2m+U\,.$$

U is a nonlocal potential:

(29) $$(1|U|1')=\int\big[(1\,2|v|1'2')-(1\,2|v|2'1')\big]\,\varrho^{(0)}(2',2)\,\mathrm{d}\tau_2\,\mathrm{d}\tau_{2'}\,.$$

To exploit the attraction of nucleons, the particles must be localized relative to each other. In the approximation admitted by the structure of Φ, this is only possible by localizing them relative to an arbitrary, but fixed point in space.

Conventionally, we choose the center of mass of $\varrho^{(0)}$ as the co-ordinate origin.

For any constant of motion $F=\sum_i f_i$, f will commute with $\mathscr{H}$ if it does with $\varrho^{(0)}$.

This is clearly not the case for $F=P$, the total linear momentum. The Φ are therefore not momentum eigenfunctions, but we have $\langle P\rangle=0$ since $P=M\dot{x}$ and the expectation value of any time derivative is zero.

$\mathscr{H}$ will in general *not* commute with the angular momentum $\boldsymbol{j}$ either. Indeed assume it did. We have then eigenfunctions ψ_{njm} of $\mathscr{H}$, and $\varrho^{(0)}$ will be of the form

$$\varrho^{(0)}(1,1') = \sum_{njm} \psi_{njm}(1)\,\psi^*_{njm}(1')\,. \tag{30}$$

This commutes with $\boldsymbol{j}$ only if for any $n\,j$ present in (30), *all* $(2j+1)$ m-values occur. This is a closed shell, and Φ has $J=0$. In all other cases, $\varrho^{(0)}$ is not a scalar, and defines an *anisotropic* well U.

The degeneracy of the H.F. problem, rooted in the arbitrariness of the localization of $\varrho^{(0)}$ in space, and of the orientation of its symmetry axes, is exploited in the theory of collective excitations.

We remark that it is always *compatible* with self-consistency that the potential well U (or $\varrho^{(0)}$) has

a) a definite parity,

b) axial symmetry *or* invariance under time reversal.

The two properties mentioned in *b*) may not be compatible. One must realize however, that such symmetry properties are *restrictive assumptions* on the variation of trial functions, and may *not* give the lowest value of $\langle H\rangle$.

In particular, lower values of $\langle H\rangle$ may be found with trial functions Φ that do not have definite parity, and are not eigenfunctions even of J_z.

3·2. *Stability of the variational solution.* – Assume a diagonal $\varrho^{(0)}$ for which $\delta\langle H\rangle \sim O(\lambda^2)$. The lowest nonvanishing terms are then given by

$$\delta\langle H\rangle = \sum \mathscr{H}(\varrho^{(0)})_{\alpha\beta}\,\varrho^{(2)}_{\beta\alpha} + \tfrac{1}{2}\sum v^A_{\alpha\beta;\gamma\delta}\,\varrho^{(1)}_{\gamma\alpha}\,\varrho^{(1)}_{\delta\beta}\,.$$

Making use of eqs. (20), (24), (26), this may be written as

$$\begin{aligned}\delta\langle H\rangle &= \sum_\sigma \varepsilon_\sigma \varrho^{(2)}_{\sigma\sigma} + \sum_\mu \varepsilon_\mu \varrho^{(2)}_{\mu\mu} + \tfrac{1}{2}\sum v^A_{\alpha\beta;\gamma\delta}\,\varrho^{(1)}_{\gamma\alpha}\varrho^{(1)}_{\delta\beta} = \\ &= \sum_{\sigma\mu}(\varepsilon_\sigma - \varepsilon_\mu)|\varrho^{(1)}_{\sigma\mu}|^2 + \sum v^A_{\mu\tau;\sigma\nu}\,\varrho^{(1)}_{\sigma\mu}\varrho^{(1)}_{\nu\tau} + \tfrac{1}{2}\sum v^A_{\mu\nu;\sigma\tau}\,\varrho^{(1)}_{\sigma\mu}\varrho^{(1)}_{\tau\nu} + \tfrac{1}{2}\sum v^A_{\sigma\tau;\mu\nu}\,\varrho^{(1)}_{\mu\sigma}\varrho^{(1)}_{\nu\tau}\,.\end{aligned} \tag{31}$$

For the trial solution to produce a (relative) minimum of $\langle H\rangle$ eq. (31) should represent a positive quadratic form. We show that this property does not hold in general.

To see it, let $F = \sum f_i$ be any one-particle operator, and define a variation of $\varrho^{(0)}$ by

$$\varrho = \exp[i\varepsilon f]\,\varrho^{(0)}\exp[-i\varepsilon f]\,. \tag{32}$$

This corresponds to replacing the trial function Φ by $\exp[i\varepsilon F]\Phi$ and to change $\langle H\rangle$ into

$$\langle\exp[-i\varepsilon F]H\exp[i\varepsilon F]\rangle = \langle H\rangle + i\varepsilon\langle[H,F]\rangle + \frac{(i\varepsilon)^2}{2!}\langle[[H,F],F]\rangle + \dots . \tag{33}$$

Clearly, if F is a constant of the motion, $[H,F]=0$ and $\delta\langle H\rangle = 0$ to order ε^2 included.

Assuming Φ is not an eigenfunction of F, $\exp[i\varepsilon F]\Phi$ is a new trial function that gives an energy degenerate with $\langle H\rangle$.

Such cases arise for $F=P$ (total momentum) and $F=J$ (total angular momentum).

3·3. *Variational problem with subsidiary condition.* – Let $\mathscr{G}=\sum_{i=1}^{A} g_i$ be a one-particle operator, with an expectation value $\langle\mathscr{G}\rangle_0 = g_0$.

We pose the problem of finding a self-consistent solution Φ giving a prescribed value $g\neq g_0$ of $\mathscr{G}$.

Let Φ_0 be the solution of the unrestricted variational problem for H, giving $\langle H\rangle_0 = E_0$.

The subsidiary condition leads to the variational problem for $H-\eta\mathscr{G}$, η being a Lagrange multiplier.

We reduce the problem to the previous one, by putting

$$\varrho = \exp[i\eta f]\varrho^{(0)}\exp[-i\eta f]\,, \tag{34}$$

$\varrho^{(0)}$ being the self-consistent (diagonal) density matrix for the unrestricted problem.

To this change in ϱ corresponds a change in Φ

$$\Phi = \exp[i\eta F]\Phi_0\,,\qquad F=\sum f_i\,.$$

Φ_0 must therefore be the self-consistent solution for

$$\left\{\begin{aligned}\widetilde{H} &= \exp[i\eta F](H-\eta\mathscr{G})\exp[-i\eta F]\,,\\ \widetilde{H} &= H+\eta(i[H,F]-\mathscr{G})+\dots=\\ &= H+\eta(\dot{F}-\mathscr{G})+\dots\end{aligned}\right. \tag{35}$$

The condition that $\widetilde{H}$ be stationary with respect to Φ_0 implies that

$$\widetilde{\mathscr{H}}(\varrho^{(0)})_{\mu\sigma} = \widetilde{\mathscr{H}}(\varrho^{(0)})_{\sigma\mu} = 0\,, \tag{36}$$

see eq. (22a). Since $\mathscr{H}(\varrho^{(0)})$ already satisfies this condition, there remains

(to order η)

$$(\dot{\mathscr{F}}(\varrho^{(0)}))_{\sigma\mu} = g_{\sigma\mu} ,$$

where

$$\dot{\mathscr{F}}_{\sigma\mu} \equiv i\{(\varepsilon_\sigma - \varepsilon_\mu) f_{\sigma\mu} + \sum_{\tau,\nu} v^A_{\sigma\tau,\,\mu\nu} f_{\nu\tau} - \sum_{\tau,\nu} v^A_{\sigma\nu,\tau\mu} f_{\tau\nu}\} . \tag{37}$$

The energy $E(\eta) = \langle H \rangle_\eta$ becomes (to order η^2)

$$\begin{cases} E(\eta) = \langle H + \eta \dot{F} + \frac{1}{2}\eta^2 [i\dot{F}, F] \rangle_0 = \\ \qquad = E(0) + \frac{1}{2}\eta^2 \langle i[\mathscr{G}, F] \rangle_0 . \end{cases} \tag{38}$$

η itself is determined by the equation

$$g(\eta) = \langle \mathscr{G} \rangle_\eta = \langle \mathscr{G} + i\eta[\mathscr{G}, F] \rangle_0 = g(0) + \eta \langle i[\mathscr{G}, F] \rangle_0 . \tag{39}$$

Clearly

$$\delta E(\eta) = \frac{1}{2}\eta(g(\eta) - g(0)) = \frac{1}{2}\frac{(g(\eta) - g(0))^2}{\langle i[\mathscr{G}, F] \rangle_0} . \tag{40}$$

4. – Time-dependent H.F. equations.

Let $\Psi(1, 2, \dots, A; t)$ be the wave function of a nonstationary state, satisfying the Schrödinger equation

$$i\frac{\partial \Psi}{\partial t} = H\Psi . \tag{41}$$

We define the two time-dependent density matrices

$$\varrho(1, 1'; t) = A\int \mathrm{d}\tau_2 \dots \mathrm{d}\tau_A \, \psi(1, 2, \dots, A; t)\, \psi^*(1', 2, \dots, A; t) ,$$

$$\varrho(1, 2; 1', 2'; t) = A(A-1)\int \mathrm{d}\tau_3 \dots \mathrm{d}\tau_A \, \psi(1, 2, 3, \dots, A; t)\, \psi^*(1', 2', 3, \dots, A; t) .$$

It then follows from (41) and its adjoint that

$$i\frac{\partial \varrho(1, 1')}{\partial t} = \sum_{1''} \big((1|t|1'')\varrho(1'', 1') - \varrho(1, 1'')(1''|t|1')\big) + \\ + \sum_{2} \sum_{1''2''} \big((1\,2|v|1''2'')\varrho(1''2'', 1'2) - \varrho(1\,2, 1''2'')(1''2''|v|1'2)\big) .$$

Introducing again $\varrho_{\alpha\beta}(t)$ and $\varrho_{\alpha\beta;\,\gamma\delta}(t)$ as in eqs. (9), (10) one has

$$(42)\qquad i\,\frac{\partial\varrho_{\alpha\beta}(t)}{\partial t}=\sum_{\gamma}(t_{\alpha\gamma}\varrho_{\gamma\beta}-\varrho_{\alpha\gamma}t_{\gamma\beta})+\sum_{\zeta}\sum_{\gamma\delta}(v_{\alpha\zeta,\,\gamma\delta}\varrho_{\gamma\delta,\,\beta\zeta}-\varrho_{\alpha\zeta,\,\gamma\delta}v_{\gamma\delta,\,\beta\zeta})\,.$$

This eq. (42) is exact; the time-dependent H.F. approximation to it follows from the condition of imposing on the two-particle density matrix *at all times* the structure

$$(43)\qquad \varrho_{\alpha\beta,\,\gamma\delta}(t)=\varrho_{\alpha\gamma}(t)\,\varrho_{\beta\delta}(t)-\varrho_{\alpha\delta}(t)\,\varrho_{\beta\gamma}(t)\,.$$

With (43), eq. (42) can be written in terms of the one-body matrix

$$(44)\qquad \mathscr{H}_{\alpha\beta}(t)\equiv\big(\mathscr{H}\big(\varrho(t)\big)\big)_{\alpha\beta}=t_{\alpha\beta}+\sum_{\gamma\delta}v^{A}_{\alpha\gamma,\,\beta\delta}\varrho_{\delta\gamma}(t)$$

as

$$(45)\qquad i\,\frac{\partial\varrho_{\alpha\beta}(t)}{\partial t}=\sum_{\gamma}\mathscr{H}_{\alpha\gamma}(t)\,\varrho_{\gamma\beta}(t)-\varrho_{\alpha\gamma}(t)\,\mathscr{H}_{\gamma\beta}(t)=[\mathscr{H}(t),\,\varrho(t)]_{\alpha\beta}\,.$$

It is seen now that the special assumption of a stationary ϱ leads directly to the Hartree-Fock condition eq. (23).

Notice also that (45) implies that the expectation value $\langle H\rangle$ of H should be independent of time

$$(46)\qquad \frac{\mathrm{d}}{\mathrm{d}t}\langle H\rangle=\mathrm{Tr}\left(\mathscr{H}(t)\,\frac{\partial\varrho}{\partial t}\right)=\frac{1}{i}\,\mathrm{Tr}\,\big(\mathscr{H}(t)[\mathscr{H},\,\varrho]\big)=0\,.$$

5. – Small-amplitude oscillations of $\varrho(t)$.

We assume that $\varrho(t)$ has the form

$$(47)\qquad \varrho(t)=\varrho^{(0)}+\varrho^{(1)}(t)+\dots$$

and that $|\varrho^{(1)}|\ll 1$; $\varrho^{(0)}$ is assumed to be a stationary H.F. solution, satisfying $\mathrm{Tr}\,\varrho^{(0)}=A$, $(\varrho^{(0)})^2=\varrho^{(0)}$, so that we have

$$\mathrm{Tr}\,\varrho^{(1)}(t)=0\,,\qquad \varrho^{(0)}\varrho^{(1)}(t)+\varrho^{(1)}(t)\,\varrho^{(0)}=\varrho^{(1)}(t)$$

(see eqs. (17)). The condition $|\varrho^{(1)}|\ll 1$ allows us to *linearize*, with respect to $\varrho^{(1)}$, the nonlinear equations of motion (45):

$$(48)\qquad i\,\frac{\partial\varrho_1}{\partial t}=[\mathscr{H}(\varrho^{(0)}),\,\varrho^{(1)}]+[v(\varrho^{(1)}),\,\varrho^{(0)}]\,,$$

where

$$v_{\alpha\beta}(\varrho) = \sum_{\gamma\delta} v^A_{\alpha\gamma,\,\beta\delta}\,\varrho_{\delta\gamma}\,.$$

(48) is simplest in a representation, in which $\varrho^{(0)}$ and $\mathscr{H}(\varrho^0)$ are diagonal; in this case only $\varrho^{(1)}_{\sigma\mu}$ and $\varrho^{(1)}_{\mu\sigma}$ are $\neq 0$ and one has

$$i\,\frac{\partial\varrho^{(1)}_{\sigma\mu}}{\partial t} = (\varepsilon_\sigma - \varepsilon_\mu)\,\varrho^{(1)}_{\sigma\mu} + \sum_{\tau,\nu} v^A_{\sigma\nu,\mu\tau}\,\varrho^{(1)}_{\tau\nu} + v^A_{\sigma\tau,\,\mu\nu}\,\varrho^{(1)}_{\nu\tau}\,, \tag{49a}$$

$$-i\,\frac{\partial\varrho^{(1)}_{\mu\sigma}}{\partial t} = (\varepsilon_\sigma - \varepsilon_\mu)\,\varrho^{(1)}_{\mu\sigma} + \sum_{\tau,\nu} v^A_{\mu\nu,\sigma\tau}\,\varrho^{(1)}_{\tau\nu} + v^A_{\mu\tau,\,\sigma\nu}\,\varrho^{(1)}_{\nu\tau}\,. \tag{49b}$$

Of course $\varrho^{(1)}_{\sigma\mu} = (\varrho^{(1)}_{\mu\sigma})^*$ and (49*b*) is the complex conjugate of (49*a*).

We may find the eigenfrequencies of oscillation by the ansatz

$$\varrho^{(1)}_{\sigma\mu} = \sum_\omega X_{\sigma\mu}(\omega)\exp[-i\omega t] + Y^*_{\sigma\mu}(\omega)\exp[i\omega t]\,,$$

which gives the equations

$$\begin{cases} (\varepsilon_\sigma - \varepsilon_\mu - \omega)\,X_{\sigma\mu} + \sum_{\tau\nu} v^A_{\sigma\nu,\,\mu\tau} X_{\tau\nu} + v^A_{\sigma\tau,\,\mu\nu}\, Y_{\tau\nu} = 0\,, \\ (\varepsilon_\sigma - \varepsilon_\mu + \omega)\,Y_{\sigma\mu} + \sum_{\tau\nu} v^A_{\mu\tau,\,\sigma\nu}\, Y_{\tau\nu} + v^A_{\mu\nu,\,\sigma\tau} X_{\tau\nu} = 0\,. \end{cases} \tag{50}$$

To display more clearly the structure of these equations, introduce the matrices

$$A_{\sigma\mu;\,\tau\nu} = (\varepsilon_\sigma - \varepsilon_\mu)\,\delta_{\sigma\tau}\delta_{\mu\nu} + v^A_{\sigma\nu,\,\mu\tau}\,, \tag{51a}$$

$$B_{\sigma\mu;\,\tau\nu} = v^A_{\sigma\tau,\,\mu\nu}\,. \tag{51b}$$

Equations (50) may then be written as

$$AX + BY = \omega X\,, \qquad A^*Y + B^*X = -\,\omega Y\,. \tag{52}$$

(A^*, B^* are the complex conjugates, not Hermitian adjoints, of A, B. A is Hermitian, and B is symmetric.)

It is interesting to notice that the same Hermitian matrix $\begin{pmatrix} A & B \\ B^* & A^* \end{pmatrix}$ as in (52) occurs in the expression for the second-order variation of $\langle H\rangle$, eq. (31). Call z a vector with elements $\varrho^{(1)}_{\sigma\mu}$; one has

$$\delta\langle H\rangle = \tfrac{1}{2}(z^*Az + zA^*z^* + zB^*z + z^*Bz^*)$$

or

$$\delta\langle H\rangle = \frac{1}{2}(z^* z)\begin{pmatrix} A & B \\ B^* & A^* \end{pmatrix}\begin{pmatrix} z \\ z^* \end{pmatrix}. \tag{53}$$

The eigenvalues of $\delta\langle H\rangle$ are therefore given by the equations

$$Az + Bz^* = \lambda z\,, \qquad B^*z + A^*z^* = \lambda z^*\,. \tag{54}$$

We have previously shown that there exist solutions z with $\lambda = 0$, indicating the degeneracy of the H.F. trial functions associated with the arbitrariness of position and orientation of the self-consistent potential well. To these correspond zero-frequency solutions of (52), with $Y = X^*$.

THOULESS has shown that if the eigenvalues λ of (54) are positive (or zero), then the eigenfrequencies of (52) are *real* (or zero). This expresses simply the physical condition that the occurrence of small-amplitude oscillations (real frequencies) of ϱ is tied to the existence of an actual minimum for $\langle H\rangle$ in the stationary case.

The proof is in itself interesting: since

$$M = \begin{pmatrix} A & B \\ B^* & A^* \end{pmatrix},$$

is Hermitian, all eigenvalues λ of (54) are real, and we assume that they are nonnegative. It follows then from (52), using $Z = \begin{pmatrix} x \\ y \end{pmatrix}$, $Z^+ = (x^+, y^+)$ that

$$Z^+ M Z = \omega(x^+ x - y^+ y)\,. \tag{55}$$

The left side of (55) is positive, unless Z is an eigenvector of M to eigenvalue zero, in this case $\lambda = \omega = 0$. In all other cases (that is, Z is *not* eigenvector of M) $Z^+ M Z > 0$; since $(x^+ x - y^+ y)$ is real, ω is then real.

The physical interpretation of these eigenfrequencies ω is clearly that of excitation energies. Indeed, we had a nonstationary state to start out with:

$$\Psi(1 \dots A, t) = \sum_n c_n \psi_n(1 \dots A) \exp[-iE_n t]\,,$$

which leads to a one-particle density matrix

$$\varrho(1, 1') = \sum_{nm} \varrho_{nm}(1, 1') \exp[i(E_m - E_n)t]\,.$$

In eq. (52), these frequencies are recovered in a certain approximation, and, as it should, in pairs $\omega, -\omega$. Indeed for every solution (X, Y) of (52) to frequency ω, there is a solution (Y^*, X^*) to frequency $-\omega$.

The main interest of eqs. (52) lies in their applications to collective excitations, which are discussed elsewhere.

BIBLIOGRAPHY

General:

G. E. Brown: *Unified Theory of Nuclear Models* (Amsterdam, 1964).
R. K. Nesbet: *Rev. Mod. Phys.*, **33**, 28 (1961).
D. J. Thouless: *The Quantum Mechanics of Many-Body Systems*, Chapt. III (New York, London, 1961).
F. Villars: *Proc. S.I.F.*, Course XXIII (New York, London, 1963).

Stability of H. F. Solution:

D. J. Thouless: *Nucl. Phys.*, **21**, 225 (1960).
D. J. Thouless: *Nucl. Phys.*, **22**, 78 (1961).

Time-dependent Hartree-Fock:

M. Baranger: *Theory of Finite Nuclei*, Chapt. 3 and 4 in: 1962 *Cargèse lectures in Theoretical Physics*. M. Lévy, ed. (New York, 1963).
D. Thouless: l.c. Chapter 5.10.
G. E. Brown: l.c. Chapter 5.4.

Rotational States and General Theory of Collective Motion.

F. VILLARS
Massachusetts Institute of Technology - Cambridge, Mass.

Introduction.

The main body of these lectures will be devoted to the « microscopic » theory of collective rotation. Indeed, collective rotation—as exhibited in the rotational spectra of many nuclei—has distinctive features; the problem of rotational excitations is quite different from that of collective multipole vibrations of spherical (or near spherical) nuclei. In this latter case, the R.P.A. or quasi-boson approximation techniques supply a satisfactory framework for a purely quantum-mechanical description of excited states.

By contrast, rotational motion is conventionally described in semi-classical terms: typically, one does not calculate $E_{J'}-E_J$, but rather finds $\delta E(\omega)$, the increase of energy with angular velocity ω of the deformed mass distribution:

$$\delta E(\omega) = \tfrac{1}{2}\Theta\omega^2 + \dots .$$

This method is sufficient to determine the moment-of-inertia parameter Θ and then—by « quantization »—an energy

$$\delta E_J = \frac{J(J+1)}{2\Theta} .$$

The *one* purely quantum-mechanical method for describing rotational states is the method of projection of the Hartree-Fock trial function on angular momentum eigenstates, due to PEIERLS and YOCCOZ, and later improved by PEIERLS and THOULESS.

Both the semi-classical and the P.Y. quantum-mechanical approach have their limitations. In the first, the construction of angular momentum eigenstates is avoided altogether, so that matrix-elements and transition rates between rotational states cannot be determined. In the second, it appears very difficult to go beyond the simple approximation given by the projection of H.F. states on J.

There are some new developments attempting to go beyond the above-mentioned approximations. One is the « generalized Hartree-Fock method » of Kerman and Klein, based on a generalized factorization of the two-body density matrix. Another method is an attempt to separate the collective dynamics from the « intrinsic » dynamics: this latter may then be handled by usual H.F. and R.P.A.-techniques, and the coupling between collective and intrinsic dynamics handled by perturbation methods.

The purpose of these lectures will be to review and discuss the established methods, and to give a brief account of some of the more recent attempts to develop new methods.

A point of particular interest that will be discussed is the relation of the microscopic—that is « fundamental »—description to the approximation embodied in the Bohr-Mottelson unified model, which has been so highly successful in accounting for many facts of nuclear collective dynamics.

1. – Semi-classical theory.

Assume that the self-consistent density $\varrho^{(0)}$ has axial symmetry, and let this symmetry axis be the z-axis (Fig. 1).

We may then ask for a solution $\varrho(t)$ of the time-dependent H.F. equation, which describes a *uniform rotation* with angular velocity ω about an axis perpendicular to the z-axis, say the x-axis. This property of $\varrho(t)$ is expressed by the equation

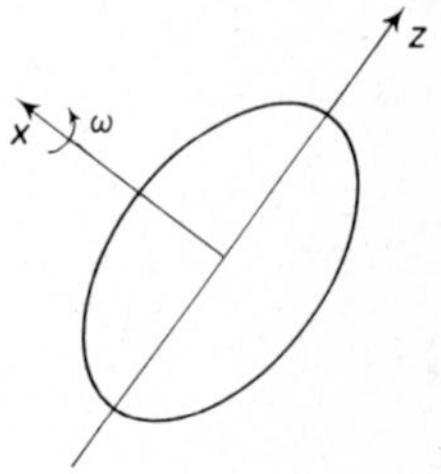

Fig. 1.

$$\varrho(t) = \exp[-i\omega j_x]\varrho(0)\exp[+i\omega j_x]\,. \tag{1}$$

Inserting this into the equation

$$i\frac{\partial\varrho}{\partial t} = [\mathscr{H}(\varrho),\,\varrho] \tag{2}$$

we obtain

$$\begin{aligned}\omega\exp[-i\omega t j_x][j_x,\,\varrho(0)]\exp[i\omega t j_x] &= [\mathscr{H}(\varrho(t)),\,\varrho(t)] = \\ &= \exp[-i\omega t j_x][\mathscr{H}(\varrho(0)),\,\varrho(0)]\exp[i\omega t j_x]\,.\end{aligned} \tag{3}$$

The last step in this equation is possible because H and J_x commute: $[H,\,J_x]=0$. The time factors therefore separate off, and we are left with the time-independent problem

$$[\mathscr{H}(\varrho(0)) - \omega J_x,\,\varrho(0)] = 0\,. \tag{4}$$

This equation tells us that $\varrho(0)$ must be the self-consistent density of the operator

$$\tilde{H} = H - \omega J_x \, .$$

Formally, the problem is thus reduced to the variational problem for $\tilde{H}$, that is a variational problem with the subsidiary condition that $\langle J_x \rangle$ has a given value; ω plays the role of the Lagrange multiplier.

The solution to this problem is well known (see preceding lecture, eqs. (34) (40)). The operator G is here the angular momentum component $J_x = \sum_{i=1}^{A} j_{ix}$, and the matrix elements $f_{\sigma\mu}$ of F are determined by

$$(\varepsilon_\sigma - \varepsilon_\mu) f_{\sigma\mu} - \sum_{\tau\nu} (v^A_{\sigma\nu,\tau\mu} f_{\tau\nu} + v^A_{\sigma\tau,\mu\nu} f_{\nu\tau}) = - i(j_x)_{\sigma\mu} \, . \tag{5}$$

The energy change due to ω is

$$\delta E = \frac{1}{2} \Theta \omega^2 = \frac{\langle J_x \rangle^2}{2\Theta}$$

and the moment of inertia is given by

$$\Theta \simeq i \langle [J_x, F] \rangle_0 = \sum_{\sigma\mu} i \big((j_x)_{\mu\sigma} f_{\sigma\mu} - f_{\mu\sigma} (j_x)_{\sigma\mu} \big) \, . \tag{6}$$

(6) is the Thouless-Valatin formula for the moment of inertia. In an approxi mation which neglects the potential-energy terms in eq. (5), one finds the Inglis cranking formula

$$\Theta \simeq 2 \sum_{\sigma\mu} \frac{|(j_x)_{\sigma\mu}|^2}{\varepsilon_\sigma - \varepsilon_\mu} \, . \tag{7}$$

The cranking approximation (7) gives good results in light nuclei, where the energy gap $(\varepsilon_\sigma - \varepsilon_\mu)$ is enhanced compared to the value expected from the positions of levels in a deformed local potential well. This is an instance where the nonlocality of the Hartree-Fock self-consistent well plays an essential role. The results stated here may be generalized in an obvious way to cases of non axially symmetric density distributions.

We notice that the result (6) remains essentially correct in a quasi-particle theory (like the BCS theory). In this theory, the « Brillouin condition » (preceding lecture, eq. (22*a*)) is replaced by

$$\langle 2 | H | 0 \rangle = 0 \, , \tag{8}$$

$|0\rangle$ being the ground state (« vacuum ») and $|2\rangle$ being any 2-quasi-particle state. Correspondingly, condition (37) of the preceding lecture:

$$\langle \Phi_{\sigma\mu} (i[H, F] - G) \Phi_0 \rangle = 0$$

is replaced by

$$\langle 2|(i[H, F]-G)|0\rangle = 0 \tag{9}$$

and the moment of inertia is simply (with $G=J_x$)

$$\Theta = i\langle 0|[J_x, F]|0\rangle . \tag{10}$$

2. – Moment of inertia from stability condition.

Assume a situation with a well-developed ground state rotational band

$$E_{0J} = E_{00} + \frac{J(J+1)}{2\Theta} . \tag{11}$$

One may then conclude that the operator

$$\tilde{H} = H - \frac{\boldsymbol{J}^2}{2\Theta} \tag{12}$$

is the Hamiltonian of the «intrinsic» (that is, nonrotational) motion: to the ground state rotational band of H corresponds now a single eigenvalue E_0 of $\tilde{H}$.

In a Hartree-Fock approximate treatment of $\tilde{H}$, this should show up as an additional degeneracy; to the extent that $\tilde{H}$ in fact describes only the intrinsic dynamics, $\tilde{H}$ commutes not only with $\boldsymbol{J}$, but also with three angular variables θ, φ, ψ.

An analogy to this exists in the translational problem: H commutes with $\boldsymbol{P}$, the total linear momentum, but the «intrinsic» Hamiltonian

$$\tilde{H} = H - \frac{\boldsymbol{P}^2}{2Am}$$

commutes in addition with X; both P and X can now be used as generators of variations of ϱ, for which

$$\delta\langle\tilde{H}\rangle \equiv 0$$

to any order. Here this idea is simply applied to rotations. The difference is that we *know* the value of $M=2Am$, the total mass, but we do not know the value of Θ.

But here we may in fact use the *condition* that an additional degeneracy should exist, to *determine* the value of Θ.

This idea is realized as follows. We construct H.F. solution for $H = \tilde{H} - (1/2\Theta)\boldsymbol{J}^2$, and assume for simplicity that we get a deformed, axially symmetric self-consistent well. (That is, the states ψ_α are eigenstates of J_z.)

The expression for the second-order variation of $\langle\tilde{H}\rangle$ now reads (see preceding lecture, eq. (31)):

$$\delta\langle\tilde{H}\rangle = \sum(\varepsilon_\sigma - \varepsilon_\mu)|\varrho^{(1)}_{\sigma\mu}|^2 + \sum\left\{v^A_{\mu\tau,\sigma\nu} - \frac{1}{\Theta}(\boldsymbol{j}_{\mu\sigma}\cdot\boldsymbol{j}_{\tau\nu} - \boldsymbol{j}_{\mu\nu}\cdot\boldsymbol{j}_{\tau\sigma})\right\}\varrho^{(1)}_{\sigma\mu}\varrho^{(1)}_{\nu\tau} + \sum\left\{v^A_{\mu\nu,\sigma\tau} - \frac{1}{\Theta}(\boldsymbol{j}_{\mu\sigma}\cdot\boldsymbol{j}_{\nu\tau} - \boldsymbol{j}_{\mu\tau}\cdot\boldsymbol{j}_{\nu\sigma})\right\}\varrho^{(1)}_{\sigma\mu}\varrho^{(1)}_{\tau\nu} + \sum\left\{v^A_{\sigma\tau,\mu\nu} - \frac{1}{\Theta}(\boldsymbol{j}_{\sigma\mu}\cdot\boldsymbol{j}_{\tau\nu} - \boldsymbol{j}_{\sigma\nu}\cdot\boldsymbol{j}_{\tau\mu})\right\}\varrho^{(1)}_{\mu\sigma}\varrho^{(1)}_{\nu\tau}. \tag{13}$$

Considering this as a bilinear form in $\varrho^{(1)}_{\sigma\mu}$ and $\varrho^{(1)}_{\mu\sigma} = (\varrho^{(1)}_{\sigma\mu})^*$ the condition for *zero* eigenvalue of $\delta\langle\tilde{H}\rangle$ is

$$(\varepsilon_\sigma - \varepsilon_\mu)\varrho^{(1)}_{\mu\sigma} + \sum\left(v^A_{\mu\tau,\sigma\nu} - \frac{1}{\Theta}(\boldsymbol{j}_{\mu\sigma}\cdot\boldsymbol{j}_{\tau\nu} - \boldsymbol{j}_{\mu\nu}\cdot\boldsymbol{j}_{\tau\sigma})\right)\varrho^{(1)}_{\nu\tau} + \sum\left(v^A_{\mu\nu,\sigma\tau} - \frac{1}{\Theta}(\boldsymbol{j}_{\mu\sigma}\cdot\boldsymbol{j}_{\nu\tau} - \boldsymbol{j}_{\mu\tau}\cdot\boldsymbol{j}_{\nu\sigma})\right)\varrho^{(1)}_{\tau\nu} = 0 \tag{14}$$

(and the complex-conjugate equation).

We see that in the terms $\sim 1/\Theta$, there appears a « coherent », factorable term, and incoherent exchange terms.

We drop the latter, by a « random phase » argument. One has then the equation

$$(\varepsilon_\sigma - \varepsilon_\mu)\,\varrho^{(1)}_{\mu\sigma} + \sum(v^A_{\mu\tau,\sigma\nu}\varrho^{(1)}_{\nu\tau} - v^A_{\mu\nu,\sigma\tau}\varrho^{(1)}_{\tau\nu}) = \boldsymbol{\omega}\cdot\boldsymbol{j}_{\mu\sigma} \tag{15}$$

with

$$\boldsymbol{\omega} = \frac{1}{\Theta}\sum_{\tau\nu}(\boldsymbol{j}_{\tau\nu}\varrho^{(1)}_{\nu\tau} + \boldsymbol{j}_{\nu\tau}\varrho^{(1)}_{\tau\nu}). \tag{16}$$

$\boldsymbol{\omega}$ is located in the x-y plane, as $(j_z)_{\tau\mu} \equiv 0$.

A comparison with eqs. (6) of the preceding lecture will show that the Θ defined by (15), (16) is again exactly the Thouless-Valatin result.

3. – Method of projected Slater determinants.

It turns out that for sufficiently deformed nuclei, (even light nuclei), the value of the angular momentum is highly indeterminate: one has $\langle\Phi_0\boldsymbol{J}\Phi_0\rangle = 0$ (even nuclei) but

$$\langle\Phi_0\boldsymbol{J}^2\Phi_0\rangle \gg 1\,. \tag{17}$$

In fact, even for light nuclei $\langle J^2 \rangle_0$ may assume values of order 10^2. One may, in this case, introduce the interpretation that Φ_0 does in fact represent a wave packet, obtained by superposition of angular momentum eigenstates of the ground-state rotational band.

According to the uncertainty relation, the definite *orientation* of the nucleus (described by a deformed trial function) has been paid by an appropriate uncertainty in angular momentum.

With this view in mind, one may try to recover the angular momentum eigenstates ψ_J by projecting out of Φ_0 the component with angular momentum J.

This procedure is very successful if condition (17) is satisfied, and we shall discuss here the main results and applications.

3·1. *Rotations and the D-functions.* – It will be necessary here to review briefly the subject of finite rotations, if only to have a clearly defined, unambiguous notation. Let $\boldsymbol{e}_x$, $\boldsymbol{e}_y$, $\boldsymbol{e}_z$ be a system of co-ordinate axes, and $\boldsymbol{e}_{x'}$, $\boldsymbol{e}_{y'}$, $\boldsymbol{e}_{z'}$ a rotated system (Fig. 2). The rotation is described by 3 Euler angles α, β, γ. We also write Ω as a shorthand notation for the set.

A point P in space has the co-ordinates xyz (in short x) with respect to the original axes, and the co-ordinates $x'y'z'$ (in short x') with respect to the rotated axes. The relation between the co-ordinates x and x' of P may be written in two ways:

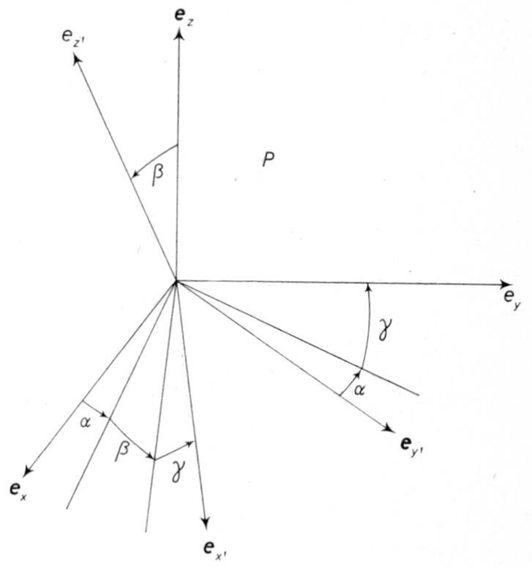

Fig. 2.

(18) $$x' = Rx$$

(that is, $x'_i = \sum R_{iK} x_K$, $x_1 = x$, $x_2 = y$, $x_3 = z$), but also as the unitary operator transformation:

(19) $$x'_i = \mathscr{R}(\Omega) x_i \mathscr{R}^{-1}(\Omega)$$

where

(20) $$\mathscr{R}(\Omega) = \exp[-i\alpha J_z] \exp[-i\beta J_y] \exp[-i\gamma J_z] .$$

This same operator $\mathscr{R}$ then also relates the values of the functions $\Phi(x')$ and $\Phi(x)$ (x' and x standing here for the set of co-ordinates of all A particles)

(21) $$\Phi(x') = \mathscr{R}(\Omega) \Phi(x) .$$

Rule for composition of rotations:

$$x' = R_1 x\,, \qquad x'' = R_2 x'\,, \qquad x'' = R_2 R_1 x\,.$$

To this corresponds

$$x' = \mathcal{R}_1 x \mathcal{R}'^{-1}_1\,, \qquad x'' = \mathcal{R}'_2 x' \mathcal{R}'^{-1}_2 = \mathcal{R}'_2 \mathcal{R}_1 x \mathcal{R}^{-1}_1 \mathcal{R}'^{-1}_2 = \mathcal{R}_1 \mathcal{R}_2 x \mathcal{R}^{-1}_2 \mathcal{R}^{-1}_1\,,$$

hence to $R = R_2 R_1$ is associated

$$\mathcal{R} = \mathcal{R}_1 \mathcal{R}_2\,. \tag{22}$$

Definition of D-function:

We define the D-function in terms of the standard matrix representation of J_x, J_y, J_z by

$$\begin{aligned} \mathcal{D}^J_{MK}(\alpha\beta\gamma) &= \langle JM|\exp[-i\alpha J_z]\exp[-i\beta J_y]\exp[-i\gamma J_z]|JK\rangle = \\ &= \exp[-iM\alpha]\langle JM|\exp[-i\beta J_y]|JK\rangle \exp[-iK\gamma] = \\ &= \exp[-iM\alpha] d^J_{MK}(\beta)\exp[-iK\gamma]\,. \end{aligned} \tag{23}$$

We also define the adjoint D-function $D^\dagger$ by

$$\mathcal{D}^{\dagger J}_{KM}(\alpha\beta\gamma) = \big(\mathcal{D}^J_{MK}(\alpha\beta\gamma)\big)^* = \langle JK|\exp[i\gamma J_z]\exp[i\beta J_y]\exp[i\alpha J_z]|JM\rangle\,. \tag{24}$$

The $D^\dagger$ are angular momentum eigenfunctions, and satisfy the relations

$$\left\{\begin{aligned} &\mathcal{J}_z \mathcal{D}^{\dagger J}_{KM}(\alpha\beta\gamma) \equiv \frac{1}{i}\frac{\partial}{\partial\alpha}\mathcal{D}^{\dagger J}_{KM} = M\mathcal{D}^{\dagger J}_{KM}\,, \\ &(\mathcal{J}_x \pm i\mathcal{J}_y)\mathcal{D}^{\dagger J}_{KM}(\alpha\beta\gamma) \equiv \exp[\pm i\alpha]\left(i\operatorname{cotg}\beta\frac{\partial}{\partial\alpha} \pm \frac{\partial}{\partial\beta} - \frac{i}{\sin\beta}\frac{\partial}{\partial\gamma}\right)\mathcal{D}^{\dagger J}_{KM} = \\ &\qquad = \sqrt{J(J+1) - M(M\pm 1)}\,\mathcal{D}^{\dagger J}_{K,M\pm 1} \end{aligned}\right. \tag{25}$$

and similar relations with respect to the operators $\mathcal{J}_{z'}$, $\mathcal{J}_{x'}$, $\mathcal{J}_{y'}$.

$$\left\{\begin{aligned} &\mathcal{J}_{z'} \mathcal{D}^{\dagger J}_{KM}(\alpha\beta\gamma) \equiv \frac{1}{i}\frac{\partial}{\partial\gamma}\mathcal{D}^{\dagger J}_{KM} = K\mathcal{D}^{\dagger J}_{KM}\,, \\ &(\mathcal{J}_{x'} \pm \mathcal{J}_{y'})\mathcal{D}^{\dagger J}_{KM}(\alpha\beta\gamma) \equiv \exp[\mp i\gamma]\left(-i\operatorname{ctg}\beta\frac{\partial}{\partial\gamma} \pm \frac{\partial}{\partial\beta} + \frac{i}{\sin\beta}\frac{\partial}{\partial\alpha}\right)\mathcal{D}^{J\dagger}_{KM} = \\ &\qquad = \sqrt{J(J+1) - (K\mp 1)}\,\mathcal{D}^{\dagger J}_{K\mp 1,M}\,. \end{aligned}\right. \tag{26}$$

These equations also embody the usual (normal) commutation relations for the $\mathcal{J}_x$, $\mathcal{J}_y$, $\mathcal{J}_z$, and the « anomalous » relations for $\mathcal{J}_{x'}$, $\mathcal{J}_{y'}$, $\mathcal{J}_{z'}$:

$$[\mathcal{J}_x, \mathcal{J}_y] = i\mathcal{J}_z\,, \qquad \text{and} \qquad [\mathcal{J}_{x'}, \mathcal{J}_{y'}] = -i\mathcal{J}_{z'}\,. \tag{27}$$

These operators $\mathscr{J}$ are Hermitian (volume element is $\mathrm{d}\Omega = \mathrm{d}\alpha\,\mathrm{d}\cos\beta\,\mathrm{d}\gamma$); it will be good to distinguish them from the operators $\boldsymbol{J} = \sum_{i=1}^{A}(\boldsymbol{x}_i \times \boldsymbol{p}_i + \frac{1}{2}\boldsymbol{\sigma}_i)$ operating on $\Phi(x)$, and used in defining the operator $\mathscr{R}$, eq. (20). They are related, however, by the basic relation

$$\int \mathrm{d}\Omega\, \mathscr{D}^{J\dagger}_{KM}(\Omega) J_K \mathscr{R}(\Omega) = \int \mathrm{d}\Omega \big(\mathscr{J}_K \mathscr{D}^{\dagger J}_{KM}(\Omega)\big)\mathscr{R}(\Omega) = \sum_{M'} \langle JM'|J_K|JM\rangle \int \mathrm{d}\Omega\, \mathscr{D}^{J\dagger}_{KM'}(\Omega)\mathscr{R}(\Omega)\,. \tag{28}$$

3·2. *The projection operator.* – The property of $D^\dagger$ displayed in eq. (28) establishes the operator

$$P^J_{KM} = \int \mathrm{d}\Omega\, \mathscr{D}^{\dagger J}_{KM}(\Omega)\mathscr{R}(\Omega) \tag{29}$$

as a projection operator on many-particle wave functions $\Phi(x)$. It is not normalized, however.

Now let $\Phi_n(x)$ be any Slater determinant.

We operate on it with P^J_{KM}, eq. (29), and obtain a function

$$\psi^J_{nKM}(x) = \int \mathrm{d}\Omega\, \mathscr{D}^{\dagger J}_{KM}(\Omega)\mathscr{R}(\Omega)\,\Phi_n(x)\,. \tag{30}$$

By using eq. (28), one sees that this function has the properties

$$\begin{cases} J_z \psi^J_{nKM}(x) = M\psi^J_{nKM}(x)\,, \\ \boldsymbol{J}^2 \psi^J_{nKM}(x) = J(J+1)\,\psi^J_{nKM}(x)\,, \end{cases} \tag{31}$$

it is therefore an eigenfunction of $\boldsymbol{J}^2$ and J_z.

The label K seems to indicate a ***third*** quantum number, but in fact K is *not* eigenvalue of an operator acting on ψ^J_{nKM}. What happens actually is that the operator P^J_{KM} first projects out of $\Phi_n(x)$ the component with $J_z = K$, $\Phi_{\mu K}$, and *then* projects out of $\Phi_{\mu K}$ a component with definite $\boldsymbol{J}^2(=J(J+1))$ and $J_z(=M)$.

If the original trial function $\Phi_n(x)$ has already a definite $J_z = K_n$, then P^J_{KM} on $\Phi_n(x)$ will give zero unless $K = K_n$.

3·3. *Some properties of the functions* $\mathscr{D}^J_{MK}(\alpha\beta\gamma)$ *and* $d^J_{MK}(\beta)$. – In order to discuss the main properties of the projected wave functions ψ^J_{nKM}, we need to tabulate some of the relevant properties of the functions $\mathscr{D}^J_{MK}(\alpha, \beta, \gamma)$ and $d^J_{MK}(\beta)$ defined by eq. (23):

i) Unitarity: The defining eq. (23) makes it clear that the $\mathscr{D}^J_{MK}(\Omega)$ for fixed Ω, are unitary matrices:

$$\sum_K \mathscr{D}^J_{MK}(\Omega)\mathscr{D}^{\dagger J}_{KM'}(\Omega) = \delta_{MM'}\ , \tag{32a}$$

$$\sum_M \mathscr{D}^{\dagger J}_{KM}(\Omega)\mathscr{D}^J_{MK'}(\Omega) = \delta_{KK'}\ . \tag{32b}$$

ii) Orthogonality: The $\mathscr{D}^{\dagger J}_{KM}$ are eigenfunctions of the three operators $\mathscr{J}_z, \mathscr{J}_{z'}$ and $\mathscr{J}^2$ to eigenvalues M, K and $J(J+1)$, respectively. These operators being Hermitian, the $\mathscr{D}$ satisfy an orthogonality relation

$$\frac{1}{8\pi^2}\int_0^{2\pi} d\alpha \int_{-1}^{1} d\cos\beta \int_0^{2\pi} d\gamma\, \mathscr{D}^{\dagger J}_{KM}(\Omega)\mathscr{D}^{J'}_{M'K'}(\Omega) = \frac{\delta_{JJ'}\delta_{MM'}\delta_{KK'}}{(2J+1)}\ . \tag{33}$$

iii) Vector addition: Products of two $\mathscr{D}$-functions may be vector-added to a single $\mathscr{D}$ function:

$$\sum_{\substack{m_1 m_2\\ k_1 k_2}} \mathscr{D}^{j_1}_{m_1k_1}(\Omega)\mathscr{D}^{j_2}_{m_2k_2}(\Omega)\langle j_1m_1j_2m_2|JM\rangle\langle j_1k_1j_2k_2|JK\rangle = \mathscr{D}^J_{MK}(\Omega) \tag{34a}$$

and

$$\mathscr{D}^{j_1}_{m_1k_1}(\Omega)\mathscr{D}^{j_2}_{m_2k_2}(\Omega) = \sum_J \langle j_1m_1j_2m_2|JM\rangle\langle j_1k_1j_2k_2|JK\rangle\mathscr{D}^J_{MK}(\Omega)\ . \tag{34b}$$

iv) Composition of 2 rotations: Let $R_1(\Omega_1)$ be a rotation characterized by the set of Euler angles Ω_1, and $R_2(\Omega_2)$ another rotation. Then $R_1R_2 = R(\Omega)$ is a rotation, with angles Ω. One has then

$$\mathscr{D}^J_{MK}(\Omega) = \sum_Z \mathscr{D}^J_{MZ}(\Omega_2)\mathscr{D}^J_{ZK}(\Omega_1) \tag{35a}$$

and

$$\mathscr{D}^{\dagger}_{KM}(\Omega) = \sum_Z \mathscr{D}^{\dagger J}_{KZ}(\Omega_1)\mathscr{D}^{\dagger J}_{ZM}(\Omega_2)\ . \tag{35b}$$

v) Structure of $d^J_{MK}(\beta) = \langle JM|\exp[-i\beta J_y]|JK\rangle$.

This function is explicitly given by the expression

$$d^J_{MK}(\beta) = \sqrt{(J+K)!(J-K)!(J+M)!(J-M)!}\,\cdot \tag{36}$$
$$\cdot\sum_\sigma \frac{(-1)^{J-K-\sigma}}{(J-K-\sigma)!(J-M-\sigma)!\sigma!(M+K+\sigma)!}\left(\cos\frac{\beta}{2}\right)^{2\sigma+M+K}\left(\sin\frac{\beta}{2}\right)^{2J-(2\sigma+M+K)}\ .$$

From this formula the following symmetry properties may be derived:

(37a) i) it is real,

(37b) ii) $d^J_{MK}(\beta) = d^J_{KM}(-\beta)$,

(37c) iii) $d^J_{MK}(\beta) = (-1)^{M-K} d^J_{KM}(\beta) = (-1)^{M-K} d^J_{-M,-K}(\beta) = d^J_{-K,-M}(\beta)$,

(37d) iv) $d^J_{MK}(\pi - \beta) = (-1)^{J-K} d^J_{-MK}(\beta) = (-1)^{J+M} d^J_{M,-K}(\beta)$.

vi) Special values of d-functions

(38a) i) $d^J_{00}(\beta) = P^J(\cos\beta) =$ Legendre polynomial,

(38b) ii) $d^J_{KK}(\beta) \underset{\beta\to 0}{\longrightarrow} 1 - \dfrac{\beta^2}{4}[J(J+1) - K^2] + \dots$,

(38c) iii) $d^J_{MK}(\beta) \underset{\beta\to 0}{\longrightarrow} \sim O(\beta^{|K-M|})$,

(38d) iv) $d^J_{KK}(\beta) \underset{\beta\to\pi}{\longrightarrow} (-1)^{J-|K|} \begin{pmatrix} J+|K| \\ J-|K| \end{pmatrix} \left(\dfrac{\beta'^2}{4}\right)^K + \dots, \qquad \beta' \equiv (\pi - \beta) \to 0$

(38e) (in particular, for $K = 0$, $\quad d^J_{00}(\beta) = (-1)^J d^J_{00}(\beta'); \quad \beta' \equiv (\pi - \beta)$).

3'4. *Orthogonality properties of projected wave functions.* – We shall here only consider axially symmetric Slater determinants, since nonaxially symmetric ones must first be expanded in such. Call them Φ_{nK}, n standing for all additional quantum numbers needed in addition to K (eigenvalue of J_z) to specify the determinants.

Let $\int d\Omega$ stand for

$$\frac{1}{8\pi^2}\int_0^{2\pi} d\alpha \int_{-1}^{+1} d\cos\beta \int_0^{2\pi} d\gamma\,.$$

The projected wave functions are

(39) $$\psi^J_{nKM}(x) = P^J_{KM}\Phi_{nK}(x) = \int d\Omega\, \mathscr{D}^{\dagger J}_{KM}(\Omega)\mathscr{R}(\Omega)\Phi_{nK}(x) = \int d\Omega\, \mathscr{D}^{\dagger J}_{KM}(\Omega)\Phi_{nK}(Rx)\,.$$

These functions, by eq. (31), are orthogonal in J and M. They are not *exactly* orthogonal in K, however; we shall calculate the overlap integral in some detail, since it serves to demonstrate a technique which is needed again and again:

(40) $$\int d\tau\, \psi^{*J'}_{n'K'M'}(x)\psi^J_{nMK}(x) = \int d\Omega\, d\Omega'\, \mathscr{D}^{J'}_{M'K'}(\Omega')\mathscr{D}^{\dagger J}_{KM}(\Omega)\int d\tau\, \Phi^*_{n'K'}(R'x)\,\Phi_{nK}(Rx)\,.$$

Now we first introduce $x' = R'x$ as new independent integration variable; $d\tau$ is not affected by this.

With $R'x = x'$ as independent variable, one has $Rx = RR'^{-1}x' = \tilde{R}x'$ in the argument of Φ_{nK}.

Let $\tilde{\Omega}$ be the angles associated with $\tilde{R} = RR'^{-1}$, since $R = \tilde{R}R'$ we have, by eq. (35*b*):

$$\mathscr{D}^{\dagger J}_{KM}(\Omega) = \sum_z \mathscr{D}^{\dagger J}_{Kz}(\tilde{\Omega})\,\mathscr{D}^{\dagger J}_{zM}(\Omega')\,.$$

Then the right-hand side of eq. (40) may be written as

$$\int \mathrm{d}\Omega'\,\mathrm{d}\tilde{\Omega}\,\mathscr{D}^{J'}_{M'K'}(\Omega') \sum_z \mathscr{D}^{\dagger J}_{Kz}(\tilde{\Omega})\,\mathscr{D}^{\dagger J}_{zM}(\Omega') \int \mathrm{d}\tau\,\Phi^*_{n'K'}(x)\,\Phi_{nK}(\tilde{R}x)\,.$$

By eq. (33), the Ω'-integration just gives $\big(1/(2J+1)\big)\delta_{JJ'}\delta_{MM'}\delta_{K'z}$ and we have

$$\int \mathrm{d}\tau\,\psi^{*J'}_{n'K'M'}\psi^{J}_{nKM} = \frac{\delta_{JJ'}\delta_{MM'}}{2J+1}\int \mathrm{d}\Omega\,\mathscr{D}^{\dagger J}_{KK'}(\Omega)\int \mathrm{d}\tau\,\Phi^*_{n'K'}(x)\mathscr{R}(\Omega)\,\Phi_{nK}(x)\,. \tag{41}$$

(We have used again $\Phi(Rx) = \mathscr{R}\Phi(x)$; see eqs. (18) and (21).)

(41) can be further reduced. First, the Φ's being eigenfunctions of J_z, one has, from eq. (20) for $\mathscr{R}(\Omega)$

$$\int \mathrm{d}\tau\,\Phi^*_{n'K'}\mathscr{R}(\Omega)\,\Phi_{nK} = \exp[-i\alpha K' - i\gamma K]\int \mathrm{d}\tau\,\Phi^*_{n'K'}(x)\exp[-i\beta J_y]\,\Phi_{nK}(x)\,.$$

The phase factors so isolated are just cancelled by corresponding factors in $\mathscr{D}^{\dagger J}_{KK'}(\Omega)$ (see eq. (24)); eq. (41) reduces to

$$\int \mathrm{d}\tau\,\psi^{*J'}_{n'K'M'}(x)\,\psi^{J}_{nKM}(x) = \frac{\delta_{JJ'}\delta_{MM'}}{2J+1}\,\frac{1}{2}\int_{-1}^{+1}\mathrm{d}\cos\beta\,d^J_{KK'}(\beta)\cdot \tag{42}$$

$$\cdot\int \mathrm{d}\tau\,\Phi^*_{n'K'}(x)\exp[-i\beta J_y]\,\Phi_{nK}(x)\,.$$

To interpret this result, we must first look at the structure of the matrix element

$$N_{n'K',nK}(\beta) \equiv \int \mathrm{d}\tau\,\Phi^*_{n'K'}(x)\exp[-i\beta J_y]\,\Phi_{nK}(x)\,. \tag{43}$$

Consider first a *diagonal element* $n'K' = nK$. Since $J_y = \sum_{i=1}^{A}(j_y)_i$; the function $\exp[-i\beta J_y]\Phi_{nK}$ is itself a determinant, with individual one particle functions $\exp[-i\beta j_y]\varphi_\lambda(x)$.

So $N(\beta)$ is the overlap of two nonorthogonal Slater determinants, and may itself be written as a determinant

$$N(\beta) = \det\|M_{\lambda\mu}(\beta)\|\,, \tag{44a}$$

where $\|M_{\lambda\mu}(\beta)\|$ is the AxA matrix with elements

(44b) $$M_{\lambda\mu}(\beta)=\int \mathrm{d}\tau\big(\varphi_\lambda^*\exp[-i\beta j_y]\varphi_\mu\big)\,.$$

Since $M_{\lambda\mu}\xrightarrow[\beta\to 0]{}\delta_{\lambda\mu}$ we write

$$M_{\lambda\mu}=\delta_{\lambda\mu}+D_{\lambda\mu}(\beta)=\delta_{\lambda\mu}-i\beta(j_y)_{\lambda\mu}-\frac{\beta^2}{2}(j_y^2)_{\lambda\mu}+\dots .$$

One has then using a well-known result:

$$N(\beta)=\exp[\mathrm{Tr}\log M(\beta)]=\exp[\mathrm{Tr}\log\big(1+D(\beta)\big)]\,,$$

the trace being taken over the space of occupied one-particle orbitals φ_λ. Expanding the logarithm, one has

(45) $$\mathrm{Tr}\log\big(1+D(\beta)\big)=\mathrm{Tr}\,\big(D(\beta)-\tfrac{1}{2}D^2(\beta)\big)=$$
$$=\sum_{\lambda=1}^{A}\left(-\frac{\beta^2}{2}(j_y^2)_{\lambda\lambda}-\frac{1}{2}(i\beta)^2\sum_\mu(j_y)_{\lambda\mu}(j_y)_{\mu\lambda}+\dots\right)=$$
$$=-\frac{\beta^2}{2}\sum_{\lambda\sigma}|(j_y)_{\lambda\sigma}|^2+O(\beta^4)=-\frac{\beta^2}{2}\langle J_y^2\rangle+O(\beta^4)\,.$$

J_y is the operator $\sum_{i=1}^{A}(j_y)_i$ and $\langle J_y^2\rangle$ is the expectation value of J_y^2 with respect to the determinant Φ_{nK}. One has in addition

(46) $$\langle J_y^2\rangle=\tfrac{1}{2}\langle J_x^2+J_y^2\rangle=\tfrac{1}{2}\langle J^2-K^2\rangle=\tfrac{1}{2}\langle J_\perp^2\rangle\,.$$

So, to order β^2 in $\log\big(1+D(\beta)\big)$, one has

(47) $$N(\beta)\simeq\exp\left[-\frac{\beta^2}{4}\langle J_\perp^2\rangle\right].$$

With values of $\langle J_\perp^2\rangle$ of order of 10^2 or more, as one finds them in strongly deformed nuclei, $N(\beta)$ is very sharply peaked about $\beta=0$.

Let us also look at values of β near $\beta=\pi$; with

$$\beta'\equiv\pi-\beta$$

one has, still for the diagonal element,

(48) $$N(\beta)=\Phi_{nK}\exp[i\beta' J_y]\big(\exp[-i\pi J_y]\Phi_{nK}\big)\,.$$

We will here stick to the convention that, unless specified otherwise, Φ_{nK} refers to a nonnegative K, $K\geqslant 0$, and the operator $\exp[-i\pi J_y]$ will be used to define the time-reversed state $\Phi_{n,-K} = \exp[-i\pi J_y]\Phi_{n,K}$. (Notice that $\Phi_{n,-(-K)} = \pm \Phi_{n,K}$, depending on whether K is integer (+) or half integer.)

Some care is needed in applying this to $K = 0$. For $K \neq 0$, one always has two distinct, orthogonal states $K, -K$.

In the case $K = 0$, the lowest states appear to be time-reversal-invariant (and have even parity):

$$\exp[-i\pi J_y]\Phi_{0,0} = +\Phi_{0,0}\,. \tag{49a}$$

We call this the normal case. It corresponds to a coupling scheme, where nucleons are stacked up pairwise in single-particle states, $j_z = m$, and their time-reversed, $j_z = -m$. Such two particle systems are then invariant under $\exp[-i\pi J_y]$ and have even parity.

But « anomalous » situations are possible, where

$$\exp[-i\pi J_y]\Phi_{n,0} = -\Phi_{n,0}\,. \tag{49b}$$

An example is the $\Phi_{n,0}$ obtained from projecting a parity impure determinant of ellipsoidal symmetry on $J_z = 0$. In this case, even-parity states satisfy (49*a*), odd-parity states (49*b*).

Applied to $N(\beta)$, eq. (43), we have, for $K = 0$

$$N_{n0,n0}(\pi-\beta) = N_{n0,n0}(\beta)\,. \tag{50a}$$

For $K > 0$ no such problem arises, and one has generally

$$N(\pi-\beta) \equiv N(\beta') \underset{\beta'\to 0}{\longrightarrow} \frac{(i\beta')^{2K}}{(2K)!}\int \mathrm{d}\tau\, \varphi^*_{nK}(J_y)^{2K}\varphi_{n,-K}\,. \tag{50b}$$

In Fig. 3 we plot this behaviour.

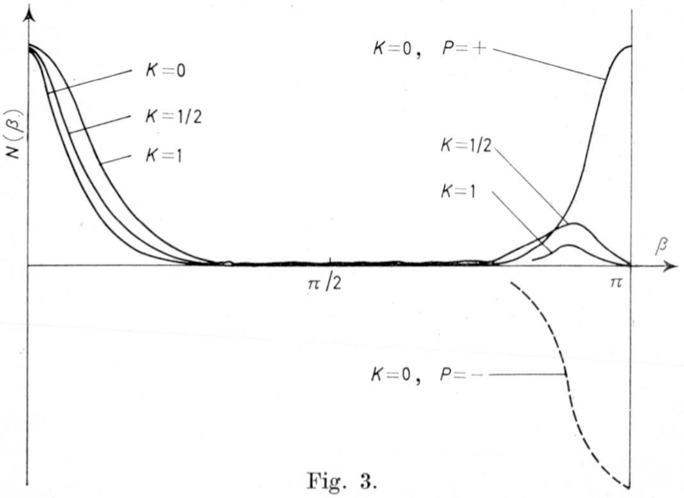

Fig. 3.

Considering *nondiagonal* elements, $n'K' \neq nK$; it is now clear that they will start at $\beta = 0$ with some power β^s, at $\beta' = (\pi - \beta) = 0$ with some power s' determined by the condition that s, s' are the *smallest* numbers, for which the matrix elements

$$\int \mathrm{d}\tau \Phi^*_{n'K'}(j_y)^s \Phi_{nK} \quad \text{and} \quad \int \mathrm{d}\tau \Phi^*_{n'K'}(j_y)^{s'} \Phi_{n,-K} \tag{51}$$

are different from zero. This means that a typical nondiagonal element has an $N(\beta)$ which looks like Fig. 4.

With this material, we are now in a position to make a few statements:

1) For $K=0$, the diagonal element $N_{nn}(\beta)$ satisfies

$$N_{nn}(\beta) = \pm N_{nn}(\pi - \beta)$$

according to eq. (42), this gets into the integral

$$\int_{-1}^{+1} \mathrm{d}(\cos\beta)\, d^J_{00}(\beta) N(\beta),$$

where

$$d^J_{00}(\beta) = P_J(\beta) = (-1)^J d^J_{00}(\pi - \beta)\,.$$

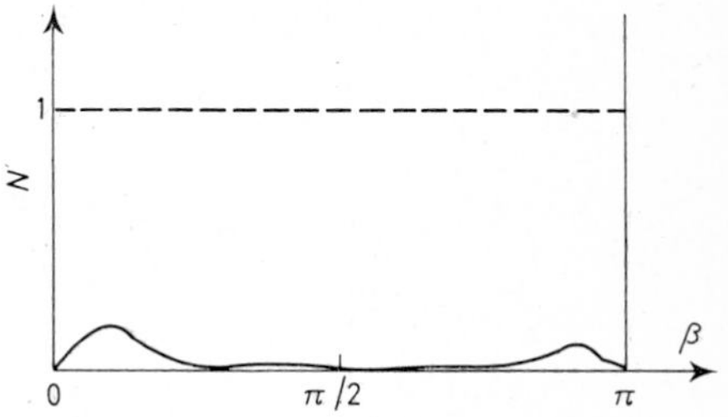

Fig. 4. – Plot of a typical nondiagonal element $N_{n'K',nK}(\beta)$.

We have therefore the result that for $K=0$ the normalization of $\psi^J_{n0,M}$ is zero (and thus ψ itself is zero) unless $(-1)^{J+P} = +1$.

The only states which exist are therefore

$$P = +\,, \qquad J = 0, 2, 4, \ldots\,,$$
$$P = -\,, \qquad J = 1, 3, 5, \ldots\,. \; (^*)$$

By contrast, for $K \neq 0$, the admissible J values are

$$J = |K|,\ |K|+1,\ |K|+2, \ldots\,.$$

2) Orthogonality of wave functions in $(nK, n'K')$: The smallness of the corresponding overlap integrals, eq. (42), depends on the necessary values of s, s' in eq. (51). If, in addition to $n' \neq n$ one also has $K' \neq K$, then not only will $N(\beta)$ be $\ll 1$ but also $d^J_{K'K}(\beta)$, according to eq. (38*c*).

A more detailed analysis shows that such nondiagonal elements (42) are at best of order $1/\langle J^2 \rangle$ compared to diagonal elements.

(*) As mentioned, there are exceptions possible to this rule.

3·5. *Matrix-elements of tensor operators.* – Tensor operators $T^{\varkappa}_{\mu}(x)$ may be characterized by their commutation relations with the angular momentum components J_q ($q=x, y, z$):

$$[J_q, T^{\varkappa}_{\mu}(x)] = \sum_{\nu} T^{\varkappa}_{\nu}(x)\langle\varkappa\nu|J_q|\varkappa\mu\rangle . \tag{52}$$

The $T^{\varkappa}_{\mu}$, being functions of the set of variables which we call here « x », satisfy the equation

$$T^{\varkappa}_{\mu}(Rx) = \mathscr{R}T^{\varkappa}_{\mu}(x)\mathscr{R}^{-1} \tag{53}$$

with R given by (20). Equation (19) is a special case of (53). Equations (20), (52) and (53) can be used to show that

$$T^{\varkappa}_{\mu}(Rx) = \sum_{\nu} T^{\varkappa}_{\nu}(x)\mathscr{D}^{\varkappa}_{\nu\mu}(\Omega)\,, \tag{54a}$$

$$T^{\varkappa}_{\mu}(R^{-1}x) = \sum_{\nu} T^{\varkappa}_{\nu}(x)\mathscr{D}^{\dagger\varkappa}_{\nu\mu}(\Omega)\,, \tag{54b}$$

Ω being the set of Euler angles associated with R.

We now construct the general expression for the diagonal and nondiagonal matrix elements of operators $T^{\varkappa}_{\mu}$ with respect to projected wave functions ψ_{nKM}

$$\int\mathrm{d}\tau\,\psi^{J'*}_{n'M'K'}(x)\,T^{\varkappa}_{\mu}(x)\,\psi_{nMK}(x) = \mathscr{M}\,. \tag{55}$$

The main application will be—for diagonal elements—the evaluation of electric and magnetic multipole moments; nondiagonal elements determine the transition rates, as in electromagnetic and β-transitions.

Matrix elements of scalar operators, as for instance the energy, are a special case. It will be seen however, that in the particular case of the energy, a higher order of approximation is needed to extract the rotational spectrum than in the calculation of multipole moments and transition amplitudes. We shall therefore reserve the discussion of the energy to a final subsection.

To evaluate an expression of type of $\mathscr{M}$, eq. (55), we proceed as in the calculation of the overlap integral of two ψ's and get

$$\mathscr{M} = \int\mathrm{d}\Omega\int\mathrm{d}\widetilde{\Omega}\sum_{\nu}\mathscr{D}^{J'}_{M'K'}(\Omega)\mathscr{D}^{\dagger\varkappa}_{\nu\mu}(\Omega)\sum_{z}\mathscr{D}^{\dagger J}_{Kz}(\widetilde{\Omega})\mathscr{D}^{\dagger J}_{zM}(\Omega)\int\mathrm{d}\tau\,\Phi^{*}_{n'K'}(x)T^{\varkappa}_{\nu}(x)\Phi_{nK}(\widetilde{R}x)\,.$$

There appears now an integration over a product of three functions $\mathscr{D}(\Omega)$. Using eqs. (34b) and (33), this Ω-integral gives:

$$\frac{\delta_{M',\mu+M}}{2J'+1}\langle J'M'|\varkappa\mu, JM\rangle\langle J'K'|\varkappa\nu, J(K'-\nu)\rangle\delta_{K',\nu+z}\,.$$

Inserting this into M, one has

(56) $$\mathscr{M} = \frac{1}{2J'+1} \langle J'M'|\varkappa\mu, JM\rangle \langle n'K'J'\|T^{\varkappa}\|nKJ\rangle ,$$

where $\langle\|T^{\varkappa}\|\rangle$ is a reduced matrix-element (but beware, we do not have a standard normalization!), and the first coefficient $\langle J'M'|\varkappa\mu, JM\rangle$ just expresses the Wigner-Eckhart theorem.

The reduced matrix element is

(57) $$\langle n'K'J'\|T^{\varkappa}\|nKJ\rangle = \sum_{\nu} \langle J'K'|\varkappa\nu, J(K'-\nu)\rangle \cdot \cdot \int \mathrm{d}\Omega\, \mathscr{D}^{\dagger J}_{K,K'-\nu}(\tilde{\Omega}) \int \mathrm{d}\tau\, \Phi^*_{n'K'}(x)\, T^{\varkappa}_{\nu}(x)\, \Phi_{nK}(\tilde{R}x) .$$

This can be further reduced, using the fact that Φ_{nK} and $(\Phi^*_{n'K'}T^{\varkappa}_{\nu})$ are eigenstates of J_z to K and $K'-\nu$, respectively. This gives the final expression

(58) $$\int \mathrm{d}\tau\, \psi^{*J'}_{n'K'M'}(x) T^{\varkappa}_{\mu}(x) \psi^{J}_{nKM}(x) = \frac{1}{2J'+1} \langle J'M'|\varkappa\mu, JM\rangle \cdot \sum_{\nu} \langle J'K'|\varkappa\nu, J(K'-\nu)\rangle \cdot \cdot \frac{1}{2}\int_{-1}^{+1} \mathrm{d}\cos\beta\, d^{J}_{K'-\nu,K}(\beta) \int \mathrm{d}\tau\, \Phi^*_{n'K'}(x) T^{\varkappa}_{\nu}(x) \exp[-i\beta J_y]\, \Phi_{nK}(x) .$$

Since this is the « general » formula, we shall introduce an additional feature.

We will assume that for any $T^{\varkappa}$, the matrix element

$$\int \mathrm{d}\tau\, \Phi^*_{n'K'}(x)\, T^{\varkappa}(x) \exp[-i\beta J_y]\, \Phi_{nK}(x)$$

goes to a value very nearly zero as $\beta \to \pi/2$. So effectively the β-integral consists of two separate parts $0<\beta<\pi/2$ and $\pi/2 \leqslant \beta \leqslant \pi$. In this latter we introduce $\beta' = \pi - \beta$ as variable, and finally $\beta'' = -\beta'$. We may then use the symmetry properties of the d-function, and the definition of $\Phi_{n,-K}$ given by eq. (48). This gives, finally,

(58a) $$\langle n'K'J'\|T^{\varkappa}\|nKJ\rangle = \sum_{\nu} \langle J'K'|\varkappa\nu, J(K'-\nu)\rangle \cdot \cdot \left\{\frac{1}{2}\int_{0}^{\pi/2} \mathrm{d}\cos\beta\, d^{J}_{K'-\nu,K}(\beta) \int \mathrm{d}\tau\, \Phi^*_{n'K'}(x)\, T^{\varkappa}_{\nu}(x) \exp[-i\beta J_y]\Phi_{nK}(x) + \right. \left. + (-1)^{J-K}\frac{1}{2}\int_{0}^{\pi/2} \mathrm{d}\cos\beta\, d^{J}_{K'-\nu,-K}(\beta) \int \mathrm{d}\tau\, \Phi^*_{n'K'}(x)\, T^{\varkappa}_{\nu}(x) \exp[-i\beta J_y]\Phi_{n,-K}(x)\right\} .$$

The most trivial and reliable results will be those referring to diagonal elements, or to transitions *within* a given rotational band. In both these cases, the *same* intrinsic wave function Φ_{nK} appears in initial and final states.

In the evaluation of eq. (58), one may use a systematic approximation procedure, based on an expansion in powers of $1/\langle J\rangle^2$. This arises as follows: In (58) one has integrals over a product

$$\int_{\beta=0}^{\pi/2} \mathrm{d}\cos\beta\, d^J_{K',K}(\beta)\, T(\beta)\,, \tag{59}$$

where $T(\beta)$ is the matrix element of $\big(T^{\varkappa}_{\nu}(x)\exp[-i\beta J_y]\big)$. $d^J_{K',K}(\beta)$ is a *slowly* varying function of β, starting like $\beta^{|K'-K|}$. $T(\beta)$ on the other hand is of type $T(\beta)\sim\beta^s\exp[-\beta^2/\beta_0^2]$, β_0^2 being of order $4/\langle J^2\rangle$, that is $\beta_0^2\ll 1$. This situation lends itself to a procedure of successive approximation, in increasing powers of β_0^2.

We have then:

1) *zero* order terms

$$K'=K\ \big(\text{in (59)}\big)\,,\qquad d^J_{KK}\simeq 1\,,\qquad T(\beta)\underset{\beta\to 0}{\rightarrow}\text{const}\neq 0\,;$$

2) *first* order terms: May arise in 3 ways

$$K'=K\,,\qquad \beta^2\text{-term of } d^J_{KK}\,,\qquad T(\beta)\underset{\beta\to 0}{\rightarrow}O(1)\,,$$

$$\text{or}\quad |K'-K|=1\,,\qquad T(\beta)\rightarrow O(\beta)$$

$$\text{or}\quad |K'-K|=2\,,\qquad T(\beta)\rightarrow O(1)\,.$$

In most cases, the zero approximation will be sufficient. A *notable* exception is the rotational energy, which must be calculated in 1st order. Also, zero-order terms may be anomalously small, or higher-order terms anomalously large; a case by case examination is needed to judge what terms must be retained.

3·6. *Some examples.*

3·6.1. Electric quadrupole moment. Conventionally, the quadrupole moment is defined as

$$Q=\int \psi^{*J}_{nKJ}Q_0^2\,\psi^J_{nKJ}\,\mathrm{d}\tau\,. \tag{60}$$

In this case, the zero-order approximation will do, and gives as leading term

$$Q=\langle JJ|20JJ\rangle\langle JK|20,JK\rangle\,\frac{\int \mathrm{d}\cos\beta\int\mathrm{d}\tau\,\Phi^*_{nK}Q_0^2\exp[-i\beta J_y]\Phi_{nK}}{\int \mathrm{d}\cos\beta\int\mathrm{d}\tau\,\Phi^*_{nK}\exp[-i\beta J_y]\Phi_{nK}}\,. \tag{61}$$

The denominator normalizes the trial function, and the ratio of the two integrals defines the « intrinsic » quadrupole moment Q_0. Inserting the values of the vector-addition coefficients, one has

(62) $$Q=\frac{3K^2-J(J+1)}{(J+1)(2J+3)}Q_0 .$$

3·6.2. Electric quadrupole transitions within a given band (nK). The transition amplitude is

$$\sim\int\psi^{*J'}_{nKM'}Q^2_\mu\psi^J_{nKM}\,\mathrm{d}\tau ,$$

which, in the same zero-order approximation, is

$$\langle J'M'|2\mu JM\rangle\langle J'K|20, JK\rangle Q_0$$

and the reduced transition probability $B(E2)$ is thus proportional to

(63) $$B(E_2)\sim|\langle J'K|20, JK\rangle|^2Q_0^2 .$$

But in both these cases there are additional « zero order » terms, due to the second term in (58*a*). They are absent for $K=0$, and $K>1$ but exist for $K=\frac{1}{2}, 1$ (generally, for $2|K|\leqslant\varkappa$ the rank of the tensor). In example, for $K=\frac{1}{2}$ one has an addition to (61):

(61*a*) $$\delta Q=\langle JJ|20JJ\rangle\langle J\tfrac{1}{2}|2|J-\tfrac{1}{2}\rangle(-1)^{J-\frac{1}{2}}\cdot$$
$$\cdot\int\mathrm{d}\cos\beta\int\mathrm{d}\tau\,\Phi^*_{n\frac{1}{2}}Q^2_1\exp[-i\beta J_y]\Phi_{n,-\frac{1}{2}}/\text{normalization} .$$

Clearly, the matrix element

$$T(\beta)=\int\Phi^*_{n\frac{1}{2}}Q^2_1\exp[-i\beta J_y]\Phi_{n,-\frac{1}{2}}$$

is in general $\neq 0$ for $\beta\to 0$.

In the β-integral, also the factor $d^J_{-\frac{1}{2},-\frac{1}{2}}(\beta)$ would occur, which we put equal to 1. So the term is formally of order zero, but small nevertheless since

$$\left|\int\mathrm{d}\tau\,\Phi^*_{n\frac{1}{2}}Q^2_0\Phi_{n\frac{1}{2}}\right|\gg\left|\int\mathrm{d}\tau\,\Phi^*_{n\frac{1}{2}}Q^2_1\Phi_{n-\frac{1}{2}}\right| ,$$

since all particles contribute to the left matrix element, but only 1 to the right one.

So some judgement is needed to evaluate matrix elements in a proper approximation.

3·6.3. Magnetic dipole moment. Here we calculate the expression up to first-order terms. The zero-order term will define the « intrinsic » g-factor g_K, the first-order term the collective or rotational g-factor g_R.

The magnetic moment μ is defined as

$$\mu = \int \psi_J^{*J} M_0^1 \psi_J^J \,\mathrm{d}\tau \,.$$

Including again the normalization of the wave function, one has

$$\mu = \langle JJ|10, JJ\rangle \cdot \Bigg\{ \langle JK|10, JK\rangle \cdot \frac{\int_0^{\pi/2} \mathrm{d}\cos\beta\big(1-(\beta^2/4)[J(J+1)-K^2]\big)\int \mathrm{d}\tau\, \Phi_{nK}^* M_0^1 \exp[-i\beta J_y]\Phi_{nK}}{\int_0^{\pi/2} \mathrm{d}\cos\beta\big(1-(\beta^2/4)[J(J+1)-K^2]\big)\int \mathrm{d}\tau\, \Phi_{nK}^* \exp[-i\beta J_y]\Phi_{nK}} +$$
$$+ \langle JK|11, JK-1\rangle \int \mathrm{d}\cos\beta\, d^J_{K-1,K}(\beta) \int \mathrm{d}\tau\, \Phi_{nK}^* M_1^1 \exp[-i\beta J_y]\Phi_{nK}/\text{norm.} +$$
$$+ \langle JK|1, -1, JK+1\rangle \int \mathrm{d}\cos\beta\, d^J_{K+1,K}(\beta) \int \mathrm{d}\tau\, \Phi_{nK}^* M_{-1}^1 \exp[-i\beta J_y]\Phi_{nK}/\text{norm.} \,.$$

This expression holds for $K \neq \frac{1}{2}$, and reduces to

$$\mu \simeq g_R J + (g_K - g_R)\frac{K^2}{J+1}\,, \tag{64}$$

a well-known result; g_K and g_R are given by

$$g_K \simeq \int \mathrm{d}\tau\, \Phi_{nK}^* M_z \Phi_{nK}/K \qquad (M_z = M_0^1, \text{ etc.}), \tag{65a}$$

$$g_R \simeq \int \mathrm{d}\tau\, \Phi_{nK}^* (M_x J_x + M_y J_y)\Phi_{nK}/\langle J_x^2 + J_y^2\rangle \,. \tag{65b}$$

An additional zero-order term arises for $K = \frac{1}{2}$.

3·6.4. Rotational energy. Here we have to deal with the expectation values of a *scalar* operator. The attention is here focused on the J-dependent 1st-order terms. For $K=0$ or $K \geqslant 1$, the expression for E, up to 1st order, reads

$$E_{nK}^J = \int_0^{\pi/2} \sin^2\beta\,\mathrm{d}\beta \left(1 - \frac{\beta^2}{4}\big(J(J+1)-K^2\big)\right) \int \mathrm{d}\tau \big(\Phi_{nK}^* H \exp[-i\beta J_y]\Phi_{nK}\big)/\text{norm.} \tag{67}$$

the normalization being the same expression, with H replaced by 1.

We may write

$$(68)\qquad \int \mathrm{d}\tau \Phi^*_{nK} H \exp[-i\beta J_y]\Phi_{nK} = \int \mathrm{d}\tau(\Phi^*_{nK} H \Phi_{nK}) \int \mathrm{d}\tau \Phi^*_{nK} \exp[-i\beta J_y]\Phi_{nK} + \\ + \sum_{n'\neq n}{}' \int (\Phi^*_{nK} H \Phi_{n'K})\, \mathrm{d}\tau \int \mathrm{d}\tau (\Phi^*_{n'K} \exp[-i\beta J_y]\Phi_{nK}) .$$

The first term on the right just gives the Hartree-Fock energy times the normalization integral; so

$$(69)\qquad E^J_{nK} = (E_{nK})_{\text{H.F.}} + \sum_{n'\neq n} H_{nn'} \int_0^{\pi/2} \mathrm{d}\cos\beta \left(1 - \frac{\beta^2}{4}\,(J(J+1) - K^2) + \ldots\right) \cdot \\ \cdot \int \mathrm{d}\tau \Phi^*_{n'K} \exp[-i\beta J_y]\Phi_{nK}/\text{norm.} .$$

Now we use again expression (47) for $N_{nK,nK}(\beta)$ (eq. (43)). For the off-diagonal element occurring in (69), one has

$$(70)\qquad N_{n'K,nK}(\beta) \simeq -\frac{\beta^2}{2}\,(J^2_y)_{n'K,nK} N_{nK,nK}(\beta) .$$

This result is based on the following observations:

Assuming that Φ_{nK} is a relative H.F. ground state, the $\Phi_{n'K}$ in (68, 69) represent two particle two hole excitations. The matrix element (70) therefore starts like β^2 at $\beta^2 = 0$. The r.h.s. of (70) may be obtained by the following argument:

Let $\Omega^\dagger_{n'n}$ be the operator with the property

$$(71)\qquad \Phi_{n'K} = \Omega^\dagger_{n'n}\Phi_{nK} , \qquad 0 = \Omega_{n',n}\Phi_{nK} ,$$

$\Omega^\dagger$ is a two particle-two hole creation operator. One has then

$$\int \mathrm{d}\tau (\Phi^*_{n'K} \exp[-i\beta J_y]\Phi_{nK}) = (\exp[-i\beta J_y])_{n'K,nK} = (\Omega_{n'n} \exp[-i\beta J_y])_{nK,nK} = \\ = \left\{\exp[-i\beta J_y]\left(\Omega_{n'n} - i\beta[\Omega_{n'n}, J_y] - \frac{\beta^2}{2}\,[[\Omega_{n'n}, J_y]J_y] + \ldots\right)\right\}_{nK,nK} .$$

Due to the nature of $\Omega_{n'n}$, also $[\Omega_{n'n}, J_y]\Phi_{nK} = 0$, and the lowest nonzero term is

$$(72)\qquad -\frac{\beta^2}{2}\,(\exp[-i\beta J_y])_{nK,nK}[[\Omega_{n'n}, J_y]J_y]_{nK,nK} = \\ = -\frac{\beta^2}{2}\,(\exp[-i\beta J_y])_{nK,nK} \int \Phi^*_{n'K} J^2_y \Phi_{nK}\, \mathrm{d}\tau .$$

In terms of $N(\beta) = N_{nK,nK}(\beta)$ we have now

$$(73) \qquad E^J_{nK} = (E_{nK})_{\text{HF}} + \sum_{n'\neq n} \left(H_{nK,n'K}(J^2_y)_{n'K,nK}\right) \cdot \frac{\int_0^{\pi/2} \beta\, d\beta\, \beta^2 N(\beta)\left[1 - (\beta^2/4)\left(J(J+1) - K^2\right)\right]}{\int_0^{\pi/2} \beta\, d\beta\, N(\beta)\left[1 - (\beta^2/4)\left(J(J+1) - K^2\right)\right]} =$$

$$= (E_{nK})_{\text{HF}} - 2\,\frac{\sum_{n'\neq n} H_{nK,n'K}(J^2_y)_{n'K,nK}}{(J^2_\perp)_{nK,nK}}\left(1 - \frac{J(J+1) - K^2}{\langle J^2_\perp\rangle}\right) =$$

$$= (E_{nK})_{\text{HF}} + \frac{1}{2\Theta}\left\{J(J+1) - K^2 - \langle J^2_\perp\rangle\right\}.$$

In this last equation, we have introduced the moment of inertia Θ, which in this formalism is given by

$$(74) \qquad \frac{1}{2\Theta} = \sum_{n'\neq n} \frac{H_{nK,n'K}(J^2_\perp)_{n'K,nK}}{(J^2_\perp)^2_{nK,nK}}.$$

Several comments are in order concerning this result:

1) The value of this method as a device to calculate rotational energies has been questioned, since the corresponding procedure—projection on a state of total *linear* momentum P—does *not* give the correct translational kinetic energy $P^2/2Am$.

Modifications of the straight projection procedure are the method of Peierls-Thouless which leads again to the Thouless-Valatin result for Θ, and the variational method applied to the projected wave functions. For this, see the notes of a seminar given by YOCCOZ.

2) The evaluation of nondiagonal elements $N_{n'K',nK}(\beta)$ has always been done in a rather flimsy way, leading to expressions like (70). Better results might be obtained from solving approximately the differential equations

$$(75) \qquad \frac{\partial^2 N_{n'K',nK}(\beta)}{\partial\beta^2} = -\sum_{n''K''} (J^2_y)_{n'K',n''K''} N_{n''K'',nK}(\beta).$$

3) The case $K = \frac{1}{2}$ is special. One has an additional first order term due to the second part of (58a).

The expression (69) is changed into

$$E^J_{n\frac{1}{2}} = (E_{n\frac{1}{2}})_{\text{HF}} + \sum_{n'\neq n} H_{nn'} \frac{I_{n'n}}{I_{nn}},$$

where

$$(76) \qquad I_{n'n} = \int_0^{\pi/2} \beta \mathrm{d}\beta \left\{ \left[1 - \frac{\beta^2}{4} \left(J(J+1) - \frac{1}{4} \right) \right] N_{n\frac{1}{2},n\frac{1}{2}}(\beta) + \right.$$

$$\left. + (-)^{J+\frac{1}{2}} \left(J + \frac{1}{2} \right) \left(\frac{\beta}{2} \right) N_{n\frac{1}{2},n-\frac{1}{2}}(\beta) \right\} .$$

This leads to the rotational energy of the form

$$(77) \qquad \frac{1}{2\Theta} \left(J(J+1) + (-)^{J+\frac{1}{2}} \left(J + \frac{1}{2} \right) a \right) ,$$

a being the so-called decoupling coefficient.

4. – Method of separation of collective variables in H.

This is an old idea, which flourished in the 50es: One introduces, in an explicit fashion, collective variables directly in the Hamiltonian, in other words, one carries out a canonical transformation. Such a transformation would be of the type

$$\begin{pmatrix} x_i \\ p_i \end{pmatrix} \rightleftarrows \begin{pmatrix} Q_s \\ P_s \end{pmatrix}, \qquad \begin{pmatrix} \xi_\sigma \\ \pi_\sigma \end{pmatrix} .$$

$i = 1 \ldots A$ « collective » variables « intrinsic » variables

If f collective variable pairs are introduced, there will be $(3A - f)$ intrinsic variable pairs.

This programme can be carried out to a certain extent, but is of limited usefulness only. The main objection is that the one-to-one correspondence of intrinsic variables ξ_σ to the co-ordinates of individual nucleon is *lost*, and with this is lost the possibility of an « independent particle », that is, Hartree Fock description of the intrinsic motion.

So the conclusion is that we must *not* carry out a canonical transformation. Nevertheless the idea of somehow separating off the collective terms in the Hamiltonian can be carried out. Let us illustrate this with an almost trivial example, that of the center-of-mass motion of the nucleus. We may write

$$(78) \qquad H(x_i, p_i) = \frac{P^2}{2Am} + H^{\text{intr}}(x_i, p_i) ,$$

where

$$(79) \qquad H^{\text{intr}}(x_i, p_i) = \sum_{i=1}^{A} \frac{p_i^2}{2m^*} + \sum_{i<j} \left(V_{ij} - \frac{p_i p_j}{Am} \right)$$

and $m^* = (A/(A-1))m$. H^{intr} *could* be written as a function of $3(A-1)$ independent variables ξ_σ, π_σ; this is demonstrated by the property of H^{intr} to commute with the canonical pair of collective variables

$$P = \sum_{i=1}^{A} p_i\,, \qquad X = \frac{1}{A}\sum_{i=1}^{A} x_i\,, \tag{80}$$

$$[H^{\text{intr}}, P] = 0\,, \qquad [H^{\text{intr}}, X] = 0\,. \tag{81}$$

Nevertheless we choose to use the expression (79) for H^{intr}, that is, to keep it as a function of the x_i and p_i.

This will enable us to apply the usual Hartree-Fock trial function, the Slater determinant, to H^{intr}. The resulting H.F. equation will be of the usual type, since H^{intr} has the same structure as H.

One way, in which eq. (81) will make itself felt is that the degeneracy of the H.F. ground state is now increased; both

$$\exp[i\lambda P]\Phi_0 \qquad \text{and} \qquad \exp[i\eta X]\Phi_0$$

give H.F. energies degenerate with $E_0 = (\Phi_0 H \Phi_0)$.

But since one has already to face the problem of zero roots in the stability problem of the H.F. solution, the existence of an additional mode with $\omega = 0$ is hardly a serious problem. Both these roots will show up as zero energy solutions in an R.P.A. treatment.

We will now apply this idea to the rotational type of collective motion. Here the separation of H analogous to (78) is not obvious; indeed one may well ask whether it exists at all. Well, it does, to a certain extent. Let us illustrate this in a two-dimensional space, where only one component of J exists

$$J = \sum (y_i p_{z_i} - z_i p_{y_i})\,. \tag{82}$$

The conjugate variable is an angle φ which must satisfy the commutation relation

$$[J, e^{i\varphi}] = e^{i\varphi}\,, \tag{83}$$

$e^{i\varphi}$ is to be defined as a symmetric function of the particle co-ordinates and momenta; one choice is

$$\exp[2i\varphi] = \frac{\sum_i (x_i + iy_i)^2}{|\sum (x_i + iy_i)|^2}\,. \tag{84}$$

(This φ measures the orientation of the principal axes of the quadrupole tensor of the mass distribution; but other choices are possible.)

The criteria for a function $f(x_i, p_i)$ to be «intrinsic» are given by the conditions

$$\begin{cases} [f(x_i, p_i), J] = 0\,, \\ [f(x_i, p_i), \varphi] = 0\,. \end{cases} \tag{85}$$

Since H already commutes with J the following decomposition may be attempted:

$$H = H^{(0)} + JH^{(1)} + \frac{J^2}{2} H^{(2)} + \dots\,, \tag{86}$$

where all terms $H^{(n)}(x_i, p_i)$ are *intrinsic* in the sense of eq. (85).

This separation can indeed be carried out.

Define

$$\varphi^{(K+1)} = i[\varphi^{(K)}, \varphi] \tag{87a}$$

and

$$\varphi^0 = H\,, \qquad \varphi^{(1)} \equiv \dot{\varphi} = i[H, \varphi]\,. \tag{87b}$$

By taking commutators of (86) with φ one has

$$\varphi^{(K)} = \sum_{n=0} \frac{J^n}{n!} H^{(n+K)} \tag{88}$$

and by inversion of (88)

$$H^{(n)} = \sum_{K=0} \frac{(-)^K}{K!} J^K \varphi^{(K+n)}\,. \tag{89}$$

One easily *checks* that each term satisfies (85), and that (86) holds.

A simplification arises if φ is defined as a function of *co-ordinates* x_i only, and the two-body interactions are given by a *local* potential. Then the series (86) stops at $n = 2$, and one has

$$H^{(0)}(x_i, p_i) = H - \dot{\varphi}J + \tfrac{1}{2}i[\dot{\varphi}, \varphi]J^2\,, \tag{90a}$$

$$H^{(1)}(x_i, p_i) = \dot{\varphi} - i[\dot{\varphi}, \varphi]J\,, \tag{90b}$$

$$H^{(2)}(x_i, p_i) = i[\dot{\varphi}, \varphi]\,. \tag{90c}$$

The eigenvalue problem for H can now be carried out as follows. We construct a trial function

$$\psi^{J'} = \exp[iJ'\varphi]\Phi^{(\text{intr})}\,,$$

J' being an *eigenvalue* of the operator J.

The eigenvalue problem for $\Phi^{(\mathrm{intr})}$ is then the eigenvalue problem of the operator

$$H^{J'} = H^{(0)} + J'H^{(1)} + \tfrac{1}{2}J'^2H^{(2)}, \tag{91}$$

notice that $H^{J'}(x_i, p_i)$ (J' is a numerical parameter) is entirely intrinsic, yet written as a function of (x_i, p_i). We may diagonalize $H^{J'}$ over any orthogonal set of wave functions $\Phi_n(x_1 \dots x_A)$. This is clearly a *redundant* basis; as a consequence, the energy levels will be degenerate. In any approximate diagonalization of $(H^{J'})_{n',n}$ this degeneracy will be removed, and the problem of recognizing *spurious states* will arise.

One approximation scheme one may think of is to determine a « ground » state determinantal wave function for $H^{J'}$ by the usual H.F. method, and *then* use the R.P.A. for the description of « intrinsic » modes of excitations (of zero angular-momentum). This ground state trial function $\Phi_{0z}^{J'}$ will be a (generally deformed) determinant, and give, to zero-th order, the ground states for each eigenvalue J' of J; that is, it will give the ground state rotational band. The rotational energies and hence the moments of inertia appear therefore, in this approach, as given in lowest order already by a simple H.F. solution for the Hamiltonian (91), without any further projection or subsidiary condition. What are the results?

The H.F. solution $\Phi_0^{J'}$ for (91) has been (formally) obtained by reduction to the problem for $J' = 0$

$$\Phi_0^{J'} = \exp[iJ'F(x, p)]\Phi_0^0 . \tag{92}$$

$F(x, p)$ is determined by the conditions that

$$\delta\langle\Phi_0^{J'}|H^{J'}|\Phi_0^{J'}\rangle = 0$$

or, equivalently,

$$\delta\langle\Phi_0^0|\exp[-iJ'F]H^{J'}\exp[iJ'F]|\Phi_0^0\rangle = 0 , \tag{93}$$

that is, Φ_0^0 must be a H.F. solution of both $H^0 = H^{J'=0}$ and of

$$(\exp[-iJ'F]H^{J'}\exp[iJ'F]) .$$

The terms proportional to J'^2 in $E^{J'}$ determine the moment of inertia Θ:

$$\frac{1}{\Theta} = \langle\Phi_0^0|H^{(2)} + i[H^{(1)}, F]|\Phi_0^0\rangle . \tag{94}$$

It can be shown that (94) is in fact nothing but the Thouless-Valatin formula again. It is noteworthy that this definite result for Θ is obtained *irrespective* of the definition of the phase angle operator φ.

We now discuss briefly the more realistic 3-dimensional case. The collective variables in this case are the 3 components J_K ($K=1, 2, 3$) of the angular momentum, and 3 Euler angles. The latter can be replaced by three orthogonal unit vectors $\boldsymbol{e}_A$ ($A=1, 2, 3$) which specify a « body fixed » system of co-ordinate axes

(95a) $$(\boldsymbol{e}_A \cdot \boldsymbol{e}_B) = \delta_{AB} ,$$

(95b) $$(\boldsymbol{e}_A \times \boldsymbol{e}_B) = \boldsymbol{e}_{[AB]} = \boldsymbol{e}_C .$$

These $\boldsymbol{e}_A$ are symmetric functions of the particle co-ordinates and momenta. With their help, one may define the body-fixed components of the angular momentum:

(96) $$J_A = (\boldsymbol{J} \cdot \boldsymbol{e}_A) = \sum_{K=1}^{3} J_K e_{KA} .$$

The J_A are scalars:

(97) $$[J_A, J_K] = 0 \qquad \text{(all } A, K\text{)}.$$

The following commutators are also essential:

(98a) $$[J_i, J_k] = iJ_l ,$$

(98b) $$[J_A, J_B] = -iJ_C$$

(i, k, l = cyclic permut. of 1, 2, 3; ABC same).

One has also

(99a) $$[J_i, e_{KA}] = ie_{[iK]A} = ie_{lA} ,$$

(99b) $$[J_A, e_{KB}] = -ie_{K[AB]} = -ie_{KC} .$$

A function $f(x_i, p_i)$ will be called intrinsic if it commutes with all the J^K and e_{KA} (of these latter, only 3 are independent).

The generalization of the decomposition (86) is now

(100) $$H = H^{(0)} + \sum_A J_A H_A^{(1)} + \tfrac{1}{2} \sum_{AB} J_A J_B H_{AB}^{(2)} + \dots ,$$

where $H^{(0)}$, $H_A^{(1)}$, $H_{AB}^{(2)}$ are intrinsic in the above-mentioned sense. To determine those terms, one needs the quantities

(101a) $$\eta_C^{(1)} = \eta_{[AB]}^{(1)} = \tfrac{1}{2}(\dot{\boldsymbol{e}}_A \cdot \boldsymbol{e}_B - \dot{\boldsymbol{e}}_B \cdot \boldsymbol{e}_A)$$

(where $\dot{e} = i[H, e]$), and

$$\eta_{AB}^{(2)} = \eta_{BA}^{(2)} = \frac{i}{2}\left([\eta_A^{(1)}, \boldsymbol{e}_C]\cdot\boldsymbol{e}_D - [\eta_A^{(1)}, \boldsymbol{e}_D]\boldsymbol{e}_C\right) \tag{101b}$$

(with BCD-cyclic perm. of 1 2 3).

One has then

$$H^{(0)} = H - \sum_A \eta_A^{(1)} J_A + \tfrac{1}{2}\sum_{AB} \eta_{AB}^{(2)} J_A J_B\,, \tag{102a}$$

$$H_A^{(1)} = \eta_A^{(1)} - \sum_B \eta_{AB}^{(2)} J_B\,, \tag{102b}$$

$$H_{AB}^{(2)} = \eta_{AB}^{(2)}\,. \tag{102c}$$

It is easily checked by means of eqs. (95)-(99), that these operators are intrinsic, that is, commute with J_A (or J_K) and $\boldsymbol{e}_A$.

The *energy eigenvalue* problem may now be handled as follows. We assume a solution ψ of the form

$$\psi^J_{nKM}(x_1 \dots x_A) = \sum_K \mathscr{D}^{\dagger J}_{KM}(e_{KA})\,\psi_n^{(JK)}(\text{intrinsic})\,,$$

the $\mathscr{D}^\dagger$ are eigenfunctions of $\boldsymbol{J}^2$ and $J_{A=3}$ (see section on rotations). The ψ_n (intr) are then eigenfunctions of the matrix operator

$$(JK|\widetilde{H}|JK') = H^{(0)}\delta_{KK'} + \sum_A H_A^{(1)}(JK|J_A|JK') + \tfrac{1}{2}\sum_{AB} H_{AB}^{(2)}(JK|J_A J_B|JK')\,. \tag{103}$$

As before, one may try a H.F. approximation on this operator:

One starts with a H.F. solution $\Phi_0^{(0)}$ for $H^{(0)}$, assuming $K = K_0$, and then defines the trial functions for (103) by

$$\begin{aligned}\Phi_0^{(JK)} &= (JK|\exp\left[i \textstyle\sum F_A(x_i p_i) J_A\right]|JK_0)\cdot\Phi_0^{(0)} = \\ &= \left\{\delta_{KK_0} + i \sum_A F_A(x_i p_i)(JK|J_A|JK_0) + \dots\right\}\Phi_0^{(0)}\,.\end{aligned} \tag{104}$$

With suitable approximations, one ends up again with the Thouless-Valatin result.

It is of some interest to investigate how the Hamiltonian (100), or the two-dimensional analogy (86), is related to the Hamiltonian of the Bohr-Mottelson unified model. Let us illustrate this in the two-dimensional case. Using eqs. (90), one can easily see that H may be written as

$$H = H^{(0)} + \frac{1}{2\Theta_0}(J - \widetilde{J})^2\,, \tag{105}$$

where

(106a) $$H^{(C)} = H - \tfrac{1}{2}\Theta_0\dot{\varphi}^2 ,$$

(106b) $$\Theta_0 \;= i[\dot{\varphi}, \varphi] ,$$

(106c) $$\tilde{J} \;= J - \Theta_0\dot{\varphi} .$$

All three operators $H^{(C)}$, Θ_0, $\tilde{J}$ are *intrinsic*, as one may easily check.

The structure (105) resembles closely the Bohr-Mottelson expression, but there are some characteristic differences: in particular $\tilde{J}$ is *not* an angular momentum, but in fact an intrinsic operator which commutes with J. One may show that for the definition (84) of φ, the operator Θ_0 is

(107) $$\Theta_0 \simeq m \frac{(\sum x^2 - \sum y^2)^2}{\sum x^2 + \sum y^2} .$$

This is exactly the « hydrodynamic » moment of inertia of the B.M. model. The effective moment of inertia, given by eq. (94) is quite different from Θ_0; but in order to obtain the correct value of Θ, the proper form of the operator $\tilde{J}$ (eq. (106c)) is quite crucial.

BIBLIOGRAPHY

Cranking formulae:

D. R. INGLIS: *Phys. Rev.*, **96**, 1059 (1954); **79**, 701 (1955).
J. G. VALATIN: *Proc. Roy. Soc.*, A **238**, 182 (1956).

Time-dependent Hartree-Fock:

D. J. THOULESS and J. G. VALATIN: *Nucl. Phys.*, **31**, 211 (1952).

« Generalized » Hartree-Fock:

A. K. KERMAN and A. KLEIN: *Phys. Rev.*, **132**, 1326 (1963).

J-projected wave functions:

R. E. PEIERLS and J. YOCCOZ: *Proc. Phys. Soc.*, A **70**, 381 (1957).
J. J. GRIFFIN and J. A. WHEELER: *Phys. Rev.*, **108**, 311 (1962).
R. E. PEIERLS and D. J. THOULESS: *Nucl. Phys.*, **38**, 154 (1962).

Rotations and D-functions:

A. R. EDMONDS: *Angular Momentum in Quantum Mechanics* (Princeton, N. J., 1957).
M. E. ROSE: *Elementary Theory of Angular Momentum* (New York, 1957).

Separation of collective variables:

F. Villars: *Elementary Theory of Nuclear Collective Rotations*, in *Nucl. Phys.*, in press.

Older attempts of this sort are reviewed in:

T. Tamura: *Fortschritte der Physik*, **6**, 109 (1958).
F. Villars: *The Collective Model of Nuclei, Annual Reviews of Nuclear Science*, vol. **7** (Palo Alto, Calif., 1957).

Approximate Methods in Nuclear-Structure Calculations.

V. Gillet

Service de Physique Théorique, C.E.N. - Saclay

1. – Introduction.

1·1. *The nuclear Hamiltonian.* – Present microscopic theories of nuclei are based on two postulates:

a) the degrees of freedom associated with the meson fields in nucle; may be replaced by potentials (including exchange forces) between nucleonsi

b) two-body forces are preponderant.

It is difficult to justify these two hypotheses otherwise than by pointing out the absence of effects depending essentially upon their violation.

Thus the nuclear Hamiltonian for A nucleons is of the form

$$H=\sum_{i=1}^{A}\frac{P_i^2}{2M}+\frac{1}{2}\sum_{i,j=1}^{A}V_{ij}\,, \tag{1}$$

where V_{ij} is a two-nucleon potential.

1·2. *The two-body force.* – The matrix elements of the nucleon-nucleon potential on the energy shell are obtained from analyses of the free nucleon-nucleon scattering data. The matrix elements of V_{ij} off the energy shell, which also contribute to the nuclear problem, cannot be obtained directly from experiment. The scattering behavior of two free nucleons is, a priori, quite different from that of two nucleons in a nucleus. In particular, in the latter case the Pauli principle limits the available final states. As a matter of fact the relationship between the nucleon-nucleon free scattering matrix and the scattering matrix in a nucleus is still an outstanding problem in microscopic theory of nuclei. A solution to this problem is suggested in the Brueckner theory [1], where the matrix of the operator V_{ij} is replaced by a matrix T_{ij} which describes the mutual scattering of two nucleons i and j in a nucleus. In the present lectures we will neglect in general this problem and describe V_{ij} by a small number of parameters to be determined by fitting a large number of experimental results. This has been the most usual procedure in shell model spectroscopy. The theoretical relationship between such an « *effective force* » and the two-body potential is outlined in Sect. **3**'1 in the framework of Green's function. The phenomenological aspect of the problem is discussed in Sect. **6**'2. We shall also report in Sect. **6**'2 on some attempts to link more directly the parameters of the effective potential to the free-scattering parameters.

1'3. *The shell structure of nuclei.* – Perhaps the most decisive step in our understanding of nuclei was the recognition that, within a certain approximation, there exists an average nuclear field. This was very surprising since it seems to be in complete contradiction with what we know of nuclear forces which are strong and of short range. However a wealth of experimental evidence such as the shell structure of nuclei, or the large resonances in neutron scattering, shows that nucleons in a nucleus behave to a certain extent as independent particles in a common potential.

Recent advances in the theory of nuclear matter [2, 3] explain in part the paradox by singling out two mechanisms which strongly reduce the effects of the strong interaction between nucleons upon the nuclear wave function.

a) The scattering of nucleons is hindered by the Pauli principle which limits the final available states to those above the Fermi level. Since two nucleons far apart interact through low Fourier components of the force, the momentum transfer is insufficient to raise them above the Fermi level. Henceforth, beyond a certain distance which WEISSKOPF *et al.* [2] call « the healing distance », the relative wave function of the two nucleons remains unperturbed. This is in sharp contrast to the scattering of two free nucleons, wherein their relative wave function remains affected to infinity.

b) The effects of the repulsive short-range part of the force on the nucleon-nucleon phase shifts are opposite to the effects of the attractive tail of the force. As a result the phase shifts due to the strong nucleon-nucleon potential at distances larger than about 1 fermi are the same as those due to an effective potential which has zero value up to a distance (which is a function of the relative momentum) called the cut-off radius [3] and thereafter it is equal to the weak attractive long-range part of the force.

A consequence of these two effects is the weakly bound nature of nuclear systems. As a matter of fact, the binding energy of the deuteron is so weak that its radius is much larger than the range of nuclear forces and it has no bound excited states. One must compare this situation to the case of the H_2 molecule which presents a complicated vibrational and rotational spectrum.

The experimental evidence for the existence of an average nuclear field within a certain approximation suggests that the microscopic theory of nuclei starts from the application of the variational principle to the class of trial wave functions consisting of independent particle functions. This is the Hartree-Fock method which leads to a separation of the initial Hamiltonian (1) into two parts

$$H = H_0 + v , \tag{2}$$

where H_0 is an independent particle Hamiltonian and v is a *residual interaction* between these particles. Both operators H_0 and v are defined in terms of the initial operators P_i and V_{ij} by the self-consistent Hartree-Fock equations which have been developed in Prof. Villars' lectures.

1·4. *The Hartree-Bogoliubov-Valatin field.* – Besides the average field effect there is another characteristic of the nucleon-nucleon force which may be reproduced by a Hamiltonian consisting of independent excitations. This is the *pairing effect* of the two-body force. Two identical particles, in the same angular momentum state, interact most strongly when the angular overlap of their wave functions is maximum, *i.e.* when they are coupled to a total angular momentum $J = 0$. The Hartree-Bogoliubov-Valatin method extends the variational principle to a class of simple trial wave functions of independent excitations or « quasi-particles », which includes these correlations. Thus one obtains a separation of H similar to (2):

$$H = H_0^{\text{QP}} + v^{\text{QP}} , \tag{3}$$

where H_0^{QP} is a Hamiltonian of independent quasi-particles and v^{QP} is a residual interaction between these quasi-particles. The derivation of the Hamiltonian (3) will be given in Prof. Elliott's lectures.

1·5. *The nuclear secular problem.* – At this stage of the theory, we have a zero-order Hamiltonian H_0 or H_0^{QP} which defines a simple base of independent particle (or quasi-particle) wave functions which hopefully contain already a large part of the effects of the interactions between nucleons. The next step consists in getting as close as possible to the true solutions $\Psi^{(n)}$ of the complete nuclear Hamiltonian

$$H\Psi^{(n)} = E^{(n)}\Psi^{(n)} . \tag{4}$$

We may expand $\Psi^{(n)}$ in a complete orthonormal set of eigenstates Φ_α of H_0:

$$\Psi^{(n)} = \sum_\alpha X_\alpha^{(n)} \Phi_\alpha . \tag{5}$$

The configurational mixing coefficients $X_\alpha^{(n)}$ and the eigenvalues $E^{(n)}$ are then solutions of the nuclear secular problem:

$$\sum_\beta \left(\mathscr{E}_\alpha \delta_{\alpha\beta} + \langle \Phi_\alpha | v | \Phi_\beta \rangle\right) X_\beta^{(n)} = E^{(n)} X_\alpha^{(n)} \tag{6}$$

where the $\mathscr{E}_\alpha$ are the eigenvalues associated with the configurational states Φ_α.

The solutions of (6) are exact as long as the expansion (5) includes all the configurations of H_0. This is clearly not feasible and even undesirable if one wants to retain some insight into the physics of the problem.

In order to simplify the nuclear secular problem three main courses of action have been taken:

a) One guesses a simplified model Hamiltonian, which retains some of the characteristics of the true Hamiltonian but which is invariant under certain groups of transformations. The representations of these groups are used then to classify and build the exact solutions of the model Hamiltonian. The supermultiplet model is thus founded on a spin and isospin invariant Hamiltonian, and the SU_3 theory adds to the preceding invariances those of a harmonic oscillator. These methods will be discussed in Prof. Elliott's lectures.

b) One retains on the contrary the complete nuclear Hamiltonian H, in the form (2) or (3), and looks for nuclear situations where the diagonalization space in (6) may be restricted to a few configurations, or enlarged in simple ways at the cost of violating somewhat the Pauli principle. Such situations arise at or near closed shells where the excitation of a particle requires a large energy, for light deformed nuclei where the degeneracies are strongly removed by the deformed field, and for even-even nuclei where the first few excited states are primarily made up of seniority 2 configurations.

c) One retains a restricted configurational space but introduces the effect of higher configurations through renormalized single quasi-particle excitations and interactions. This approach is systematized in Prof. Migdal's lectures, from the point of view of Landau theory of Fermi liquids. Some of its concepts are somewhat implicit in the methods of *b*) when a phenomenological effective interaction is used along with experimental single-particle energies.

The present lectures will review the methods, calculations and results of *b*) above. We will concern ourselves mainly with the description of low-lying bound states. We will also recall, from a historical point of view, some of the results obtained for unbound states (mainly the giant resonance) using a configuration space of bound configurations. The correct treatment of continuum states, which consists in solving the secular eq. (6) for unbound as well as bound configurations Φ_α of H_0 will be given in Prof. Bloch's lectures.

PART I

2. – The formalism of the second quantization (*).

2·1. *Antisymmetrized states of A nucleons.* – The separation, which is basic to all methods of approximation, of the nuclear Hamiltonian into an independent particle Hamiltonian H_0

$$H_0 = \sum_{i=1}^{A}(T_i + \hat{V}_i) = \sum_{i=1}^{A} h_i \tag{7}$$

and a residual interaction v assigns an important rôle to the independent particles eigenstates of H_0. These will be called the *configurations* of the system. We use the isospin formalism and we consider all nucleons as identical particles. The Pauli principle requires that the configurations be antisymmetrized in the co-ordinates of the A nucleons. Such states can be represented by Slater determinants $\Psi_{\{\alpha\}}$:

$$\Psi_{\{\alpha\}} = \frac{1}{\sqrt{A!}}\begin{pmatrix} \varphi_{\alpha_1}(x_1) & \varphi_{\alpha_1}(x_2) & \dots & \varphi_{\alpha_1}(x_A) \\ \varphi_{\alpha_2}(x_1) & \varphi_{\alpha_2}(x_2) & \dots & \varphi_{\alpha_2}(x_A) \\ \vdots & \vdots & & \vdots \\ \varphi_{\alpha_A}(x_1) & \varphi_{\alpha_A}(x_2) & \dots & \varphi_{\alpha_A}(x_A) \end{pmatrix}. \tag{8}$$

The $\varphi_{\alpha_i}(x)$ form a complete set of single-particle wave functions obtained as solutions of eq. (7), *i.e.*,

$$h(x)\varphi_{\alpha_i}(x) = \varepsilon_{\alpha_i}\varphi_{\alpha_i}(x)\,, \tag{9}$$

and orthonormalized according to

$$\int \varphi_{\alpha_i}(x)\varphi_{\alpha_j}(x)\,\mathrm{d}x = \delta_{\alpha_i\alpha_j}\,.$$

Here x represents the space, spin and isospin co-ordinates, and the indices α_i represent all the quantum numbers which are necessary to define completely the single-particle states α_i.

The Slater determinants $\Psi_{\{\alpha\}}$, where $\{\alpha\} = \alpha_1, \alpha_2, \dots, \alpha_A$ specifies the A occupied single-particle states, form a complete orthonormal set. In par-

(*) For a more detailed treatment we refer for example the reader to *Lectures on the nuclear many-body problem*, by C. BLOCH (Bombay, 1962).

ticular, we shall be concerned in correctly antisymmetrized eigenstates of H_0 which are *also* eigenstates of the total angular-momentum operator. These will be given as a linear combination of Slater determinants

$$\Psi^J = \sum_{\alpha} C^J_{\{\alpha\}} \Psi_{\{\alpha\}} ,$$

where $C^J_{\{\alpha\}}$ are appropriate geometrical recoupling coefficients.

The Slater determinants are somewhat cumbersome and we shall develop now a more convenient representation of these states, the « occupation number » representation.

2·2. *The occupation number representation.* – Except for a phase, the determinant $\Psi_{\{\alpha\}}$ can be specified completely by the series of indices $\alpha_1, \alpha_2, \dots, \alpha_i, \dots$ of the occupied states. The phase arbitrariness is removed by adopting a standard order for these indices. From now on we shall denote by $\{\alpha\}$ the series of indices of the occupied states in that order.

We shall consider now the occupation number representation, which will be denoted as the O.N. representation. Its vectors are of the form

$$|N_\alpha N_\beta N_\gamma \dots N_\delta \dots\rangle , \tag{10}$$

where $\alpha, \beta, \gamma, \dots \delta, \dots$ is the infinite series of indices of all the independent particle states in the standard order and N_δ are the eigenvalues of the occupation number operator:

$$N_\delta = 0 \text{ if the state } \delta \text{ is not occupied,}$$

$$N_\delta = 1 \text{ if the state } \delta \text{ is occupied.}$$

Values for N_δ greater than 1 are forbidden by the Pauli principle. It may be shown that all the states (10) form a complete orthonormal set.

It is possible to establish a one-to-one correspondence between each Slater determinant and a vector of the occupation number representation

$$\Psi_{\{\alpha\}} \Rightarrow |N_\alpha N_\beta N_\gamma \dots N_\delta \dots\rangle ,$$

with the eigenvalues

$$N_{\alpha_1} = N_{\alpha_2} = N_{\alpha_3} = \dots = N_{\alpha_A} = 1$$

in the standard order corresponding to $\{\alpha\} = \alpha_1, \alpha_2, \alpha_3 \dots$ and all other eigenvalues

$$N_\delta = 0 .$$

2'3. *Creation and annihilation operators.* – The O.N. representation is somewhat inconvenient as it requires a complete specification of all nonoccupied states for which $N_\delta = 0$ as well as the occupied states in the standard order for which $N_{\alpha_i} = 1$. Moreover the changes in sign arising from permutations of rows and columns (these being required during the actual evaluation of the matrix elements) make it necessary to follow the standard order throughout the calculation.

These inconveniences can be removed by introducing particle creation and annihilation operators $\eta_m^\dagger$ and η_m. They are defined by their action upon the vectors of the occupation number representation

$$(11)\qquad \begin{cases} \begin{cases} \eta_m^\dagger | N_\alpha, N_\beta, \dots, N_m = 1, \dots, N_\delta, \dots \rangle = 0\,, \\ \eta_m^\dagger | N_\alpha, N_\beta, \dots, N_m = 0, \dots, N_\delta, \dots \rangle = \\ \qquad = (-)^\nu | N_\alpha, N_\beta, \dots, N_m = 1, \dots, N_\delta, \dots \rangle\,; \end{cases} \\ \begin{cases} \eta_m | N_\alpha, N_\beta, \dots, N_m = 1, \dots, N_\delta, \dots \rangle = \\ \qquad = (-)^\nu | N_\alpha, N_\beta, \dots, N_m = 0, \dots, N_\delta, \dots \rangle\,, \\ \eta_m | N_\alpha, N_\beta, \dots, N_m = 0, \dots, N_\delta, \dots \rangle = 0\,. \end{cases} \end{cases}$$

In other words a particle can only be created in state m if that state is not occupied (Pauli principle) and similarly a particle may be annihilated in state m only if that state is occupied. The quantity ν denotes the number of occupied states (such as $N_{\alpha_1} = N_{\alpha_2} = \dots = 1$) which precede the state m in the standard order $\alpha, \beta, \gamma, \dots, m, \dots$.

The sign $(-)^\nu$ which enters in definitions (11) brings about the following anticommutation relations:

$$(12)\qquad [\eta_i, \eta_j]_+ = 0\,, \qquad [\eta_i^\dagger, \eta_j^\dagger]_+ = 0\,, \qquad [\eta_i, \eta_j^\dagger]_+ = \delta_{ij}\,.$$

The vacuum state wherein all particle states are empty shall be denoted as follows:

$$|0\rangle = |N_\alpha = 0,\ N_\beta = 0,\ N_\gamma = 0, \dots N_\delta = 0, \dots \rangle\,.$$

Therefore, according to (11), we find

$$(13)\qquad \eta_m |0\rangle = 0 \qquad \text{for all } m.$$

2'4. *Representation of state vectors.* – For every state of the O.N. representation it is possible to establish the one-to-one correspondence,

$$(14a)\qquad |N_\alpha, N_\beta, N_\gamma, \dots, N_\delta, \dots \rangle \Rightarrow \eta_i^\dagger \eta_j^\dagger \eta_k^\dagger \dots \eta_l^\dagger \dots |0\rangle\,,$$

where the series $i, j, k, \ldots, l, \ldots$ corresponds to the occupation numbers $N_i = N_j = N_k = \ldots = N_l = 1$ of the series $N_\alpha, N_\beta, N_\gamma, \ldots, N_\delta, \ldots$ in the standard order. It is not difficult to verify that the action of the operators $\eta^\dagger_m$ and η_m upon the kets $\eta^\dagger_i\eta^\dagger_j\eta^\dagger_k \ldots \eta^\dagger_l \ldots |0\rangle$ yields the relations (11).

A similar correspondence exists for the Slater determinants

$$\Psi_{\{\alpha\}} = \Psi_{\alpha_1, \alpha_2, \ldots, \alpha_A} \Rightarrow \eta^\dagger_{\alpha_1}\eta^\dagger_{\alpha_2} \ldots \eta^\dagger_{\alpha_A}|0\rangle \tag{14b}$$

($\alpha_1, \alpha_2, \ldots, \alpha_A$ in the standard order).

Indeed, according to the anticommutation relation (12), the normalization of the Slater determinant (the series $\alpha'_1, \alpha'_2, \ldots, \alpha'_A$ and $\alpha_1, \alpha_2, \ldots, \alpha_A$ being both in the standard order)

$$\langle \Psi_{\alpha'_1\alpha'_2 \ldots \alpha'_A} | \Psi_{\alpha_1\alpha_2 \ldots \alpha_A} \rangle = \delta_{\alpha'_1\alpha_1}\delta_{\alpha'_2\alpha_2} \ldots \delta_{\alpha'_A\alpha_A}$$

corresponds to

$$\langle 0|\eta_{\alpha'_1}\eta_{\alpha'_2} \ldots \eta_{\alpha'_A}, \eta^\dagger_{\alpha_1}\eta^\dagger_{\alpha_2} \ldots \eta^\dagger_{\alpha_A}|0\rangle = \delta_{\alpha'_1\alpha_1}\delta_{\alpha'_2\alpha_2} \ldots \delta_{\alpha'_A\alpha_A}$$

setting

$$\langle 0|0\rangle = 1 .$$

Similarly the antisymmetry of the $\Psi_{\{\alpha\}}$ is maintained in the operator description

$$\Psi_{\alpha_1\alpha_2 \ldots \alpha_A} = -\Psi_{\alpha_2\alpha_1 \ldots \alpha_A} \Rightarrow \eta^\dagger_{\alpha_1}\eta^\dagger_{\alpha_2} \ldots \eta^\dagger_{\alpha_A}|0\rangle = -\eta^\dagger_{\alpha_2}\eta^\dagger_{\alpha_1} \ldots \eta^\dagger_{\alpha_A}|0\rangle ,$$

$$\Psi_{\alpha_1\alpha_1 \ldots \alpha_A} = 0 \qquad \Rightarrow \eta^\dagger_{\alpha_1}\eta^\dagger_{\alpha_1} \ldots \eta^\dagger_{\alpha_A}|0\rangle = 0 .$$

Hereafter we shall utilize the vectors (14) rather than the Slater determinants

2·5. *Representation of one-body and two-body operators.* – We need only consider the one-body operators Θ_1 and the two-body operators Θ_2. These operators must be symmetrized with respect to the nucleon co-ordinates in order to reflect the indistinguishability of the particles

$$\begin{cases} \Theta_1 = \sum\limits_{i=1}^{A} \theta_1(x_i) , \\ \Theta_2 = \frac{1}{2} \sum\limits_{i \neq j=1}^{A} \theta_2(x_i, x_j) . \end{cases} \tag{15}$$

In order to express these operators in the O.N. representation we shall first consider their off-diagonal matrix elements as calculated with Slater determinants.

In the case of the one-body operator it is clear that the series $\{\alpha'\}$ and $\{\alpha\}$ which appear in the matrix element

$$\langle \Psi_{\{\alpha'\}} | \sum_{i=1}^{A} \theta_1(x_i) | \Psi_{\{\alpha\}} \rangle$$

differ at most by a single index since each $\theta_1(x_i)$ acts upon a single particle transferred from state a to b. We can bring out these states a and b by writing the Slater determinants in the form

$$\Psi_{\{\alpha\}} = (-)^{\nu_a} \sum_P \frac{(-)^P}{\sqrt{A}} \varphi_a(x_i) \frac{1}{\sqrt{(A-1)!}} |A-1|_{\{\alpha-a\}} ,$$

$$\Psi_{\{\alpha'\}} = (-)^{\nu_b} \sum_{P'} \frac{(-)^{P'}}{\sqrt{A}} \varphi_b(x_i) \frac{1}{\sqrt{(A-1)!}} |A-1|_{\{\alpha'-b\}} .$$

The signs $(-)^{\nu_a}$ and $(-)^{\nu_b}$ are associated with the permutations which bring respectively the rows of φ_a's and φ_b's from their standard position to the first row. The sums over P and P' are carried out over all permutations of the co-ordinates x_i with all the others. The signs $(-)^P$ and $(-)^{P'}$ guarantee the anti-symmetrization of the particle in state φ_a or φ_b with respect to all others. The two determinants $|A-1|_{\{\alpha-a\}}$ and $|A-1|_{\{\alpha'-b\}}$ are identical otherwise the orthogonality of the φ's yields a zero result. The operator $\theta_1(x_i)$, which acts upon the co-ordinate x_i, can only yield a nonzero result if the co-ordinate x_i appears in φ_a and φ_b, *i.e.* for a given permutation $P = P'$. Therefore,

(16) $$\langle \Psi_{\{\alpha'\}} | \Theta_1 | \Psi_{\{\alpha\}} \rangle = (-)^{\nu_a+\nu_b} \langle b | \theta_1 | a \rangle ,$$

where

(17) $$\langle b | \theta_1 | a \rangle = \mathop{\sum\!\!\!\!\!\!\int} \varphi_a(x) \varphi_b(x) \theta_1(x) \, dx .$$

The expression for the one-body operator in the O.N. representation, denoted by $\tilde{\Theta}_1$, must fulfil the following condition:

(18) $$\langle 0 | \eta_\alpha \eta_\beta \ldots \eta_b \ldots \eta_\delta \ldots \tilde{\Theta}_1 \eta_\alpha^\dagger \eta_\beta^\dagger \ldots \eta_a^\dagger \ldots \eta_\delta \ldots | 0 \rangle = (-)^{\nu_a+\nu_b} \langle b | \theta_1 | a \rangle .$$

At this point it is convenient to introduce the concept of the substitution operator $\eta_b^\dagger \eta_a$. The action of such an operator upon the ket $\eta_\alpha^\dagger \eta_\beta^\dagger \ldots \eta_a^\dagger \ldots | 0 \rangle$ yields the state

$$(\eta_b^\dagger \eta_a) \eta_\alpha^\dagger \eta_\beta^\dagger \ldots \eta_a^\dagger \ldots \eta_\delta \ldots | 0 \rangle = (-)^{\nu_a+\nu_b} \eta_\alpha^\dagger \eta_\beta^\dagger \ldots \eta_b^\dagger \ldots \eta_\delta \ldots | 0 \rangle ,$$

where the initially occupied state a has been replaced by the occupied state b in their standard position. The sign $(-)^{\nu_a+\nu_b}$ corresponds to the permutations which bring the operator $\eta_a^\dagger$ into leading position from its initial standard position and which relegate the operator η_b from its initial leading position to its standard position. It should be noted that if a is not occupied or if b is occupied in the initial ket, then

$$(\eta_b^\dagger \eta_a)\eta_\alpha^\dagger \eta_\beta^\dagger \dots \eta_\delta^\dagger \dots |0\rangle = 0 .$$

The application of the substitution operator in (18) leads to the following definition for $\tilde{\Theta}_1$;

$$\tilde{\Theta}_1 = \sum_{i,j} \langle i|\theta_1|j\rangle\, \eta_i^\dagger \eta_j \,, \tag{19}$$

where the one-body element $\langle i|\theta_1|j\rangle$ has been defined in equation (17).

The expression for the two-body operator (15) is obtained in the same fashion. Let us consider the case of off-diagonal matrix elements. First of all we note that the matrix element

$$\langle \Psi_{\{\alpha'\}}|\Theta_2|\Psi_{\{\alpha\}}\rangle$$

can only differ from zero if the series $\{\alpha'\}$ and $\{\alpha\}$ of states occupied before and after the interaction contain at most two different indices since $\theta_2(x_i, x_j)$ acts upon two particles only. We bring out the states m and n initially occupied by these two particles

$$|\Psi_{\{\alpha\}}\rangle = (-)^{\nu_m+\nu_n} \sum_{PP'} \frac{(-)^{P+P'}}{\sqrt{A(A-1)}} \frac{1}{\sqrt{2}} \begin{vmatrix} \varphi_m(x_i)\varphi_m(x_j) \\ \varphi_n(x_i)\varphi_n(x_j) \end{vmatrix} \frac{1}{\sqrt{(A-2)!}} |A-2|_{\{\alpha-n-m\}} \,. \tag{20}$$

The summations must be carried out over all permutations of the co-ordinates x_i and x_j with all the others. The sign $(-)^{\nu_n+\nu_m}$ is related to these permutations which bring the states m and n from their standard position to rows 1 and 2. Similarly in the final state,

$$|\Psi_{\{\alpha'\}}\rangle = (-)^{\nu_r+\nu_s} \sum_{PP'} \frac{(-)^{P+P'}}{\sqrt{A(A-1)}} \frac{1}{\sqrt{2}} \begin{vmatrix} \varphi_r(x_i)\varphi_r(x_j) \\ \varphi_s(x_i)\varphi_s(x_j) \end{vmatrix} \frac{1}{\sqrt{(A-2)!}} |A-2|_{\{\alpha'-r-s\}} \,.$$

The two determinants $|A-2|_{\{\alpha-n-m\}}$ and $|A-2|_{\{\alpha'-r-s\}}$ must be identical, therefore

$$\langle \Psi_{\{\alpha'\}}|\Theta_2|\Psi_{\{\alpha\}}\rangle = (-)^{\nu_r+\nu_s+\nu_n+\nu_m} \langle rs|\theta_2|\widetilde{mn}\rangle = \tfrac{1}{2}(-)^{\nu_r+\nu_s+\nu_n+\nu_m} \langle \widetilde{rs}|\theta_2|\widetilde{mn}\rangle \,, \tag{21}$$

according to whether the two-particle wave functions are antisymmetrized solely on the right or on both sides. We shall always utilize two-body matrix elements which are antisymmetrized solely on the right and we shall omit the corresponding symbol $|\tilde{\ }\rangle$:

$$(22)\qquad \langle rs|\theta_2|\widetilde{mn}\rangle \equiv \langle rs|\theta_2|mn\rangle = \\ = \iint \mathrm{d}x_1\,\mathrm{d}x_2\,\varphi_r(x_1)\varphi_s(x_2)\theta_2(x_1,x_2)\{\varphi_m(x_1)\varphi_n(x_2)-\varphi_m(x_2)\varphi_n(x_1)\}\,.$$

The expression for the two-body operator in the O.N. representation thus requires two substitution operators, one which replaces $\eta_m^\dagger$ by $\eta_r^\dagger$ and the other $\eta_n^\dagger$ by $\eta_s^\dagger$ and

$$(\eta_r^\dagger\eta_m)(\eta_s^\dagger\eta_n) = \eta_r^\dagger\eta_s^\dagger\eta_n\eta_m\,.$$

The application of these substitution operators yields the following expression for the two body operators in the O.N. representation:

$$(23)\qquad \tilde{\Theta}_2 = \tfrac{1}{4}\sum_{\alpha\beta\gamma\delta}\langle\alpha\beta|\theta_2|\gamma\delta\rangle\,\eta_\alpha^\dagger\eta_\beta^\dagger\eta_\delta\eta_\gamma\,,$$

where the two-body matrix element is antisymmetrized on the right according to (22). It may be seen that expression (23) yields eq. (21). The antisymmetrization is doubly guaranteed by the definition of the matrix element (22) and by the anticommutation properties of the $\eta^\dagger$'s and the η's. This gives four times too many terms whereby the factor $\frac{1}{4}$ appearing in the definition (23).

2·6 *Graphical representation of states. The reference state.* – A state of the O.N. representation can be represented graphically by associating a vertical line k to each of its occupation numbers for which $N_k = 1$, Fig. 1.

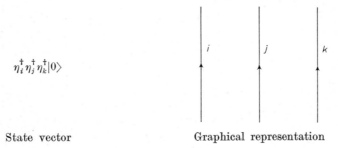

$\eta_i^\dagger\eta_j^\dagger\eta_k^\dagger|0\rangle$

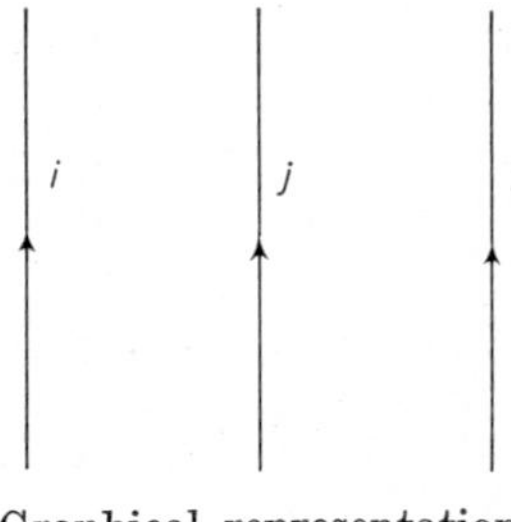

State vector — Graphical representation

Fig. 1.

The number of lines going up is equal to the number of particles A which is generally large and thus the diagram so defined is rather inconvenient.

In order to simplify the graphical representation it is convenient to choose a particular state and to represent it by the absence of line. This so-called « reference state » for a system of independent particles is generally the nondegenerate ground state wherein all the levels are completely filled up to the Fermi level F of Fig. 2.

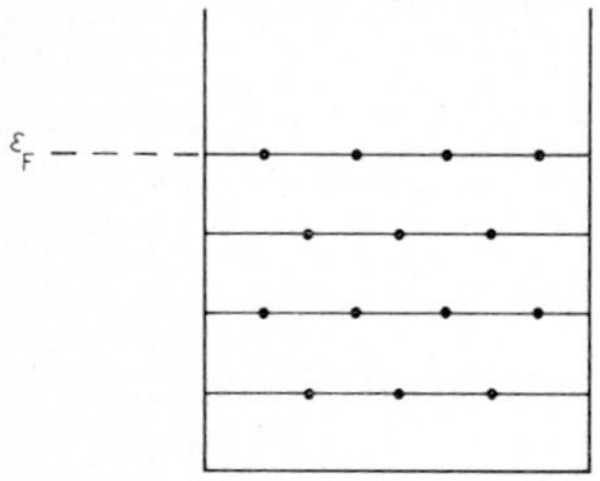

Reference state Graphical representation

Fig. 2.

This reference state is denoted by the ket $|\Phi_0\rangle$, where

$$|\Phi_0\rangle = \eta_1^\dagger \eta_2^\dagger \dots \eta_F^\dagger |0\rangle .$$

The notion of reference state can only be useful if the configurational states to be considered differ from that state by a small number of single-particle states, whether they be occupied or not. The absence of a particle below the Fermi level appears as a hole and is represented graphically by a line going down. The presence of a particle above the Fermi level is denoted by a line going up. From here on we shall denote the states above the Fermi level by capital letters $A, B, C \dots$ and the states below the Fermi level by lower case letters $a, b, c \dots$. A system of A nucleons, n_1 of which occupy levels above ε_F and for which n_2 single-particle states below ε_F are unoccupied, is therefore represented by n_1 lines going up and n_2 going down as shown in Fig. 3.

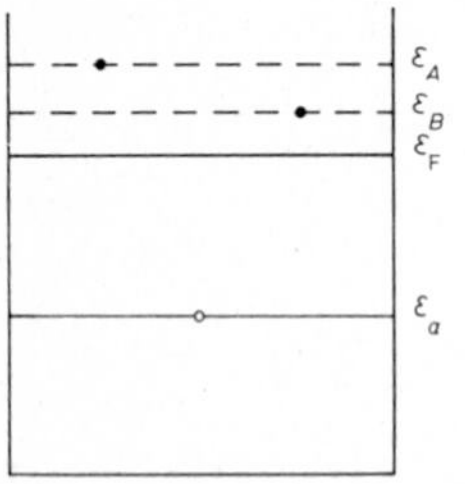

$$\eta_A^\dagger \eta_B^\dagger \eta_a |\Phi_0\rangle$$

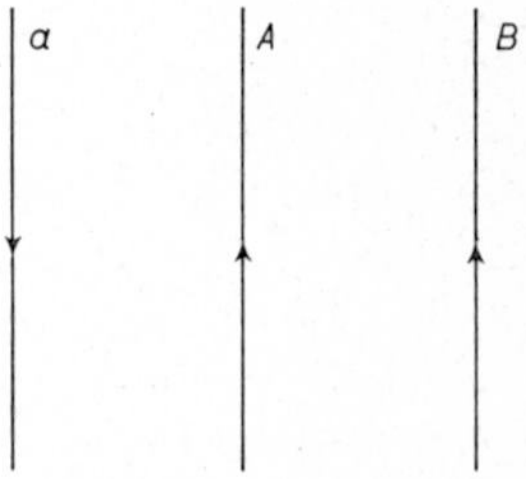

State Vector Graphical representation

Fig. 3.

2'7. *A simple example of quasi-particles.* – It is convenient to consider the reference state as a vacuum. It is not a vacuum with respect to particles, for indeed

$$\eta_a|\Phi_0\rangle \neq 0 \qquad\qquad (\varepsilon_a \leqslant \varepsilon_{\rm F})\,.$$

It is rather a vacuum with respect to so-called « quasi-particles » which represent holes when their energy is below $\varepsilon_{\rm F}$ and particles when their energy is above $\varepsilon_{\rm F}$. The annihilation operators ξ_α for these quasi-particles are defined as follows:

$$\xi_\alpha|\Phi_0\rangle = 0 \qquad\qquad \text{for all } \alpha\,.$$

The quasi-particle operators $\xi^\dagger$, ξ can be expressed in terms of the particle operators $\eta^\dagger$, η through the transformation

$$(24)\qquad \begin{cases} \begin{cases} \xi^\dagger_{j_\alpha m_\alpha} = \eta^\dagger_{j_\alpha m_\alpha} \\ \xi_{j_\alpha m_\alpha} = \eta_{j_\alpha m_\alpha} \end{cases} & \text{if } \varepsilon_\alpha > \varepsilon_{\rm F}\,; \\ \begin{cases} \xi_{j_\alpha m_\alpha} = (-)^{j_\alpha - m_\alpha}\eta^\dagger_{j_\alpha - m_\alpha} \\ \xi^\dagger_{j_\alpha m_\alpha} = (-)^{j_\alpha - m_\alpha}\eta_{j_\alpha - m_\alpha} \end{cases} & \text{if } \varepsilon_\alpha \leqslant \varepsilon_{\rm F}\,. \end{cases}$$

This transformation is said to be *canonical* since it conserves the anticommutation relations:

$$(25)\qquad [\xi_i, \xi_j]_+ = 0\,, \qquad [\xi^\dagger_i, \xi^\dagger_j]_+ = 0\,, \qquad [\xi_i, \xi^\dagger_j]_+ = \delta_{ij}\,.$$

The quasi-particles defined by the transformation (24) are fermions.

2·8. *Graphical representation of one-body and two-body operators.* – We may likewise give a graphical representation of the operators.

The diagram representing a one-body operator consists of a point associated with the one-body matrix element, of one incoming line and of one outgoing line associated respectively with the creation and annihilation operators according to the correspondence table of Fig. 4.

	$\varepsilon_a \leqslant \varepsilon_{\rm f}$	$\varepsilon_A > \varepsilon_{\rm F}$
$\eta^\dagger$	ξ_a a	$\xi^\dagger_A$ A
η	$\xi^\dagger_a$ a	ξ_A A

Fig. 4.

We thus obtain the following four possible situations, according to the positions of the single particle states relative to the Fermi level, graphically represented on Fig. 5.

$$a)\ \langle A|\theta_1|B\rangle\, \eta_A^\dagger\, \eta_B \equiv \langle A|\theta_1|B\rangle\, \xi_A^\dagger\, \xi_B\ ,$$

$$b)\ \langle a\,|\theta_1|b\rangle\ \eta_a^\dagger\, \eta_b \equiv \langle a\,|\theta_1|b\rangle\ \xi_a\, \xi_b^\dagger\ ,$$

$$c)\ \langle A|\theta_1|b\rangle\ \eta_A^\dagger\, \eta_b \equiv \langle A|\theta_1|b\rangle\ \xi_A^\dagger\, \xi_b^\dagger\ ,$$

$$d)\ \langle a\,|\theta_1|B\rangle\, \eta_a^\dagger\, \eta_B \equiv \langle a\,|\theta_1|B\rangle\, \xi_a\, \xi_B\ .$$

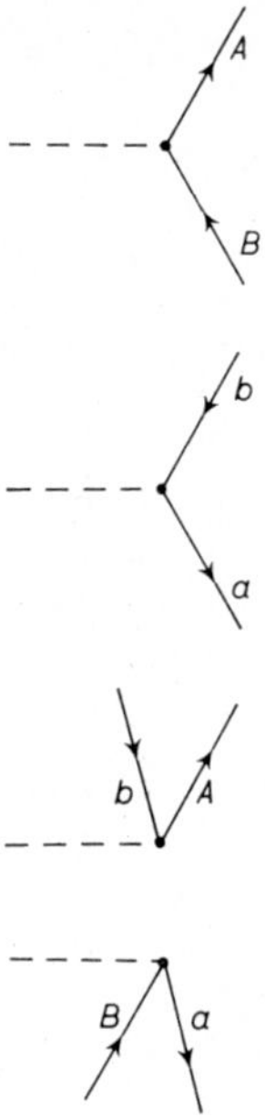

Fig. 5.

As an illustrative example let us suppose that the operator θ_1 describes the absorption of a photon. In the language of the new representation where the quasi-particles are « particles » when above ε_F and « holes » when below ε_F the absorption of the photon is accompanied respectively in the four preceding cases by *a*) the scattering of a « particle », *b*) the scattering of a « hole », *c*) the creation of a particle-hole pair, *d*) the annihilation of a particle-hole pair.

The graphical representation of a two-body operator will be similar. However we must now distinguish between the direct and the exchange terms as shown in Fig. 6.

$\langle AB|\theta_2|CD\rangle_{\text{direct}}\,\eta_A^\dagger\,\eta_B^\dagger\,\eta_D\,\eta_C$ $\quad$ $\langle BA|\theta_2|CD\rangle_{\text{exchange}}\,\eta_A^\dagger\,\eta_B^\dagger\,\eta_D\,\eta_C$

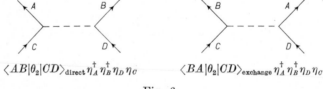

Fig. 6.

In order to avoid this distinction we may use the antisymmetric matrix element (22). The operator is then represented by a point on which we terminate two incoming lines and two outgoing lines, corresponding to the four fermions operators according to the correspondence table of Fig. 4. A few examples are given on Fig. 7.

$$\tfrac{1}{4}\langle AB|\theta_2|CD\rangle\, \eta_A^\dagger \eta_B^\dagger \eta_D \eta_C = \\ = \tfrac{1}{4}\langle AB|\theta_2|CD\rangle\, \xi_A^\dagger \xi_B^\dagger \xi_D \xi_C\,,$$

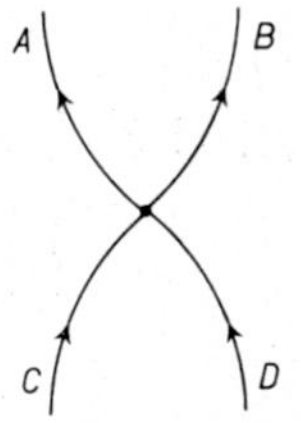

$$\tfrac{1}{4}\langle ab\ |\theta_2|CD\rangle\, \eta_a^\dagger \eta_b^\dagger \eta_D \eta_C = \\ = \tfrac{1}{4}\langle ab\ |\theta_2|CD\rangle\, \xi_a \xi_b \xi_D \xi_C\,,$$

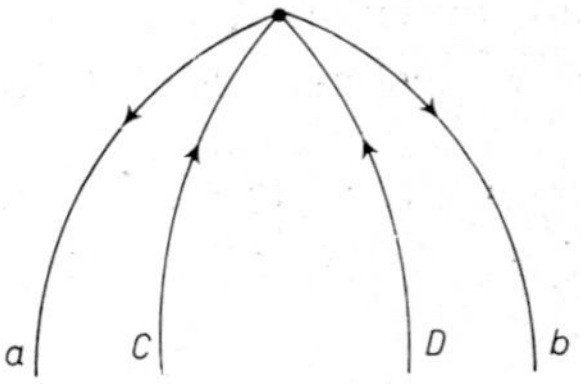

$$\tfrac{1}{4}\langle AB|\theta_2|Cd\rangle\, \eta_A^\dagger \eta_B^\dagger \eta_d \eta_C = \\ = \tfrac{1}{4}\langle AB|\theta_2|Cd\rangle\, \xi_A^\dagger \xi_B^\dagger \xi_d^\dagger \xi_C\,,$$

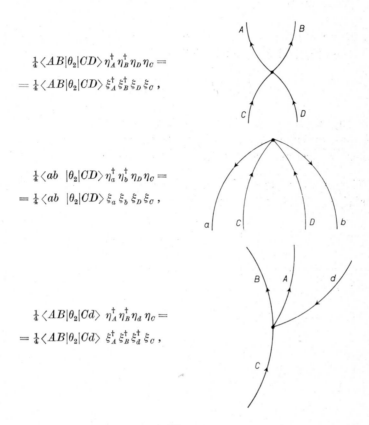

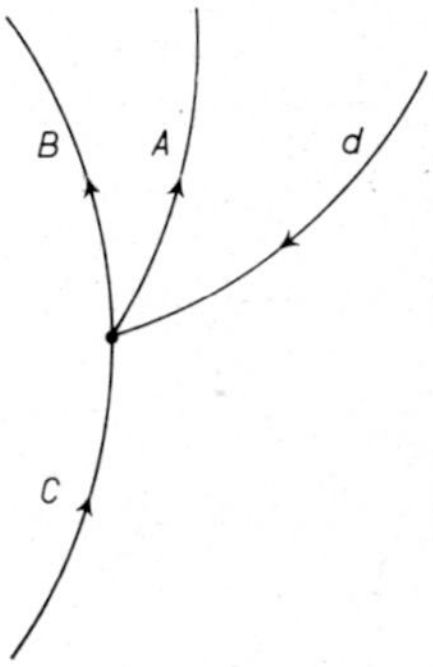

Fig. 7.

2·9. *The Wick theorem.* – The evaluation of matrix elements in the O.N. representation requires the determination of the mean value of product of annihilation and creation operators relative to their « vacuum », $|\Phi_0\rangle$. For example, the two-body matrix element between an initial state $|i\rangle$ and a final state $|n\rangle$ is

$$\langle f|\Theta_2|i\rangle = \tfrac{1}{4}\sum_{r,s,m,n} \langle rs|\theta_2|mn\rangle\langle f|\xi_r^\dagger\xi_s^\dagger\xi_n\xi_m|i\rangle = \\ = \tfrac{1}{4}\sum_{r,s,m,n} \langle rs|\theta_2|mn\rangle\langle \Phi_0|\xi_{\alpha'}\xi_{\beta'}\,\dots\,\xi_r^\dagger\xi_s^\dagger\xi_n\xi_m\xi_\alpha^\dagger\xi_\beta^\dagger\dots|\Phi_0\rangle\,.$$

The evaluation of the mean value is done by the successive applications of the anticommutation relations (25), in order to bring on the right all the annihilation operators, which then give zero when acting on the vacuum. The calculation is greatly simplified by the Wick theorem. Before stating this theorem, we shall define the normal product, the contraction and the contracted normal product.

2·9.1. Normal product. The normal product of n operators $\xi_i^\dagger \xi_j^\dagger \xi_k \xi_l \xi_n^\dagger$ is denoted by $:\xi_i^\dagger \xi_j^\dagger \xi_k \xi_l \xi_n^\dagger:$ and is defined as follows:

$$:\xi_i^\dagger \xi_j^\dagger \xi_k \xi_l \xi_n^\dagger: = (-)^\nu \xi_i^\dagger \xi_j^\dagger \xi_n^\dagger \xi_k \xi_l \,, \tag{26}$$

where the annihilation operators have been brought to the left. The quantity ν is the number of permutations necessary for this reordering.

The normal product has the following properties:

1) The mean value of a normal product of annihilation and creation operators $\xi^\dagger, \xi \ldots$ relative to their vacuum $|\Phi_0\rangle$ is zero,

$$\langle \Phi_0| :\xi^\dagger \xi^\dagger \xi^\dagger \ldots : |\Phi_0\rangle = 0 \,.$$

This important property explains the usefulness of the normal product in simplifying matrix element calculations.

2) Anticommutativity.

$$:\xi_i^\dagger \xi_j^\dagger \xi_k: = -:\xi_j^\dagger \xi_i^\dagger \xi_k: \,.$$

3) Distributivity.

$$:(u\xi_i + v\xi_j^\dagger)\xi_k^\dagger \xi_l^\dagger: = u:\xi_i \xi_k^\dagger \xi_l^\dagger: + v:\xi_j^\dagger \xi_k^\dagger \xi_l^\dagger: \,.$$

2·9.2. Contraction. The contraction of two operators ξ_α, ξ_β is the mean value of their product relative to a reference state and is denoted by $\overline{\xi_\alpha \xi_\beta}$. The contraction is defined relative to a particular reference state. For example the table of contractions of the operators $\xi^\dagger, \xi \ldots$ defined in eq. (24) relative to their vacuum $|\Phi_0\rangle$ is

$$\left\{ \begin{aligned} \overline{\xi_m \xi_n} &= \langle \Phi_0| \xi_m \xi_n |\Phi_0\rangle = 0 \,, \\ \overline{\xi_m^\dagger \xi_n} &= \langle \Phi_0| \xi_m^\dagger \xi_n |\Phi_0\rangle = 0 \,, \\ \overline{\xi_m^\dagger \xi_n^\dagger} &= \langle \Phi_0| \xi_m^\dagger \xi_n^\dagger |\Phi_0\rangle = 0 \,, \\ \overline{\xi_m \xi_n^\dagger} &= \langle \Phi_0| \xi_m \xi_n^\dagger |\Phi_0\rangle = \delta_{mn} \,, \end{aligned} \right. \tag{27}$$

while the table of contractions of the ξ's relative to the true vacuum $|0\rangle$ (absence of particles) is as follows:

$$
(28)\qquad \left\{
\begin{aligned}
&\overline{\xi_m\xi_n} = \langle 0|\xi_m\xi_n|0\rangle = 0\,,\\
&\overline{\xi_m^\dagger\xi_n} = \langle 0|\xi_m^\dagger\xi_n|0\rangle \begin{cases} = 0 & \text{if } \varepsilon_n > \varepsilon_F\,,\\ = \delta_{mn} & \text{if } \varepsilon_n \leqslant \varepsilon_F\,,\end{cases}\\
&\overline{\xi_m^\dagger\xi_n^\dagger} = \langle 0|\xi_m^\dagger\xi_n^\dagger|0\rangle = 0\,,\\
&\overline{\xi_m\xi_n^\dagger} = \langle 0|\xi_m\xi_n^\dagger|0\rangle \begin{cases} = \delta_{mn} & \text{if } \varepsilon_n > \varepsilon_F\,,\\ = 0 & \text{if } \varepsilon_n \leqslant \varepsilon_F\,.\end{cases}
\end{aligned}\right.
$$

2'9.3. Contracted normal product. A contracted normal product is defined as,

$$
(29)\qquad :\xi_i\overline{\xi_j\xi_k^\dagger\xi_l^\dagger}\,\overline{\xi_m^\dagger\xi_n^\dagger}\ldots: = (-)^\nu\,\overline{\xi_j\xi_l^\dagger}\,\overline{\xi_m^\dagger\xi_n^\dagger}:\xi_i\xi_k^\dagger\ldots:\,,
$$

where ν is the number of permutations which bring the contracted operators next to each other. The contracted factors, which are pure numbers, are then taken out of the normal product. The following are two simple examples of contracted normal products:

$$
:\xi_i^\dagger\overline{\xi_j\xi_k^\dagger\xi_l}: = -\,\overline{\xi_j\xi_l}:\xi_i^\dagger\xi_k^\dagger:\,,
$$

$$
:\overline{\xi_i^\dagger\xi_j}\,\overline{\xi_k^\dagger\xi_l}: = \overline{\xi_i^\dagger\xi_j}\,\overline{\xi_k^\dagger\xi_l}\,.
$$

This last example shows that the definition includes the completely contracted normal product.

We can now state the *Wick theorem*:

A product of creation and annihilation operators is equal to the sum of all its contracted normal products (including the uncontracted term).

As examples we apply the theorem to the products $\eta_m^\dagger\eta_n$ and $\eta_r^\dagger\eta_s^\dagger\eta_n\eta_m$ which appear in the expressions (19) and (23) for $\widetilde{\Theta}_1$ and $\widetilde{\Theta}_2$:

$$
(30)\qquad \eta_m^\dagger\eta_n = :\eta_m^\dagger\eta_n: + \overline{\eta_m^\dagger\eta_n}\,,
$$

$$
\begin{aligned}
(31)\qquad \eta_r^\dagger\eta_s^\dagger\eta_n\eta_m = {}&\overline{\eta_s^\dagger\eta_n}\,\overline{\eta_r^\dagger\eta_m} - \overline{\eta_s^\dagger\eta_m}\,\overline{\eta_r^\dagger\eta_n} + \overline{\eta_r^\dagger\eta_s^\dagger}\,\overline{\eta_n\eta_m} + \overline{\eta_s^\dagger\eta_n}:\eta_r^\dagger\eta_m: + \overline{\eta_r^\dagger\eta_m}:\eta_s^\dagger\eta_n: -\\
&- \overline{\eta_s^\dagger\eta_m}:\eta_r^\dagger\eta_n: - \overline{\eta_r^\dagger\eta_n}:\eta_s^\dagger\eta_m: + \overline{\eta_r^\dagger\eta_s^\dagger}:\eta_n\eta_m: + \overline{\eta_n\eta_m}:\eta_r^\dagger\eta_s^\dagger: + :\eta_r^\dagger\eta_s^\dagger\eta_n\eta_m:.
\end{aligned}
$$

We thus obtain the following result, relative to the quasi-particle vacuum

$|\Phi_0\rangle$ defined above,

$$(32)\qquad \begin{cases} \langle\Phi_0|\eta_r^\dagger\eta_s^\dagger\eta_n\eta_m|\Phi_0\rangle = 0 & \text{if } \varepsilon_n,\ \varepsilon_m > \varepsilon_F,\\ \qquad = \delta_{sn}\delta_{rm} - \delta_{sm}\,\delta_{rm} & \text{if } \varepsilon_n,\ \varepsilon_m \leqslant \varepsilon_F. \end{cases}$$

2'10. *The nuclear Hamiltonian in second-quantized form.* – In the O.N. representation the nuclear Hamiltonian is of the form (cf. eqs. (19) and (23))

$$(33)\qquad H = \sum_{m,n} \langle m|T|n\rangle \eta_m^\dagger \eta_n + \tfrac{1}{4}\sum_{rsmn} \langle rs|V|mn\rangle \eta_r^\dagger\eta_s^\dagger\eta_n\eta_m\,,$$

where the single-particle wave functions entering in the matrix elements may be the members of any complete orthonormal set.

A particular choice for such a set are the single-particle wave functions which diagonalize the Hartree-Fock Hamiltonian (cf. Prof. Villars' lectures)

$$(34)\qquad \sum_m \{\langle m|T|n\rangle + \sum_{b\leq F} \langle mb|V|nb\rangle\}\varphi_m = \varepsilon_n\varphi_n\,.$$

In that representation the nuclear Hamiltonian takes the form

$$(35)\qquad H = E_0 + \sum_m \varepsilon_m :\eta_m^\dagger\eta_m: + \tfrac{1}{4}\sum_{rsmn}\langle rs|V|mn\rangle :\eta_r^\dagger\eta_s^\dagger\eta_n\eta_m:\,,$$

where E_0 is the Hartree-Fock energy of the independent particle state $|\Phi_0\rangle$ where all the levels are filled up to the Fermi level.

Let us discuss the meaning of the normal products which appear in the above expression for H. The reference state is $|\Phi_0\rangle$. The normal products are relative to the operators $\xi^\dagger$, ξ whose vacuum is $|\Phi_0\rangle$. The first normal product $:\eta_m^\dagger\eta_m:$ gives two terms when going to the ξ's according to the transformation (24); for a hole state

$$:\eta_a^\dagger\eta_a: = :\xi_a\xi_a^\dagger: = -\,\xi_a^\dagger\xi_a\,,$$

and for a particle state

$$:\eta_A^\dagger\eta_A: = :\xi_A^\dagger\xi_A: = \xi_A^\dagger\xi_A\,.$$

It is convenient to redefine the single-particle energy $\tilde{\varepsilon}_i$ such that

$$(36)\qquad \begin{cases} \tilde{\varepsilon}_i = \varepsilon_i & \text{if } \varepsilon_i > \varepsilon_F,\\ \tilde{\varepsilon}_i = -\,\varepsilon_i & \text{if } \varepsilon_i \leqslant \varepsilon_F; \end{cases}$$

therefore

$$\sum_i \varepsilon_i :\eta_i^\dagger \eta_i: = \sum_i \tilde{\varepsilon}_i \xi_i^\dagger \xi_i .$$

Now we consider the second term of (35) which is the « *residual interaction* » of shell model calculations,

$$v = \tfrac{1}{4} \sum_{rsmn} \langle rs|V|mn\rangle :\eta_r^\dagger \eta_s^\dagger \eta_n \eta_m: . \tag{37}$$

Here the normal product excludes all systems of contraction between the four operators $\eta_r^\dagger \eta_s^\dagger \eta_m \eta_n$. These contributions are precisely the ones which are included in the Hartree-Fock field (34). We note however that, at this stage, the residual interaction is in principle given by the matrix elements of the nucleon-nucleon force and not by those of some renormalized operator. In going to the language of « particles » and « holes » by substituting the ξ's for the η's in (37) according to the transformation (24), we obtain 16 terms corresponding to the various possibilities for the four single-particle states r, s, m and n to be above or below the Fermi level. The various types of terms are the following (we keep the convention $\varepsilon_A, \varepsilon_B, \varepsilon_C, \varepsilon_D > \varepsilon_F$; $\varepsilon_a, \varepsilon_b, \varepsilon_c, \varepsilon_d \leqslant \varepsilon_F$)

a) The « particle-particle » interaction operator,

$$\tfrac{1}{4} \sum_{\substack{AB\\CD}} \langle AB|V|CD\rangle \xi_A^\dagger \xi_B^\dagger \xi_D \xi_C . \tag{38}$$

b) The « hole-hole » interaction operator,

$$\tfrac{1}{4} \sum_{\substack{ab\\cd}} \langle ab|V|cd\rangle \xi_d^\dagger \xi_c^\dagger \xi_a \xi_b . \tag{39}$$

c) The « particle-hole » interaction operator,

$$-\tfrac{1}{2} \sum_{\substack{Ab\\cD}} \langle Ab|V|cD\rangle \xi_A^\dagger \xi_c^\dagger \xi_D \xi_b . \tag{40}$$

In this summation we necessarily have $A \neq b$ and $D \neq c$, hence the factor $\frac{1}{2}$ instead of $\frac{1}{4}$. The sign results from the reordering of the normal product.

d) Pair creation or pair annihilation interaction operators.

Although the number of nucleons is conserved, the number of particle-hole pairs need not be. We get for example terms corresponding to the scattering of a « particle » or a « hole » accompanied by the absorption or creation of a particle-hole pair, cf. the third diagram in Fig. 7.

There is also a term wherein two particle-hole pairs are created. This term may be interpreted as resulting from correlations between nucleons in the Hartree-Fock ground state $|\Phi_0\rangle$ since it is the contribution of two particles initially in states c and d below the Fermi level which scatter each other into states A and B above,

$$\frac{1}{4}\sum_{\substack{AB\\cd}} \langle AB|V|cd\rangle \xi_A^\dagger \xi_B^\dagger \xi_d \xi_c \,.$$

Likewise there is also a term wherein 2 pairs are annihilated, cf. the second diagram in Fig. 7.

We shall also need the nuclear Hamiltonian in the « quasi-particle » representation. Let us define the quasi-particle annihilation and creation operators by the linear transformation

$$\text{(41)}\qquad \begin{cases} \xi_{jm}^\dagger = u_j \eta_{jm} + (-)^{j-m} v_j \eta_{j-m}^\dagger \,, \\ \xi_{jm} = u_j \eta_{jm}^\dagger + (-)^{j-m} v_j \eta_{j-m} \,. \end{cases}$$

In order to preserve the anticommutation relations for the ξ's, the coefficients of the transformation (41) must satisfy the relation

$$u_i^2 + v_i^2 = 1 \,.$$

The particle-hole transformation (24) is a special case of (41). The inverse transformation is

$$\text{(42)}\qquad \begin{cases} \eta_{jm}^\dagger = u_j \xi_{jm}^\dagger - (-)^{j-m} v_j \xi_{j-m} \\ \eta_{jm} = u_j \xi_{jm} - (-)^{j-m} v_j \xi_{j-m}^\dagger \,. \end{cases}$$

If we adopt for « vacuum » or reference state the BCS state of energy E_{BCS} (cf. the lectures of J. P. ELLIOTT), H has the form

$$\text{(43)}\qquad H = E_{\text{BCS}} + \sum_i \widetilde{E}_i \xi_i^\dagger \xi_i + v^{\text{Q.P.}} \,,$$

where the quasi-particle energies $\widetilde{E}_i$ may be written as functions of the gap Δ_i, the Hartree-Fock energy ε_i and the chemical potential λ,

$$\text{(44)}\qquad \widetilde{E}_i = \sqrt{(\varepsilon_i - \lambda)^2 + \Delta_i^2} \,.$$

The residual interaction between these quasi-particles includes 16 terms. Denoting for simplicity $\xi_{rm_{j_r}}^\dagger$, $\xi_{rm_{j_r}}$ by $\xi_r^\dagger$, ξ_r; $\xi_{r-m_{j_r}}^\dagger$, $\xi_{r-m_{j_r}}$ by $\xi_{-r}^\dagger$, ξ_{-r}; $(-)^{j_r-m_r} v_{j_r}$

by $\tilde{v}_r$ etc... we obtain

$$v^{\text{Q.P.}} = \tfrac{1}{4}\sum_{rsmn}\langle rs|V|mn\rangle :(u_r\xi_r^\dagger - \tilde{v}_r\xi_{-r})(u_s\xi_s^\dagger - \tilde{v}_s\xi_{-s})\cdot \tag{45}$$

$$\cdot(u_n\xi_n - \tilde{v}_n\xi_{-n}^\dagger)(u_m\xi_m - \tilde{v}_m\xi_{-m}^\dagger): = \tfrac{1}{4}\sum_{rsmn}\langle rs|V|mn\rangle :\{u_r u_s u_n u_m \xi_r^\dagger\xi_s^\dagger\xi_n\xi_m +$$

$$+ \tilde{v}_r\tilde{v}_s\tilde{v}_n\tilde{v}_m\xi_{-n}^\dagger\xi_{-m}^\dagger\xi_{-r}\xi_{-s} + \tilde{v}_r\tilde{v}_s\tilde{v}_n\tilde{v}_m\xi_{-n}^\dagger\xi_{-r}\xi_{-s}\xi_m + 13 \text{ terms...}\}: .$$

3. – Introduction to the Green's function method.

3·1. *Definitions and properties.* – The use of Green's functions in nuclear-spectroscopy calculations is still rather limited. The knowledge of the Green's functions of a system permits to calculate the position of the excited states relative to the ground state and their transition rates to the ground state. The Green's functions do not yield the absolute energies and since they contain less information than the wave functions they are in principle easier to calculate. Furthermore they give a well-defined framework for the semi-phenomenological approaches of the nuclear problem whereas parts of the theory are replaced by experimental quantities. This aspect of the use of Green's functions in nuclear physics is developed in Prof. Migdal's lectures. In the present lectures we shall only use Green's functions incidentally as an alternate way to derive the equations of the random phase approximation and as a perturbative framework for higher approximations. We will need however a certain number of definitions, results and rules for the diagrammatic representation of the perturbation expansion of Green's functions, which are outlined in this Section.

Let us consider a system of A nucleons whose true ground state will be denoted by $|g\rangle$. The n-particles Green's function of the system is defined as

$$G^{(n)}(1, 2, \ldots, 2n) = (i)^n\langle g|T\{\bar{\eta}_1(u_1)\bar{\eta}_2(u_2)\ \ldots\ \bar{\eta}_n(u_n)\bar{\eta}_{n+1}^\dagger(u_{n+1})\ \ldots\ \bar{\eta}_{2n}^\dagger(u_{2N})\}|g\rangle\,, \tag{46}$$

where

$$u = it/\hbar\,,$$

t is the time and $\bar{\eta}_j(u_j)$ is the annihilation operator of a fermion occupying state j in the Heisenberg representation:

$$\bar{\eta}_j(u_j) = \exp[u_jH]\eta_j\exp[-u_jH]\,. \tag{47}$$

The time-ordering operator T reorders the time-dependent operators $\bar{\eta}(u)$, $\bar{\eta}^\dagger(u)$ in order of increasing time from right to left:

$$T\{A_1(u_1)A_2(u_2)\ldots\} = (-)^\nu A_\alpha(u_\alpha)A_\beta(u_\beta)\ldots$$

with $u_\alpha > u_\beta \dots$. The sign $(-)^\nu$ is associated to the permutation which brings the series $1, 2, \dots$ in the order $\alpha, \beta \dots$.

We will be mainly concerned with the one-body Green's function

$$G^{(1)}(1,2) = i\langle g|T\{\bar\eta_1(u_1)\bar\eta_2^\dagger(u_2)\}|g\rangle\,, \tag{48}$$

where of course conservation laws require that states 1 and 2 be identical, and the two-body Green's function

$$G^{(2)}(1,2,3,4) = -\langle g|T\{\bar\eta_1(u_1)\bar\eta_2(u_2)\bar\eta_3^\dagger(u_3)\bar\eta_4^\dagger(u_4)\}|g\rangle\,. \tag{49}$$

If our A nucleon system can be represented in zero-order approximation by a nondegenerate independent particle wave function Φ_0, then we can use $|\Phi_0\rangle$ as our reference state or vacuum (cf. Sect. **2**·6). Now then we shall be concerned with excitations of this system corresponding to particle transitions from states below to states above the Fermi level and vice-versa, *i.e.* to the creation or annihilation of « particle-hole » pairs. These processes may be described most conveniently by the use of a special form of the two-body Green's function, namely the *particle-hole Green's function* defined as follows:

$$G^{(2)}_{\text{ph}}(b, A, B, a; u-u') = \langle g|T\{\bar\eta_a^\dagger(u)\bar\eta_A(u)\bar\eta_B^\dagger(u')\bar\eta_b(u')\}|g\rangle\,, \tag{50}$$

where we have constrained the original definition given in eq. (49) by requiring that the times u_1, u_2, u_3, u_4 verify

$$u_1 = u_3 = u'\,,$$

$$u_2 = u_4 = u\,.$$

The particle-hole Green's function is now solely a function of the time interval $\Delta u = u - u'$, and may be written explicitly as

$$G^{(2)}_{\text{ph}}(b, A, B, a; \Delta u) = \begin{cases} \langle g|\bar\eta_a^\dagger\eta_A \exp[-\Delta u(H-E_g)]\eta_B^\dagger\eta_b|g\rangle\,, & \text{for } \Delta u > 0\,, \\ \langle g|\eta_B^\dagger\eta_b \exp[+\Delta u(H-E_g)]\eta_a^\dagger\eta_A|g\rangle\,, & \text{for } \Delta u < 0\,. \end{cases} \tag{51}$$

The physical interpretation of the Green's functions is clear from their definition. Let us consider for example the particle-hole Green's function (51). It is the probability amplitude for the process whereby a particle-hole pair having been added in state Bb at time u' to the system in its true ground state $|g\rangle$, the particle-hole pair is found at time u in the state Aa, the rest of the system being again in its true ground state. We consider now the Fourier transform of the particle-hole Green's function:

(52)
$$i\mathscr{G}^{(2)}_{\text{ph}}(b, A, B, a; \omega) = \frac{i}{2\pi}\int\limits_{-\infty}^{\infty} \exp[+ i\omega t/\hbar] G(b, A, B, a; t)\,\mathrm{d}t =$$
$$= \sum_{n\neq g} \left\{ \langle g|\eta_a^\dagger \eta_A|n\rangle \frac{1}{E_n - E_g - \omega - i\varepsilon} \langle n|\eta_B^\dagger \eta_b|g\rangle + \right.$$
$$\left. + \langle g|\eta_B^\dagger \eta_b|n\rangle \frac{1}{E_n - E_g + \omega - i\varepsilon} \langle n|\eta_a^\dagger \eta_A|g\rangle \right\},$$

where ε is the usual convergence factor and where we have introduced the projector on the true excited states $|n\rangle$ of the system,

$$\sum_n |n\rangle\langle n| = 1 .$$

Thus the poles of $\mathscr{G}^{(2)}_{\text{ph}}$ are the excitation energies E_n of the system relative to the ground state energy E_g.

Furthermore the transition rates T between the true ground state $|g\rangle$ and an excited state $|n\rangle$ are given by the residues of $\mathscr{G}^{(2)}_{\text{ph}}$. Indeed,

$$T \propto |\langle n|\tilde{\Theta}_1|f\rangle|^2 ,$$

and substituting the expression (19) for $\tilde{\Theta}_1$ we obtain

(53)
$$T \propto \sum_{\substack{Aa\\Bb}} \{(\langle g|\eta_a^\dagger \eta_A|n\rangle\langle n|\eta_B^\dagger \eta_b|g\rangle)\langle B|\theta_1|b\rangle\langle a|\theta_1|A\rangle +$$
$$+ (\langle g|\eta_B^\dagger \eta_b|n\rangle\langle n|\eta_a^\dagger \eta_A|g\rangle)\langle a|\theta_1|A\rangle\langle B|\theta_1|b\rangle\} .$$

Its remains to calculate the Green's functions.

3·2. *The perturbation expansion.* – Since the Hamiltonian H may be written in the form $H = H_0 + v$, we shall seek a perturbation expansion for $G^{(p)}$ in powers of v. We shall use the interaction representation,

(54)
$$\begin{cases} v(u) = \exp[uH_0]v \;\exp[-uH_0] , \\ \eta_i(u) = \exp[uH_0]\eta_i \exp[-uH_0] , \end{cases}$$

whereas the operator $\bar{\eta}_i(u_j)$ defined in eq. (47) is given in the Heisenberg representatiou. Next we shall express the true ground state $|g\rangle$ of the system in terms of $|\Phi_0\rangle$, utilizing the time translation operator,

(55)
$$U(u, u_0) = \exp[uH_0] \exp[-(u - u_0)H] \exp[-u_0 H_0] ,$$

we obtain (cf. [4])

$$(56)\qquad |g\rangle = \lim_{\beta\to+\infty} \exp[\beta(E_g - H_0)]U(\beta, 0)|\Phi_0\rangle/\langle g|\Phi_0\rangle ,$$

since

$$\lim_{\beta\to+\infty} \exp[\beta(E_g - H_0)]U(\beta, 0)|\Phi_0\rangle = \lim_{\beta\to+\infty} \exp[\beta(E_g - H)]|\Phi_0\rangle =$$

$$= \lim_{\beta\to+\infty} \sum_n \exp[\beta(E_g - E_n)]\langle n|\Phi_0\rangle|n\rangle \simeq \langle g|\Phi_0\rangle|g\rangle .$$

Substituting eq. (55) and eq. (56) for $|g\rangle$ into eq. (46) for the Green's function $G^{(n)}$, we obtain

$$(57)\qquad G^{(n)}(1, 2, 3, \dots, 2n) = \lim_{\substack{\beta'\to-\infty\\ \beta\to+\infty}} \frac{\exp[(E_g - E_0)(\beta' - \beta)]}{|\langle g|\Phi_0\rangle|^2}(i)^n \cdot$$

$$\cdot\langle\Phi_0|T\{U(\beta, u_1)\eta_1(u_1)U(u_1, u_2)\dots\eta_{2n}(u_{2n})U(u_{2n}\beta')\}|\Phi_0\rangle .$$

The perturbation expansion for G in powers of v is finally obtained by substituting for the U's their iteration expansion [5]

$$(58)\qquad U(u, u_0) = \sum_{p=0}^{\infty} \frac{(-)^p}{p!} \int_{u_0}^{u} du_p \int_{u_0}^{u} du_{p-1} \dots \int_{u_0}^{u} du_1 T\{v(u_p)v(u_{p-1}) \dots v(u_1)\} .$$

In order to evaluate directly this expression it is necessary to compute the average value of products of fermion operators by application of Wick's theorem (Sect. 2·9). Such a calculation is quite complicated. Instead we shall construct a diagrammatic representation of the various terms of the perturbation expansion. This will permit us to carry out the necessary discussion in terms of diagrams rather than the complicated explicit form of the expansion. Before stating the rules which we shall need for tracing these diagrams we must introduce the concept of T-contractions.

3·3. *T-contractions.* – The fermion operators $\eta(u)$, $\eta^\dagger(u)$ in the interaction representation which appear in the various terms of the expansion are ordered by the time-ordering operator T. According to Wick's theorem, the time ordered product of two such operators is

$$T\{A_j(u_j)A_i(u_i)\} = \begin{cases} :A_j(u_j)A_i(u_i): + \overline{A_j(u_j)A_i(u_i)} , & \text{if } u_j > u_i , \\ :A_j(u_j)A_i(u_i): - \overline{A_i(u_i)A_j(u_j)} , & \text{if } u_j < u_i , \end{cases}$$

where the A's are fermion creation or annihilation operators. The time condition is cumbersome. We can eliminate it by defining the T-contraction relative to a reference state

$$\underbrace{A_j(u_j)A_i(u_i)} = \langle \Phi_0 | T\{A_j(u_j)A_i(u_i)\} | \Phi_0 \rangle \,. \tag{60}$$

Accordingly for any u_j, u_i,

$$T\{A_j(u_j)A_i(u_i)\} = :A_j(u_j)A_i(u_i): + \underbrace{A_j(u_j)A_i(u_i)} \,.$$

Thus the product of fermion operators entering in eq. (57) may be evaluated by means of Wick's theorem wherein T-contractions replace ordinary contractions.

It may be seen from its definition (60) that the T-contraction of the operators $\eta^\dagger(u)$, $\eta(u)$ ... is just the one-particle Green's function for a system of Hamiltonian H_0. More explicitly, relatively to the reference state $|\Phi_0\rangle$ and setting $u_\alpha - u_\beta = \Delta u$,

$$\underbrace{\eta_\alpha(u_\alpha)\eta_\beta(u_\beta)} = \underbrace{\eta^\dagger_\alpha(u_\alpha)\eta^\dagger_\beta(u_\beta)} = 0 \,,$$

$$\underbrace{\eta_\alpha(u_\alpha)\eta^\dagger_\beta(u_\beta)} = \begin{cases} iP_{\alpha\beta}\exp[-\Delta u\,\tilde{\varepsilon}_\alpha] & \text{if } \Delta u > 0, \quad (61a)\\ -i(1-P_{\alpha\beta})\exp[\Delta u\,\tilde{\varepsilon}_\alpha] & \text{if } \Delta u < 0, \quad (61b)\end{cases}$$

where

$$P_{\alpha\beta} = \langle \Phi_0 | \eta_\alpha \eta^\dagger_\beta | \Phi_0 \rangle = \begin{cases} \delta_{\alpha\beta} & \text{if } \varepsilon_\alpha > \varepsilon_F, \\ 0 & \text{if } \varepsilon_\alpha \leqslant \varepsilon_F, \end{cases} \tag{62}$$

and the $\tilde{\varepsilon}_\alpha$ are the Hartree-Fock energies defined in (36). Expressions (61*a*) describe the propagation of a « particle » and (61*b*) of a « hole » in the average potential.

3'4. *Rules for drawing diagrams.* – A diagram may be associated with each system of contraction given by the application of Wick's theorem to each term of eq. (57). These diagrams are drawn according to the following rules:

To each interaction $v(u)$ is associated a point at time u.

To each noncontracted fermion operator $\eta^\dagger_j(u_j)$, $\eta_j(u_j)$ is associated an oriented line j, ending at time u_j according to the correspondence table of Fig. 4.

To each T-contracted pair of operators, $\underbrace{A_j(u)A_j(u')}$ is associated a particle line j joining the times u and u', if $\varepsilon_j > \varepsilon_F$, or a hole line j if $\varepsilon_j \leqslant \varepsilon_F$. (A particle line is a line with an arrow pointing upward, direction of increasing times:

a hole line is a line with an arrow pointing downward.) Figure 8 gives an example of 3rd-order diagram.

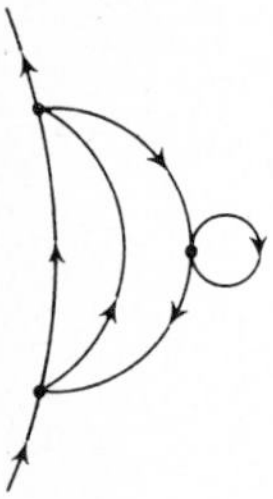

Fig. 8.

Conversely the rules for evaluating the contribution associated with a given diagram are as follows:

To each point with incoming lines r, s and outgoing lines m, n is associated the antisymmetrized matrix element $\langle rs|V|mn\rangle$ of eq. (22).

To each line j, joining the interaction at time u and u' is associated a T-contraction defined in eq. (61).

To each semi-infinite line ending at time u_j is associated an operator $\eta_j(u_j)$ or $\eta_j^\dagger(u_j)$ according to the correspondence table of Fig. 4.

The over-all sign of the contribution is $(-)^{n_1+n_2+n_3}$, where (*),

n_1 is the order of the diagram,

n_2 is the number of closed loops,

n_3 is the parity of the permutation which orders the noncontracted time-dependent operators according to eq. (46).

3·5. *Elimination of connected graphs.* – Equation (57) for Green's function may be simplified by eliminating connected graphs. A *connected* graph is one which connects vacuum to vacuum, while a *linked* graph is one which does not contain any connected parts. These are illustrated in Fig. 9. The elimination of connected graph is accomplished by applying the exponential formula of Goldstone-Hugenholtz-Bloch [4, 6].

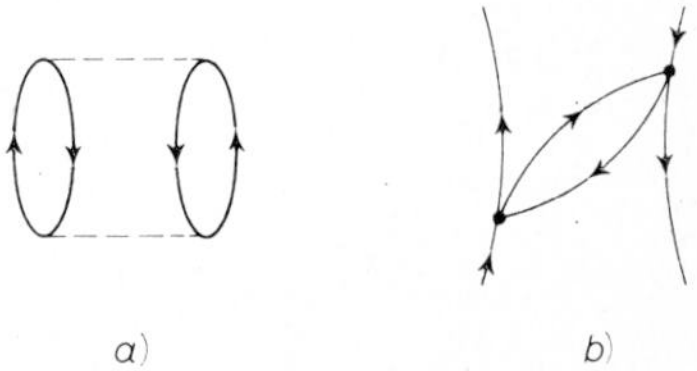

Fig. 9. – Diagram *a*) is a connected graph; diagram *b*) is a linked graph.

$$\langle\Phi_0|U(\beta,\beta')|\Phi_0\rangle = \exp[-(\beta-\beta')(E_g-E_0)]|\cdot$$
$$\cdot\langle g|\Phi_0\rangle|^2 = \exp[\langle\Phi_0|U(\beta,\beta')]|\Phi_0\rangle_C$$

and its corollary

$$(63)\quad \langle\Phi_0|UAU\ldots AU|\Phi_0\rangle = \langle\Phi_0|UAU\ldots AU|\Phi_0\rangle_L \exp[\langle\Phi_0|U(\beta,\beta')|\Phi_0\rangle_C]\,,$$

where the indices C and L denote that only connected diagrams or linked diagrams respectively must be taken into account when evaluating the matrix element. Substituting eq. (63) in eq. (57), the general expression for the n-body

(*) With the ordinary contractions, eq. (27), each hole line contributes a minus sign. This sign is included in the definition (60) of the T-contraction.

Green's function $G^{(n)}$ reduces to

$$(64)\qquad G^{(n)}(1, 2, 3, \dots, 2n) = \lim_{\substack{\beta' \to -\infty \\ \beta \to +\infty}} \langle \Phi_0 | T\{U(\beta, u_1)\eta_1(u_1) \cdot \cdot U(u_1, u_2) \dots \eta^{\dagger}_{2n}(u_{2n}) U(u_{2n}, \beta')\} | \Phi_0 \rangle_L ,$$

where only linked diagrams need be considered. It should be noted that the normal products entering in the definition of v exclude contractions between fermion operators associated with the same interaction, and therefore the corresponding diagrams containing parts of the type illustrated in Fig. 10 must be omitted.

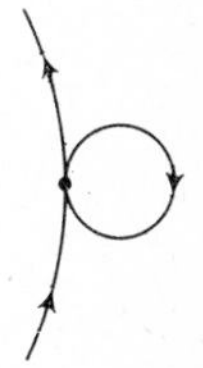
Fig. 10.

3·6. *The integral equation.* – First we shall consider the one-particle Green's function given by eq. (48). Let us define the one-particle *irreducible* diagram $s^{(1)}(j; \alpha_1 - \alpha_2)$ between times α_1 and α_2. It is a diagram with one incoming and one outgoing line, both of index j, which cannot be reduced to two irreducible diagrams by cutting any one of the internal lines. See the examples of Fig. 11 of irreducible and reducible diagrams.

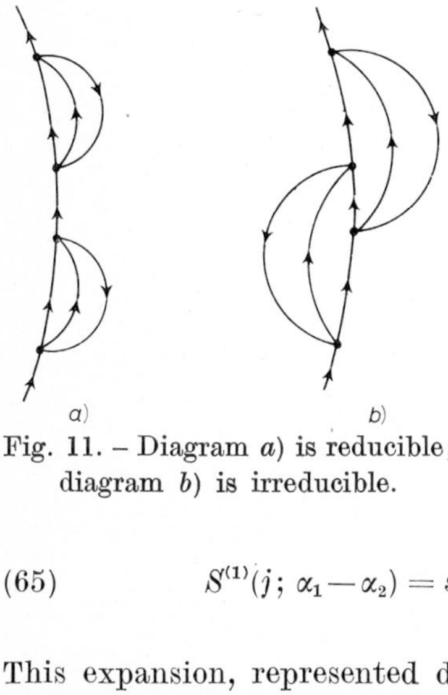

Fig. 11. – Diagram *a*) is reducible; diagram *b*) is irreducible.

The expansion of the Green's function may be reordered according to the various powers of $S^{(1)}(j; \alpha_1 - \alpha_2)$ where $S^{(1)}$ is the family of all possible irreducible one-body diagrams,

$$(65)\qquad S^{(1)}(j; \alpha_1 - \alpha_2) = s_1^{(1)}(j; \alpha_1 - \alpha_2) + s_2^{(1)}(j; \alpha_1 - \alpha_2) + \dots .$$

This expansion, represented diagrammatically in Fig. 12*a* may be rewritten by factoring out the last $S^{(1)}$ contribution, as shown in Fig. 12*b*. It may be seen that the expansion between parentheses is just the one-particle Green's function $G^{(1)}(j; \alpha - v)$, hence the integral equation for $G^{(1)}$ which is represented in Fig. 12*c* may be written as follows:

$$(66)\qquad G^{(1)}(j; u - v) = G_0^{(1)}(j; u - v) + G_0^{(1)}(j; u - \alpha_1) S^{(1)}(j; \alpha_1 - \alpha_2) G^{(1)}(j; \alpha_2 - v) ,$$

where $G_0^{(1)}(j; u_1 - u_2)$ is the free one-body propagator between times u_1 and u_2,

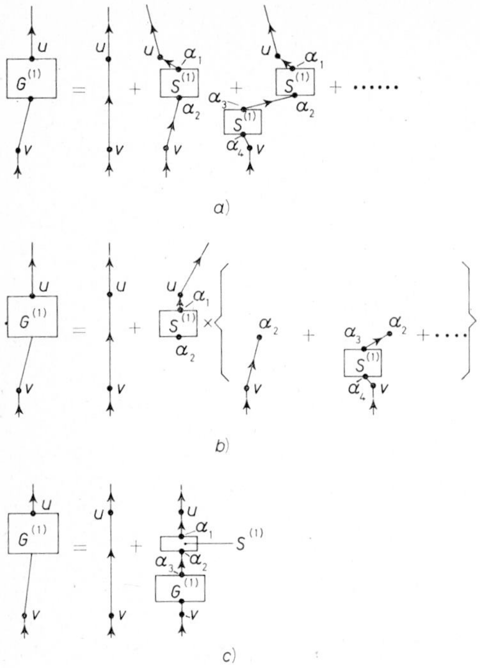

Fig. 12.

i.e. the T-contraction defined in eq. (61). The repeated time indices are integrated between $-\infty$ and $+\infty$.

We consider now the two-particle Green's function, defined by eq. (49). In this case the diagrammatic expansion may be written, in powers of the family $S^{(2)}(j_1 u_1, j_2 u_2, j_3 u_3, j_4 u_4)$ of all irreducible two-particle diagrams. These are diagrams with two incoming and two outgoing lines, with indices j_1, j_2, j_3, j_4, at times u_1, u_2, u_3, u_4, respectively, and such that they cannot be separated into two diagrams of the same type when cutting any two internal lines. As before $S^{(2)}$ may be factored out, the remaining series being $G^{(2)}$. Hence the integral equation is now

$$
\begin{aligned}
(67)\qquad G^{(2)}(1,2,3,4) &= G^{(1)}(1-2)G^{(1)}(3-4) - G^{(1)}(1-4)G^{(1)}(3-2) - \\
&- G^{(1)}(1-5)\,G^{(1)}(6-2)S^{(2)}(5,6,7,8)\{G^{(2)}(8,7,3,4) - G^{(1)}(8-7)G^{(1)}(3-4)\}\,,
\end{aligned}
$$

where we have used the condensed notation $G^{(1)}(1-2)$ for $G^{(1)}(j_1; u_1 - u_2)\delta_{j_1 j_2}$ and $G^{(2)}(1,2,3,4)$ for $G^{(2)}(j_1 u_1; j_2 u_2; j_3 u_3; j_4 u_4)$.

The general particle-hole Green's function is defined as the two-particle Green's function with the following conditions imposed upon the times:

$$u_1, u_2 > u_3, u_4$$

or

$$u_3, u_4 > u_1, u_2\,.$$

In this particular case the integral equation (67) reduces to

$$
\begin{aligned}
(68)\qquad G^{(2)}_{\text{ph}}(1,2,3,4) &= -G^{(1)}(1-4)G^{(1)}(3-2) - G^{(1)}(1-5)\,G^{(1)}(6-2)\,\cdot \\
&\cdot S^{(2)}(5,6,7,8)G^{(2)}_{\text{ph}}(8,7,3,4)\,.
\end{aligned}
$$

3·7. *Time independent formulation.* – In order to remove the time dependence, we shall apply to the Green's function a Fourier transformation. Here we are particularly concerned with the case of the particle-hole propagator of eq. (51), which may be used for the description of double-closed-shell nuclei, where all single-particle states up to the Fermi level are occupied.

We require $u_5 = u_6 = u''$ and $u_7 = u_8 = u'$. With this definition, while the diagram of Fig. 13*a* is reducible, the diagram of Fig. 13*b* should be considered as irreducible. $S^{(2)}$ is now a function of the difference $u'' - u'$ and $G^{(2)}$ a function of $u - u_0$, where $u = u_1 = u_2$ and $u_0 = u_3 = u_4$. With this restriction on the times, the right-hand side of expression (68) becomes a convolution product.

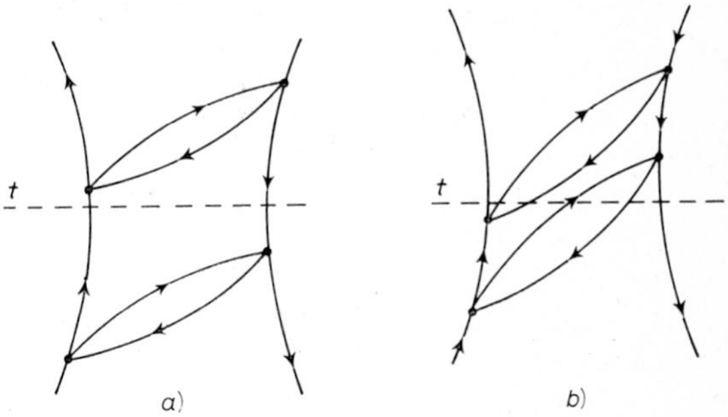

Fig. 13.

Let $i\mathscr{S}^{(2)}(i, j, n, p; \omega)$ and $i\mathscr{G}^{(2)}_{\text{ph}}(i, j, k, l; \omega)$ be the Fourier transform of $S^{(2)}(i, j, n, p; u''-u')$ and of $G^{(2)}_{\text{ph}}(i, j, k, l; u-u_0)$. The Fourier transform of (68) is, therefore,

$$(69)\qquad \mathscr{G}^{(2)}_{\text{ph}}(i, j, k, l; \omega) = -\mathscr{F}(i, j; \omega)\{\delta_{il}\delta_{jk} - \sum_{np}\mathscr{S}^{(2)}(i, j, n, p; \omega)\mathscr{G}^{(2)}_{\text{ph}}(p, n, k, l; \omega)\}\,,$$

where $i\mathscr{F}(i, j; \omega)$ is the Fourier transform of $G^{(1)}(i; u)G^{(1)}(j; -u)$,

$$(70)\qquad \mathscr{F}(i, j; \omega) = \sum_{\lambda\lambda'} \frac{\langle g|\eta_i|\lambda\rangle\langle\lambda|\eta_i^\dagger|g\rangle\langle g|\eta_j^\dagger|\lambda'\rangle\langle\lambda'|\eta_j|g\rangle}{(E_\lambda - E_g) + (E_{\lambda'} - E_g) - \omega - i\delta} + \sum_{\lambda\lambda'} \frac{\langle g|\eta_j|\lambda\rangle\langle\lambda|\eta_j^\dagger|g\rangle\langle g|\eta_i^\dagger|\lambda'\rangle\langle\lambda'|\eta_i|g\rangle}{(E_\lambda - E_g) + (E_{\lambda'} - E_g) + \omega - i\delta}\,.$$

In this expression $|g\rangle$ is the true ground state of the double-closed-shell system, $|\lambda\rangle$ and $|\lambda'\rangle$ are the true excited states of the systems with plus or minus one nucleon, respectively. The excitation energies $(E_\lambda - E_g)$ and $(E_{\lambda'} - E_g)$ are the true excitation energies of the systems with plus or minus a nucleon respectively, relative to the ground state of the double-closed-shell system.

If we assume that the true single-particle propagator can be approximated by the free single-particle propagator, then

$$(71)\qquad \mathscr{F}(i, j; \omega) \simeq \frac{P_i(1-P_j)}{\tilde{\varepsilon}_i + \tilde{\varepsilon}_j - \omega - i\delta} + \frac{P_j(1-P_i)}{\tilde{\varepsilon}_i + \tilde{\varepsilon}_j + \omega - i\delta}$$

and eq. (69) takes the following matrix form in the particle-hole configuration space:

$$\big(\mathscr{M}(\omega) - \nu\omega\big)\mathscr{G}^{(2)}_{\text{ph}}(\omega) = 1 ,$$

where

(72) $$\big(\mathscr{M}(\omega)\big)_{i,j;n,p} = (\tilde{\varepsilon}_i + \tilde{\varepsilon}_j)\delta_{ip}\delta_{jn} + \mathscr{S}^{(2)}(i, j, n, p; \omega) ,$$

(73) $$(\nu)_{i,j;n,p} = \delta_{ip}\delta_{jn}\big(-P_i(1-P_j) + P_j(1-P_i)\big) .$$

The poles of $\mathscr{G}^{(2)}_{\text{ph}}(\omega)$ were shown previously to be the frequencies of the system $\omega_n = E_n - E_g$. They are obtained as the solution of the following equation:

$$\det\big(\mathscr{M}(\omega_n) - \nu\omega_n\big) = 0 ,$$

which is equivalent to the nonlinear secular problem

(74) $$\mathscr{M}(\omega_n)X^n = \nu\omega_n X^n .$$

The residue of $\mathscr{G}^{(2)}_{\text{ph}}$ at the pole ω_n is just $X^{n\dagger}X^n$.

The Green's function formulation of the nuclear problem gives a theoretical framework to the usual semi-phenomenological procedures of shell model calculations. These are essentially of two kinds, which will be discussed in details latter on:

a) Replacement of the Hartree-Fock energies $\tilde{\varepsilon}_i + \tilde{\varepsilon}_j$ in (72) by experimental energies from the low-lying spectrum of the neighbouring odd-A nuclei. This procedure replaces the free particle-hole propagator (71) by the dressed « quasi-particle » propagator (70), assuming that only one state $\lambda = i$ and one state $\lambda' = j$ contribute respectively to the sum in (71), with a numerator equal to unity.

b) Replacement of the function $\mathscr{S}^{(2)}(i, n, p, j; \omega)$ in (72) by an effective interaction obtained from experimental considerations.

From another point of view the Green's function method provides an exact formulation of the nuclear problem in terms of a microscopic two-body interaction, as long as all possible irreducible graphs are taken into account. The method provides a framework for developing successive approximations where one tries to guess the dominant irreducible graphs.

PART II

4. – Excitations of « nondegenerate » nuclei.

4·1. *The « nondegenerate » nuclei.* – The various methods for obtaining an approximate solution to the nuclear problem which we shall discuss are based on the separation of the nuclear Hamiltonian into two parts: an independent-particle or quasi-particle Hamiltonian H_0, and a residual interaction v between these particles or quasi-particles. The form in which these operators are written in the Hartree-Fock or Hartree-Bogoliubov theories has been given in Sect. **2** eqs. (35), (43) and (45). Furthermore, these methods are primarily concerned with nuclear systems whose ground state can be represented in first approximation by a *nondegenerate* eigenstate $|\Phi_0\rangle$ of H_0,

$$H_0|\Phi_0\rangle = E_0|\Phi_0\rangle\,,$$

where E_0 is the lowest eigenvalue of H_0 for an N-particle system. As examples of « nondegenerate » nuclei, corresponding to the various possible types of the self-consistent unperturbed Hamiltonian H_0, let us list:

a) The doubly closed-shell nuclei, ^{16}O, ^{40}Ca and ^{208}Pb (^{12}C may be added to the list if we consider it doubly closed in j-j coupling) which correspond to the spherical solution of the Hartree-Fock equations. The state $|\Phi_0\rangle$ is a Slater determinant wherein all the single-particle states are occupied up to the Fermi level ε_{F}.

b) The light deformed nuclei with $N=4n$ nucleons (^{20}Ne, ^{24}Mg, ... etc) which correspond to deformed solutions of the Hartree-Fock equations. These may be considered as nondegenerate nuclei if isospin is a good quantum number, and invariance under time reversal holds for H_0; each unperturbed single-particle deformed orbital level is then four-fold degenerate. The unperturbed single-particle ground state $|\Phi_0\rangle$ is again a Slater determinant in which all the deformed orbitals are occupied up to the Fermi level.

c) The even-even spherical SCS (single closed shell) nuclei, *i.e.* the isotopes of Ni, Sn and Pb ($Z=20$, 50 and 82), and the isotones with $N=50$, 82 and 126. These nuclei have *either* neutrons *or* protons outside a doubly closed shell. Due to the pairing effect between the identical nucleons outside the doubly closed core, the ground state is represented in first approximation by a BCS wave function, *i.e.* an independent quasi-particle eigenstate corresponding to the lowest energy of the Hartree-Bogoliubov Hamiltonian.

d) The even-even heavy deformed nuclei. The degeneracies expected in spherical shell model configurations are partly lifted by the strong deformation of the average field. Furthermore the neutrons outnumber the protons to such an extent that those which are nearest to the Fermi level occupy quite different orbitals. Accordingly the neutron-proton interaction is relatively small and may be totally included within the residual interaction v while the neutron and the proton systems may be individually described by a non-degenerate BCS wave function, wherein the quasi-particles occupy deformed orbitals. The approximate ground state $|\Phi_0\rangle$ is then the product of the protons and the neutrons BCS states.

The theoretical importance of these nuclei stems from the fact that the main features of their spectrum can easily be understood qualitatively and even quantitatively. Furthermore they exhibit strongly coherent excitation modes in terms of which we can form a simple model describing approximately the spectrum of neighbouring « degenerate » nuclear systems. The odd-even nuclei shall not be considered here. From now on we shall consider for convenience $|\Phi_0\rangle$ as a reference state, according to the definition of Sect. **2**. We shall denote it as a « vacuum » associated with the creation and annihilation operators $\xi^\dagger_\alpha$ and ξ_α for a quasi-particle in state α. In the case of the Hartree-Bogoliubov field these quasi-particle operators are given by eqs. (41) where the u's and the v's are obtained by the BCS variational method. In the case of the Hartree-Fock field the quasi-particles are « particles » and « holes », defined by the transformation (24), according as to whether the single-particle state α is above or below the Fermi level.

4·2. *The configurational space.* – The spectrum of H_0, for a « nondegenerate » system, is quite characteristic and is similar for a Hartree-Fock and a Hartree-Bogoliubov field as shown on Fig. 14. Schematically it starts with an energy gap, followed by successive groups of fairly closely spaced levels; the number of levels in the first group is fairly small but it increases rapidly in each group as the energy increases.

In the case of the Hartree-Fock field the minimum excitation energy is that required to promote a particle from a state a below the Fermi level to an unoccupied state A above the Fermi level. For spherical nuclei this energy is fairly large (15 MeV for ^{16}O, 8 MeV for ^{40}Ca and 5 MeV for ^{208}Pb) since it corresponds to the separation energy $\hbar\omega$ between two successive shells. More precisely, the first excited configurations of H_0 for doubly closed-shell nuclei are one particle-one hole pairs,

$$|\Phi_{Aa}\rangle = \xi^\dagger_A \xi^\dagger_a |\Phi_0\rangle \tag{75}$$

with unperturbed energies $\tilde{\varepsilon}_A + \tilde{\varepsilon}_a$, where the $\tilde{\varepsilon}_i$ are defined in eq. (36). These excitations are of odd-parity. The next odd-parity excitations will be much higher in energy, corresponding either to a single particle-hole pair with the particle jumping 3 major shells or to two particle-hole pairs where the particles jump respectively 2 shells and 1 shell. We shall see that deformed Hartree-Fock fields exhibit similar spectra with large energy gaps.

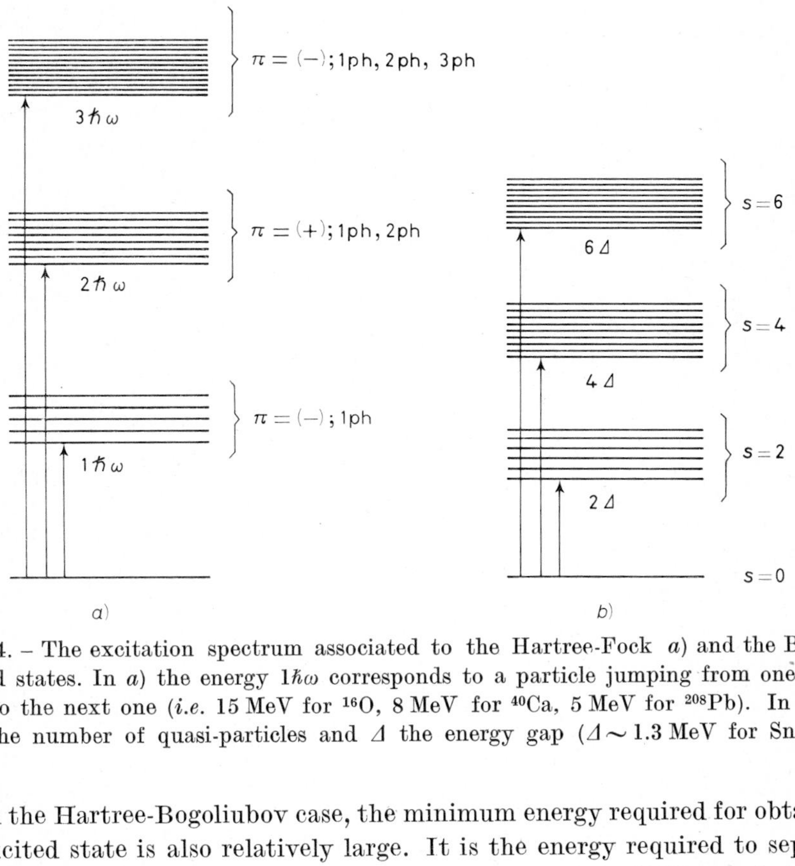

Fig. 14. – The excitation spectrum associated to the Hartree-Fock *a*) and the BCS *b*) ground states. In *a*) the energy $1\hbar\omega$ corresponds to a particle jumping from one major shell to the next one (*i.e.* 15 MeV for ^{16}O, 8 MeV for ^{40}Ca, 5 MeV for ^{208}Pb). In *b*) s is the number of quasi-particles and Δ the energy gap ($\Delta \sim 1.3$ MeV for Sn).

In the Hartree-Bogoliubov case, the minimum energy required for obtaining an excited state is also relatively large. It is the energy required to separate two paired particles and is equal to twice the value of the BCS gap Δ. Therefore the first unperturbed excited states correspond to configurations made up of two quasi-particle states,

$$|\Phi_{\alpha\beta}\rangle = \xi^{\dagger}_{\alpha}\xi^{\dagger}_{\beta}|\Phi_0\rangle\,. \tag{76}$$

This is a configuration, with energy $\tilde{E}_\alpha + \tilde{E}_\beta$, where $\tilde{E}_\alpha$ and $\tilde{E}_\beta$ are the quasi-particle energies defined in (44). Following the group of 2 quasi-particle configurations come the groups of states of 4, 6 etc. quasi-particles at excitation energies of about 4Δ, 6Δ, etc. For the low-lying excited states of the system, the secular problem is enormously reduced by the fact that the residual interaction mixes together the levels within the lowest group, to a first approximation, excluding those from other groups. The weak coupling between the configurations of the first group and those of other groups is due to the following:

1) the large energy separating groups of the same parity,

2) the small magnitude of the matrix elements connecting configurations of the lowest group with others and which may be attributed to *a*) the radial integrals over orbitals having different number of nodes and consequently small overlap, and *b*) the angular integrals which are small when connecting configurations involving a different number of quasi-particles.

In order that the simple mixture of configurations described above remains valid it is necessary to select judiciously the zero-order Hamiltonian. For example, in the case of ^{16}O, the elementary particle-hole configurations of the spherically symmetric Hartree-Fock field are of odd parity and lead to an adequate description of the low-lying odd-parity states. However, the existence in ^{16}O of low-lying even-parity states requires in the spherical representation an admixture of configurations involving at least two particle-hole pairs which are quite numerous. As we shall see in Sect. **7**, the description can be considerably simplified by selecting a deformed zero-order field.

4'3. *The two-quasi-particles secular problem.* – We shall now derive the matrix of the nuclear secular problem (4) limited to the subspace corresponding to two quasi-particle configurations in which the 1 particle-1 hole configurations become a special case. We consider the case of a spherically symmetric zero-order field. The modifications required in the nonspherical case are readily carried out.

The two-quasi-particle coupled configuration is defined as

$$|\Phi_{\alpha\beta}^{\mathscr{J}M}\rangle = [\xi_\alpha^\dagger \xi_\beta^\dagger]_M^{\mathscr{J}} |\Phi_0\rangle = \sum_{\substack{m_\alpha \\ m_\beta}} (j_\alpha j_\beta m_\alpha m_\beta | JM) \xi_\alpha^\dagger \xi_\beta^\dagger |\Phi_0\rangle \tag{77}$$

and the nuclear secular problem (4) restricted to the two-quasi–particle subspace becomes

$$\sum_{\gamma,\delta} \{(\widetilde{E}_\alpha + \widetilde{E}_\beta)\delta_{\alpha\gamma}\delta_{\beta\delta} + \langle\Phi_{\alpha\beta}^{\mathscr{J}}|v|\Phi_{\gamma\delta}^{\mathscr{J}}\rangle\} X_{\gamma\delta}^{n,\mathscr{J}} = E_{n,\mathscr{J}} X_{\alpha\beta}^{n,\mathscr{J}}, \tag{78}$$

where $\widetilde{E}_\alpha + \widetilde{E}_\beta$ are the configurational two-quasi–particle energies, the $E_{n,\mathscr{J}}$'s are the eigenvalues and the $X_{\alpha\beta}^{n,\mathscr{J}}$'s are the amplitudes of the corresponding wave functions $\Psi^{(n)}$ defined in (5).

In the particle-hole limit (cf. (24)), the configurations are

$$|\Phi_{Aa}^{\mathscr{J},M}\rangle = [\xi_A^\dagger \xi_a^\dagger]_M^{\mathscr{J}} |\Phi_0\rangle = \sum_{\substack{m_A \\ m_a}} (-)^{j_a - m_a} (j_A j_a m_A m_a | \mathscr{J} M) \eta_{Am_A}^\dagger \eta_{a-m_a} |\Phi_0\rangle \tag{79}$$

and the matrix element

$$(80)\qquad \tfrac{1}{4}\sum_{rsmn}\langle rs|V|mn\rangle\langle\Phi_0|[\xi_a\xi_A]^{\mathscr{I}}_M:\eta_r^\dagger\eta_s^\dagger\eta_n\eta_m:[\xi_B^\dagger\xi_b^\dagger]^{\mathscr{I}}_M|\Phi_0\rangle =$$

$$=\sum_{\substack{m_a m_b\\ m_A m_B}}(-)^{j_a-m_a+j_b-m_b}(j_B j_b m_B m_b|\mathscr{I}M)(j_A j_a m_A m_a|\mathscr{I}M)\langle Am_A, b-m_b|V|a-m_a, Bm_B\rangle =$$

$$=\langle \overset{\mathscr{I}M}{\overline{Ab}}|V|\underset{\mathscr{I}M}{\underline{aB}}\rangle\,,$$

where the last term is the antisymmetrized two-body matrix element defined in (22), with state A coupled to state a and state B coupled to state b in that order. For convenience we introduce the following particle-hole ket notation:

$$(81)\qquad \langle\!\langle (Aa)\mathscr{I}M|V|(Bb)\mathscr{I}M\rangle\!\rangle = \langle \overset{\mathscr{I}M}{\overline{Ab}}|V|\underset{\mathscr{I}M}{\underline{aB}}\rangle$$

and the particle-hole secular problem is written as

$$(82)\qquad \sum_{Bb}\{(\tilde{\varepsilon}_A+\tilde{\varepsilon}_a)\delta_{AB}\delta_{ab}+\langle\!\langle (Aa)\mathscr{I}|V|(Bb)\mathscr{I}\rangle\!\rangle\}X^{n,\mathscr{I}}_{Bb} = E_{n,\mathscr{I}}X^{n,\mathscr{I}}_{Aa}\,.$$

In the general case we can use expression (45) for the residual two-body interaction and the two-quasi–particle matrix elements become

$$(83)\qquad \langle\Phi^{\mathscr{I}}_{\alpha\beta}|v|\Phi^{\mathscr{I}}_{\gamma\delta}\rangle = (1+\delta_{\alpha\beta})^{-\frac{1}{2}}(1+\delta_{\gamma\delta})^{-\frac{1}{2}}\cdot$$
$$\cdot[-\langle\!\langle(\alpha\beta)\mathscr{I}|V|(\gamma\delta)\mathscr{I}\rangle\!\rangle(u_\alpha v_\beta u_\gamma v_\delta + v_\alpha u_\beta v_\gamma u_\delta)-$$
$$-(-)^{j_\alpha-j_\beta+\mathscr{I}}\langle\!\langle(\alpha\beta)\mathscr{I}|V|(\delta\gamma)\mathscr{I}\rangle\!\rangle(u_\alpha v_\beta v_\gamma u_\delta + v_\alpha u_\beta u_\gamma v_\delta)+$$
$$+\langle(\alpha\beta)\mathscr{I}|V|(\gamma\delta)\mathscr{I}\rangle(u_\alpha u_\beta u_\gamma u_\delta + v_\alpha v_\beta v_\gamma v_\delta)]\,.$$

The first two terms of the right-hand side are the particle-hole matrix elements, defined in (80), while the third term is the usual antisymmetrized particle-particle matrix element (α coupled to β and γ to δ in that order). In the particle-hole limit, one obtains again (80). Except in the case where all four states α, β, γ and δ are near the Fermi level, it is readily seen that the particle-hole term in (83) is larger than the particle-particle term due to the factors involving products of u's and v's.

4·4. *Collective states and the schematic model.* – While the solution of the nuclear secular problem yields results in reasonable agreement with experiment, as will be shown in Sect. **6**, the mechanism for the appearance of the so-called collective states is not readily understandable from the general expression (82). These collective states generally referred to as *vibrational states* are characterized by their position somewhat removed from the unperturbed two-quasi–particle energies and by the unexpected strength of their transition probabilities which considerably exceeds the predictions of the independent-particle model. The schematic model of Brown and Bolsterli [7] is a simplified version of the secular nuclear problem which relates the appearance of the collective states to certain properties of the two-body particle-hole matrix element.

The schematic model assumes that the particle-hole matrix element (81) may be separated into a product of one-body matrix elements:

$$\langle\!\langle Aa|V|Bb\rangle\!\rangle = \lambda\langle a|\theta|A\rangle\langle B|\theta|b\rangle\,, \tag{84}$$

where θ denotes a one-body operator, and λ a strength constant. Apart from providing a simplified solution to the secular problem, the relation (84) defines a phase relationship between the two-body particle-hole matrix element and the one-body matrix element. This phase relationship will be essential in explaining the enhancement of transition properties of the collective solutions. Accordingly we shall first discuss the assumption of separability (84) by comparing it to the exact matrix element. It may be shown that the direct $S=0$ (nonspin-flip) part of the particle-hole matrix element is of the form

$$\langle\!\langle (Aa)\mathcal{J}|V|(Bb)\mathcal{J}\rangle\!\rangle_D = \langle B\|F_{\mathcal{J}}\|b\rangle\langle a\|F_{\mathcal{J}}\|A\rangle\cdot \cdot\iint r_1^2\,\mathrm{d}r_1 r_2^2\,\mathrm{d}r_2\varphi_A(r_1)\varphi_a(r_1)f_{\mathcal{J}}(r_1,r_2)\varphi_B(r_2)\varphi_b(r_2)\,, \tag{85}$$

where the quantities $\langle A\|F_{\mathcal{J}}\|a\rangle$ are reduced matrix elements resulting from the integration over the angular and isospin variables. We note that the radial part of a multipole of order $\mathcal{J}$ of a short-range force, having for example Gaussian radial dependence, may be written as

$$f_{\mathcal{J}}(r_1,r_2)\propto \exp\left[-\left(\frac{r_1}{\mu}\right)^2\right]\exp\left[-\left(\frac{r_2}{\mu}\right)^2\right]i^{\mathcal{J}}j_{\mathcal{J}}\left(i\,\frac{2r_1r_2}{\mu^2}\right)\simeq \simeq\frac{\exp[-(r_1/\mu)^2]\exp[-(r_2/\mu)^2]2^{\mathcal{J}}}{((2\mathcal{J}+1)!!)^2}\left\{\left(\frac{r_1}{\mu}\right)^{\mathcal{J}}\left(\frac{r_2}{\mu}\right)^{\mathcal{J}}\right\}. \tag{86}$$

The quantity in the bracket is the first term of the expansion for the Bessel function. Strictly speaking this approximation is only valid near the origin. None the less we can apply it over all space since the exponential factors fall so rapidly. Thus the direct ($S=0$) particle-hole matrix element is approximately of the form (84), with $\theta \sim Y_{\mathscr{I}} r^{\mathscr{I}}$, this being the one-body operator associated with an electric multipole transition of order $\mathscr{I}$. This result only holds true for the direct particle-hole term. However, as long as the direct-term contribution is larger than that of the exchange term, the phase relationship (84) still holds. This is normally the case in practice.

Considering now the two-quasi–particle matrix element (83), these results are no longer true for the particle-particle part and only apply to the direct particle-hole part.

When the interaction is written in the separated form (84), the eigenvalues E of the secular problem (82) are given by the implicit equation

$$\sum_{Aa} \frac{|\langle A|\theta|a\rangle|^2}{\tilde{\varepsilon}_A + \tilde{\varepsilon}_a - E} = -\frac{1}{\lambda}\,; \tag{87}$$

the normalized amplitudes are

$$X_{Aa} = \mathscr{N} \frac{\langle A|\theta|a\rangle}{\tilde{\varepsilon}_A + \tilde{\varepsilon}_a - E}\,, \tag{88}$$

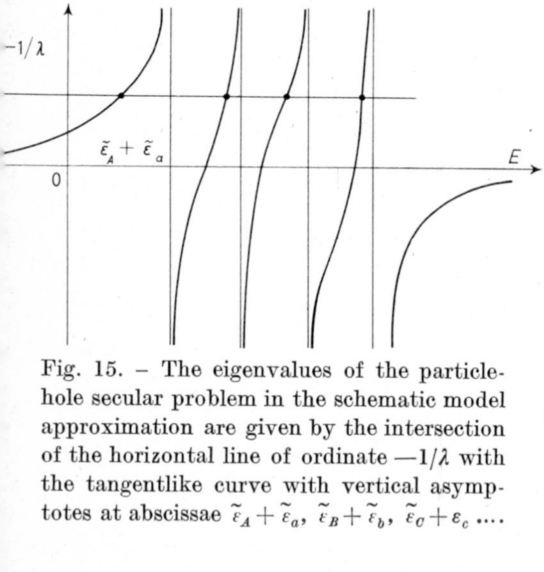

Fig. 15. – The eigenvalues of the particle-hole secular problem in the schematic model approximation are given by the intersection of the horizontal line of ordinate $-1/\lambda$ with the tangentlike curve with vertical asymptotes at abscissae $\tilde{\varepsilon}_A + \tilde{\varepsilon}_a$, $\tilde{\varepsilon}_B + \tilde{\varepsilon}_b$, $\tilde{\varepsilon}_C + \varepsilon_c$ ....

where $\mathscr{N}$ is the normalization constant,

$$\mathscr{N}^{-2} = \sum_{Aa} \left(\frac{\langle A|\theta|a\rangle \cdot}{\tilde{\varepsilon}_A + \tilde{\varepsilon}_a - E} \right)^2 . \tag{88a}$$

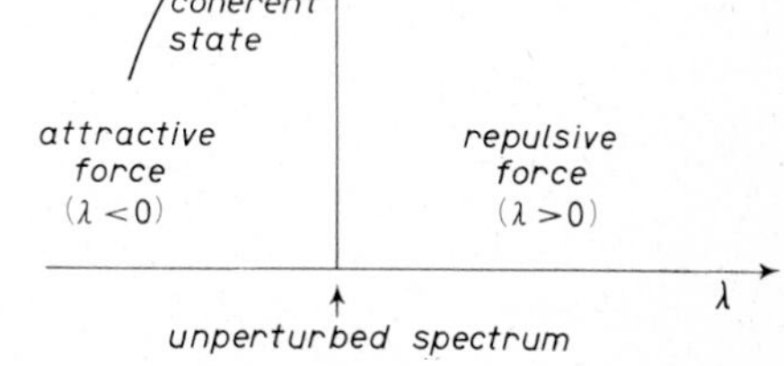

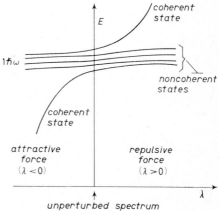

Fig. 16. – Variation of the energy spectrum as a function of the particle-hole interaction according to the schematic model.

It should be noted that the relative phases between the amplitudes of the wave function X_{Aa}, X_{Bb}, etc... are given by the relative phases between the corresponding one-body matrix elements $\langle A|\theta|a\rangle$, $\langle B|\theta|b\rangle$ etc... times the sign of the energy denominators.

The eigenvalues of the schematic model may be determined by graphical solution of eq. (87) (cf. Fig. 15) and the resulting energy spectrum is presented as a function of λ on Fig. 16. A striking characteristic of the spectrum is that only one root can be appreciably shifted by the residual interaction; namely the highest root for a repulsive interaction and the lowest one for an attractive interaction. All the other roots are trapped between the unperturbed configurational energies (this is only true of the schematic model and does not hold for the more general eigenvalue problem (82)).

Next we shall consider the transition properties of the eigenstates of the schematic model. The transition rate is given by

$$T = |\langle n|t|\Phi_0\rangle|^2 ,$$

where t is the one-body transition operator

$$t = \sum_{\alpha,\beta} \langle\alpha|t|\beta\rangle \eta_\alpha^\dagger \eta_\beta .$$

The final state $|n\rangle$ is here described in terms of particle-hole excitations and therefore the single-particle states β and α are respectively below and above the Fermi level, thus

$$T = |\sum_{Aa} X_{Aa}^n \langle A|t|a\rangle|^2 = \mathcal{N}^2 \left| \sum_{Aa} \frac{\langle A|t|a\rangle\langle a|\theta|A\rangle}{\tilde{\varepsilon}_A + \tilde{\varepsilon}_a - E} \right|^2 . \tag{89}$$

All the numerators in the summation are of the same sign, as long as the radial integrals of θ and t have the same sign which is generally the case for an electric transition. Considering the denominators it may be seen that all terms add up coherently for the upper root when $\lambda > 0$, or for the lowest root when $\lambda < 0$, resulting in an enhancement of the transition rate. In the case of the other roots which are trapped between unperturbed eigenvalues, some terms will partially cancel others in the summation and the transition rate will be reduced.

The behaviour and the nature of the collective state is strikingly illustrated in the limit of the degenerate case where all the unperturbed energies $\tilde{\varepsilon}_A + \tilde{\varepsilon}_a$ are equal to ε. One root is then shifted as shown above, while all others remain at energy ε. The amplitudes of the wave functions corresponding to the shifted root are as follows:

$$X_{Aa} = \frac{\mathcal{N}\langle A|\theta|a\rangle}{\varepsilon - E} = \frac{\langle A|\theta|a\rangle}{\left(\sum_{Aa} |\langle A|\theta|a\rangle|^2\right)^{\frac{1}{2}}} , \tag{90}$$

where we have used the value given by eq. (88*a*) for the normalization constant. The root obtained from eq. (87) may now be written as follows:

$$E = \varepsilon + \lambda \sum_{Aa} |\langle A|\theta|a\rangle|^2 , \tag{91}$$

i.e. the energy shift is equal to the sum of all the diagonal matrix elements; and the transition rate for the displaced state is

$$T = \frac{1}{\sum_{Aa} |\langle A|\theta|a\rangle|^2} \left| \sum_{Aa} \langle A|t|a\rangle\langle a|\theta|A\rangle \right|^2 . \tag{92}$$

If all the matrix elements $\langle A|\theta|a\rangle$ are equal,

$$T = \sum_{Aa} |\langle A|t|a\rangle|^2 , \tag{93}$$

i.e. the transition probability of the displaced state is equal to the sum of all the transition probabilities to the unperturbed states. The transition probabilities to all the other degenerate states, at energy ε, are equal to zero.

4·5. *Summary.* – A detailed comparison between theoretical predictions based on the preceding discussions and the behaviour of the spectrum of actual nuclei will be carried out in Sect. **6**. At this time we shall merely review what may be expected, considering the nature of the residual interaction.

Two types of states are predicted:

1) *Incoherent states*: These states are formed in the energy region of the unperturbed particle-hole or two-quasi–particle configurations. The contributions to the transition probabilities of the various configurations add up incoherently. Transition rates are smaller than those of the independent-particle model particularly when there are many closely spaced unperturbed levels.

2) *Coherent state*: A single coherent state appears with a pronounced energy shift and with strongly enhanced transition probability. The collective nature of this level is due to the coherent superposition of the contributions to the transition probabilities of elementary particle-hole or two-quasi–particle configurations. Its position depends upon the sign of the interaction. For a realistic two-body force, the interaction is attractive when protons and neutrons move in phase and is repulsive otherwise.

In the former case the schematic model predicts the existence of a low-lying collective state experimentally observed as *vibration*; in the latter case a high-lying state is predicted, *the giant resonance.*

These features will be most pronounced in the case of many closely spaced unperturbed eigenstates. This is strikingly illustrated in the giant resonance of ^{208}Pb where 30 unperturbed particle-hole 1^- configurations lie between 5 and 8 MeV as shown in Fig. 17*a*. The effect of the two-body residual interaction limited to these configurations is illustrated in Fig. 17*b* where it may be seen that all the incoherent states below 8 MeV have practically zero transition probability while a collective state appears 4 MeV higher.

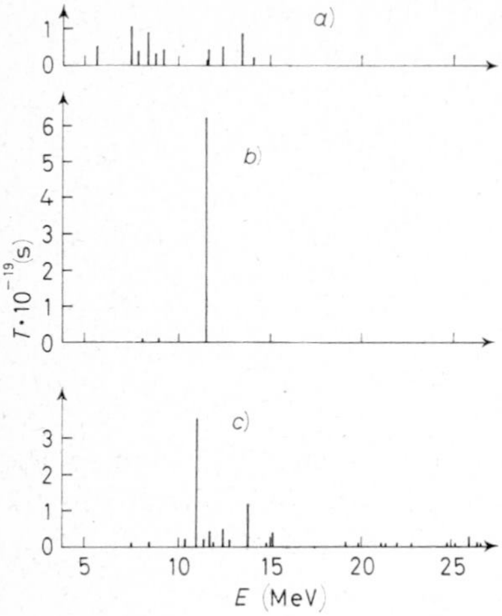

Fig. 17. – The dipole state in ^{208}Pb (GILLET, GREEN and SANDERSON [8]): *a*) unperturbed dipole strength; *b*) perturbed dipole strength keeping all configurations up to 8 MeV only; *c*) dipole state with all configurations up to 30 MeV.

5. – The random phase approximation.

5·1. *Introduction.* – According to the program outlined in Sect. **1**, successively more accurate approximations to the nuclear secular problem should consist in extending the subspace of configurations $|\Phi_\alpha\rangle$, the eigenstates of H_0, over which the residual interaction matrix is diagonalized. However it is a rather formidable task to construct configurations for a number of particle-holes or quasi-particles which are properly antisymmetrized and are eigenstates of $\mathscr{I}$.

Following a method developed to treat the electron gas, the particle-hole or 2-quasi-particle model described in Sect. **4** has been extended to include in a simple fashion excitations of more than one particle-hole pair or of seniority greater than 2. The simplicity of the formulation is obtained at the cost of some violation of the Pauli principle. This generalization of the model may be derived in various fashions, namely:

a) the quasi-boson formalism where pairs of fermions are treated as bosons;

b) the perturbation expansion of the particle-hole Green's function of the system, with resummation of some special subseries of diagrams;

c) the time-dependent Hartree-Fock method with linearization of the equation of motion.

In the lowest order, these various approaches all lead to the same non-Hermitian problem, known as the random phase approximation (R.P.A.).

However they are not quite equivalent in their point of view nor in the physical insight they give into the R.P.A. Furthermore each of them is the starting point for different higher approximations. Accordingly we shall briefly review the derivation of the R.P.A. equations by these various methods. In order to simplify the discussion, we will limit ourselves to the case of particle-hole excitations; the extension to quasi-particles is readily achieved.

5·2. *The quasi-boson approximation.* – Let $|g\rangle$ be the ground state of the system. We make the fundamental assumption that the excited states $|n\rangle$ differ from $|g\rangle$ by the presence or absence of at most one particle-hole pair, *i.e.*

$$|nJM\rangle = Q^\dagger_{nJM}|g\rangle\,, \tag{94}$$

where

$$Q^\dagger_{nJM} = \sum_{Aa}\{X^n_{Aa}\Omega^\dagger_{JM}(Aa) - Y^n_{Aa}\Omega_{JM}(Aa)\} \tag{95}$$

and where $\Omega^\dagger_{JM}(Aa)$ and $\Omega_{JM}(Aa)$ are respectively creation and annihilation operators for the particle-hole pair Aa, *i.e.*

$$\Omega^\dagger_{JM}(Aa) = \sum_{\substack{m_a\\ m_A}}(j_A j_a m_A m_a|JM)\xi^\dagger_{j_A m_A}\xi^\dagger_{j_a m_a}\,. \tag{96}$$

Hereafter we shall generally omit the indices J and M for simplicity. Since the ground state cannot contain any component of the excited states,

$$Q_n|g\rangle = 0 \qquad \text{for all } n\,. \tag{97}$$

This condition requires that only configurations with an even number of particle-hole pairs enter in the ground-state wave function.

The total nuclear Hamiltonian in the Hartree-Fock representation (eq. (35)) acting on vectors which consist solely of particle-hole combinations has the same effect as the following model Hamiltonian:

$$\begin{aligned} H' = {} & \sum_{Aa}(\tilde\varepsilon_A + \tilde\varepsilon_a)\Omega^\dagger(Aa)\Omega(Aa) + \\ & + \tfrac{1}{2}\sum_{\substack{Aa\\ Bb}}\langle Ab|V|aB\rangle :\{\Omega^\dagger(Aa)\Omega(Bb) + \Omega(Aa)\Omega^\dagger(Bb)\}: + \\ & \qquad + \tfrac{1}{4}\sum_{\substack{Aa\\ Bb}}\langle ab|V|AB\rangle :\{\Omega^\dagger(Aa)\Omega^\dagger(Bb) + \Omega(Aa)\Omega(Bb)\}:\,, \end{aligned} \tag{98}$$

where we have used the fact that the interaction matrix is real and symmetric.

The operators Ω satisfy the following commutation relations:

$$(99)\qquad \begin{cases} [\Omega_{JM}(Aa),\ \Omega_{J'M'}(Bb)] = 0\,, \\ [\Omega^\dagger_{JM}(Aa),\ \Omega^\dagger_{J'M'}(Bb)] = 0\,, \\ [\Omega_{JM}(Aa),\ \Omega^\dagger_{J'M'}(Bb)] = 0 \qquad \text{if } Aa \neq Bb\,, \\ [\Omega_{JM}(Aa),\ \Omega^\dagger_{J'M'}(Aa)] = \delta_{JJ'}\delta_{MM'}(1 - N_A - N_a)\,, \end{cases}$$

where N_A and N_a are the occupation number operators $\xi^\dagger\xi$. The condition $J=J'$ and $M=M'$ follows from the orthonormality of the Clebsch-Gordan coefficients entering in the definition of the Ω's. The quasi-boson approximation consists in setting

$$(100)\qquad \langle g|N_A|g\rangle = \langle g|N_a|g\rangle = 0\,,$$

i.e. the probability for the particle-hole states Aa to be occupied in the ground state is assumed to be negligible. In other words, it is assumed that the ground state $|g\rangle$ differs very little from the Hartree-Fock ground state $|\Phi_0\rangle$ relative to which the occupation numbers are zero. The condition under which this assumption is valid is that

$$n \ll \mathcal{N}\,,$$

where n is the number of excited particle-hole pairs in the ground state, and $\mathcal{N}$ the number of available particle-hole states. In the nuclear case, the degeneracies of the shells are small especially for light nuclei, therefore the applicability of assumption (100) may be questionable (cf. Sect. **5**·7).

Denoting by E_n the energy of the state $|n\rangle$ relative to the energy E_g of the approximate ground state $|g\rangle$ (*i.e.* we use $E_g = 0$ as origin), the equations of motion are

$$(101)\qquad [H, Q_n^\dagger]|g\rangle = [H', Q_n^\dagger]|g\rangle = E_n Q_n^\dagger|g\rangle\,.$$

We obtain readily the expression for the left-hand side of eq. (101) utilizing the boson commutation relations (99-100)

$$(102)\qquad E_n Q_n^\dagger = \sum_{Bb}[H', X^n_{Bb}\Omega^\dagger(Bb) - Y^n_{Bb}\Omega(Bb)] =$$
$$= \sum_{Bb}\sum_{A'a'}\big[\big((\tilde{\varepsilon}_{A'} + \tilde{\varepsilon}_{a'})\delta_{A'B}\delta_{a'b} + \langle A'b|V|a'B\rangle\big)\big(X^n_{Bb}\Omega^\dagger(A'a') - Y^n_{Bb}\Omega(A'a')\big) +$$
$$+ \langle A'B|V|a'b\rangle\big(X^n_{Bb}\Omega(A'a') - Y^n_{Bb}\Omega^\dagger(A'a')\big)\big]\,.$$

The coupled equations for the amplitudes X^n_{Aa} and Y^n_{Aa} are obtained by taking the commutators of eqs. (102) with $\Omega(Aa)$ and $\Omega^\dagger(Aa)$ respectively and utilizing again the boson commutation relations (99-100)

$$(103)\quad \begin{cases} E_n X^n_{Aa} = (\tilde{\varepsilon}_A + \tilde{\varepsilon}_a) X^n_{Aa} + \sum_{Bb} (\langle Ab|V|aB\rangle X^n_{Bb} - \langle AB|V|ab\rangle Y^n_{Bb}) , \\ E_n Y^n_{Aa} = -(\tilde{\varepsilon}_A + \tilde{\varepsilon}_a) Y^n_{Aa} - \sum_{Bb} (\langle Ab|V|aB\rangle Y^n_{Bb} - \langle AB|V|ab\rangle X^n_{Bb}) . \end{cases}$$

Using again the notation defined in Sect. **4**, eq. (81), for the particle-hole matrix elements, we introduce the real symmetric matrix $\mathscr{A}$ whose elements

$$\langle\!\langle (Aa)\mathscr{I}M|\mathscr{A}|(Bb)\mathscr{I}M\rangle\!\rangle = (\tilde{\varepsilon}_A + \tilde{\varepsilon}_a)\delta_{AB}\delta_{ab} + \langle\!\langle (Aa)\mathscr{I}M|V|(Bb)\mathscr{I}M\rangle\!\rangle$$

connect particle-hole configurations $|(Aa)\mathscr{I}M\rangle\!\rangle$ to particle-hole configurations $|(Bb)\mathscr{I}M\rangle\!\rangle$, and the real symmetric matrix $\mathscr{B}$ whose elements

$$(104)\quad \langle\!\langle (Aa)\mathscr{I}M|\mathscr{B}|(bB)\mathscr{I}M\rangle\!\rangle = \langle \overbrace{A\,B|V|a}^{\mathscr{I}M}\!\!\!\underbrace{\;\;b}_{\mathscr{I}M}\rangle$$

connect particle-hole configurations $|(Aa)\mathscr{I}M\rangle\!\rangle$ to *hole-particle* configurations $|(bB)\mathscr{I}M\rangle\!\rangle$.

The right-hand side of eq. (104) denotes the two-body matrix element defined in eq. (22) wherein the particle A is coupled to the hole a and the hole b is coupled to the particle B, in that order, for given $\mathscr{I}M$. The secular problem of eq. (103) becomes

$$(105)\quad \begin{pmatrix} \mathscr{A} & \mathscr{B} \\ \mathscr{B} & \mathscr{A} \end{pmatrix} \begin{pmatrix} X^n \\ Y^n \end{pmatrix} = E_n \begin{pmatrix} X^n \\ -Y^n \end{pmatrix} .$$

These are the R.P.A. equations. The problem is non-Hermitian due to the minus sign appearing in front of the Y component in the second member.

The R.P.A. in the more general case of 2-quasi-particle excitation is obtained by substituting into the definition of the matrix $\mathscr{A}$, the quasi-particle energies $\tilde{E}$ for the $\tilde{\varepsilon}$, and the matrix elements between 2-quasi-particle states, defined in eq. (83), for the particle-hole matrix elements. The $\mathscr{B}$ matrix in the 2-quasi-particle space takes the form

$$(106)\quad \langle(\alpha\beta)\mathscr{I}M|\mathscr{B}|(\delta\gamma)\mathscr{I}M\rangle = (1+\delta_{\alpha\beta})^{-\frac{1}{2}}(1+\delta_{\gamma\delta})^{-\frac{1}{2}} \cdot$$
$$\cdot [-\langle\!\langle(\alpha\beta)\mathscr{I}M|V|(\gamma\delta)\mathscr{I}M\rangle\!\rangle(u_\alpha v_\beta v_\gamma u_\delta + v_\alpha u_\beta u_\gamma v_\delta) -$$
$$-(-)^{j_\gamma - j_\delta + \mathscr{I}} \langle\!\langle(\alpha\beta)\mathscr{I}M|V|(\delta\gamma)\mathscr{I}M\rangle\!\rangle (u_\alpha v_\beta u_\gamma v_\delta + v_\alpha u_\beta v_\gamma u_\delta) -$$
$$-\langle(\alpha\beta)\mathscr{I}M|V|(\delta\gamma)\mathscr{I}M\rangle(u_\alpha u_\beta v_\gamma v_\delta + v_\alpha v_\beta u_\gamma u_\delta)] ,$$

where the two first terms are the particle-hole matrix elements, and the third one the ordinary 2-particle matrix element.

5'3. *The Green's function approach.* – In Sect. **6** it was shown that certain properties of a nondegenerate system (viz. the energies and one-body transition probabilities relative to the exact ground state) could be obtained from the knowledge of its particle-hole Green's function defined in eq. (50). The formal procedure consists in resumming the perturbation expansion of the particle-hole Green's function in terms of a geometrical series of successive powers of irreducible particle-hole diagrams, and yields the nonlinear matrix eq. (74) which may be written as

$$\mathscr{M}(E)X = \nu EX\,, \tag{107}$$

where E is the eigenenergy, and ν is the matrix (73). The matrix $\mathscr{M}(E)$ which spans the space of particle-hole and (time-reversed) hole-particle configurations as indicated in eqs. (72), (73) was obtained as the Fourier transform of all irreducible particle-hole diagrams. The nonlinearity of eq. (107) which appears through the dependence of $\mathscr{M}$ upon E stems from the fact that the equation provides an exact formulation of the problem (*) although it is defined over a restricted configuration space. However, it is impossible to include *all* irreducible diagrams into eq. (69). The R.P.A. selects the two simplest irreducible particle-hole diagrams, *i.e.* those which are of first order in v. These two diagrams correspond respectively to the scattering of a particle-hole pair and to the creation or annihilation of a particle-hole pair (cf. Sect. **2**). Such a choice of time-independent irreducible diagrams leads to a matrix $\mathscr{M}$ which is energy-independent. It is represented schematically on Fig. 18. The sub-matrix appearing in the first quadrant of Fig. 18 (depicting the scattering of a particle-hole pair) corresponds to the particle-hole approximation described in Sect. **4**, while the added presence of the off-diagonal sub-matrices corresponding to creation and annihilation terms completes the R.P.A. secular problem. Therefore, from the Green's function point of view, the particle-hole approximation is equivalent to selecting the scattering of a particle-hole pair as the irreducible diagram which is used to build up the power series shown on Fig. 19*a*; to that series the R.P.A. adds the series indicated on Fig. 19*b* where, at any given time t, there may exist any number of excited pairs. It should be noted that the processes indicated on Fig. 19*b* violate the Pauli principle since particles in states A and B, for example, are not antisymmetrized. This defect could be corrected by the addition of suitable exchange diagrams, however such diagrams are precisely neglected in the R.P.A.

(*) Except for the approximation made on the one-body propagators as discussed in Sect. **3'7**.

It might appear that the derivation of the R.P.A. within the formalism of the Green's function could provide a justification for its application in the nuclear case. However the question is still open. The R.P.A. is not necessarily preferable to the particle-hole approximation, although it invokes more terms

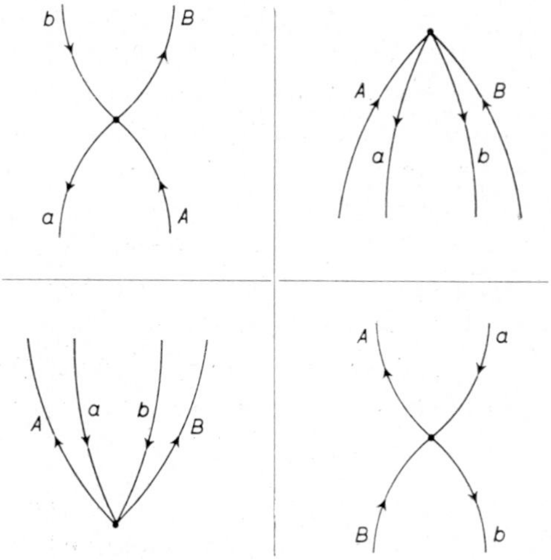

Fig. 18.

in the perturbation expansion. The inclusion of extra terms might even prove detrimental if some of the neglected terms could have exactly cancelled the newly included ones. In the case of the R.P.A. the neglected exchange terms have precisely that effect upon some of the added terms which violate the Pauli principle.

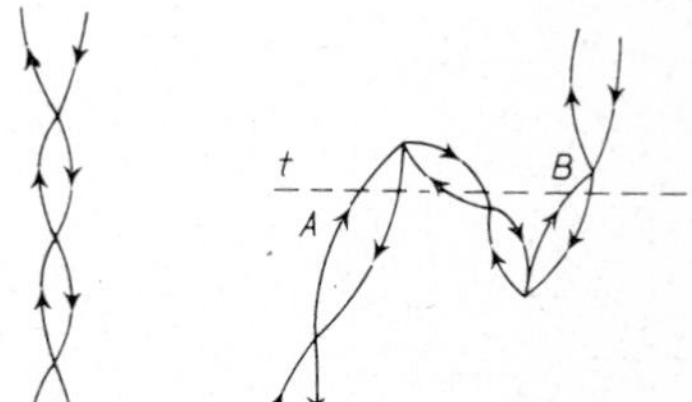

Fig. 19.

For infinite systems, such as the electron gas, the R.P.A. can be shown to be exact in the limit of infinite density, when the range of the forces between the particles is much larger than the average distance $\boldsymbol{r}$ between them. In that limit the Fermi surface is very large, *i.e.* the phase space inside which can vary the momenta $\boldsymbol{k}$ of both the particles and holes is very large; on the contrary the momentum transfer $\boldsymbol{q}$ in a collision between two particles is bound to remain small. When computing the contribution of a perturbation term the conservation of linear momentum eliminates a variable $\boldsymbol{k}_i$ (whose domain of integration in phase space is large) for each independent momentum transfer

$\boldsymbol{q}_i$ (whose domain of integration is small). Therefore the dominant contribution to the Green's function will come from diagrams containing the minimum number of independent q's. These are precisely the diagrams of Fig. 19 where a particle-hole pair of total momentum q is transformed into another similar pair of same total momentum q. The perturbation terms of Fig. 19, with only one transfer momentum q, are accordingly the dominant ones at each order.

Although it is difficult to make such an argument for a finite system where the notion of linear momentum transfer no longer holds, one might inquire about the applicability of a high-density approximation to nuclear systems. Nuclei are often considered as consisting of low-density matter; but this point of view is based on the effects of the short-range part of nuclear forces, while in our present analysis we are primarily concerned with the effects of the long-range part. The ratio of the range of this force to the average internucleon distance is of the order of one. One may be willing to consider such nuclear matter as «high-density», since nuclei exhibit many features characteristic of high-density systems such as the presence of an average common potential well with associated collective degrees of freedom.

5.4. *The time-dependent Hartree-Fock method.* – The best physical insight into the meaning of the R.P.A. is perhaps obtained from its derivation in the framework of the time-dependent Hartree-Fock method; this derivation is given in Prof. Villars' lectures and will not be repeated here. We shall only recall the basic assumptions. The first assumption is the existence of an average self-consistent field which varies slowly in time; the nuclear wave function may be represented at each instant t by a determinantal wave function. The other assumption is that the time-dependent Hartree-Fock state differs very little from the static Hartree-Fock state, so that the equation of motion may be linearized relative to the amplitudes around the static solution. These are precisely the assumptions which enter in the phenomenological unified model of Bohr and Mottelson, the experimental consequences of which have been largely verified.

5.5. *Properties of the solutions of the R.P.A.*

5.5.1. Eigenvalues. If N is the dimension of the $\mathscr{A}$ or $\mathscr{B}$ matrices, the non-Hermitian R.P.A. secular problem (105) possesses $2N$ eigenvalues which may be real or complex. For each eigenvalue E_n associated to the eigenvector (X, Y), there is also an eigenvalue $-E_n$ corresponding to the eigenvector (Y^*, X^*).

5.5.2. Normalization. The normalization of the eigenvectors $|n\rangle$ (eq. (94)), associated with *real positive eigenvalue*, gives

$$\langle n|n\rangle = \langle g|Q_n Q_n^\dagger|g\rangle = \langle g|[Q_n, Q_n^\dagger]|g\rangle = 1 ,$$

where we have used condition (100). Replacing the Q's by their definition (95) and using the quasi-boson approximation (100) for evaluating the commutators we obtain

$$\sum_{Aa}\{|X^n_{Aa}|^2-|Y^n_{Aa}|^2\}=1\,. \tag{108}$$

5·5.3. Stability conditions. The appearance of imaginary eigenvalues in the R.P.A. does carry physical significance. It indicates that the initial static Hartree-Fock solution does not yield a local minimum for the unperturbed energy E_0, or as stated in Thouless's theorem:

« If the static Hartree-Fock solution is a local minimum, then all eigenvalues of the R.P.A. secular problem are real ».

It should be emphasized that the theorem only holds if the zero-order field is the result of a true static Hartree-Fock calculation. Since this is not the case in practical calculations the usefulness of the theorem is limited.

5·5.4. The spurious C.M. state. The use of independent-particle wave functions in a fixed average potential well introduces one extra degree of freedom associated with the motion of the center of mass of the particles in the well. The quantum numbers of this state are $\mathscr{I}=1$, $\pi=(-)$, $T=0$, since it is generated by the application of the total linear momentum operator on the ground state. Accordingly the solutions of the particle-hole approximation (cf. Sect. **4**) which have these quantum numbers will contain components of that spurious state which may be removed by suitable projection.

In principle, this difficulty is avoided in the R.P.A. secular problem since it may be shown that the spurious state is an eigenstate of the R.P.A. problem (and is therefore orthogonal to the other eigenstates), and that its eigenvalue is zero. Again this result can only be applied to the case when the initial field is the static Hartree-Fock solution.

5·5.5. Computation of transition rates. Let us consider a transition from the ground state $|g\rangle$ to the excited state $|n\rangle$ arising from the action of the one-body operator t. The transition rate is given by

$$T\propto|\langle n|t|g\rangle|^2\,.$$

Substituting eqs. (94) and (19) into the above equation yields

$$T\propto|\sum_{Aa}\langle A|t|a\rangle X_{Aa}+\langle a|t|A\rangle Y_{Aa}|^2\,. \tag{109}$$

For example, if t represents the absorption of a photon, the first term on the right corresponds to the creation and the second term to the annihilation of a particle-hole pair. The latter process is only possible because the R.P.A. allows the existence of excited particle-hole pairs in the ground state.

5·6. *Comparison between the solutions of the R.P.A. and of the particle-hole approximation.* – In order to compare the behaviour of the eigenvalues and transition rates obtained in the R.P.A. with the results of the previous Section, we shall again use the schematic model. Assuming that the particle-hole matrix element has the separable form given by eq. (84), the secular problem of the R.P.A. reduces to

$$(\tilde{\varepsilon}_A + \tilde{\varepsilon}_a - E)X_{Aa} = -\lambda\langle A|\theta|a\rangle\{\sum_{Bb} X_{Bb}\langle B|\theta|b\rangle + Y_{Bb}\langle b|\theta|B\rangle\},$$

$$(\tilde{\varepsilon}_A + \tilde{\varepsilon}_a + E)Y_{Aa} = -\lambda\langle a|\theta|A\rangle\{\sum_{Bb} X_{Bb}\langle B|\theta|b\rangle + Y_{Bb}\langle b|\theta|B\rangle)\}.$$

The quantity in brackets is a constant. Therefore we have

$$(110)\qquad \begin{cases} X_{Aa} = \dfrac{\mathcal{N}\langle A|\theta|a\rangle}{\tilde{\varepsilon}_A + \tilde{\varepsilon}_a - E}, \\ Y_{Aa} = \dfrac{\mathcal{N}\langle a|\theta|A\rangle}{\tilde{\varepsilon}_A + \tilde{\varepsilon}_a + E}, \end{cases}$$

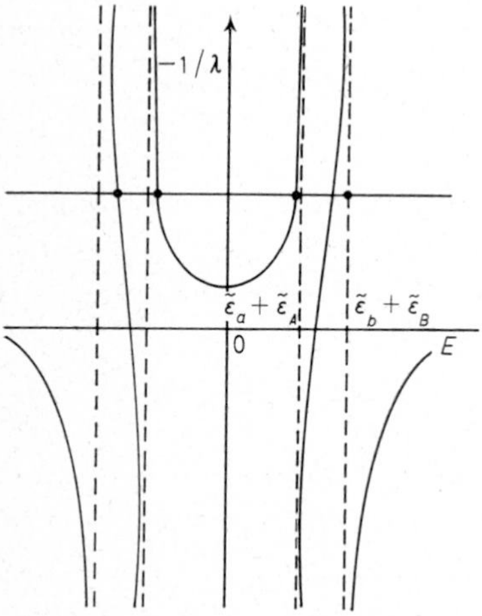

Fig. 20. – Graphical solution of the schematic R.P.A. problem.

where $\mathcal{N}$ is the appropriate normalization factor as per eq. (108). The eigenvalues E are given by the implicit equation

$$(111)\qquad \sum_{Aa} \frac{2|\langle A|\theta|a\rangle|^2(\tilde{\varepsilon}_A + \tilde{\varepsilon}_a)}{(\tilde{\varepsilon}_a + \tilde{\varepsilon}_A)^2 - E^2} = -\frac{1}{\lambda}.$$

The graphical solution of this problem is shown on Fig. 20. The main difference with the solution of the particle-hole approximation (87) is found in the behaviour of the lowest root corresponding to an attractive force, $\lambda < 0$. As $-\lambda$ increases, this root goes to zero much faster than previously; there is a critical value $-\lambda_c$ beyond which the lowest root becomes pure imaginary.

The large energy shift of the lowest root ($\lambda < 0$) is also illustrated in the limit of the degenerate case, when all $\tilde{\varepsilon}_A + \tilde{\varepsilon}_a$ are equal to ε; in that case

$$(112)\qquad E = \sqrt{\varepsilon^2 + 2\lambda\varepsilon \sum_{Aa} |\langle A|\theta|a\rangle|^2}$$

which should be compared with eq. (91) obtained in the particle-hole approximation.

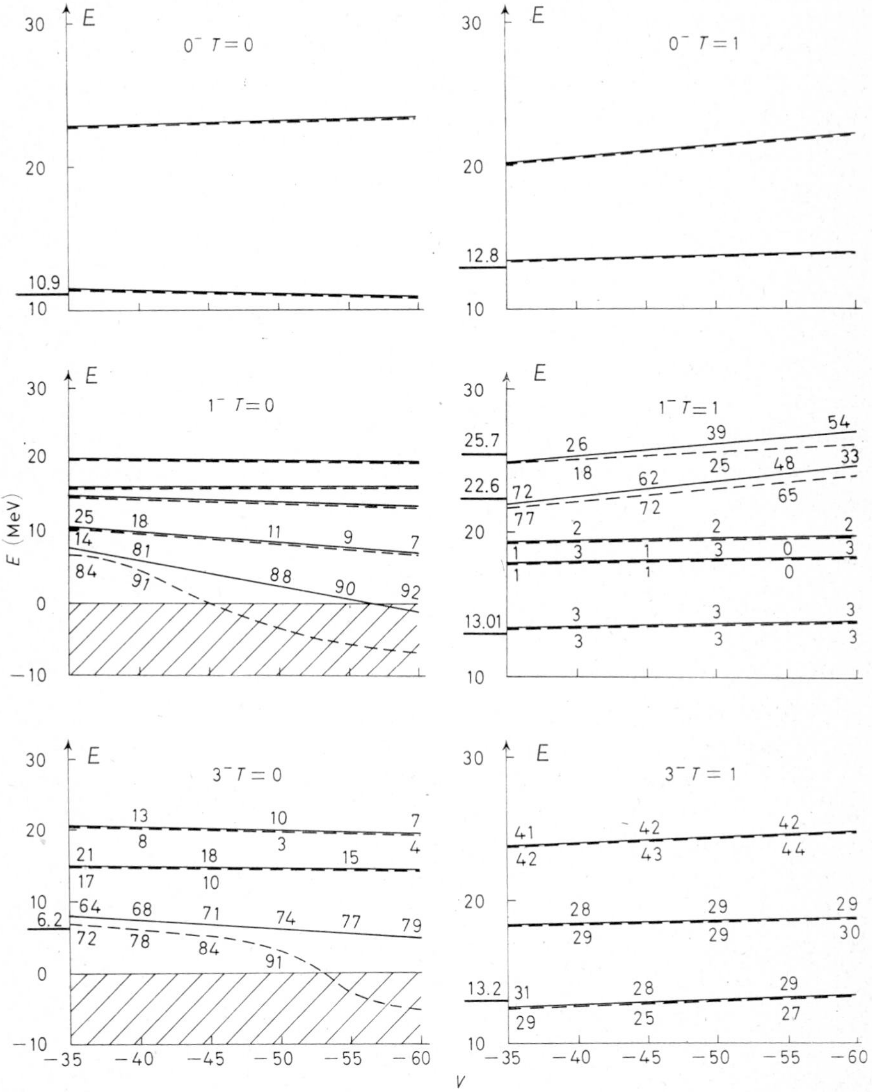

Fig. 21. – Dependence of some selected levels of ^{16}O on the potential depth parameter V (in MeV). The levels predicted by the particle-hole approximation and the R.P.A. are represented respectively by the solid and the dashed curves. The experimental positions of the known levels are given on the vertical axes. The shaded regions correspond to the appearance of imaginary roots in the R.P.A.; in this case the quantity plotted is the modulus of E multiplied by a negative sign. The relative radiative intensities, normalized to 100, are marked along the curves. The configurations which are taken into account and their energies are listed in ref. [9].

More generally the eigenvalues obtained with the R.P.A. are lower than those obtained with the particle-hole approximation, whether the interaction be attractive or repulsive, *i.e.* the energy shift of states which are lowered is increased, the energy shift of the states which are raised is decreased.

Considering now the effect of the R.P.A. on transition rates, we shall examine the limit of the degenerate case in the schematic model; applying the normalization condition (108) and assuming that all the amplitudes $\langle A|\theta|a\rangle$ are equal we find that the state which is shifted in energy, has the following transition rate:

$$T = \frac{\varepsilon}{E}\sum_{Aa} |\langle A|t|a\rangle|^2 .$$

Comparing this result with the transition rate predicted by the particle-hole approximation, eq. (93), we see that the R.P.A. increases the transition rate of the state which is shifted down ($\lambda < 0$) and decreases it for the state which is shifted upwards ($\lambda > 0$). The enhancement of the transition rate of the low-lying states may be quite large since E may be several times smaller than ε ($\varepsilon/E \sim 2$ to 4).

We compare the behaviour of the two types of solutions in a realistic case on Fig. 21. We have represented some selected levels of ^{16}O computed with a Gaussian force. The depth of the force V is varied, all other parameters of the exchange mixture being kept fixed at the values given in [9]. We see that the $T=1$ solutions are shifted upwards while the $T=0$ solutions are shifted downwards relative to the unperturbed energies. We note that many states experience very little shift, which reflects in part the importance of the unperturbed energies compared to the residual interaction. For these states both approximations give the same result. The only states which are strongly shifted are the lowest 3^- $T=0$ state, the lowest 1^- $T=0$ (largely spurious) state and the two upper 1^- $T=1$ (the giant resonance).

5·7. *Validity of the R.P.A. in the nuclear case.* – As will be shown in Sect. **6**, the R.P.A. will prove to be essential in describing the properties of the low-lying collective states in doubly closed-shell nuclei. However, from the previous discussions, it is clear that the R.P.A. still needs justification. The results of the R.P.A. have been compared with exact solutions of simplified systems [10] but it is difficult to extend the conclusions drawn from such comparisons to nuclei. A realistic complete calculation has been done by COHEN, LAWSON and SODA [11] for two, four and six particles in the *s-d* shell; the results have been compared with those of the R.P.A. applied to two quasi-particle excitations. However the accuracy of the approximate solution depends not only upon the validity of the R.P.A. but also upon the validity of the BCS wave functions.

Another approach might consist in estimating the contribution of the first neglected exchange diagrams. There are reasons to believe that their contribution is very small as they are obtained by uncoupling the particle-hole scheme and recoupling it in a particle-particle or hole-hole scheme. The resulting summations over angular momenta include many terms each of which is small and of random sign. These conditions should lead to near cancellations and we might therefore expect that the R.P.A. would provide a good approximation by living up to its name.

While it appears difficult to check directly the validity of the R.P.A., we can at least verify its internal consistency by showing that the basic assumption of the quasi-boson derivation given in Sect. **5**·3, $\langle g|N_A|g\rangle \approx 0$ and $\langle g|N_A|g\rangle \approx 0$, is satisfied by the solution provided by the R.P.A. We shall write the R.P.A. ground state as [12]

$$|g\rangle = \frac{1}{\sqrt{C}}\left(1 + \sum_{n,\mathscr{I}} \sum_{\substack{Aa\\Bb}} \alpha^{n,\mathscr{I}}_{AaBb}[\Omega^\dagger_{\mathscr{I}}(Aa)\Omega^\dagger(Bb)]^0_0 + \dots\right)|\Phi_0\rangle\,,$$

where $|\Phi_0\rangle$ is the Hartree-Fock uncorrelated ground state, and where we limit the expansion to its first term wherein two particle-hole pairs are coupled to $\mathscr{I}=0$, $M=0$. The contributions of 4, 6 ... particle-hole pairs are neglected in conformity with the R.P.A. which assumes that $|g\rangle$ is close to $|\Phi_0\rangle$. The quantity C is the appropriate normalization constant. The mixing coefficients $\alpha^{n,\mathscr{I}}_{AaBb}$ are directly related to the amplitudes X and Y of the R.P.A. secular problem; using eq. (97) we obtain the following linear system for the α's:

$$X^{n,\mathscr{I}}_{Aa} = -2\sum_{Bb} \alpha^{n,\mathscr{I}}_{AaBb} Y^{n,\mathscr{I}}_{Bb}\,. \tag{113a}$$

The expectation values of the particle and hole occupation numbers relative to $|g\rangle$ are given by

$$(113b)\quad \begin{cases} N_{Aj_Am_A} = \langle g|\eta^\dagger_{Aj_Am_A}\eta_{Aj_Am_A}|g\rangle = \dfrac{1}{(2j_A+1)}\dfrac{1}{C}\sum\limits_{\substack{Bba\\n,\mathscr{I}}} |\alpha^{n,\mathscr{I}}_{AaBb}|^2\,, \\ N_{aj_am_a} = 1 - \langle g|\eta^\dagger_{aj_am_a}\eta_{aj_am_a}|g\rangle = \dfrac{1}{(2j_a+1)}\dfrac{1}{C}\sum\limits_{\substack{ABb\\n,\mathscr{I}}} |\alpha^{n,\mathscr{I}}_{AaBb}|^2\,. \end{cases}$$

It should be noted that the simplicity of expressions (113*a*) and (113*b*) is due to the neglect of Pauli correlations between different particle-hole pairs, in accordance with the quasi-boson approximation. Accordingly the occupation numbers calculated with eq. (113*b*), using the α's obtained from the R.P.A. amplitudes X, Y, do not constitute a test of the theory but rather a check of consistency. GOSWAMI and PAL [12] have calculated the N_A and N_a for ^{12}C, where, as we shall see, the effect of the R.P.A. is very strong relative to the ordinary particle-hole approximation. The calculated values are shown in Table I. They are small in spite of the particularly important rôle played by the ground-state correlations in the transition probabilities of ^{12}C (see Sect. **6**'4). As indicated above this constitutes only a consistency check. For a real test of the R.P.A., one should substitute the values of Table I in the commutator of eq. (99), carry out with the complete commutator the calculation of (101) and check if the new eigenstates are much modified by the correction.

TABLE I. – *Average values of the particle and hole occupation numbers in the ground state of* ^{12}C (GOSWAMI and PAL [12]).

	Levels	$\bar{N}$
Holes	$1s$	0.05
	$1p_{\frac{3}{2}}$	0.11
Particles	$1p_{\frac{1}{2}}$	0.201
	$1f_{\frac{7}{2}}$	0.101
	$1f_{\frac{5}{2}}$	0.013
	$2p_{\frac{3}{2}}$	0.007
	$2p_{\frac{1}{2}}$	0.005
	$1d_{\frac{3}{2}}$	0.081
	$1d_{\frac{5}{2}}$	0.101
	$1g_{\frac{9}{2}}$	0.007
	$1g_{\frac{7}{2}}$	0.001
	$2d_{\frac{5}{2}}$	0.006
	$2d_{\frac{3}{2}}$	0.007

6. – Application to spherical nuclei.

6'1. *Introduction.* – In this Section we shall review the main features and the results of calculations performed 1) on doubly closed-shell nuclei in terms of elementary particle-hole excitations, and 2) on single closed-shell nuclei in terms of two-quasi-particle excitation. We shall call Approximation I the particle-hole or two quasi-particle approximation of Sect. **4**, and Approximation II the random phase approximation described in Sect. **5**. We shall seek to answer two questions. First, how well does the model work? Secondly, what has been achieved by the R.P.A. which could not have been obtained with Approximation I alone. Such questions are difficult to answer unambiguously because of the large part played in the results by the phenomenological adjustment of parameters. These parameters enter in the Hartree-Fock problem which we do not know how to solve explicitly as yet, and in the simplified effective two-body forces which are used in practical calculations. We shall first discuss briefly the choice of these parameters.

6·2. *The phenomenological determination of the Hartree-Fock field.* – Since we do not know how to solve exactly the Hartree-Fock problem for single particles, eq. (34), we take for φ the wave functions corresponding to some simple potential, and for ε we substitute experimental values. We shall first discuss the single-particle energies, and then the single-particle wave functions.

In the case of doubly closed-shell nuclei containing A nucleons, the particle and hole energies $\tilde{\varepsilon}_\alpha$ may be obtained from the experimental low-lying spectra of the neighbouring $A \pm 1$ nuclei. It might appear that such a procedure assumes that these spectra can be described by pure shell-model configurations, while in fact they contain small configuration mixing even in the best possible situation. However the contention is that substituting the experimental energies for the true shell energies constitutes an improvement as it is an approximate way of introducing the contribution of the interaction Hamiltonian into the single-particle propagators. However as discussed in Sect. **3**·1 in the Green's function framework, one retains a simple secular problem only if the Fourier expansion of the true one-particle or one-hole propagator can be approximated by the contribution of only one pole. This means that the experimental determination of single-particle energies is limited to the first few excited states of the $A \pm 1$ nuclei, which have the same parity as the ground state. The states with opposite parity are generally the result of an important configurational mixing, as shown by their position, transition properties and multiplicity.

In the case of s.c.s. nuclei, the Hartree-Fock energies, which enter into the B.C.S. calculation, are not directly attainable experimentally, since the odd-even nuclei spectra are associated to quasi-particle excitations. In practice one considers the Hartree-Fock energies as parameters which are determined by fitting through a B.C.S. calculation the spectra of odd-even nuclei considered as pure quasi-particle spectra; however this assumption is not verified in many cases. Alternatively one may eliminate the problem raised by the unknown Hartree-Fock energies by taking the quasi-particle energies $\widetilde{E}_\alpha$ and the occupational numbers u's and v's from the result of stripping experiments, rather than calculating them by solving the gap equations. The number of adjustable parameters is considerably reduced, but some rigor is lost since the relationship between the experimental and theoretical quantities is not always too clear.

In practically all calculations carried out to date the single-particle wave functions are approximated by those of an infinite harmonic oscillator, the parameters of the well being chosen for example so as to reproduce the r.m.s. radius observed in electron scattering experiments. These are necessarily

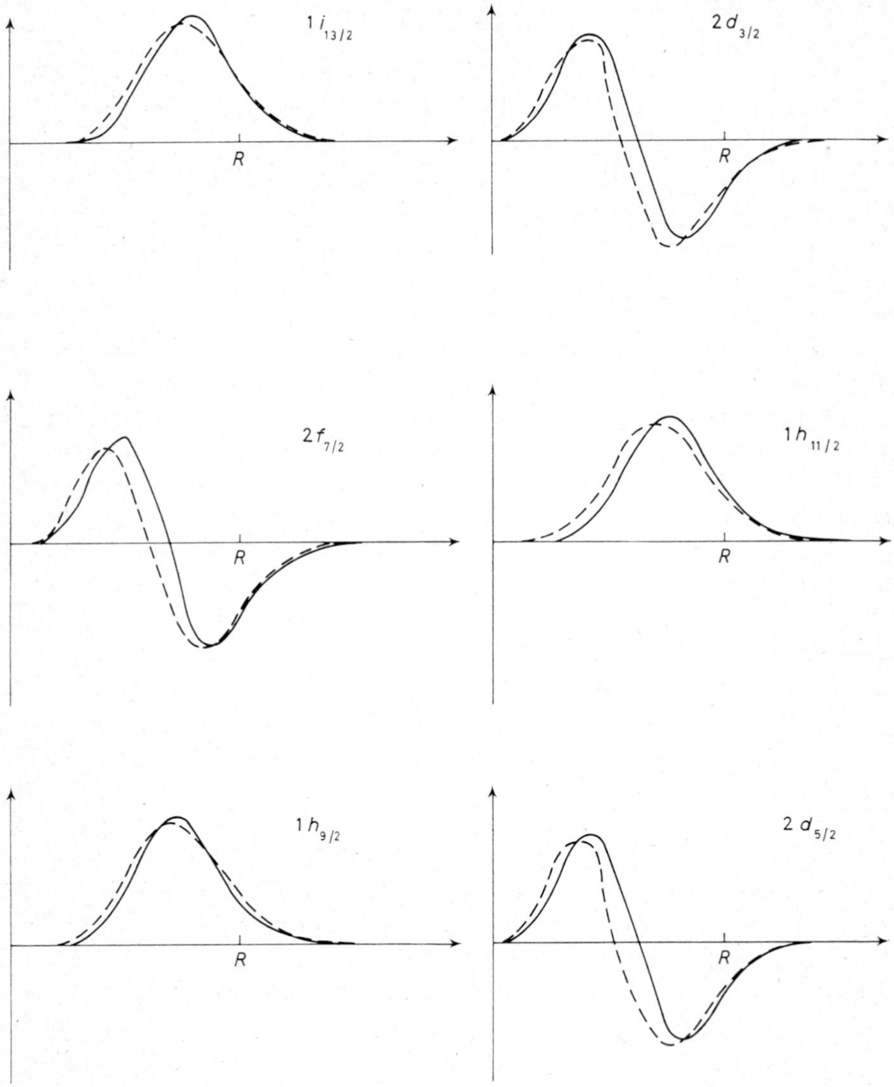

Fig. 22. – Single-particle orbitals in an infinite oscillator well [13] (dashed line) and in a Saxon-Wood well [14] (solid line) for ^{208}Pb ($R = r_0 A^{\frac{1}{3}}$).

nonconsistent wave functions. However the main objection to these functions is that they are derived in a well which exhibits a totally wrong behaviour outside the nucleus. This indeed affects drastically the positive energy (unbound) single-particle states. On the other hand it is well known that the bound-particle wave functions in an infinite well corresponding to negative energy states are quite similar to those found in a finite well. This is shown in Fig. 22 which displays some single-particle wave functions for ^{208}Pb computed respectively in an infinite oscillator well (with $\sqrt{m\omega/\hbar}=0.63$ as determined by TRUE and FORD [13]) and in the finite semi-consistent Saxon-Wood well of Blomquist and Wahlborn [14]. The agreement is generally satisfactory (especially if one considers the effect on the matrix elements, always inferior to 10 %). Finite-well effects are generally thought to be important for the high angular momenta; this is not substantiated by Fig. 22 where the discrepancies do not increase with the angular momentum, but rather with the number of nodes.

6'3. *The effective two-body force.* – Considering the very scant information which exists on the nucleon-nucleon scattering matrix which must be used in shell model calculations, the most common procedure has been to assume an effective force, of simple « well behaved » form (Gaussian or Yukawa), static and central. This permits the introduction of a limited number of parameters: a potential depth V, a range μ and an exchange mixture. The most common effective forces used in shell model calculations, such as the Rosenfeld, the Ferrell-Visscher or the Meshkov-Soper forces exhibit widely different characteristics which reflect the strong dependence of these forces on the particular model used in their determination. Furthermore in almost every shell-model calculation all or some of the force parameters are varied to optimize agreement between theory and experiment. Thus the final parameter values are not absolute since they are adjusted to correct for the inadequacies of the nuclear models, for the differences which may exist between the phenomenological quantities introduced (such as the single-particle state energies) and the theoretical quantities they replace, and for the numerical oversimplification of ordinary shell-model calculations. The central question which arises then is this: how important is the role played by phenomenology in the success of a model? It is not possible to give a clear-cut answer to this question. However one may try to obtain some theoretical results which are independent of the parameters: 1) either by computing a much larger number of quantities than the number of parameters and determining the force parameters through a least squares fit, 2) or by using a simplified « realistic » force which fits the scattering length and the binding energy of the deuteron and which gives saturation. From a fundamental point of view the second approach is the only justifiable one. However, in practice, considering the inherent limitations of ordinary shell-model calculations (non-consistent zero-order field; well with the wrong asymptotic behaviour etc...) the first procedure may bring out some strong characteristics of the solutions which are not affected by the uncertainties of the parameters. As an example we shall now briefly describe results obtained for ^{16}O and ^{12}C through a least squares search and those obtained by utilizing a «realistic» force.

6·3.1. A χ^2 search for an effective two-body force in ^{12}C and ^{16}O. The effective two-body force is assumed to be static and central. There are still four possible types of exchange potentials which are generally given the same spatial dependence, so that

$$V(|\boldsymbol{r}_1-\boldsymbol{r}_2|)=f\left(\frac{|\boldsymbol{r}_1-\boldsymbol{r}_2|}{\mu}\right)V_0(W+BP_\sigma-HP_\tau+MP_\sigma P_\tau)\,. \tag{114}$$

We define for a set α of the force parameters the quantity $\chi^2(\alpha)$:

$$\chi^2(\alpha)=\frac{1}{N}\sum_{i=1}^{N}\left(E^{(i)}_{\text{exp}}-E^{(i)}_{\text{cal}}(\alpha)\right)^2,$$

i.e. the square of the average error between the energies $E^{(i)}_{\text{exp}}$ of N experimental levels and the corresponding theoretical energies $E^{(i)}_{\text{cal}}(\alpha)$ computed with the set α. The χ^2 search is carried out for ^{12}C and ^{16}O respectively, utilizing the experimental levels of Table II, for a Gaussian force.

TABLE II. – *The states of ^{12}C and ^{16}O used in the least squares search, where $\mathscr{I}$ is the spin, π the parity, T the isobaric spin and E the experimental energy in* MeV.

	$\mathscr{I}$	π	T	E
^{16}O	0	—	0	10.9
	0	—	1	12.8
	1	—	1	13.0
	1	—	1	22.6
	1	—	1	25.7
	2	—	1	13.0
	3	—	0	6.2
	3	—	1	13.2
^{12}C	1	—	1	17.5
	1	—	1	22.5
	1	+	1	15.1
	2	+	0	4.4
	2	+	1	16.1
	3	—	0	9.8

This choice was limited by the necessity for considering only well-identified levels which could be considered reasonably well-described by the particle-hole models. This condition eliminates the even-parity states of ^{16}O, although in the case of ^{12}C three even parity states have been kept because of the large

$0\hbar\omega$ component in their wave functions. Some results of the χ^2 study are presented in Fig. 23, where the values of the χ^2 are given in terms of two of the force parameters, namely the Heisenberg component H and the excess

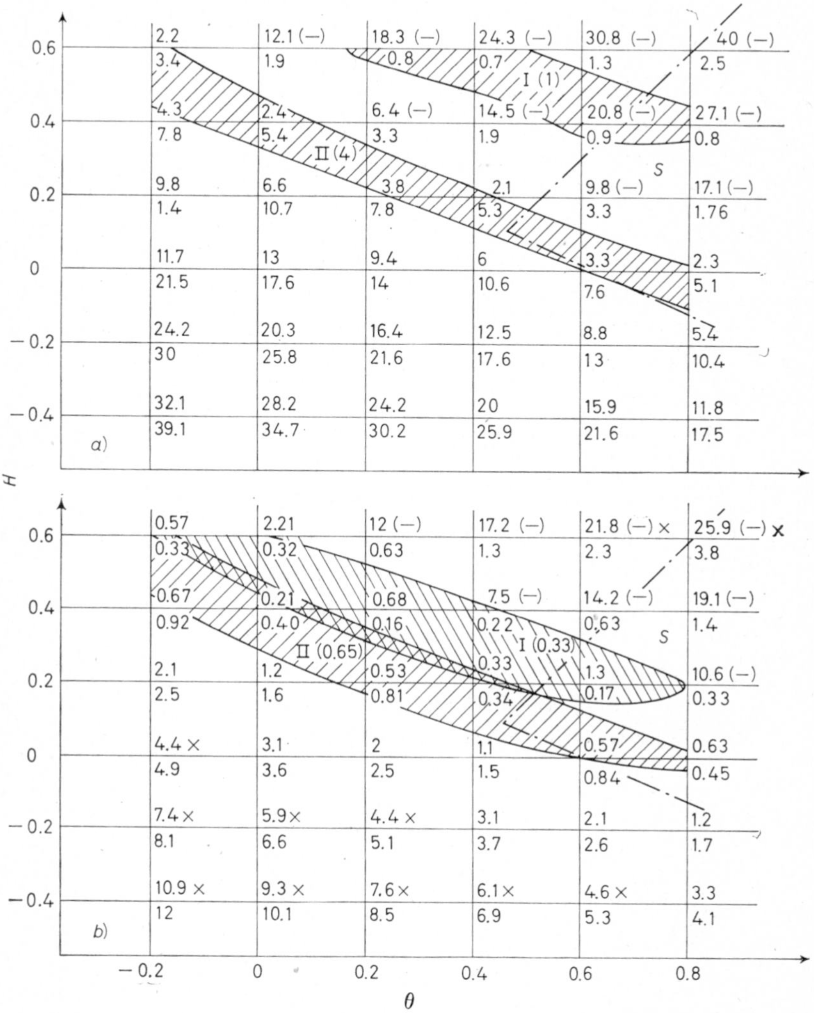

Fig. 23. – The regions of best agreement for *a*) ^{12}C and *b*) ^{16}O as functions of the Heisenberg component H and the excess θ of the Majorana force over the Wigner force.

of Majorana over Wigner force $\theta = M - W$. The other parameters are kept constant at the values $V_0 = -40$ MeV; $\mu/b = 1$ (b is the oscillator length) and $M + W - H - B = 0.6$ for ^{12}C and 0.4 for ^{16}O ($M + W + H + B = 1$). At every point of the arrays of Fig. 23 the upper number represents the value of the χ^2 obtained with Approximation II; the lower number gives the χ^2

value obtained in Approximation I. The region of best agreement is enclosed by the curve of smallest constant χ^2 which can be drawn considering the rather large steps adopted for the arrays. The values of the χ^2 on these « equipotential » curves are given in parentheses in the areas they enclose. The areas of best fit are shaded for more clarity. Each figure shows two shaded areas, indicated respectively as I and II, and corresponding to the best fits reached with Approximations I and II, respectively. The points of the arrays indicated by the sign (—) correspond to values of the force parameters for which Approximation II yields an imaginary eigenvalue for the lowest 3^-, $T=0$, state, in the case of ^{16}O, and for the lowest 2^+, $T=0$, state, in the case of ^{12}C. In these regions the nucleus would be spherically unstable if the true self-consistent spherical Hartree-Fock solutions had been used for the zero-order representation. The points of the arrays indicated by the symbol ($\times$) correspond to effective forces for which the energy of the spurious center-of-mass motion obtained in Approximation II is imaginary. Finally the region marked S in Fig. 23 is the domain of the force parameter space where the five nuclear saturation conditions of Breit and Wigner are fulfilled. Similar figures may be drawn by varying the other parameters, ref. [15].

The results of such a χ^2 analysis may be summarized as follows:

The regions of best agreement are rather extensive; the computed levels do not depend critically on the values of the force parameters. One of the reasons for this is the large contribution of the unperturbed energies in the final levels, as compared to the contribution of the residual interaction. The regions of best agreement are partially determined by the various phenomenological corrections which are brought in by a χ^2 fit. However they exhibit some strong characteristics which should still hold when the treatment of ^{12}C or ^{16}O is improved, namely 1) the Heisenberg component is positive (~ 0.2, 0.4); 2) the Majorana component is equal to or greater than the Wigner component ($\theta = M - W \sim 0 \div 0.4$); 3) the singlet to triplet strength ratio is of the order of $0.4 \div 0.7$.

Both Approximations I and II give an equally good agreement in ^{12}C and ^{16}O provided that the parameters of the force are varied from one nucleus to the other. For example in ^{16}O the lowest χ^2 obtained are of the order of 0.3 MeV in Approximation II and even less in Approximation I.

However it is only with the use of the R.P.A. that we obtain the same region of best agreement in ^{12}C and ^{16}O, showing that the renormalization effects are not as important for Approximation II as for Approximation I.

6'3.2. Use of a « realistic » force in ^{16}O. A convenient framework for such a calculation is the separation method of Moszkowski and Scott [3], used by Kallio and Kolltveit [16]. The free two-body force with hard core is separated into a short-range and a long-range part, with the requirement that the short-range part should give no scattering in the collision of two free nucleons, *i.e.* the attractive short-range potential should exactly cancel the

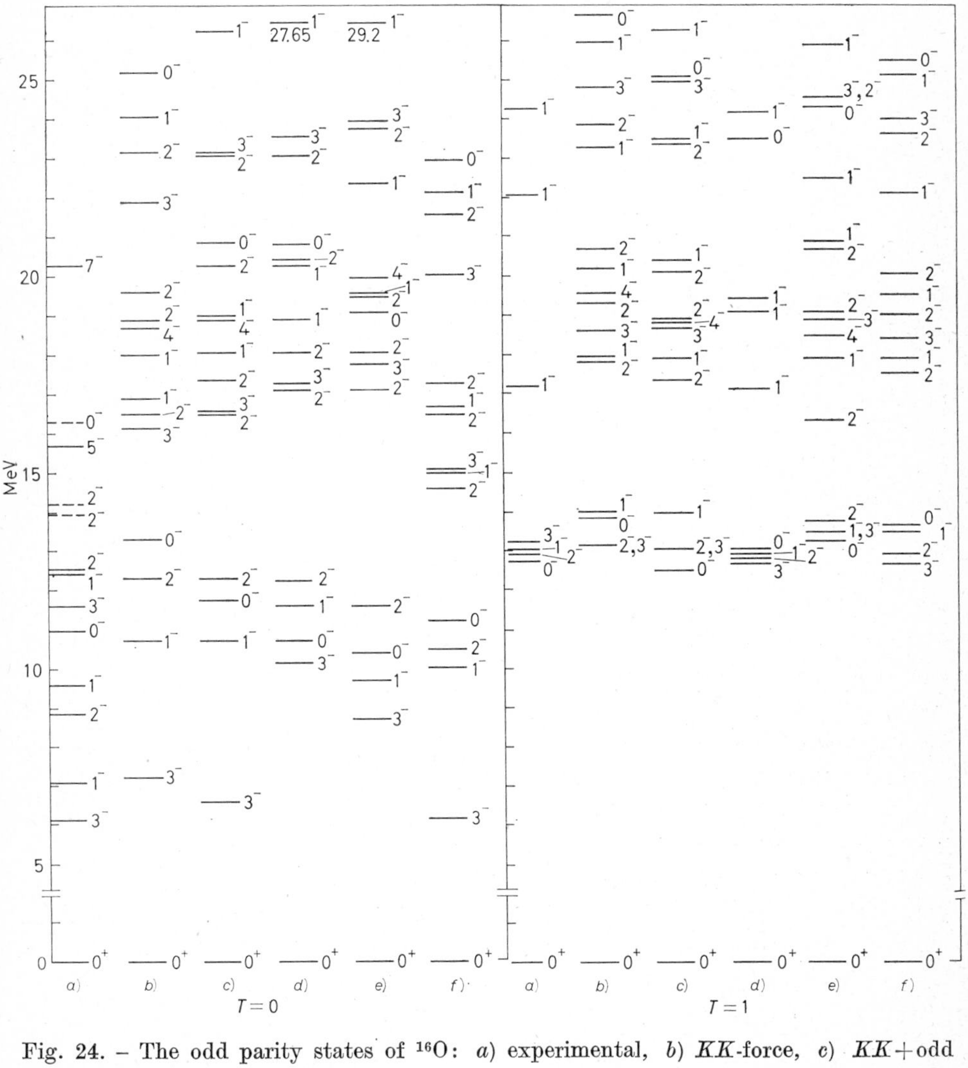

Fig. 24. – The odd parity states of ^{16}O: *a*) experimental, *b*) *KK*-force, *c*) *KK*+odd state force, *d*) Hamada-Johnston potential, *e*) BGT-potential, *f*) results with the « best » effective force of ref. [15]. All results are with the random phase approximation. (A. KALLIO, ref. [17]).

effect of the repulsive hard core upon the phase shifts. The long-range part is a very simple potential which remains zero up to a distance called the « separation distance » and then takes the form of an attractive Yukawa tail. The separation distance as given by *t*-matrix calculations [3] is a slowly varying function of the relative momentum in free scattering and is assumed to be a constant quantity independent of the relative energy. Assuming that the short-range potentials play a negligible role, as shown by nuclear-matter calculations, the effective potential is of a simple form.

The odd-parity states of ^{16}O computed in Approximation II, using the separation method and various «realistic» potentials are presented on Fig. 24. Column *a*) gives the experimental positions of the levels whose spins are well identified. Column *b*) shows the results obtained with the hard-core potential determined by KALLIO and KOLLTVEIT [16] which fits the scattering length and binding energy of the deuteron. It is a potential which acts only in relative *s*-states with no tensor force included. In column *c*) an odd-state tensor force is added to the preceding potential. Only one state is sensitive to this added force, the 0^- state, which shows improved agreement with experience. Columns *d*) and *e*) correspond respectively to the Hamada-Johnston potential and the Brueckner-Gammel-Thaler potential. The uncertainties in the realistic potential parameters clearly have an important effect on the position of the calculated levels. Column *f*) gives the spectrum obtained with the effective force determined by the least squares fit shown in Fig. 23.

When using a «realistic» potential it is necessary to include all the relevant configurations, as no renormalization of the force may be substituted for their effect. The importance of higher-order configurations for the low-lying odd-parity spectrum of closed-shell nuclei is discussed in the seminar of G. E. BROWN, (this volume p. 524).

6·4. *Summary of results for doubly-closed-shell nuclei.* – In 1956 WILKINSON suggested that the odd-parity states of ^{16}O be described in terms of independent particle-hole excitations [18]. This was followed by the pioneering work of ELLIOTT and FLOWERS [19] who introduced with great success the effect of the residual interaction between these particle-hole configurations. Since then a considerable amount of computational work has been devoted to ^{12}C, ^{16}O, ^{40}Ca and ^{208}Pb, and individual references may be found in [9]. We shall review the main features of the results obtained so far.

According to the arguments given in Sect. 4, the particle-hole models should apply to odd-parity states. Therefore, we should expect three types of odd-parity excitations, namely *a*) collective modes lying much below the $1\hbar\omega$ energy region, corresponding to modes where the nuclear particle-hole interaction matrix is attractive. With realistic forces this corresponds to a motion where protons and neutrons are in phase ($T=0$ states for light nuclei); *b*) collective modes lying much above the $1\hbar\omega$ energy region, corresponding to the repulsive particle-hole interaction when protons and neutrons move with opposite phases ($T=1$ states for light nuclei); *c*) states in the $1\hbar\omega$ region with more or less reduced transition properties relative to the independent-particle predictions.

6·4.1. Low-lying collective states. Both approximations I and II predict a large energy shift for the states listed in Table III, which is in general agreement with experiment. We have included in the list an even-parity state,

TABLE III.

	a	b	c	I	II	d
^{12}C, 2^+ $T=0$	4.4	1/6	13.77	8.2	4.8	4
^{16}O, 3^- $T=0$	6.1	3	11.51	7.4	6.2	3
^{40}Ca, 3^- $T=0$	3.7	20	6.7	5.5	3.8	1.5
^{208}Pb, 3^-	2.6	45	4.3	3.2	2.7	0.5

the 2^+ $T=0$ state of ^{12}C at 4.43 MeV, described with $0\hbar\omega$ and $2\hbar\omega$ one particle-one hole configurations and neglecting $2\hbar\omega$ $2p$-$2h$ configurations; the justification for this is on the one hand the importance of the $0\hbar\omega$ excitation $1p_{\frac{1}{2}}1p_{\frac{3}{2}}$ in describing that state, and on the other hand the rather unexpected success of this description in predicting both its energy and its excitation properties as we will see below. Column a gives the experimental energies. Column b gives the dimension of the $1p$-$1h$ configurational space. Column c gives the energy of the lowest unperturbed particle-hole configuration. For the 2^+ state in ^{12}C the next $1p$-$1h$ configurations taken into account lie much higher above 25 MeV. For the 3^- state of ^{16}O, the $1\hbar\omega$ space is limited to only 3 configurations respectively at 11.51 MeV ($1p_{\frac{1}{2}}1d_{\frac{5}{2}}$), 17.65 MeV ($1p_{\frac{3}{2}}1d_{\frac{5}{2}}$) and 22.7 MeV ($1p_{\frac{3}{2}}1d_{\frac{3}{2}}$). The first neglected configurations

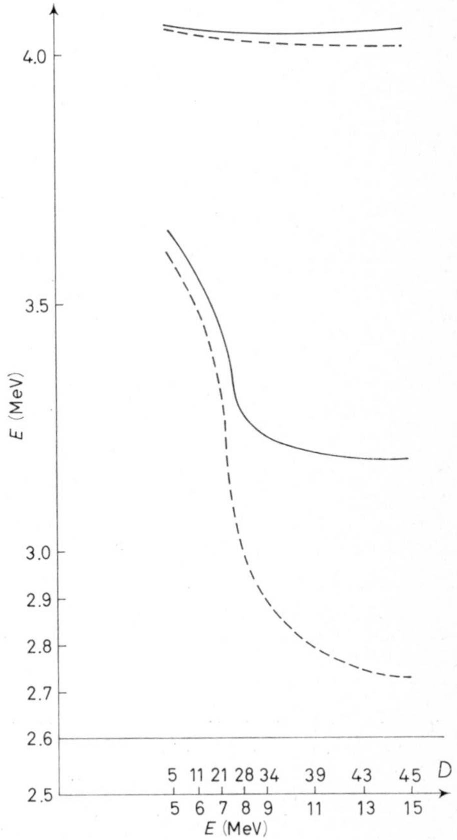

Fig. 25. – Position of the octupole state of ^{208}Pb as a function of the number of configurations included (indicated along the horizontal axis as well as the corresponding unperturbed energies). The solid line is given by Approximation I and the dashed line by the R.P.A. (from ref. [8]).

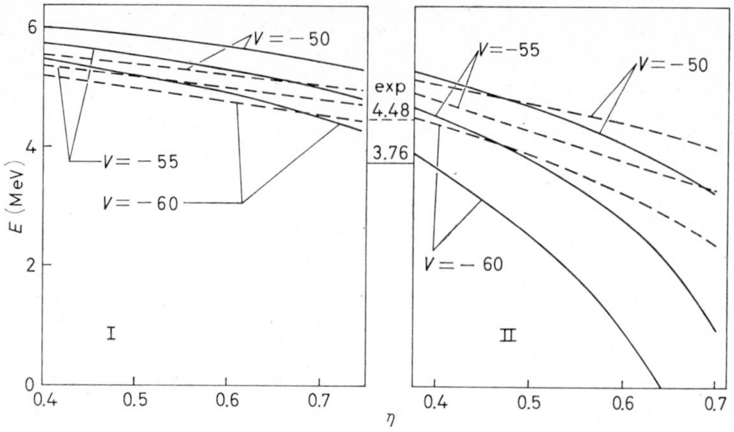

Fig. 26. – The lowest 3^- and 5^- states of ^{40}Ca calculated with the average Coulomb field effects included, in approximation I (left) and approximation II (right), V is the depth of the Gaussian well, η the singlet to triplet strength ratio ($\eta = W + M - B - H$). The values of the other force parameters are given in ref. [21]. ——— 3^- $T = 0$, — — 5^- $T = 0$.

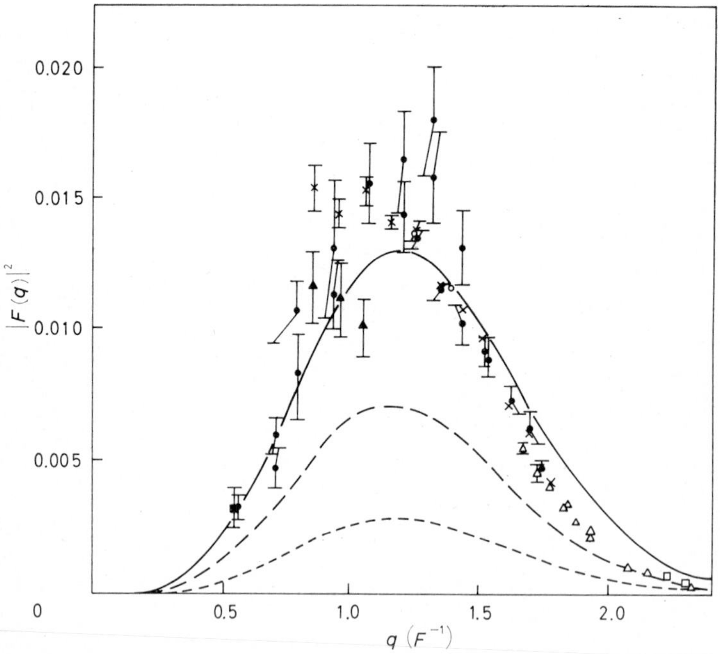

Fig. 27. – The inelastic electron scattering form factor for the $T = 0$, 2^+, 4.4 MeV state of ^{12}C calculated in the independent-particle model (- - -), in Approximation I (— — —) and in the RPA (solid line ref. [22]). ■ $E_i = 80$ MeV; ▲ $E_i = 150$ MeV; • $E_i = 187$ MeV; × $E_i = 250$ MeV; ○ $E_i = 300$ MeV; △ $E_i = 600$ MeV; □ $E_i = 800$ MeV.

are $3\hbar\omega$ and lie above 30 MeV. Considering the high excitation energy of the first neglected configurations these rather limited configurational spaces for the 2^+ and the 3^- states should and indeed provide an adequate description of the collective properties of these levels. On the other hand the 3^- states of ^{40}Ca and ^{208}Pb are characterized respectively by 20 and 45 $1\hbar\omega$ configurations and it is important to include them all in order to obtain a correct description. This is shown in Fig. 25, where the position of the octupole state of ^{208}Pb is given as a function of the dimension D of the diagonalization space. Column d of Table III gives roughly the average values of the particle-hole matrix elements for the nucleus in question. These have to be compared to the experimental and theoretical energy shift of the state in order to appreciate the importance of the coherent effect of the off-diagonal matrix elements, shown by the schematic model in eqs. (87) and (111).

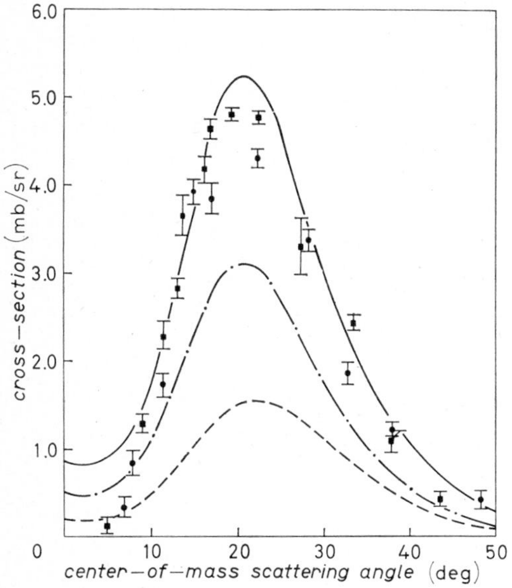

Fig. 28. – Inelastic scattering of 156 MeV proton on the $T=0$, 2^+, 4.4 MeV state of ^{12}C, calculated in the independent-particle model (—·—) $(1p^{\frac{3}{2}})^{-1}1p^{\frac{1}{2}}$, in approximation I (– – –) and in the RPA (—— ref. [23]): • 155 MeV, ▪ 185 MeV.

We may summarize the results as follows:

Both approximations I and II can give in the cases shown in Table III equally good agreement for the energy spectra.

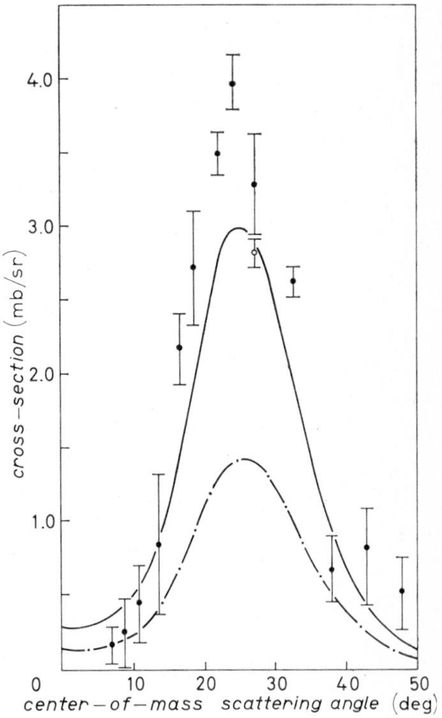

Fig. 29. – Inelastic scattering of 156 MeV protons on the 3^-, $T=0$, 6.1 MeV state of ^{16}O, ref. [23], approximation I (—·—), RPA (——). ○ 150 MeV, • 185 MeV.

However, only the R.P.A. gives with the same set of parameters (obtained by a best fit of 14 levels in ^{12}C and ^{16}O, see Fig. 23) the positions of the 2^+ 4.4 MeV state in ^{12}C, the 3^- 6.1 MeV state in ^{16}O and the 3^- 2.6 MeV state in ^{208}Pb. The theoretical energies obtained with that set of force parameters are listed in columns I and II for approximations I and II, respectively.

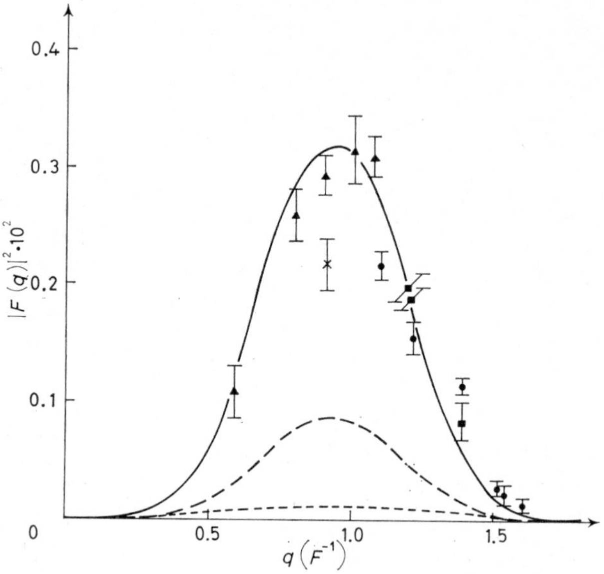

Fig. 30. – Form factor for the 3^- $T = 0$, 3.73 MeV state of ^{40}Ca. (· · · ·) *IP* model; (— — —) approximation I; (solid line) approximation II (ref. [22]): ▲ $E_i = 120$ MeV; ▪ $E_i = 150$ MeV; • $E_i = 180$ MeV; × $E_i = 220$ MeV.

^{40}Ca requires a different set of force parameters, which may come from the fact that the experimental particle and hole energies used in the calculations were uncertain. Even so, only the R.P.A. yields the correct order of the 3^- and 5^- states as shown on Fig. 26, where the positions of these 2 levels are given as a function of the singlet to triplet strength ratio for 3 values of the depth V_0 [21].

Finally a more stringent test of the theory is given by the transition properties of the above-mentioned collective states. Here the R.P.A. always enhances strongly the calculated transition rates or cross-sections, as compared to Approximation I, and thus improves agreement with experiment. For example, the experimental transition rate of the 3^- state in ^{208}Pb is about 20 Weisskopf units (cf. Blatt and Weisskopf [20], p. 627); Approximation I gives ~ 8 and the R.P.A. ~ 18 Weisskopf units. This result is quite general as shown by computations of electron scattering form factors [22] and of high-energy (156 MeV) inelastic scattering of protons [23] from ^{12}C, ^{16}O and

^{40}Ca. In these calculations there are no free parameters, once the force parameters are determined by a best fit to the energies. In the case of electron scattering the parameter of the well is given by the elastic electron scattering data and the electromagnetic interaction is well known. There are no free parameters either in the high-energy proton scattering calculation. The distorted waves are determined by optical model analyses of the elastic scattering data while the interaction with the incoming particle is given by the free two-body scattering matrix. Some of these results are shown on Figs. 27, 28, 29 and 30, which compare the predictions of the independent-particle model, with those of Approximations I and II. The agreement between experiment and the results of the R.P.A. is remarkable in every case.

6·4.2. The giant resonance. The observation of a strongly excited dipole mode at an energy somewhat above the $1\hbar\omega$ energy region was the original motivation for the particle-hole model [18]. However the model has been much less successful here than in the case of low-lying collective bound states. These failures seem to be due to certain oversimplifying assumption rather than to a basic defect of the model. The mean features of the theoretical results are as follows:

The results of the R.P.A. are very close to those of Approximation I. The position of the upper 1^- $T=1$ states calculated in the R.P.A. are slightly lower and the transition properties somewhat weaker than in the case of Approximation I.

In the light nuclei ^{12}C, ^{16}O and ^{40}Ca most of the shift comes from diagonal matrix elements and the effect of off-diagonal elements is relatively weak. In ^{208}Pb, on the contrary, as shown previously in Fig. 17, the coherent effect of off-diagonal matrix elements is very strong. Although the average value of the matrix element is ~ 0.5 MeV, the group of unperturbed particle-hole states below 8 MeV drives on one state several MeV higher.

Although the position of the main peaks have been satisfactorily reproduced by the particle-hole model for the doubly closed-shell nuclei, two important failures have appeared, the failure to reproduce the transition rates and the detailed structure of the giant resonance.

1) Failure to reproduce the transition rates.

While for ^{208}Pb the agreement in the transition rates between experiment and theory is satisfactory, this is not the case for ^{16}O. Here the single-particle model predicts that the transition rates to the $1\hbar\omega$ states are far more important than transitions to higher energy states such as $3\hbar\omega$, $5\hbar\omega$, etc. However the total experimental γ-absorption corresponding to transitions to the $1\hbar\omega$ states amounts to about half of the theoretical values, and in fact exhausts only half of the Thomas-Reiche-Kuhn dipole sum rule; indeed γ-absorption experiments indicate that a large strength still lies above the giant resonance region. It has been suggested that these difficulties are due to neglect of short-range nucleon-nucleon correlations although such calculations have never yet been attempted.

2) Failure to reproduce the detailed structure of the giant resonance.

The fact that the giant resonance of ^{16}O contains more peaks than available particle-hole configurations has been considered a failure of the model and has even been offered as a proof for the existence of nuclear fluctuations [24]. As described in Prof. Bloch's lectures, this additional structure may be the result of higher configurational mixing. The residual interaction gives rise in the giant resonance region to a few quasi-bound 1^- $T=1$ states predominantly constituted of $2p$-$2h$ configurations. Although these states cannot be coupled to the ground state by a one-body operator, they may affect the cross-section through configuration mixing with the unbound one particle-one hole configurations and show up as additional structure in the giant resonance region [25].

6·4.3. Non-collective states. Apart from the coherent states which we have been considering so far, the states in the $1\hbar\omega$ region experience a relatively small shift primarily due to the diagonal term of the particle-hole

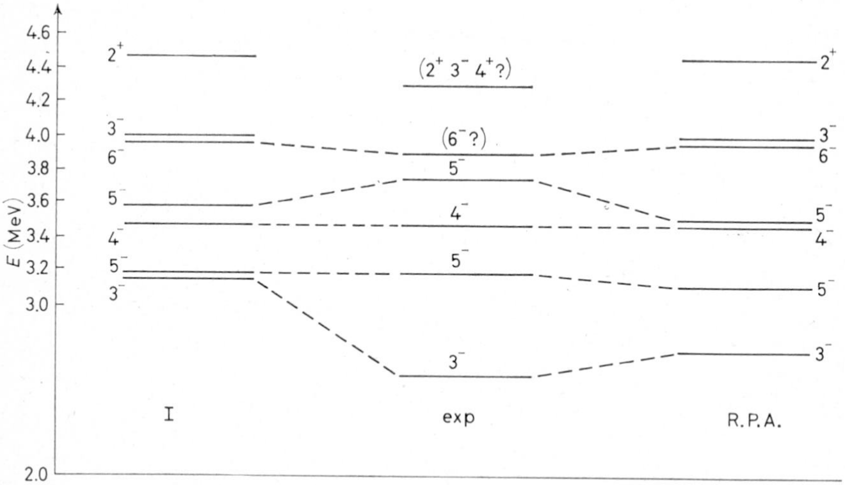

Fig. 31. – The low-lying states of ^{208}Pb (ref. [8]).

residual interaction. In these cases, both the R.P.A. and Approximation I give similar results. The energies are primarily determined by the value chosen for the experimental particle and hole energies, and are not very sensitive to variations in the force parameters. Therefore the good overall agreement with experiment obtained for these states is due to the choice of phenomenological single-particle energies. However it is gratifying to obtain with the same model and the same force parameters the proper position of both the collective levels which are strongly shifted in energy and of the noncollective ones. For example, among the few identified low-lying levels of ^{208}Pb, only one (the octupole state) is strongly shifted by the residual interaction. All the others are only slightly displaced in agreement with observation as shown in Fig. 31.

6'5. *Summary of results for single-closed-shell nuclei.* – The standard treatment of these nuclei consists: 1) in neglecting the particle-hole excitations of the doubly closed core; 2) in taking into account the strong pairing correla-

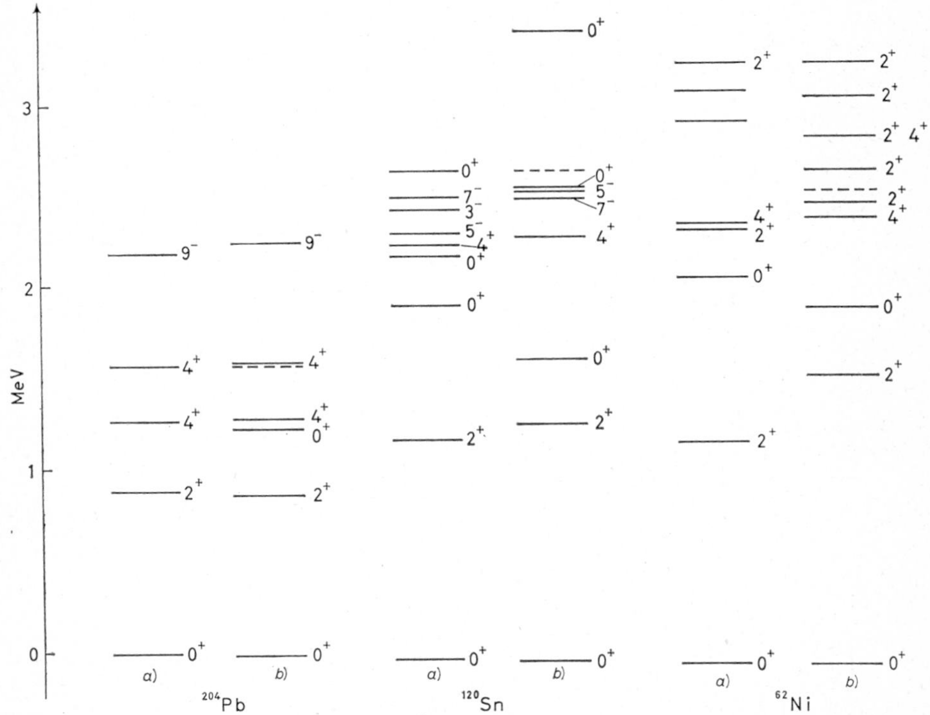

Fig. 32. – Comparison between the experimental levels of ^{204}Pb, ^{120}Sn and ^{62}Ni (columns *a*)) and the theoretical values given by the BCS and R.P.A. approximations (columns *b*)). The dashed lines in columns *b*) give the position of the lowest 2-quasi-particle configuration (R. Arvieu *et al.*, ref. [27]).

tions between the particles of the partially filled shell by means of the Bogoliubov-Valatin transformation; 3) in diagonalizing the residual interaction defined in eq. (45) between the quasi-particles, while restricting the configurational space to 2-quasi-particle excitations. The calculations may be carried out either in Approximation I (corresponding to the secular problem of eq. (83)) or in the R.P.A. (where the $\mathscr{B}$ matrix corresponding to correlations in the BCS ground state is defined in eq. (106)).

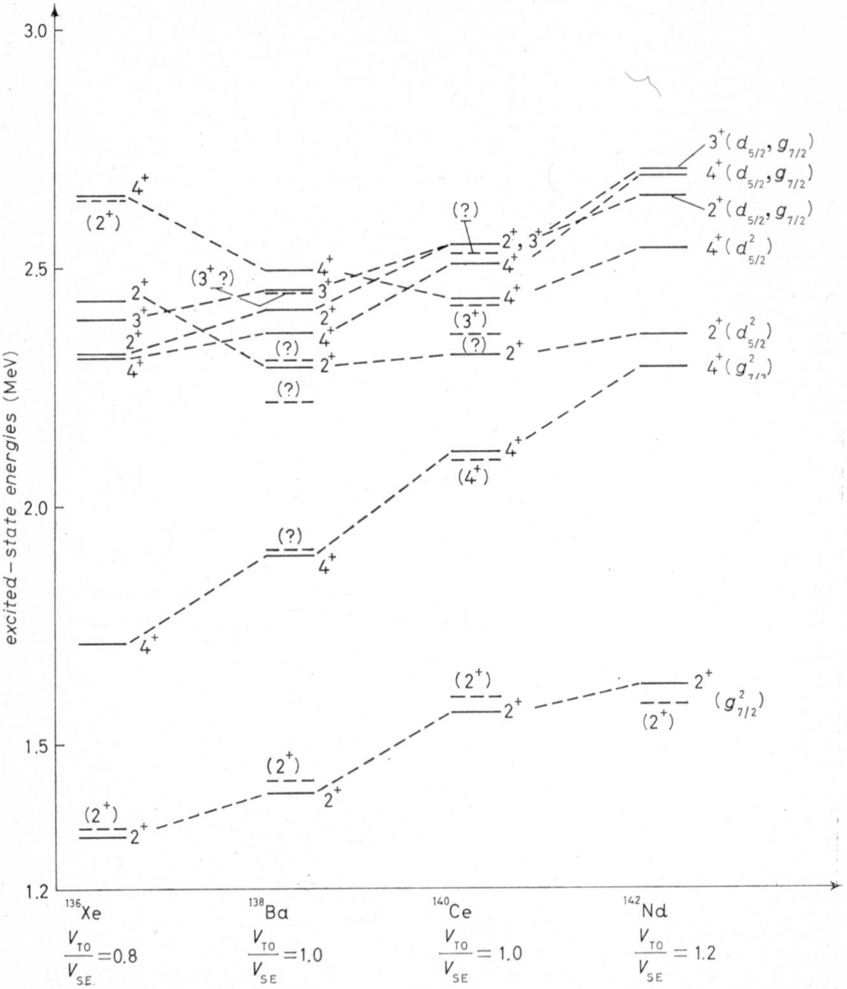

Fig. 33. – Level spectra for $J_\pi = 2^+, 3^+, 4^+$. The far right entry in parenthesis corresponds to the dominant component of the wave function. The force is gaussian. The ratio V_{TO}/V_{SE} has to be varied between 0.8 and 1.2 as indicated (M. Rho, ref. [28]). —— J, theoretical; – – – – (J) experimental; – – – (?) experimental with spins unidentified or tentative.

Many such calculations have been carried out on the s.c.s. (single closed shell) nuclei. Most of these utilize simple separable potentials and a list of references will be found in Kisslinger and Sørensen [26]. Figures 32 and 33 show the agreement obtained with observation with a Gaussian force in the case of the Ni, Sn and Pb isotopes (ARVIEUX and VENERONI [27]), and of the $N=82$ isotones (RHO) [28]. These results are quite typical and their features may be summarized as follows:

The residual interaction is quite effective in pushing down a few states into the gap region. This may be seen on Fig. 32 where the dashed lines in columns *b* represent the position of the lowest 2 quasi-particle configurations.

The R.P.A. gives almost the same results as Approximation I (except for the lowest and almost entirely spurious 0^+ state which is not shown on the figure), since the $\mathscr{B}$ matrix is multiplied by products of u's and v's (cf. eq. (106)) which are quite small for quasi-particle states near the Fermi level.

The agreement between theoretical and experimental energies improves with increasing A. It is satisfactory in the case of the isotopes of Pb, but rather poor for the isotopes of Ni. This is due in part to a better knowledge of the Hartree-Fock energies obtained in the former case from the experimental spectrum of ^{207}Pb, and primarily to the improvement of the validity of the BCS method with increasing number of particles.

It does not appear feasible to reach consistent detailed agreement with experiment in a given nuclear region with a single set of force parameters. For example, in Rho's results, a different ratio of triplet-odd to singlet-even potential is required to obtain an acceptable fit for the 2^+ and 4^+ states in each nucleus considered. Similar problems arise for the Ni and Sn isotopes in attempting to fit simultaneously the quasi-particle energies, the even-odd mass difference, and the spectrum of the even-even isotopes [29]. This necessary renormalization of the force parameters indicates the importance of the neglected higher configurations which stems from the fact that the energy gap is not much larger than the average value of the interaction matrix element, and of the core excitations which we shall discuss presently.

The strong electromagnetic transition probabilities of the low-lying states of the Sn, Pb and Ni isotopes cannot be reproduced with an approximation which only takes into account the open neutron shell. Likewise the calculated transition rates of the isotones $N=82$, using R.P.A. wave functions which include only the protons configurations of the open shell, are found to be markedly smaller than the experimental values [30].

These difficulties in obtaining a consistent fit with experimental energies and transition rates may be attributed in part to the important rôle played by the particle-hole excitations of the doubly closed shell constituting the core. The unperturbed energies of the core show up some distance above the lowest 2 quasi-particle excitations (for example in Sn, for the 3^- state, the lowest particle-hole unperturbed core excitations appear at $(5.5\div 6.5)$ MeV, while the lowest 2-quasi-particle unperturbed energies are found at $(3\div 3.5)$ MeV). None the less they give rise to coherent effects and their importance is indicated by the calculations of YOSHIDA [31], VEJE [32] and LOMBARD [33]. Although these calculations were performed with schematic separable potentials, they provide a comparison between the relative importance of the various effects. We report here part of the work of LOMBARD who used a pairing plus a quadrupole force in calculating the quadrupole state of the isotones $N=82$. In Table IV we compare the results of these calculations using Approximation I and the R.P.A. for the energies and the transition rates relative to the single-particle predictions. In columns *a* the core and the open shell are included; the quadrupole force parameters are different in Approximations I and II, since they are determined in each approximation so as to fit the position of the 2^+ state of ^{140}Ce. In columns *b*, only the open-shell configurations are taken into account; the quadrupole force parameters are the same as in the corresponding *a* columns. In columns *c* only the open-shell configurations are taken into account as in columns *b*, however the quadrupole force parameters are renormalized so as to fit the experimental energy of the 2^+ state in ^{140}Ce. Schematic separable forces generally exaggerate the enhancement effects of the R.P.A. and of distant configurations, as compared to more realistic forces. None the less, we may draw the following conclusions from Table IV:

TABLE IV. – *Core effects and role of the R.P.A. for the* 2^+ *state of* ^{138}Ba, ^{140}Ce, ^{142}Nd *with a pairing+quadrupole force* (LOMBARD [33]).

	I						II (R.P.A.)					
	E			$BE(2)/B_{SP}$			E			$BE(2)/B_{SP}$		
	a	*b*	*c*	*a*	*b*	*c*	*a*	*b*	*c*	*a*	*b*	*c*
^{138}Ba	1.43	1.73	1.43	13	2.2	3.1	1.44	1.79	1.45	30	4.9	9.4
^{140}Ce	1.57	2.00	1.57	18	3.1	4.4	1.57	2.08	1.57	43	6.3	11
^{142}Nd	1.56	2.10	1.57	23	4.1	5.7	1.57	1.58	1.52	57	13	23

A comparison of columns *a* and *b* shows that including the core effects is important both for the energies and the transition rates.

Renormalization of the force permits one to obtain the same results *for the energies*, with or without the R.P.A. (see columns I*a* and II*a*) and with or without inclusion of core effects (see columns *a* and *c* in I or in II).

However renormalization of the force is unable to reproduce the enhancement of the transition probabilities due to the use of the R.P.A. (see the $BE(2)$ values of columns *a*, *b*, *c* in I and II) or to the inclusion of core effects (see the $BE(2)$ values of columns *a* and *c* in I and II respectively).

These results are quite general and point out the necessity for including all the relevant configurations.

7. – Description of deformed nuclei.

7·1. *Introduction.* – We shall consider here the excitation spectrum of light deformed nuclei in the s, d shell which may be treated relatively simply, in view of the small degeneracies of the shell structure in that region of the periodic table. Our discussion will be primarily concerned with the method of deformed orbitals, a simplified version of the Hartree-Fock approximation wherein it is assumed that most of the particles in the core do not contribute to the nuclear deformation.

It is an experimental fact that all light nuclei exhibit deformations in their ground and/or their excited states. Even the doubly closed-shell nucleus ^{16}O has recently been found to have rotational bands [34]. In the light of the shell model these deformations may be attributed to: 1) the fact that orbital wave functions in a spherical well have a nonspherical distribution for $l \neq 0$ (therefore it is already clear that they cannot give rise to a self-consistent field except for doubly closed-shell nuclei); 2) the alignment effect of the two-body force whose low multipole components tend to align nucleon orbital angular momenta so as to maximize overlap between individual particle wave functions.

We shall begin with a qualitative description of the procedures which will be developed in latter Sections.

We consider first ^{16}O which behaves both as a spherical and a deformed nucleus. The theoretical description of its spectrum can be given in principle by diagonalizing a residual interaction v on the complete space of all the eigenstates of the spherically symmetric Hartree-Fock Hamiltonian. We have seen in the previous Section that the lowest odd-parity vibrational states are thus obtained as a mixture of one particle-hole excitations of energy $1\hbar\omega$. The mixture of the next set of configurations corresponding to an excitation energy of $2\hbar\omega$ (two particle-hole or one particle-hole configurations) give rise to even-parity states which are situated above the vibrational levels. Experimentally, however, the lowest state is found to have even parity (0^+, 6.05 MeV), and there are a number of low-lying excited states of both parities which cannot be explained by the simple $1\hbar\omega$ and $2\hbar\omega$ configuration mixing. In the case of ^{16}O these include for example the 1^-, $T=0$, 7.1 MeV, the 2^-, $T=0$, 8.8 MeV and the 2^+, $T=0$, 7.8 MeV states. The existence of such states in a spherically symmetric zero-order field can only be understood as a mixture of higher configurations. The presence of configurations involving four particle-hole states at relatively low energy may appear surprising in view of the large excitation energy required to promote four particles say from the p to the s-d shell. However, it can be understood by the fact that the four particles may have a higher mutual interaction energy in the s-d than in

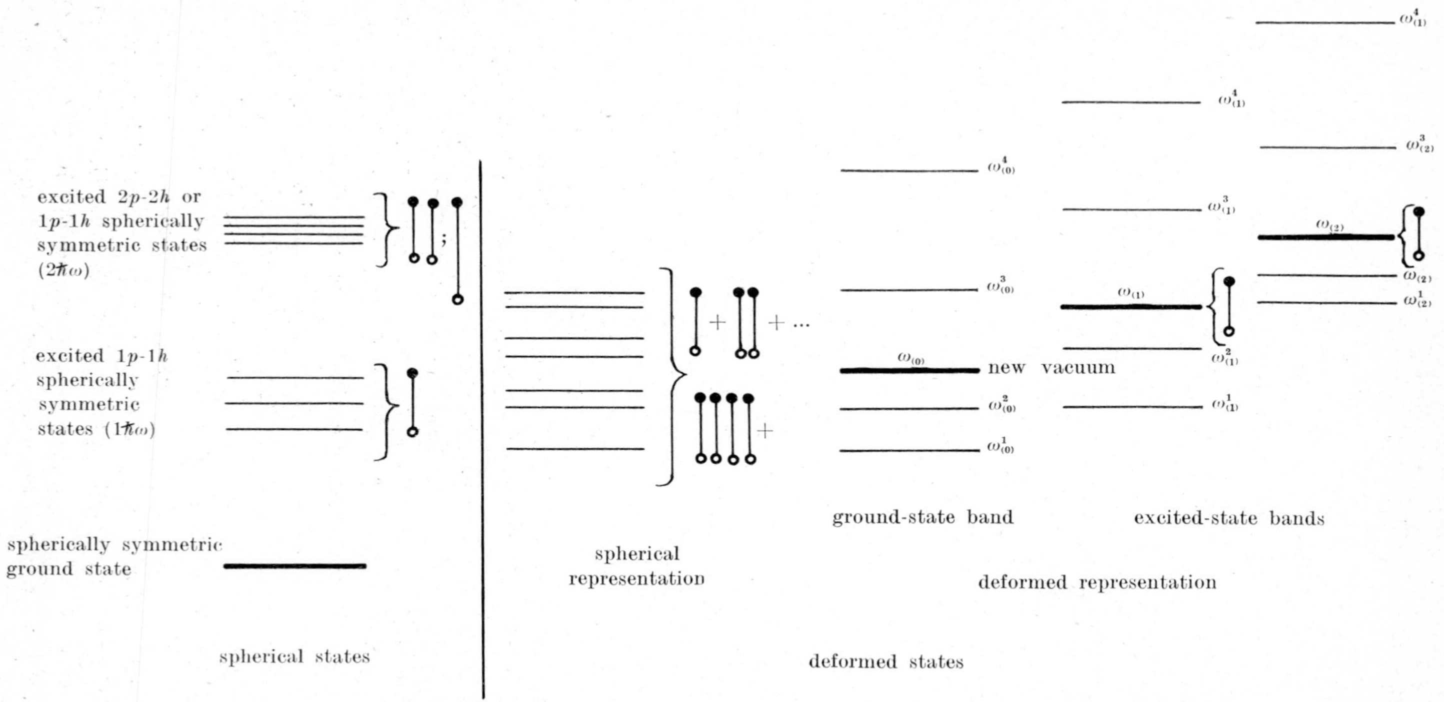

Fig. 34. – Schematic description of computed spectra for a doubly-closed-shell nucleus.

the p-shell. Of course the secular problem in such an extensive configurational space becomes quite formidable. Rather than attempting to include the complete residual interactions between the excited particles, we shall first treat in a simplified Hartree-Fock method those effects which may be represented by an average deformed field yielding a new Hartree-Fock ground state.

As shown on Fig. 34 this new Hartree-Fock ground state of energy $\omega_{(0)}$ can in turn give rise to a series of vibrational states $\omega_{(1)}, \omega_{(2)}, \ldots$ formed by the mixing of simple one particle-hole pairs occupying deformed orbital states.

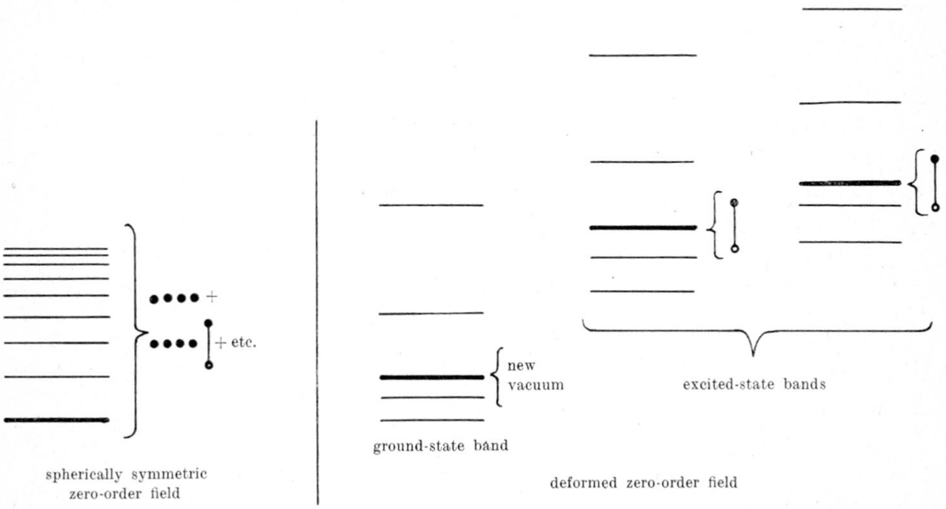

Fig. 35. – Schematic description of computed spectra for a doubly closed-shell nucleus plus 4 nucleons.

However the states $\omega_{(1)}, \omega_{(2)}, \ldots$ are not eigenstates of J since they arise from a nonspherically symmetric Hamiltonian. True eigenstates of J can be obtained from the former by projection giving rise to the bands of energy $\omega^1_{(0)}, \omega^2_{(0)}, \ldots$ $\omega^1_{(1)}, \omega^2_{(1)}, \ldots$ which represent the excited states in this approximation. We shall see later that they may be associated with a series of rotational bands.

In the case of a nucleus consisting of a doubly closed shell plus n nucleons, the solution of the secular problem requires diagonalization over a large configuration space when starting from spherically symmetric Hartree-Fock states. This is due to the high degree of degeneracy exhibited by the configurations of n nucleons in a partially filled shell. For example the low-lying excited states of ^{20}Ne (cf. Fig. 35) are obtained by diagonalizing in the space of the configurations with four particles, five particles and one hole etc. As in the previous case it is preferable to single out that part of the mutual interaction among nucleons which is primary responsible for the average field. A Hartree-Fock calculation limited to the nucleons outside the core yields a deformed nondegenerate Hartree-Fock ground state which may then be used as a reference or new vacuum state (cf. Sect. **2** and Fig. 2) defining particle-hole excitations in deformed orbitals. If the energy associated with an elementary particle-hole excitation is large, then the low-lying excited states may be adequately represented by restricting the secular problem to the one particle-hole pair configuration subspace. The proper eigenstates of the system are obtained by projecting out states of given angular momentum giving rise to bands associated with the deformed Hartree-Fock ground state and with each particle-hole vibrational state (cf. Fig. 35).

The limited Hartree-Fock method and the projection procedure just outlined appear as approximate ways of treating the mixing among the configurations of a given large number of particles. Mixing between these configurations and simpler ones treated in another scheme, for example particle-hole excitations in a spherical scheme, may have to be taken into account. This aspect of the problem is treated in the seminar of G. E. BROWN (this volume p. 524).

7·2. *Method of deformed orbitals.* – Since a general approach to the Hartree-Fock problem is difficult we assume that we have the solution $|\Phi_0^N\rangle$ of a spherical Hartree-Fock problem for an N-particle system and that we know the corresponding single particle energies ε_i, and the associated vectors $|j_i m_i\rangle$ entering in $|\Phi_0^N\rangle$.

We seek a trial determinantal wave function whose domain of variation is not restricted to spherical symmetry, for a system of $A = N + n$ nucleons, where n may be positive, negative or zero. Following an extension due to G. RIPKA of the deformed-orbitals method of LEVINSON and KELSON [35] and of DIETRICH *et al.* [36] we will choose the trial wave function in the form

$$|\Phi^{N+n}\rangle = b^\dagger_{X_1} \dots b^\dagger_{X_k} b_{x_1} \dots b_{x_l} |\Phi_0^N\rangle\,, \tag{115}$$

where k particles and l holes are created in nonspherically symmetric orbits and

$$k - l = n\,.$$

The actual values assigned to k and l partly define the model and must be chosen by trial and error. For example, in the case of ^{16}O we shall see that the value $k=4$ (4 particles-4 holes) gives a lower Hartree-Fock energy than $k=2$ (2 particles-2 holes).

The definition of $|\Phi^{N+n}\rangle$ contains the main hypothesis of the deformed-orbitals method: namely only k particles and l holes will participate in the construction of the deformed field. In other words it is assumed that the core is stable against deformation. The orbitals of the created particles or holes are of the general form

$$b_X^\dagger = \sum_A C_A^X \eta_A^\dagger \,, \tag{116}$$

$$b_x = \sum_a C_a^x \eta_a \,, \tag{117}$$

where $A = \tau_A j_A m_A$ and $a = \tau_a j_a m_a$ represent complete sets of quantum numbers denoting spherical single-particle states above and below the Fermi level, respectively. The fermion operators $\eta_A^\dagger$ and η_a respectively create and annihilate nucleons in the spherical states A and a.

If certain invariances are demanded of the system (axial symmetry, parity or others) these expansions become restricted as will be discussed later.

The C's are the variational parameters of the problem. They will be given as eigenvectors of a Hermitic operator (the Hartree-Fock Hamiltonian) and accordingly they satisfy the relations

$$\sum_\lambda C_i^\lambda C_{i'}^\lambda = \delta_{ii'} \,, \qquad \sum_i C_i^\lambda C_i^{\lambda'} = \delta_{\lambda\lambda'} \,. \tag{118}$$

The variational principle applied to the class of determinantal trial wave functions (115) yields the self-consistent problem

$$h|\lambda\rangle = E_\lambda|\lambda\rangle \,, \tag{119}$$

where h is the Hartree-Fock Hamiltonian, $|\lambda\rangle$ the deformed self-consistent orbital λ and E_λ the corresponding eigenvalue. In the spherical representation $|jm\rangle$, h is given by

$$\langle jm|h|j'm'\rangle = \langle jm|T|j'm'\rangle + \tfrac{1}{2}\sum_\varrho \langle jm\varrho|V|j'm'\varrho\rangle \,, \tag{120}$$

where the ϱ summation must be taken over all occupied single-particle states, and the Hartree-Fock problem (119) may be written as

$$\sum_{j'm'} \langle jm|h|j'm'\rangle C_{j'm'}^\lambda = E_\lambda C_{jm}^\lambda \,. \tag{121}$$

The deformed orbitals method consists in selecting certain trial values for the C's and calculating $\langle jm|h|j'm'\rangle$; the new C's are then obtained by diagonalizing eq. (121). The process is repeated until the new C's are identical to the trial ones.

In order to solve eq. (121), we need the explicit form of the matrix element $\langle jm|h|j'm'\rangle$ which may be written as

$$\langle jm|h|j'm'\rangle = \{\langle jm|T|j'm'\rangle + \tfrac{1}{2}\sum_a \langle jma|V|j'm'a\rangle\} + \\ + \tfrac{1}{2}\sum_X \langle jmX|V|j'm'X\rangle - \tfrac{1}{2}\sum_x \langle jmx|V|j'm'x\rangle \,, \tag{122}$$

where the a summation is over all the states below the Fermi level of the reference spherical state $|\Phi_0^N\rangle$ and where we have used the fact that

$$(123)\qquad \sum_x \langle jmx|V|j'm'x\rangle = \sum_{abx} C_a^x C_b^x \langle jma|V|j'm'b\rangle = \sum_{a'} \langle jma'|V|j'm'a'\rangle\,,$$

where the summation extends over the unoccupied spherical single-particle states a' which are assumed to form a complete set. The quantity appearing in the bracket of eq. (122) is diagonal in the spherical Hartree-Fock representation

$$(124)\qquad \langle jm|T|j'm'\rangle + \tfrac{1}{2}\sum_a \langle jma|V|j'm'a\rangle = \varepsilon_j \delta_{jj'}\delta_{mm'}\,,$$

therefore

$$(125)\quad \langle jm|h|j'm'\rangle = \varepsilon_j\delta_{jj'}\delta_{mm'} + \tfrac{1}{2}\sum_X \langle jmX|V|j'm'X\rangle - \tfrac{1}{2}\sum_x \langle jmx|V|j'm'x\rangle\,.$$

In a self-consistent calculation, the ε_j's would be determined according to the Hartree-Fock procedure from the two-body force V. However a realistic interaction complicates the problem beyond practical bounds while a simple central effective two-body interaction cannot give the proper spin-orbit splitting nor the binding energies. A practical compromise consists in replacing the ε_j's by experimental values as described in Sect. **5**·2 and assuming that the single-particle spherical vectors $|jm\rangle$ may be represented by the wave functions of a phenomenological well usually taken as an infinite oscillator well.

A further simplification of the problem consists in limiting the expansions of the deformed orbitals (116, 117) to a few spherical states, taking advantage of the large energy gap between shells. Most calculations have been limited to $1p$, $2s$ and $1d$ states.

The intrinsic trial wave function need not have all the invariance properties of the total Hamiltonian H. However we may restrict the variational space by requiring that the intrinsic trial wave function be invariant under certain transformations (such as parity, rotation about some axes, reflection). Thus, the number of independent parameters, C_i^λ, is reduced.

The principal restrictions which may be imposed upon the total trial wave function are:

a) The requirement that it must have intrinsic parity, which limits the summation in (116, 117) over spherical states of same parity.

b) The requirement of axial symmetry, *i.e.* $|\Phi^{N+n}\rangle$ must be an eigenstate of J_z. Therefore the deformed orbitals must also be eigenstates of J_z with eigenvalues K. This limits the summation over spherical states $|jm\rangle$ with m equal to K.

c) The requirement of invariance through a rotation $R_y(\pi)$ of π around an axis y perpendicular to the axis of symmetry. Since we have

$$R_y(\pi)|jm\rangle = (-)^{j-m}|j-m\rangle$$

for each single particle wave function contained in $|\Phi_0^{N+n}\rangle$,

$$|\lambda\rangle = \sum_{jm} C_{jm}^{\lambda}|jm\rangle\,,$$

these must also exist in $|\Phi_0^{N+n}\rangle$ the time reversed state,

$$|-\lambda\rangle = \sum_{jm} C_{jm}^{\lambda}(-)^{j-m}|j-m\rangle\,,$$

where the same coefficients C_{jm}^{λ} appear in both functions.

d) The charge invariance is obtained by requiring that each single-particle state occupied by a proton be matched with an identical state occupied by a neutron.

e) The invariance relative to the reflection through a plane containing the axis of symmetry $0z$ may be also required. It is the product of a rotation $R_y(\pi)$ of π around the axis $0y$ and of a reflection S_0 through the origin. It results in a two-fold degeneracy of the Hartree-Fock solution, $|\Phi_0, J_z = M\rangle$ and $|\Phi_0, J_z = -M\rangle$ having the same energy. The case $J_z = 0$ is of particular interest. We have two degenerate solutions for which

$$(125a)\qquad |\Phi, J_z = 0\rangle = R_y(\pi)S_0|\Phi, J_z = 0\rangle = \sum_{J,\varepsilon}(-)^{J+\varepsilon}a_{J\varepsilon}|J, \varepsilon, J_z = 0\rangle\,.$$

Here the Hartree-Fock state is expanded in terms of components with good angular momentum J and parity ε. It follows from eq. (125*a*) that the projected (J, ε) states will form two groups; namely,

$$(-)^{J+\varepsilon} = 1 \Rightarrow \begin{cases} 0^+\ 2^+\ 4^+\ \ldots\,, \\ 1^-\ 3^-\ 5^-\ \ldots\,. \end{cases}$$

7·3. *Deformed orbitals for s-d shell nuclei.* – KELSON and LEVINSON [35] have applied the approximate Hartree-Fock system (121) to the *s-d* shell nuclei. The ^{16}O core is taken as inert ($l = 0$ in eq. (115)) and the variational space is limited to the $2s$ and $1d$ states. Axial symmetry around $0z$ and reflexion symmetry relative to the xy-plane are imposed on the trial wave function. The basic two-body interaction entering in (125) is a Rosenfeld mixture with a Yukawa shape and the single-particle energies ε_j are given by the ^{17}O spectrum. The deformed orbitals (116) given by the iteration

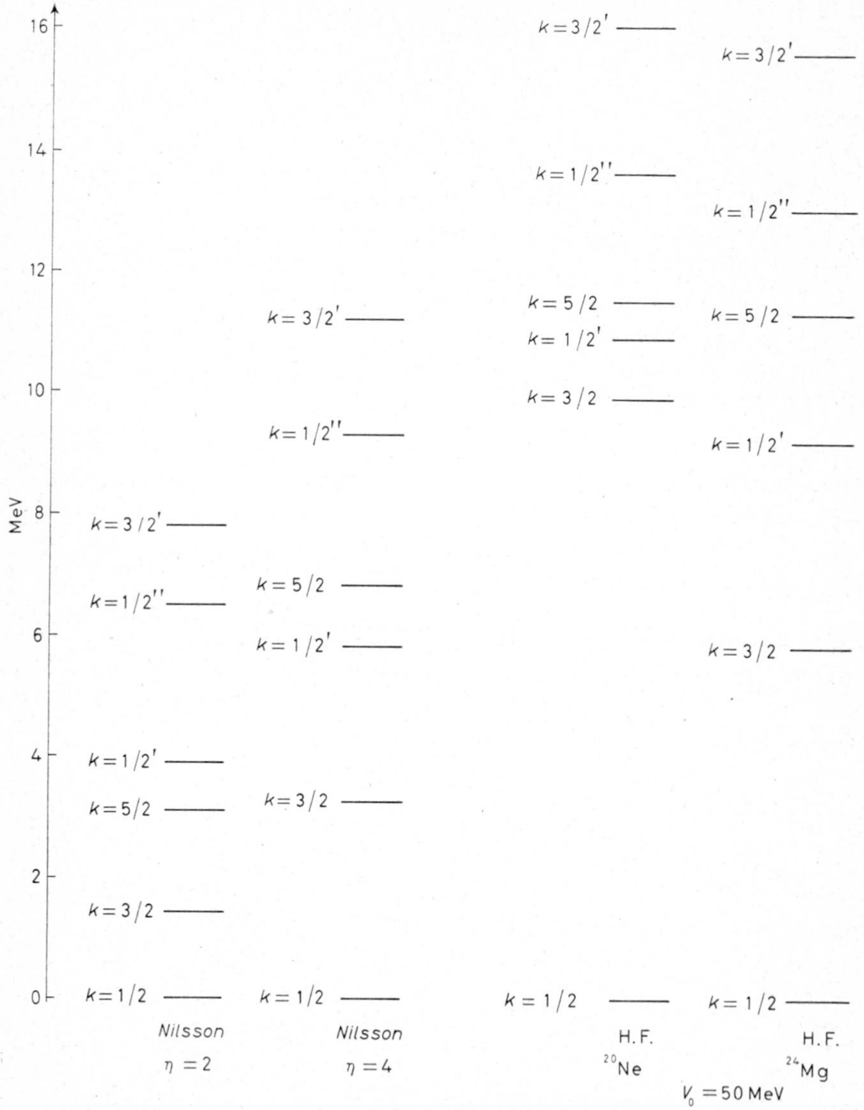

Fig. 36. – Comparison between the deformed harmonic oscillator spectrum and the self-consistent particle spectrum (KELSON and LEVINSON, ref. [35]).

of (121) show a strong configuration mixing between the spherical single-particle basis vectors, thus indicating that the interaction between the few particles outside the closed core yields large deformations. Indeed the amplitudes C_i^x for the deformed orbitals are quite similar to the components of the corresponding Nilsson's states for large values of the deformation parameter ($\eta \sim 0.2$, 0.4). This similarity for the orbitals does not hold for the single-particle energies, as shown by Fig. 36 where the deformed oscillator spectrum ($\eta = 0.2 \div 0.4$) of NILSSON and MOTTELSON is compared to the self-consistent single particle spectrum of KELSON and LEVINSON (for ^{20}Ne and ^{24}Mg since the spectrum in the self-consistent calculation depends strongly on the nature of the occupied levels). The most striking feature of this comparison concerns the energy gap between filled and unfilled levels. It is much larger in the self-consistent calculations. The difference between the single particle spectra of Fig. 36 indicates the importance of the nonlocal self-consistent potential which is brought in by the exchange parts of the interaction matrix in (121) while it is missing in the simple Nilsson's potential.

The large energy gap in the self-consistent single-particle spectrum has two important consequences for the moments of inertia and for the computation of excited intrinsic states.

a) The moment of inertia $\mathcal{I}$ associated to the deformed Hartree-Fock state is strongly reduced as compared to the moment of inertia of the Nilsson's determinantal states. This is simply seen with the Inglis cranking formula

$$\mathcal{I} = \sum_{X_1, X_2} \frac{|\langle X_1 | J_x | X_2 \rangle|^2}{E_{X_1} - E_{X_2}}, \tag{126}$$

where $|X_1\rangle$ and $|X_2\rangle$ are respectively occupied and unoccupied deformed orbitals, and E_{X_1}, E_{X_2} the corresponding energies. Since the Nilsson's and the self-consistent single-particle wave functions do not differ greatly, the numerators of (126) are similar in both cases. However the denominators, as seen from Fig. 36, are quite different. The departure from the rigid moment of inertia is large enough to bring a very satisfactory agreement with experimental values, as shown on Fig. 37.

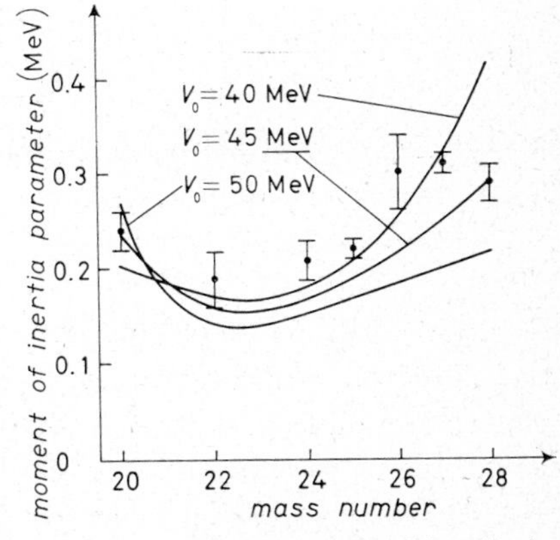

Fig. 37. – The moments of inertia in the *s*-*d* shell (ref. [35]).

b) The lowest intrinsic excited states of the nuclei corresponding to completely filled deformed states (*i.e.* ^{20}Ne, ^{24}Mg, ^{28}Si ...) should be well represented by the mixing of configurations with only one particle-hole pair, the rôle of higher configurations being reduced by the large energy gap. The situation is thus similar to the one encountered in doubly closed shell nuclei. Some calculations, using the R.P.A., have been performed for ^{20}Ne by BASSICHIS *et al.* [37].

7·4. *The deformed states of* ^{16}O. – The low-lying even-parity states of ^{16}O are not properly described by the mixing of spherical $2\hbar\omega$ configurations. For example, electron form factors computed from such wave functions are too small by factors ranging from 40 to 1000 [38]. Recent experimental data show that certain of these excited states belong to rotational bands [34]. KELSON [39] and BASSICHIS and RIPKA [40] have performed a deformed-orbital calculation for ^{16}O; although the first of these calculations includes odd-parity mixing, both lead to similar results for the even-parity intrinsic state, and we shall report here on the latter. The variational procedure is successively carried out for the case of 2 particles-2 holes, *i.e.* $l=k=2$ in (115) and the case of 4 particles-4 holes, *i.e.* $l=k=4$. The trial wave functions are required to have intrinsic parity and to be invariant under rotations about an axis and under reflection in the plane perpendicular to the axis of symmetry. With these requirements one finds three linearly independent 2p-2h and one 4p-4h trial wave functions. The Hartree-Fock equations are solved for each of these, utilizing a Rosenfeld force with a Gaussian shape, and experimental spherical single-particle energies (obtained from ^{15}O and ^{17}O spectra). The resultant Hartree-Fock energies are given on Fig. 38, as a function of the potential depth parameter V_0. It may be seen that for $V_0 > 30$ MeV the 4p-4h solution is separated by a large energy gap from the three others which are of the 2p-2h type; this result suggests that even in a more realistic calculation the mixing between 2p-2h and 4p-4h configurations should be small. The 4p-4h solution having energy E_{HF} may be interpreted as the intrinsic state of a rotational band; the lowest state of this rotational band having energy E_0 is identified as the lowest 0^+ state of ^{16}O appearing experimentally at 6.05 MeV. The relation between E_0 and E_{HF} can easily be obtained within the adiabatic hypothesis of the unified model. The intrinsic (space-oriented) Hartree-Fock state $|\Phi\rangle$ is a wave packet built up as the linear superposition of rotating states Ψ_J, eigenstates of $\boldsymbol{J}$ (see Prof. Villar's notes), *i.e.*

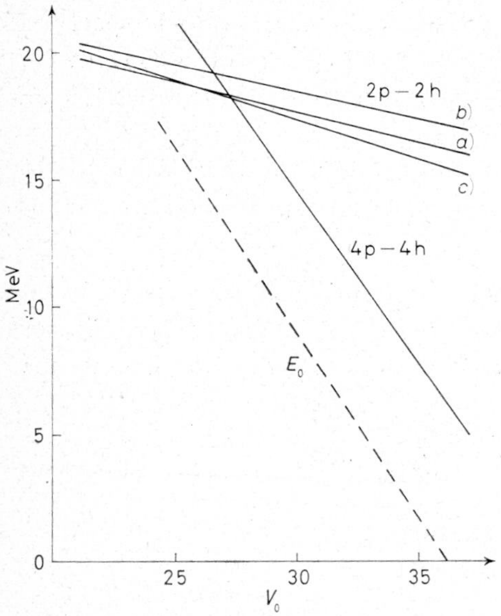

Fig. 38. – The 2p-2h and the 4p-4h Hartree-Fock states in ^{16}O (BASSICHIS and RIPKA, ref. [40]).

$$|\Phi\rangle = \sum_J A^J \Psi^J, \qquad \text{with } \sum_J |A^J|^2 = 1,$$

therefore,

$$E_{\text{HF}} = \langle \Phi | H | \Phi \rangle = \sum_J E_J |A^J|^2 \simeq \sum_J \left(E_0 + \frac{\hbar^2}{2\mathscr{I}} J(J+1) \right) |A^J|^2 = \tag{127}$$

$$= E_0 + \frac{\hbar^2}{2\mathscr{I}} \langle \Phi | J^2 | \Phi \rangle .$$

The value E_0 calculated from eq. (127) with the 4p-4h solution E_{HF} and with the moment of inertia given by the cranking formula (126), is represented by the dashed line on Fig. 38. The experimental energy of the 0^+ state corresponds to $V_0 = 32$ MeV. Finally, though the 4p-4h H-F state is lower than the 2p-2h H-F states, the 8p-8h H-F state comes much higher at $+30$ MeV.

KELSON [39] obtains likewise a low-lying deformed odd-parity intrinsic state 0^-, associated to 3p-3h excitations ($k = l = 3$ in eq. (115)).

Projecting out the angular momentum as discussed in the next Section KELSON has obtained the bands of Fig. 39 which agree quite well with the experimental situation.

Of course, one must expect some mixing between « deformed » and « spherical » solutions. This aspect of the problem is discussed by BROWN and GREEN [41] and KELSON [39], who show that such mixing is limited to a few per cent (see G. E. BROWN, this volume p. 524).

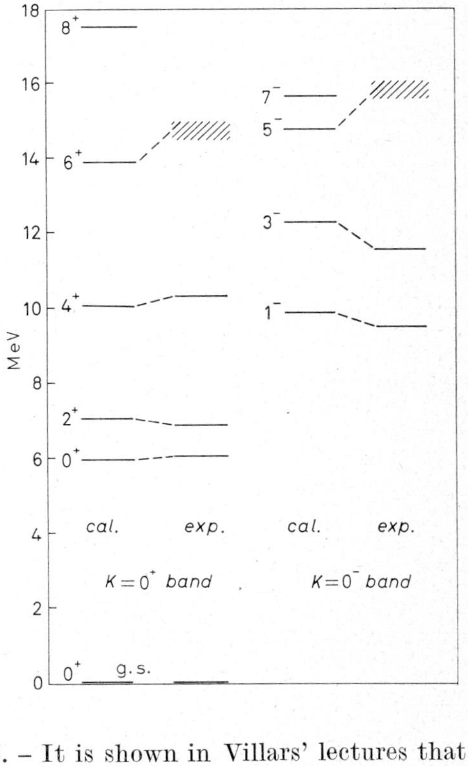

Fig. 39. – Comparison between the experimental and the calculated $K=0^+$ and $K=0^-$ bands in ^{16}O, ref. [39].

7'5. *Rotational bands in the s-d shell.* – It is shown in Villars' lectures that the removal of the degeneracy associated with the space orientation of the deformed Hartree-Fock state Φ leads to a band of physical states with definite angular momentum J, M. The energies of this « rotational band » are given by

$$E_J = \frac{\langle \Phi | H P_{JM} | \Phi \rangle}{\langle \Phi | P_{JM} | \Phi \rangle} , \tag{128}$$

TABLE V. – *The rotational bands of* ^{18}O, ^{18}F, ^{19}F and ^{20}Ne. *The energies are given relative to the* (H.F.) *ground state of* ^{16}O (ref. [42]).

Nucleus	J^π	Experimental	Calculated	Configuration
^{18}O	0^+	— 12.19	— 11.5	2p
	0^+	— 8.56	— 8.7	2p
	0^+	— 6.86	— 6.0	4p-2h
	0^+	—	1.53	2p
	2^+	— 10.21	— 9.8	2p
	2^+	— 8.27	— 8.2	2p
	2^+	— 6.94	— 4.6	4p-2h
	2^+	—	— 2.7	2p
	3^+	— 6.82	— 6.6	2p
	4^+	— 8.64	— 8.7	2p
	4^+	—	— 1.7	4p-2h
^{18}F	1^+	— 13.28	— 13.4	2p
	1^+	— 11.58	— 9.7	2p
	1^+	—	— 8.9	4p-2h
	1^+	—	— 7.9	2p
	2^+	—	— 10.1	2p
	2^+	—	— 8.0	4p-2h
	3^+	— 12.34	— 12.8	2p
	3^+	—	— 9.0	2p
	3^+	—	— 7.3	4p-2h
	3^+	—	— 4.3	2p
	4^+	—	— 7.3	2p
	4^+	—	— 5.3	4p-2h
	5^+	— 12.15	— 12.4	2p
	5^+	—	— 4.6	4p-2h
^{20}Ne	0^+	— 40.11	— 40.8	4p
	2^+	— 38.48	— 39.6	4p
	4^+	— 35.86	— 37.0	4p
	6^+	— 32.51	— 33.4	4p
	8^+	—	— 29.63	4p
^{19}F	$1/2^+$	— 23.72	— 24.1	3p
	$3/2^+$	— 22.17	— 22.0	3p
	$5/2^+$	— 23.53	— 23.4	3p
	$7/2^+$	—	— 18.7	3p
	$9/2^+$	— 20.93	— 21.5	3p
	$11/2^+$	—	— 15.4	3p
	$13/2^+$	—	— 19.4	3p
	$1/2^-$	— 23.61	— 22.6	4p-1h
	$3/2^-$	— 22.27	— 21.0	4p-1h
	$5/2^-$	— 22.38	— 21.5	4p-1h
	$7/2^-$	—	— 18.1	4p-1h
	$9/2^-$	—	— 19.0	4p-1h
	$11/2^-$	—	— 14.2	4p-1h

where P_{JM} is the projector

$$P_{JM} = \sum_{\alpha} |\alpha J M\rangle\langle\alpha J M| \,. \tag{129}$$

An explicit expression for P_{JM} may be obtained starting from the definition of the rotation matrix $D^J_{MM'}(\Omega)$ in terms of the rotation operator $R(\Omega)$ (Ω denotes the 3 Euler angles), see Prof. Villars' lectures,

$$P_{JM} = \frac{2J+1}{8\pi^2} \int \mathrm{d}\Omega D^{J*}_{MM'}(\Omega) R(\Omega) \,. \tag{130}$$

The expression for E_J, (128), together with the explicit form (130), have been utilized by BASSICHIS, GIRAUD and RIPKA [42] for computing the rotational bands of ^{18}O, ^{18}F associated with the 4p-2h ($k=4$, $l=2$ in (115)) Hartree-Fock states, the rotational bands of ^{19}F associated with the 3p and the 4p-1h H-F states, and the band of ^{20}Ne associated with the 4p H-F state. The trial wave functions have intrinsic parity and have both axial and reflexion symmetry. The force is a central Gaussian Rosenfeld mixture. The spherical Hartree-Fock energies are obtained from the spectra of ^{15}O and ^{17}O. The results of BASSICHIS, GIRAUD and RIPKA are summarized in Table V which includes also the states of ^{18}O and ^{18}F given by diagonalization in the 2-particle configuration space. They obtain very satisfactory agreement with 26 experimental levels using a single set of parameters. It may be noted that the odd-parity states of ^{19}F come at the same position as the even-parity states, although they require the excitation of an extra particle-hole pair.

7·6. *Comparison between the deformed-orbital method and the complete diagonalization.* – The deformed-orbital method for k particles and l holes is clearly an approximation to the complete problem of diagonalizing the residual interaction in the space of all the configurations with k particles and l holes.

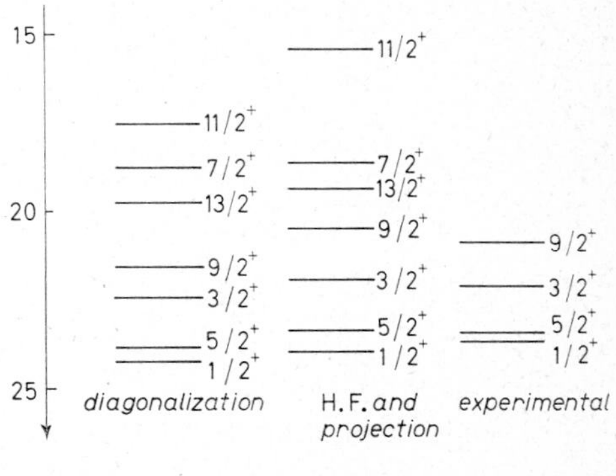

Fig. 40. – Binding energies of the ^{19}F positive-parity states (relative to the ^{16}O binding energy) obtained by exact diagonalization of the Hamiltonian in the three-particle subspace and by projecting angular momentum from the H.F. state. A Rosenfeld force with strength $V_0 = 53.25$ MeV was used in both calculations, RIPKA *et al.*, ref. [42].

In order to test the accuracy of the method, BASSICHIS, GIRAUD and RIPKA [42] have compared the even-parity states of ^{19}F given by the deformed-orbital method ($k=3$, $l=0$) with the results of an exact diagonalization of the force over all possible 3-particle configurations in the s-d shell. (This involves matrices of the order of 45×45.) The agreement, as shown on Fig. 40, is quite good. This agreement may be understood from the large binding energy of the H.F. state which separates it from the excited configurational states by a large energy. The corrections to the deformed-orbital method which would come from the mixing between the projected state of given J and the remaining far away configurational states of same J is likely to be small.

* * *

The author gratefully acknowledges the collaboration of Prof. M. MELKANOFF in the preparation of these lecture notes, and is thankful to Dr. M. RHO for clarifying discussions.

REFERENCES

General references

M. BARANGER: *Theory of Finite Nuclei*, 1962 Cargese Lectures (New York, 1962).
C. BLOCH: *Lectures on nuclear many-body problems*, Tata Institute, Bombay (1962).
G. E. BROWN: *Unified Theory of Nuclear Models* (Amsterdam, 1964).

[1] K. A. BRUECKNER and J. L. GAMMEL: *Phys. Rev.*, **109**, 1023 (1958).
[2] L. C. GOMES, J. D. WALECKA and V. F. WEISSKOPF: *Ann. Phys.*, **3**, 241 (1958).
[3] S. A. MOSZKOWSKI and B. L. SCOTT: *Ann. of Phys.*, **11**, 65 (1960).
[4] C. BLOCH: *Nucl. Phys.*, **7**, 451 (1958).
[5] S. S. SCHWEBER: *Introduction to Relativistic Quantum Field Theory* (New York, 1963).
[6] J. GOLDSTONE: *Proc. Roy. Soc.*, A **239**, 267 (1957).
[7] G. E. BROWN and M. BOLSTERLI: *Phys. Rev. Lett.*, **3**, 472 (1959).
[8] V. GILLET, A. M. GREEN and E. A. SANDERSON: *Phys. Lett.*, **11**, 44 (1964).
[9] V. GILLET and N. VINH MAU: *Nucl. Phys.*, **54**, 321 (1964).
[10] A. GLICK, H. J. LIPKIN and N. MESHKOV: *Proc. Rutherford Conference* (London, 1961), p. 299.
[11] S. COHEN, R. D. LAWSON and M. SODA: unpublished.
[12] A. GOSWAMI and M. K. PAL: *Nucl. Phys.*, **44**, 294 (1963).
[13] W. TRUE and K. FORD: *Phys. Rev.*, **109**, 1675 (1958).
[14] J. BLOMQUIST and S. WAHLBORN: *Ark. Fys.*, **16**, 545 (1959).
[15] V. GILLET: *Nucl. Phys.*, **51**, 410 (1964).
[16] A. KALLIO and K. KOLLTVEIT: *Nucl. Phys.*, **53**, 87 (1964).

[17] A. KALLIO: *Annales Acad. Scient. Fennicae, A, VI. Physica* 163 (1964).
[18] D. H. WILKINSON: *Physica*, **23**, 1039 (1956).
[19] J. P. ELLIOTT and B. H. FLOWERS: *Proc. Roy. Soc.*, A **242**, 57 (1957).
[20] J. M. BLATT and V. F. WEISSKOPF: *Theoretical Nuclear Physics* (New York, 1952).
[21] V. GILLET and E. SANDERSON: *Nucl. Phys.*, **54**, 472 (1964).
[22] V. GILLET and M. MELKANOFF: *Phys. Rev.*, **133**, B 1190 (1964).
[23] H. MACMANUS and R. M. HAYBRON: to be published.
[24] R. G. ALLAS, S. S. HANNA, L. MEYER-SCHÜTZMEISTER, R. E. SEGEL, P. P. SINGH and Z. VAGER: *Phys. Rev. Lett.*, **13**, 628 (1964).
[25] U. FANO: *Phys. Rev.*, **124**, 1866 (1961); C. BLOCH and V. GILLET: *Phys. Lett.*, **16**, 62 (1965); V. GILLET and C. BLOCH: *Phys. Lett.*, **18**, 58 (1965).
[26] L. S. KISSLINGER and R. A. SØRENSEN: *Rev. Mod. Phys.*, **35**, 853 (1963).
[27] R. ARVIEU and M. VÉNÉRONI: *Congrès de Physique Nucléaire* (Paris, 1964), p. 518.
[28] M. RHO: *Congrès de Physique Nucléaire* (Paris, 1964), p. 440.
[29] R. ARVIEU and M. VÉNÉRONI: *Phys. Lett.*, **5**, 142 (1963).
[30] M. RHO: *Nucl. Phys.*, **65**, 497 (1965).
[31] S. YOSHIDA: *Nucl. Phys.*, **38**, 380 (1962).
[32] C. J. VEJE: *Phys. Lett.*, **15**, 145 (1965).
[33] R. J. LOMBARD: private communication.
[34] E. B. CARTER, G. E. MITCHELL and R. H. DAVIS: *Phys. Rev.*, **131**, B 1421 (1964).
[35] I. KELSON and C. A. LEVINSON: *Phys. Rev.*, **134**, B 269 (1964).
[36] K. DIETRICH, H. J. MANG and J. PRADAL: UCRL report 11213 (1964), p. 40.
[37] W. H. BASSICHIS, I. KELSON and C. A. LEVINSON: *Phys. Rev.*, **136**, B 380 (1964).
[38] J. M. EISENBERG, B. M. SPICER and M. E. ROSE: to be published.
[39] I. KELSON: *Phys. Lett.*, **16**, 143 (1965).
[40] W. H. BASSICHIS and G. RIPKA: *Phys. Lett.*, **15**, 320 (1965).
[41] G. E. BROWN and A. M. GREEN: *Nucl. Phys.*, **75**, 401 (1966).
[42] W. H. BASSICHIS, B. GIRAUD and G. RIPKA: private communication.

Effective Interactions in the Shell Model.

J. P. Elliott

University of Sussex - Brighton, Sussex

1. – The inter-nucleon potential.

Before we become immersed in the techniques of pairing forces etc., I thought it would be a good thing to take a look at the two-body data to see what they tell us about the internucleon potential. This, after all, should be the starting point for any theory of nuclear structure.

1·1. *Information from two-body data.* – The two-particle system has four distinct charge-spin states:

$$(1)\qquad \left|\begin{array}{l} {}^{13}\Gamma \to T=0, \quad S=1 \ \text{(triplet-even)}\,, \\ {}^{31}\Gamma \to T=1, \quad S=0 \ \text{(singlet-even)}\,, \\ {}^{11}\Gamma \to T=0, \quad S=0 \ \text{(singlet-odd)}\,, \\ {}^{33}\Gamma \to T=1, \quad S=1 \ \text{(triplet-odd)}\,. \end{array}\right.$$

We shall often use the notation ${}^{2T+1,2S+1}\Gamma$ above but the alternative, in brackets, is more familiar in two-body literature. In that notation, one specifies the spin multiplicity and the parity of the orbital state. This choice of notation is due to the antisymmetry of the wave function which ensures that if the symmetries in two of the three spaces orbit, spin, isospin are chosen, then the symmetry in the third is automatically fixed. In spin-space, the $S=1$ state is, of course, symmetric while the $S=0$ state is antisymmetric and in isospin space an exactly analogous situation occurs.

The potential is assumed to be invariant (scalar) under rotation and inversion of axes. It is then convenient to classify the possible terms in the potential by their rotation properties in spin and orbit separately. These rotation properties are specified by an index k (like the angular momentum l of a wave function) which is the degree of a spherical tensor. It is necessary that both spin and orbit have the same k in order that a scalar product may be formed. Because the spin-space of a single particle has dimension only two it is impossible to construct a two-body spin operator of degree $k>2$. Hence, we are restricted to $k=0$, 1 or 2.

A term with $k=0$ is scalar in both spin and orbit and hence will be simply $V(r)$ if we exclude any momentum dependence. It is usually referred to as a central force and the shape $V(r)$ will in general be different in each charge-spin state (1).

A term with $k=1$ is a vector in both spin and orbit and must have the form

$$V(r)(\boldsymbol{S}\cdot\boldsymbol{L})\,, \tag{2}$$

where $\boldsymbol{S}=\frac{1}{2}(\boldsymbol{\sigma}_1+\boldsymbol{\sigma}_2)$ is the total spin and $\boldsymbol{L}=\frac{1}{2}(\boldsymbol{r}_1-\boldsymbol{r}_2)\wedge(\boldsymbol{p}_1-\boldsymbol{p}_2)$ is the relative angular momentum of the pair. It is called a vector or spin-orbit force, is of first order in the momentum and is nonzero only in the triplet states. The shape $V(r)$ will generally be different in the odd and even states and different also from the central force shape.

A term with $k=2$ is a second-degree tensor in both spin and orbit and, if it is to be momentum-independent, must have the form $3V(r)\boldsymbol{S}^{(2)}\cdot\boldsymbol{R}^{(2)}$ where $S^2_q=(\boldsymbol{\sigma}_1\times\boldsymbol{\sigma}_2)^{(2)}_q$ and $R^{(2)}_q=\{(\boldsymbol{r}_1-\boldsymbol{r}_2)\times(\boldsymbol{r}_1-\boldsymbol{r}_2)\}^{(2)}_q$ are tensor products in Racah's notation. It may also be written as

$$V(r)S_{12}=V(r)\{3r^{-2}(\boldsymbol{\sigma}_1\cdot\boldsymbol{r})(\boldsymbol{\sigma}_2\cdot\boldsymbol{r})-(\boldsymbol{\sigma}_1\cdot\boldsymbol{\sigma}_2)\}\,, \tag{3}$$

where $\boldsymbol{r}=(\boldsymbol{r}_1-\boldsymbol{r}_2)$. This term, which is called a tensor force, is again nonzero only in triplet states and the $V(r)$ is independent of all previous shapes. From a static, one-pion exchange, field-theoretic calculation one deduces a potential, in units of MeV,

$$3.72(\boldsymbol{\tau}_1\cdot\boldsymbol{\tau}_2)\left\{(\boldsymbol{\sigma}_1\cdot\boldsymbol{\sigma}_2)+\left(1+\frac{3}{x}+\frac{3}{x^2}\right)S_{12}\right\}\frac{e^{-x}}{x} \tag{4}$$

where $x=(r/1.42)f$.

It is known however that this O.P.E.P. is reliable only at long range $r>2$ fermi and that multiple pion exchange processes are important at shorter range. In fact the potential (4) is too weak by a factor 4 to explain the low-energy S-state interaction of two nucleons. When more than one pion is exchanged it is possible to generate spin-orbit forces which were not present in the O.P.E.P., (4). Furthermore, a relativistic correction to the O.P.E.P. gives rise to a quadratic spin-orbit [1] term of the form

$$V(r)\left[(\boldsymbol{\sigma}_1\cdot\boldsymbol{\sigma}_2)\,\boldsymbol{L}^2-\tfrac{1}{2}\{(\boldsymbol{\sigma}_1\cdot\boldsymbol{L})(\boldsymbol{\sigma}_2\cdot\boldsymbol{L})+(\boldsymbol{\sigma}_2\cdot\boldsymbol{L})(\boldsymbol{\sigma}_1\cdot\boldsymbol{L})\}\right]=V(r)L_{12}\,. \tag{5}$$

In the absence of any reliable field-theoretic calculations for the exchange of more than one pion the more accurate potentials available are those deduced phenomenologically, from the nucleon-nucleon scattering phase shifts. Typical of these is the Hamada-Johnston [2] potential which contains the O.P.E.P. plus a parameterized mixture of shorter-range potentials of all types, central, tensor, spin-orbit and quadratic spin-orbit. Altogether, 28 parameters were used to fit all available two-body data below 315 MeV. In all such fits, it is found necessary to make the potential strongly repulsive at short distances and, for simplicity, hard cores (*i.e.* $V = +\infty$) have been used. HAMADA and JOHNSTON use a hard core radius 0.485 fermi in all states. The main features of such phenomenological potentials, apart from the core, are i) a tensor force, strongly attractive in the triplet even state and repulsive in the triplet odd state, ii) an attractive spin-orbit force in the triplet odd state, iii) attractive central forces in even states, the singlet being the stronger, iv) weak central forces in odd states.

1·2. *Repulsive cores and the many-body problem.* – We now turn our attention from the two-nucleon potential to the problem of finding approximations to its eigenfunctions in a many-particle system. Here, « many » means greater than four because with fewer nucleons, a direct attempt at solving the Schrödinger equation is just feasible. Practically all attempts begin from the idea of independent-particle motion in some average field and the experimental evidence for shell structure suggests that this may be a good starting point. However, if one introduces a field H_0 and proposes to write $H = H_0 + (H - H_0)$ with $(H - H_0)$ as a perturbation, then the hard core immediately introduces an infinite repulsion in first order. Much work has been done to justify the shell model in spite of the hard core and the simplest approach stems from an idea of MOSKOWSKI and SCOTT [3]. They introduce a separation distance d to divide the potential into short- and long-range parts $V = V_s + V_l$ such that $V_s = 0$ for $r > d$ and $V_l = 0$ for $r < d$.

The value of d is chosen so that V_s gives a zero phase shift for free-particle scattering. In other words, V_s includes just enough of the attractive part of the potential to compensate for the hard core. With a core radius of $c = 0.4$ fermi, the separation distance d is of the order of 1 fermi and is comparatively insensitive to the relative energy of the pair. The effect of V_s is to build in the proper correlations, due to the hard core, in the region $r < 1$ fermi, (with the wave function vanishing in $r < c$ for example). In the outer region, the wave function of the pair is just as if they were noninteracting. This provides a very attractive picture for the foundation of the shell model beginning with a system of particles moving under these short-range, zero phase shift, interactions V_s only. The remaining part V_l of the potential is then sufficiently weak that perturbation theory may be used. The average field in which the particles move will be generated in a self-consistent manner from V_l leaving residual interactions which give rise to the splitting or mixing of configurations. The residual interactions would then be given, essentially, by the free internucleon potential beyond the separation distance d. This is, of course, a greatly simplified picture. For example, the separation distance depends on the relative momentum, so that V_l will be momentum-dependent and the scattering of nucleons in a nucleus is modified, due to the Pauli principle, from the scattering for free particles. The « reference spectrum » method of BETHE, BRANDOW and PETSCHEK [4] attempts to overcome these difficulties, but I do not wish to pursue this problem here. A number of shell-model calculations have recently been made with residual interactions obtained simply by taking V_l. The results seem promising [5].

1·3. *Information from shell-model calculations.* – Let us now ask what may be deduced about the effective internucleon potential from shell-model calculations themselves, for example from the calculations made in the p-shell, d-s shell, near ^{40}Ca, ^{90}Zr and ^{208}Pb. Most work has been done with a pure central two-body force in addition to a single-particle spin-orbit force. The shape of the potential did not seem important and for example in the p-shell it enters the calculations only through a single ratio L/K of integrals. In the exchange properties it is necessary to take attractions in $^{13}\Gamma$ and $^{31}\Gamma$ states with the $^{13}\Gamma$ greater. A repulsion in $^{33}\Gamma$ seems to be needed in order to get the observed isobaric structure for different T, see for example ^{12}C-^{12}B [6] or ^{19}O-^{19}F [7]. The $^{11}\Gamma$ state does not seem to play much part in most shell-model calculations.

In a few isolated cases, the need for a tensor force has been pointed out. The vanishingly small β-decay matrix element in $^{14}\text{C} \to {}^{14}\text{N}$ cannot be explained with central plus $(\boldsymbol{s}\cdot\boldsymbol{l})$ forces whereas a tensor force of the same sign as that in the O.P.E.P will do the trick [8]. There is, of course, always the possibility, that configuration mixing would also suffice [9] here. Recently in ^{210}Bi [10, 11] the need for a tensor force has again been demonstrated but these are isolated cases.

No need has ever been shown for an explicit two-body $(\boldsymbol{S}\cdot\boldsymbol{L})$ force although the $(\boldsymbol{s}\cdot\boldsymbol{l})$ term must be derived from some noncentral force. The most natural origin is simply from the $(\boldsymbol{S}\cdot\boldsymbol{L})$ force between a particle and a closed shell which gives rise to a simple $(\boldsymbol{s}\cdot\boldsymbol{l})$ force on the particle. There is also a theory that in higher order (*i.e.* through configuration mixing) the tensor force can generate the splitting of $j = l \pm \frac{1}{2}$ levels which characterizes the $(\boldsymbol{s}\cdot\boldsymbol{l})$ force.

There is one approach to shell-model calculations, pioneered by TALMI, which avoids the details of the two-body force. It first assumes that the chosen energy levels may be described by a pure j-j configuration or, in a few cases, by a mixture of two configurations. Then, within this set of wave functions, there is a finite number of two-body matrix elements of the kind

$(j_1 j_2 J|H|j_1' j_2' J)$ which are then treated as completely free parameters in a least squares fit to the data. In this approach it was unnecessary to assume any form for H except that it contains only two-body forces.

The fits obtained in this way are excellent, but DE-SHALIT has pointed out that this does not imply that the assumed configurations are pure, but simply that the relations between energies, deduced from this assumption, are true. He has shown for example that the second-order perturbation corrections due to excitations of the kind $(j^2)_0 \to (j'^2)_0$ will preserve the relations. The matrix elements deduced from the fit will then contain perturbation additions.

Recently, some attempts have been made to deduce a best potential from shell-model calculations themselves. COHEN and KURATH [12] have fitted a set of about 50 energy levels in the p-shell to a set of 13 matrix elements in L-S coupling. Assuming oscillator wave functions, the matrix elements are presented in the scheme of relative co-ordinates, such elements as triplet-odd $(1p|V_{LS}|1p)$ and triplet-even $(1d|V_{\text{tensor}}|2s)$ being determined from the fit. Without assuming any radial shape for the potentials these authors argue that the signs of their matrix elements are consistent with the major components of the Hamada-Johnston potential. They have difficulty with the sign of the triplet-odd central force and triplet-even spin-orbit force. They have an interesting difficulty with the sign of the important triplet-even tensor force, finding it impossible to agree with the usual attraction found in the H-J (and all other such potentials) unless the quadratic spin-orbit term is included. CLARK and myself [33] have been trying something similar. But instead of taking a lot of data from a simple shell we have used simple data from a lot of nuclei. In other words, we have chosen energy levels from nuclei of any mass which we believe could be well described by pure configurations. We have taken as our starting point the matrix elements deduced by various authors in fitting energy levels in various pure configurations. We have also included data from simple two-particle and particle-hole systems. We then tried to fit all these matrix elements with a two-body potential of general type. As a first run, we took a common Gaussian shape $\exp[-r^2/a^2]$ with range $a = 1.8$ fermi for all components and then treated the eight strengths as free parameters

$$V_{ij} = \{A + BS_{ij} + C(\boldsymbol{S}\cdot\boldsymbol{L})\}\exp[-r^2/a^2]\,. \tag{6}$$

The parameter A may have different values in the four charge-spin states (1) while B and C are nonzero only in the triplet states.

An indication of the data used has been given in Table I while Table II gives the resulting values for the eight potential strengths together with a statistical estimate for the standard deviation as a measure of the reliability of each value. As might be expected, these deviations are appreciable but not overwhelming. We have not attempted, at this stage, to make a detailed

TABLE I. – *The data.*

Configuration	Mass range	Number of matrix elements	r.m.s. deviation (MeV)	Reference
$(1p_{\frac{1}{2}})^2$	13 ÷ 16	1	0.54	[21]
$(1p_{\frac{1}{2}}2s_{\frac{1}{2}})$ $(1p_{\frac{1}{2}}1d_{\frac{5}{2}})$	13 ÷ 17	4	0.32	[20, 13]
$(1d_{\frac{5}{2}})^2$ $(2s_{\frac{1}{2}})^2$ $(1d_{\frac{5}{2}}2s_{\frac{1}{2}})$	18 ÷ 20	8	0.70	[14]
$(2s_{\frac{1}{2}}1d_{\frac{3}{2}})$	31 ÷ 33	2	0.31	[15]
$(1d_{\frac{3}{2}})^2$	33 ÷ 40	25	0.61	[21]
$(1d_{\frac{3}{2}}1f_{\frac{7}{2}})$	38 ÷ 41	4	0.27	[15, 16]
$(1f_{\frac{7}{2}})^2$	41 ÷ 56	2	1.07	[21]
$(1g_{\frac{9}{2}})^2$ $(2p_{\frac{1}{2}})^2$ $(1g_{\frac{9}{2}}2p_{\frac{1}{2}})$	89 ÷ 93	9	0.42	[17]
$(2d_{\frac{5}{2}})^2$	91 ÷ 96	3	0.22	[18]
$(2g_{\frac{9}{2}}1h_{\frac{9}{2}})$	210	10	0.17	[19]
$(1h_{\frac{9}{2}})^2$	210	3	0.22	[19]

comparison between our effective potential and a realistic potential such as that of Hamada and Johnston. Nevertheless, a qualitative comparison should be meaningful unless one believes that the shell model is so far removed from reality that the effective interaction bears no resemblance with the real one. In the last two rows of Table II we compare our integrated potential strengths, defined as the appropriate strength constant multiplied by $\int_0^\infty \exp[-r^2/a^2]r^2\,dr$ with the one computed by integrating the H-J potentials out from a separation distance $d = 0.7$ fermi. The idea of a separation distance was introduced by MOSKOWSKI and SCOTT [3] as a simple way of compensating for the repulsive core. For the purposes of our qualitative comparison, the exact choice of d is unimportant. The comparison reveals a most encouraging

TABLE II. – *Results* (energies in MeV).

	Central			
	Triplet even A^{13}	Singlet even A^{31}	Singlet odd A^{11}	Triplet odd A^{33}
Strengths of potential I	− 41.5 (±13.5)	− 38.0 (7.8)	97.3 (35.4)	14.8 (9.3)
Integrated strengths of potential I	−107.3	− 98.0	251.3	38.2
Integrated strengths of Hamada-Johnston	− 60.7	−114.7	63.6	−4.4

	Tensor		Spin-orbit	
	Triplet even B^{13}	Triplet odd B^{33}	Triplet even C^{13}	Triplet odd C^{33}
Strengths of of potential I	− 95.2 (38.8)	12.0 (11.6)	5.8 (31.2)	53.3 (17.5)
Integrated strengths of potential I	−245.6	31.2	15.0	137.9
Integrated strengths of Hamada-Johnston	−120.4	30.1	5.1	−42.9

similarity. Both potentials have i) attractive even-state central forces, ii) strong tensor forces which are attractive in the triplet-even state and repulsive in the triplet-odd, the former being the greater. There also seems to be agreement that the singlet-odd central force is repulsive while the triplet-odd central force is small, but the deviations on our parameters are large in these odd states. There seems to be no similarity at all in the spin-orbit forces, which may be due to the fact that HAMADA and JOHNSTON also include a quadratic spin-orbit force in their potential. We should however make it clear that we have only used information from the residual interactions between nucleons in *j-j* coupled orbits. The main rôle of the spin-orbit force is presumably in generating the average field in which the particles move and we have included no information from this field, such as the single-particle energies, in our fit.

We have made a calculation for a shorter-range spin-orbit force, more in keeping with that of Hamada and Johnston, but this does not affect the sign we deduce. It seems to be significant that we have difficulty in obtaining sufficient binding in the $(j^2)_{J=0}$ states. This may well be due to impurity in the configurations but, in our fit, it appears to be responsible for forcing the conflicting sign onto C^{33}.

An indication of how well the data are reproduced by our potential is given in column 4 of Table I where, for each configuration, we give the r.m.s. deviation on the matrix elements in that configuration. The inaccuracy of the fit and the deviations in the potential strengths are due to two main causes: *a*) the assumption of pure configurations and *b*) the simplicity of the potential, particularly its radial shape. Corrections due to *a*) are believed to be appreciable and are being incorporated into the fit by perturbation theory. A second fit is also being made with an improved radial dependence which takes into account some results of field theory and includes a quadratic spin-orbit force.

2. – Definition of pairing forces.

Although we have just argued in Sect. 1·2 that the residual interaction is of long range, meaning of the order of 1 fermi and greater, this is still quite short compared with the nuclear diameter, which varies from about 6 fermi in a light nucleus to about 18 fermi in a heavy nucleus. It makes sense therefore, to investigate the consequences of a δ-function potential.

We shall also define an idealization of the δ-force which is called a « pairing force ». The reason for making this idealization is that there are very simple methods for diagonalizing a « pairing force » in a many-particle system whereas the δ-force is almost as difficult to diagonalize as a completely general two-body interaction.

2·1. *The δ-force and pairing forces in L-S coupling.* – We gain a little more insight into these matters if we work in L-S coupling, in which case the orbital states may be either symmetric (even L) or anti-symmetric (odd L). The over-all antisymmetry is then achieved simply on multiplying by an appropriate charge spin function (1). In this case the matrix element in an $m_1 m_2$ representation is simply

$$(lm_1 lm_2|\delta(r_1-r_2)|l'm_1' l'm_2') = \int d^3r\, Y^*_{lm_1} Y^*_{lm_2} Y_{l'm_1'} Y_{l'm_2'} u^2_{nl} u^2_{n'l'}\,, \tag{7}$$

where the Y_{lm} are spherical harmonics and u_{nl} the radial functions. Using standard techniques to integrate spherical harmonics, this becomes

$$(8)\qquad A\sum_{L'}\frac{(2l+1)(2l'+1)}{4\pi(2L'+1)}(ll00|L'0)(l'l'00|L'0)(llm_1m_2|L'M)(l'l'm_1'm_2'|L'M')\,,$$

where $M=m_1+m_2=m_1'+m_2'$ and, for brevity,

$$A=\int r^2\,\mathrm{d}r\,u_{nl}^2u_{n'l'}^2\,.$$

Going over to an L-M representation we have, immediately,

$$(9)\qquad E_L=(l^2LM|\delta(r_1-r_2)|l'^2LM)=\frac{(2l+1)(2l'+1)A}{4\pi(2L+1)}(ll00|L0)(l'l'00|L0)\,.$$

As one would expect, the expression (9) vanishes for odd L through the Wigner coefficients. For even L, the only large matrix element occurs for $L=0$; in fact for large $l=l'$ the energies E_L satisfy $E_{L+2}/E_L=((L+1)/(L+2))^2$ so that E_L/E_0 has values 1, 1/4, 9/64 etc. for $L=0$, 2, 4 etc.

The reason why the $L=0$ state is singled out in this way is simply that the overlap of the wave functions of the two particles is greatest in that state. The probability amplitude that both particles lie in unit volume at the point $\boldsymbol{r}$ is given by putting $\boldsymbol{r}_1=\boldsymbol{r}_2=\boldsymbol{r}$ in the two-particle wave function. Thus, for $\varphi(l^2LM)$, the amplitude is

$$(10)\qquad \sum_{m_1(m_2)}(llm_1m_2|LM)Y_{lm_1}Y_{lm_2}u_{nl}^2=u_{nl}^2\frac{(ll00|L0)(2l+1)}{\sqrt{4\pi(2L+1)}}Y_{LM}\,.$$

The Y_{LM} is a normalized angular function, so that the amplitude depends on L through $(ll00|L0)/\sqrt{2L+1}$ as in (9) and this factor decreases sharply with L. It is instructive to follow this overlap argument in the m_1m_2 representation of (7). We ask for which m-values the matrix element (7) will be greatest and for chosen nl, $n'l'$ this is simply a question of the overlap of four spherical harmonics. The overlap of two spherical harmonics is greatest when their $|m|$ values are the same. If, in looking for the greatest overlaps in (7) we therefore ask that each spherical harmonic shall have the same value for $|m|$ as one other of the four, we are led to the following two possibilities, bearing in mind that $m_1+m_2=m_1'+m_2'$. Either

i) $m_1=-m_2$ so that $m_1'=-m_2'$ and $M=0$, or

ii) $m_1=m_2=m_1'=m_2'=\frac{1}{2}M$.

If we now consider the matrix, for given M, generated by the set of $\varphi(l^2 m_1 m_2)$ with $m_1 + m_2 = M$ we see that for $M \neq 0$ there will be only one such large matrix element, namely on the diagonal where $m_1 = m_2 = \frac{1}{2}M$. On the other hand, for $M = 0$ there will be large matrix elements *in every position.* We notice that the signs of these matrix elements for $M = 0$ are given, from (7), by

$$(11) \qquad \int d^3r\, Y^*_{lm_1} Y^*_{l-m_1} Y_{l'm'_1} Y_{l'-m'_1} u^2_{nl} u^2_{n'l'} = \int d^3r\, u^2_{nl} u^2_{n'l'} (-1)^{m_1+m'_1} |Y_{lm_1}|^2 |Y_{l'm'_1}|^2 ,$$

i.e. by the factor $(-1)^{m_1+m'_1}$ where we have used the Condon and Shortley phase convention $Y^*_{lm} = (-1)^m Y_{l-m}$.

Keeping to L-S coupling of nucleons in a single orbit nl there are now two completely equivalent ways of defining a pairing force: i) such that in the L-M representation all matrix elements are zero except for $L = 0$, and ii) such that, in the $m_1 m_2$ representation, the matrix elements are all zero except for $M = 0$ in which case they all have equal magnitude but with signs $(-1)^{m_1+m'_1}$. These definitions are natural developments from the overlap argument given above. That they define the same potential follows on inspection of the $M = 0$ matrix defined by ii). It is a $(2l+1)$-dimensional matrix $A_{mm'} = (-)^{m+m'}$. It is immediately seen that the column vector ψ^0 with components $\psi^0_{m'} = (-1)^{m'}$ is an eigenvector with eigenvalue $(2l+1)$, for

$$(12) \qquad \sum_{m'} A_{mm'} \psi^0_{m'} = \sum_{m'} (-1)^{m+m'+m'} = (-1)^m \sum_{m'} = (2l+1)(-)^m = (2l+1)\psi^0_m .$$

Every other eigenvector ψ has eigenvalue zero because from orthogonality $\sum_{m'} \psi_{m'} \psi^0_{m'} = 0$, *i.e.* $\sum_{m'} (-1)^{m'} \psi_{m'} = 0$, but this leads to

$$\sum_{m'} A_{mm'} \psi_{m'} = \sum_{m'} (-1)^{m+m'} \psi_{m'} = 0 .$$

Thus the definition ii) leads, on diagonalization, to the result that only a single state ψ_0 has nonzero energy. This is clearly the S-state, for

$$\psi_0 = \sum_{m'} (-1)^{m'} \varphi(l^2 m' - m') = \sqrt{2l+1}\, \varphi(l^2 L = M = 0) ,$$

using $(llm' - m'|00) = (-1)^{m'}/\sqrt{2l+1}$. Numerically, a definition ii) of equal matrix elements of magnitude $(-1)^{m+m'}$ is equivalent to giving the S-state an energy $(2l+1)$ in definition i).

This L-S coupling pairing force is a good approximation to the δ-force since, not only does the δ-force depress only the S-state by an appreciable amount, but also both forces leave all odd-L states unperturbed.

2·2. *The δ-force and pairing forces in j-j coupling.* – In j-j coupling the situation is a little more complicated. From antisymmetry, the odd J go with $T=0$ and the even J with $T=1$. The matrix elements of the δ-force in a j^2 configuration are now

$$E_J = (j^2JM|\delta(r_1-r_2)|j^2JM) = \tag{13}$$

$$= \frac{(2j+1)^2}{8\pi}\int r^2 \mathrm{d}r u_{nl}^4 \left\{\begin{pmatrix} j & j & J \\ \frac{1}{2} & -\frac{1}{2} & 0\end{pmatrix}^2 + \begin{pmatrix} j & j & J \\ -\frac{1}{2} & -\frac{1}{2} & 1\end{pmatrix}^2\right\}.$$

For large j and even J these energies are, as in the L-S case, given by the expression $E_{J+2}/E_J = \big((J+1)/(J+2)\big)^2$ while for odd J,

$$E_{J(\text{odd})} = \left(\frac{J}{J+1}\right) E_{J-1(\text{even})}\,.$$

This large-j approximation is remarkably accurate even for $j=\frac{7}{2}$. Although there is a great similarity with the L-S coupling case, the states with odd J are now perturbed and in particular the $J=1$ level is depressed appreciably by half the amount for $J=0$. The reason for this becomes clear if you compare the two coupling schemes. The S-state for two particles may have charge-spin states ${}^{13}S_1$ and ${}^{31}S_0$ with $J=1$ and 0 respectively. Thus, since we know that the δ-force depresses the S-state, we should expect the $\varphi(j^2J=1)$ state to be depressed also because it will contain a proportion of the ${}^{13}S_1$ state.

We may define a pairing force in a single j orbit in exact analogy with that in L-S coupling, *viz.* by either of the equivalent definitions:

$$\text{(14)}\quad \begin{cases} \text{i)} & (j^2J|V|j^2J) = -(j+\frac{1}{2})G\delta_{J0} \\ & \text{or} \\ \text{ii)} & (j^2m_1m_2|V|j^2m_1'm_2') = \frac{1}{2}G_{m_1,-m_2}\delta_{m_1',-m_2'}(-1)^{m_1+m_1'}\,. \end{cases}$$

Here, the state $\varphi(j^2m_1m_2)$ is a product wave function, not antisymmetrized. If it were the antisymmetrized state then the factor $\frac{1}{2}$ would disappear from the r.h.s. of (14, ii)).

It should be noticed that the j-j and L-S pairing forces are not physically equivalent, the latter being closer to the δ-force. The former leaves the $J=1$ state unperturbed whereas the latter does not. The L-S pairing force is zero in the odd states but has equal strength in the triplet even and singlet-even states. The j-j pairing force on the other hand is nonzero only in the singlet-even state. The H-J potential is, in fact, weak in the odd states and has its strongest central force component in the singlet-even state. The triplet-even state of the H-J potential is dominated by the tensor force and since this is not a short-range potential, there may be some justification for treating the short-range part of the internucleon potential by the j-j pairing force, which operates only in the singlet even state. If one is dealing with a system of neutrons (or protons) only outside the closed shells then, of course, only the even J can occur and the j-j pairing force becomes close to the δ-force also.

The pairing forces defined so far have been in a pure configuration but it is a simple matter to extend the definition (14, ii)) to a system of nucleons in a set of orbits, by taking V to have zero matrix elements except for

$$((nlj)^2 m - m|V|(n'l'j')^2 m' - m') = -G(-1)^{l+l'+m+m'+j+j'} . \tag{15}$$

The set of orbits to which one might extend the definition of the pairing force in this way would be determined partly by their proximity in single-particle energy and partly by their having large radial overlaps $\int r^2 dr u_{nl}^2 u_{n'l'}^2$ in (11). It is of course a rather crude approximation to assume that G is independent of $nln'l'$.

The diagonalization of (15) in the two-particle system follows exactly the argument of (12) leading to the depression of a single state

$$\psi^0 = \sum_{n,l,j,m} (-1)^{l+m+j}\varphi((nlj)^2 m - m) = \sum_{n,l,j} (-1)^{l+1}\sqrt{2j+1}\,\varphi((nlj)^2 J = 0) ,$$

using $(jjm - m|00) = (-1)^{j-m}/\sqrt{2j+1}$. Thus only a single combination of the $J=0$ states is depressed, all orthogonal combinations, though still having $J=0$, being unperturbed. The amount of the depression of ψ^0 is now $G\sum_{nlj}(2j+1)$ which is again simply G multiplied by the number of single-particle states in the chosen set.

2·3. *The occupation number technique.* – The occupation number representation, or second quantization formalism, is ideal for working with pairing forces and the definition (15) would then be

$$V = -\tfrac{1}{4}G \sum_{nljm} \sum_{n'l'j'm'} a^\dagger_{nlj-m} a^\dagger_{nljm} a_{n'l'j'm'} a_{n'l'j'-m'} (-)^{l+j+m+l'+m'+j'} \tag{16}$$

if the particles under consideration were all neutrons (or protons).

It is convenient to introduce a formal symbol ν to represent the set $nljm$, with the convention that $-\nu$ then represents $nlj-m$, and the abbreviation $P_\nu = (-)^{l+m+j}$ with $-P_\nu = P_{-\nu} = (-)^{l-m+j}$ since m is half-integral. Then

$$V = -\tfrac{1}{4}G \sum_{\nu\nu'} a^\dagger_{-\nu} a^\dagger_\nu a_{\nu'} a_{-\nu'} P_\nu P_{\nu'} , \tag{17}$$

where, as usual, the $a_\nu^\dagger$ and a_ν operators satisfy the anticommutation relations

$$\{a_\nu, a_{\nu'}\} = \{a_\nu^\dagger, a_{\nu'}^\dagger\} = 0 , \qquad \{a_\nu, a_{\nu'}^\dagger\} = \delta_{\nu\nu'} .$$

If we define $A = \sum_{\nu'} P_{\nu'} a_{\nu'} a_{-\nu'}$ so that $A^\dagger = \sum_\nu P_\nu a_{-\nu}^\dagger a_\nu^\dagger$ then simply

$$V = -\tfrac{1}{4} G A^\dagger A \tag{18}$$

where A is an operator which destroys the depressed $J=0$ state, while $A^\dagger$ creates such a state with amplitude $2\sqrt{\sum_{nlj}(2j+1)}$. When considering a system of neutrons and protons we must, for charge independence, allow pairing equally in the three substates $M_T = \pm 1, 0$ of $T=1$. In other words we must allow both n-n, p-p and n-p pairing in the $T=1$ state. We shall reserve the operator a for neutrons and introduce b for protons. Hence if we define

$$A_1 = \sum_\nu P_\nu a_\nu a_{-\nu} , \qquad A_{-1} = \sum_\nu P_\nu b_\nu b_{-\nu} , \qquad A_0 = \sqrt{2} \sum_\nu P_\nu a_\nu b_{-\nu} , \tag{19}$$

the potential

$$V_{jj} = -\tfrac{1}{4} G (A_1^\dagger A_1 + A_{-1}^\dagger A_{-1} + A_0^\dagger A_0)$$

will be charge-independent.

In L-S coupling, there are six charge-spin states $^{31}\Gamma$, $^{13}\Gamma$ for the S-states so that the corresponding potential would be

$$V_{L\text{-}S} = -G \sum_{i=1}^{6} A_i^\dagger A_i , \tag{20}$$

where

$$A_1 = \sum_{lm} (-)^{l-m} a_{m\uparrow} b_{-m\uparrow} , \qquad A_2 = \sum_{lm} (-)^{l-m} a_{m\uparrow} a_{-m\downarrow} ,$$

$$A_3 = \sum_{lm} (-)^{l-m} a_{m\downarrow} b_{-m\downarrow} , \qquad A_4 = \sum_{lm} (-)^{l-m} b_{m\uparrow} b_{-m\downarrow} ,$$

$$A_5 = \sqrt{\tfrac{1}{2}} \sum_{lm} (-)^{l-m} (a_{m\uparrow} b_{-m\downarrow} + a_{m\downarrow} b_{-m\uparrow}) , \qquad A_6 = \sqrt{\tfrac{1}{2}} \sum_{lm} (-)^{l-m} (a_{m\uparrow} b_{-m\downarrow} - a_{m\downarrow} b_{-m\uparrow}) .$$

These six operators destroy a pair in the states

$$T = M_T = 0,\ S = M_S = 1; \qquad T = M_T = 1,\ S = M_S = 0;$$

$$T = M_T = 0,\ S = -M_S = 1; \qquad T = -M_T = 1,\ S = M_S = 0;$$

$$T = M_T = M_S = 0,\ S = 1; \qquad S = M_S = M_T = 0,\ T = 1 ,$$

respectively. The arrows ↑ and ↓ indicate spin up or down. Then (20) represents a purely orbital pairing force, charge- and spin-independent. In the two-particle S-state the potential (20) has matrix element $-(2l+1)G$. On transforming to a j-j scheme we see that it is numerically the same as the potential (16)-(18) with the addition of the $J=1$ state interaction as discussed above. In j-j coupling this $J=0$ energy of $-(2l+1)G$ is divided between the $j=l\pm\frac{1}{2}$ orbits according to (14, i)). Simply, $(j+\frac{1}{2})=(l+1)$ or l in these two cases the sum being $(2l+1)$. This also follows immediately from the transformation

$$\varphi(j^2J=0)=\sum_{L(S)}\sqrt{(2S+1)(2L+1)(2j+1)}\begin{Bmatrix}\frac{1}{2} & l & j\\ \frac{1}{2} & l & j\\ S & L & 0\end{Bmatrix}\varphi(l^2SLJ=0)\,,$$

so that, if only the $L=0$ state contributes to the energy, we have

$$(j^2J=0|V|j^2J=0)=(2j+1)^2\begin{Bmatrix}\frac{1}{2} & l & j\\ \frac{1}{2} & l & j\\ 0 & 0 & 0\end{Bmatrix}^2(l^2S=L=0|V|l^2S=L=0)=$$

$$=\frac{(j+\frac{1}{2})}{(2l+1)}(l^2,\,S=L=0|V|l^2,\,S=L=0)\,.$$

3. – Pairing forces with degenerate single-particle energies, exact solutions.

Having given some justification for the pairing force in a two-particle system we move on to the problem of its eigensolution in a system of many particles. We first restrict ourselves to the situation in which all orbits nlj involved in the definition of the pairing force have the same single-particle energy in the average field. In this case there are exact solutions which we shall describe by elementary algebra. We shall also give, briefly, a group-theoretical description of these solutions, which throws some light on the algebraic technique.

3·1. *Neutrons only, in j-j coupling.* – Consider first the all-neutron potential (18). We notice that

$$[A^\dagger, A]=4(N-j-\tfrac{1}{2})$$

and hence

$$[V, A^\dagger]=GA^\dagger(N-j-\tfrac{1}{2})\,,$$

where $N = \sum_\nu a_\nu^\dagger a_\nu$ is the number operator. Using also the relations $[N, A^\dagger] = 2A^\dagger$ and $[N^2, A^\dagger] = 4A^\dagger(N+1)$, it then follows that

$$[V - \tfrac{1}{4}GN^2 + \tfrac{1}{2}(j + \tfrac{3}{2})GN, A^\dagger] = 0 . \tag{21}$$

If we denote the particle vacuum by $|0)$ and write

$$\tilde{V} = V + \tfrac{1}{4}G\{(2j+3)N - N^2\},$$

then, immediately from (21), the n-particle states $(A^\dagger)^{n/2}|0)$ are eigenstates of both $\tilde{V}$ and V for

$$\tilde{V}(A^\dagger)^{n/2}|0) = (A^\dagger)^{\frac{1}{2}n}\tilde{V}|0) = 0 ,$$

since both $V|0) = 0$ and $N|0) = 0$ and also

$$N(A^\dagger)^{\frac{1}{2}n}|0) = n(A^\dagger)^{\frac{1}{2}n}|0) ,$$

leading to

$$V(A^\dagger)^{\frac{1}{2}n}|0) = -\tfrac{1}{4}G\{(2j+3)n - n^2\}(A^\dagger)^{\frac{1}{2}n}|0) . \tag{22}$$

We have not yet solved the problem, since we have constructed only one eigenstate for each even number of particles and none at all for odd numbers. The complete solution follows very quickly however by a chain process with the introduction of the seniority number v, which is an integer, odd or even with the number of particles concerned. We begin by defining the states $(A^\dagger)^{\frac{1}{2}n}|0)$, already constructed, to have seniority $v=0$ and if we introduce a notation $|nvJ)$ they would be $|n00)$ since the $A^\dagger$ operator is a scalar ($J=0$). We next label all the states of two particles other than $|200)$ by a seniority $v=2$, *viz.* $|22J)$. From the very definition of the pairing force or from the property $A|22J)=0$ which follows from the orthogonality $(200|22J)=0$, we see that the states $|22J)$ are eigenstates of V with zero energy. We then define the seniority-two states for any even number n by

$$|n2J) = (A^\dagger)^{\frac{1}{2}(n-2)}|22J) . \tag{23}$$

They have the same set of J values for all even n and are orthogonal to the $|n00)$. In the same way define all four-particle states not included in (22) or (23) to have seniority 4, denoted by $|44J)$. It is not at all obvious what set of J values they will have or even whether it may be necessary to introduce a further label (as is in general the case except for small j) to distinguish the set. The important point to realize is that in discussing the energies these questions do not arise. As in (23) we define the seniority $v=4$ states of n particles by

$$|n4J) = (A^\dagger)^{\frac{1}{2}(n-4)}|44J) \tag{24}$$

or generally

$$|nvJ) = (A^\dagger)^{\frac{1}{2}(n-v)}|vvJ)\,. \tag{25}$$

The full-seniority state $|vvJ)$ always has the property that $A|vvJ)=0$. This may be shown by arguing that $(v-2\gamma|A|vvJ)=0$ where γ denotes any state of $(v-2)$ particles. But this is obvious for

$$(v-2\gamma|A|vvJ) = \overline{(vvJ|A^\dagger|v-2\gamma)} = 0$$

because $A^\dagger|v-2\gamma)$ must be a state of v particles with seniority $\leqslant v-2$, and by definition, $|vvJ)$ is orthogonal to all such states. Precisely the same procedure applies for odd n and we notice that for $v=1$ only $J=j$ is possible.

It is now clear that the $|nvJ)$ are eigenfunctions of V for

$$\begin{aligned} V|nvJ) &= [\widetilde{V}-\tfrac{1}{4}G\{(2j+3)N-N^2\}](A^\dagger)^{\frac{1}{2}(n-v)}|vvJ) = \\ &= [\widetilde{V}-\tfrac{1}{4}G\{(2j+3)n-n^2\}]\,(A^\dagger)^{\frac{1}{2}(n-v)}|vvJ) = \\ &= (A^\dagger)^{\frac{1}{2}(n-v)}[\widetilde{V}-\tfrac{1}{4}G\{(2j+3)n-n^2\}]\,|vvJ) = \\ &= (A^\dagger)^{\frac{1}{2}(n-v)}[V+\tfrac{1}{4}G\{(2j+3)N-N^2\}-\tfrac{1}{4}G\{(2j+3)n-n^2\}]\,|vvJ) = \\ &= (A^\dagger)^{\frac{1}{2}(n-v)}\tfrac{1}{4}G\{(2j+3)(v-n)-(v^2-n^2)\}\,|vvJ) = \\ &= -\tfrac{1}{4}G(n-v)(2j+3-n-v)|nvJ)\,. \end{aligned} \tag{26}$$

Bearing in mind that $v\leqslant n$, the lowest energy is given by the smallest v for chosen n. Thus, for even n, seniority zero, with $J=0$ only, is lowest, while for odd n, seniority one with $J=j$ only is lowest. For even n, the first excited states occur in a degenerate group, at an excitation $(j+\frac{1}{2})G$ with spins $J=2, 4, \ldots, 2j-1$ exactly as for two particles. These ground-state spins are, of course, just what are generally observed but the excited states for even n show large departures from degeneracy.

3·2. *Charge-independent pairing force in j-j coupling.* – The method of Sect. **3**·1 extends readily to the charge-independent potential (19). The crux of the method is to find an operator like $\widetilde{V}$ in the previous Section, which commutes with $A_1^\dagger$, $A_{-1}^\dagger$ and $A_0^\dagger$. Since these three operators are the components of a vector in isospin space, any isoscalar which commutes with one will commute with all three. We first notice that

$$(27)\qquad [A_q, A_{q'}] = [A_q^\dagger, A_{q'}^\dagger] = [A_1^\dagger, A_{-1}] = [A_{-1}^\dagger, A_1] = 0$$

while $[A_{\pm 1}^\dagger, A_0] = \mp 4T_{\pm 1}$ and $[A_q^\dagger, A_q] = 2N - 4j - 2 + 4qT_0$.

Thus, whereas previously only the operator N occurred on commuting $A^\dagger$ and A, we now find the isospin operators T_q coming in also. After a little manipulation one sees that the definition

$$(28)\qquad \widetilde{V} = V - \tfrac{1}{2}GT^2 - \tfrac{1}{8}GN^2 + \tfrac{1}{2}(j+2)GN$$

ensures that $[\widetilde{V}, A_q^\dagger] = 0$. The definition of seniority is now extended and one new quantum number, the reduced isotopic spin t, is introduced. The seniority-zero states of n (even) particles are the set

$$(A_{+1}^\dagger)^x (A_{-1}^\dagger)^y (A_0^\dagger)^z |0)$$

with x, y, z integers satisfying $x \leqslant j + \frac{1}{2}$, $y \leqslant j + \frac{1}{2}$ and $x + y + z = \frac{1}{2}n$. They will all have $J = 0$ but different values for M_T. By writing down these values, running through the possible choices for x, y, z it follows that for $n \leqslant (2j+1)$ this set contains isospins $T = n/2$, $(n/2) - 2$, $(n/2) - 4$, ... 0 or 1, depending on whether $n/2$ is even or odd. For each T, of course, $M_T = T, T-1, ..., -T$. It is convenient to introduce the notation $P(nTM_T)$ for that homogeneous polynomial of degree $n/2$ in the $A_{\pm 1}^\dagger$, $A_0^\dagger$ which has definite T and M_T (of course, $M_T = x - y$).

As before, the seniority-two states of two particles are those orthogonal to the seniority-zero states, *i.e.* $T = 0$, odd J and $T = 1$, even $J \neq 0$. The seniority-two states of n particles are the set constructed by taking all polynomials of degree $\frac{1}{2}(n-2)$ in the $A_{\pm 1}^\dagger$, $A_0^\dagger$ multiplied into these two-particle states. In addition to the seniority label v we now include also a « reduced isotopic spin t » which is the isospin of the full-seniority state; *e.g.* for $v = 2$, $t = 1$ or 0.

Thus we build up a set

$$(29)\qquad |nv\widetilde{T}tTM_TJ) = \sum_{\widetilde{M}_T(m_t)} (\widetilde{T}t\widetilde{M}_T m_t|TM_T) P(n - v\widetilde{T}\widetilde{M}_T)|vtm_tJ)\,,$$

where the full seniority state $|vv0ttm_tJ)$ has been abbreviated to $|vtm_tJ)$.

In this notation we have also included an « additional isospin $\widetilde{T}$ » quantum number.

The same procedure goes through for odd n. It is interesting to notice that for the cases $v = 0$ and $v = 1$ of most physical interest, both the reduced or additional isospins are superfluous quantum numbers since they are uniquely determined, $t=0$, $\tilde{T}=T$ for $v=0$ and $t=\frac{1}{2}$, $\tilde{T}=T\pm\frac{1}{2}$ for $v=1$, depending on $(n/2)+T$ being even or odd.

As before, the full-seniority states have the property

$$A_q|vtm_tJ)=0\,, \tag{30}$$

which with (28) enables us to show that we have constructed eigenstates of V. For

$$\begin{aligned}
(31)\qquad V|nv\tilde{T}tTM_TJ) &= [\tilde{V}+\tfrac{1}{8}G\{4T^2+N^2-4(j+2)N\}]\cdot \\
&\cdot \sum_{\tilde{M}_T(m_t)} (\tilde{T}t\tilde{M}_Tm_t|TM_T)P(n-v\tilde{T}\tilde{M}_T)|vtm_tJ) = \\
&= \sum_{\tilde{M}_T(m_t)} (\tilde{T}t\tilde{M}_Tm_t|TM_T)P(n-v\tilde{T}\tilde{M}_T)\cdot \\
&\quad\cdot[\tilde{V}+\tfrac{1}{8}G\{4T(T+1)+n^2-4(j+2)n\}]|vtm_tJ) = \\
&= \sum_{\tilde{M}_T(m_t)} (\tilde{T}t\tilde{M}_Tm_t|TM_T)P(n-v\tilde{T}\tilde{M}_T)\cdot \\
&\quad\cdot[V-\tfrac{1}{8}G\{4T^2+N^2-4(j+2)N\}+\tfrac{1}{8}G\{4T(T+1)+n^2-4(j+2)n\}]|vtm_tJ) = \\
&= [\tfrac{1}{2}G\{T(T+1)-t(t+1)\}-\tfrac{1}{8}G(n-v)\,4j+8-n-v)]|nv\tilde{T}tTM_TJ)\,.
\end{aligned}$$

This eigenvalue is similar to (26) with the addition of the $T(T+1)$ term. It, of course, reduces to (26) if we take $T=n/2$, $t=v/2$ which implies having all neutrons. Notice that, while (31) is independent of $\tilde{T}$, it does depend on t.

From (30) one sees that the lowest seniority is lowest in energy. For odd n, $v=1$ is lowest and then all $\frac{1}{2}$-integral values for T are possible being simply ordered by $\frac{1}{2}GT(T+1)$. However, for even n, $v=0$ is lowest and this contains only even T for even values of $n/2$ and odd T for odd values of $n/2$. Thus the ground state has even T if $n/2$ is even and odd T if $n/2$ is odd. For a nucleus specified by N and Z one must examine $\frac{1}{2}(N+Z)$ to decide whether the ground state has $T=\frac{1}{2}(N-Z)$ or $\frac{1}{2}(N-Z)+1$.

3·3. *Charge-spin-independent pairing force in L-S coupling.* – The extension to the L-S coupling pairing force (20) follows the same pattern. Whereas the previous solution rested on the charge independence and the consequent degeneracy of the charge multiplet M_T, with T a good quantum number the present problem rests on the complete charge-spin independence and the degeneracy of the Wigner supermultiplet. We shall not describe supermultiplet theory in detail here but simply point out the parallel with isospin.

In isospin, there are three operators T_q $(q = \pm 1, 0)$ and so far as their behaviour under the T_q is concerned, functions may be classified by a label T (integer or half-integer) such that for each T there is a set of $(2T+1)$ functions labelled by $M_T = T, T-1, \ldots, -T$ which transform among themselves under the operators T_q. The operator T^2 is invariant, $[T^2, T_q] = 0$ and has the same eigenvalue $T(T+1)$ for all M_T of some chosen T. This is of course simply the algebra of angular momentum operators.

In supermultiplet theory, there are fifteen operators T_q, S_q and $Y_{qq'} = \frac{1}{2}\sum_i \sigma_q(i)\tau_{q'}(i)$ and functions may be classified by a label $(PP'P'')$ with the P's integer or half-integer and $P \geqslant P' \geqslant P''$. In each $(PP'P'')$ there is a set of TS multiplets with the usual $M_T M_S$ values. The operator $\mathscr{C} = (T^2 + S^2 + Y^2)$ is invariant under the T_q, S_q, $Y_{qq'}$ and has eigenvalues

$$P(P+4) + P'(P'+2) + (P'')^2 \tag{32}$$

for all states belonging to $(PP'P'')$. Just as we may write

$$T^2 = \tfrac{1}{4}\sum_i\sum_j (\tau_i \tau_j) = \tfrac{1}{4}\sum_i \tau_i^2 + \tfrac{1}{2}\sum_{i<j}(\tau_i \cdot \tau_j) = \tfrac{1}{4}n\langle\tau^2\rangle +$$
$$+ \tfrac{1}{2}\sum_{i<j}(2P_{ij}^{\tau} - 1) = \tfrac{3}{4}n - \tfrac{1}{4}n(n-1) + \sum_{i<j} P_{ij}^{\tau} = -\tfrac{1}{4}n(n-4) - \sum_{i<j} P_{ij}^{sl},$$

where P_{ij}^{τ} is the isospin exchange operator and P_{ij}^{sl} $(= -P_{ij}^{\tau}$ in antisymmetric states) is the spin-orbit exchange operator, so also may we write

$$\mathscr{C} = -\tfrac{1}{4}n(n-16) - 2\sum_{i<j} P_{ij}^{r}$$

where P_{ij}^{r} is the space-exchange operator. The operator $\sum_{i<j} P_{ij}^{r}$ is the Majorana operator.

Returning to the L-S pairing problem, we see that the operators $A_i^{\dagger}$ generate the operators T_q, S_q and $Y_{qq'}$ when commuted with A_j and hence it is possible to construct

$$\tilde{V} = V - \tfrac{1}{2}G\mathscr{C} - \tfrac{1}{8}GN^2 + G(l+2)N \tag{33}$$

which satisfies $[\tilde{V}, A_i^{\dagger}] = 0$.

Hence, defining seniority v and reduced supermultiplet symmetry $(pp'p'')$ we construct eigenfunctions $|nv(pp'p'')(PP'P''); TSJ\rangle$ with eigenvalues

$$\tfrac{1}{2}G\{P(P+4) + P'(P'+2) + (P'')^2 - p(p+4) - p'(p'+2) - (p'')^2\} - \tfrac{1}{8}G(n-v)(8l + 16 - n - v)\,. \tag{34}$$

We have not defined an additional supermultiplet symmetry in analogy with $\tilde{T}$, although this is possible, since it plays no part in the eigenvalues of V and is useful, in classification, only for rather excited states. For seniority zero, $p=p'=p''=0$ and the n-particle eigenfunction is simply a polynomial of degree $n/2$ in the $A_i^\dagger$. From this, it follows that $P'=P''=0$ and then $P=n/2$, $(n/2)-2, \dots 0$ or 1 depending on whether $n/2$ is even or odd.

For seniority one, $p=p'=p''=\frac{1}{2}$ and $P'=P''=\frac{1}{2}$. These states of low seniority will again lie lowest in energy from (34).

3·4. *The use of projection operators.* – We now show how the solution to the charge-independent problem may be deduced by an isospin projection from the solutions for neutrons and protons separately. Let us define the full-seniority states to satisfy (30) as before. For $v=0$ or 1, this is trivial. It then follows, from the argument leading to (31) that

$$P_T(A_{+1}^\dagger)^x (A_{-1}^\dagger)^y (A_0^\dagger)^z |vtm_t J\rangle \tag{35}$$

is another way of writing an eigenstate of V with eigenvalue (31). Here P_T is the isospin projection operator and x, y, z satisfy $x+y+z=\frac{1}{2}(n-v)$, $x-y=M_T-m_t$.

We have essentially replaced the vector coupling in (29) by a projection. There remains freedom in x, y, z, particularly since the energy is independent of M_T. There are two interesting choices. The first, which we call *a*), has $z=0$ in which case (35) is an isospin projection from a solution to the charge-dependent potential

$$V_1 = -\tfrac{1}{4}G(A_1^\dagger A_1 + A_{-1}^\dagger A_{-1})$$

which excludes n-p interaction. Choice *b*) has $x=y=0$ making (35) an isospin projection from a solution to the charge-dependent potential

$$V_0 = -\tfrac{1}{4}G A_0^\dagger A_0\,,$$

which excludes n-n and p-p interaction. The solution of V_1 reduces immediately to the all-neutron problem of Sect. **3·1** since the neutrons and protons are noninteracting. The solution of V_0 is also mathematically the same as the solution of (18), the pairing being now between a neutron with label jm, and a proton with label $j-m$. Thus for V_0 we must interpret ν as an abbreviation for $nljm\, m_t$ with $-\nu$ for $nlj-m-m_t$ and the $\sum_\nu$ running over twice as many states.

We shall find this projection most useful in the nondegenerate problem, in particular using choice *a*). As an indication of the technique, we now rederive the eigenvalue (31) using V_1 and the earlier result (26).

The eigenvalues of V_1 are the sums of two terms like (26) *viz.*

$$E = -\tfrac{1}{4}G\{(n_n - v_n)(2j + 3 - n_n - v_n) + (n_p - v_p)(2j + 3 - n_p - v_p)\}$$

with suffixes indicating neutron and proton parts. The corresponding eigenfunctions are

$$\varphi_a = (A_1^\dagger)^{\frac{1}{2}(n_n - v_n)}(A_{-1}^\dagger)^{\frac{1}{2}(n_p - v_p)}|vtm_tJ)$$

with $v = v_n + v_p$, $m_t = \frac{1}{2}(v_n - v_p)$.

The relation

$$[\tfrac{1}{4}GA_0^\dagger A_0 + \tfrac{1}{2}G(T^2 - T_0^2 - \tfrac{1}{2}N),\ A_{\pm 1}^\dagger] = 0 \tag{36}$$

may be derived using (27) and since by definition $A_q|vtm_tJ) = 0$ we have finally

$$VP_T\varphi_a = P_T V\varphi_a =$$

$$= P_T\left[V_1 - \left\{\tfrac{1}{4}GA_0^\dagger A_0 + \tfrac{1}{2}G\left(T^2 - T_0^2 - \frac{N}{2}\right)\right\} + \frac{1}{2}G\left(T^2 - T_0^2 - \frac{N}{2}\right)\right]\varphi_a =$$

$$= P_T\left[E - \frac{1}{2}G\left\{t(t+1) - m_t^2 - \frac{v}{2}\right\} + \frac{G}{2}\left(T^2 - T_0^2 - \frac{n}{2}\right)\right]\varphi_a =$$

$$= \left[E + \frac{G}{2}\{T(T+1) - t(t+1)\} - \frac{G}{4}\{(n-v) + 2(T_0^2 - m_t^2)\}\right]P_T\varphi_a =$$

$$= \left[\frac{G}{2}\{T(T+1) - t(t+1)\} - \frac{G}{4}\{(n-v)(2j+4) - \tfrac{1}{2}(n^2 - v^2)\}\right]P_T\varphi_a =$$

$$= \left[\frac{G}{2}\{T(T+1) - t(t+1)\} - \frac{G}{8}(n-v)(4j + 8 - n - v)\right]P_T\varphi_a\,,$$

which agrees with (31). Notice how the dependence on $(v_n - v_p)$ and $(n_n - n_p)$ disappears in the final result.

A similar projection method, but now with respect to the supermultiplet label (P, P', P''), may be applied to the L-S coupling problem.

4. – Pairing forces with nondegenerate single-particle levels.

When the pairing force operates between a number of nondegenerate single-particle levels, these exact methods are no longer applicable. Approximate techniques have been developed for the case of neutrons only and we shall briefly describe these. We shall also show how this simple solution may be extended to the charge- and charge-spin-independent problem without further complication.

4·1. *Neutrons only, in j-j coupling.* – A single-particle energy term must now be added to the potential (18) to give a Hamiltonian

$$H = \sum_\nu \varepsilon_\nu a_\nu^\dagger a_\nu - \tfrac{1}{4} G A^\dagger A \,. \tag{37}$$

For reference, we briefly outline the B.C.S., Bogoliubov-Valatin method of quasi-particles to obtain an approximate solution to (37).

Define

$$\begin{cases} \beta_\nu = u_\nu a_\nu + P_\nu v_\nu a_{-\nu}^\dagger \,, \\ \beta_\nu^\dagger = u_\nu a_\nu^\dagger + P_\nu v_\nu a_{-\nu} \,, \end{cases} \tag{38}$$

where $u_\nu = u_{-\nu}$, $v_\nu = v_{-\nu}$ and $u_\nu^2 + v_\nu^2 = 1$. The quasi-particle (q—p) operators β then obey the usual fermion anticommutation relations. Inverting (38) we get

$$\begin{cases} a_\nu = u_\nu \beta_\nu - P_\nu v_\nu \beta_{-\nu}^\dagger \,, \\ a_\nu^\dagger = u_\nu \beta_\nu^\dagger - P_\nu v_\nu \beta_{-\nu} \,. \end{cases} \tag{39}$$

Substituting into (37) and putting the resulting expression into normal form *i.e.* with the $\beta_\nu^\dagger$ operators to the left of all β_ν operators we find

$$H = H_{00} + H_{11} + H_{20} + H_{02} + H_{40} + H_{04} + H_{31} + H_{13} + H_{22} \,,$$

where the two suffixes denote the numbers of $\beta^\dagger$ and β operators respectively. In detail

$$\begin{cases} H_{00} = \sum_\nu \varepsilon_\nu v_\nu^2 - \dfrac{\Delta^2}{G} - \dfrac{1}{2} G \sum_\nu v_\nu^4 \,, \\ H_{11} = \sum_\nu \beta_\nu^\dagger \beta_\nu \{(\varepsilon_\nu - G v_\nu^2)(u_\nu^2 - v_\nu^2) + 2\Delta u_\nu v_\nu\} \,, \\ H_{20} + H_{02} = \sum_\nu P_\nu (\beta_{-\nu}\beta_\nu + \beta_\nu^\dagger \beta_{-\nu}^\dagger) \left\{\dfrac{\Delta}{2}(u_\nu^2 - v_\nu^2) - (\varepsilon_\nu - G v_\nu^2) u_\nu v_\nu\right\} \,, \end{cases} \tag{40}$$

where we define $\Delta = (G/2) \sum_\nu u_\nu v_\nu$.

The standard solution is then obtained by choosing the variational parameters v_ν (and hence also u_ν) to make $H_{20} + H_{02}$ vanish. This is precisely equivalent to choosing the u_ν to minimize H_{00}. If one then neglects the remaining terms, which contain four q-p operators, the Hamiltonian is a pure single q-p one. This neglect however destroys the number-conservation property of the Hamiltonian so that the solutions are mixtures of functions representing different numbers of particles. If we wish to approximate to a chosen number n of particles, we use the Lagrange multiplier technique to restrict the variational freedom by applying the subsidiary condition that the expectation value of the number operator shall be equal to n. We therefore subtract from H a term λN which modifies (40) by replacing ε_ν with $\varepsilon_\nu - \lambda$. Thus the u_ν and v_ν are to be determined from the equations

$$\frac{\Delta}{2}(u_\nu^2 - v_\nu^2) - (\varepsilon_\nu - \lambda - G v_\nu^2) u_\nu v_\nu = 0 \,, \tag{41}$$

$$\sum_\nu v_\nu^2 = n \,, \tag{42}$$

$$u_\nu^2 + v_\nu^2 = 1 \,. \tag{43}$$

The practical problem of solving these equations can be greatly simplified if one writes $\tilde{\varepsilon}_\nu = \varepsilon_\nu - G v_\nu^2$ and treats the $\tilde{\varepsilon}_\nu$ as known. Of course, the ε_ν are known but the v_ν are the very objects being determined. However, it is usually assumed that the $G v_\nu^2$ may be neglected and the $\tilde{\varepsilon}_\nu$ are interpreted as the known single-particle energies. Then from (41) we have

$$(\tilde{\varepsilon}_\nu - \lambda)^2 4 u_\nu^2 v_\nu^2 = \Delta^2 (u_\nu^2 - v_\nu^2)^2 = \Delta^2 (1 - 4 u_\nu^2 v_\nu^2) \,,$$

giving:

$$\left\{ \begin{aligned} 2 u_\nu v_\nu &= \Delta / \sqrt{(\tilde{\varepsilon}_\nu - \lambda)^2 + \Delta^2} \,, \\ u_\nu^2 - v_\nu^2 &= (\tilde{\varepsilon}_\nu - \lambda) / \sqrt{(\tilde{\varepsilon}_\nu - \lambda)^2 + \Delta^2} \,. \end{aligned} \right. \tag{44}$$

Hence

$$\left\{ \begin{aligned} u_\nu^2 &= \tfrac{1}{2}\{1 + (\tilde{\varepsilon}_\nu - \lambda)/\sqrt{(\tilde{\varepsilon}_\nu - \lambda)^2 + \Delta^2}\}, \\ v_\nu^2 &= \tfrac{1}{2}\{1 - (\tilde{\varepsilon}_\nu - \lambda)/\sqrt{(\tilde{\varepsilon}_\nu - \lambda)^2 + \Delta^2}\}, \end{aligned} \right. \tag{45}$$

expressing all the u_ν, v_ν in terms of the *two* unknowns λ and Δ. These two unknowns are then found from (44), after summing both sides, and (42) using (45) *viz.*

$$\frac{4}{G} = \sum_\nu \frac{1}{\sqrt{(\tilde{\varepsilon}_\nu - \lambda)^2 + \Delta^2}} \tag{46}$$

and

$$n = \tfrac{1}{2} \sum_\nu \{1 - (\tilde{\varepsilon}_\nu - \lambda)/\sqrt{(\tilde{\varepsilon}_\nu - \lambda)^2 + \Delta^2}\}. \tag{47}$$

The lowest energy, corresponding to no q-p (the q-p vacuum) is then given simply by the number H_{00}. However, this vacuum, which may be written as

(48) $$\varphi = \prod_{\nu} \beta_\nu |0) \propto \prod_{\substack{\nu \\ (m>0)}} \left(1 + P_\nu \left(\frac{v_\nu}{u_\nu}\right) a^\dagger_{-\nu} a^\dagger_\nu\right) |0)$$

contains only even numbers of particles. The lowest energy for an odd number of particles is described by a single q-p state with energy given by the coefficient of $\beta^\dagger\beta$ in H_{11}. This simplifies using (44) and (45) to give

(49) $$E_\nu = \sqrt{\Delta^2 + (\lambda - \tilde{\varepsilon}_\nu)^2}\,.$$

The ordering of the single q-p levels E_ν will depend on λ and Δ which in turn depend on n so that the ordering changes smoothly with n. Excited states in an even nucleus can only be formed by taking two q-p states. If Δ is large this implies a large excitation energy (gap) in even nuclei but no gap in odd nuclei, since $E_\nu - E_{\nu'}$ is not large with Δ.

4·2. *A small improvement in the B.C.S. method using a number projection.* – The neglect of Gv_ν^2 in $\tilde{\varepsilon}$ may be avoided by the following device which actually simplifies the calculation of energies while making them more accurate. Starting from the expression (40) for H, defined by (37), we write $H = H_1 + H_2$, where

$$H_2 = -\tfrac{1}{2} G \sum_\nu v_\nu^4 - G \sum_\nu \beta_\nu^\dagger \beta_\nu v_\nu^2 (u_\nu^2 - v_\nu^2) + G \sum_\nu P_\nu (\beta_{-\nu}\beta_\nu + \beta_\nu^\dagger \beta_{-\nu}^\dagger) u_\nu v_\nu^3$$

contains the offending terms in GV^2 previously neglected. It may be shown that the operator

(50) $$H_2' = H_2 - \frac{G}{4}\{(N - \langle N \rangle)^2 - 2N + \mathcal{N}\}$$

where $\mathcal{N}$ is the q-p number operator, contains only four q-p type operators and that, in the degenerate case, those of the form $\beta^\dagger\beta^\dagger\beta^\dagger\beta^\dagger$, $\beta^\dagger\beta^\dagger\beta^\dagger\beta$, $\beta^\dagger\beta\beta\beta$ and $\beta\beta\beta\beta$ cancel with $H_{40} + H_{31} + H_{13} + H_{04}$. Now construct the solution of H_1 using the method above except that now $\tilde{\varepsilon}_\nu = \varepsilon_\nu$, the real single-particle energies. Denote the vacuum again by φ and consider the number projection $P_n \varphi$. Then

$$HP_n\varphi = P_n(H_1 + H_2)\varphi \approx P_n\left[E_0 + \frac{G}{4}\{(N - \langle N \rangle)^2 - 2N + \eta\}\right]\varphi$$

if we neglect the four q-p creation terms in H_1 and H_2'. Thus

$$HP_n\varphi \approx \left[E_0 + \frac{G}{4}\{(n-\langle N\rangle)^2 - 2n\}\right] P_n\varphi\,, \tag{51}$$

where $E_0 = \sum_\nu \varepsilon_\nu v_\nu^2 - \Delta^2/G$ is the vacuum energy of H_1, see (40). If, in the usual way, we choose $\langle N\rangle = n$ the new approximation to the ground-state energy is

$$E_0 - \tfrac{1}{2}Gn\,, \tag{52}$$

which is lower than the previous energy by an amount

$$\tfrac{1}{2}Gn - \tfrac{1}{2}G\sum_\nu v_\nu^4 = \tfrac{1}{2}G\sum_\nu (v_\nu^2 - v_\nu^4) = \tfrac{1}{2}G\sum_\nu u_\nu^2 v_\nu^2\,.$$

For the one q-p states of an odd system we would construct $P_n\beta_\nu^\dagger\varphi$ and find

$$HP_n\beta_\nu^\dagger\varphi = \left[E_0 - E_\nu + \frac{G}{4}\{(n-\langle N\rangle)^2 - 2n + 1\}\right] P_n\beta_\nu^\dagger\varphi\,,$$

which with the choice $\langle N\rangle = n$ gives an energy

$$E_0 + E_\nu - \frac{G}{4}(2n-1)\,. \tag{53}$$

It is interesting to see that the exact answer is obtained by this method in the degenerate case and furthermore this is so for any choice of $\langle N\rangle$.

In the degenerate limit putting $\varepsilon_\nu = 0$, (42) leads to $v^2 = n/(2j+1)$, $u^2 = 1 - n/(2j+1)$ so that

$$\Delta^2 = \tfrac{1}{4}G^2 n(2j+1-n)$$

and from (46),

$$\lambda = \tfrac{1}{4}G(2n-2j-1)\,.$$

Hence

$$E_0 - \tfrac{1}{2}Gn = -\tfrac{1}{4}Gn(2j+1-n) - \tfrac{1}{2}Gn = -\tfrac{1}{4}Gn(2j+3-n) \tag{54}$$

which agrees with (26) for $v = 0$.

In an odd system, (53) reduces to

$$-\tfrac{1}{4}Gn(2j+3-n) + \tfrac{1}{4}G(2j+2) = -\tfrac{1}{4}G(n-1)(2j+2-n)\,,$$

which agrees with (26) for $v = 1$.

4·3. *Charge-independent pairing force in j-j coupling* [23]. – The Hamiltonian is

$$H = \sum_\nu \varepsilon_\nu^n a_\nu^\dagger a_\nu + \sum_\nu \varepsilon_\nu^p b_\nu^\dagger b_\nu - \tfrac{1}{4}G(A_1^\dagger A_1 + A_{-1}^\dagger A_{-1} + A_0^\dagger A_0)$$

in the notation of (19). Following the ideas developed in Sect. 3·4 we write

$$H = H_n + H_p - \tfrac{1}{4}GA_0^\dagger A_0 ,$$

where H_n and H_p are the separate neutron and proton pairing Hamiltonians. Solve H_n and H_p separately to form a product vacuum $\varphi = \varphi_n\varphi_p$ with average numbers n_n and n_p of neutrons and protons. We then notice that the combination

$$H' = \tfrac{1}{4}GA_0^\dagger A_0 + \tfrac{1}{2}G(T^2 - T_0^2 - \tfrac{1}{2}N) \tag{55}$$

has the property that, when expressed in terms of the neutron and proton *q-p* operators, it contains no terms with fewer than four *q-p* operators in normal form and that, in the degenerate limit, all terms of the kind H_{40}, H_{31}, H_{13} or H_{04} vanish. It has a property very like that of (50) in fact and this enables us to find a solution for H. We shall use the improved method of Sect. 4·2 for solving the separate neutron and proton problems and then consider

$$HP_T P_{n_n} P_{n_p}\varphi = P_T P_{n_n} P_{n_p}\{H_n + H_p - H' + \tfrac{1}{2}G(T^2 - T_0^2 - \tfrac{1}{2}N)\}\varphi .$$

Neglecting, as usual, the four *q-p* creation terms in $H_n + H_p - H'$ we have

$$\begin{aligned} HP_T P_{n_n} P_{n_p}\varphi &\approx P_T P_{n_n} P_{n_p}\{E_n + E_p + \tfrac{1}{2}G(T^2 - T_0^2 - \tfrac{1}{2}N)\}\varphi = \\ &= [E_n + E_p + \tfrac{1}{2}G\{T(T+1) - \tfrac{1}{4}(n_n - n_p)^2 - \tfrac{1}{2}(n_n + n_p)\}]\, P_T P_{n_n} P_{n_p}\varphi , \end{aligned} \tag{56}$$

where E_n and E_p are the separate neutron and proton energies given by (52).

For the one *q-p* states, describing the low levels of an odd nucleus, we have in a similar way, solutions

$$P_T P_{n_n} P_{n_p}\beta^\dagger\varphi \tag{57}$$

with energies given again by (56). In this case either n_n or n_p is odd so that either E_n or E_p contains a *q-p* energy.

It is again true that (56) gives the exact answer (31) in the degenerate limit. We have already shown that, in this limit, E_n and E_p take the exact values, see (54), so that the energy in (56) becomes

$$-\tfrac{1}{4}Gn_n(2j+3-n_n)-\tfrac{1}{4}Gn_p(2j+3-n_p)+\tfrac{1}{2}G\{T(T+1)-\tfrac{1}{4}(n_n-n_p)^2-\tfrac{1}{2}n\}=$$
$$=\tfrac{1}{2}GT(T+1)-\tfrac{1}{4}G\{n(2j+3)-n_n^2-n_p^2+\tfrac{1}{2}(n_n-n_p)^2+n\}=$$
$$=\tfrac{1}{2}GT(T+1)-\tfrac{1}{4}G\{n(2j+4)-\tfrac{1}{2}(n_n+n_p)^2\}=$$
$$=\tfrac{1}{2}GT(T+1)-\tfrac{1}{8}Gn(4j+8-n)\,,$$

which is (31) with $v=t=0$.

In an odd system, (56) again gives the exact answer in this limit for, if we take n_n to be odd, for definiteness, we get

$$-\frac{G}{4}(n_n-1)(2j+2-n_n)-\frac{G}{4}n_p(2j+3-n_p)+\frac{G}{2}\left\{T(T+1)-\frac{1}{4}(n_n-n_p)^2-\frac{n}{2}\right\}=$$
$$=\frac{G}{2}T(T+1)-\frac{G}{4}\{n(2j+3)-n_n^2-n_p^2+\tfrac{1}{2}(n_n-n_p)^2+n-(2j+2)\}=$$
$$=\frac{G}{2}T(T+1)-\frac{G}{4}\left\{n(2j+4)-\frac{n^2}{2}-(2j+2)\right\},$$

which agrees with (31) when $v=1$ and $t=\tfrac{1}{2}$.

In the degenerate limit, the energy is independent of $M_T=\tfrac{1}{2}(n_n-n_p)$, as it should be for a charge-independent force. Generally, because of the approximations, this is not so and a choice must be made. We choose $M_T=T$ since this tends to eliminate all $T'<T$ from the vacuum. The usual minimization procedure then builds up the component of the vacuum with the chosen T. We used the word « tends » because the usual number uncertainty applies to both n_n and n_p and hence to M_T.

With this choice, the energy (56) for chosen T and n simplifies to

$$(58)\qquad E_n+E_p+\tfrac{1}{2}G\{T(T+1)-T^2-\tfrac{1}{2}n\}=E_n+E_p-\tfrac{1}{2}G(\tfrac{1}{2}n-T)\,,$$

where E_n, E_p are determined for $n_n=\tfrac{1}{2}n+T$, $n_p=\tfrac{1}{2}n-T$.

The symmetries for even n discussed in Sect. 3·2, namely that seniority zero includes only such T values for which $(n/2)-T$ is even, persist also in this nondegenerate problem. This may be seen if we construct that part of the vacuum with a definite number of particles. The choice of n_n and n_p given above automatically incorporates this symmetry for if $(n/2)-T$ is even then both n_p, n_n are even while if $(n/2)-T$ is odd then both n_p, n_n are odd. Thus in the former case both E_n, E_p take their lowest (vacuum) values while in the latter they must both contain a q-p excitation. Thus, T-values for which $(n/2)-T$ is odd will enter only at a $2q$-p excitation. These remarks apply only for even n because when n is odd then, necessarily either n_n or n_p is odd and the other is even.

Suppose then that we are given a nucleus specified by N and Z so that $n = N + z$ and $M_T = \frac{1}{2}(N - Z)$ which implies $T \geqslant \frac{1}{2}(N - Z)$. To find the energy for the smallest $T = \frac{1}{2}(N - Z)$, the choice above implies taking $n_n = N$ and $n_p = Z$. To find the energy for $T = \frac{1}{2}(N - Z) + 1$ we must put $n_n = N + 1$, $n_p = Z - 1$ etc. For an odd nucleus, this invariably leads to a lowest energy for the smallest T-value and hence for the ground-state energy one should simply take $n_n = N$ or $n_p = Z$, which seems natural. For an even-even nucleus this is also the case with $T = \frac{1}{2}(N - Z)$ for the ground state being constructed from the separate neutron and proton vacua. For an odd-odd nucleus however this smallest value implies odd n_n and n_p and so can only be constructed from $2q$-p excitations. It will then be generally true that the next $T = \frac{1}{2}(N - Z) + 1$ for which one takes $n_n = N + 1$, $n_p = Z - 1$ will lie lowest since these are both even and so give vacuum energies.

4·4. *Comparison with exact results for a simple system.* – Some exact calculations have been made by HECHT [24] for the charge-independent pairing problem in a simple system. He has taken four equally spaced, doubly degenerate levels, *i.e.* $j = \frac{1}{2}$, with ε denoting the energy between adjacent levels. We compare his result with ours in Fig. 1 and 2 for $n = 6$ and 8 res-

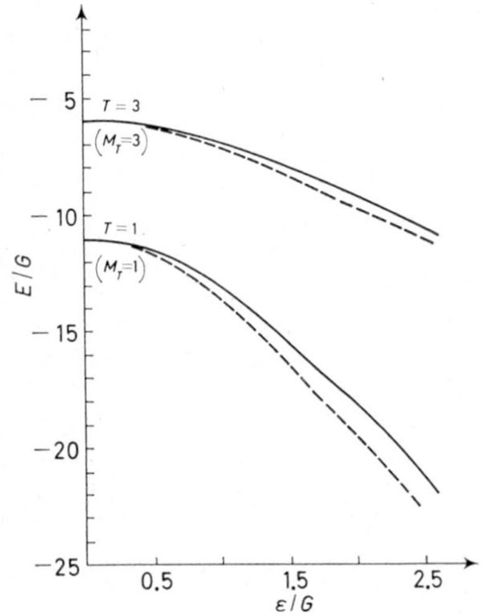

Fig. 1. – $n = 6$; ——— exact (HECHT), ——— B.C.S. (ELLIOTT and LEA).

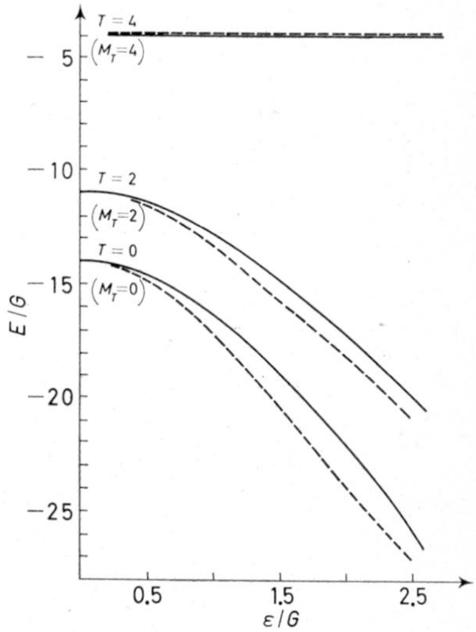

Fig. 2. – $n = 8$; ——— exact, ——— B.C.S.

pectively, as a function of the single-particle splitting ε/G, in units of the pairing strength G. The errors at large ε, *i.e.* small G, are present in the usual B.C.S. treatment. The B.C.S. solution is already on the asymptote at

$\varepsilon/G=2$ whereas the exact solution approaches it more slowly. We show only the lowest $J=0$ levels with $(T-n/2)$ even, the other T values would require two q-p excitations which would involve an energy of about $4G$ at $\varepsilon/G=1$.

The behaviour of these curves as functions of ε/G is uninteresting and so, for odd nuclei, we give the results only at $\varepsilon/G=1$. Exact results are available only for $n=5$ and Table III compares them with our B.C.S. solutions for the single q-p states.

TABLE III.

	$T=\frac{1}{2}$		$T=\frac{3}{2}$		$T=\frac{5}{2}$	
	B.C.S.	Exact	B.C.S.	Exact	B.C.S.	Exact
Level 4	-9.3	-9.6	-6.5	-6.3	-5.2	-5.3
Level 3	-10.0	-10.5	-7.5	-7.4	-5.5	-6.0
Level 2	-10.4	-11.3	-8.5	-8.6	-5.1	-5.2
Level 1	-10.1	-10.3	-9.5	-9.6	-4.4	-4.3

Because all four levels have $j=\frac{1}{2}$ we have distinguished them by numbers, level 1 being that with lowest single-particle energy etc. The $T=\frac{5}{2}$ result is just that for all neutrons, of course, but one sees that the errors are not greater for the lower T-values where the new method has been used. It is interesting to notice how the $T=\frac{3}{2}$ results in this treatment have exactly the single-particle energy spacing. This is simply because, taking $M_T=T=\frac{3}{2}$ for $n=5$ implies $N=4$, $Z=1$ so that the odd system has just one particle. The exact results agree very closely with this answer. It is clear that this result generalizes to any system with $T=(n/2-1)$.

4'5. *Application to spherical nuclei.* – Extensive work has been carried out by KISSLINGER and SØRENSEN both to semi-closed shell nuclei and to others [25, 26]. They use a pairing force between neutrons and between protons but have no n-p pairing force. They include also a charge-independent quadrupole force.

We have not fully investigated the effect on their conclusions caused by making the pairing force properly charge-independent but at first sight there would not seem to be any great change. The vacuum energy is lowered by an amount $(G/2)n_p$. The wave function is now a T-projection but we can ask what errors whould be introduced by omitting the projections. After all, one normally omits the number projection at a cost of $(G/2)\sum_\nu U_\nu^2 V_\nu^2$ in the vacuum energy. If one were to omit the projection and simply take the vacuum in fact used by KISSLINGER and SØRENSEN one would lose an amount $(G/2)\sum_\nu U_\nu^2(n)V_\nu^2(p)$ in the vacuum energy which is of the same order of magnitude as the errors due to number uncertainty. Whether the omission of the T-projection leads to greater errors in other calculated quantities remains to be seen.

4·6. *Charge-spin-independent pairing force in L-S coupling.* – The Hamiltonian is

$$H = \sum_{\nu,s} \varepsilon_l^n a_{\nu s}^\dagger a_{\nu s} + \sum_{\nu,s} \varepsilon_l^p b_{\nu s}^\dagger b_{\nu s} - G \sum_{i=1}^{6} A_i^\dagger A_i \tag{59}$$

in the notation of (20) and where ν represents lm and s denotes the spin $\uparrow$ or $\downarrow$. We are again able to write

$$H = H_n + H_p - G(A_1^\dagger A_1 + A_3^\dagger A_3 + A_5^\dagger A_5 + A_6^\dagger A_6)$$

where H_n contains only neutron pairing etc. Now

$$H_n = \sum_{lms} \varepsilon_l^n a_{lms}^\dagger a_{lms} - G A_2^\dagger A_2 = \sum_\mu \varepsilon_\mu a_\mu^\dagger a_\mu - \tfrac{1}{4} G D^\dagger D\,, \tag{60}$$

where

$$D = 2A_2 = 2\sum_{lm} (-)^{l-m} a_{lm\uparrow} a_{l-m\downarrow} = \sum_{lm} (-)^{l-m} (a_{lm\uparrow} a_{l-m\downarrow} - a_{l-m\downarrow} a_{lm\uparrow}) = \sum_\mu P_\mu a_\mu a_{-\mu}$$

with $P_\mu = (-)^{l-m+\frac{1}{2}-m s}$ and μ is an abbreviation for lms with $-\mu$ for $l-m-s$. Thus (61) is of just the all-neutron form (37) with $2(2l+1)$ states μ in place of $(2J+1)$.

It may be shown that the operator

$$H' = G(A_1^\dagger A_1 + A_3^\dagger A_3 + A_5^\dagger A_5 + A_6^\dagger A_6) + \tfrac{1}{2} G(\mathscr{C} - 2s_n^2 - 2s_p^2 - T_0^2 - 2N) \tag{61}$$

has the property of (55) with respect to the q-p operators for $H_n + H_p$. If we then project out a supermultiplet symmetry ($P00$) from the vacuum, bearing in mind that from symmetry arguments only this type may occur in the vacuum we have, as in (56) an energy

$$E_n + E_p + \tfrac{1}{2} G\{P(P+4) - \tfrac{1}{4}(n_n - n_p)^2 - 2n\}\,. \tag{62}$$

Here we have used the result that the spin S of the neutron or proton vacua is zero since the operators $A_2^\dagger A_4^\dagger$ are spin scalars.

In the degenerate limit, $E_n = -\frac{1}{4} G n_n (4l + 4 - n_n)$ etc. from (54) so that (62) becomes

$$\tfrac{1}{2} GP(P+4) - \tfrac{1}{4} G n_n (4l+4-n_n) - \tfrac{1}{4} G n_p (4l + 4 - n_p) - \tfrac{1}{8} G (n_n - n_p)^2 - nG =$$
$$= \tfrac{1}{2} GP(P+4) - Gn(l+1) + \tfrac{1}{8} G n^2 - nG =$$
$$= \tfrac{1}{2} GP(P+4) - \tfrac{1}{8} Gn(8l + 16 - n)\,,$$

which is the exact result (34) with $v = p = p' = p'' = P' = P'' = 0$. The exact result also emerges for the one q-p solution in an odd system.

5. – Quadrupole forces.

The pairing forces do not produce any of the collective effects observed. The only correlation between one pair and another is due to the Pauli principle. This is not surprising since, by definition, a collective effect involves many particles moving together and this implies the presence of long-range forces capable of feeling more than just one other particle. For the short-range limit we have investigated the δ-force and its idealization, the pairing force. What can we construct for long range?

5·1. *Long-range forces.* – Consider a Gaussian shape $\exp[-r^2/a^2]$ and let the range $a \to \infty$. This is a somewhat delicate process because $r = |\boldsymbol{r}_i - \boldsymbol{r}_j|$ also tends to infinity but suppose we are working within a shell-model configuration so that the wave functions all drop off for large r. Then expanding simply we have

$$\exp[-r^2/a^2] = 1 - \frac{r^2}{a^2} + \frac{r^4}{2a^4} + \dots \tag{63}$$

so that

$$\sum_{i<j} \exp[-r_{ij}^2/a^2] = \frac{1}{2}\, n(n-1) - \frac{1}{a^2}\sum_{i<j} r_{ij}^2 + \frac{1}{a^4}\sum_{i<j} r_{ij}^4 \,.$$

The first term will not split the levels, being a constant, and since

$$2\sum_{i<j} r_{ij}^2 = \Big(\sum_i \boldsymbol{r}_i\Big)^2 - \sum_i r_i^2 \,,$$

the second term gives the single-particle oscillator field $\sum r_i^2$ apart from the centre-of-mass term $\big(\sum_i \boldsymbol{r}_i\big)^2$ which causes no splitting.

This confirms our idea that the long-range part of the force generates the field. It is the third term of (63) which first introduces splitting in a configuration. Now

$$r_{ij}^4 = (r_i^2 + r_j^2 - 2r_i r_j \cos\theta_{ij})^2 = r_i^4 + r_j^4 + 2r_i^2 r_j^2 - r_i r_j (r_i^2 + r_j^2)\cos\theta_{ij} +$$

$$+ 4r_i^2 r_j^2 \cos^2\theta_{ij} = r_i^4 + r_j^4 + \frac{10}{3} r_i^2 r_j^2 + \frac{8}{3} r_i^2 r_j^2 P_2(\cos\theta_{ij}) - 4r_i r_j (r_i^2 + r_j^2) P_1(\cos\theta_{ij}).$$

The last term has odd parity in each particle so that, although it plays an important part in the particle-hole calculations involving core excitations, it contributes nothing to a configuration of orbits with the same parity. The first two terms modify the oscillator field and the third has the same value in all two-particle states. The only term remaining

$$V_a = \sum_{i<j} r_i^2 r_j^2 P_2(\cos\theta_{ij}) \tag{64}$$

is referred to as the quadrupole force and we shall see that this does in fact give rise to collective effects.

The justification for this force may be argued also by a numerical approximation to the potential within a certain distance r. For very small r the Gaussian is constant, for larger r its decrease can be approximated by the form $\alpha-\beta r^2$ and for larger r still, the r^2 decrease must be halted, giving the form $\alpha-\beta r^2+\gamma r^4$ with α, β, γ all positive. This leads of course to the correct sign for r^2 if we take an attractive Gaussian and the quadrupole force is then an attractive one. In a more general way, expand any

$$V(r_{ij}) = \sum_k v_k(r_i, r_j)\, P_k(\cos\theta_{ij}) \tag{65}$$

and consider particles with the same values for r_i and r_j a situation which is very roughly approximated in a shell-model configuration. The range of the force is then identified with the angular distance θ_{ij} between the particles. The functions P_k have the property that they drop off sharply in a distance proportional to $1/k$.

Thus the shorter the range of the force the greater will be the importance of the terms with large k in (65), and vice-versa for a long-range force one would expect the low k to dominate. We have seen this effect in the long-range expansion of the Gaussian where only $k=1$ and $k=2$ occurred in the first three terms. For a δ-force it may be shown that

$$v_k(r_i, r_j) = \frac{2k+1}{4\pi r_i r_j}\,\delta(r_i - r_j)\,,$$

which increases with k, so that the high multipoles are important.

5·2. *Quadrupole forces in an oscillator potential.* – Here I want to discuss briefly an idealization of the quadrupole force which, within an oscillator configuration, lends itself to an exact solution. Consider a spherically symmetric oscillator potential and let $a_x^\dagger = (x - il^2 p_x)/l\sqrt{2}$ be the Cartesian creation operator for oscillator quanta in the x co-ordinate. The oscillator potential separates $H_0 = H_x + H_y + H_z$ in Cartesian co-ordinates. The operators $a^\dagger$, a now satisfy the Bose commutation relations. The nine operators $A_{ij} = \frac{1}{2}(a_i^\dagger a_j + a_j a_i^\dagger)$ with $i, j = x, y$ or z break up into a scalar H_0, a vector L_q (the angular momentum) and a second-rank tensor

$$Q_q^{(2)} = \sqrt{\frac{4\pi}{5}}\,\{r^2 Y_q^2(\theta_r\,\varphi_r) + p^2 Y_q^2(\theta_p, \varphi_p)\}/b^2\,,$$

where θ_r, φ_r are the polar angles of $\boldsymbol{r}$ and θ_p, φ_p those of $\boldsymbol{p}$. The operators A_{ij}

satisfy $[A_{ij}, A_{kl}] = \delta_{jk} A_{il} - \delta_{il} A_{kj}$ and they all commute with the oscillator Hamiltonian $H_0 = \sum_i A_{ii}$. Now within a chosen oscillator configuration, (*i.e.* fixed single-particle energy) the operator $Q_q \equiv \sqrt{(16\pi/5)}\, r^2 Y_q^2/b^2$ because of the symmetry between r and p in the oscillator. If we then take a system of particles and use the same notation Q_q for the symmetric operator $Q_q = \sum_i Q_q(i)$ where i runs over the particles, we have for the scalar product

$$\sum_{i<j} \big(Q(i)\cdot Q(j)\big) \equiv \sum_{i<j} \frac{16\pi}{5} r_i^2 r_j^2 \big(Y_q^2(i)\cdot Y_q^2(j)\big) = 4 \sum_{i<j} r_i^2 r_j^2 P_2(\cos\theta_{ij}) ,$$

so that

$$(Q\cdot Q) \equiv 8 \sum_{i<j} r_i^2 r_j^2 P_2(\cos\theta_{ij}) + \sum_i \big(Q(i)\cdot Q(i)\big) .$$

If we define

$$\tilde{Q}_q = \sum_i \sqrt{\frac{16\pi}{5}}\, r_i^2 Y_q^2(i)$$

as the quadrupole moment operator then

$$(\tilde{Q}\cdot\tilde{Q}) \equiv (Q\cdot Q) - \sum_i \big(Q(i)\cdot Q(i)\big) + 4 \sum_i r_i^4$$

so that, apart from single-particle terms, the operator $(Q\cdot Q)$ is equivalent to the quadrupole force or the operator $(\tilde{Q}\cdot\tilde{Q})$. We shall consider $(Q\cdot Q)$ writing

$$(66) \qquad (Q\cdot Q) = Q_0^2 + Q_2 Q_{-2} + Q_{-2} Q_2 - Q_1 Q_{-1} - Q_{-1} Q_1 =$$
$$= Q_0^2 + \tfrac{1}{2}(Q_2 + Q_{-2})^2 - \tfrac{1}{2}(Q_2 - Q_{-2})^2 - \tfrac{1}{2}(Q_1 + Q_{-1})^2 + \tfrac{1}{2}(Q_1 - Q_{-1})^2 .$$

Now $Q_0 = 2A_{zz} - A_{xx} - A_{yy}$ and $\sqrt{\tfrac{1}{6}}(Q_2 + Q_{-2}) = (A_{xx} - A_{yy})$ so that Q_0 and $Q_2 + Q_{-2}$ may be simultaneously diagonalized and if H_0 is also diagonalized this implies diagonalization of the three one-dimensional oscillators in x, y and z.

Take a number k of particles in an oscillator shell, each with single-particle energy $(n + \tfrac{3}{2})$. Construct the function φ with greatest eigenvalue of Q_0 and if, as is usually the case, there are several such, choose the one with the greatest value for $Q_2 + Q_{-2}$. Then φ has the properties

$$(67) \qquad A_{zx}\varphi = A_{zy}\varphi = A_{xy}\varphi = 0$$

since otherwise these operations would produce a state with greater values for Q_0 or $Q_2 + Q_{-2}$, violating our definition of φ. Transforming into the spherical tensors L_q, Q_q this means that

$$(Q_1 - Q_{-1} - \sqrt{6}\, iL_y)\varphi = (Q_1 + Q_{-1} - \sqrt{6}\, L_x)\varphi = (Q_2 - Q_{-2} - \sqrt{6}\, L_z)\varphi = 0 ,$$

so that

$$(68)\qquad \{(Q_2-Q_{-2})^2+(Q_1+Q_{-1})^2-(Q_1-Q_{-1})^2\}\varphi = \\ =\{6(L_x^2+L_y^2+L_z^2)-24(A_{zz}-A_{yy})\}\varphi\,.$$

Let us denote the eigenvalue of $A_{xx}-A_{yy}$ by μ and that of $2A_{zz}-A_{xx}-A_{yy}$ by $2\lambda+\mu$, so that $\mu=N_x-N_y$, $\lambda=N_z-N_x$ in terms of the total Cartesian oscillator numbers.

A set of eigenfunctions of (66) are now given by the angular momentum projections $P_L\varphi$. We show this by putting $(Q\cdot Q)=H_1+H_2$ where $H_1=Q_0^2+ +\frac{1}{2}(Q_2+Q_{-2})^2$ and H_2 the remaining terms of (66). Now by definition

$$H_1\varphi=\{(2\lambda+\mu)^2+3\mu^2\}\varphi=4(\lambda^2+\mu^2+\lambda\mu)\varphi$$

and from (68)

$$\{H_2+3L^2-12(\lambda+\mu)\}\varphi=0\,,$$

so that

$$(69)\qquad HP_L\varphi=P_LH\varphi=P_L(H_1+H_2)\varphi= \\ =P_L\{4(\lambda^2+\mu^2+\lambda\mu)+12(\lambda+\mu)-3L^2\}\varphi= \\ =\left[4\{(\lambda^2+\mu^2+\lambda\mu)+3(\lambda+\mu)\}-3L(L+1)\right]P_L\varphi\,.$$

Thus, with an attractive quadrupole force, there is a rotational spectrum in L. The L-values are just those which are contained in the « intrinsic function » φ.

To construct more eigenfunctions, for the same configuration, we choose φ' to satisfy the same conditions as φ and also be orthogonal to all $P_L\varphi$. Then again $P_L\varphi'$ are eigenfunctions of H and, since the value of $(2\lambda'+\mu')$ must be less than $(2\lambda+\mu)$, this « band » of levels will lie higher in energy than those first constructed.

The explicit projection operator is

$$(70)\qquad P_{KLM}=(2L+1)\int \mathrm{d}\Omega D^L_{MK}(\Omega)\mathscr{R}(\Omega)\,,$$

where Ω represents three Euler angles and $\mathscr{R}(\Omega)$ is the rotation operator. Hence the $\psi(KLM)=P_{KLM}\varphi$ are all eigenfunctions of H with energies given by (69). The label M is the usual projection of L on the fixed z-axis. The label $K=0$ if φ is axially symmetric but otherwise takes a range of values. It may be shown that $\psi(-KLM)$ and $\psi(KLM)$ are identical except for phase but, for different $|K|$, the $\psi(KLM)$ are generally linearly independent, though not orthogonal. Thus for nonaxially symmetric φ, a set of K-bands arises. Although two states with the same L and different K are degenerate under the pure quadrupole force a more realistic potential preserves the $L(L+1)$ pattern for each K and introduces a K-splitting roughly proportional to K^2. The details of these matters are published elsewhere [27].

As examples, consider ^{20}Ne and ^{24}Mg in the *d-s* shell. The single-particle function with greatest value for Q_0 is $a_z^\dagger a_z^\dagger|0)$. Thus for ^{20}Ne the Pauli principle permits four nucleons in this state and φ has the rotational properties of the axially symmetric function z^8 which contains $L=0, 2, 4, 6, 8$. In this case $\lambda=8$, $\mu=0$ and $K=0$. For ^{24}Mg, the last four nucleons fill the next most favoured level, *viz.* $a_z^\dagger a_x^\dagger|0)$ and φ then has the rotational properties of the function $z^8 y^4$. This intrinsic function is not axially symmetric and contains values $|K|=0, 2, 4$.

Experimentally, both ^{20}Ne and ^{24}Mg possess rotational spectra and ^{24}Mg has a low-lying $K=2$ band whereas ^{20}Ne does not, in agreement with the discussions above.

5'3. *Some applications to light nuclei.* – These eigenfunctions of $(Q\cdot Q)$ which are generally referred to as U_3 functions (see Sect. **6'**5) are in pure L-S coupling so that, without the inclusion of at least a $\sum(s\cdot l)$ force, they will be of use only in even-even nuclei and even in such cases only semi-quantitative agreement can be expected. Rotational spectra are predicted for every even-even nucleus except a closed shell and, even there, the even-parity excited states are predicted to fall into rotational bands. There is in fact just such a situation emerging in the observed spectrum for ^{16}O with $K=0$ and 2 bands beginning at 6 and 7 MeV excitation.

Recent work in ^{16}O suggests that these rather strongly deformed excited configurations mix appreciably with the lowest configuration to produce much larger values for quadrupole matrix elements (*e.g.* in $E2$ transitions) than one would expect, even allowing for an effective charge chosen to fit the quadrupole properties of the very low states. It is interesting to notice that, in the nuclei with $A=15$, the ground state is oblate while the admixing state is prolate, leading to a cancellation in quadrupole effects whereas in the $A=17$ nuclei, for example, both states are prolate and enhancements occur. Experimental work in Oxford suggests this to be the case.

Inclusion of the $\sum(s\cdot l)$ force is not easily accomplished. In the limit that such a force is large compared with the $L(L+1)$ splitting but small compared with the energy difference between states of different K and $\lambda\mu$, calculations may simply be done [28] and electromagnetic effects in the first half of the *d-s* shell are in fair agreement with this picture. At the end of the shell the approximation appears to break down, which is to be expected since the *j-j* scheme appears to be applicable in this region.

An intermediate coupling sketch of the entire *d-s* shell has also been carried out [29] making use of the U_3 functions in the L-S limit. Then, with the help of calculated end points, slopes and asymptotes an interpolation is performed. The pattern of levels is reproduced for almost every nucleus using essentially only one intermediate coupling parameter.

The structure of the U_3 functions, as projections from intrinsic functions, suggests however that the spin-orbit force should be incorporated in the average field which also acquires a nonspherical shape from the quadrupole force. This is of course the basis of the Nilsson model. In the future it seems that a self-consistent nonspherical field approach with a final angular momentum projection is the most promising although there are difficulties here too (see the lectures of Villars).

In this discussion we have omitted the pairing force altogether. When collective features predominate its role seems to be a minor one, modifying the calculations in a quantitative manner rather than introducing new effects. The proper place for it is surely in modifying the intrinsic wave function and, in such a formulation, the omission of the $T=0$ component of the force may perhaps be excused with the argument that a substantial part of the $T=0$ interaction, being of longer range, has been included in the field.

Away from the collective regions, the quadrupole force has been used, especially by KISSLINGER and SØRENSEN [25, 26], as a correction to be applied after a *q-p* treatment of the pairing forces. Qualitatively the inclusion of such a term is essential to pull down a collective combination of the two *q-p* states with an appreciable quadrupole matrix element.

6. – A group-theoretical interpretation of the degenerate problems.

6·1. *Neutrons only, in j-j coupling.* – The commutation relations

$$(71)\qquad [A^\dagger, A] = 4(N - j - \tfrac{1}{2}), \qquad [N, A^\dagger] = 2A^\dagger, \qquad [N, A] = -2A,$$

given just before (21) are reminiscent of those satisfied by the angular momentum operators $J_\pm = J_x \pm iJ_y$ and J_0 *viz.*

$$[J_+, J_-] = 2J_0, \qquad [J_0, J_\pm] = \pm J_\pm .$$

In fact, the operators $\frac{1}{2}A^\dagger$, $\frac{1}{2}A$, $\frac{1}{2}(N - j - \frac{1}{2})$ commute precisely like the operators J_+, J_- and J_0 respectively. Let us now digress for a moment.

It is well known that the angular-momentum operators are also the infinitesimal operators from which rotations in three dimensions may be generated, the group R_3. It is also well known that functions may be classified according to their rotation properties by the familiar labels JM, where the symbol J

is an integer or half-integer and the number $J(J+1)$ is the eigenvalue of the operator J^2. Here M is the eigenvalue of J_0. Any rotation on a function $\varphi(JM)$ produces a linear combination of the M but the J-value remains the same. The transformation is, in fact, given by the rotation matrices $D^J_{MM'}(\Omega)$. Thus the $(2J+1)$-dimensional vector space of the $\varphi(JM)$ with fixed J is invariant under rotations and furthermore is irreducible, that is it may not be further reduced in size and remains invariant. Within this space, the label J is in fact the greatest eigenvalue M of J_0. A more general continuous group is defined by a set of infinitesimal operators X_α which commute among themselves (as do the $J_\pm$, J_0) defining structure constants $C^\gamma_{\alpha\beta}$

$$[X_\alpha, X_\beta] = \sum_\gamma C^\gamma_{\alpha\beta} X_\gamma \,. \tag{72}$$

The transformation properties of functions under this group may be classified by two sets of labels $J_1, J_2 \ldots$ and $M_1, M_2 \ldots$, where the set J_i distinguish one irreducible invariant space from another while the M_i distinguish independent functions within one of these spaces. Such an irreducible invariant space is said to provide an irreducible representation (i, r) of the group and the set J_i labels this irreducible representation. The number of labels in each set is the same and is referred to as the « rank » of the group. Unfortunately this labelling is not complete except for small groups like R_3 so that in general there will be several linearly independent functions with the same M_i in any but the simple $i{\cdot}r$'s.

Given the X_α one determines the rank and these labels by finding the largest subset of the X_α which are mutually commuting and may therefore be simultaneously diagonalized. The rank is just the number of such operators and the M_i their eigenvalues. The J_i are then the greatest values for M_i within the particular invariant subspace, *i.e.* M_1 is the greatest value of J_1, and within the set of functions with this M_1, the greatest value of J_2 is denoted by M_2 etc.

It is always possible to construct a set of Casimir operators $\mathscr{C}_i$, polynomials in the X_α, for which $[\mathscr{C}_i, X_\alpha] = 0$ for all α. All functions of an irreducible representation are then eigenfunctions of each $\mathscr{C}_i$ with eigenvalue dependent only on the J_i and not on the M_i. Of most interest is the quadratic Casimir operator

$$\mathscr{C}_1 = \sum_{\alpha\beta} g^{\alpha\beta} X_\alpha X_\beta \,, \tag{73}$$

where $g^{\alpha\beta}$ is the inverse of $g_{\alpha\beta} = \sum_{\gamma\delta} C^\delta_{\alpha\gamma} C^\gamma_{\beta\delta}$. The group R_3 has rank one, with J_0 diagonalized and $\mathscr{C}_1 = J^2$.

Returning to the relations (71) it follows that the operators $A^\dagger$, A, $N - j - \frac{1}{2}$

describe, abstractly, a group R_3 and therefore that the behaviour of functions under these operators will exactly follow that of angular momentum functions. Let us write:

$$J_+ = \tfrac{1}{2}A^\dagger, \qquad J_- = \tfrac{1}{2}A, \qquad J_0 = \tfrac{1}{2}(N - j - \tfrac{1}{2}),$$

remembering of course that although these operators behave algebraically like the usual angular-momentum operators they have nothing at all to do, physically, with rotation in physical space or with angular momentum. The pairing potential then becomes

$$V = -GJ_+J_- = -G(J^2 - J_0^2 + J_0).$$

The problem of diagonalizing V is then simply one of the simultaneous diagonalization of J^2 and J_0. But we are familiar with this problem and the eigenfunctions are $\varphi(JM)$ with energies

$$-G\{J(J+1) - M^2 + M\}. \tag{74}$$

To interpret this result in terms of particle number and seniority we notice that, in the chosen shell, $0 \leqslant n \leqslant (2j+1)$ so that $-\frac{1}{2}(j+\frac{1}{2}) \leqslant M \leqslant \frac{1}{2}(j+\frac{1}{2})$ and therefore $J \leqslant \frac{1}{2}(j+\frac{1}{2})$.

First consider the maximum $J = \frac{1}{2}(j+\frac{1}{2})$ with substates $M = -\frac{1}{2}(j+\frac{1}{2})$, $-\frac{1}{2}(j-\frac{3}{2})$, ... $\frac{1}{2}(j+2)$ corresponding to $n = 0, 2, ..., (2_j + 1)$.

This set of solutions with $J = \frac{1}{2}(j+\frac{1}{2})$ therefore occurs for all even n. Next consider $J = \frac{1}{2}(j-\frac{1}{2})$ with $n = 1, 3, ..., 2j$, giving a solution for all odd n. Continuing the process $J = \frac{1}{2}(j-\frac{3}{2})$ contains $n = 2, 4, ..., (2j-1)$ giving a solution only for $2 \leqslant n \leqslant (2j-1)$, and so on.

The link with seniority should now be clear, we must define $v = (j+\frac{1}{2}) - 2J$ so that, as in Sect. **3**·1, v is the smallest number of particles for which states of that J occur. The energy (74) is then

$$-\frac{G}{4}\left\{\left(j+\frac{1}{2}-v\right)\left(j+\frac{5}{2}-v\right)-\left(j+\frac{1}{2}-n\right)^2+2\left(n-j-\frac{1}{2}\right)\right\} =$$
$$= -\frac{G}{4}(n-v)(2j+3-n-v),$$

which agrees with (26).

The procedure above was in fact quite general. The $A^\dagger$, A operators with the inclusion of the number operators were seen to commute among themselves. By this we do not mean that the commutator of any pair is zero but that it gives a linear combination of operators in the set. They could therefore be associated with the infinitesimal operators of a continuous group. The Hamiltonian could, moreover, be written in terms of the Casimir operators of the group and the subset of the infinitesimal operators which could be simultaneously diagonalized (in the previous case simply J_0).

6·2. *Charge-independent pairing force in j-j coupling.* – In the charge independent problem, (27) shows that the six $A_q^\dagger, A_q$ operators together with the three isospin operators T_q and N commute among themselves. By inspection, these commutation relations may be identified with those of the group R_5 (or the isomorphic group Sp_4). The group R_5 has rank two and the operators $\tilde{N} = \frac{1}{2}(N-2j-1)$ and T_0 may be simultaneously diagonalized.

It is not possible in this case to express V in terms of the Casimir operator, $\tilde{N}$ and T_0. However, the operators T_q form a group (isospin group) on their own, so that they form a subgroup of R_5. Since the Casimir operator T^2 of this group commutes with $\tilde{N}$ and T_0, the functions may be labelled, additionally, by T. We thus have at our disposal one more simultaneously diagonalizable operator T^2 and this does the trick, for we may now write

$$V = -\frac{G}{2}\{\mathscr{C}(R_5) - T^2 - \tilde{N}^2 + 3\tilde{N}\}\,. \tag{75}$$

Rewriting this as

$$V - \frac{1}{2}G(T^2 + \tilde{N}^2 - 3\tilde{N}) = -\frac{G}{2}\mathscr{C}(R_5)\,,$$

which gives

$$V - \frac{1}{2}GT^2 - \frac{1}{8}GN^2 + \frac{1}{2}(j+2)GN = -\frac{G}{2}\mathscr{C}(R_5) + \frac{1}{8}G(2j+1)(2j+2)\,,$$

we see the left-hand side of this expression is simply $\tilde{V}$ of (28). This is to be expected since we constructed $\tilde{V}$ to have the property of commuting with the $A_q^\dagger$ and thus with the A_q but since it is an isoscalar it also commutes with the T_q and hence with all operators of R_5. But this is exactly the property of the Casimir operator $\mathscr{C}(R_5)$ and the remaining term on the right-hand side, above, is a constant.

Thus, if we diagonalize $\mathscr{C}$, T^2 and $\tilde{N}$ simultaneously we have eigenfunctions of V. But the eigenvalues of $\mathscr{C}$ are well known [30] to be $J_1(J_1+3) + J_2(J_2+1)$ in the irreducible representation (J_1, J_2) of R_5 where J_1 is the greatest value of $\tilde{N}$ and J_2 the greatest value of T_0 for that J_1. Thus V has eigenvalues

$$-\frac{G}{2}\left\{J_1(J_1+3) + J_2(J_2+1) - T(T+1) - \frac{1}{4}(N-2j-1)^2 + \frac{3}{2}(N-2j-1)\right\}$$

and if we define seniority $v = 2j + 1 - 2J_1$, and reduced isospin $t = J_2$ this becomes

$$-\frac{G}{8}\{(2j+1-v)(2j+7-v) + 4t(t+1) - 4T(T+1) - (2j+1-n)^2 + \\ + 6(n-2j+1)\} = \frac{1}{2}G\left\{T(T+1) - t(t+1) - \frac{1}{8}G(n-v)(4j+8-n-v)\right\},$$

which agrees with (31). Thus v and t, as introduced earlier label an irreducible representation of R_5 and again have the physical significance that, for states of that irreducible representation, v is the smallest number of particles which occurs and for that number, t is the greatest value of T_0 and thus of T which occurs. It may be shown that there is in fact only this one value of T for $n = v$.

6·3. *Charge-spin-independent pairing force in L-S coupling.* – Moving on to the L-S coupling case, the twelve operators $A_i^\dagger$, A_i need the inclusion of T_q, S_q, $Y_{qq'}$, and N, a total of 28 operators, before they are closed under commutation. The commutation relations may be identified with R_8 while the T_q, S_q, $Y_{qq'}$, describe the supermultiplet group R_6 (or SU_4) which is a subgroup of R_8. The operators T_q and S_q describe the product group $R_3 \times R_3$ which is again a further subgroup of R_6. Representations of R_8 are labelled by $(J_1\, J_2\, J_3\, J_4)$ there being four commuting operators N, T_0, S_0 and Y_{00}, being essentially the number operators in each of the four charge-spin states of a single particle.

The Casimir operator of R_8 has eigenvalues

$$J_1(J_1+6) + J_2(J_2+4) + J_3(J_3+2) + J_4^2$$

and we may write

$$v = -\frac{G}{2}\{\mathscr{C}(R_8) - \mathscr{C}(R_6) - N' + 6N'\} \tag{76}$$

where $N' = \frac{1}{2}(N - 4l - 2)$ and the Casimir operator $\mathscr{C}(R_6)$, already introduced in Sect. **3**·3, has eigenvalues given by (32). Hence the eigenvalues of V are

$$-\frac{G}{2}\{J_1(J_1+6) + J_2(J_2+4) + J_3(J_3+2) + J_4^2 - P(P+4) - \\ - P'(P'+2) - P''^2 - \tfrac{1}{4}(n-4l-2)^2 + 3(n-4l-2)\}.$$

Defining $v = 4l + 2 - 2J_1$, $p = J_2$, $p' = J_3$, $p'' = J_4$, this becomes

$$\tfrac{1}{2}G\{P(P+4) + P'(P'+2) + P''^2 - p(p+4) - p'(p'+2) - p''^2\} - \\ - \tfrac{1}{8}G\{(4l+2-v)(4l+14-v) - (4l+2-n)^2 + 12(n-4l-2)\} = \\ = \tfrac{1}{2}G\{P(P+4) + P'(P'+2) + P''^2 - p(p+4) - p'(p'+2) - p''^2\} - \\ - \tfrac{1}{8}G(n-v)(8l+16+n+v),$$

which agrees with (34). The interpretation of v, p, p', p'' now follows that of v, t in the previous problem.

6·4. *Use of group theory to solve the nondegenerate problem.* – The nondegenerate all-neutron pairing Hamiltonian is

$$V = \sum_\nu \varepsilon_\nu a_\nu^\dagger a_\nu - \tfrac{1}{4} G A^\dagger A = \sum_j \varepsilon_j \sum_m a_{jm}^\dagger a_{jm} - G \sum_{jj'} A^\dagger(j) A(j') . \tag{77}$$

In the notation of Sect. **6**·1 we define, for each j, the operators

$$J_+(j) = \tfrac{1}{2} A^\dagger(j) , \quad J_-(j) = \tfrac{1}{2} A(j) \quad \text{and} \quad J_0(j) = \tfrac{1}{2}\Big(\sum_m a_{jm}^\dagger a_{jm} - j - \tfrac{1}{2}\Big)$$

so that (77) becomes

$$V = 2 \sum_j \varepsilon_j J_0(j) + \sum_j \varepsilon_j (j + \tfrac{1}{2}) - G(J^2 - J_0^2 + J_0) , \tag{78}$$

where

$$J_q = \sum_j J_q(j) .$$

Now the $J_q(j)$ are just like the angular momentum operators for a « particle » j, with J_q as the total angular momentum. One must remember however that this a purely mathematical analogy, with j actually labelling the nondegenerate orbits. There are hence as many « particles » as nondegenerate orbits. The problem of diagonalizing (78) thus reduces to a problem of evaluating matrix elements of an unsymmetric single-body angular-momentum operator in a complete set of coupled wave functions of « particles » with different single-particle spins. Using Wigner coefficients a matrix may be set up and diagonalized numerically. This has been done [31] and compared with the q-p solutions, confirming their validity.

For the charge-independent pairing problem a similar technique has been developed by HECHT [24] using the Wigner coefficients for R_5. It is however not easy to compute these coefficients and applications have been made only to systems with small j.

HECHT does however produce perturbation formulae from both the strong and weak pairing limits which are relatively simple. It was Hecht's results which we quoted in Sect. **4**·4 for comparison with our q-p solutions.

In L-S coupling one could compute R_8 Wigner coefficients and obtain an exact solution in the same way. There is however little merit in getting exact solutions to idealized potentials if it involves heavy computation. The only justification is as a thorough test of the approximate solution and in this respect the work of HECHT (and of KERMAN, LAWSON and MCFARLANE) has been extremely helpful.

6·5. *Use of group theory for the quadrupole force.* – A very similar procedure works here also. The operators A_{ij} are closed under commutation, they all commute with H_0 and there are nine of them. Their commutation relations are just those of the group U_3 and the removal of H_0 leaves them closed under commutation in which case they provide the eight operators of the group SU_3. This fact is the reason for the well-known degeneracies (*e.g.* *sd*, *pf*, *sdg*) in the oscillator field.

The many-body operators $\sum_p A_{ij}(p)$, summed over particles p, have the same commutation relations and the operator $\frac{1}{4}\{Q\cdot Q + 3(L\cdot L)\}$ is the Casimir operator of the group with eigenvalues $(\lambda^2+\mu^2+\lambda\mu)+3(\lambda+\mu)$. Hence, if we choose an n-particle wave function belonging to an irreducible representation $(\lambda\mu)$ of SU_3 such that it also diagonalizes the Casimir operator L^2 of the subgroup R_3 then we shall have constructed an eigenfunction of $(Q\cdot Q)$ with eigenvalue

$$4\{(\lambda^2+\mu^2+\lambda\mu)+3(\lambda+\mu)\}-3L(L+1)$$

as was also given in (69).

7. – Concluding remarks.

In these lectures we first discussed briefly some attempts to deduce an effective shell-model inter-nucleon potential from shell-model calculations themselves. We compared this with the most up-to-date potential deduced from two-body data and found broad similarities.

For the rest of the time we studied the simple solutions for certain idealized potentials which typify short- and long-range components of the force. There are two ways of regarding such potentials. In the first [25], one tries to describe nuclear properties through the idealized potentials alone. In the second [27, 32], one uses the set of eigenfunctions of some idealized potential as a physically significant complete set of functions in which to diagonalize some more realistic potential. The first type of calculation has the advantage of simplicity but the disadvantage that it cannot be expected to give more than qualitative agreement and it also contains free parameters which reduce the significance of any agreement with experimental data. The second type, although free from parameters once the effective potential is chosen, is necessarily more complicated. If the residual interaction (by which we mean that part of the interaction not represented by the idealized potential) is large, there may be so much mixing of the eigenfunctions of the idealized potential that it is simpler to use some arbitrary complete set chosen for its simplicity.

REFERENCES

[1] N. Hoshizaki and S. Machida: *Progr. Theor. Phys.*, **24**, 1325 (1960).
[2] T. Hamada and I. D. Johnston: *Nucl. Phys.*, **34**, 382 (1962).
[3] S. A. Moskowski and B. L. Scott: *Ann. Phys.*, **11**, 65 (1960).
[4] H. A. Bethe, B. H. Brandow and A. G. Petschek: *Phys. Rev.*, **129**, 225 (1963).
[5] A. Kallio and K. Kolltveit: *Nucl. Phys.*, **53**, 87 (1964).
[6] D. Kurath: *Phys. Rev.*, **101**, 216 (1956).
[7] J. P. Elliott and B. H. Flowers: *Proc. Roy. Soc.*, A **229**, 536 (1955).
[8] J. P. Elliott: *Phil. Mag.*, **1**, 503 (1955).
[9] E. Baranger and S. Meshkov: *Phys. Rev. Lett.*, **1**, 30 (1958).
[10] P. A. Mello and J. Flores: *Nucl. Phys.*, **47**, 177 (1963).
[11] Y. E. Kim and J. O. Rasmussen: *Nucl. Phys.*, **47**, 184 (1963).
[12] S. Cohen and D. Kurath: *Nucl. Phys.*, **73**, 1 (1965).
[13] I. Talmi and I. Unna: *Phys. Rev.*, **112**, 452 (1958).
[14] S. Cohen, R. D. Lawson, M. H. Macfarlane and M. Soga: *Phys. Lett.*, **9**, 180 (1964).
[15] S. Goldstein and I. Talmi: *Phys. Rev.*, **105**, 995 (1957).
[16] S. Goldstein and I. Talmi: *Phys. Rev.*, **102**, 589 (1956).
[17] S. Cohen, R. D. Lawson, M. H. MacFarlane and M. Soga: *Phys. Lett.*, **10**, 195 (1964).
[18] I. Talmi: *Phys. Rev.*, **126**, 2116 (1962).
[19] K. Helmers: *Nucl. Phys.*, **23**, 594 (1961).
[20] I. Talmi and I. Unna: *Ann. Rev. Nucl. Sci.*, **10**, 353 (1960).
[21] I. Talmi and R. Thieberger: *Phys. Rev.*, **103**, 718 (1956).
[22] A. K. Kerman: *Ann. of Phys.*, **12**, 300 (1961).
[23] J. P. Elliott and D. A. Lea: *Phys. Lett.*, **19**, 291 (1965).
[24] K. T. Hecht: *Nucl. Phys.*, **63**, 177 (1965); *Phys. Rev.*, **139**, 794 (1965).
[25] L. S. Kisslinger and R. A. Sørensen: *Mat. Fys. Medd. Dan. Vid. Selsk.*, **32**, No. 9 (1960).
[26] L. S. Kisslinger and R. A. Sørensen: *Rev. Mod. Phys.*, **35**, 853 (1963).
[27] J. P. Elliott and M. Harvey: *Proc. Roy. Soc.*, A **272**, 557 (1963).
[28] J. P. Elliott and C. E. Wilsdon: to be published.
[29] M. C. Bouten, J. P. Elliott and J. A. Pullen: to be published.
[30] G. Racah: *Rend. Lincei*, **8**, 108 (1950).
[31] A. K. Kerman, R. D. Lawson and M. H. MacFarlane: *Phys. Rev.*, **124**, 162 (1961).
[32] R. Arvieu, E. Baranger, M. Vénéroni, M. Baranger and V. Gillet: *Phys. Lett.*, **4**, 119 (1963).
[33] J. M. Clark and J. P. Elliott: *Phys. Lett.*, **19**, 294 (1965).

The Method of Interacting Quasi-Particles in the Theory of the Nucleus.

A. MIGDAL

Kurchatov Institute - Moscow

1. – Introduction.

Nearly all problems theoretical physics has recently dealt with involve the many-body problem, *i.e.*, taking into account the interaction of many particles. In particular, this problem arises in quantum electrodynamics where we can apply perturbation theory, *i.e.*, take advantage of the fact that the quantum-electron interaction is weak. This means that the electron charge in dimensionless units is small. The electron-quantum interaction is given by a small dimensionless quantity

$$\alpha = e^2/\hbar c = 1/137 .$$

In other problems involving elementary particles the interaction cannot be treated as weak. The nucleon charge determining the interaction of a neutron or proton with π-mesons in dimensionless units is not small any longer

$$g^2/\hbar c = 12 \div 14 ,$$

and perturbation theory cannot be used.

This is why calculation methods without perturbation theory requiring no assumption that the particle interaction is weak had to be worked out. Thus, a dispersion theory of elementary particles was developed which does not assume the smallness of the interaction but takes advantage of the fact that some quantities vary little in the energy region of interest and can be replaced by constants.

Exact relations between observed quantities are obtained after the constants determined from experiment (particle masses and charges determining their interaction) have been introduced.

The methods developed in the theory of elementary particles have been applied very intensely several years ago for investigating systems of strongly interacting particles such as metal electrons, liquid helium or the atomic nuclei (*).

If a system of strongly interacting particles has, as in the case of the nucleus, 100 or 200 particles, the problem is obviously hopeless as far as the precise solution is concerned. As a matter of fact even the three-body problem cannot be solved in general form.

If the system is not gaslike, with rare particle interactions, we cannot develop an approximate method taking into account only pair particle collisions. However, actually particle-particle distances in the nucleus are of the same order as the range of forces and several particles interact simultaneously. Besides, the energy of this interaction is comparable with kinetic energy so that the interaction cannot be treated as weak.

Other approximate methods must be developed. The idea of these methods is the same as in the dispersion theory of elementary particles, where the particle masses and the constants describing their interaction are introduced empirically. We must introduce the constants characterizing the motion of neutrons and protons in the nucleus as well as the constants describing the interaction of nucleons inside the nucleus. This interaction strongly differs from the interaction of two nucleons in vacuum.

After these constants have been introduced, all nuclear processes involving low energies (less than 40 MeV) can be precisely calculated. In other words, having found the constants from a few processes we can explain quantitatively all the other experimental data of low-energy nuclear physics.

To describe single-particle excitations in a finite system we have to introduce, besides the effective mass of quasi-particles, the parameters of the effective potential well in which quasi-particles are moving. For systems with a short range of forces r_0 these parameters include the depth and width of the well and the width of the layer ($\sim r_0$) over which the density goes from its value inside the system to zero.

For all these quantities we can obtain expressions in the form of perturbation series, which enable us to make rough estimates even when the interaction is not small. To first order in particle interaction, the effective potential reduces to the Hartree-Fock self-consistent field.

In the nucleus where the interaction is not small the potential well parameters must be found by comparing the theoretical and experimental single-particle energies.

The shell model is used extensively and effectively in nuclear physics. In this model the nucleon energy levels are determined as in a gas of noninteracting

(*) L. D. Landau: *Sov. Phys. JETP*, **35**, 97 (1958); A. A. Abrikosov, L. P. Gorkov and I. E. Dzaloshinsky: *Methods of Quantum Field Theory in Statistical Physics* (Moscow, 1962).

Fermi particles placed into the potential well. Theoretically satisfactory results obtained by the shell model could not be explained since there is a strong interaction between particles, and the cases when several particles interact simultaneously cannot be neglected.

The Green function method allows a conclusive explanation of this fact. In spite of the strong interaction there are single-particle excitations. The role of multiple collisions reduces simply to this: the single-particle states in the well (quasi-particle states) must be calculated with a somewhat changed mass (comparison with experiment shows that this change does not exceed 10 to 20%).

The response of the system to an external field (intensities and frequencies of transitions; magnetic and quadrupole moments, etc.) reduces to the problem of behavior in the external field of the gas of interacting quasi-particles placed into the potential well. In this case it is sufficient to take into account the pair collisions of quasi-particles. Multiple particle collisions are taken into account by the theory precisely but lead to a change of the interaction between quasi-particles and an effective « charge » for the interaction between the quasi-particles and external field. The effective « charge » can in most cases be found from general considerations (charge, energy, momentum conservation etc.).

All these results can be explained in very simple and visualizable terms. Suppose that a not very strong field acts on the system so that the change of each particle's energy in this field is small compared with its kinetic energy. Then the state of the system corresponds to the appearance of several quasi-particles and several quasi-holes. The number of the newly arisen quasi-particles accounts for a small fraction of the total number of particles in the system. If the average distance between particles is of the order of the range of forces, the average distance between quasi-particles will be much larger than the interaction range and hence the quasi-particles make up a gas, *i.e.*, we can neglect the cases when three or more quasi-particles collide simultaneously. The interaction between quasi-particles is of the same order as that between particles but differs from it essentially. We shall see that in some cases attraction may be replaced by repulsion due to the effect of other nucleons which, unlike quasi-particles, occur in large numbers and next to the two quasi-particles under considerations.

Thus, though the interaction between quasi-particles is not small, the problem becomes immensely simplified since it is sufficient to consider the collision of only two quasi-particles each time.

As for the « charge » of a quasi-particle with respect to an external field, this « charge » describes the interaction with the field of that set of particles which makes up the quasi-particle and leads to the difference between the effective mass and the mass of the particle. Suppose an electrical field which acts only on protons is applied to the nucleus. Since the charge is conserved in the interaction of a proton with other particles of the nucleus, the entire set making the proton quasi-particle has the same charge as the proton. In this case the charge of the quasi-particle equals that of the particle. In the case of other external fields (for a magnetic field, for example) the quasi-particle field interaction differs from the corresponding quantity for the particle.

A moving neutron in vacuum interacts with a magnetic field only due to its internal magnetic moment. Since the moving neutral quasi-particle sets into motion the neighbouring protons, as a result of which there originates an electrical current, the interaction with the magnetic field changes. In the neutron quasi-particles there arises orbital magnetism, *i.e.*, magnetism connected with their orbital movement. If there is no interaccion, it is only the protons which have orbital magnetism.

Thus for many processes the nucleus can be regarded as a gas of two types of interacting quasi-particles placed into the potential well. The effective interaction between neutron and proton quasi-particles is characterized by several constants which are identical for all nuclei and all types of transitions within the same accuracy that the average density of nuclear matter is constant.

2. – Graph technique and Green functions.

2'1. *Representation of processes by graphs.* – The Feynman graph method is extensively used to obtain relations in the elementary-particle theory. The same method is used in other many-body problems and in particular in that approach to the theory of the nucleus which will be discussed later on.

We begin by drawing graphs representing various physical processes which may occur with particles. The movement of a quantum of light is represented by a dashed line

The movement of particles is represented by a line

The picture

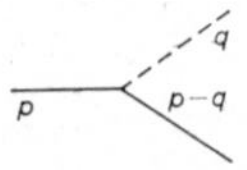

denotes that a charged particle, say, an electron, has emitted a quantum of light. The solid line is broken to show that the electron acquires another momentum following the emission of a quantum.

Suppose we have two noninteracting particles

If they interact we draw this picture

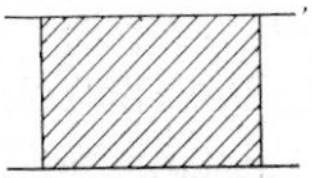

If their interaction is effected via quanta of light (and hence is a Coulomb interaction) the lines are connected by a dashed line

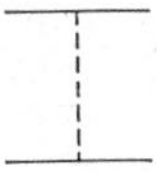

If these are two nucleons and the interaction is effected by the transfer of a π-meson we draw a wavy line between the lines of the particles

This graph shows that two nucleons have interacted once. If they had interacted twice the picture would be

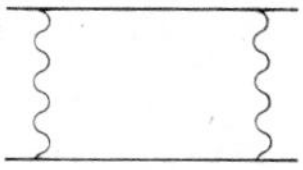

The graph

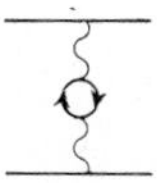

represents a more complex process: a nucleon has emitted a π-meson which has then disintegrated into a nucleon and an antinucleon. These two particles are converted again into a π-meson which is absorbed by the second nucleon.

More complex particle processes can be represented similarly.

To impart a quantitative (and not only purely illustrative) meaning to these graphs, let us take each graph to mean the amplitude of the transition from one state at the initial time to another state at the final time. The square of the transition amplitude gives the probability for the final state at the final time. Thus, the above graph for the emission of a quantum denotes the amplitude of the transition of a charged particle with momentum p into a state with a quantum of momentum q and a particle with momentum $p-q$.

According to the superposition principle, the total transition amplitude, usually called the Green function, is the sum of all possible physically different transition amplitudes.

By way of illustration let us derive the relation connecting the two-particle scattering amplitude and the interaction potential. The scattering amplitude can, according to the superposition principle, be represented by the sum of graphs

$\Gamma =$ 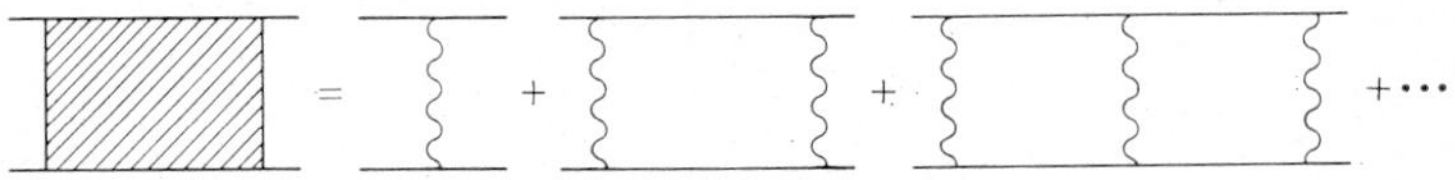

The first of these graphs represents the interaction between particles. The second one corresponds to the double interaction of particles. Between the two interaction events there is the amplitude for the transition of two non-interacting particles.

Let the first graph correspond to the particle interaction potential

$\mathscr{V} =$ 

and the line to the Green function, *i.e.*, the transition amplitude of a free particle G. Then the second graph can be denoted

 $= \mathscr{V}GG\mathscr{V}$,

since the two-particle transition amplitude equals the product of the Green function of each particle. For the scattering amplitude we obtain the series

$$\Gamma = \mathscr{V} + \mathscr{V}GG\mathscr{V} + \mathscr{V}GG\mathscr{V}GG\mathscr{V} + \dots .$$

The expression in the second and subsequent terms to the right of $\mathscr{V}GG$ again makes the sum giving Γ. For Γ we obtain the equation

$$\Gamma = \mathscr{V} + \mathscr{V}GG\Gamma .$$

The function G in this equation can readily be found. If the Ψ-function of a particle at the initial moment is the superposition of different eigenfunctions, the problem of finding G reduces to the wave-packet spread problem. If, on the other hand, the particle is at the initial moment in a state with a definite energy, the transition amplitude is determined quite simply. Obviously, the expression for Γ is a symbolic notation of the scattering amplitude equation well-known from quantum mechanics

$$\Gamma(\boldsymbol{p}_1, \boldsymbol{p}_2) = \mathscr{V}(\boldsymbol{p}_1 - \boldsymbol{p}_2) + \int \mathscr{V}(\boldsymbol{p}_1 - \boldsymbol{p}') \frac{\Gamma(\boldsymbol{p}', \boldsymbol{p}_2)}{\varepsilon_{p_1} - \varepsilon_{p'} + i\gamma} \frac{\mathrm{d}^3 \boldsymbol{p}'}{(2\pi)^3}.$$

Comparing both equations for Γ we can readily establish the precise correspondence of the graphic and analytical expressions.

Similarly we can connect the Green function of a particle in an external field $\tilde{G}$ with the Green function of a free particle G. The Green function in a field $\tilde{G}$ will be represented by the sum of partial transition amplitudes

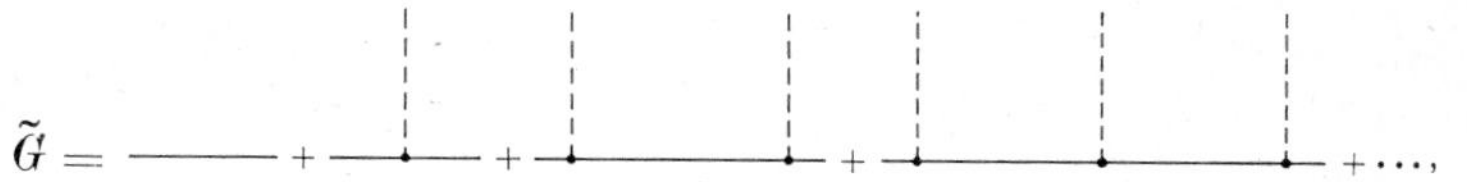

where each dot-and-dash line represents one external field action event:

$V =$ 

Collecting all graphs in $\tilde{G}$ to the right of V, we obtain again $\tilde{G}$. Thus

$$\tilde{G} = G + GVG + GVGVG + \ldots = G + GV\tilde{G}.$$

Comparing the correction to G to the first order of perturbation theory with respect to V

$$G^{(1)} = GVG,$$

with the well-known quantal expression, we can readily establish the meaning in which the multiplication in the symbolic formula for $\tilde{G}$ should be understood.

Thus, the idea of the graph technique is to establish, using simple examples, the correspondence between graph elements and analytical expressions after which we can learn how to decode any graphs consisting of these elements. Obtaining relations by this technique is so much simpler than doing it analytically that complex problems which seem unsolvable analytically can be treated successfully by this method.

Below we establish the analytical correspondence for all graphs describing the processes at work in the system of interacting particles, which will make it possible to obtain readily quantitative relations.

2'2. *Definition of the Green function.* – The usual method of solving quantal problems is to find the Ψ-function of the system satisfying the Schrödinger equation

$$i\frac{\partial \Psi}{\partial t} = H\Psi .$$

The function Ψ completely determines the physical properties of the system under study. We shall see that in many cases it is more convenient to find from the Ψ-function the amplitude of the transition from one state to another; this amplitude just as the Ψ-function gives all the physical properties of the system. Let us determine the amplitude of the transition $G(\xi, \xi', \tau, t)$ by the relation

$$\Psi(\xi, t+\tau) = C_N\int G(\xi, \xi', \tau, t)\Psi(\xi', t)\,d\xi'. \tag{2.1}$$

Here ξ is the set of variables describing the state of the system. To simplify the coefficients, the normalizing factor C_N can conveniently be chosen in the following formulae equal to

$$C_N = i^N ,$$

where N is the number of particles in the system.

The transition amplitude $G(\xi, \xi', \tau, t)$ makes it possible to express the Ψ-function at the moment $t+\tau$ by the Ψ-function at the moment t. The quantity G is usually called the Green function. When the Hamiltonian of the system does not depend explicitly on time, the Green function depends only on the time difference τ. The quantity G has an advantage over the Ψ-function, as we shall see later: to find it, we can use the graph technique mentioned in the Introduction and used for the first time in quantum electrodynamics.

Equation (2.1) contains G only at $\tau > 0$. For the sake of definiteness let us assume that

$$G(\xi, \xi', \tau, t) = 0 , \qquad \tau < 0 .$$

For the function $\Psi(t+\tau)$ to go over to $\Psi(t)$ at τ tending to zero on the side of positive values ($\tau = +0$), we put

$$C_N G(\xi, \xi', \tau, t)\,|_{\tau=+0} = \delta(\xi - \xi') . \tag{2.2}$$

Then the transition amplitude G satisfies the following inhomogeneous equation

$$-iC_N\left(i\frac{\partial G}{\partial \tau} - HG\right) = \delta(\tau)\delta(\xi - \xi') . \tag{2.3}$$

Indeed, at $\tau > 0$, G must satisfy the same equation as Ψ, *i.e.*, the Schrödinger equation; the correctness of the coefficient $\delta(\tau)$ is checked by integrating eq. (2.3) over an infinitely small interval τ including the point $\tau = 0$. Thus we obtain

$$C_N\big(G|_{\tau=+0} - G|_{\tau=-0}\big) = C_N G|_{\tau=+0} = \delta(\xi - \xi')\,,$$

i.e., the condition (2.2).

Let us show that the physical properties of the system are determined by the function G to the same extent as by the eigenfunctions of the Hamiltonian H

$$H\Psi_S = E_S \Psi_S\,.$$

Let us write G in the form

$$G(\xi, \xi', \tau) = \sum C_S \Psi_S^*(\xi')\Psi_S(\xi) \exp[-iE_S\tau]\Theta(\tau)\,,$$

where

$$\Theta(\tau) = \begin{cases} 1\,, & \tau > 0\,, \\ 0\,, & \tau < 0\,. \end{cases}$$

The substitution of this expression in eq. (2.3) gives

$$C_N G(\xi, \xi', \tau) = \sum \Psi_S^*(\xi')\Psi_S(\xi) \exp[-iE_S\tau]\Theta(\tau)\,. \tag{2.4}$$

Let us pass to the Fourier representation in τ

$$\begin{aligned} C_N G(\xi, \xi', \varepsilon) &= C_N \int G(\xi, \xi', \tau) \exp[i\varepsilon\tau] \mathrm{d}\tau = \\ &= \sum_S \Psi_S^*(\xi')\Psi_S(\xi) \int_0^\infty \exp[i(\varepsilon - E_S)\tau] \mathrm{d}\tau = i \sum_S \frac{\Psi_S^*(\xi')\Psi_S(\xi)}{\varepsilon - E_S + i\gamma}\,, \end{aligned} \tag{2.5}$$

where $\gamma = +0$, the sign of γ being chosen so that $G(\tau) = 0$ for $\tau < 0$. Thus, the poles of $G(\varepsilon)$ lying on the real axis ε, yield the eigenvalues of the energy of the system and the residue of G at each pole is

$$\operatorname{Res}(-iC_N G) = \varrho_S = \Psi_S^*(\xi')\Psi_S(\xi)\,,$$

and determines the physical properties of the system in the state S.

The transition amplitude has another important property on which we shall draw extensively. It is directly clear from the definition (2.1) that the transition amplitude satisfies

$$C_N G(\xi, \xi', t - t') = C_N^2 \int G(\xi, \xi_1, t - t_1) G(\xi_1, \xi', t_1 - t') \mathrm{d}\xi_1\,, \qquad t > t_1 > t'. \tag{2.6}$$

Indeed, the Ψ-function at the moment t can be obtained from the Ψ-function at the moment t' in two stages. At first we obtain the Ψ-function at the moment t_1

$$\Psi(\xi_1, t_1) = C_N \int G(\xi_1, \xi', t_1 - t')\Psi(\xi', t')\, d\xi' .$$

Then we have

$$\Psi(\xi, t) = C_N \int G(\xi, \xi_1, t - t_1)\Psi(\xi_1, t_1)\, d\xi_1 = \\ = C_N^2 \int G(\xi, \xi_1, t - t_1) G(\xi_1, \xi', t_1 - t')\Psi(\xi', t')\, d\xi_1 d\xi' .$$

A comparison with eq. (2.1) yields eq. (2.6).

2·3. *The Green function of one particle.* – Let us consider in more detail the Green function for one particle. It was indicated in the Introduction that the system of strongly interacting particles for weak excitations behaves like a gas of quasi-particles, and the Green function describing the behavior of a quasi-particle differs little from the Green function for the case when the system consists of one particle.

Let the system of eigenfunctions be given by the formula

$$H\varphi_\lambda(\boldsymbol{r}) = \varepsilon_\lambda^0 \varphi_\lambda(\boldsymbol{r}) ,$$

$$H = \frac{p^2}{2m} + U(r) ,$$

where $U(r)$ is the potential well.

We shall see that in the case of the nucleus the eigenfunctions and energies of quasi-particles are given by the same equation in which the mass of free particles has been replaced by the effective mass m^* and the potential $U(r)$ has the form represented in Fig. 1 where R is the nuclear radius and r_0 is the diffuse edge width, *i.e.*, the width of the region over which U passes from a constant value inside to a value outside the nucleus. Apart from the potential represented in Fig. 1 U contains also corrections connected with the Coulomb and spin-orbit interactions between particles. The Green function of the particle in the co-ordinate representation on the basis of eq. (2.5) ($C_N = i^N = i$) has the form

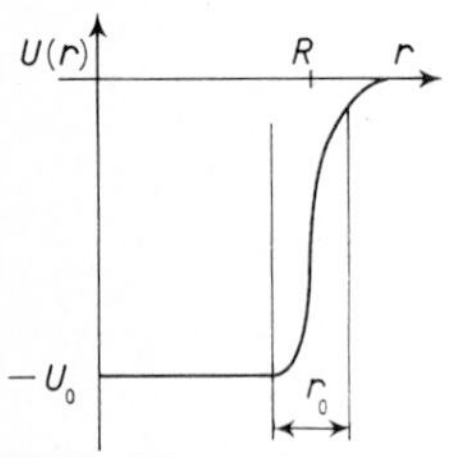

Fig. 1

$$G(\boldsymbol{r}, \boldsymbol{r}', \varepsilon) = \sum \frac{\varphi_\lambda^*(\boldsymbol{r}')\varphi_\lambda(\boldsymbol{r})}{\varepsilon - \varepsilon_\lambda^0 + i\gamma} .$$

The Green function has an especially simple form in the λ, ε representation

$$(2.5') \qquad G_{\lambda\lambda'}(\varepsilon) = \int G(\boldsymbol{r}, \boldsymbol{r}', \varepsilon)\varphi_\lambda(\boldsymbol{r}')\varphi^*_{\lambda'}(\boldsymbol{r})\,\mathrm{d}\boldsymbol{r}\,\mathrm{d}\boldsymbol{r}' = \delta_{\lambda\lambda'}\frac{1}{\varepsilon - \varepsilon^0_\lambda + i\gamma} \equiv G_\lambda(\varepsilon)\delta_{\lambda\lambda'}\,.$$

Let us also write the Green function in the λ, τ representation

$$(2.4') \qquad \begin{cases} G_\lambda(\tau) = \int G_\lambda(\varepsilon)\exp[-i\varepsilon\tau]\dfrac{\mathrm{d}\varepsilon}{2\pi} = -i\exp[-i\varepsilon^0_\lambda\tau]\,, & \tau > 0, \\ G_\lambda(\tau) = 0\,, & \tau < 0, \end{cases}$$

in agreement with eq. (2.4). The normalizing factor $C_N = C_1 = i$ is selected so that we should obtain a simple expression (2.5′) as we go over to the λ, ε representation.

2·4. *Quasi-particle Green function.* – The amplitude of the transition from a state with one quasi-particle λ to a state with one quasi-particle, *i.e.*, the quasi-particle Green function can readily be obtained by analogy with the Green function of one particle. For one particle we had in the λ-representation

$$G^0_{\lambda\lambda'}(\tau) = \delta_{\lambda\lambda'}\begin{cases} -i\exp[-i\varepsilon^0_\lambda\tau]\,, & \tau > 0, \\ 0\,, & \tau < 0. \end{cases}$$

To obtain the quasi-particle Green function we need only to replace the free-particle energy ε^0_λ by the quasi-particle energy ε_λ and take into account the fact that the transition amplitude, *i.e.*, the Green function depends on the occupation numbers of the quasi-particles. Below we shall give a more rigorous derivation but for the time being we confine ourselves to a less rigorous but more visualizable method.

The transition probability is proportional to the number of vacancies in the initial and final states. The number of vacancies in the state λ is, according to the Pauli principle, equal to $1 - n_\lambda$ where n_λ is the number of quasi-particles in the state λ. Consequently, the quasi-particle Green function depends on the occupation numbers of the quasi-particles n_λ as follows:

$$G^+_{\lambda\lambda'}(\tau) = f_{\lambda\lambda'}\sqrt{(1-n_\lambda)(1-n_{\lambda'})}\,,$$

where $f_{\lambda\lambda'}$ does not depend on the occupation numbers. Since at $n_\lambda = 0$ we must obtain the Green function of one particle (with replacement ε^0_λ by ε_λ), we have

$$(2.7) \qquad G^+_{\lambda\lambda'}(\tau) = -i(1-n_\lambda)\delta_{\lambda\lambda'}\begin{cases} \exp[-i\varepsilon_\lambda\tau]\,, & \tau > 0, \\ 0\,, & \tau < 0. \end{cases}$$

Let us now obtain the expression for the quasi-hole transition amplitude. Since the number of hole vacancies in the level λ is proportional to n_λ, we obtain similarly to the quasi-particle case

$$G^-_{\lambda\lambda'}(\tau) = -in_\lambda\delta_{\lambda\lambda'}\begin{cases}\exp[-i\varepsilon^-_\lambda\tau]\,, & \tau>0\,,\\ 0\,, & \tau<0\,.\end{cases} \tag{2.8}$$

Here ε^-_λ is the hole energy or, more accurately, the difference between the energies of the system after and before the appearance of the hole, as we shall see below.

As follows from the definition of the Green's function, the quantity $iG^+_\lambda(+0)$ must equal unity if $n_\lambda=0$ and the quantity $iG^-_\lambda(+0)$ must equal unity at $n_\lambda=1$. Equations (2.7) and (2.8) satisfy these conditions. We shall see by examples that the eqs. (2.7) and (2.8) are also correct for the case when

$$n_\lambda \neq 0, 1\,.$$

Let the following graphs correspond to the quantities $G^+_\lambda(t_1-t_2)$ and $G^-_\lambda(t_1-t_2)$

$$\begin{cases} G^+_\lambda(t_1-t_2)_{t_1>t_2} = \overset{\lambda t_2 \qquad \lambda t_1}{\longrightarrow}\,,\\ -G^-_\lambda(t_1-t_2)_{t_1>t_2} = \overset{\lambda t_2 \qquad \lambda t_1}{\longleftarrow}\,.\end{cases} \tag{2.9}$$

The minus sign in the second formula is taken to simplify the graphic notation of the production of a particle and hole in an external field which we shall soon consider.

In some cases it proves convenient to introduce the quasi-particle Green function G_λ determined as follows

$$G_\lambda(\tau) = \begin{vmatrix} G^+_\lambda(\tau) & \tau>0\\ -G^-_\lambda(-\tau) & \tau<0\end{vmatrix} = \overset{\lambda t_2 \qquad\quad \lambda t_1}{\overline{\qquad\qquad\qquad}}\,, \tag{2.10}$$

where $\tau = t_1 - t_2$.

We shall see in the next Section that the variation of the Green function in an external field is represented more simply by the function G_λ than by the functions G^+_λ and G^-_λ. We shall obtain the expression for the functions $G^+_\lambda(\varepsilon)$, $G^-_\lambda(\varepsilon)$ and $G_\lambda(\varepsilon)$, in the Fourier-transformed representations of eqs. (2.7), (2.8) and (2.10). These expressions will often be used in what follows. The Fourier representation $G(\varepsilon)$ is connected with the function $G(\tau)$ by the relations

$$G_\lambda(\tau) = \int_{-\infty}^{\infty} G_\lambda(\varepsilon)\exp[-i\varepsilon\tau]\frac{d\varepsilon}{2\pi}\,,$$

$$G_\lambda(\varepsilon) = \int_{-\infty}^{\infty} G_\lambda(\tau)\exp[i\varepsilon\tau]\,d\tau\,.$$

Using eqs. (2.7), (2.8) and (2.10) we obtain

$$
(2.11)\quad
\begin{cases}
G^{+}_{\lambda}(\varepsilon) = -i(1-n_{\lambda})\displaystyle\int_0^{\infty}\exp[-i\varepsilon_{\lambda}\tau + i\varepsilon\tau]\mathrm{d}\tau = \dfrac{1-n_{\lambda}}{\varepsilon-\varepsilon_{\lambda}+i\gamma}\,,\\[2ex]
G^{-}_{\lambda}(\varepsilon) = -\,in_{\lambda}\displaystyle\int_0^{\infty}\exp[-i\varepsilon^{-}_{\lambda}\tau + i\varepsilon\tau]\mathrm{d}\tau = \dfrac{n_{\lambda}}{\varepsilon-\varepsilon^{-}_{\lambda}+i\gamma}\,,\\[2ex]
G_{\lambda}(\varepsilon) = -i(1-n_{\lambda})\displaystyle\int_0^{\infty}\exp[-i\varepsilon^{+}_{\lambda}\tau + i\varepsilon\tau]\mathrm{d}\tau + \\[2ex]
\qquad + in_{\lambda}\displaystyle\int_{-\infty}^{0}\exp[i\varepsilon^{-}_{\lambda}\tau + i\varepsilon\tau]\,\mathrm{d}\tau = \dfrac{1-n_{\lambda}}{\varepsilon-\varepsilon^{+}_{\lambda}+i\gamma} + \dfrac{n_{\lambda}}{\varepsilon+\varepsilon^{-}_{\lambda}-i\gamma}\,,
\end{cases}
$$

where $\gamma\to+0$.

2'5. *The system of noninteracting quasi-particles in an external field.* – We considered above the Green function in a field for one particle. In the system of particles in an external field there appear processes like the production of a particle and hole. In this case the graph method requires the study of the analytical and graphic expressions for pair production and in particular the explanation of the choice of signs in the graphic representations (2.9) for G^{+}_{λ} and G^{-}_{λ}. For the sake of simplicity we confine ourselves for the time being to the case of noninteracting quasi-particles. The amplitude of the transition of a particle from a point $\lambda_2 t_2$ to a point $\lambda_1 t_1$ in the first order in the external field is composed of three graphs

1) 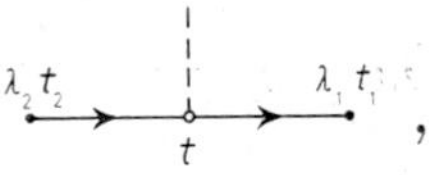

, $\quad t_2 < t < t_1$.

Here the instant of action of the external field lies between the times t_2 and t_1. The next term in the transition amplitude has the form

2) 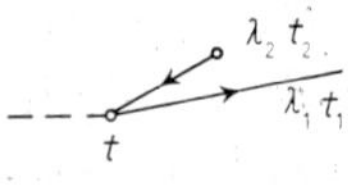

$\quad t < t_2 < t_1$.

A particle and hole originate at the moment t. The arrival of the hole at point

$\lambda_2 t_2$ is equivalent to the departure of the particle and hence the graph 2) also expresses the transition of the particle from $\lambda_2 t_2$ to $\lambda_1 t_1$.

Finally the third graph is represented as

3) 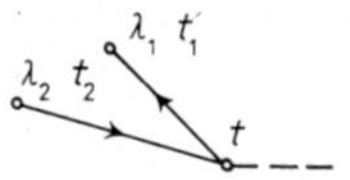 $t_2 < t_1 < t$.

Here the pair is absorbed by the field. According to eq. (2.9), the sum of these graphs corresponds to the following analytical expression:

(2.12)
$$G^{(1)}_{\lambda_1\lambda_2}(t_1, t_2) = \int_{t_2}^{t_1} G^+_{\lambda_1}(t_1 - t) V_{\lambda_1\lambda_2}(t) G^+_{\lambda_2}(t - t_2)\,dt -$$
$$- \int_{-\infty}^{t_2} G^+_{\lambda_1}(t_1 - t) V_{\lambda_1\lambda_2}(t) G^-_{\lambda_2}(t_2 - t)\,dt - \int_{t_1}^{\infty} G^-_{\lambda_1}(t - t_1) V_{\lambda_1\lambda_2}(t) G^+_{\lambda_2}(t - t_2)\,dt\,.$$

Just as before (p. 7) the external field corresponds to the graph $V_{\lambda_2\lambda_1}(t) =$

$=$ 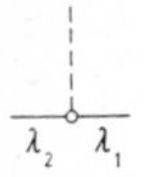 . Now it can readily be seen that the notation (2.10) simplifies considerably both analytical and graphic representations of the Green function in a field.

Indeed, from the last expression we obtain with the aid of eq. (2.10)

(2.12′)
$$G^{(1)}_{\lambda_1\lambda_2}(t_1, t_2) = \int_{-\infty}^{+\infty} G_{\lambda_1}(t_1 - t) V_{\lambda_1\lambda_2}(t) G_{\lambda_2}(t - t_2)\,dt =$$  .

Now the lines have no arrows in accordance with eq. (2.10). Let us now make sure that eqs. (2.9) give the correct transition amplitude. To this end it is sufficient to consider some simple case which can be obtained analytically and compare the results with a formula derived by the graph method.

Let us consider the second of the graphs entering $G^{(1)}$ at $t_2 \to t_1 - 0$ in a field of frequency ω. This graph describes the production of a particle and hole in the field. The particle and hole production amplitude $g_{\lambda_1\lambda_2}$ can be obtained by multiplying the expressions corresponding to the second term in eq. (2.12) by i. As a result we obtain

$$g_{\lambda_1\lambda_2}(t_1) = -i\int_{-\infty}^{t_1} G^+_{\lambda_1}(t_1-t)\,V_{\lambda_1\lambda_2}(t)\,G^-_{\lambda_2}(t_1-t)\,\mathrm{d}t =$$

$$= +i\int_{-\infty}^{t_1} \exp[-i\varepsilon_{\lambda_1}(t_1-t)]\exp[-i\omega t]\exp[-i\varepsilon^-_{\lambda_2}(t_1-t)]\mathrm{d}t\,V^0_{\lambda_1\lambda_2}(1-n_{\lambda_1})n_{\lambda_2} =$$

$$= V^0_{\lambda_1\lambda_2}\frac{(1-n_{\lambda_1})n_{\lambda_2}}{\varepsilon^+_{\lambda_1}+\varepsilon^-_{\lambda_2}-\omega}\exp[-i\omega t_1]\,.$$

Substituting for $\varepsilon^-_{\lambda_2} = -\varepsilon^+_{\lambda_2} \equiv -\varepsilon_{\lambda_2}$, we obtain at $t_1 = 0$

$$g_{\lambda_1\lambda_2}(0) = \frac{V^0_{\lambda_1\lambda_2}(1-n_{\lambda_1})n_{\lambda_2}}{\varepsilon_{\lambda_1}-\varepsilon_{\lambda_2}-\omega}\,.$$

This expression coincides with that derived in perturbation theory for the amplitude of the state λ_1 provided the particle prior to the inclusion of the field was in the state λ_2.

Thus, our expressions lead to the correct formulae for the transition amplitude.

2·6. *Creation and annihilation operators of quasi-particles.* – The functions G^+_λ, G^-_λ and G_λ can be written in a form more convenient for generalization with the aid of second quantization operators.

Let $b^\dagger_\lambda$ and b_λ be the production and annihilation operators of a quasi-particle in the state λ. Then we have

$$b^\dagger_\lambda b_\lambda = \hat{n}_\lambda\,, \qquad b_\lambda b^\dagger_\lambda = 1-\hat{n}_\lambda\,,$$

where $\hat{n}_\lambda$ is the operator of the number of quasi-particles in the state λ. The function describing the quasi-particle which appears at the moment t_2 in the state λ_2 has the form

$$\Phi_{\lambda_2}(t_2) = b^\dagger_{\lambda_2}\Phi_0\exp[-iE_0(N)t_2]\,,$$

where Φ_0 is the wave function, and $E_0(N)$ is the energy of the ground state of the system of N particles. The same function at the moment t_1 is

$$\Phi_{\lambda_2}(t_1) = \exp[-iH(t_1-t_2)]b^\dagger_{\lambda_2}\Phi_0\exp[-iE_0(N)t_2]\,.$$

Note that since the state with one quasi-particle is the eigenstate, the function $\Phi_{\lambda_2}(t)$ is the eigenfunction of the Hamiltonian of the system just as the corresponding function describing the quasi-hole.

The amplitude of the transition from the state $\lambda_2 t_2$ to the state $\lambda_1 t_1$ is determined by the admixture in the function $\Phi_{\lambda_2}(t_1)$ of the Ψ-function

$$\Phi_{\lambda_1}(t_1) = b^\dagger_{\lambda_1}\Phi_0 \exp[-iE_0(N)t_1],$$

or, to put it differently, by the matrix element

$$(\Phi_0 \exp[iE_0 t_1] b_{\lambda_1} \exp[-iH(t_1-t_2)] b^\dagger_{\lambda_2} \exp[-iE_0 t_2]\Phi_0).$$

Since $G^+_{\lambda_1\lambda_2}$ differs from the transition amplitude by the factor $-i$ we obtain

$$G^+_{\lambda_1\lambda_2}(t_1, t_2) = -i\theta(t_1-t_2)(\Phi_0, b_{\lambda_1}(t_1) b^\dagger_{\lambda_2}(t_2)\Phi_0), \tag{2.7'}$$

where

$$\theta(\tau) = \begin{cases} 1, & \tau > 0, \\ 0, & \tau < 0, \end{cases} \qquad b_\lambda(t) = \exp[iHt] b_\lambda \exp[-iHt].$$

If the Hamiltonian H depends explicitly on time, we must write instead of Ht

$$\int_0^t H \mathrm{d}t.$$

Similarly to $G^+_{\lambda_1\lambda_2}(t_1, t_2)$ we can write

$$G^-_{\lambda_1\lambda_2}(t_1, t_2) = -i\theta(t_1-t_2)\langle\Phi_0 b^\dagger_{\lambda_1}(t_1) b_{\lambda_2}(t_2)\Phi_0\rangle. \tag{2.8'}$$

From eqs. (2.7′) and (2.8′) we immediately obtain eqs. (2.7) and (2.8). Let us, for example, obtain eq. (2.8) from eq. (2.8′). We represent the transition amplitude in the form

$$(\Phi_0, b^\dagger_{\lambda_1}(t_1) b_{\lambda_2}(t_2)\Phi_0) = \sum_S (\Phi_0 b^\dagger_{\lambda_1}(t_1)\Phi_S)(\Phi_S b_{\lambda_2}(t_2)\Phi_0) =$$
$$= \sum (\Phi_0 b^\dagger_{\lambda_1}\Phi_S)(\Phi_S b_{\lambda_2}\Phi_0) \exp[-i[E_S(N-1) - E_0(N)](t_1-t_2)].$$

By definition of a quasi-hole in the absence of external field, the state obtained under the action of the operator b_{λ_2},

$$\Phi_{\lambda_2} = b_{\lambda_2}\Phi_0,$$

is the eigenstate of the system of $N-1$ particles, corresponding to the energy $E^{(\lambda_2)}(N-1) = E_S(N-1)$. The same state must be obtained by the action of the operator b_{λ_1} and therefore we have $\lambda_1 = \lambda_2$ (we assume that λ completely determines the state).

Thus, only one state remains in the sum and we obtain

$$\left(\Phi_0 b^\dagger_{\lambda_1}(t_1) b_{\lambda_2}(t_2)\Phi_0\right) = \exp\left[-i[E^{\lambda_2}(N-1) - E_0(N)]\tau\right] \sum_S |(\Phi_0 b^\dagger_{\lambda_1}\Phi_S)|^2 \delta_{\lambda_1\lambda_2} ,$$

i.e., the expression coinciding with eq. (2.8). Thereby we have clarified what should be understood by the energy of the quasi-particle and quasi-hole in eqs. (2.7) and (2.8)

$$\text{(2.13)} \qquad \begin{cases} \varepsilon_\lambda = E^{(\lambda)}_\nu(N+1) - E_0(N) , \\ \varepsilon_\lambda^- = E^{(\lambda)}(N-1) - E_0(N) . \end{cases}$$

We have written eqs. (2.7′) and (2.8′) in the form which permits a natural generalization for the case of external field when the Hamiltonian H depends explicitly on time. In this case the functions $G^\pm_{\lambda_1\lambda_2}(t_1, t_2)$ do not contain the factor $\delta_{\lambda_1\lambda_2}$ and do not depend on the difference $t_1 - t_2$ only.

The function $G^-_{\lambda_1\lambda_2}(t_1, t_2)$ at $t_1 \to t_2 + 0$ has a simple physical meaning, *viz.*, it is expressed by the quasi-particle density matrix. The quasi-particle density matrix is

$$\text{(2.14)} \qquad \varrho_{\lambda_2\lambda_1}(t) = \left(\Phi_0(t) b^\dagger_{\lambda_1} b_{\lambda_2} \Phi_0(t)\right) ,$$

where $\Phi_0(t)$ is the function obtained from Φ_0 under the action of the external field

$$\Phi_0(t) = \exp\left[i\int_0^t H\,\mathrm{d}t'\right] \cdot \Phi_0 .$$

The quantity $\varrho_{\lambda_2\lambda_1}(t)$ enables us to find the averaged values of the operators expressed by the sum of some quantities over quasi-particles, *i.e.*, operators of the form

$$\hat{A} = \sum_n \hat{A}(\xi_n) .$$

The summation is performed over all quasi-particles; ξ_n is the set of operators acting on the n-th quasi-particle. Such operators are known to be expressed by second quantization operators as follows:

$$\sum_n \hat{A}(\xi_n) = \sum_{\lambda_1\lambda_2} (\varphi_{\lambda_1} A(\xi_n) \varphi_{\lambda_2}) b^\dagger_{\lambda_1} b_{\lambda_2} .$$

The average value of the operator $\hat{A}$ is determined by $\varrho_{\lambda_2\lambda_1}(t)$ using the following formula:

$$\langle \hat{A} \rangle = \sum_{\lambda_1\lambda_2} A_{\lambda_1\lambda_2} \varrho_{\lambda_2\lambda_1} = \mathrm{Tr}\, \hat{A}\varrho .$$

It is clear from eq. (2.8′) that the density matrix is connected with $G^-_{\lambda_1\lambda_2}$ by the relation

$$\varrho_{\lambda_2\lambda_1}(t) = iG^-_{\lambda_1\lambda_2}(t+0,\, t)\,. \tag{2.15}$$

The Green function $G_{\lambda_1\lambda_2}(t_1, t_2)$ uniting the functions $G^+_{\lambda_1\lambda_2}$ and $G^-_{\lambda_1\lambda_2}$ is written as follows:

$$G_{\lambda_1\lambda_2}(t_1, t_2) = \begin{Bmatrix} G^+_{\lambda_1\lambda_2}(t_1, t_2)\,, & t_1 > t_2 \\ -G^-_{\lambda_1\lambda_2}(t_2, t_1)\,, & t_1 < t_2 \end{Bmatrix} = -i\langle Tb_{\lambda_1}(t_1)b^\dagger_{\lambda_2}(t_2)\rangle\,, \tag{2.16}$$

where $\langle\;\rangle$ denotes the averaging over the ground-state of the system, and the symbol T is defined by

$$Tb_{\lambda_1}(t_1)b^\dagger_{\lambda_2}(t_2) = \begin{cases} b_{\lambda_1}(t_1)b^\dagger_{\lambda_2}(t_2)\,, & t_1 > t_2\,, \\ -b^\dagger_{\lambda_2}(t_2)b_{\lambda_1}(t_1)\,, & t_1 < t_2\,. \end{cases}$$

The expression in brackets in eq. (2.16) is known as a T-product.

3. – Pairing correlation.

3·1. *Influence of near levels on the Green function.* – If the system has an excited state with the same constants of motion as, and an energy close to, the single quasi-particle state, both states are mixed, and the expression for the quasi-particle Green function becomes more complex.

If we imagine that the transitions to this competing state are forbidden the quasi-particle transition amplitude has the simple form which we assumed above.

To obtain the quasi-particle Green function taking into account the competing state, let us write the corresponding graph equation, understanding by thin lines the quasi-particle Green functions without taking into account the transitions into the competing state. The precise Green function will be denoted by a thick line. Then we obtain for the Green function the equation

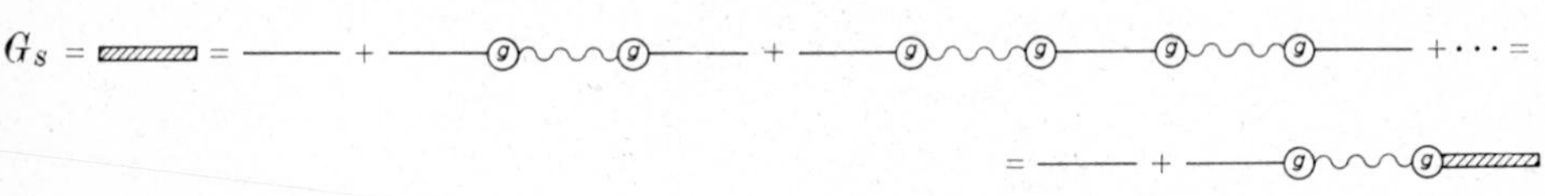

Here the block 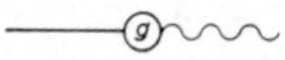 describes the irreducible amplitude of the transition g from the single quasi-particle to a competing state. By the irreducible amplitude we mean the amplitude which does not contain parts connected by a straight or wavy line (which represents the Green function of the competing state). The equation for G_s can be written as follows:

$G_s =$ 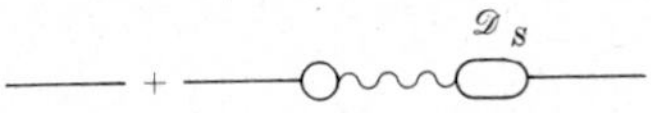 ,

where $\mathscr{D}_s$ denotes the reducible transition amplitude whose meaning is clear from the graphs.

Apart from the equation for G_s we must write a similar equation for $\mathscr{D}_s$ and the equation for the irreducible amplitude g. Solving this set of equations we obtain the final energies and Ψ-functions of the states under consideration.

To write the equations for g and $\mathscr{D}_s$ we must know the structure of the competing states.

Thus, in an unclosed shell of a nucleus with an extra quasi-particle, the state with two particles and one hole often proves close in energy to the single quasi-particle state. In some cases the competing state is the state with one quasi-particle and collective excitations.

We shall now analyse this process in more detail in the case of pair correlation.

3·2. *Pairing correlation in an infinite system.* – In infinite Fermi systems two particles with opposite spins and momenta may in some cases be in a bound state with energies close to the Fermi energy; in other words, these particles make a « Cooper pair ». In such cases an energy gap in the spectrum of single-particle excitations appears. As a result the system becomes superfluid or in the case of charged particles superconductive. In terms of the Green functions this means that a quasi-particle may pass into a hole plus Cooper pair state or a quasi-hole may pass to a quasi-particle minus Cooper pair state. In other words, the state with one quasi-particle against the background of N particles is mixed with the state of one quasi-hole against the background of $N+2$ particles, and the state with one quasi-hole is mixed with the state of one quasi-particle against the background of $N-2$ particles.

Let us introduce irreducible blocks for such transitions similar to the block g of the previous Section:

$i\Delta^+ =$ 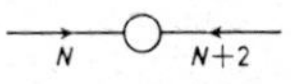 , $i\Delta^- =$ 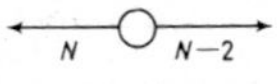 .

The number of background particles is shown below the lines.

The amplitudes representing the reverse process are the respective complex conjugates. Thus we have

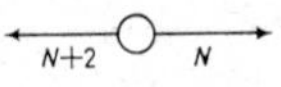 $= i(\Delta^+)^*$.

Using the above quasi-particle production operators we can represent these blocks analytically. In λ-representation we obtain in particular

$$\Delta^{-}_{-\lambda,\lambda} = \langle \Phi_0^*(N-2) b_\lambda b_{-\lambda} \Phi_0(N) \rangle \, .$$

Here $-\lambda$ denotes the state matching λ. If, for example, a pair with total zero spin and total zero momentum is produced, $-\lambda$ is the state with the momentum and spin opposite to those of the state λ. The same expression can be interpreted as the block of transition of a correlated pair into two quasi-particles

$\Delta^{-}_{\bar{\lambda},\lambda} =$ 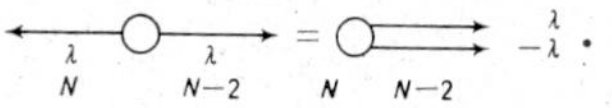

The graphs entering the Green function are represented, taking into account the pairing, by

$G_S^+(1,2) =$ 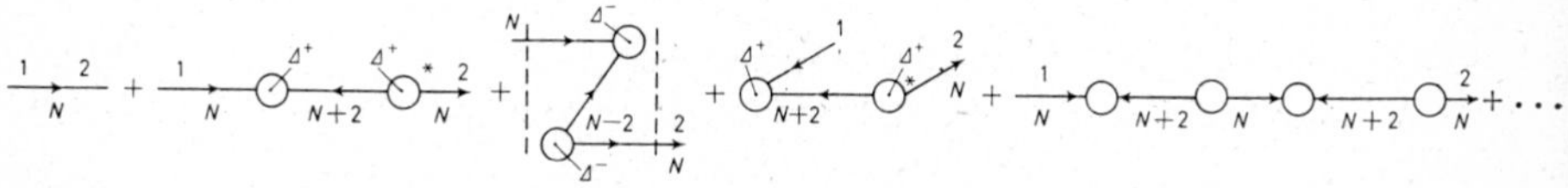

The second of these graphs corresponds to a process in which a quasi-particle moves at first freely, and then there occurs the transition to the state with a hole against the background $N+2$ and then the reverse transition and free movement to point 2.

The third graph has the following meaning. The correlated pair in the system of N particles has transformed into two particles against the background of $N-2$ particles. Then one of these particles and the initial particle make a pair in the system of N particles, which is followed by the free movement of the initial particle to point 2.

The graphs for G_S^- are represented similarly.

In a sufficiently large system the difference between Δ^+ and $(\Delta^-)^*$ can be neglected. Indeed we have

$$\Delta^+(N) = (\Delta^-(N+2))^* \simeq (\Delta^-(N))^*,$$

and at large N the difference is inessential. Besides, we assume that the Green functions of quasi-particles against the background of N, $N+2$ and $N-2$ particles coincide. This also introduces an error vanishing with the growth of N.

In this case we can introduce the Green function determined for both positive and negative times (similarly to the way it was done above for the system of quasi-particles in an external field) and unite the equations for G_S^+ and G_S^-

$G_S(1,2) =$ 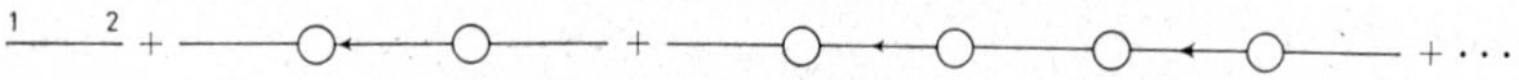

Now the arrow between the blocks denotes the Green function with the reverse sequence of the incoming and outgoing times which we shall denote G^T. Since the sum of all graphs to the right of the second of the blocks Δ forms exactly a function $G_S^{\cdot}$, we obtain the equation

(3.1) $G =$ 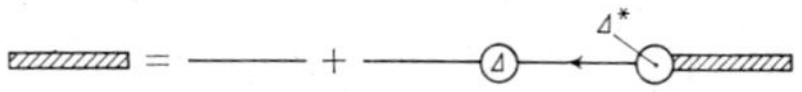 .

Note that between the blocks Δ there is a thin line since all graphs with recurring blocks Δ are taken into account in the function $G_S^{\cdot}$ to the right of Δ.

Analytically, eq. (3.1) can be written as

$$G_S(1, 2) = G(1, 2) - \int G(1, 3)\Delta(3, 4)\, G^T(4, 5)\Delta^*(5, 6) G_S(6,2)\, d\tau_3 d\tau_4 d\tau_5 d\tau_6 , \tag{3.1'}$$

where

$$G^T(4, 5) = G(5, 4) .$$

Let us go over to the momentum representation. Since all quantities in an infinite uniform system are nonzero only for equal incoming and outgoing momenta, we obtain from eq. (3.1′) the following algebraic equation:

$$G_S(p) = G(p) - G(p)\Delta(p)G(-p)\Delta^*(p)G_S(p) ,$$

or

$$G_S(p) = \frac{G(p)}{1 + G(p)|\Delta|^2 G(-p)} = \frac{G^{-1}(-p)}{G^{-1}(p)G^{-1}(-p) + |\Delta|^2} .$$

If the energies are measured from the Fermi energy, we have

$$G^{-1}(p) = \varepsilon - \varepsilon_p , \qquad G^{-1}(-p) = -\varepsilon - \varepsilon_{-p} = -(\varepsilon + \varepsilon_p) .$$

Substituting into the previous equation, we obtain

$$G_S(p) = \frac{\varepsilon + \varepsilon_p}{\varepsilon^2 - \varepsilon_p^2 - \Delta^2} .$$

The pole of the function $G_S(p)$ as a function of ε gives a new quasi-particle energy taking into account the pair correlation

$$E(p) = \pm\sqrt{\varepsilon_p^2 + \Delta^2}.$$

The two signs correspond, as we shall see later, to particles and holes. The minimum particle energy corresponds to $p = p_F$ $(\varepsilon_{p_F} = 0)$ and is

$$E_{min} = \Delta .$$

The minimum particle and hole production energy is 2Δ. On the other hand, the expression for G_S can be written in the form (p. 183)

$$G_S = \frac{1-n_p}{\varepsilon - E_p + i\gamma} + \frac{n_p}{\varepsilon + E_p^- - i\gamma},$$

where E_p^- is the hole energy and n_p is the number of quasi-particles with momentum p.

Comparing the two expressions of $G_S(p)$ we obtain

$$E_p = E_p^- = \sqrt{\varepsilon_p^2 + \Delta^2}, \qquad n(p) = \frac{E_p - \varepsilon_p}{2E_p}. \tag{3.2}$$

This comparison also yields the pole enclosure rules in the formula we have obtained for G_S.

It should be noted that from the equation for Δ obtained below it follows that $\Delta(p)$ is a slowly varying function of p and can be replaced by its values at $|p| = p_F$, $\varepsilon = \varepsilon_F$. At $\Delta \to 0$ eq. (3.2) for $n(p)$ goes into the conventional Fermi distribution

$$n_p \underset{\Delta \to 0}{=} \begin{cases} 1, & p < p_F, \\ 0, & p > p_F. \end{cases}$$

3·3. *Pairing correlation in nuclei.* – A process similar to the Cooper pair correlation occurs in nuclei. Two quasi-particles (two neutrons or two protons) make a state with zero total angular momentum so that the Ψ-function of these particles is a superposition of single-particle states of the form

$$\Psi(\boldsymbol{r}_1, \boldsymbol{r}_2) = \sum_{\nu,m} C_\nu \varphi_{\nu,m}(\boldsymbol{r}_1)\varphi_{\nu,-m}(\boldsymbol{r}_2),$$

where ν is the set of the other quantum numbers and m is the projection of the total angular momentum.

Let us assume j-j coupling which is known to exist in all nuclei except the lightest. In other words, we assume that the quasi-particle state is characterized by the quantum numbers $\lambda = n, l, j$ and m.

Owing to the pair correlation there arises the amplitude of the transition from the state with one quasi-particle to the state with one quasi-hole and correlated pair. In other words, the following block arises:

$i\Delta_{\lambda}'(\varepsilon) =$ 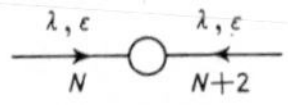

transferring a particle against the background of N particles into a hole against the background of $N+2$ particles, and a similar block transferring a hole into a particle. Below we shall obtain the equation for $\Delta_\lambda(\varepsilon)$ from which it will be clear that $\Delta_\lambda(\varepsilon)$ depends weakly on ε and can be replaced by the value at $\varepsilon=\varepsilon_F$:

$$\Delta_\lambda(\varepsilon) \simeq \Delta_\lambda(\varepsilon_F) = \Delta_\lambda .$$

To simplify the formulae let us neglect the difference between the energies $E_0(N+2)-E_0(N)$ for the addition and $E_0(N)-E_0(N-2)$ for the subtraction of two particles and replace ε_λ^- by $-\varepsilon_\lambda$. Besides, we have

$$\Delta^{+*}(N) = \Delta^-(N+2) \simeq \Delta^-(N) .$$

Then similarly to the case of an infinite system we can write the equations for G_S^+ and G_S^- as one equation for G_S.

The equation for the Green function G_S can then be written as

$G_{S\lambda}(\varepsilon) =$ 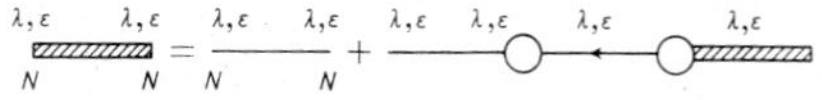

or analytically

$$\left[\varepsilon-\varepsilon_\lambda-\frac{|\Delta_\lambda|^2}{\varepsilon+\varepsilon_\lambda}\right] G_{S\lambda}=1 .$$

To generalize for the case when an external field is applied it is more convenient to write this equation in the form of two equations

$$\text{(3.3)} \qquad \begin{cases} (\varepsilon-\varepsilon_\lambda)\, G_{S\lambda}+\Delta_\lambda F_\lambda=1 , \\ (\varepsilon+\varepsilon_\lambda) F_\lambda=-\Delta_\lambda^* G_{S\lambda} . \end{cases}$$

The quantity F we have introduced denotes the total amplitude of the transition from the hole state to the quasi-particle state. We have denoted by F the quantity

$F =$ 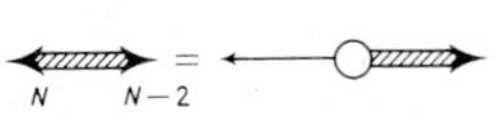 .

If there are no external fields we shall assume that

$$\Delta_\lambda=\Delta_\lambda^* \qquad \text{and} \qquad F_\lambda=F_\lambda^* .$$

Using eq. (3.3) and the rules for the enclosure of the poles we obtain

$$\text{(3.4)} \qquad \begin{cases} G_\lambda=\dfrac{1-n_\lambda}{\varepsilon-E_\lambda+i\gamma}+\dfrac{n_\lambda}{\varepsilon+E_\lambda-i\gamma} , \\ F_\lambda=\dfrac{-\Delta_\lambda}{2E_\lambda}\left(\dfrac{1}{\varepsilon-E_\lambda+i\gamma}-\dfrac{1}{\varepsilon+E_\lambda-i\gamma}\right) . \end{cases}$$

It can readily be seen that our equations (together with the equation for Δ obtained below) are invariant under the transformation

$$G' = G\,, \qquad F' = e^{i\varphi}F\,, \qquad \Delta' = e^{-i\varphi}\Delta\,.$$

Therefore, we can choose the phase φ so that Δ' be real, as is done in eq. (3.4).

Let us write eq. (3.3) in the co-ordinate representation:

$$\left\{\begin{aligned}&\left(i\frac{\partial}{\partial\tau}-H\right)G_s(\mathbf{r},\mathbf{r}',\tau)+\Delta(\mathbf{r})F(\mathbf{r},\mathbf{r}',\tau)=\delta(\mathbf{r}-\mathbf{r}')\delta(\tau)\,,\\&\left(i\frac{\partial}{\partial\tau}+H\right)F(\mathbf{r},\mathbf{r}',\tau)=-\Delta^*(\mathbf{r})G_s(\mathbf{r},\mathbf{r}',\tau)\,.\end{aligned}\right. \tag{3.5}$$

When the equations are written in the form (3.5) it is clear how an external field should be introduced. In the case of fields which do not change as t is replaced by $-t$ we must add to the Hamiltonian H the effective field acting on the quasi-particle. In the case of fields which change sign as t is replaced by $-t$, such as the magnetic field, for example, in the first equation the effective field V must still be added and in the second equation $V(-t)$ is subtracted from H since the change of the sign at H is connected with time inversion. The connection between the effective and external field and the equations for G and F in an external field will be considered in detail below.

These formulae must be complemented by the equation for determining Δ which can readily be obtained by the graph method (*). Here we shall give the final result

$$\Delta_{\lambda\lambda'} = \sum(\varphi^*_{\lambda}\varphi_{\lambda}\gamma(r)\varphi^*_{\lambda_1}\varphi_{\lambda_2})F_{\lambda_1,\lambda_2}(\tau)_{\tau=0}\,.$$

The dependence of the quantity $\gamma(r)$ on r takes into account the change of the interaction between quasi-particles in the transition from the internal to the external region of the nucleus.

4. – Interaction between quasi-particles.

4·1. *The mechanism of the interaction.* – The interaction between two quasi-particles in the nucleus strongly differs from that of two nucleons in vacuum. Indeed, the latter interaction occurs by the exchange of one meson or several mesons, while inside nuclear matter there may be, apart from this mechanism,

(*) A. Migdal: *The Theory of Finite Fermi Systems and the Properties of Nuclei*, Interscience Edition series (in the press).

also the interaction owing to particle and hole exchange. Graphically the two mechanisms can be represented as follows

$F =$ 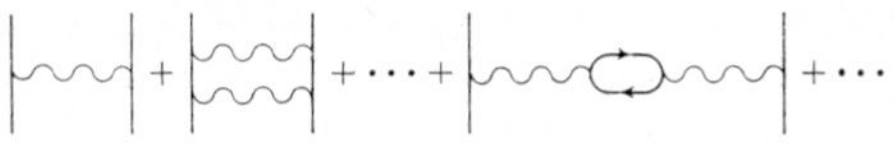

The wavy lines denote the meson Green functions.

The graphs corresponding to particle-hole exchange should not be confused with those representing nucleon-antinucleon pair exchange (which can be regarded as included into the meson lines). Thus, the additional interaction is the interaction owing to medium polarization and is similar to that arising between charged particles in a medium with a nonunity dielectrical constant. Besides, on account of the Pauli principle, even those interaction graphs which are not connected with polarization, change because some states are occupied by the remaining nucleons and inaccessible for interacting particles.

To find the interaction in matter from the interaction of two nucleons in vacuum is a complicated problem since the effect of the medium changes very strongly the vacuum interaction. This problem is not considered here. The interaction between quasi-particles will be expressed by several constants, which are not subtracted but must be found from comparing theory and experiment. These constants are identical for all nuclei within the same accuracy that the nuclear matter density is constant.

The graphs entering the scattering amplitude can be divided into two types: 1) graphs describing the effective interaction between nucleons in a medium and 2) graphs describing the scattering of quasi-particles.

The graphs of the first type correspond to the medium-altered quasi-particle interaction potential. The range of action of this potential is approximately the same as the range r_0 of the vacuum interaction potential. Indeed, the nuclear density is determined by the condition that the distance between particles must be of the order r_0. Consequently, the Fermi surface momentum which is determined by the density is connected with r_0 by the relation ($\hbar = m = 1$)

$$p_0 r_0 \sim 1 .$$

The depth of the effective potential well in which nuclear particles are moving is of the order

$$U \sim \frac{p_0^2}{2} \sim \frac{1}{r_0^2} .$$

Thus, all quantities in nuclear matter, and consequently the range of effective interaction forces are determined by the quantity r_0 as the only quantity of the dimension of a length characterizing both the vacuum interaction and the additional interaction caused by the polarizability of nuclear matter.

4'2. *Scattering amplitude at small momentum transfers. Local interaction.* – In many cases the problem is to find the scattering amplitude not at large but at small 4-momentum transfer.

We shall see that all problems involving an external field, with a frequency ω small and wave vectors small compared with the Fermi momentum reduce to finding the scattering amplitude with small momentum transfers ($K \ll p_F$, $\omega \ll \varepsilon_F$). In this case to obtain a convenient equation, the graphs entering Γ should be classified in a different way. *Viz.*, let us collect into a block all graphs which do not contain parts connected by two lines, one of a quasi-particle and the other of a quasi-hole. The block $\mathcal{F}$ will contain the following graphs:

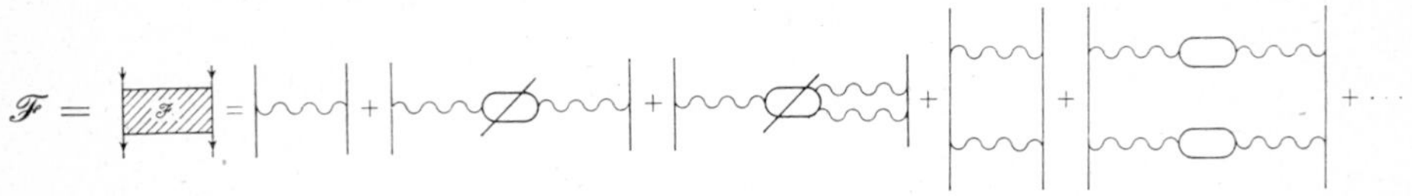

Those graphs which do not by definition enter the block $\mathcal{F}$ are crossed out. These graphs will be shown to depend essentially at small momentum transfers on the scattering particle states.

All graphs except those crossed out correspond at small momentum transfers to the δ-like contributions to the block $\mathcal{F}$. Indeed, the first, third and fifth graphs describe the interaction of free nucleons and are therefore characterized by the radius r_0, the fourth graph weakly depends on momentum transfer and hence is also characterized by the only quantity r_0 of length dimensionality entering the problem. In general all graphs containing more than two lines in the particle-hole channel weakly depend on momentum transfer since large momenta and energies ($p \sim p_F$, $\varepsilon \sim \varepsilon_F$) are essential in the integration over 4-momenta of the internal lines.

Let us elucidate this proposition.

Consider a graph of the form

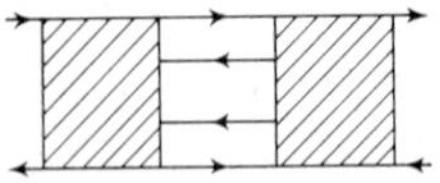

Let us show that the integration over 4-momenta of the internal lines is determined by energies far removed from the Fermi surface.

Each Green function contributes the factor $1/(\varepsilon - \varepsilon_p)$, and besides the integration over the angles p_1, two integrations over $d\varepsilon_1$ and $d\varepsilon_{p_1}$. The 4-momentum conservation law contributes 4 relations, 2 out of which restrict the region of the angles and the other 2 restrict the values ε_i and ε_{p_i} as a result of which the number of integrations over $d\varepsilon_i d\varepsilon_{p_i}$ decreases by 2. As a result we obtain the following integral

$$\mathscr{F} = \int \Phi \frac{d^6\xi}{\xi^4} ,$$

in which the integration region near the Fermi surface ($\varepsilon = \varepsilon_F$, $p = p_F$, $\xi = 0$) makes a small contribution. Since in the momentum representation the appreciable variation region $\sim \varepsilon_F$, p_F, in the co-ordinate representation the graph under consideration is δ-like with a spread width $\sim r_0$.

With the aid of the block $\mathscr{F}$ all graphs entering Γ, can be classified as follows: 1) graphs which do not contain two lines in the quasi-particle-quasi-hole channels (block $\mathscr{F}$) and 2) graphs in which the block $\mathscr{F}$ comes first in the quasi-particle-quasi-hole channel, then follow two lines (of a quasi-particle and quasi-hole) and then the sum of all graphs transferring the quasi-particle and quasi-hole into a new state (*i.e.*, Γ).

Graphically the equation for Γ can be represented as

(4.1) $\Gamma =$ 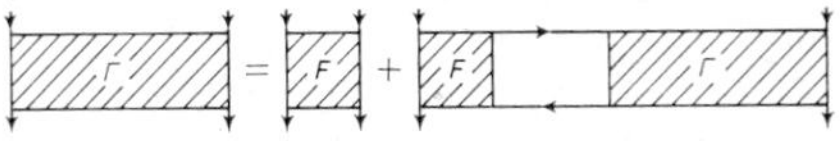

.

Here just as in the previous Section we must take into account the graphs of two types

In the second of these graphs the particle and hole exchange places. Both types of graphs are united if we introduce the Green function defined for negative times

$$\mathscr{F}G^+G^-\Gamma + \mathscr{F}G^-G^+\Gamma = \mathscr{F}GG\Gamma .$$

Therefore, the equation for Γ takes the form

$$\Gamma = \mathscr{F} + \mathscr{F}GG\Gamma \text{ (*)} . \tag{4.2}$$

Since the block $\mathscr{F}$ does not contain two lines, it is δ-like in time difference. The same applies, on the basis of eq. (4.2), to Γ. Therefore, both Green functions are taken for the same time. The transition amplitude corresponding to the free movement of a particle and a hole was calculated when the system of quasi-particles in a field was considered (p. 185). Let the transferred 4-th component in Γ be ω

$$\big(\Gamma(t) \to \Gamma \exp[-i\omega t]\big) .$$

(*) Here and below the factor $-i$ is omitted in the symbolic product.

Then we have

$$-i\int G_{\lambda_1}(t_1-t)\,G_{\lambda_2}(t-t_1)\exp[-i\omega t_1]\,\mathrm{d}t_1=\exp[-i\omega t]\cdot\frac{n_{\lambda_1}-n_{\lambda_2}}{\varepsilon_{\lambda_1}-\varepsilon_{\lambda_2}+\omega}\,.$$

For Γ we obtain the equation

$$(\lambda_1\lambda_2|\Gamma|\lambda_3\lambda_4)=(\lambda_1\lambda_2|\mathscr{F}|\lambda_3\lambda_4)+\sum_{\lambda\lambda'}(\lambda_1\lambda_2|\mathscr{F}|\lambda'\lambda)\frac{n_\lambda-n_{\lambda'}}{\varepsilon_\lambda-\varepsilon_{\lambda'}+\omega}(\lambda'\lambda|\Gamma|\lambda_3\lambda_4)\,. \tag{4.3}$$

Since the block $\mathscr{F}$ in the co-ordinate representation is δ-like and is determined by the region of radius r_0 near the point under study, we shall call the quantity $\mathscr{F}$ the local interaction amplitude or simply local interaction.

When the pair correlation is essential or when near the Fermi surface there are levels competing with single-particle states, the expression for G_λ becomes more complex and the equation for Γ has no longer the simple form (4.3).

Now we can prove that the graphs containing a particle and a hole tend to zero as momentum transfer increases. The graphs of this type are collected into the second term of eq. (4.3). In the momentum representation we have

$$\frac{n_\lambda-n_{\lambda'}}{\varepsilon_\lambda-\varepsilon_{\lambda'}+\omega}\to\frac{n(\boldsymbol{p}'+\boldsymbol{k}/2)-n(\boldsymbol{p}'-\boldsymbol{k}/2)}{\omega+\boldsymbol{k}\boldsymbol{p}'}\,. \tag{4.4}$$

As momentum transfer increases $k\to\infty$ or $\omega\to\infty$ this expression tends to zero and the second term is absent in eq. (4.3).

4·3. *Local interaction in homogeneous nuclear matter.* – It has been said above that the effective local interaction between quasi-particles is characterized by several numbers.

Let us first consider homogeneous nuclear matter and then introduce the corrections due to the finiteness of the nuclear size. In the momentum representation the local interaction amplitude depends on 2 momenta p_1 and p_2 and momentum transfer q

$\mathscr{F}=$ 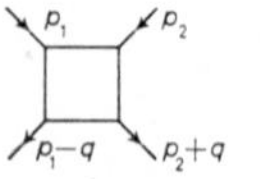

Since the block $\mathscr{F}$ weakly depends on the momenta (varies appreciably as the momenta change by a quantity $\delta p\sim p_{\mathrm{F}}$, $\delta\varepsilon\sim\varepsilon_{\mathrm{F}}$) we can if the momentum transfer is small assume that $q=0$ (accurately to within $\sim k/p_{\mathrm{F}}$ and $\omega/\varepsilon_{\mathrm{F}}$). If, moreover we take into account that in the expression p' lies at small k near the Fermi surface, it is sufficient for the investigation of the amplitude Γ near the Fermi surface to know $\mathscr{F}$ at $|\boldsymbol{p}_1|=|\boldsymbol{p}_2|=p_{\mathrm{F}}$ and $\varepsilon_1=\varepsilon_2=\varepsilon_{\mathrm{F}}$. Therefore

$\mathscr{F}$ depends only on the angle between the incoming momenta $\boldsymbol{p}_1$ and $\boldsymbol{p}_2$. The interaction between quasi-particles depends, moreover, on the spin of quasi-particles and isotopic spin. Assuming isotopic invariance, we obtain

$$\mathscr{F} = C\{f + f'\boldsymbol{\tau}_1\boldsymbol{\tau}_2 + (g + g'\boldsymbol{\tau}_1\boldsymbol{\tau}_2)\boldsymbol{\sigma}_1\boldsymbol{\sigma}_2\}\,, \tag{4.5}$$

where f, f' and g, g' are functions of the angle between $\boldsymbol{p}_1$ and $\boldsymbol{p}_2$, and $\boldsymbol{\tau}$ and $\boldsymbol{\sigma}$ are the isotopic and spin matrices. We choose the normalizing factor C to be

$$C = \frac{\pi^2}{m^* p_{\mathrm{F}}}\,.$$

Then f, f', g and g' are dimensionless quantities of the order of unity.

We have not included in eq. (4.5) the terms of the form $\boldsymbol{p}_1\boldsymbol{\sigma}_1$, $\boldsymbol{p}_2\boldsymbol{\sigma}_2$ which originate as a relativistic spin-orbit correction.

The tensor forces are proportional to q^2 and therefore are not included in eq. (4.5) though, of course, they have affected the numerical value of the terms taken into account.

Let us expand $\mathscr{F}$ in Legendre polynomials depending on the cosine of the angle between $\boldsymbol{p}_1$ and $\boldsymbol{p}_2$

$$\begin{cases} x = \dfrac{\boldsymbol{p}_1\boldsymbol{p}_2}{p_{\mathrm{F}}^2}\,, \\ \mathscr{F} = \sum\limits_l \mathscr{F}_l P_l(x)\,. \end{cases} \tag{4.6}$$

The numbers f_l, f'_l, g_l and g'_l must be found from comparing theory with experiment. Let us note that this expansion has nothing in common with the conventional expansion of the scattering amplitude in partial waves in which the expansion is performed in the functions P_l of the deflection angle while in $\mathscr{F}$ the deflection angle is assumed to be zero ($k = 0$). Comparison with experiment shows that the zero harmonics of this expansion play the main role in nuclei, *i.e.*, the local interaction of quasi-particles little depends on their velocities.

Let us see how the quantities f, f', g and g' are connected with the interaction amplitude of two identical and two different particles.

To obtain $\mathscr{F}^{\mathrm{np}}$, we must replace in $\mathscr{F}$ the quantity $\boldsymbol{\tau}_1\boldsymbol{\tau}_2$ by $(\tau_1)_{\alpha\alpha}(\tau_2)_{\alpha\alpha} = 1$, and to obtain the nonexchange part of $\mathscr{F}^{\mathrm{np}}$ replace $\boldsymbol{\tau}_1\boldsymbol{\tau}_2$ by $(\tau_1)_{\alpha\alpha}(\tau_2)_{\beta\beta} = -1$. Finally, to obtain the exchange part of $\mathscr{F}^{\mathrm{np}}$, $\mathscr{F}^{\mathrm{np}}_{\mathrm{exc}}$ when charge is transferred by the particle-hole channel, we must replace $\boldsymbol{\tau}_1\boldsymbol{\tau}_2$ by $(\tau_1)_{\alpha\beta}(\tau_2)_{\beta\alpha} = 2$.

Thus we obtain

$$\begin{cases} \mathscr{F}^{\mathrm{nn}} = \mathscr{F}^{\mathrm{pp}} = C[f + f' + (g + g')\boldsymbol{\sigma}_1\boldsymbol{\sigma}_2]\,, \\ \mathscr{F}^{\mathrm{np}} = C[f - f' + (g - g')\boldsymbol{\sigma}_1\boldsymbol{\sigma}_2]\,, \\ \mathscr{F}^{\mathrm{np}}_{\mathrm{exc}} = 2C[f' + g'\boldsymbol{\sigma}_1\boldsymbol{\sigma}_2]\,. \end{cases} \tag{4.7}$$

4'4. *Effect of finite sizes.* – The equation for the effective fields in an infinite system contains $\mathcal{F}$ at momentum transfer q equal to the 4-vector of the external field. Therefore, in sufficiently uniform fields we can in $\mathcal{F}$ assume that $q=0$ (accurately to within k/p_F, ω/ε_F).

In a finite system the effective field V is not uniform even in a uniform external field but varies appreciably over distances of the order R. Therefore, we must have the expression for $\mathcal{F}$ at $k\sim 1/R$, and in this case we can assume that $\omega=0$ if $\omega\ll\varepsilon_F$. Since we have $k/p_F\sim 1/p_F R\sim 1/A^{\frac{1}{3}}$ it is sufficient in $\mathcal{F}$ to take into account only the terms linear in q and neglect the terms in q^2 and hence neglect the tensor forces which contain q^2. The most general expression, linear in q, symmetric over the signs of the particles and unchanged if t is replaced by $-t$, is

$$\mathcal{F}^{sl}=\hat{\varkappa}(\boldsymbol{\sigma}_1+\boldsymbol{\sigma}_2)\times(\boldsymbol{p}_1-\boldsymbol{p}_2)\cdot\boldsymbol{q}\,.$$

If $1\rightleftarrows 2$, $q=p_1-p_1'$ goes into $p_2-p_2'=-q$. The quantity $\varkappa$ differs for identical and different nuclei. It can be shown that $\varkappa=\frac{1}{2}(\varkappa^{nn}+\varkappa^{np})$ determines the spin-orbit addition to the Hamiltonian of one quasi-particle

$$\delta V=-\varkappa\frac{1}{r}\frac{dn}{dr}\boldsymbol{\sigma}\boldsymbol{l}\,.$$

The interaction $\mathcal{F}^{sl}$ leads to the spin-orbit correction for the nuclear magnetic moments.

The expression for $\mathcal{F}$ at $|\boldsymbol{p}_1|=|\boldsymbol{p}_2|=p_F$, which corresponds to δ-like forces in the co-ordinate representation was given in the previous Section. We can introduce in $\mathcal{F}$ additional constants, expanding $\mathcal{F}$ in the powers of $p_1^2-2m^*\varepsilon_F$ and $p_2^2-2m^*\varepsilon_F$ and thus take into account the finiteness of the interaction range. Incidentally, the finiteness of the range of forces produces the greatest effect on the processes occurring near the nuclear surface where the quantity $\mathcal{F}$ varies strongly as it is, since outside the nucleus $\mathcal{F}$ assumes a different value.

Let us proceed to the transition of $\mathcal{F}$ from its value inside to that outside the nucleus. To determine the regularity of the law for this transition we can use the approximate method employed in the nucleon-nucleon scattering theory at low energies. The nucleon-nucleon interaction is described by the limiting condition

$$\frac{d}{dr}\ln r\Psi\bigg|_{r=r_1-r_2=0}=\alpha(r_1)\,.$$

The determination of $\mathcal{F}(r)$ reduces to the determination of the scattering amplitude of two nucleons placed in a potential well, the quantity $\alpha(r)$ having different values inside and outside the well. For $\alpha(r)$ we can take, for example, the transition law obtained in the gas approximation

$$\alpha(r) = \alpha_0 + \alpha_1 \frac{\sqrt{2m^*(\varepsilon_F - U(r))}}{\sqrt{2m^*\varepsilon_F}} .$$

The character of the transition of α to the vacuum value does not affect the result too strongly. Indeed, the equation for the effective field contains the matrix elements of $\mathcal{F}$ for the functions φ_λ with energies close to the Fermi energy. Near the nuclear surface these functions do not vary very strongly over the width $\sim r_0$ across which the transition of $\mathcal{F}$ from the internal to the external value occurs.

It should be noted that outside the nucleus $\mathcal{F}$ may differ appreciably from the free-nucleon scattering amplitude because of a distortion of the Ψ-functions of nucleons near the nuclear surface. It is only at distances from the nucleus exceeding several times the nuclear radius that $\mathcal{F}$ goes into the value corresponding to free nucleons. The determination of $\mathcal{F}$ outside the nucleus is a complex problem which has not yet been solved. By way of first approach we can characterize $\mathcal{F}$ outside the nucleus by constants determined from experiment.

Let us assume that $\mathcal{F}(r)$ has the form

$$\mathcal{F}(r) = \mathcal{F} + \frac{\mathcal{F}_{ex} - \mathcal{F}}{1 + \exp[-\alpha'(r - R')]} . \tag{4.8}$$

Inside the nucleus we obtain the value $\mathcal{F}$ and outside the nucleus we have $\mathcal{F}_{ex}$. The quantities α' and R' must differ little from the corresponding values α and R for the density variation, but strictly speaking they must also be found from experiment. The above expression for $\mathcal{F}_{ex}$ corresponds to the δ-function forces. In other words, neglecting all harmonics except the zero harmonic, $\mathcal{F}$ has the following form in the co-ordinate representation:

$$\mathcal{F}(\boldsymbol{r}_1, \boldsymbol{r}_2, \boldsymbol{r}_3, \boldsymbol{r}_4) = \mathcal{F}_0(\boldsymbol{r}_1)\delta(\boldsymbol{r}_1 - \boldsymbol{r}_2)\delta(\boldsymbol{r}_1 - \boldsymbol{r}_3)\delta(\boldsymbol{r}_1 - \boldsymbol{r}_4) .$$

For the processes for which the region near the nuclear surface is essential we must take into account the finiteness of the range of forces, *i.e.*, replace the δ-functions by a more complicated expression (such as the Gaussian curve with width depending on r).

The values of $(f_0)_{ex}$ and $(f_0')_{ex}$ (zero harmonics of the expansion (4.6)) are found from the comparison of the theoretical and experimental values of the quadrupole moments and isotope shift (at $\alpha' = \alpha$, $R' = R$). In this case it appears that $(f_0)_{ex}$ strongly differs from the value inside the nucleus

$$f_0 \simeq 1 \pm 0.2 , \qquad (f_0)_{ex} = -3 \pm 0.8 .$$

Therefore, all processes involving f_0 must be calculated by the interpolation formula (4.8).

Let us give the values of the constants entering $\mathcal{F}$ found from the comparison with experiment.

The isotope shift and quadrupole moments are well explained with the following values of the constants:

$$f_0 = 1 \pm 0.2\,, \qquad (f_0)_{\rm ex} = -3 \pm 0.8\,, \qquad f_0' = 0.35 \pm 0.2 \simeq (f_0')_{\rm ex}\,.$$

The comparison of theory with experiment yields for the magnetic moments

$$g_0 \simeq 0.5\,, \qquad |g_0 - g_0'| \lesssim 0.1\,.$$

From the estimate of the orbital magnetism of neutrons (see p. 231) we obtain

$$\tfrac{1}{3} f_1^{\rm np} \lesssim 0.1\,.$$

From the estimate of the effective mass we have

$$\tfrac{1}{3}(f_1^{\rm nn} + f_1^{\rm np}) \lesssim 0.1\,.$$

Thus already the first harmonic (which always has the factor $\frac{1}{3}$) makes comparatively small corrections. These values of the constants are in agreement with other experimental data.

4·5. *Symmetry energy and compressibility. Nuclear matter stability conditions.* – Let us find the change of the Fermi energy (*i.e.*, the chemical potential of quasi-particles) as the neutron and proton concentration varies, *i.e.*, in the transition from the nucleus with $N = Z$ to nuclei with $N > Z$ for the same A. The change of the Fermi energy is caused first by a change in the density of particles of a given kind and second by a change in the potential-well depth. The density change is

$$\delta n^{\rm n} = \frac{N-Z}{2V}\,, \qquad \delta n^{\rm p} = -\frac{N-Z}{2V}\,.$$

This change causes the following potential-well change for neutrons and protons

$$\delta U^{\rm n} = \mathcal{F}_0^{\rm nn}\delta n^{\rm n} + \mathcal{F}_0^{\rm np}\delta n^{\rm p} = \mathcal{F}_0^- \frac{N-Z}{2V} = \frac{4}{3}\varepsilon_{\rm F} f_0' \frac{N-Z}{A}\,,$$

$$\delta U^{\rm p} = \mathcal{F}_0^{\rm pp}\delta n^{\rm p} + \mathcal{F}_0^{\rm pn}\delta n^{\rm n} = -\mathcal{F}_0^- \frac{N-Z}{2V} = -\frac{4}{3}\varepsilon_{\rm F} f_0' \frac{N-Z}{A}\,,$$

where $\mathscr{F}_0^- = \mathscr{F}_0^{nn} - \mathscr{F}_0^{np} = \mathscr{F}_0^{pp} - \mathscr{F}_0^{pn}$. Such simple expressions for δU are obtained only if the density variation is uniform over the nucleus. When a small number of particles is added and the density variation is nonuniform over the nucleus, the equation for the effective field in the nucleus must be solved (see Sect. **5**). Therefore, the results obtained below apply only at $N-Z \gg 1$ when the density of added particles is uniform over the nuclear volume. As a result the Fermi energy change is

$$\delta\varepsilon_F^n = \frac{d\varepsilon_F}{dN}\frac{N-Z}{2} + \frac{4}{3}\varepsilon_F f_0' \frac{N-Z}{A} = \frac{2}{3}\varepsilon_F(1+2f_0')\frac{N-Z}{A},$$

$$\delta\varepsilon_F^p = -\frac{2}{3}\varepsilon_F(1+2f_0')\frac{N-Z}{A}.$$

On the other hand, the difference of these quantities gives with minus sign the difference of chemical potential which is obtained by differentiating the term $\beta((N-Z)^2/A)$ of Weizsäcker's formula over N with a constant A. From the comparison we obtain

$$\beta = \frac{\varepsilon_F}{3}(1+2f_0'). \tag{4.9}$$

At $f_0'=0.35$ and $\varepsilon_F=40$ we obtain

$$\beta = 22 \text{ MeV}.$$

A similar reasoning leads us to the expression for the nuclear matter compressibility $\mathscr{K}$ determined as coefficient in the expression for the energy density variation under compression

$$\delta E = \mathscr{K}\frac{(n-n_0)^2}{2n_0}.$$

For $\mathscr{K}$ we obtain the expression

$$\mathscr{K} = \frac{2\varepsilon_F}{3}(1+2f_0). \tag{4.10}$$

Equations (4.9) and (4.10) impose restrictions on possible values of the constants f_0' and f_0 in infinite nuclear matter

$$f_0' > -\tfrac{1}{2}, \qquad f_0 > -\tfrac{1}{2}.$$

These relations are a particular case of more general nuclear matter stability conditions obtained from the requirement that the energy of the system must increase as a quasi-particle or quasi-hole appears.

We obtain the following conditions:

$$1+\frac{2}{2l+1}f_l>0\,, \qquad 1+\frac{2}{2l+1}f'_l>0\,,$$

$$1+\frac{2}{2l+1}g_l>0\,, \qquad 1+\frac{2}{2l+1}g'_l>0\,.$$

These relations generalize similar conditions obtained for a matter consisting of particles of one kind.

If the gas approximation could be applied in the nucleus, the real part of the scattering amplitude of free nucleons at energies close to the Fermi energy would coincide with $\mathscr{F}$. It appears that this assumption not only contradicts the values of f, f', g and g' given above but even violates the stability condition. Indeed, the real part of the free nucleon amplitude gives the following values of the constants:

$$(f_0)_{\text{fr}}=-1.4\,, \qquad (f_1)_{\text{fr}}=\quad 0.04\,,$$

$$(f'_0)_{\text{fr}}=-0.01\,, \qquad (f'_1)_{\text{fr}}=-0.3\,,$$

$$(g_0)_{\text{fr}}=\quad 0.36\,, \qquad (g_1)_{\text{fr}}=\quad 0.01\,,$$

$$(g'_0)_{\text{fr}}=\quad 0.40\,, \qquad (g'_1)_{\text{fr}}=\quad 0.38\,.$$

The value $(f_0)_{\text{fr}}=-1.4$ contradicts the stability condition. The nuclear matter therefore must compress until the repulsive forces come into play and change f_0 towards positive values.

4·6. *Interaction through the core.* – The effective interaction is known to be introduced in many nuclear calculations with different constants for different cases. The most frequent use is made of the quadrupole-quadrupole interaction which is written in the λ-representation as follows:

$$\mathscr{F}^{QQ}=CQ_{\lambda_1\lambda_2}Q_{\lambda_3\lambda_4}\,,$$

where $Q_{\lambda_1\lambda_2}$ is the matrix element of the quadrupole moment

$$Q_{\lambda_1\lambda_2}=\int\varphi^*_{\lambda_1}r^2P_2(\cos\theta)\varphi_{\lambda_2}\mathrm{d}r\,.$$

The octupole-octupole and other interactions are written similarly. All these interactions have played an important role for the qualitative systematization of the experimental evidence.

We shall see that all these interactions are an approximation (with an error of the order of unity) of similar interactions which are rigorously derivable from the equation for the scattering amplitude and are expressed by the constants of the local interaction $\mathscr{F}$.

Let us neglect for the sake of simplicity the pair correlation and obtain the effective interaction between particles belonging to one shell.

Let us write the equation for the scattering amplitude in the form

$$\Gamma(\nu_1, \nu_2^*) = \mathscr{F}(\nu_1, \nu_2^*) + \sum_{\nu} \mathscr{F}(\nu_1, \nu^*) \mathscr{A}(\nu) \Gamma(\nu, \nu_2^*) .$$

Here ν_1 denotes the total set of the indices $\lambda_1 \lambda_1'$ of the particle before and after the collision, and $\nu_2 = (\lambda_2, \lambda_2')$ corresponds to the same for the second particle, while ν' corresponds to the same for the intermediate state.

Graphically we have

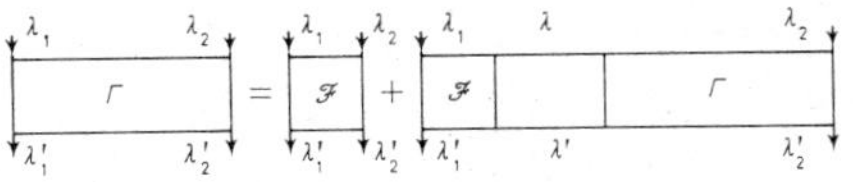

The summation in this equation is performed over all states of λ and λ' out of which one is above and the other below the Fermi energy in accordance with the value

$$\mathscr{A}(\nu) = \frac{n_\lambda - n_{\lambda'}}{\varepsilon_\lambda - \varepsilon_{\lambda'} + \omega} .$$

We can perform such a renormalization of the equation for Γ that the summation will occur only over the states of the shell to which the scattered particles belong. For example, over the states of the last open shell. Instead of the local interaction $\mathscr{F}$ the renormalized equation will contain the nonlocal interaction $\mathscr{F}'$ which will include part of the interaction due to the other shells (excitation of the core). Indeed, let us introduce the quantity $\mathscr{F}'$ by the formula

$$\mathscr{F}' = \mathscr{F} + \mathscr{F}' \mathscr{A}_2 \mathscr{F} = (1 + \mathscr{F}' \mathscr{A}_2) \mathscr{F} . \tag{4.11}$$

The subscript 2 of $\mathscr{A}$ shows that the summation is performed over all shells except that to which the scattered particles belong. Let us multiply the equation

$$\Gamma = \mathscr{F} + \mathscr{F} \mathscr{A} \Gamma,$$

on the left by $1 + \mathscr{F}' \mathscr{A}_2$. Then we have

$$\Gamma + \mathscr{F}' \mathscr{A}_2 \Gamma = \mathscr{F}' + \mathscr{F}' \mathscr{A} \Gamma, \qquad \Gamma = \mathscr{F}' + \mathscr{F}' \mathscr{A}_1 \Gamma. \tag{4.12}$$

Here the subscript 1 denotes that the summation is performed over the states of the indicated shell only.

Since the summation over only the states of the last shell is usually performed in nuclear calculations as the interaction is taken into account, the formulae must contain the complex quantity $\mathscr{F}'$ instead of the simple local interaction $\mathscr{F}$. This explains the need for introducing different constants for different processes. Yet according to eq. (4.11) $\mathscr{F}'$ is expressed by the quantity $\mathscr{F}$ which is identical for all nuclei (except the lightest) and all types of transitions. In some cases eq. (4.11) can be solved by the iteration method since the quantity

$$\mathscr{A}_{\lambda,\lambda'} = \frac{n_\lambda - n_{\lambda'}}{\varepsilon_\lambda - \varepsilon_{\lambda'} + \omega}$$

contains large denominators (ε_λ and $\varepsilon_{\lambda'}$ differ by two shells).

In the zero approximation we have $\mathscr{F}' = \mathscr{F}$.

In the next approximation we obtain

$$\mathscr{F}' = \mathscr{F} + \mathscr{F}\mathscr{A}_2\mathscr{F}'.$$

It can be shown that the second term is negative at small ω and corresponds to the attraction owing to the exchange of core excitations. The quantity $\mathscr{F}'$, just as $\mathscr{F}$, cannot be represented as the product of two factors

$$(\lambda_1\lambda_2|\mathscr{F}'|\lambda_3\lambda_4) \neq CQ_{\lambda_1\lambda_2}Q_{\lambda_3\lambda_4}\,.$$

For example, the simplest form $\mathscr{F}$ if the terms depending on the velocities are neglected is

$$(\lambda_1\lambda_2|\mathscr{F}|\lambda_3\lambda_4) = \mathscr{F}_0\int \varphi^*_{\lambda_1}\varphi_{\lambda_2}\varphi^*_{\lambda_3}\varphi_{\lambda_4}\,\mathrm{d}^3r\,,$$

i.e., is not divisible into factors.

To investigate the quadrupole excitations, for example, it is necessary to form with the entering states of $\mathscr{F}'$ and $\mathscr{F}$ a superposition with angular momentum 2 and solve the corresponding equation for radial matrix elements.

The representation of $\mathscr{F}'$ as a product distorts the radial dependence of this quantity and may lead to appreciable errors. The solution of eqs. (4.11) and (4.12) (after the separation of angular variables) on a computer is such a simple problem that it is pointless to introduce assumptions which simplify the interaction $\mathscr{F}'$. We shall call $\mathscr{F}'$ the effective interaction in an open shell or simply the effective interaction.

5. – Nuclei in an external field.

5·1. *Effective field.* – Let us determine the change of the Green function of a quasi-particle in an external field. For the sake of simplicity we confine ourselves to the first approximation of perturbation theory with respect to the field. However, the interaction between particles will be taken into account precisely. Let us write several graphs entering the Green function of a quasi-particle in the field $\tilde{G}$:

(5.1) $\tilde{G} =$ 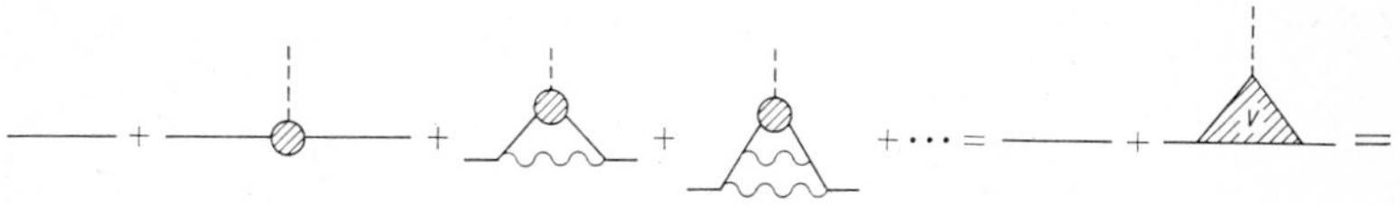

$$= G + GVG\,.$$

Here the circle denotes the direct interaction of quasi-particles with the external field V^0

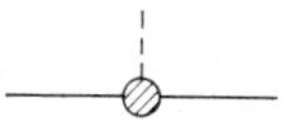 $= e_q V^0\,.$

e_q is the « charge » of the quasi-particle. We shall see that for some types of fields $e_q \neq 1$, which denotes the difference of the external field acting on quasi-particles from that applied to particles. For noninteracting particles we have

$\tilde{G}_0 =$ 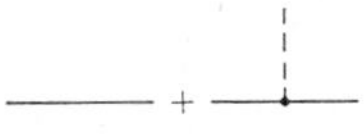 $= G_0 + G_0 V^0 G_0\,.$

Thus the cross-hatched triangle in eq. (5.1) replaces the point on this graph and corresponds to the effective field V acting on a quasi-particle.

Let us obtain the equation for the field V. Among the graphs entering V there is one graph which does not contain the interaction between quasi-particles ($e_q V^0$). All the other graphs have the following structure. If we move from the apex of the triangle, we meet at first the circle ($e_q V^0$); then the two lines, one of a particle and the other of a hole (GG) and then the total sum of all graphs beginning with and ending in an interaction and transferring the particle and hole to a new state, *i.e.*, the quantity which we have termed the scattering amplitude Γ.

Thus we obtain

(5.2) $V =$ 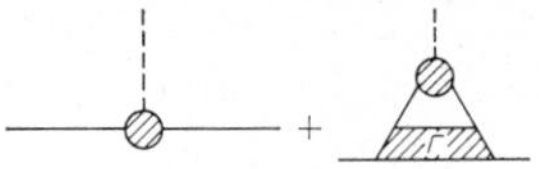 $= V^0 + \Gamma G G e_q V^0 .$

This expression can readily be written in a different form, using the equation for Γ (Sect. **4**·2)

$$\Gamma = \mathcal{F} + \mathcal{F} G G \Gamma .$$

Substituting into eq. (5.2) we obtain

$$V = e_q V^0 + \mathcal{F} G G e_q V^0 + \mathcal{F} G G \Gamma G G e_q V^0 = e_q V^0 + \mathcal{F} G G V , \tag{5.3}$$

or graphically

$V =$ 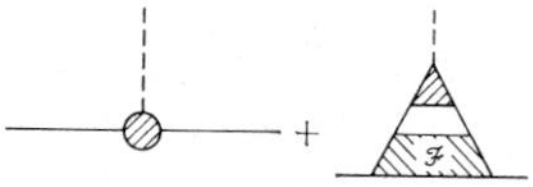 .

The first term in V describes the direct effect of the external field of the quasi-particle. The second term gives an additional field originating owing to the polarization of the medium, *i.e.*, caused by the force effect of the redistributed nuclear nucleons.

In the λ-representation we obtain for the external field of frequency ω (eq. (4.3))

$$V_{\lambda_1\lambda_2} = e_q V^0_{\lambda_1\lambda_2} + \sum (\lambda_1 \lambda_2 | \mathcal{F} | \lambda' \lambda) \mathcal{A}_{\lambda\lambda'} V_{\lambda\lambda'} , \tag{5.3'}$$

where

$$\mathcal{A}_{\lambda\lambda'} = - i \int G_\lambda(t) G_{\lambda'}(-t) \exp[-i\omega t] dt . \tag{5.4}$$

In those cases when $G_\lambda(t)$ and $G_{\lambda'}(t)$ have the above simple form, we obtain

$$\mathcal{A}_{\lambda\lambda'} = \frac{n_\lambda - n_{\lambda'}}{\varepsilon_\lambda - \varepsilon_{\lambda'} - \omega} . \tag{5.4'}$$

When the pair correlation is essential or when there are close competing levels the expression for $\mathcal{A}_{\lambda\lambda'}$ becomes more complex.

In the equation for V we have omitted the isotopic indices. Equation (5.3) describes the effective field acting on both protons (V^p) and neutrons (V^n).

Let us write eq. (5.3) displaying the isotopic indices. Let the external field act in the protons (V^{0p}) and neutrons (V^{0n}). Then we shall have

$$(5.3'')\qquad \begin{cases} V^{p} = e_q^{pp}V^{0p} + e_q^{pn}V^{0n} + \mathscr{F}^{pp}\delta G^{p} + \mathscr{F}^{pn}\delta G^{n}, \\ V^{n} = e_q^{nn}V^{0n} + e_q^{np}V^{0p} + \mathscr{F}^{nn}\delta G^{n} + \mathscr{F}^{np}\delta G^{p}. \end{cases}$$

We shall see that for the scalar external field we have $e_q^{np} = 0$, $e_q^{pp} = e_q^{nn} = 1$. However, in other cases it will appear that $e_q^{np} \neq 0$, *i.e.*, the external field applied only to protons acts directly on neutron quasi-particles as well. Incidentally, in all cases investigated so far the nondiagonal charge e_q^{np} is numerically small ($\lesssim 0.1$). The connection between the quantities $\mathscr{F}^{pp} = \mathscr{F}^{nn}$ and $\mathscr{F}^{np} = \mathscr{F}^{pn}$ with the isotopic components of $\hat{\mathscr{F}}$ is given in Sect. **4**.3.

Equation (5.3) can be simplified considerably if it is assumed that the proton Green functions differ little from their neutron counterparts. This is possible in those cases when in the sums over states the main contribution comes from states which are not very close to the Fermi energy. Then adding and subtracting eq. (5.3′), we obtain two independent equations

$$V^{+} = e_q^{+}V^{0+} + \mathscr{F}^{+}GGV^{+},$$
$$V^{-} = e_q^{-}V^{0-} + \mathscr{F}^{-}GGV^{-},$$

where

$$V^{+,-} = V^{p} \pm V^{n}, \qquad \mathscr{F}^{+,-} = \mathscr{F}^{pp} \pm \mathscr{F}^{pn},$$
$$e_q^{+,-} = e_q^{pp} \pm e_q^{pn}, \qquad V^{0+,-} = V^{0p} \pm V^{0n}.$$

5.2. *Effective interaction of quasi-particles in an open shell.* – For the processes involving transitions inside the last open shell it is convenient to carry out such a renormalization of eq. (5.3) that the summation be performed only over the states of the last shell.

Let us divide $\mathscr{A}$, as it was done when the interaction through the core was introduced in Sect. **4**.6, into two terms:

$$\mathscr{A} = \mathscr{A}_1 + \mathscr{A}_2 .$$

$(\mathscr{A}_2)_{\lambda\lambda'}$ is not zero only when both states lie outside the last shell, and $(\mathscr{A}_1)_{\lambda\lambda'}$ is not zero when one state or both states lie in the last shell. Since in $\mathscr{A}_2$ both Green functions are sufficiently far from the Fermi surface, the pair correlation and in general the effect of any near-Fermi-surface states can always be neglected in them. Therefore, $\mathscr{A}_2$ is given by the simple expression (5.4).

Let us write the equation for V symbolically

$$V = e_q V^0 + \mathscr{F}\mathscr{A}_1 V + \mathscr{F}\mathscr{A}_2 V .$$

In the third term we replace V with the aid of the right-hand side of this equation. Repeating this operation just as it was done in the previous Section we obtain

$$V = e_q\{1 + \mathscr{F}\mathscr{A}_2 + \mathscr{F}\mathscr{A}_2\mathscr{F}\mathscr{A}_2 + \dots\}V^0 + \{\mathscr{F} + \mathscr{F}\mathscr{A}_2\mathscr{F} + \mathscr{F}\mathscr{A}_2\mathscr{F}\mathscr{A}_2\mathscr{F} + \dots\}\mathscr{A}_1 V.$$

The expression in brackets before $\mathscr{A}_1 V$ is denoted by $\mathscr{F}'$:

(5.5) $$\mathscr{F}' = \mathscr{F} + \mathscr{F}\mathscr{A}_2\mathscr{F} + \mathscr{F}\mathscr{A}_2\mathscr{F}\mathscr{A}_2\mathscr{F} + \dots = \mathscr{F} + \mathscr{F}\mathscr{A}_2\mathscr{F}'.$$

In the λ-representation we have

(5.5') $$(\lambda_1\lambda_2|\mathscr{F}'|\lambda_3\lambda_4) = (\lambda_1\lambda_2|\mathscr{F}|\lambda_3\lambda_4) + \sum{}''(\lambda_1\lambda_2|\mathscr{F}|\lambda'\lambda)\frac{n_\lambda - n_{\lambda'}}{\varepsilon_\lambda - \varepsilon_{\lambda'} + \omega}(\lambda\lambda'|\mathscr{F}'|\lambda_3\lambda_4).$$

The sign $''$ of the sum denotes that neither λ nor λ' lie in the last shell.

This is the equation for the effective interaction of quasi-particles in the last shell. Since the denominator of $\mathscr{A}_2$ contains large energy differences corresponding to the distance between two shells, eq. (5.5) can be solved by the iteration method in many cases.

Let us now denote by V' the quantity

(5.6) $$V' = e_q\{1 + \mathscr{F}\mathscr{A}_2 + \mathscr{F}\mathscr{A}_2\mathscr{F}\mathscr{A}_2 + \dots\}V^0 =$$
$$= e_q V^0 + \mathscr{F}\mathscr{A}_2\{e_q V^0 + \mathscr{F}\mathscr{A}_2 V^0 + \dots\} = e_q V^0 + \mathscr{F}\mathscr{A}_2 V'.$$

In these notations the equation for V takes the form

(5.7) $$V = V' + \mathscr{F}'\mathscr{A}_1 V.$$

In eq. (5.7) the summation is performed over the states out of which one state or two states lie in the last shell. The quantity $\mathscr{A}_1$ in eq. (5.7) must be determined taking into account the distortion of the Green function due to the effect of near levels. In the next Section we shall consider the most important cause of this distortion: pair correlation.

5·3. *Effective field in the case of pair correlation.* – Let us first of all write the equation for V in such a form as would be valid regardless of the form of the quasi-particle Green functions. The second term in the equation for V can always be represented as

(5.8) $$V - e_q V^0 = \mathscr{F}\delta G,$$

where δG is the change of the Green function in the field. Indeed if we move from the side of the free ends, the graphs $V - e_q V^0$ begin with an interaction, and if we isolate the block $\mathscr{F}$ which does not contain two lines, we meet further the graphs beginning with and ending in a quasi-particle and containing an external field, *i.e.*, a change of the Green function in the field. In a particular case when

$$\delta G = GVG\,,$$

we obtain the earlier expression for V. In the case of the pair correlation δG is given by a more complex expression.

Let us note that eq. (5.8) has an easily visualizable meaning. Since $\mathcal{F}$ is δ-like in time, $\delta G(t_1, t_2)$ in eq. (5.8) is taken at identical times. Let us assume that we take $\delta G(t_1, t_2)$ at $t_2 = t_1 + 0$. Then the Green function $G(t_1, t_1 + 0)$ coincides, as we have seen in Sect. **3**.3, with the density matrix

$$\varrho_{\lambda'\lambda}(t) = G_{\lambda\lambda'}(t, t+0)\,.$$

Therefore, the right-hand side of eq. (5.2) can be written in the form

$$(V - e_q V^0)_{\lambda_1\lambda_2} = (\mathcal{F}\delta G)_{\lambda_1\lambda_2} = \sum (\lambda_1\lambda_2|\mathcal{F}|\lambda\lambda')\,\delta\varrho_{\lambda'\lambda}\,.$$

In this form eq. (5.2) acquires a simple physical meaning: an additional field due to the polarization of the medium is determined as the matrix product of the local interaction of quasi-particles by a matrix density change. In particular, if $\mathcal{F}$ does not depend on velocities and spins, *i.e.*, has this form in the co-ordinate representation

$$\mathcal{F}(\boldsymbol{r}_1, \boldsymbol{r}_2, \boldsymbol{r}_3, \boldsymbol{r}_4) = \mathcal{F}_0\delta(\boldsymbol{r}_1 - \boldsymbol{r}_2)\delta(\boldsymbol{r}_1 - \boldsymbol{r}_3)\delta(\boldsymbol{r}_3 - \boldsymbol{r}_4)\,,$$

we obtain

$$(\mathcal{F}\delta\varrho)_{\lambda_1\lambda_2} = \mathcal{F}_0 \sum_{\lambda\lambda'} \int \varphi^*_{\lambda_1}\varphi_{\lambda_2}\varphi^*_{\lambda}\varphi_{\lambda'}\,\mathrm{d}^3r\,(\delta\varrho)_{\lambda'\lambda}\,.$$

However, the quantity

$$\delta n(\boldsymbol{r}, t) = \sum (\delta\varrho)_{\lambda'\lambda}\varphi^*_{\lambda}(\boldsymbol{r})\varphi_{\lambda'}(\boldsymbol{r})$$

is the change of the quasi-particle density, and the additional field in the co-ordinate representation is

$$V - e_q V^0 = \mathcal{F}_0\delta n(\boldsymbol{r}, t)\,,$$

as it can well be expected for the δ-like interaction. Thus we have found that in eq. (5.8) by δG we must understand δG^-. It can readily be shown that this specification is essential only in static fields.

Thus our aim is to find in the case of a pairing correlation the change $\delta\varrho$ of the density matrix in an external field. For this purpose let us find the change of G in the external field. In Sect. **3**'3 it was shown how the effective field is introduced into the equation for the functions G and F. Now some more precise reservations must be made. Equation (3.5) for G and F in a field assumes the form

$$(5.9)\qquad \begin{cases} \left(i\dfrac{\partial}{\partial t}-H-V\right)\tilde{G}=-\tilde{\Delta}\tilde{F}+\delta(\boldsymbol{r}-\boldsymbol{r}')\delta(t-t'),\\[2mm] \left(i\dfrac{\partial}{\partial t}+H-V^T\right)\tilde{F}=-\tilde{\Delta}^*\tilde{G}. \end{cases}$$

The field V^T in the equation for F is connected with the field

$$V=V(\omega)\exp[-i\omega t],$$

by the relation (*)

$$V^T(t)=\pm V(-\omega)\exp[-i\omega t].$$

The plus sign corresponds to even fields and the minus sign to odd fields with respect to the replacement of t by $-t$.

We have introduced here the quantity $\tilde{\Delta}$ instead of Δ since the change of Δ in the field must also be taken into account which we did not mention in Sect. **3**'8 for the sake of simplicity.

Thus eq. (5.9) must be complemented by the equation for Δ in the field.

Keeping only the first term of the expansion we obtain after trivial algebraic transformations

$$(5.10)\qquad \begin{cases} \delta G=GVG-F^*V^TF+Gd^{(1)}F-F^*d^{(2)}G,\\ \delta F=Fd^{(1)}F+G^Td^{(2)}G+FVG+G^TV^TF, \end{cases}$$

where

$$d^{(1)}=\delta\Delta=\tilde{\Delta}-\Delta,\qquad d^{(2)}=\delta\Delta^*=\widetilde{\Delta^*}-\Delta^*.$$

We shall take up the determination of $d^{(1)}$ and $d^{(2)}$ later.

5'4. *Density matrix variation. Set of equations for the effective field.* – To obtain the change of the density matrix in the field we must find

$$\varrho_{\lambda'\lambda}=-i\big(\delta G(t_1-t_2)\big)_{\lambda\lambda'}\big|_{t_2=t_1+0}=\int_{\tau\to 0}\big(\delta G(\varepsilon)\big)_{\lambda\lambda'}\exp[-i\varepsilon\tau]\frac{d\varepsilon}{2\pi i}.$$

(*) A. MIGDAL: *The Theory of Finite Fermi Systems and the Properties of Nuclei*, Interscience Edition series (in the press).

Let us write eq. (5.10) in the λ, ε representation (assuming that $F^* = F$) for the field $V_0(t) = V_0 \exp[i\omega t]$

$$(\delta G)_{\lambda\lambda'} = G_\lambda(\varepsilon) V_{\lambda\lambda'} G_{\lambda'}(\varepsilon+\omega) - F_\lambda(\varepsilon) V_{\lambda\lambda'} F_{\lambda'}(\varepsilon+\omega) + \\ + G_\lambda(\varepsilon) d^{(1)}_{\lambda\lambda'} F_{\lambda'}(\varepsilon+\omega) - F_\lambda(\varepsilon) d^{(2)}_{\lambda\lambda'} G_{\lambda'}(\varepsilon+\omega) .$$

Similarly we can write the second eq. (5.10). The quantities $d^{(1)}$ and $d^{(2)}$ depend weakly on ε and can be taken at $\varepsilon = \varepsilon_F$ just as V.

Let us write the integral of G over dε, *i.e.*, $\delta\varrho$ in the form

$$(\delta\varrho)_{\lambda\lambda'} = \varrho'_{\lambda\lambda'} = \mathscr{L}_{\lambda\lambda'} V_{\lambda\lambda'} + \mathscr{M}^{(1)}_{\lambda\lambda'} d^{(1)}_{\lambda\lambda'} + \mathscr{M}^{(2)}_{\lambda\lambda'} d^{(2)}_{\lambda\lambda'} . \tag{5.11}$$

We can readily obtain, using eq. (3.4) for G and F

$$\left\{\begin{aligned} \mathscr{L}_{\lambda_1\lambda_2} &= -\frac{(E_{\lambda_1} - E_{\lambda_2})(E_{\lambda_1}E_{\lambda_2} - \varepsilon_{\lambda_1}\varepsilon_{\lambda_2} + \Delta_{\lambda_1}\Delta_{\lambda_2} T) + \omega(\varepsilon_{\lambda_2}E_{\lambda_1} - \varepsilon_{\lambda_1}E_{\lambda_2})}{2E_{\lambda_1}E_{\lambda_2}[(E_{\lambda_1}+E_{\lambda_2})^2 - \omega^2]} , \\ \mathscr{M}^{(1)}_{\lambda_1\lambda_2} &= \frac{\Delta_{\lambda_2}(-\omega E_{\lambda_1} + \varepsilon_{\lambda_1}(E_{\lambda_1}+E_{\lambda_2}))}{2E_{\lambda_1}E_{\lambda_2}[(E_{\lambda_1}+E_{\lambda_2})^2 - \omega^2]} , \\ \mathscr{M}^{(2)}_{\lambda_1\lambda_2} &= +\mathscr{M}^{(1)}_{\lambda_2\lambda_1}(-\omega) . \end{aligned}\right. \tag{5.12}$$

We denote by T the operation giving the field V^T from the field V

$$TV(\omega) = V^T(\omega) = \pm V(-\omega) .$$

5·5. *Conservation of the number of quasi-particles.* – Since near the Fermi surface the change of the quasi-particle density matrix $\delta\varrho$ differs by only a factor from the change of the particle density matrix $\delta\varrho^a$, quasi-particle conservation follows from particle conservation. *Viz.*, we have

$$\frac{\partial n'(\boldsymbol{r})}{\partial t} + \operatorname{div} \boldsymbol{j} = 0 ,$$

where $n'(\boldsymbol{r})$ is the density n and $\boldsymbol{j}$ is the quasi-particle current density.

Symbolically the change of the quasi-particle density matrix can be written as

$$\delta\varrho = \mathscr{L}V + \mathscr{M}^{(1)}d^{(1)} + \mathscr{M}^{(2)}d^{(2)}.$$

The change of the quasi-particle density $n'(\boldsymbol{r})$ is

$$n'(\boldsymbol{r}) = \sum \{\mathscr{L}V + \mathscr{M}^{(1)}d^{(1)} + \mathscr{M}^{(2)}d^{(2)}\}_{\lambda_1\lambda_2} \varphi^*_{\lambda_1}(\boldsymbol{r}) \varphi_{\lambda_2}(\boldsymbol{r}) .$$

The quasi-particle current density is given by the expression

$$j_\alpha(\boldsymbol{r}) = \sum \{\mathscr{L}V + \mathscr{M}^{(1)}d^{(1)} + \mathscr{M}^{(2)}d^{(2)}\}_{\lambda_1\lambda_2} \cdot \frac{1}{2m_i^*}\left(\varphi^*_{\lambda_1}\frac{\partial}{\partial r_\alpha}\varphi_{\lambda_2} - \varphi_{\lambda_2}\frac{\partial}{\partial r_\alpha}\varphi^*_{\lambda_1}\right) .$$

Let us calculate $\operatorname{div} \boldsymbol{j} = \partial j_\alpha / \partial r_\alpha$. From the equation for φ_λ we obtain

$$\frac{\partial}{\partial r_\alpha}\left\{\varphi^*_{\lambda_1}\frac{\partial \varphi_{\lambda_2}}{\partial r_\alpha} - \varphi_{\lambda_2}\frac{\partial \varphi^*_{\lambda_1}}{\partial r_\alpha}\right\} = (\varphi^*_{\lambda_1}\Delta\,\varphi_{\lambda_2} - \varphi_{\lambda_2}\Delta\varphi^*_{\lambda_1}) = 2m^*(\varepsilon_{\lambda_1} - \varepsilon_{\lambda_2})\varphi^*_{\lambda_1}\varphi_{\lambda_2}\,.$$

Thus we have

$$\operatorname{div} \boldsymbol{j} = -i\sum\{\mathscr{L}V + \mathscr{M}^{(1)}d^{(1)} + \mathscr{M}^{(2)}d^{(2)}\}(\varepsilon_{\lambda_1} - \varepsilon_{\lambda_2})\varphi^*_{\lambda_1}\varphi_{\lambda_2}\,.$$

Substituting the discontinuity equation

$$(5.13)\qquad \sum\{\mathscr{L}V + \mathscr{M}^{(1)}d^{(1)} + \mathscr{M}^{(2)}d^{(2)}\}_{\lambda_1\lambda_2}(\omega + \varepsilon_{\lambda_1} - \varepsilon_{\lambda_2})\varphi^*_{\lambda_1}(\boldsymbol{r})\varphi_{\lambda_2}(\boldsymbol{r}) = 0\,.$$

This equation can be used for determining $d^{(1)}$ and $d^{(2)}$ if we employ also the relation

$$(5.14)\qquad d^{(2)}_{\lambda_1\lambda_2}(\omega) = Td^{(1)}_{\lambda_1\lambda_2}(\omega) = \pm\, d^{(1)}_{\lambda_1\lambda_2}(-\omega)\,,$$

where T is the time-reversal operation. The plus sign corresponds to even fields and the minus sign to odd fields with respect to time reversal. This relation follows from the fact that $d^{(1)}$ describes the process inverse to that described by $d^{(2)}$. The change of the sign of ω corresponds to the replacement of quantum emission by quantum absorption.

We use eq. (5.13) for determining $d^{(1)}$ and $d^{(2)}$ when investigating collective vibrations.

5'6. *Set of equations in the case of a scalar field.* – To illustrate the relations obtained above let us consider in more detail the case of the scalar external field. We reduce the equations for V, $d^{(1)}$ and $d^{(2)}$ to a more convenient form in which they will be used for calculating the quadrupole moments and investigating collective vibrations.

Let us neglect the velocity dependence of the interaction forces and the spin-orbit term in $\mathscr{F}$. Then we have

$$\left(\frac{\mathrm{d}n}{\mathrm{d}\varepsilon_{\mathrm{F}}}\right)\mathscr{F} = \hat{f}_0 + \hat{g}_0\,\bar{\sigma}_1\bar{\sigma}_2\,.$$

We denote by $\hat{f}_0$ and $\hat{g}_0$ the corresponding isotopic matrices. In the case of a scalar field the term $\hat{g}_0\bar{\sigma}_1\bar{\sigma}_2$ does not enter the effective field equation. Indeed, this term would make an addition to the effective field of the form

$$\hat{g}_0\bar{\sigma}\,\mathrm{Tr}\,\bar{\sigma}\delta\varrho\,,$$

which is zero since the scalar field causes no changes in the spin distribution of particles.

The effective field equation takes the form

$$V_{\lambda_1\lambda_2} = V^0_{\lambda_1\lambda_2} + \left(\frac{\mathrm{d}n}{\mathrm{d}\varepsilon_F}\right)^{-1} \sum (\varphi^*_{\lambda_1}\varphi_{\lambda_2}\hat{f}_0\varphi^*_{\lambda}\varphi_{\lambda'})(\delta\varrho)_{\lambda'\lambda}\,, \tag{5.15}$$

where $\delta\varrho$ equals

$$(\delta\varrho)_{\lambda'\lambda} = \{\mathscr{L}V + \mathscr{M}^{(1)}d^{(1)} + \mathscr{M}^{(2)}d^{(2)}\}_{\lambda\lambda'}\,,$$

and $d^{(1)}$ and $d^{(2)}$ are determined from the eq. (5.13). For the time being we omit the isotopic indices. We assume that $\hat{f}_0(r)$ is a function of r in order to take into account the transition of $\hat{f}_0$ from the value inside the nucleus to the value outside (see p. 232).

Multiplying eq. (5.15) by φ_{λ_1} and summing over λ_1 we obtain

$$V(\boldsymbol{r}) = V_0(\boldsymbol{r}) + \left(\frac{\mathrm{d}n}{\mathrm{d}\varepsilon_F}\right)^{-1} \hat{f}_0(\boldsymbol{r}) \sum \varphi^*_{\lambda}(\boldsymbol{r})\varphi_{\lambda'}(\boldsymbol{r})(\delta\varrho)_{\lambda'\lambda} = V_0(\boldsymbol{r}) + \left(\frac{\mathrm{d}n}{\mathrm{d}\varepsilon_F}\right)^{-1} \hat{f}_0(\boldsymbol{r})n'(\boldsymbol{r})\,, \tag{5.16}$$

where $n'(\boldsymbol{r})$ is the change of the quasi-particle density.

Let us reduce eq. (5.16) to a more convenient form. Since the matrix elements $V_{\lambda_1\lambda_2}$ are not zero only for the same projection of the angular momentum in the states $\lambda_1\lambda_2$ the phases of the functions φ_{λ_1} and φ_{λ_2} cancel out and the functions can be regarded as real. Besides, since V is a function of only the co-ordinates, we have $V_{\lambda_1\lambda_2} = V_{\lambda_2\lambda_1}$. Since the field does not change under T transformation, we have according to eq. (5.14)

$$d^{(2)}_{\lambda_1\lambda_2}(\omega) = d^{(1)}_{\lambda_1\lambda_2}(-\omega)\,.$$

Let us introduce the notations

$$\begin{cases} d^{\alpha}_{12}(\omega) = \frac{1}{2}\big(d^{(1)}_{12}(\omega) - d^{(1)}_{12}(-\omega)\big)\,, \\ d^{\beta}_{12}(\omega) = \frac{1}{2}\big(d^{(1)}_{12}(\omega) + d^{(1)}_{12}(-\omega)\big)\,, \end{cases} \tag{5.17}$$

(1, 2 replace λ_1, λ_2). Substituting eq. (5.12) into eq. (5.13), we obtain after trivial algebraic transformations

$$\sum_{1,2}\varphi^*_1(\boldsymbol{r})\varphi_2(\boldsymbol{r})\left\{\frac{\omega V_{12}[(E_1+E_2)(E_1E_2-\varepsilon_1\varepsilon_2+\Delta_1\Delta_2)}{\mathscr{D}_{12}} + \frac{(\varepsilon_1-\varepsilon_2)(\varepsilon_2E_1-\varepsilon_1E_2)}{\mathscr{D}_{12}} + \frac{(E_1+E_2)(\varepsilon_1-\varepsilon_2)(\Delta_2\varepsilon_1-\Delta_1\varepsilon_2)-\omega^2(E_1\Delta_2+E_2\Delta_1)}{\mathscr{D}_{12}}d^{\alpha}_{12} + \omega\frac{(E_1+E_2)(\Delta_2\varepsilon_1+\Delta_1\varepsilon_2)-(\varepsilon_1-\varepsilon_2)(E_2\Delta_1-E_1\Delta_2)}{\mathscr{D}_{12}}d^{\beta}_{12}\right\} = 0\,. \tag{5.18}$$

Here $\mathscr{D}_{12}$ denotes $\mathscr{D}_{12}=2E_1E_2[(E_1+E_2)^2-\omega^2]$. The operator T in $\mathscr{L}$ equals 1 since we have $TV(\omega)=V(-\omega)=V(\omega)$. This expression contains two unknown quantities d^α and d^β. However, the expression with d^β changes sign in the transition across the Fermi surface ($\varepsilon_{1,2}$ are counted from the Fermi energy). The sum receives a substantial contribution from the levels lying in the layer $\sim\Delta$ on both sides of the Fermi surface. Therefore, in those cases when several levels can fit within the energy interval $\sim 2\Delta$, the term with d^β makes a considerably smaller contribution than the term with d^α. The equations for d^α and d^β can readily be obtained from eq. (5.17); it appears that the quantities d^α and V enter the equation for d^β with factors changing sign in the transition across the Fermi surface and thus we have $d^\beta \ll d^\alpha$. In the following we shall assume that $d^\beta=0$. For precise calculations it is necessary to solve the equations for d^α and d^β. Integrating eq. (5.18) over the volume we obtain

$$2\sum_1 \frac{V_{11}E_1\Delta_1^2}{\mathscr{D}_{11}}=\omega\sum_1\frac{E_1\Delta_1}{\mathscr{D}_{11}}d_{11}^\alpha\,. \tag{5.19}$$

From this relation it follows that the diagonal elements d^α have a pole at $\omega\to 0$. The addition of the constant V changes the residue at this pole. Let us count V from the quantity $\bar{V}$ chosen so that d^α have no pole at $\omega=0$.

The addition to V of the constants $\bar{V}$ entails, as is clear from eq. (5.19), the addition of the quantity $(2\Delta_1/\omega)\bar{V}$ to d_{11}^α. Therefore, we have

$$2\sum V_{11}\frac{E_1\Delta_1^2}{\mathscr{D}_{11}}=2\bar{V}\sum\frac{E_1\Delta_1^2}{\mathscr{D}_{11}}+2\sum\frac{V'_{11}E_1\Delta_1^2}{\mathscr{D}_{11}}=\omega\sum\frac{E_1\Delta_1 d_{11}^{\alpha'}}{\mathscr{D}_{11}}+2\bar{V}\sum\frac{E_1\Delta_1^2}{\mathscr{D}_{11}}\,.$$

Let us choose $\bar{V}$ from the condition that the quantity $\sum(V'_{11}E_1\Delta_1^2/\mathscr{D}_{11})$ converts to zero. Then $d^{\alpha'}$ will have no pole at $\omega=0$. We obtain

$$\bar{V}=\frac{\sum V_{11}\big(\Delta_1^2/E_1(4E_1^2-\omega^2)\big)}{\sum\big(\Delta_1^2/E_1(4E_1^2-\omega^2)\big)}\,. \tag{5.20}$$

Since $d^{\alpha'}$ is an odd function of ω having no pole at $\omega=0$, $d^{\alpha'}\sim\omega$ can be discarded at small ω. Therefore, we can assume that $d^\alpha=0$ for the static field, but count V from the quantity given by eq. (5.20). We shall deal with the case of determining d^α for nonstatic fields in the investigation of collective vibrations. Thus the equations for the scalar field have the form (5.16) where $n'(\boldsymbol{r})$ is given by the expression

$$n'(\boldsymbol{r})=\sum\frac{(E_1+E_2)(E_1E_2-\varepsilon_1\varepsilon_2+\Delta_1\Delta_2)}{\mathscr{D}_{12}}V'_{12}\varphi_1(\boldsymbol{r})\varphi_2^*(\boldsymbol{r})-$$
$$-\omega\sum\frac{E_1\Delta_2+E_2\Delta_1}{\mathscr{D}_{12}}d_{12}^\alpha\varphi_1(\boldsymbol{r})\varphi_2^*(\boldsymbol{r})\,, \tag{5.21}$$

where d^α has no pole any longer at $\omega = 0$ (we omit the prime of $d^{\alpha'}$).
Similar expressions entering eq. (5.13) are used to obtain eq. (5.21).
When Δ_λ depends weakly on λ, eq. (5.21) becomes simpler. We obtain

$$\sum \frac{[(\varepsilon_1 - \varepsilon_2)^2 - \omega^2] d_{12}^\alpha + 2\Delta\omega V_{12}}{\mathscr{D}_{12}} (E_1 + E_2)\varphi_1\varphi_2^* = a \,. \tag{5.22}$$

5'7. *Change of density matrix vs. number of particles.* – The change of the quasi-particle density matrix as an external field is superimposed was shown to be given by the expression

$$\varrho' = \mathscr{A} V .$$

On the other hand, for V we had

$$V = e_q V^0 + \mathscr{F} \varrho' .$$

Substituting into the expression for ϱ' we obtain the equation for the change of the quasi-particle density matrix in a field:

$$\mathscr{A}^{-1} \varrho' = e_q V^0 + \mathscr{F} \varrho' \,.$$

In the λ-representation for the case when the pair correlation is inessential we can use eq. (5.4′) for $\mathscr{A}$. Then we have

$$(\omega - \varepsilon_\lambda + \varepsilon_{\lambda'}) \varrho'_{\lambda\lambda'} = (n_\lambda - n_{\lambda'}) \{ e_q V^0_{\lambda\lambda'} + \sum (\lambda\lambda' | \mathscr{F} | \lambda_1 \lambda_2) \cdot \varrho'_{\lambda_1\lambda_2} \} \,.$$

This equation coincides precisely with the kinetic equation for the density matrix of a gas of particles with the interaction $\mathscr{F}$ and charge e_q. This equation can be obtained very simply if we consider a gas of noninteracting quasi-particles in the field V.

The Hamiltonian of this gas has the form

$$H = \sum \varepsilon_\lambda b_\lambda^\dagger b_\lambda + \sum b_\lambda^\dagger b_{\lambda'} V_{\lambda\lambda'}(t) \,.$$

Commuting the quantity $b_{\lambda_1}^\dagger b_{\lambda_2}$ with the Hamiltonian, we obtain

$$[H, b_{\lambda_1}^\dagger b_{\lambda_2}] = (\varepsilon_{\lambda_1} - \varepsilon_{\lambda_2}) b_{\lambda_1}^\dagger b_{\lambda_2} + \sum_\lambda V_{\lambda\lambda_1} b_\lambda^\dagger b_{\lambda_2} - \sum_{\lambda'} V_{\lambda_2\lambda'} b_{\lambda_1}^\dagger b_{\lambda'} \,.$$

The density matrix is by definition (p. 187)

$$\varrho_{\lambda_2\lambda_1}(t) = \big(\Phi^*(t) b_{\lambda_1}^\dagger b_{\lambda_2} \Phi(t) \big) \,,$$

where $\Phi(t)$ is the function originating from the ground state under the action of the field V and satisfying the Schrödinger equation

$$i\frac{\partial\Phi}{\partial t}=H\Phi\,,$$

$$i\frac{\partial\varrho_{\lambda_1\lambda_2}}{\partial t}=-(\Phi[H,\,b^\dagger_{\lambda_2}b_{\lambda_1}]\Phi)=(\varepsilon_{\lambda_1}-\varepsilon_{\lambda_2})\varrho_{\lambda_1\lambda_2}+\sum V_{\lambda_1\lambda}\varrho_{\lambda\lambda_2}-\sum\varrho_{\lambda_1\lambda'}V_{\lambda'\lambda_2}\,.$$

Before the superimposition of the external field the density matrix is

$$\varrho^0_{\lambda_1\lambda_2}=n_{\lambda_1}\delta_{\lambda_1\lambda_2}\,.$$

To first order in the field V we obtain

$$\left[i\frac{\partial}{\partial t}-\varepsilon_{\lambda_1}+\varepsilon_{\lambda_2}\right]\varrho^{(1)}_{\lambda_1\lambda_2}=(n_{\lambda_2}-n_{\lambda_1})V_{\lambda_1\lambda_2}\,,$$

i.e., the equation coinciding with that obtained above.

The role of the particle interaction reduces to the field V differing from the external field V^0.

Thus in the case when there is no pair correlation the effective field equation can also be obtained without the Green functions. When the pair correlation is essential there is no simple equation for ϱ and obtaining the effective field equations without Green functions is an extremely cumbersome problem.

Let us consider the change of the density matrix *vs.* the number of particles in a system. Suppose the quasi-particle occupation numbers change by δn_λ. It will be shown below how δn_λ must be determined.

The expression for the change of the nondiagonal part of the density matrix

$$(\delta\varrho)_{\lambda_1\lambda_2}=\mathscr{A}_{\lambda_2\lambda_1}V_{\lambda_1\lambda_2}$$

remains valid in the absence of an external field if V is understood to mean the effective field originating from the rearrangement of the occupation numbers

(5.23) $$V_{\lambda_1\lambda_2}=\sum_{\lambda\lambda'}(\lambda_1\lambda_2|\mathscr{F}|\lambda\lambda')(\delta\varrho)_{\lambda'\lambda}(1-\delta_{\lambda\lambda'})+ \\ +\sum_{\lambda}(\lambda_1\lambda_2|\mathscr{F}|\lambda\lambda)\delta n_\lambda=\sum_{\lambda\lambda'}(\lambda_1\lambda_2|\mathscr{F}|\lambda\lambda')\mathscr{A}_{\lambda\lambda'}V_{\lambda\lambda'}+\sum_{\lambda}(\lambda_1\lambda_2|\mathscr{F}|\lambda\lambda)\delta n_\lambda\,.$$

Thus, if δn_λ are known, we can find V and the nondiagonal part of the density matrix. For the change of the density matrix we have the nonhomogeneous equation

(5.24) $$(\delta\varrho)_{\lambda_1\lambda_2}=\delta_{\lambda_1\lambda_2}\delta n_{\lambda_1}+(1-\delta_{\lambda_1\lambda_2})\mathscr{A}_{\lambda_1\lambda_2}\sum_{\lambda\lambda'}(\lambda_1\lambda_2|\mathscr{F}|\lambda\lambda')\delta\varrho_{\lambda'\lambda}\,.$$

Using the equation for the amplitude Γ we can represent eqs. (5.23) and (5.24) in a different form.

Equation (5.23) denotes symbolically

$$V = \mathscr{F}\delta^0\varrho + \mathscr{F}\mathscr{A}V,$$

where

$$(\delta^0\varrho)_{\lambda_1\lambda_2} = \delta_{\lambda_1\lambda_2}\delta n_{\lambda_1} .$$

Let us compare this equation with the equation for $\Gamma\delta_0\varrho$

$$\Gamma\delta_0\varrho = \mathscr{F}\delta_0\varrho + \mathscr{F}\mathscr{A}\Gamma\delta_0\varrho .$$

Thus we have

$$V = \Gamma\delta_0\varrho , \tag{5.25}$$

or in the λ-representation

$$V_{\lambda_1\lambda_2} = \sum_{\lambda} (\lambda_1\lambda_2|\Gamma|\lambda\lambda)\,\delta n_\lambda .$$

Similarly, eq. (5.24) can be written in the form

$$\delta\varrho = \delta_0\varrho + A\mathscr{F}\delta\varrho = \delta_0\varrho + A\mathscr{F}\delta_0\varrho + A\mathscr{F}A\mathscr{F}\delta_0\varrho + \dots = (1 + A\Gamma)\delta_0\varrho . \tag{5.26}$$

Let us now see how $\delta_0\varrho$, *i.e.*, the diagonal part of the change of the quasi-particle density matrix, is determined. The effective field changes the quasi-particle energy. To first order in V we have

$$\tilde{\varepsilon}_\lambda = \varepsilon_\lambda + V_{\lambda\lambda} .$$

The new occupation numbers $\tilde{n}_\lambda$ are obtained from the minimum condition for the energy of the system. If the level spacing near the Fermi surface is large compared with the interaction energy, the energy minimum requirement reduces to the condition

$$\tilde{n}_\lambda(\tilde{\varepsilon}_\lambda) = \begin{cases} 1 & \text{if } \tilde{\varepsilon}_\lambda < \tilde{\mu} , \\ 0 & \text{if } \tilde{\varepsilon}_\lambda > \tilde{\mu} , \end{cases} \tag{5.27}$$

where $\tilde{\mu}$ is a new chemical potential determined by the change of the total number of particles in the system

$$\delta N = \sum_{\lambda} \{\tilde{n}_\lambda(\tilde{\varepsilon}_\lambda) - n_\lambda(\varepsilon_\lambda)\} .$$

If the energy change in ε_λ, *i.e.*, $V_{\lambda\lambda}$ is smaller than the distance to the nearest level, the change of n_λ reduces to the settlement of the added particles on the nearest vacancies. If, on the other hand, the effective field V is so large that the levels cross, we have a more complex rearrangement of occupation numbers in accordance with the condition (5.27). When an odd particle is added to a closed shell, the resulting field can readily be shown to be of the order $V \sim \varepsilon_0/A$, which is smaller than the distance to the nearest level. Therefore, the added particle settles in this case on the nearest level and the change in the occupation numbers is

$$\delta n_\lambda = \delta_{\lambda\lambda_0} .$$

In the case of pair correlation, for all levels except the level λ_0 on which lies the odd particle and the level $-\lambda_0$ where there is a hole, the change of occupation numbers is given by a small change of the chemical potential and energies ε_λ

$$\text{(5.28)} \qquad \left\{ \begin{aligned} &\delta n_\lambda \underset{\substack{\lambda \neq \lambda_0 \\ \lambda \neq -\lambda_0}}{=} \frac{E_\lambda(\tilde\mu) - (\tilde\varepsilon_\lambda - \tilde\mu)}{2E_\lambda(\tilde\mu)} - \frac{E_\lambda(\mu) - (\varepsilon_\lambda - \mu)}{2E_\lambda(\mu)} , \\ &E_\lambda = \sqrt{\Delta_\lambda^2 + (\varepsilon_\lambda - \mu)^2} . \end{aligned} \right.$$

For $\lambda = \lambda_0$ and $\lambda = -\lambda_0$ the new occupation numbers are

$$\tilde n_{\lambda_0} = 1 , \qquad \tilde n_{-\lambda_0} = 0 .$$

Therefore the change of n_λ is given by the formula

$$\text{(5.28')} \qquad \left\{ \begin{aligned} (\delta n)_{\lambda_0} &= 1 - n_{\lambda_0} , \\ (\delta n)_{-\lambda_0} &= -n_{\lambda_0} . \end{aligned} \right.$$

Thus as long as there is no level crossing, δn_λ is determined very simply. If the levels cross, δn_λ is determined as follows. Assigning a certain rearrangement of particles over levels, we must determine $\delta\varrho$. Then we determine V by $\delta\varrho$ and new energies $\tilde E_\lambda$ with the aid of $\tilde\varepsilon_\lambda$. Then we calculate the energy of the system of quasi-particles taking into account the interaction $\mathcal{F}$. This calculation must be made for several trial distributions of $\tilde n_\lambda$: The distribution with the lowest energy gives the ground state of the system.

Thus in the external fields responsible for the crossing of levels the determination of δn_λ taking into account the quasi-particle interaction is a complex problem which must be solved afresh for each specific nucleus.

In the limiting case of quite strong fields the problem is simplified again since in this case many levels are involved and the change of the density matrix can be found using the quasi-classical approximation.

5·8. *Calculation of mean values.* – In the determination of the static nuclear moments (*e.g.* magnetic or quadrupole moments) we shall encounter the problem of calculating the mean value over the ground state of the operator of the form

$$\hat{Q} = \sum_{\lambda\lambda'} a_\lambda^\dagger a_{\lambda'} Q_{\lambda\lambda'} .$$

The mean value is expressed by the particle density matrix

$$Q = \langle \hat{Q} \rangle = \sum_{\lambda\lambda'} \varrho^a_{\lambda'\lambda} Q_{\lambda\lambda'} .$$

Suppose that the value of $\langle Q \rangle$ for some nucleus is known. Then we have

$$\delta\langle Q \rangle = \sum (\delta\varrho^a)_{\lambda'\lambda} Q_{\lambda\lambda'} ,$$

where $\delta\varrho^a$ is the change of the particle density matrix in the transition from the nucleus having the value $\langle Q \rangle$ to the nucleus under consideration. The change of $\delta\varrho^a$ can be expressed by the change of the quasi-particle density matrix $\delta\varrho$ determined from eq. (5.26).

We quote only the result, namely the following formula for calculating the mean values:

$$\delta\langle Q \rangle = \sum e_q (\delta\varrho)_{\lambda'\lambda} Q_{\lambda\lambda'} , \tag{5.29}$$

where e_q is the quasi-particle charge corresponding to the field Q.

Equation (5.29) has a very simple meaning. The change of the energy of the system under the action of the static field Q can be written as the change of the energy of the system of quasi-particles with charge e_q. Then, using eqs. (5.26) and (5.25) we obtain

$$\delta Q = e_q Q \delta\varrho = e_q Q (1 + \mathscr{A}\Gamma) \delta_0 \varrho = e_q V[Q] \delta_0 \varrho . \tag{5.30}$$

Here $V[Q]$ denotes the effective field caused by the external field Q. Thus, the change of the mean values is determined by the following simple formula:

$$\delta Q = e_q \sum_\lambda V_{\lambda\lambda}[Q] n_\lambda . \tag{5.30'}$$

Let one particle be added to the magic nucleus. Since in this case there is no crossing of terms and the interaction between quasi-particles is smaller than the distance to the near level, the nucleus receives one quasi-particle in the state λ_0 above the closed levels of the magic nucleus. Therefore

$$\delta n_\lambda = \delta_{\lambda\lambda_0}$$

and in this case the change of the mean value is given by the diagonal matrix elements of the effective field with respect to the state λ_0

$$\delta Q = e_q V_{\lambda_0\lambda_0}[Q] .$$

5·9. *Frequencies and probabilities of transitions.* – Let us write the equation for V in a more convenient form. We assume that the equation for $d^{(1)}$ and $d^{(2)}$ has been solved in the form

$$d^{(1)} = \mathscr{K}^{(1)} V, \qquad d^{(2)} = \mathscr{K}^{(2)} V.$$

Let us denote

$$\mathscr{L} + \mathscr{M}^{(1)}\mathscr{K}^{(1)} + \mathscr{M}^{(2)}\mathscr{K}^{(2)} = A .$$

Then the equation for V can be written as

$$V = e_q V^0 + \mathscr{F} A V.$$

Here $\delta\varrho = AV$ is the change of the density of quasi-particles in a field. The eigenfrequency ω_S of some state S is given by the condition

$$V_{\lambda\lambda'} \underset{\omega \to \omega_S}{=} \frac{\chi^{(S)}_{\lambda\lambda'}}{\omega - \omega_S} + V^r_{\lambda\lambda'} .$$

The residue of V at the pole ω_S satisfies the equation

(5.31) $$\chi^{(S)} = \mathscr{F} A_S \chi^{(S)}.$$

The solution of this equation gives the proper frequencies ω_S and the functions $\chi^{(S)}_{\lambda\lambda'}$ by which the transition probability is expressed (as we shall see later). Since eq. (5.31) determines χ accurately to within a constant factor we have only to find the normalization of χ. Substituting the expression of V near the pole into the equation for V we obtain

$$V^r(\omega - \omega_S) = e_q V^0(\omega - \omega_S) + \mathscr{F}_0 \frac{\mathrm{d}A}{\mathrm{d}\omega} \chi(\omega - \omega_S) + \mathscr{F} A_S V^r(\omega - \omega_S),$$

or

$$V^r = e_q V^0 + \mathscr{F} \frac{\mathrm{d}A}{\mathrm{d}\omega} \chi + \mathscr{F} A_S V^r .$$

Multiplying by χA and using eq. (5.31) we obtain

$$\chi A V^r = e_q \chi A V^0 + \chi \frac{\mathrm{d}A}{\mathrm{d}\omega} \chi + \chi A V^r .$$

Thus, χ is normalized as follows

$$\sum_{\nu} \chi(\nu) \frac{\mathrm{d}A(\nu)}{\mathrm{d}\omega} \chi(\nu) = -e_q \sum_{\nu} \chi(\nu) A(\nu) V^0(\nu) , \tag{5.32}$$

where ν denotes the set of symbols $\lambda_1\lambda_2$. We have now only to express the transition probability by the quantities χ and A. Let the external field perturb the Hamiltonian of the system as follows:

$$H' = \sum_{\lambda\lambda'} a_\lambda^\dagger a_{\lambda'} V^0_{\lambda\lambda'} \exp[-i\omega t] ,$$

where $a_\lambda^\dagger$, a_λ are the particle (and not quasi-particle) production and annihilation operators. Then the number of transitions per unit time to the state S is given by the well-known formula

$$W_{0S} = 2\pi |M_{0S}|^2 \delta(\omega - \omega_S) , \qquad \omega_S = E_S - E_0 , \tag{5.33}$$

where the transition amplitude M_{0S} is

$$M_{0S} = \sum_{\lambda\lambda'} (\Phi_0 a_\lambda^\dagger a_{\lambda'} \Phi_S) V^0_{\lambda\lambda'} .$$

The transition probability can be expressed very simply by the mean value of the perturbation over the perturbed ground state

$$\langle H' \rangle = (\Phi' H' \Phi') = -\sum_S \left[\frac{|M_{0S}|^2}{E_S - E_0 - \omega + i\gamma} + \frac{|M_{0S}|^2}{E_S - E_0 + \omega - i\gamma} \right] ;$$

the transition probability is

$$W_{0S} = 2 \operatorname{Im} \langle H' \rangle_S , \tag{5.34}$$

where $\langle H' \rangle_S$ is the term in $\langle H' \rangle$ corresponding to the transition to the state S. However, $\langle H' \rangle$ can be expressed by the change of the density matrix of quasi-particles in a field:

$$\langle H' \rangle = e_q V^0 \delta\varrho = \sum_{\lambda\lambda'} e_q V^0_{\lambda\lambda'} (\delta\varrho)_{\lambda\lambda'} = e_q V^0 A V .$$

Introducing V near the pole we obtain

$$\langle H' \rangle = e_q V^0 A V = e_q V^0 A \frac{\chi}{\omega - \omega_S + i\gamma} ,$$

whence from eq. (5.34) we have

$$W_{0S} = 2\pi e_q \sum_\nu V^0(\nu) A(\nu) \chi(\nu) \delta(\omega - \omega_S) . \tag{5.35}$$

Let us denote by ϱ' the residue at the pole of the density matrix in the field

$$\delta\varrho = AV \underset{\omega\to\omega_S}{=} \frac{\varrho'}{\omega - \omega_S}, \qquad \varrho' = A\chi .$$

Then from the renormalization of χ we obtain the normalization for ϱ'

$$e_q V^0 \varrho' = \varrho' \frac{\mathrm{d}A^{-1}}{\mathrm{d}\omega} \varrho', \tag{5.36}$$

and W_{0S} can also be written in the form

$$W_{0S} = 2\pi \sum_\nu \varrho'(\nu) \frac{\mathrm{d}A^{-1}}{\mathrm{d}\omega} \varrho'(\nu) . \tag{5.37}$$

The results obtained so far are suitable for both single-particle and collective transitions.

For single-particle transitions we can obtain a more visualizable expression for the transition probability and energy which is specially simple for small transition frequencies.

Let us renormalize the equation for V similarly to the way it was done when the effective interaction in an open shell was introduced. Let a single-particle excitation correspond to a transition of a quasi-particle from the state λ_0 to the state λ_1. Let ν denote the set of symbols λ, λ'. The equation for V can be written as

$$V(\nu) = e_q V^0(\nu) + \sum_{\nu'} \mathscr{F}(\nu, \nu') A(\nu') V(\nu') ,$$

where

$$V(\nu) = V_{\lambda\lambda'} , \qquad \mathscr{F}(\nu, \nu') = (\lambda\lambda'|\mathscr{F}|\lambda''\lambda''') .$$

Let us isolate in the sum the term $\nu' = \nu_0 = \lambda_0, \lambda_1$ corresponding to the transition under study. Repeating the renormalization (5.5) we obtain

$$V(\nu) = e_q V_1(\nu) + \mathscr{F}_1(\nu, \nu_0) A(\nu_0) V(\nu_0) , \tag{5.38}$$

where

$$V_1 = V^0 + \mathscr{F}_1 A_1 V^0, \qquad \mathscr{F}_1 = \mathscr{F} + \mathscr{F} A_1 \mathscr{F}_1 , \tag{5.39}$$

A_1 denotes that in the sum there is no term with $\nu' = \nu_0$. Thus neither V_1 nor $\mathscr{F}_1$ contain the small denominator corresponding to $\omega = \varepsilon_{\lambda_0} - \varepsilon_{\lambda_1}$.

From the equation for V we obtain

$$V(\nu_0) = \frac{e_q V_1(\nu_0)}{1 - \mathscr{F}_1(\nu_0, \nu_0) A(\nu_0)} . \tag{5.40}$$

The transition frequency is given by relation

$$1 = \mathscr{F}_1(\nu_0, \nu_0) A(\nu_0) . \tag{5.41}$$

When the pair correlation is inessential we have

$$V_{\lambda_0\lambda_1} = \frac{e_q V_{1\lambda_0\lambda_1}(\omega - \varepsilon_{\lambda_1} + \varepsilon_{\lambda_0})}{\omega - \varepsilon_{\lambda_1} + \varepsilon_{\lambda_0} - (\lambda_0 \lambda_1 | \mathscr{F}_1 | \lambda_0 \lambda_1)(n_{\lambda_0} - n_{\lambda_1})} . \tag{5.42}$$

The pole of this expression gives the transition frequency

$$\omega = \varepsilon_{\lambda_1} - \varepsilon_{\lambda_0} + (\lambda_0 \lambda_1 | \mathscr{F}_1 | \lambda_0 \lambda_1)(n_{\lambda_0} - n_{\lambda_1}) . \tag{5.43}$$

To obtain the transition probability we transform the expression for the mean perturbation value

$$\begin{aligned}\langle H' \rangle = e_q V^0 A V = e_q \{V^0 A_0 V + V^0 A_1 [e_q V_1 + \mathscr{F}_1 A_0 V]\} = \\ = e_q (V^0 + V^0 A_1 \mathscr{F}_1) A_0 V + e_q^2 V^0 A_1 V_1 = e_q V_1 A_0 V + e_q^2 V^0 A_1 V_1 .\end{aligned}$$

Here A_0 denotes $A_0 = A(\nu_0)\delta_{\nu\nu_0}$. The second term has no pole which would correspond to our transition, and therefore, the transition probability is

$$W_{0S} = 2\,\mathrm{Im}\langle H' \rangle = 2\pi e_q V_1(\nu_0) A(\nu_0) \chi(\nu_0) \delta(\omega - \omega_S) ,$$

where $\chi(\nu_0)$ is the residue at the pole V equal, according to eq. (5.40), to

$$\chi(\nu_0) = -\frac{e_q V_1(\nu_0)}{(\mathrm{d}/\mathrm{d}\omega)(\mathscr{F}_1 A)} ,$$

or otherwise

$$W_{0S} = 2\pi e_q^2 \frac{|V_1(\nu_0)|^2}{\mathrm{d}A^{-1}/\mathrm{d}\omega - \mathrm{d}\mathscr{F}_1/\mathrm{d}\omega} \delta(\omega - \omega_S) . \tag{5.44}$$

Since $\mathscr{F}_1$ is an even function of ω, we obtain for small transition frequencies

$$\frac{\mathrm{d}\mathscr{F}_1}{\mathrm{d}\omega} = 2\omega \frac{\mathrm{d}\mathscr{F}_1}{\mathrm{d}\omega^2} \ll 1 . \tag{5.45}$$

It can readily be shown that the frequency smallness criterion is

$$\omega \ll \frac{\varepsilon_F}{A^{\frac{1}{3}}},$$

if only the sum of the equation for $\mathscr{F}_1$ contains no terms with anomalously small denominators. Let us assume moreover, that the pair correlation is inessential. Then we have

$$W_{0s} = 2\pi e_q^2 |V_{1\lambda_0\lambda_1}|^2 (n_{\lambda_0} - n_{\lambda_1}) \delta(\omega - \omega_s) . \tag{5.46}$$

This expression differs from the transition probability of noninteracting particles by the replacement of the matrix element $V^0_{\lambda_0\lambda_1}$ by the matrix element of the static effective field since we can assume that in V_1 $\omega = 0$. Besides, there appears the factor e_q^2, and the transition frequency ω_s is not equal to $\varepsilon_{\lambda_1} - \varepsilon_{\lambda_0}$ but is determined by the relation (5.41).

For a weak particle interaction when there is no pair correlation, ϱ' satisfies the equation

$$(\varepsilon_\lambda - \varepsilon_{\lambda'} + \omega) \varrho'_{\lambda\lambda'} = (n_\lambda - n_{\lambda'}) \sum_{\lambda_1\lambda_2} (\lambda\lambda' | \mathscr{F} | \lambda_1\lambda_2) \varrho'_{\lambda_1\lambda_2} \approx 0 ,$$

and consequently $\varrho'_{\lambda\lambda'}$ is not zero only under the condition

$$\omega = \varepsilon_{\lambda_0} - \varepsilon_{\lambda_1} > 0 .$$

Therefore, we have

$$\varrho'(\nu) = C\delta(\nu, \nu_0) ,$$

where $\nu_0 = (\lambda_0, \lambda_1)$.

The coefficients C are found from the normalization condition (5.36)

$$C = \frac{e_q V^0(\nu_0)}{dA^{-1}(\nu_0)/d\omega} .$$

Substituting in the expression for W_{0s} and assuming that $e_q = 1$ we obtain the well-known expression for the number of transitions

$$W_{0s} = |V^0_{\lambda_0\lambda_1}|^2 (n_{\lambda_0} - n_{\lambda_1}) \delta(\varepsilon_{\lambda_0} - \varepsilon_{\lambda_1} - \omega) .$$

Similarly, we check the limiting transition to a weak interaction ($\mathscr{F} \to 0$) taking into account the pair correlation.

We obtain the expression coinciding with the transition probability obtained with the aid of the canonical Bogolyubov transformation.

In nuclei the interaction $\mathscr{F}$ is not small, and the formulae obtained as $\mathscr{F} = 0$ can only be used for qualitative estimates.

5.10. *Conservation laws and quasi-particle charges for different fields.* – Conservation laws impose strong restrictions on the quasi-particle charge e_q. A formal derivation of the results given below can be found elsewhere (*). We shall confine ourselves to inductive physical considerations.

First of all let us consider the physical consequences following from the gauge invariance requirement.

The physical meaning of this requirement is as follows. Let vector fields $\partial f_n/\partial x_i$ and $\partial f_p/\partial x_i$ be imposed on neutrons and protons. Such fields are known to produce no physical changes in the system. In particular there occurs no polarization of the medium and the effective field acting on quasi-particles coincides with the external field. From this fact it follows that in the case of a scalar field acting on protons the charge of the proton quasi-particle equals that of a neutron quasi-particle.

For the vector field we obtain a more complicated expression which we shall give below.

Further information on quasi-particle charges can be obtained by taking advantage of the fact that in some fields (no longer fictitious) no redistribution of particles occurs and consequently the effective field equals the external field. Thus, in a uniform field acting equally on both kinds of particles the system oscillates as a whole without any internal changes. From this requirement we can readily obtain

$$V^{\mathrm{p}}_{\lambda\lambda'}(p^{\mathrm{p}}_{\alpha}+p^{\mathrm{n}}_{\alpha})=p_{\alpha}=(e^{\mathrm{pp}}_q+e^{\mathrm{np}}_q)\,p_{\alpha}\,,$$

i.e.,

$$e^{\mathrm{pp}}_q+e^{\mathrm{pn}}_q=e^{\mathrm{nn}}_q+e^{\mathrm{np}}_q=1\,.$$

Similarly, we can conclude that the sum $e^{\mathrm{pp}}_q+e^{\mathrm{np}}_q=1$ for any perturbation commuting with the Hamiltonian and having only diagonal matrix elements in the λ-representation, *i.e.*, for a perturbation of the form

$$H'=\sum a^{\dagger}_{\lambda}a^{}_{\lambda}Q_{\lambda\lambda}\,,$$

if the operator H' commutes with H.

Indeed, it can be shown that this perturbation produces no medium polarization. We shall call this perturbation diagonal.

Let us obtain the expression for the effective charge in the case of a perturbation of the form $\bar{\sigma}\cdot\bar{H}$. Since the charge e_q is given by the local particle interaction, the quantity in the nucleus little differs from the corresponding quantity in unlimited nuclear matter of the same density. Since the spin-orbit interaction

(*) A. Migdal: *A Theory of Finite Fermi Systems and the Properties of Atomic Nuclei* (Moscow, 1965).

in the nuclear matter is small, the total spin operator commutes with the Hamiltonian. Besides, in a sufficiently large system the spin-orbit correction to the quasi-particle Hamiltonian is inessential and can be omitted. The functions are then the eigenfunctions of the operator σ_z. Thus the perturbation is diagonal and

$$e_q^{\mathrm{pp}} + e_q^{\mathrm{np}} = 1 \,.$$

Let us write this condition in the form

$$e_q^{\mathrm{pp}} = 1 - \zeta_S \,, \qquad e_q^{\mathrm{pn}} = \zeta_S \,.$$

The quantity ζ_S is not calculated and must be found from experiment. The same quantity enters into the renormalization of the axial constants of β-decay in the nucleus. For allowed transitions the interaction with an electron-neutron field yields in the nuclear Hamiltonian a perturbation proportional to the Gamov-Teller transition. Let us find the effective charge for this external field.

Let us consider first the field $\tau_z\sigma_z$

$$\tau_z\sigma_z = \frac{1+\tau_z}{2}\sigma_z - \frac{1-\tau_z}{2}\sigma_z = \sigma_z^p - \sigma_z^n \,.$$

The nonhomogeneous term of the equation for V containing the external field is

$$e_q V^0[\tau_z\sigma_z] = e_q[\tau_z\sigma_z]\tau_z\sigma_z = e_q[\sigma_z^{\mathrm{p}}]\sigma_z - e_q[\sigma_z^{\mathrm{n}}]\sigma_z =$$

$$= \begin{Bmatrix} e_q^{\mathrm{pp}} - e_q^{\mathrm{pn}} \\ e_q^{\mathrm{np}} - e_q^{\mathrm{nn}} \end{Bmatrix} \sigma_z = \begin{Bmatrix} 1 - 2\zeta_S \\ -(1 - 2\zeta_S) \end{Bmatrix} \sigma_z = (1 - 2\zeta_S)\tau_z\sigma_z \,.$$

Thus we have

$$e_q[\tau_z\sigma_z] = 1 - 2\zeta_S \,.$$

Owing to the isotopic invariance, we shall have the same charge for the field $(\tau_x \pm i\tau_y)\sigma_z$. For the field $\tau_x \pm i\tau_y$ of the Fermi transition we obtain (considering first the field τ_z) $e_q = 1$.

Let us tabulate the charges e_q for different fields

Field	Charge
Scalar field $f(r)$	$e_q^{\mathrm{pp}} = 1, \quad e_q^{\mathrm{pn}} = 0$
Vector field p_α	$e_q^{\mathrm{pp}} = 1 - \frac{1}{3}(f_1^{\mathrm{np}}/m^*), \quad e_q^{\mathrm{pn}} = \frac{1}{3}(f_1^{\mathrm{np}}/m^*)$
Spinor field σ_α	$e_q^{\mathrm{pp}} = 1 - \zeta_S, \quad e_q^{\mathrm{pn}} = \zeta_S$
Orbital field $\boldsymbol{r} \times \boldsymbol{p}$	$e_q^{\mathrm{pp}} = 1 - \frac{1}{3}(f_u^{\mathrm{pp}}/m^*), \quad e_q^{\mathrm{pn}} = \frac{1}{3}(f_q^{\mathrm{pn}}/m^*)$
β-decay field $\tau_x \pm i\tau$,	$e_p = 1$
$(\tau_x \pm i\tau\ )\sigma_z$	$e_q = 1 - 2\zeta_S$

Since the charges e_q are given by the local properties of the medium, the same expressions are conserved if the above fields are multiplied by smooth functions of the co-ordinates. For the same reason the charge for the orbital field equals that for the vector field.

6. – Nuclear moments.

6·1. *Scheme for the calculation of moments.* – A change of nuclear energy in a static external field, in an electric or magnetic field of atomic electrons, for example, is given by different static moments. An energy change in a uniform magnetic field is given by the dipole magnetic moment of the nucleus, which is usually called simply magnetic moment. If the nonuniformity of the magnetic field is essential, octupole magnetic moments have to be introduced. The interaction of atomic electrons with an electric field is determined practically by two moments, the mean square of the nuclear electric radius which enters the formula for the isotope shift of atomic spectral lines and the quadrupole moment which is found from hyperfine splitting. All these quantities are expressed as averages with respect to the ground state of the nucleus for the corresponding operator. The moment Q is

$$Q = \left(\Phi_0, \sum_n Q_n \Phi_0\right),$$

or with the aid of the second quantization operators we obtain

$$Q = \left(\Phi_0 \sum a^\dagger_\lambda a_{\lambda'} Q_{\lambda\lambda'} \Phi_0\right) = \sum_{\lambda\lambda'} \underset{\sim}{\varrho}^a_{\lambda\lambda'} Q_{\lambda\lambda'} = \mathrm{Tr}\, \underset{\sim}{\varrho}^a Q\,,$$

where $\underset{\sim}{\varrho}^a$ is the particle density matrix.

We have seen ((5.7), (5.8)), that the change of the mean value *vs.* the number of particles in the nucleus can be calculated by the change of the quasi-particle density matrix $\delta\underset{\sim}{\varrho}$ or still more simply by finding the effective field induced by the external field Q (*i.e.*, the addition of the form $H' = \sum a^\dagger_\lambda a_{\lambda'} Q_{\lambda\lambda'}$ to the Hamiltonian) and determining the change in the quasi-particle occupation numbers occurring in the transition from one nucleus to the other. The change of the moment Q is

$$\delta Q = \mathrm{Tr}\, e_q \delta \underset{\sim}{\varrho} \widehat{Q} = \sum_\lambda V_{\lambda\lambda}[Q] \delta n_\lambda\,, \tag{6.1}$$

where e_q is the quasi-particle charge with respect to the field Q.

Since even-even nuclei have no magnetic moments, for the calculation of the magnetic moments of an even-odd or odd-even nucleus it is sufficient to find the density matrix change as one particle is added to the even-even nucleus. The quadrupole moments in the region of spherical nuclei for even-even nuclei are zero, and therefore for the calculation of the quadrupole moments of an adjacent nucleus it is also sufficient to know the density matrix change as one particle is added.

Thus, the scheme for the calculation of static moments is as follows.

The effective field $V[Q]$ corresponding to the field is obtained by the calculations derived in Sect. **5**.1 or Sect. **5**.5. The field Q equals $r^2P_2(\cos\theta)$ in the case of quadrupole moments, the quantity r^2 in the case of an isotope shift and finally the operator of the magnetic moment of one particle when the nuclear magnetic moment is calculated. Then we determine by the relations (5.6) the change of the number of quasi-particles at the level δn_λ as one particle is added. Thereupon Q is calculated by eq. (6.1).

In the simplest case the addition of one particle to a twice magic nucleus yields

$$\delta n_\lambda = \delta_{\lambda\lambda_0}\,,$$

where λ_0 is the state at which an odd quasi-particle appears.

In this case we have

$$Q = V_{\lambda_0\lambda_0}[Q]\,.$$

Let us write these relations with isotopic indices.

Let the operator Q act, as in the case of quadrupole moments and an isotope shift, on protons alone. Then we have

$$\delta Q = \delta Q^{\text{p}} = Q^{\text{p}}\delta\varrho^{\text{p}} = \sum V^{\text{p}}_{\lambda\lambda}[Q^{\text{p}}]\delta n^{\text{p}}_\lambda + V^{\text{n}}_{\lambda\lambda}[Q^{\text{p}}]\delta n^{\text{n}}_\lambda\,,$$

$$V^{\text{p}}[Q^{\text{p}}] = Q^{\text{p}} + \Gamma^{\text{pp}}A^{\text{p}}Q^{\text{p}}\,,\qquad V^{\text{n}}[Q^{\text{p}}] = \Gamma^{\text{np}}A^{\text{p}}Q^{\text{p}}\,.$$

The magnetic moments, to which contributions are made by both the proton and neutron parts of the moment operator, are calculated similarly.

6.2. *Magnetic moments.* – The operator of the dipole magnetic moments of one nucleon can be written as the sum of two terms:

$$\mu = \mu^J + \mu^S,$$

$$\mu^J = \frac{1+\tau_z}{2}J\,,\qquad \mu^S = \left[\frac{1+\tau_z}{2}\left(\gamma_{\text{p}} - \frac{1}{2}\right) + \frac{1-\tau_z}{2}\gamma_{\text{n}}\right]\sigma_z\,,$$

where $(1+\tau_z)/2$ and $(1-\tau_z)/2$ are the matrices corresponding to the proton and neutron states, the total moment $\boldsymbol{J} = \boldsymbol{l} + \frac{1}{2}\boldsymbol{\sigma}$ where $\boldsymbol{l}$ is the orbital moment, and γ_{p} and γ_{n} are the proton and neutron gyromagnetic numbers.

We must find the effective field $V[\mu]$ corresponding to the operator μ and calculate the magnetic moment by the formula

$$\langle\mu\rangle = \sum_\lambda V_{\lambda\lambda}[\mu]\delta n_\lambda\,.$$

The magnetic moments of higher multipolarities are calculated by a similar scheme. The operator of the moments of an arbitrary multipolarity has the form

$$\Omega^L = \sum a^\dagger_\lambda a_{\lambda'} \mu^L_{\lambda\lambda'} ,$$

$$\mu^L = \left\{ \frac{1+\tau_z}{2} \left[\left(\gamma_p - \frac{1}{L+1} \right) \boldsymbol{\sigma} + \frac{2}{2L+1} \boldsymbol{j} \right] + \frac{1-\tau_z}{2} \gamma_n \boldsymbol{\sigma} \right\} \nabla (r^L Y_{LM}) .$$

At $L=1$ we obtain the above operator of the dipole magnetic moment; $L=3$ corresponds to the octupole moment.

Just as in the case of the dipole magnetic moment, the orbital part of the octupole differs little from the inclusion of the interaction.

After the separation of angular variables, the equation for the spin part reduces to a set of equations for two functions of r^2. The experimental and calculated values of the magnetic moments and octupole magnetic moments are tabulated in Tables I and II.

TABLE I. – *Dipole magnetic moments.*

Element	State	μ_{exp}	$\mu_{\text{sh m}}$	μ_{theor}
^{33}S	$1d_{3/2}$	0.64	1.14	0.80
^{35}S	$1d_{3/2}$	1.00	1.14	1.05
^{37}Cl	$1d_{3/2}$	0.68	0.12	0.65
^{39}K	$1d_{3/2}$	0.39	0.12	0.30
^{41}Ca	$1f_{7/2}$	−1.59	−1.91	−1.71
^{43}Ca	$1f_{7/2}$	−1.31	−1.91	−1.35
^{45}Sc	$1f_{7/2}$	4.75	1.1	4.85
^{47}Ti	$1f_{5/2}$	−0.79	−1.36	−0.75
^{49}Ti	$1f_{7/2}$	−1.10	−1.91	−1.10
^{51}Vn	$1f_{7/2}$	5.15	5.8	5.25
^{55}Mn	$1f_{5/2}$	3.47	4.14	3.60
^{57}Mn	$1f_{7/2}$	5.05	5.8	5.10
^{57}Co	$1f_{7/2}$	4.65	5.8	4.95
^{67}Zn	$1f_{5/2}$	0.88	1.36	0.90
^{85}Rb	$1f_{5/2}$	1.35	0.86	1.40
^{87}Rb	$2p_{3/2}$	2.75	3.8	2.70
^{91}Zr	$2d_{5/2}$	−1.30	−1.91	−1.45
^{95}Mo	$2d_{5/2}$	−0.93	−1.91	−1.20
^{97}Mo	$2d_{5/2}$	−0.95	−1.91	−1.00
^{135}Ba	$2d_{3/2}$	0.84	1.14	0.85
^{137}Ba	$2d_{3/2}$	0.93	1.14	0.95
^{143}Nd	$2f_{7/2}$	−1.00	−1.91	−1.05
^{201}Hg	$3p_{3/2}$	−0.61	−1.91	−0.70
^{205}Tl	$3p_{1/2}$	1.62	2.79	1.85
^{209}Bi	$1h_{9/2}$	4.08	2.62	3.40

TABLE II. – *Octupole magnetic moments.*

Element	State λ_0	$\Omega_{\lambda_0}/r^2_{\lambda_0}$ (shell model)	$\Omega_{\lambda_0}/r^2_{\lambda_0}$ experimental	$\Omega_{\lambda_0}/r^2_{\lambda_0}$ theoretical
^{127}I	$(d_{5/2})\,p$	2.8	0.7	1.5
^{115}In	$(g_{9/2})\,p$	4.7	2.1	2.9
^{113}In	$(g_{9/2})\,p$	4.7	2.1	2.9
^{83}Kr	$(g_{9/2})\,n$	-2.1	-0.7	-0.9
^{81}Br	$(p_{3/2})\,p$	1.7	0.6	-0.85
^{79}Ba	$(p_{3/2})\,p$	1.7	0.6	-0.85
^{71}Ga	$(p_{3/2})\,p$	1.7	0.7	0.8
^{69}Ga	$(p_{3/2})\,p$	1.7	0.9	0.8
^{35}Cl	$(d_{3/2})\,p$	-0.1	-0.15	0
^{37}Cl	$(d_{3/2})\,p$	-0.1	-0.15	0

6·3. *Quadrupole moments and isotope shift.* – To calculate the quadrupole moments it is necessary to find the effective field induced by an external scalar field equal to $V^0 = r^2 P_2(\cos\theta)$. The isotopic shift is given by the field $V^0 = r^2$. The change of the quadrupole moments and the quantity $\langle r^2 \rangle$ were calculated in ref. (*). The equation for the effective field was solved on computers. The dependence $\hat{f}_0(r)$ was taken of the form

$$\hat{f}_0(r) = \hat{f}_0 + [\hat{f}_{0\,\mathrm{ex}} - \hat{f}_0]\,\frac{n(0) - n(r)}{n(0)}\,,$$

where $n(r)$ is the density of particles in the nucleus.

Let us give the tables of comparison of the theoretical and experimental values of $\delta\langle r^2 P_2\rangle$ and $\delta\langle r^2\rangle$.

In all cases we obtain an agreement with experimental values within 30 % to 40 % (except light elements).

Without taking into account the dependence $\hat{f}_0(r)$, agreement with the data cannot be obtained.

For the constants f_0, f_0', $f_{0\,\mathrm{exp}}$ and $f'_{0\,\mathrm{ex}}$ we obtain the following values

$$f_0 = 1 \pm 0.2\,, \qquad f_0' = 0.35 \pm 0.2\,, \qquad f_{0\,\mathrm{ex}} = -3 \pm 1\,, \qquad f'_{0\,\mathrm{ex}} = 0.3 \div 0.5\,.$$

The discrepancies seem to be explained by the roughness of the formula for $\hat{f}_0(r)$. The formula of p. 201 should have been written for $\hat{f}_0(r)$ and the constants α' and R' have been also selected from comparison with experiment.

(*) G. G. BUNATYAN and N. A. MIKULINSKY: *Nucl. Phys. (Soviet)*, **1**, 38 (1965); V. A. BELIAKOV and S. V. CHUDIAKOV: *Nucl. Phys. (Soviet)*, **1**, 744 (1965).

TABLE III. – *Isotope shift constant.*

Element	A_1-A_2	State	$C_{th}\cdot 10^3$ cm (by precise functions)	$C_{th}\cdot 10^3$ cm (by oscillator functions)	$C_{exp}\cdot 10^3$ cm
$_{37}$Rb	85- 87	$1g_{9/2}$	—	12	8 ± 12
$_{38}$Sr	84- 86	$1g_{9/2}$	—	12	0
$_{44}$Ru	96- 98	$1g_{7/2}$	—	13	34 ± 9
	98-100	$1g_{7/2}$	—	22	(and over all isotopes)
	100-102	$1g_{7/2}$	—	22	—
	102-104	$2d_{5/2}$	—	35	—
$_{46}$Rd	106-108	$2d_{5/2}$	55	—	42 ± 9
	108-110	$2d_{5/2}$	55	—	36 ± 5
$_{47}$Ag	107-109	$2d_{5/2}$	55	—	38 ± 6
$_{48}$Cd	108-110	$2d_{5/2}$	58	—	32 ± 4
$_{50}$Sn	112-114	$1g_{7/2}$	65	34	40 ± 10
	114-116	$1g_{7/2}$	65	34	40 ± 10
	116-118	$1g_{7/2}$	65	34	30 ± 10
	118-120	$1g_{7/2}$	65	34	30 ± 10
	120-122	$1h_{11/2}$	29	30	15 ± 10
	122-124	$1h_{11/2}$	29	30	15 ± 10
$_{54}$Xe	132-134	$1h_{11/2}$	40	38	18 ± 4
	134-136	$1h_{11/2}$	49	38	26 ± 6
$_{56}$Ba	134-136	$1h_{11/2}$	63	44	44 ± 9
	136-138	$1h_{11/2}$	63	44	67 ± 13
$_{58}$Ce	136-138	$1h_{11/2}$	63	—	36
	138-140	$1h_{11/2}$	63	—	36
	140-142	$2f_{7/2}$	131	—	147 ± 30
$_{60}$Nd	142-144	$2f_{9/2}$	142	—	187 ± 35
$_{75}$Re	185-187	$1i_{13/2}$	170	—	157 ± 40
$_{76}$Os	186-188	$1i_{13/2}$	175	—	176 ± 27
	188-190	$1i_{13/2}$	185	—	150 ± 23
	190-192	$1i_{13/2}$	186	—	130 ± 20
$_{77}$Ir	191-193	$1i_{13/2}$	185	—	130 ± 30
$_{78}$Pt	194-196	$1i_{13/2}$	188	—	135 ± 25

TABLE III (*continued*).

Element	A_1-A_2	State	$C_{th}\cdot 10^3$ cm (by precise functions)	$C_{th}\cdot 10^3$ cm (by oscillator functions)	$C_{exp}\cdot 10^3$ cm
$_{80}$Hg	198-200	$1i_{13/2}$	265	—	240 ± 27
	200-202	$1i_{13/2}$	267	—	270 ± 30
	202-204	$1i_{13/2}$	270	—	267 ± 30
$_{81}$Tl	203-205	$1i_{13/2}$	270	—	280 ± 40
$_{82}$Pb	204-206	$1i_{13/2}$	270	—	280 ± 31
	206-208	$1i_{13/2}$	270	—	315 ± 35
	208-210	$2g_{9/2}$	609	—	548 ± 61

$$C=\frac{R_\infty}{3}\left[\frac{1+b}{\Gamma(1+2b)}\right]^2\left(\frac{2ZR}{a}\right)^{2b}\frac{[\delta\langle r^2\rangle]\lambda_0}{ZR^2}$$

where R_∞ is Rydberg's constant, $b\equiv\sqrt{1-(Z/137)^2}$, Γ is the gamma-function, R is radius of the nucleus.

7. – Electromagnetic and β-decay transitions.

7·1. *Dipole excitations.* – Let us consider dipole transitions under the action of γ-quanta of not very large energy $\omega \ll 40$ MeV. Then we can neglect the nonuniformity of the field within the nuclear radius ($k^2R^2 \ll 1$). To investigate the excitations of the nucleus and not its motion as a whole, it is convenient to go over to the centre-of-inertia system. In this case, apart from the electrical field acting on the protons, there arises an inertial field as a result of which the perturbation of the Hamiltonian of the system takes the form ($e=1$)

$$H'=\boldsymbol{E}\left\{\frac{N}{A}\sum_{\mathrm{p}}\boldsymbol{r}_i-\frac{Z}{A}\sum_{\mathrm{n}}\boldsymbol{r}_i\right\}.$$

The effective field originating in the perturbation H' satisfies the equation

$$\text{(7.1)}\qquad\left\{\begin{aligned}V^{\mathrm{p}}&=\frac{N}{A}E_x+\mathcal{F}^{\mathrm{pp}}A^{\mathrm{p}}V^{\mathrm{p}}+\mathcal{F}^{\mathrm{pn}}A^{\mathrm{n}}V^{\mathrm{n}}\,,\\ V^{\mathrm{n}}&=-\frac{Z}{A}E_x+\mathcal{F}^{\mathrm{nn}}A^{\mathrm{n}}V^{\mathrm{n}}+\mathcal{F}^{\mathrm{np}}A^{\mathrm{p}}V^{\mathrm{p}}\,.\end{aligned}\right.$$

For the position of the maximum of the giant resonance curve we obtain

$$\omega_S^2=\omega_0^2(1+2f_0')=\omega_0^2\,\frac{3\beta}{\varepsilon_F}\,.$$

TABLE IV. – *Isomeric shift constant.*

Isotope	λ_0	λ_1	ΔE (keV)	τ	$C\cdot 10^3$ cm	$C\cdot 10^3$ cm (sh. model)
$^{69}_{30}$Zn	$2p_{1/2}$	$1g_{9/2}$	436	13.8 h	-3	4
$^{85}_{36}$Kr	$-1g_{9/2}$	$-2p_{1/2}$	305	4.4 h	-4	6
$^{87}_{38}$Sr	$-1g_{9/2}$'	$-2p_{1/2}$	390	2.8 h	-4	8
$^{87}_{39}$Y	$2p_{1/2}$	$1g_{9/2}$	384	14 h	$+2$	23
$^{89}_{39}$Y	$2p_{1/2}$	$1g_{9/2}$	913	14 sec	$+2$	23
$^{91}_{39}$Y	$2p_{1/2}$	$1g_{9/2}$	555	51 min	$+2$	23
$^{89}_{40}$Zn	$-1g_{9/2}$	$-2p_{1/2}$	588	4.4 min	-4	8
$^{113}_{48}$In	$3s_{1/2}$	$1h_{11/2}$	—	5.1 y	-10	19
$^{113}_{49}$In	$-1g_{9/2}$	$-2p_{1/2}$	390	1.73 h	-7	$+48$
$^{115}_{49}$In	$-1g_{9/2}$	$-2p_{1/2}$	335	4.5 h	-7	$+48$
$^{127}_{52}$Te	$-2d_{3/2}$	$-1h_{11/2}$	88.5	113 d	3	-20
$^{129}_{52}$Te	$-2d_{3/2}$	$-1h_{11/2}$	106	34 d	3	-20
$^{133}_{52}$Te	$-2d_{3/2}$	$-1h_{11/2}$	300	63 min	3	-20
$^{133}_{54}$Xe	$-2d_{3/2}$	$-1h_{11/2}$	232	2.3 d	4	-20
$^{135}_{54}$Xe	$-2d_{3/2}$	$-1h_{11/2}$	520	15.3 min	4	-24
$^{135}_{56}$Ba	$-2d_{3/2}$	$-1h_{11/2}$	269	28.7 h	5	-28
$^{137}_{56}$Ba	$-2d_{3/2}$	$-1h_{11/2}$	661	2.6 min	5	-28

λ_0: ground state;
λ_1: excited state;
ΔE: excitation energy;
τ: lifetime.

A similar relation is obtained for the maximum width

$$\Gamma^2 = \Gamma_0^2 \frac{3\beta}{\varepsilon_F},$$

where Γ_0 is the width obtained for a system of noninteracting particles in a diffuse edge well. These results are in satisfactory agreement with experiment.

Taking into account the velocity dependence of inter-quasi-particle forces changes the sum rule for dipole transitions. We obtain

$$\int \sigma(\omega)\,\mathrm{d}\omega = 2\pi^2 \frac{NZ}{A} \frac{1+\frac{2}{3}f'_1}{1+\frac{2}{3}f_1}\,.$$

At $f_1^{\mathrm{np}} = 0$, which denotes the absence of exchange forces the sum rule assumes the conventional form.

TABLE V. – *Quadrupole moments of isomeric states.*

Isotope	λ_0	λ_1	$Q_{\mathrm{th}}\cdot 10^{24}$ (cm²)	$Q^*_{\mathrm{th}}\cdot 10^{24}$ (cm²)	$Q_{\mathrm{exp}}\ 10^{24}$ (cm²)	$Q^*_{\mathrm{exp}}\cdot 10^{24}$ (cm²)	ΔE (keV)	$\tau\cdot 10^9$ (s)	$\frac{\delta\langle r^2\rangle}{R^2}\cdot 10^4$	$\frac{\delta\langle r^2\rangle}{R^2}\cdot 10^4$ sh. mod.
${}^{61}_{28}\mathrm{Ni}$	$2p_{3/2}$	$1f_{5/2}$	-0.14	-0.13	—	—	68	5.2	-15	25
${}^{67}_{30}\mathrm{Zn}$	$-1f_{5/2}$	$-2p_{3/2}$	0.14	0.11	0.16	—	93	$9.5\cdot 10^3$	-16	25
${}^{119}_{50}\mathrm{Sn}$	$3s_{1/2}$	$2d_{3/2}$	0	-0.10	0	-0.08	24	18	-2.5	4
${}^{125}_{52}\mathrm{Te}$	$-3s_{1/2}$	$-2d_{3/2}$	0	0.16	0	0.20	35	1.4	2.8	4
${}^{129}_{53}\mathrm{I}$	$1g_{7/2}$	$2d_{5/2}$	-0.36	-0.36	-0.50	-0.69	27	10	15	-40
${}^{129}_{54}\mathrm{Xe}$	$3s_{1/2}$	$2d_{3/2}$	0	-0.13	0	—	40	0.7	-2	3
${}^{131}_{54}\mathrm{Xe}$	$2d_{3/2}$	$3s_{1/2}$	-0.13	0	-0.12	—	80	0.3	-2	3

λ_0 and λ_1 are the ground and excited states,
Q_{th} and Q^*_{th} the theoretical values of the quadrupole moment in the ground and excited states,
Q_{exp} and Q^*_{exp} the experimental values, and
$\delta\langle r^2\rangle/R^2$ the change of the mean quadratic radius in isomeric transitions.

7·2. *Quadrupole transitions.* – There is a large number of well-studied quadrupole transitions with low frequencies. Therefore for these transitions we must write expressions taking into account the pair correlation.

To investigate quadrupole transitions, we must find the effective field induced by the external field

$$V^0 = r^2 P_2(\cos\theta) \equiv Q\,.$$

TABLE VI *a*. – *Quadrupole moments of odd nuclei.*

Nucleus	J	$q \cdot 10^{24}$ (cm^2)	$Q_{th} \cdot 10^{24}$ (cm^2)	$Q_{exp} \cdot 10^{24}$ (cm^2)
$^{11}_{5}B$	3/2	0.022	0.068	0.058
$^{17}_{8}O$	5/2	0	−0.017	−0.026
$^{25}_{12}Mg$	5/2	0	0.18	0.15
$^{25}_{13}Al$	5/2	0.058	0.34	—
$^{27}_{13}Al$	5/2	0.060	0.24	1.152
$^{29}_{13}Al$	5/2	0.061	0.23	—
$^{27}_{14}Si$	5/2	0	0.19	—
$^{31}_{14}Si$	3/2	0	−0.063	—
$^{33}_{16}S$	3/2	0	−0.071	−0.064
$^{35}_{16}S$	3/2	0	0.045	0.054, 0.038
$^{37}_{16}S$	7/2	0	−0.093	—
$^{33}_{17}Cl$	3/2	−0.045	−0.10	—
$^{35}_{17}Cl$	3/2	−0.046	−0.077	−0.079
$^{37}_{17}Cl$	3/2	−0.047	−0.066	−0.062
$^{37}_{18}A$	3/2	0	0.029	—
$^{39}_{18}A$	7/2	0	−0.066	—
$^{39}_{19}K$	3/2	0.047	0.062	0.070
$^{41}_{19}K$	3/2	−0.048	−0.068	−0.085
$^{41}_{20}Ca$	7/2	0	−0.051	—
$^{47}_{20}Ca$	7/2	0	0.16	—
$^{49}_{20}Ca$	3/2	0	−0.087	—
$^{41}_{21}Sc$	7/2	−0.10	−0.14	—
$^{45}_{21}Sc$	7/2	−0.11	−0.17	−0.22
$^{40}_{21}Sc$	7/2	−0.11	−0.22	—
$^{49}_{22}Ti$	7/2	0	0.20	—
$^{53}_{24}Cr$	3/2	0	0.13	0.03

TABLE VI *a* (*continued*).

Nucleus	J	$q \cdot 10^{24}$ (cm^2)	$Q_{th} \cdot 10^{24}$ (cm^2)	$Q_{exp} \cdot 10^{24}$ (cm^2)
$^{57}_{27}$Co	7/2	0.12	0.49	—
$^{59}_{27}$Co	7/2	0.12	0.53	0.5
$^{59}_{28}$Ni	3/2	0	0.31	—
$^{61}_{28}$Ni	3/2	0	—0.14	—
$^{63}_{29}$Cu	3/2	—0.072	—0.27	—0.16, —0.19
$^{65}_{29}$Cu	3/2	—0.072	—0.23	—0.16, —0.15
$^{67}_{30}$Zn	5/2	0	0.18	0.18
$^{71}_{30}$Zn	9/2	0	—0.13	—
$^{67}_{31}$Ga	3/2	0.073	0.24	0.22
$^{69}_{31}$Ga	3/2	0.074	0.17	0.20
$^{71}_{31}$Ga	3/2	0.075	0.15	0.12
$^{69}_{32}$Ge	5/2	0	0.11	—
$^{73}_{32}$Ge	9/2	0	—0.15	—0.20
$^{77}_{35}$Br	3/2	0.077	0.16	—
$^{79}_{35}$Br	3/2	0.077	0.16	0.32
$^{81}_{35}$Br	3/2	0.078	0.18	0.27
$^{83}_{35}$Br	3/2	0.079	0.20	0.45
$^{85}_{36}$Kr	9/2	0	0.25	0.30
$^{85}_{37}$Rb	5/2	0.11	0.17	0.27
$^{87}_{38}$Sr	9/2	0	0.18	0.36
$^{89}_{38}$Sr	5/2	0	—0.16	—
$^{87}_{37}$Rb	3/2	0.080	0.17	0.14, —0.2
$^{93}_{41}$Nb	9/2	—0.18	—0.30	—0.13

J: is the spin of nuclei;
q: shell-model quadrupole moment;
Q_{th}: theoretical quadrupole moment;
Q_{exp}: experimental quadrupole moment.

TABLE VI *b*. – *Quadrupole moments.*

Element	State	$Q_{th}\cdot 10^{24}$ (cm^2)	$\Delta Q_{th}\cdot 10^{24}$ (cm^2)	$Q_{exp}\cdot 10^{24}$ (cm^2)	$\Delta Q_{exp}\cdot 10^{24}$ (cm^2)
$_{85}$Kr	$(1g_{9/2})\,n$	0.28	0.28	0.25, —0.4	0.25, —0.14
$_{93}$Nb	$(1g_{9/2})\,p$	—0.3	—0.04	—0.2	0.06
$_{201}$Hg	$(3p_{3/2})\,n$	0.58 (*)	0.58	0.65	0.65
$_{209}$Bi	$(1h_{9/2})\,p$	—0.26 (*)	0.02	—0.4	—0.12

Q: total quadrupole moment.
ΔQ: the difference between the total quadrupole moment and the quadrupole moment calculated by the shell model.
(*) Calculated with precise functions.

We have seen (5.16) that the equation for the effective scalar field has the form

$$V^{p}(\boldsymbol{r}) = V^{0}(\boldsymbol{r}) + [f^{pp}(\boldsymbol{r})\,\delta n^{p}(\boldsymbol{r}) + f^{pn}(\boldsymbol{r})\,\delta n^{n}(\boldsymbol{r})]\left(\frac{\mathrm{d}n}{\mathrm{d}\varepsilon_F}\right)^{-1},$$

where $\delta n^{p}(\boldsymbol{r})$ and $\delta n^{n}(\boldsymbol{r})$ are the changes of the density of protons and neutrons in the field.

In the investigation of quadrupole collective vibrations we usually employ the so-called quadrupole-quadrupole interaction which has the form

$$(\lambda_1\lambda_2|\mathscr{F}^{Q}|\lambda_3\lambda_4) = -\varkappa Q_{\lambda_1\lambda_2}Q_{\lambda_3\lambda_4}\,.$$

The only reason for this choice of the interaction is that eq. (6.1) reduces in this case to an algebraic equation.

The interaction $\mathscr{F}^{Q}$ leads to an effective field of the form

$$V = C(\omega)\,V^{0},$$

i.e., is equivalent to the assumption that the density change in the field is

$$\delta n(\boldsymbol{r}) = \alpha(r)P_2(\cos\theta) = C_1 r^2 P_2(\cos\theta)\,.$$

This assumption distorts the radial dependence of $\delta n(\boldsymbol{r})$ and hence the quantities $V - V^{0}$. The error is especially large in those cases when states with a large moment are essential. In this case the main contribution to $V - V^{0}$ is determined by the values of r near the nuclear surface where the quantities $f_0(r)$ and $\delta n(r)$ vary sharply with r.

For several cases when the pair correlation is inessential the single-particle quadrupole transition intensities were calculated in (*). As is clear from the Table, a satisfactory agreement with experimental data is obtained. The quantity $\hat{f}_0(r)$ entering the solution is taken to be the same as in the calculation of quadrupole moments and isotope shifts.

In the case of the pair correlation, besides single-particle quadrupole states, there arises a state with energies $\lesssim 2\Delta$ known as a collective state. The calculation of the intensity and frequency of these transitions, just as single-particle quadrupole transitions, is made as follows. The angular variables are separated by the usual technique in the equation for the effective field and in the equations for d^α and d^β. The equations for the radial matrix elements V and $d^{\alpha\beta}$ are solved on computers with the function $f(\boldsymbol{r})$ the form of which is given in (4.4).

For a qualitative analysis we can make the assumption

$$V = C(\omega)Q\,, \qquad d^\alpha = \mathscr{D}(\omega)Q\,.$$

Multiplying the equations for V and d^α by Q and integrating we can readily obtain the quantities $C(\omega)$ and $\mathscr{D}(\omega)$. From this approach it can be concluded that the neglect of the quantity d^α, as is often done in nuclear calculations, introduces at $\omega \ll 2\Delta$ appreciable errors and at $\omega/2\Delta \simeq 1$ distorts the result completely. This is not surprising since the neglect of d^α violates the conservation of the number of particles.

7·3. *Magnetic transitions.* – The intensities of single-particle or collective transitions are calculated by the same scheme as electric transitions.

The equations for the effective field differ from the equations used in the calculation of magnetic moments only by the presence of the frequency ω in the denominator of $A_{\lambda\lambda'}$. At low frequencies the probability for the transition from the state λ_0 to the state λ_1 is given by the static effective field matrix element $V_{\lambda_0\lambda_1}$ which replaces in the single-particle model transition formulae the quantity $V^0_{\lambda_0\lambda_1}$.

For low-frequency transitions the interaction of configurations is usually essential, which leads to additional selection rules.

The interaction of configurations must be calculated by the same scheme as in the shell model but as the interaction we must take the effective interaction in the last shell $\mathscr{F}'$ (5.5) which must be found from the equation

$$\mathscr{F}' = \mathscr{F} + \mathscr{F}A'\mathscr{F}'\,,$$

where A' denotes that the summation is performed over all shells but the last.

(*) S. Kamezdjiev: *Nucl. Phys. (Soviet)*, in press.

7·4. β-*decay*. – It is well known that β-transitions in nuclei (β-decay, K-capture, μ-capture) are caused by the following perturbation:

$$H' = G_\nu \int \bar{\psi}\tau_+ \gamma_\mu (1 + C_1\gamma_5)\psi \bar{\varphi}_e \gamma_\mu (1+\gamma_5)\varphi_\nu \mathrm{d}^3\tau_1 \,,$$

where $\bar{\psi} = \psi^\dagger \gamma_4$, $\psi^\dagger$ and ψ are the nucleon production and annihilation operators, φ_ν and φ_e are the neutrino and electron or muon (in the case of μ-capture) functions. The factor C_1 equals the relation of the pseudovector and vector interaction constants

$$C_1 = \frac{G_A}{G_V} = -1.2 \,.$$

The isotopic matrix transforming a proton into a neutron τ_+ is

$$\tau_+ = \tfrac{1}{2}(\tau_x + i\tau_y) = \begin{vmatrix} 0 & 1 \\ 0 & 0 \end{vmatrix} .$$

Neglecting the relativistic corrections for the nucleons, we obtain

$$\bar{\psi}\tau_+\gamma_\mu(1 + C_1\gamma_5)\psi = \delta_{\mu 0}\psi^\dagger\tau_+\psi + C_1\delta_{\mu\alpha}\psi^\dagger\tau_+\sigma_\alpha\psi \,,$$

where $\alpha = 1, 2, 3$.

In the λ-representation we obtain

$$H' = G_\nu \sum_{\lambda\lambda'} a_\lambda^\dagger a_{\lambda'} [(\tau_+ j_0)_{\lambda\lambda'} + C_1(\tau_+\sigma_\alpha j_\alpha)_{\lambda\lambda'}] \,, \tag{7.2}$$

where $j_\mu = j_0$, j_α is the current density for light particles.

To obtain H' in the case of allowed transitions we regard $j_\mu(\boldsymbol{r})$ as independent of r (the Coulomb function of an electron is replaced by its value on the nuclear surface).

In the case of Fermi transitions the difference of the effective field is due only to the Coulomb corrections since if the Coulomb field is neglected the perturbation

$$H' = \sum a_\lambda^\dagger a_{\lambda'} (T_\pm)_{\lambda\lambda'}$$

does not, because of isotopic invariance, cause the polarization of the medium, no more than the perturbation

$$H' = \sum a_\lambda^\dagger a_{\lambda'} (T_z)_{\lambda\lambda'} = T_z$$

causes it. The equation for $V(\tau_+)$ shows that the corrections of only the second order with respect to V_Q/ε_F, where V_Q is the Coulomb field, are involved.

Therefore, the corrections to the Fermi matrix element calculated under the assumption of strict isotopic invariance prove to be negligibly small ($\sim 0.3\%$).

TABLE VII. – *Mirror β-transitions of the* $1p$, $1d_{\frac{5}{2}}$, $2s$ $1d_{\frac{3}{2}}$ *subshells.*

Transition	Initial state	Final state	$\lg f\tau_{exp}$	$(M_0)^2_{GT}$	$\left(\frac{M_{ex}}{M_0}\right)_{GT}$	$\left(\frac{M_{th}}{M_0}\right)_{GT}$
^{11}C -^{11}B	$1p_{3/2}$	$1p_{3/2}$	3.62	1.67	0.44 ± 0.01	0.39
^{13}N -^{13}C	$1p_{1/2}$	$1p_{1/2}$	3.67	0.33	0.83 ± 0.02	0.90
^{15}O -^{15}N	$1p_{1/2}$	$1p_{1/2}$	3.64	0.33	0.92 ± 0.02	0.90
^{17}F -^{17}O	$1d_{5/2}$	$1d_{5/2}$	3.36	1.40	0.93 ± 0.04	0.82
^{19}Ne-^{19}F	$1d_{5/2}$	$1d_{5/2}$	3.25	1.60	1.03 ± 0.05	0.69
^{21}Na-^{21}Ne	$1d_{5/2}$	$1d_{5/2}$	3.59	0.92	0.63 ± 0.07	0.60
^{23}Mg-^{23}Na	$1d_{5/2}$	$1d_{5/2}$	3.74	0.92	0.31 ± 0.02	0.54
^{25}Al -^{25}Mg	$1d_{5/2}$	$1d_{5/2}$	3.63	1.40	0.46 ± 0.03	0.49
^{27}Si -^{27}Al	$1d_{5/2}$	$1d_{5/2}$	3.64	1.40	0.45 ± 0.02	0.47
^{29}P -^{29}Si	$2s_{1/2}$	$2s_{1/2}$	3.68	3.00	0.26 ± 0.03	0.57
^{31}S -^{31}P	$2s_{1/2}$	$2s_{1/2}$	3.71	3.00	0.21 ± 0.01	0.60
^{33}Cl -^{33}S	$1d_{3/2}$	$1d_{3/2}$	3.72	0.60	0.43 ± 0.12	0.48
^{35}A -^{35}Cl	$1d_{3/2}$	$1d_{3/2}$	3.75	0.32	0.45 ± 0.15	0.54
^{37}K -^{37}A	$1d_{3/2}$	$1d_{3/2}$	3.66	0.32	0.85 ± 0.08	0.64
^{39}Ca -^{39}K	$1d_{3/2}$	$1d_{3/2}$	3.64	0.60	0.70 ± 0.03	0.77
^{57}Ni -^{57}Co	$2p_{3/2}$	$2p_{3/2}$	5.4	1.66	0.10 ± 0.02	0.11
^{59}Cu-^{59}Ni	$2p_{3/2}$	$2p_{3/2}$	5.0	1.66	0.16 ± 0.03	0.22
^{61}Cu-^{61}Ni	$2p_{3/2}$	$2p_{3/2}$	4.94	1.66	0.17 ± 0.02	0.18
^{63}Zn-^{63}Cu	$2p_{3/2}$	$2p_{3/2}$	5.37	1.66	0.10 ± 0.02	0.12

$(M_0)_{GT}$ is the Gamov-Teller matrix element without interaction.

The equations for the effective field in the case of Gamov-Teller transitions are closely similar to the equations for the effective field corresponding to the spin part of the magnetic moment.

The quasi-particle charge for the field $\tau_+\sigma_\alpha$ is (Sect. **5**·10)

$$e_q = 1 - 2\xi .$$

In the sums over λ and λ' one state refers to neutrons and the other to protons. Just as in the case of the spin part of the magnetic moment the main role belongs to the terms of the sum with λ and λ' differing only by the sign of the spin projection on the direction of the moment j.

In the case of mirror nuclei the Gamov-Teller matrix element M is expressed rigorously by the magnetic moment of the daughter or parent nucleus in the ground state. The substitution of the observed magnetic moments yields amplitudes of β-transitions coinciding with those observed within the instrumental accuracy.

The calculation of the allowed β-transition probabilities taking approximately into account the pair correlation is given by U. GAPONOV [*Nucl. Phys.* (*Soviet*), in press].

The comparison of the theoretical and experimental values is tabulated in Table VII. It is clear from this Table that in all cases when there is no configuration perturbation we obtain a satisfactory agreement between the absolute transition probabilities and experimental values. The spin-spin interaction constant figuring in the calculation is taken the same as in the case of magnetic moments.

7·5. *l-forbidden transitions.* – Among magnetic transitions and allowed β-transitions there are transitions in which the orbital moment changes by two units.

Such l-forbidden transitions are impossible in the single-particle model since the matrix element σ_α or $\sigma_\alpha\tau_+$ is zero for transitions changing the orbital moment.

The following explanation of l-forbidden transitions is given.

The transition probability contains the matrix element of the effective and not of the external field. Now, the effective field in the case of the external field σ and in the case of the field $\sigma_\alpha\tau_+$ has the form

$$V_\alpha = V_1(r^2)\sigma_\alpha + V_2(r^2)\frac{r_\alpha r_\beta}{r^2}\sigma_\beta \,.$$

The second term in this expression has matrix elements for states with orbital moments differing by two units. Thus calculated, the intensities are in satisfactory agreement with the experimental probabilities of l-forbidden transitions.

7·6. *μ-capture.* – In contrast to β- and K'-capture, the neutrino-carried momentum in μ-capture is large and the nucleus receives an energy of the order of 10 to 15 MeV. In the perturbation (7.2) the current of light particles cannot be regarded as independent of r. Besides this perturbation must be complemented by the induced pseudoscalar interaction which makes a negligible contribution in the case of β-decay but yields an appreciable correction in μ-capture. Otherwise, the calculation is performed by the same scheme as the calculation of dipole and quadrupole transitions for high excitation energies. The summation over the states in the effective equation is performed in the quasi-classical approximation in ref. (*). The formula obtained for the dependence of the μ-capture time on A and Z is in satisfactory agreement with experiment. More accurate results are obtained in ref. (**) in the numerical solution

(*) M. URIN and V. NOVIKOV: *Nucl. Phys.* (*Soviet*), **3**, 419 (1965).
(**) G. BUNATYAN: *Nucl. Phys.* (*Soviet*), **3**, 833 (1966).

of the equation for the corresponding effective field. The comparison of the theoretical and experimental data on the μ-capture time is given in Table VIII borrowed from this investigation.

TABLE VIII. – *Probability of μ-capture* (Λ is in units $10^5\ s^{-1}$).

Element	Λ_{th} (precise calculation)	Λ_{exp}	$\Lambda_{sh\ mod}$
^{16}O	0.885	0.97 ± 0.03	1.57
^{35}Cl	16.55	18.02 ± 0.49	37.00
^{37}Cl	11.465	12.51 ± 0.52	25.64
^{40}Ca	22.73	26.8 ± 0.4; 24.44 ± 0.5; 25.5 ± 0.5	45.21
^{44}Ca	16.03	17.93 ± 0.4	31.92
^{48}Ti	22.16	26.3 ± 0.6	43.04
^{51}V	26.99	31.3 ± 0.7; 33.7 ± 0.6	52.02
^{50}Cr	36.51	38.25 ± 0.5	70.65
^{52}Cr	32.64	34.52 ± 0.47	63.88
^{53}Cr	31.19	32.97 ± 0.45	60.61
^{54}Cr	29.74	30.57 ± 0.42	58.04
^{55}Mn	37.61	40.4 ± 0.8; 36.7 ± 0.8; 35.3 ± 0.8	71.36
^{56}Fe	46.15	45.3 ± 1; 46.5 ± 0.5	89.62
^{59}Co	46.68	50.6 ± 0.9; 46.4 ± 0.3	90.83
^{58}Ni	58.5	61.1 ± 0.5	113.4
^{60}Ni	53.4	55.62 ± 0.97	103.3
^{62}Ni	45.4	47.16 ± 0.95	88.6
^{108}Ag	111.00	108.6 ± 0.3; 112.5 ± 5; 114.5 ± 5.7	260.66
^{112}Cd	109.3	100.5 ± 5.0	254.5
^{112}Sn	119.3	—	280.00
^{119}Sn	95.69	112 ± 7; 107 ± 1.4	224.12
^{124}Sn	75.81	—	179.87
^{122}Sb	94.36	116 ± 10; 104.6 ± 1.4	222.2
^{201}Hg	127.51	134 ± 8	468.8
^{206}Pb	125.4	136.1	464.5
^{207}Pb	121.62	129.5; 117.0 ± 7.5; 132 ± 11	451.3
^{208}Pb	120.12	129.8	442.5
^{210}Pb	117.31	—	435.4
^{209}Bi	124.6	132.6;122 ± 7.5	459.0

8. – Conclusion.

The general aim of the above approach to the calculation of nuclei is to formulate in rigorous terms and express by the universal constants of the theory all problems which have been solved semi-quantitatively with the aid of simple models.

The preliminary result is a more or less satisfactory agreement of different processes of nuclear physics. We have seen that for this purpose it is sufficient to introduce the interaction between quasi-particles characterized by the constants f_0, f_0', g_0 and g_0' inside the nucleus and similar constants outside of it. To obtain more reliable results, the interaction between quasi-particles must be made more accurate. The most vulnerable spot of the theory is the law for the transition of constants from the values inside to those outside the nucleus. The improvement of the theory in this respect is possible in two directions: either we ought to introduce the new constants α' and R' characterizing the transition law or we should try to obtain the transition law from theoretical considerations. It can be expected that the gas approximation applies even with a small decrease of the near-nuclear-surface density, and therefore it is reasonable to try to obtain the transition law from the gas approximation.

Furthermore, the interaction values outside the nucleus are rather sensitive to the interacting-particle energy value since the scattering amplitude conserves the pole at low energies. This pole affects little the interaction F since the latter enters the sums where the energy in the two-particle channel is not fixed but varies within a rather wide interval.

This process can readily be taken into account by using as interaction amplitude outside the nucleus the function of the sum of the 4-components of particles of the pole type.

The interaction constants outside the nucleus can be obtained theoretically by considering nucleons near the nuclear surface and introducing the known interaction of free nucleons. Then the number of constants of the theory will decrease appreciably.

A more accurate comparison of the theory with experiment will make it possible to obtain the following harmonic of the expansion of $\mathcal{F}$ in the angle between the incoming particle moments.

Let us enumerate several problems which have not yet been solved.

Let us begin with the nuclear reactions.

To consider the reactions with the production of an intermediate nucleus we can readily reformulate the calculations in terms of the interacting quasi-particles, making use as above, of the gas approximation for quasi-particles.

More interesting results can be obtained from considering direct nuclear reactions. The latter were investigated in detail in ref. (*) by isolating the pole parts of the corresponding graphs. In this case the constants characterizing the nonpole parts of graphs have to be introduced just as in the approach presented above.

In the simplest cases these constants can be expressed by the quasi-particle interaction constants we have introduced.

(*) J. Shapiro: *Theory of Direct Reactions* (Moscow, 1962).

First of all the elastic and inelastic scattering of nucleons is described by the scattering amplitude graphs

$\Gamma =$ 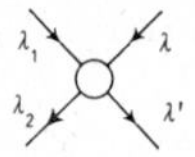

Here λ_1 and λ_2 are the initial and final states of the scattered nucleon, and λ and λ' correspond to a single-particle excitation.

Thus this reaction is expressed by the interaction constants entering $\mathcal{F}$.

Furthermore, the block

$g =$ 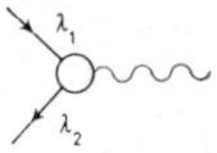

corresponding to the scattering with the production of a collective excitation is the residue at the corresponding pole of the scattering amplitude and therefore is expressed by $\mathcal{F}$.

Nor do the reactions (γn) and (γp) require the introduction of new constants.

The reactions with the production of deutons or α-particles for processes near the Fermi surface can be described by one additional constant.

In the case of α-particles the same constant will enter the specified theory of α-decay. Indeed, the irreducible block characterizing the production of an α-particle from quasi-particles lying near the Fermi surface in the co-ordinate representation is δ-like and is characterized by one constant.

Interesting processes are involved in the leadlike changes of the radii and shapes of nuclei as particles are added.

As a small number of particles is added to the magic nucleus, the re-distribution of the density is smooth without change of the nuclear radius as long as the field of the added particles does not cause a crossing of the terms. The density at the nuclear center exceeds the mean value corresponding to a formula $R = r_0 A^{\frac{1}{3}}$. With a sufficiently large number of added particles, the radius or shape of the nuclear surface makes a jump and the mean density value is restored. This process could be observed in Hofstadter-type experiments.

Of considerable interest is the calculation with the effective interaction $\mathcal{F}'$ of all cases of configurations mixing leading to strong changes in the transition probabilities or nuclear moments.

The calculation of the interaction constants and the constants characterizing the potential well through the interaction of free nucleons involves very considerable difficulties and lies beyond the theory under discussion.

The current approximate methods of solving this problem proceed in this or other form from the assumption that the interaction is small or that the gas approximation is applicable, for which there are no theoretical grounds.

If, however, the correct values for those interaction constants which are already known were obtained from such calculations, other results obtained from them might be credited as well.

The Alpha-Particle Model of Light Nuclei.

D. BRINK
Clarendon Laboratory - Oxford

1. – Introduction.

The shell model and its extensions, in particular the random-phase approximation have been very successful in describing certain forms of collective motion in nuclei in terms of an individual-particle model. The ground state of a double-closed-shell nucleus like ^{16}O is assumed to be well represented by a single Slater-determinant wave function. The simplest excited states are linear combinations of one particle-one hole states. A residual particle-hole interaction causes a coherent mixing of the one particle-hole states and some states acquire certain collective properties. These collective characteristics are enhanced if the calculations are extended using the random-phase approximation. We have seen that this description has been very successful in accounting for the properties of some collective states in double-closed-shell nuclei.

More recently these shell-model calculations have been extended to include two particle-two hole (2p-2h) excited states in double-closed-shell nuclei and improvements involving higher random-phase approximations have been suggested. Such calculations become very involved and, as there are indications that 3p-3h and 4p-4h states may also be important, the picture is discouraging. It may be a good idea to look for other ways of specifying nuclear states which are different from the particle-hole description. The α-particle model provides an example of another possible approach.

The α-particle model of the nucleus is older than the proton-neutron model. It was first introduced by GAMOW in 1929 as a natural extension of his successful investigation of α-decay. The idea went out of favour when the neutron was discovered and HEISENBERG and MAJORANA had developed their simple and satisfying theories of nuclear structure.

Subsequently the α-particle model has been revived in three different forms:

i) The first of these (resonating-group method) was introduced by WHEELER [1] in 1937 when he tried to construct a wave function for ^8Be consisting of two α-clusters:

$$(1)\qquad \begin{cases} \Phi = \mathscr{A}[\Phi(\boldsymbol{r}_{i1}-\boldsymbol{R}_1)\Phi(\boldsymbol{r}_{j2}-\boldsymbol{R}_2)\chi(\boldsymbol{R}_1-\boldsymbol{R}_2)]\,, \\ \boldsymbol{R}_l = \frac{1}{4}\sum_{i=1}^{4}\boldsymbol{r}_{il}\,. \end{cases}$$

In this wave function $\Phi(\boldsymbol{r}_{i1}-\boldsymbol{R}_1)$ and $\Phi(\boldsymbol{r}_{j2}-\boldsymbol{R}_2)$ describe α-clusters with centers of mass $\boldsymbol{R}_1$ and $\boldsymbol{R}_2$ respectively, $\chi(\boldsymbol{R}_1-\boldsymbol{R}_2)$ describes the relative motion of the clusters and $\mathscr{A}$ is the antisymmetrization operator. EDWARDS [2], WILDERMUTH [3], NEUDACHIN [4] and coworkers have also adopted this approach.

ii) The second approach was introduced by MARGENAU [5] in 1941. He also constructed a wave function for ^{8}Be consisting of two α-clusters:

$$(2)\qquad \Phi = \mathscr{A}[\psi_{\boldsymbol{R}}(\boldsymbol{r}_1, \dots, \boldsymbol{r}_4)\psi_{\boldsymbol{S}}(\boldsymbol{r}_5, \dots, \boldsymbol{r}_8)]\,.$$

In this wave function $\psi_{\boldsymbol{R}}(\boldsymbol{r}_1, \dots, \boldsymbol{r}_4)$ and $\psi_{\boldsymbol{S}}(\boldsymbol{r}_5, \dots, \boldsymbol{r}_8)$ describe α-clusters with « fixed » centers; $\boldsymbol{R}$ and $\boldsymbol{S}$ are the mean positions of the centers of mass of the two clusters and $\mathscr{A}$ is the antisymmetrization operator. BLOCH has investigated this idea in some unpublished work in 1952. Many of the investigations described in these lectures were made by him then. BIEL [6] has made similar investigations.

The wave functions (1) and (2) have a very similar appearance. They differ because in (1) $\boldsymbol{R}_1 = \frac{1}{4}(\boldsymbol{r}_1+\boldsymbol{r}_2+\boldsymbol{r}_3+\boldsymbol{r}_4)$ and $\boldsymbol{R}_2$ are dynamical co-ordinates of the centers of mass of the two clusters, while in (2) $\boldsymbol{R}$ and $\boldsymbol{S}$ are parameters specifying the fixed mean positions of the two clusters. The first wave function has several advantages over the second. For example the function $\chi(\boldsymbol{R}_1-\boldsymbol{R}_2)$ describing the relative motion of the two clusters may be chosen in a best way by a variation method. Also the first type of wave function is an eigenstate of angular momentum while the second is not. On the other hand antisymmetrization is much easier in the second method than in the first and calculations may be extended to heavier nuclei with little trouble, while the first method becomes hopelessly complicated. The physical ideas are the same in both approaches. Only the mathematics is different.

iii) A third, physically different, approach was introduced by WEFELMEIER [7] and developed by WHEELER [8], DENNISON [9] and KAMENY [10]. It is assumed that ^{8}Be may be treated as a system of two α-particles with no internal structure which obey Bose-Einstein statistics.

In these lectures we will follow up the line suggested by the work of MARGENAU [5] and BLOCH. The development will be based on two assumptions:

i) There is a nuclear Hamiltonian with two-body interactions

$$H = \sum_{i=1}^{A} T_i + \sum_{i<j} V_{ij} .$$

ii) We investigate the action of this operator on a subspace generated by Slater-determinant wave functions Φ_ν which contain α-clustering effects. The states do not form a complete set and in particular all states have $T=0$ and $S=0$.

The approach differs from others described at this Course in that no average nuclear field is introduced. We try to find a best wave function in our chosen set using the energy variation principle.

2. – Specification of wave functions.

In order to describe configurations with α-particle-like clustering in a nucleus with $4N$ nucleons we take a set of N single-particle wave functions

$$(3) \qquad \varphi_i(\boldsymbol{r}) = A \exp[-(\boldsymbol{r}-\boldsymbol{R}_i)^2/2b^2] , \qquad i=1, 2, ..., N; \qquad A = [b^3\pi^{\frac{3}{2}}]^{-\frac{1}{2}},$$

depending on N vectors $\boldsymbol{R}_1, ..., \boldsymbol{R}_N$ as parameters. The wave function φ_i describes the motion of a single nucleon in a $1s$ harmonic oscillator orbit centered at the point $\boldsymbol{R}_i$. A $4-N$ nucleon state may be constructed from these N orbital wave functions by requiring that each orbital state should be occupied by two protons and two neutrons, and then forming the corresponding $4-N$ particle normalized Slater-determinant wave function $\Phi(\boldsymbol{R}_1, ..., \boldsymbol{R}_N)$. The resultant wave function describes a state with maximum orbital symmetry in the sense of Wigner supermultiplet theory (*i.e.* it has $[4, 4, 4, ..., 4]$ symmetry) and has $T=0$ and $S=0$. There is a tendency for two protons and two neutrons to cluster about each of the points $\boldsymbol{R}_i$; but this clustering is inhibited by the Pauli exclusion principle if the points $\boldsymbol{R}_1, ..., \boldsymbol{R}_N$ are close together. The size of the clusters is determined by the parameter b. If there is a tendency to form α-particle clusters in light nuclei then the class of wave functions described here contains the possibility for describing such clustering. The basic set of wave functions is not an orthogonal set, but as shown in the Appendix, this does not create any difficulties for the construction of S. D. wave functions.

3. – Matrix elements of the kinetic and potential energy.

Let Φ and Ψ be two $4N$-nucleon wave functions constructed from the orbital wave functions of the type specified in eq. (3) with the same radius parameter b, but possibly different sets of parameter vectors $\boldsymbol{R}_1, \ldots, \boldsymbol{R}_N$; $\boldsymbol{S}_1, \ldots, \boldsymbol{S}_N$. We have to calculate some matrix elements of standard operators.

3·1. *The overlap matrix.* – We may use the formula (A.11) given in the Appendix:

$$\text{(A.11)} \qquad \langle \Phi, \Psi \rangle = (\det \langle \varphi_i, \psi_j \rangle)^4 / (\det \langle \varphi_i, \varphi_j \rangle \det \langle \psi_i, \psi_j \rangle)^2 .$$

In our case the single-particle orbital wave functions are simple and the overlap matrix elements may be calculated explicitly. They are

$$(4) \qquad B_{ij} = \langle \varphi_i, \psi_j \rangle = \exp[-(\boldsymbol{R}_i - \boldsymbol{S}_j)^2/4b^2] ,$$

$$(5) \qquad \langle \varphi_i, \varphi_j \rangle = \exp[-(\boldsymbol{R}_i - \boldsymbol{R}_j)^2/4b^2] ,$$

$$(6) \qquad \langle \psi_i, \psi_j \rangle = \exp[-(\boldsymbol{S}_i - \boldsymbol{S}_j)^2/4b^2] .$$

3·2. *The kinetic-energy matrix element.* – From eq. (A.13) of the Appendix we have a formula for the matrix elements of an arbitrary spin-isospin independent one-body operator. We may use this to calculate matrix elements of the kinetic energy:

$$(7) \qquad \langle \Phi, T\Psi \rangle = 4 \langle \Phi, \Psi \rangle \sum_{ij} \langle \varphi_i, t\psi_j \rangle (B^{-1})_{ji} ,$$

where B^{-1} is the inverse of the overlap matrix B given in eq. (4). The single-particle matrix element of the kinetic energy in (7) may be evaluated explicitly:

$$(8) \qquad \langle \varphi_i, t\varphi_j \rangle = \hbar\omega B_{ij} \left[\frac{3}{4} - \frac{1}{8b^2} (\boldsymbol{R}_i - \boldsymbol{S}_j)^2 \right] ,$$

where $\hbar\omega = \hbar^2/Mb^2$.

3·3. *The potential energy.* – Equation (A.14) of the Appendix gives an expression for the matrix element of a general central exchange potential

$$(9) \qquad \begin{cases} V = u(r)(W + BP_\sigma - HP_\tau - MP_\sigma P_\tau) , \\ \langle \Phi, V\Psi \rangle = X_d V_d + X_e V_e , \end{cases}$$

where

$$X_d = 8W + 4B - 4H - 2M , \qquad X_e = 8M + 4H - 4B - 2W ,$$

and the direct and exchange matrix elements V_d and V_e are

$$(10a) \qquad V_d = \langle \Phi, \Psi \rangle \sum_{ijkl} \langle \varphi_i \varphi_j | u | \psi_k \psi_l \rangle (B^{-1})_{ki} (B^{-1})_{lj} ,$$

$$(10b) \qquad V_e = \langle \Phi, \Psi \rangle \sum_{ijkl} \langle \varphi_i \varphi_j | u | \psi_k \psi_l \rangle (B^{-1})_{kj} (B^{-1})_{li} .$$

If $u(r)$ is a local potential then the orbital two-body matrix elements may be calculated explicitly:

$$\langle\varphi_i, \varphi_j|u|\psi_k\psi_l\rangle = A^4\int \exp\left[-\frac{1}{2b^2}[(\boldsymbol{r}_1-\boldsymbol{R}_i)^2+(\boldsymbol{r}_2-\boldsymbol{R}_j)^2+ + (\boldsymbol{r}_1-\boldsymbol{S}_k)^2+(\boldsymbol{r}_2-\boldsymbol{S}_l)^2]\right] u(\boldsymbol{r}_1-\boldsymbol{r}_2)\,\mathrm{d}\boldsymbol{r}_1\,\mathrm{d}\boldsymbol{r}_2 .$$

This expression for the matrix element can be simplified using the identity

$$(\boldsymbol{r}_1-\boldsymbol{R}_i)^2+(\boldsymbol{r}_1-\boldsymbol{S}_k)^2 = 2\big(\boldsymbol{r}_1-\tfrac{1}{2}(\boldsymbol{R}_i+\boldsymbol{S}_k)\big)^2+\tfrac{1}{2}(\boldsymbol{R}_i-\boldsymbol{S}_k)^2,$$

and a similar one involving $\boldsymbol{r}_2$, $\boldsymbol{R}_j$ and $\boldsymbol{S}_l$. We get

$$\text{(11)}\quad \langle\varphi_i\varphi_j|u|\psi_z\psi_l\rangle = B_{ik}B_{jl}A^4\int\exp\left[-\frac{1}{b^2}\left[\big(\boldsymbol{r}_1-\tfrac{1}{2}(\boldsymbol{R}_i+\boldsymbol{S}_k)\big)^2+\big(\boldsymbol{r}_2-\tfrac{1}{2}(\boldsymbol{R}_j+\boldsymbol{S}_l)\big)^2\right]\right]\cdot \cdot u(\boldsymbol{r}_1-\boldsymbol{r}_2)\,\mathrm{d}\boldsymbol{r}_1\,\mathrm{d}\boldsymbol{r}_2 = B_{ik}B_{jl}\,I(\boldsymbol{R}_i+\boldsymbol{S}_k-\boldsymbol{R}_j-\boldsymbol{S}_l)\,,$$

where

$$\text{(12)}\qquad I(\boldsymbol{\rho}) = \frac{A^2}{\sqrt{8}}\int\exp\left[-\left(\boldsymbol{r}-\frac{\boldsymbol{\rho}}{2}\right)^2\Big/2b^2\right]u(\boldsymbol{r})\,\mathrm{d}\boldsymbol{r}\,.$$

If $u(r)$ is a Gaussian potential or a sum of Gaussian potentials then the integral $I(\varrho)$ can be evaluated explicitly. If

$$u(r) = u_0\exp[-r^2/\beta^2]\,,$$

then

$$\text{(13)}\qquad I(\varrho) = a_0a^3\exp[-\varrho^2(1-a^2)/8b^2]\,,$$

where

$$a^2 = 1/\big(1+2(b/\beta)^2\big)\,.$$

If on the other hand $u(r)$ is a general local potential $I(\varrho)$ may be expressed in terms of Talmi integrals

$$\text{(14)}\qquad I(\varrho) = \exp[-\varrho^2/8b^2]\sum_n(\varrho^2/8b^2)^nI_n/n!\,,$$

$$I_n = \frac{2}{(2b^2)^{n+\frac{3}{2}}\Gamma(n+\frac{3}{2})}\int\exp[-r^2/2b^2]\,r^{2n+2}u(r)\,\mathrm{d}r\,.$$

The series (14) for $I(\varrho)$ converges rapidly for all ϱ unless the range of the potential $u(r)$ is much greater than the harmonic oscillator radius parameter b which gives the size of the α-clusters.

4. – Examples of α-cluster wave functions.

i) ^{8}Be: Suppose we take a system of two α-clusters specified by the two orbital wave functions

$$\varphi_1(\boldsymbol{r}) = A \exp\left[-\frac{1}{2b^2}(\boldsymbol{r}-\boldsymbol{d})^2\right], \qquad \varphi_2(\boldsymbol{r}) = A \exp\left[-\frac{1}{2b^2}(\boldsymbol{r}+\boldsymbol{d})^2\right].$$

The 8-nucleon S. D. wave function constructed from these two orbital wave-functions represents two α-clusters with mean positions $\boldsymbol{d}$ and $-\boldsymbol{d}$ separated by a distance $2d$. Suppose we choose $\boldsymbol{d}$ parallel to the z-axis and investigate the behaviour of the S. D. wave functions as $\boldsymbol{d}\to 0$. In this limit the two orbital wave functions become identical and the unormalized S.D. wave function vanishes. At the same time, however, the normalization constant (A.6) becomes infinite and the normalized S.D. wave function tends to a definite nonzero limit. To see what this is it is convenient to introduce orthogonal linear combinations of φ_1 and φ_2

$$\chi_1 = \varphi_1 + \varphi_2\,, \qquad \chi_2 = \frac{1}{d}(\varphi_1 - \varphi_2)\,.$$

As $\boldsymbol{d}\to 0$

$$\chi_1 \to 2A \exp[-r^2/2b^2]\,, \qquad \chi_2 \to \frac{4A\boldsymbol{r}\cdot\boldsymbol{d}}{d2b^2}\exp[-r^2/2b^2] = 2\frac{Az}{b^2}\exp[-r^2/2b^2]\,.$$

In other words χ_1 tends to a $1s$ spherical state and χ_2 tends to a $1p$ state.

The limiting form of the cluster wave function as $\boldsymbol{d}\to 0$ is just a harmonic-oscillator shell-model function with 4 nucleons in the $1s$-shell and 4 nucleons in the $1p$-shell [in the orbital state (0, 0, 1)]. This is a deformed intrinsic state of the type considered by ELLIOTT in his SU_3 model. If we project out angular momentum eigenstates (with $L=0, 2, 4$) we obtain the lowest states in the shell-model description of ^{8}Be in (L, S) coupling.

ii) ^{12}C: suppose we take a system of 3α-clusters whose centers form an equilateral triangle with side d in the x, y plane and investigate the behaviour of the normalized S.D. wave function as $d\to 0$. As in the previous case we obtain a harmonic-oscillator shell-model wave function in the limit with configuration $(0\,0\,0)^4(1\,0\,0)^4(0\,1\,0)^4$; $((n_x, n_y, n_z)$ represents the harmonic oscillator state with n_x, n_y, n_z quanta in the x, y, z directions respectively). This state is a deformed intrinsic state and projecting out angular momentum eigenstates (with $L=0, 2, 4$) we get the lowest states of ^{12}C in the L, S shell-model description.

We might also consider a system of 3 α-clusters in a line parallel to the x-axis. The shell-model limit as the clusters move together is the configuration $(0\ 0\ 0)^4(1\ 0\ 0)^4(2\ 0\ 0)^4$ with 4 nucleons in each of the $1s$, $1p$, $2s$, $1d$ shells respectively. In other words it is a 4 particle-4 hole excitation from the ground-state shell-model configuration.

If we expand a three-α-particle configuration lying somewhere between the equilateral triangle and linear configuration in terms of harmonic-oscillator shell-model states we obtain a superposition of 1 particle-1 hole, 2 particle-2 hole, 3 particle- 3 hole and 4 particle- 4 hole states.

iii) ^{16}O: a tetrahedral configuration of 4α-clusters goes over to the double-closed-shell configuration in the limit of overlapping clusters. A plane configuration in the x, y plane goes over to a 4 particle-4 hole excited state in which 4 nucleons are excited from the $(0\ 0\ 1)$ $1p$-shell state to a state in the $2s$, $1d$-shell. The orbital state of these sd nucleons depends on the geometrical configuration of the α-clusters. For example if the α-clusters lie at the corners of a square then the orbital configuration of the four sd-nucleons is $1/\sqrt{2}\,[(2\ 0\ 0)-(0\ 2\ 0)]$. For other shapes the orbital wave function of the sd-nucleons in the limit of overlaping clusters will be $[\alpha(2\ 0\ 0)+\beta(0\ 2\ 0)]$ where the coefficients α and β depend on the geometrical shape.

The most deformed 4p-4h wave function in the SU_3 classification belongs to the (8 4) representation and the intrinsic state has a shell-model configuration $(0\ 0\ 0)^4(1\ 0\ 0)^4(0\ 1\ 0)^4(2\ 0\ 0)^4$, quite similar to a coplanar configuration of four α-clusters.

We see from the above examples that the shell model is a limiting case of the α-cluster model. The α-cluster model may be thought of as an extension of the shell model just as the particle-hole model is an extension of the shell-model. A shell-model calculation involves diagonalization of a nuclear Hamiltonian in a finite subspace of shell-model states chosen out of a complete set. A selection of a few α-cluster states may give a better approximation to the true wave functions of the system than many 1p-1h, 2p-2h, 3p-3h and 4p-4h states.

5. – The nucleon-nucleon interactions.

Now we must investigate the important question of which interaction to use in our calculations. All the α-cluster states considered have a certain « closed shell » structure because each orbital state is occupied by four nucleons. They all have maximum orbital symmetry in the Wigner supermultiplet sense and all have $T=0$ and $S=0$. Because they all have spin-zero, matrix elements of the spin-orbit force and the tensor force vanish identically. (The spin-orbit force and the tensor force are tensors of rank one and two respectively in spin, hence their matrix elements between spin-zero states vanish by the Wigner-Eckart theorem.) These two noncentral forces contribute only in second order by admixtures of $S=1$ and $S=2$ states which do not have the α-cluster structure. In the present calculations we neglect these admixtures and consider only central forces.

It was shown in the last Section that only certain combinations of the exchange parameters in the general central force

$$V(r) = u(r)(W + BP_\sigma - HP_\tau - MP_\sigma P_\tau)\,, \tag{15}$$

occur in expressions for matrix elements of the potential energy in the α-cluster model, namely

$$X_d = 8W + 4B - 4H - 2M \qquad \text{and} \qquad X_e = 8M + 4H - 4B - 2W.$$

In other words two different exchange forces with the same values of X_d and X_e would have the same effect in the α-cluster model. This is because the α-cluster wave functions have maximum orbital symmetry.

In light nuclei a central nucleon-nucleon interaction with a large space-exchange interaction tends to push down states with maximum orbital symmetry in spite of the spin-orbit force which tends to break this symmetry. It is probable therefore that calculated energies of low states in light even-even nuclei are mainly sensitive to the combinations X_d and X_e of the exchange parameters, so that these parameters should be well determined by fitting the energies of low excited states. Many of the self-consistent field calculations made recently in the s-d shell have used a Rosenfeld exchange mixture. It is probable that the results would be almost the same if a simple mixture of Wigner and Majorana exchange force were used with the appropriate values of X_d and X_e.

In Table I we list values of the parameters X_e and X_d for some common exchange mixtures.

The classical condition for saturation with exchange forces and without a hard core in the nucleon-nucleon interaction is

$$X_d \leqslant 0\,,$$

hence the interactions (v) and (vi) are saturating; (iii) and (iv) almost saturate while (i) and (ii) do not saturate. Also listed in the last two columns of the Table are values of

$$Y_{\text{even}} = \frac{1}{6}(X_d + X_e) \qquad \text{and} \qquad Y_{\text{odd}} = \frac{1}{10}(X_d - X_e)\,, \tag{16}$$

TABLE I.

	W	M	B	H	X_d	X_e	Y_{even}	Y_{odd}
i) SERBER	0.5	0.5	0	0	3	3	1	0
ii) SOPER [11]	0.40	0.33	0.17	0.10	2.82	1.56	0.73	0.14
iii) FERREL and VISSCHER [12]	0.32	0.50	0	0.18	0.84	4.08	0.82	−0.32
iv) GILLET [13] (^{16}O best)	0.35	0.35	−0.1	0.4	0.1	4.1	0.7	−0.4
v) GILLET [13] (^{12}C best)	0.40	0.40	−0.2	0.4	0.0	4.8	0.8	−0.5
vi) ROSENFELD [14]	−0.13	0.93	0.46	−0.26	0.0	4.8	0.8	−0.5
vii) MAJORANA mixture	$1-M$	M	0	0	$8-10M$	$10M-2$	1	$1-2M$
ix) ELLIOTT [15]					0.0	6.0	1	−0.6

which measure the strength of the interaction in even and odd states of relative angular momentum of two nucleons. Most of the phenomenological interactions are quite strongly repulsive in odd relative angular-momentum states.

Evidence from nucleon-nucleon scattering experiments suggests that the nucleon-nucleon interaction has a repulsive core and most people believe that the saturation property of nuclear forces is due partially to the repulsive core and partially to the exchange character of the force. In the classical saturation problem, the saturation is produced by a repulsive interaction in odd states of relative motion which balances the attraction in even states. For a nuclear force with a repulsive core the saturation is a consequence of the hard core which acts most strongly in relative S-states and of a weaker repulsion in odd angular-momentum states due to exchange effects.

Let us look at the nucleon-nucleon interaction in relative p-states as determined from nucleon-nucleon scattering. The interaction is repulsive in the $^1P_1$ and $^3P_1$ states and attractive in the $^3P_0$ and $^3P_2$ states. One may try to calculate the matrix elements of the interactions in relative p-states using some procedure to take account of the repulsive core, then evaluate the average over spin states appropriate for nuclear states with maximum spatial symmetry. The average p-state interaction turns out to be rather small, either zero or slightly repulsive depending upon the nucleon-nucleon potential used, and the prescription for eliminating the repulsive core. These results suggest that the saturation property of nuclear forces is due to the repulsive core rather than to the repulsion in odd angular-momentum states, and that for the purposes of nuclear structure calculations the central part of the nucleon-nucleon interaction might be well represented by a hard core plus an attractive Serber exchange mixture or even by a hard-core potential plus an attraction which acts only in s-states of relative motion (MOSKOWSKI and SCOTT [16], KALLIO and KOLTVEIT [17]).

A phenomenological force has been used in the calculation described in these lectures. We must determine restrictions which have to be placed on this interaction in order that the calculation would give sensible results. The most important of these is that the force should have reasonable saturation properties for the range of nuclei considered. In the particle-hole model this restriction is not so important because of the way in which the calculations are made. Although the model is based on the Hartree-Fock theory, and the single-particle energies and residual interactions should be calculated from the same nuclear force, this is never done in practice. The single-particle energies are taken from experimental energy levels and the residual interaction between particles or particles and holes is parametrized independently. Energies of excited states are calculated relative to the ground state and the ground-state binding energy is assumed to have its experimental value. This procedure is not self-consistent although it may give good results in cases where the core is not strongly excited. The lack of self-consistency shows up, for example, in spurious states which do not appear at zero energy as they should if the calculations were made correctly.

In the α-cluster theory there is no possibility of making a separation into core and valence nucleons. All nucleons in the nucleus are treated on the same footing. Consequently there is no place in the theory for an average nuclear field or for single-particle energy levels. We do not calculate energies of excited states relative to the ground state; but calculate the total energy of each nuclear state, and subtract the calculated ground-state energy in order to get the energies of excited states. Because we evaluate energies of the nucleus as a whole it is necessary to be careful about the saturation properties of the internucleon interactions. In order to illustrate these remarks we consider the ground state of ^{16}O. We may want to calculate the stability of the shell-model ground-state against deformation into four α-clusters arranged in a tetrahedral configuration. We do this by calculating the expectation value of the nuclear energy for several tetrahedral deformations and locating the deformation which gives a minimum energy. For the result of such a calculation to make sense it is necessary that the forces used should give the correct binding energy of ^{16}O relative to the binding energy of four independent α-particles. These considerations are also important if we are trying to calculate the effect of a core deformation in a nucleus with an ellipsoidal deformation in its ground-state.

The internucleon interaction used in the present calculations was developed by VOLKOV [18] for use in some self-consistent calculations with p-shell nuclei. It is a mixture of a Wigner and a Majorana interaction

$$V(r) = u(r)(W + MP_M) , \tag{17}$$

where

$$u(r) = -60 \exp[-(r/1.80)^2] + 60 \exp[-(r/1.01)^2] \text{ MeV} .$$

The form of a weakly repulsive core followed by an attractive tail was chosen so that the radial shape of the potential resembled the long range part of a potential obtained from a Moskowski-Scott [16] separation method. The potential has the following properties:

i) It is saturating for light nuclei and gives a reasonable binding energy and equilibrium size for ^{4}He and ^{16}O if the wave functions of these nuclei are represented by harmonic-oscillator shell-model wave functions. (To give the correct binding energy for ^{16}O, M must lie between 0.6 and 0.65).

ii) It gives good order-of-magnitude values for the two-body low-energy parameters.

The interaction (17) also has some defects. It is not saturating in infinite nuclear matter and it does not give enough binding in ^{8}Be and ^{12}C. These two defects may be related and, if possible, a better effective interaction should be found.

6. – Calculations of equilibrium deformations.

Although the main purpose of these lectures is to discuss α-clustering, in the first part of this Section we will consider ellipsoidal deformations of light nuclei.

This problem is discussed by BAR TOUV and GILLET in seminars and lectures at this Course, within the framework of Hartree-Fock theory in a restricted subspace, namely the spherical oscillator states in the s-d shell. Recently THOULESS and HAYWARD [19] have considered the deformation problem from a different point of view and I have also made some calculations to compare with the results of α-cluster calculations.

The idea is to take a set of single-particle wave functions defined by a deformed harmonic-oscillator potential to construct Slater-determinant wave functions and to calculate the mean energy of the nucleus as a function of the deformation. THOULESS and HAYWARD used standard effective interactions (GILLET, SOPER, etc.) and varied the oscillator parameters with a constant volume restriction. My calculations used the interaction (17), which has reasonable saturation properties for light nuclei, and a search was made for an unrestricted minimum.

The expectation value of the energy was calculated using the standard shell model formula

$$\langle E\rangle = \sum_{\alpha} \langle\alpha|t|\alpha\rangle + \tfrac{1}{2}\sum_{\alpha\beta}\{\langle\alpha\beta|v|\alpha\beta\rangle - \langle\alpha\beta|v|\beta\alpha\rangle\}\,, \tag{18}$$

where the sums are to be taken over the occupied (orthogonal) single-particle states α. The single-particle orbital states are labeled with quantum numbers n_x, n_y, n_z, giving the number of quanta in the x, y and z directions respectively. It is possible to calculate the two-body matrix elements $\langle\alpha\beta|v|\alpha\beta\rangle$ by making a Talmi transformation to relative and center-of-mass co-ordinates in the rectangular representation. The two-body matrix elements are given in terms of matrix elements

$$V(n_x, n_y, n_z) = \langle n_x n_y n_z|v|n_x n_y n_z\rangle\,,$$

between deformed oscillator states $|n_x n_y n_z\rangle$ describing the relative motion of two nucleons. (If the many-nucleon wave function is an eigenstate of N_x, N_y, N_z then only diagonal matrix elements of v occur in the expression for the expectation value of the potential energy.) Hence the expectation value of the potential energy of any nuclear state may be expressed in the form

$$\langle V\rangle = \sum c(n_x, n_y, n_z)\, V(n_x, n_y, n_z)\,, \tag{19}$$

where the coefficients $c(n_x, n_y, n_z)$ are pure numbers which depend only on the nuclear state considered, but not on the form of the potential used nor on the deformation of the wave functions. They may be calculated once and for all for any state of interest. The matrix elements $V(n_x, n_y, n_z)$ depend on the internucleon interaction potential and the deformation of the wave functions.

We will consider the case of ^{12}C as an example, assuming a configuration $(0\,0\,0)^4(0\,1\,0)^4(0\,0\,1)^4$. In shell-model language the $1s$, $1p_y$ and $1p_z$ orbits are each occupied by four nucleons. The expectation value for the total energy of this state is

$$\langle E\rangle = \langle T\rangle + Y_{\text{even}}\langle V_{\text{even}}\rangle + Y_{\text{odd}}\langle V_{\text{odd}}\rangle\,, \tag{20}$$

where

$$\langle T\rangle = 2.75\hbar\omega_x + 4.75(\hbar\omega_y + \hbar\omega_z)\,,$$

(the center-of-mass kinetic energy has been subtracted) Y_{even} and Y_{odd} are the interaction strengths in even and odd angular momentum states of relative motion of two nucleons, and are defined in eq. (16), in terms of the exchange parameters. Also

$$\langle V_{\text{even}}\rangle = 27V(0\,0\,0) + 3V(0\,2\,0) + 3V(0\,0\,2) + V(0\,1\,1)\,,$$
$$\langle V_{\text{odd}}\rangle = 15V(0\,1\,0) + 15V(0\,0\,1)\,.$$

Calculations of $\langle E\rangle$ as a function of ω_x, ω_y, ω_z with the potential (17) ($M = 0.65$) give the following results:

i) The lowest-energy configuration has $\omega_y = \omega_z$ *i.e.* the x-axis is an axis of symmetry as expected.

ii) There is a gain in binding energy of about 4.5 MeV in going from the best spherical wave functions ($\hbar\omega_x = \hbar\omega_y = \hbar\omega_z \approx 16$ MeV) to the best deformed wave function ($\hbar\omega_x \simeq 18$ MeV, $\hbar\omega_y = \hbar\omega_z \approx 14$ MeV). The nuclear volume is approximately preserved.

Similar calculations were made to determine the excitation energy of a simple 4particle-4hole excited state in ^{16}O with configuration $(0\,0\,0)^4(1\,0\,0)^4(0\,1\,0)^4(2\,0\,0)^4$. The ground-state configuration was assumed to be $(0\,0\,0)^4(1\,0\,0)^4(0\,1\,0)^4(0\,0\,1)^4$ *i.e.* four nucleons were excited from the $(0\,0\,1)$ state to the $(2\,0\,0)$ state. Results of these calculations are summarized in Table II.

TABLE II.

	BE (spherical)	BE_{eq}	$\hbar\omega_x$ (eq)	$\hbar\omega_y = \hbar\omega_z$ (eq)	ΔE
^{12}C	64.6	69.1	18	14	4.5
^{16}O g.s.	117	117	16	16	0
^{16}O 2p-2h	85.4	88.8	12	16	3.4
^{16}O 4p-4h	67.6	79.0	10	14	11.4

The first column BE (spherical) gives binding energies calculated with spherical wave function ($\hbar\omega = 16$), BE_{eq} is the equilibrium binding energy, $\hbar\omega_x$(eq) etc. give the equilibrium deformation and ΔE is the energy gained on deformation. All numbers are in MeV. There was a gain in binding energy of 11 MeV on deformation and the nuclear volume was considerably less in the excited state compared with the ground state. The 4p-4h state was much too high at 38 MeV, however, to correspond to the observed 6.06 MeV 0^+ state in ^{16}O even after projection of angular momentum.

THOULESS and HAYWARD [19] made similar calculations on the same 4p-4h state in ^{16}O using a wide range of exchange mixtures. They found that the deformation energy was very sensitive to the exchange mixture used. Forces which were strongly repulsive in odd angular-momentum states, for example the Rosenfeld mixture or the Gillet force, gave a large deformation energy and brought the 4p-4h state low down in energy so that it could reasonably correspond to the 6.06 MeV 0^+ state.

The fact that the deformation energies are large (calculations made with interaction (17) in ^{19}F and ^{20}Ne also give values of the order of 10 MeV) suggests that investigations using Hartree-Fock theory restricted to spherical single-particle states in the *s-d* shell of the type described by GILLET and BAR-TOUV cannot be considered completely satisfactory, even though the results of such calculation agree remarkably well with experiment.

In the second part of this Section we give examples of the binding energies and equilibrium deformations of same α-cluster configurations and compare them with the calculations using deformed ellipsoidal wave functions. In all the calculations the harmonic oscillator radius parameter $b=(\hbar/M\omega)^{\frac{1}{2}}$ which determines the size of the α-clusters was fixed at 1.61 fermi ($\hbar\omega=16$ MeV). This was the equilibrium value in the ground-state wave function of ^{16}O. In each example a certain geometrical arrangement of α-clusters was chosen and its binding energy calculated as a function of the separation of the clusters. When the separation of the α-clusters was small ($\leqslant 0.5$ fermi) the cluster wave functions approached a spherical harmonic-oscillator shell-model wave function with $\hbar\omega=16$ MeV. The equilibrium deformation and the deformation energy were determined for each configuration.

The results of some calculations are given in Table III. The first column in the Table specifies the configuration, the second (BE ($d=0$)) gives the binding energy of the shell model limit of overlapping clusters, BE_{eq} is the equilibrium binding energy and d_{eq} is the equilibrium separation of the nearest pair of α-clusters in the configuration. ΔKE is the decrease in kinetic energy on deformation and ΔE is the gain in binding energy.

TABLE III.

	BE ($d=0$)	BE_{eq}	ΔKE	ΔE	d_{eq} (fermi)
^{12}C triangle	64.6	67.6	19	3	2.5
^{12}C linear	23.5	59.8	66	35.3	3.5
^{16}O tetrahedron	117.0	117.0	0	0	0
^{16}O square	64	85.0	77	21	3.0
^{16}O diamond	67	88.5	58	21	3.0

In the triangular configuration of ^{12}C the α-clusters lie at the corners of an equilateral triangle with side d. The α-cluster wave function when $d=0$ coincides with the ellipsoidal state in the limit of zero deformation. The gain in binding energy on deformation is in fact larger for the ellipsoidal wave function than for the α-cluster wave function, but the α-cluster wave function is not an eigenstate of parity and we should project parity in order to compare them. In any case there is a large overlap between the oblate ellipsoidal configuration and the cluster wave function.

The linear configuration for ^{12}C (three equidistant α-clusters in a straight line) is interesting because of the large gain in energy on distorting into 3α-clusters and the fact that the equilibrium energy is 7.8 MeV above the ground-state triangular configuration. It could correspond to the well known 0^+ state in ^{12}C near 7 MeV. The shell-model limit of the linear configuration is a 4p-4h excited state.

If we consider the tetrahedral configuration of ^{16}O we find that the state of lowest energy occurs in the shell-model limit $d = 0$. In other words, for the interaction used, the spherical shell model representation of the ground-state of ^{16}O is stable. There is no tendency for it to deform into a tetrahedral configuration of four α-clusters. We should remember, however, that this cluster configuration is neither an eigenstate of angular momentum nor of parity. We should project angular momentum and parity before we can say conclusively that the spherical shell-model state is the state of lowest energy. We will return to this problem later.

The coplanar configurations of four α-clusters lie at quite a high excitation energy above the ground-state of ^{16}O. They also show a strong tendency to deform into four rather widely separated clusters. A diamond-shaped configuration seems to have the lowest energy. It is about 10 MeV lower than the lowest deformed ellipsoidal 4p-4h configuration.

Looking at Table III we see that the decrease in kinetic energy due to deformation is very large in all cases where the α-clusters separate. This reduction in kinetic energy is due to the Pauli exclusion principle. If two clusters are separated by a distance large compared with $2b$ all the nucleons in each cluster occupy a $1s$ orbital state. On the other hand if two clusters overlap completely then, because of the Pauli principle, four nucleons must move up to a $1p$ state and the kinetic energy increases by $2\hbar\omega$.

If the nucleon-nucleon interaction used in the calculations has a large Majorana exchange component then the consequent repulsive interaction between nucleons in odd angular momentum states favours a separation of α-clusters. The kinetic energy also favours a separation of α-clusters. The strong attractive nucleon-nucleon interaction in even states tends to pull them together.

The Majorana exchange component in the nucleon-nucleon interaction was varied in some calculations in the tetrahedral cluster configuration of ^{16}O. If the Majorana strength M was increased to 0.75 then the spherical shape became unstable and a deformed tetrahedral cluster configuration was favoured, even without projecting angular momentum and parity. This calculation illustrates the effects of repulsion between clusters due to a large Majorana component in the nucleon-nucleon interaction.

We will end this Section by pointing out a possible pitfall in Hartree-Fock calculations made in a limited subspace of single-particle states. Such calculations may find local minima which would in fact correspond to saddle-point if the space of single-particle states were extended. This point is illustrated by the coplanar configurations in the α-cluster model. The « best » coplanar configuration is diamond shaped, but if we relax the restriction of coplanarity the diamond-shaped plane configuration can fold about a diagonal and pass continuously over into the tetrahedral configuration which has a lower energy.

7. – The Hill-Wheeler method.

An α-cluster state is represented by a Slater-determinant wave function $\Phi(\beta)$ where β denotes the vectors $\boldsymbol{R}_1, \ldots, \boldsymbol{R}_N$ specifying the centers of the clusters. Up to this point we have investigated the variation of the expectation value of the energy

$$\langle E(\beta)\rangle = \langle \Phi(\beta),\, H\Phi(\beta)\rangle\,, \tag{21}$$

as a function of the parameters β and looked for the state $\Phi(\beta_0)$ which minimizes $\langle E(\beta)\rangle$.

These wave functions are unsatisfactory from several points of view. The mean positions of the centers of the α-clusters are fixed and the wave functions do not allow dynamical oscillations of the cluster structure. Also the S.D. states are not eigenstates of angular momentum and often they are not eigenstates of parity.

We can always obtain a better wave function by allowing linear combinations of the cluster wave functions corresponding to different parameters

$$\Phi = \int c(\beta)\Phi(\beta)\,\mathrm{d}\beta\,. \tag{22}$$

If we determine a « best » wave function Φ by the variation principle:

$$\delta(\langle \Phi,\, H\Phi\rangle / \langle \Phi,\, \Phi\rangle) = 0\,, \tag{23}$$

we obtain an integral equation for the coefficients $c(\beta)$

$$\int\{H(\beta,\beta') - EB(\beta,\beta')\}c(\beta')\,\mathrm{d}\beta' = 0\,, \tag{24}$$

where

$$H(\beta,\beta') = \langle \Phi(\beta),\, H\Phi(\beta')\rangle$$

and

$$B(\beta, \beta') = \langle \Phi(\beta), \Phi(\beta') \rangle .$$

These are the well-known equations of the Hill-Wheeler [20] method.

If $\beta_1 - \beta_2$ is small enough then

$$\langle \Phi(\beta_1), \Phi(\beta_2) \rangle \simeq 1 \qquad \text{and} \qquad \Phi(\beta_1) \simeq \Phi(\beta_2) .$$

For example in the α-cluster wave functions a shift in the position of one cluster by 0.5 fermi does not change the wave function very much. Hence one may get a quite good wave function by taking a finite linear combination of cluster wave functions

$$\Phi = \sum_{i=1}^{n} c_i \Phi(\beta_i) , \tag{25}$$

instead of the integral combination in eq. (22). The variation principle (23) then leads to an algebraic eigenvalue problem for the coefficients c_i instead of the integral eq. (24)

$$\sum_j (H_{ij} - EB_{ij}) c_j = 0 . \tag{26}$$

This method was suggested by BORYSOWICZ who has made some calculations with it in the α-cluster model. It has one very attractive feature: it leads to an algebraic equation instead of an integral equation. This is a great simplication because the space of variation of the parameters β (which stand for a set of N vectors) is very complicated. Also eq. (26) is not just an approximation to the integral eq. (24). It is a variational equation in its own right.

If we solve the eigenvalue problem (26) the lowest eigenvalue should give an approximation to the ground-state energy of our nucleus and other low eigenvalues may give approximations to low excited states. By choosing a trial wave function of the form (25) we are diagonalizing the Hamiltonian of the system in a finite subspace of states spanned by the states $\Phi(\beta_i)$, $i = 1, ..., n$.

In what way are the eigenvalues of the truncated problem related to the eigenvalues of the complete Hamiltonian? This question arises in all shell-model calculations and is answered by the Mini-Max Theorem (COURANT and HILBERT, HALMOS [21]).

THEOREM. – Let H be a self-adjoint operator with discrete eigenvalues $\lambda_1 \leqslant \lambda_2 \leqslant \lambda_3 \leqslant ...$ and $\psi_1, \psi_2, ..., \psi_n$ be any linearly independent set of n-vectors. Let $\mu_1 \leqslant \mu_2 \leqslant \mu_3 \leqslant ... \leqslant \mu_n$ be the eigenvalues of H restricted to the subspace $\mathscr{V}_n$ of linear combinations of $\psi_1, ..., \psi_n$. Then

$$\lambda_1 \leqslant \mu_1, \quad \lambda_2 \leqslant \mu_2, \quad \lambda_3 \leqslant \mu_3, \quad ..., \quad \lambda_n \leqslant \mu_n .$$

Proof. We will first show that there is at least one normalized vector in $\mathscr{V}_n$ with the property

$$\langle\psi, H\psi\rangle \geqslant \lambda_n .$$

Let $\varphi_1, \ldots, \varphi_n$ be the eigenstates of $\lambda_1, \ldots, \lambda_n$ and $\varphi_{n+1}, \ldots$ be the eigenstates of $\lambda_{n+1}, \ldots$. Also $\mathscr{W}_n$ is the set of all linear combinations of $\varphi_1, \ldots, \varphi_n$ and P_n is a projection operator on $\mathscr{W}_n$; $Q_n = 1 - P_n$.

Let ψ be any vector in $\mathscr{V}_n$ and consider the projected vector $P_n\psi$ in $\mathscr{W}_n$. There are two possibilities:

i) $P_n\psi \neq 0$ for all vectors ψ in $\mathscr{V}_n$;

ii) there exists a vector ψ_0 in $\mathscr{V}_n$ such that $P_n\psi_0 = 0$.

In case ii) ψ_0 is a linear combination of $\psi_{n+1}, \ldots$.

Hence $\langle\psi_0, H\psi_0\rangle \geqslant \lambda_{n+1} \geqslant \lambda_n$.

In case i) if ψ_1, ψ_2 are two vectors in $\mathscr{V}_n$ then $P_n\psi_1 \neq P_n\psi_2$ (otherwise $P_n(\psi_1 - \psi_2) = 0$), *i.e.* every vector in $\mathscr{V}_n$ leads to a different vector in $\mathscr{W}_n$ as both $\mathscr{V}_n$ and $\mathscr{W}_n$ have the same dimension there must be a one-to-one correspondence between the vectors of $\mathscr{V}_n$ and $\mathscr{W}_n$ induced by P_n. It follows that there must exist a normalized vector ψ in $\mathscr{V}_n$ with the property

$$P_n\psi = \alpha\varphi_n .$$

Put $\psi = \alpha\varphi_n + \beta\chi_n$ where χ_n is a linear combination of $\varphi_{n+1} \ldots$

$$\langle\psi, H\psi\rangle = |\alpha|^2\lambda_n + |\beta|^2\langle\chi_n, H\chi_n\rangle \geqslant \lambda_n .$$

and (a) is proved.

Because μ_n is the maximum eigenvalue of H restricted to $\mathscr{V}_n$

$$\mu_n \geqslant \langle\psi, H\psi\rangle \geqslant \lambda_n \qquad i.e. \qquad \mu_n \geqslant \lambda_n .$$

We may now reduce the problem to one in a vector space of $n-1$ dimensions by taking $\mathscr{V}_{n-1}$ to be the set of all vectors in $\mathscr{V}_n$ orthogonal to the eigenvector belonging to μ_n and proceed by induction to prove $\mu_{n-1} \geqslant \lambda_{n-1}$ and so on.

The eigenvalue problem (26) has a nonstandard form and we should discuss some of its properties. The problem (26) arises from the variation problem (23) when Φ is restricted to the subspace of linear combinations of the states $\Phi(\beta_1), \ldots, \Phi(\beta_n)$. The nonstandard form occurs only because this basic set of states is not orthonormal. Some features of the variation problem are independent of the choice of basic states.

a) Orthogonality. Two wave functions

$$\Phi = \sum c_i\Phi_i \qquad \text{and} \qquad \Phi' = \sum c'_i\Phi_i \qquad (\text{here } \Phi_i = \Phi(\beta_i)),$$

belonging to different eigenvalues E and E' must be orthogonal, *i.e.*

$$\langle \Phi, \Phi' \rangle = \sum_{ij} c_i^* \langle \Phi_i, \Phi_j \rangle c'_j = \sum_{ij} c_i^* B_{ij} c'_j = 0 . \tag{27}$$

Equation (27) gives the orthogonality condition for solutions $\{c_i\}$ of the eigenvalue problem (26).

b) Properties of the overlap matrix $B_{ij} = \langle \Phi_i, \Phi_j \rangle$. As above if $\Phi = \sum c_i \Phi_i$ then

$$\langle \Phi, \Phi \rangle = \sum c_i^* B_{ij} c_j .$$

There are two possibilities:

i) the set $\Phi_i (i = 1, ..., n)$ is linearly independent: then $\Phi \neq 0 \langle \Phi, \Phi \rangle > 0$ and $\sum c_i^* B_{ij} c_j > 0$ for all $\{c_i\}$ *i.e.* the matrix B_{ij} is positive definite and is nonsingular;

ii) the set $\Phi_i (i = 1, ..., n)$ is linearly dependent; then there exists a set $\{c_i\}$ of coefficients such that $\Phi = 0$ *i.e.*

$$\sum c_i^* B_{ij} c_j = 0 ;$$

in this case the matrix B_{ij} is positive semidefinite and is singular.

In many practical problems it may happen that the matrix is not singular, but is almost singular. In other words the matrix B_{ij} may have one or several very small eigenvalues. If the states Φ_i are normalized then the diagonal matrix elements of B are all unity and $\mathrm{Tr}(B) = n$. B would be almost singular if there were an eigenvalue μ_n with the property $0 < \mu_n \ll 1$. Suppose Φ is a normalized eigenfunction corresponding to this eigenvalue. Then

$$1 = \langle \Phi, \Phi \rangle = \sum c_i^* B_{ij} c_j = \mu_n \sum |c_i|^2 ,$$

$$\sum_{i=1}^{n} |c_i|^2 = \frac{1}{\mu_n} \gg 1 .$$

The coefficients c_i in the expansion of Φ are large and one might say that the representation of the state Φ in terms of the set Φ_i is ill conditioned. In general one might say that the expansion $\Phi = \sum c_i \Phi_i$ is ill conditioned if

$$\sum |c_i|^2 / \langle \Phi, \Phi \rangle \gg 1 . \tag{28}$$

If this condition holds then a small error in the matrix elements of H_{ij} or B_{ij} can lead to a larger error in the energy. It is hoped therefore that the physically important states, *i.e.* those which have the lowest energy, correspond to small values of the ratio (28).

Suppose H' and B' denote small changes in H and B, then to first order in H' and B' the change in an eigenvalue E with unperturbed eigenfunction $\{c_i\}$ is given by

$$\delta E = \Big(\sum_{ij} c_i^* (H'_{ij} - EB'_{ij}) c_j\Big) \Big/ \Big(\sum_{ij} c_i^* B_{ij} c_j\Big) . \tag{29}$$

If $0 < \sum_{ij} c_i^* B_{ij} c_j \ll 1$ when $\{c_i\}$ is normalized by $\sum |c_i|^2 = 1$ then a small change in H' or B' can produce a large change in δE.

8. – Spurious states of center-of-mass motion.

If a nuclear state is represented by a shell-model wave function the center of mass of the nucleus is confined to a small region of space. As a consequence the center of mass energy is not zero but has some finite positive value. There are other, more serious, consequences of this defect of shell-model wave functions. It may happen that certain linear combinations of excited shell-model configurations do not represent an intrinsic excitation of the nucleus; but rather an excitation of the center of mass motion. These shell-model configurations are called *spurious states*. In shell-model calculations it is important to have some criterion for distinguishing between real intrinsic excitations and these spurious states.

The same problem exists in the α-cluster model as soon as we consider the more general trial wave function (25). The solution of the eigenvalue problem (26) may give a good representation of the nuclear ground state, but other eigenvalues could be spurious states rather than real intrinsic excitations.

The general problem of spurious states of center-of-mass motion is discussed by YOCCOZ in a seminar at this course. Fortunately the solution of this problem in the α-cluster model is simple because of a special property of the cluster wave functions. A particular term in the expansion of a Slater-determinant wave function Φ representing a cluster configuration will contain a product of orbital wave functions

$$\prod_i \left[\exp\left[-\frac{1}{2b^2}(\boldsymbol{r}_i - \boldsymbol{S}_{\alpha(i)})^2\right]\right] = \exp\left[-\frac{1}{2b^2}\sum_i(\boldsymbol{r}_i - \boldsymbol{S}_{\alpha(i)})^2\right],$$

where the i-th nucleon is moving in the cluster with center $\boldsymbol{S}_{\alpha(i)}$. If we let $\boldsymbol{R}$ denote the center of mass of the nucleus and $\boldsymbol{S}$ the mean position of the cluster centers, then

$$\exp\left[-\frac{1}{2b^2}\sum_i(\boldsymbol{r}_i - \boldsymbol{S}_{\alpha(i)})^2\right] = \tag{30}$$

$$= \exp\left[-\frac{1}{2b^2}\sum_i(\boldsymbol{r}_i - \boldsymbol{R} - (\boldsymbol{S}_{\alpha(i)} - \boldsymbol{S}))^2\right]\exp\left[-\frac{1}{2b^2}(\boldsymbol{R} - \boldsymbol{S})^2\right].$$

The first factor on the right-hand side of (30) depends only on the relative co-ordinates of the nucleons and the second factor only on the center of mass co-ordinate. Each term in the expansion of Φ will factor in the same way. Hence we obtain

$$\Phi = \Phi_{\text{int}} \exp[-(\boldsymbol{R}-\boldsymbol{S})^2/2b^2] , \tag{31}$$

where Φ_{int} is an intrinsic wave function depending only on the relative co-ordinates of the nucleons.

If we take a linear combination of α-cluster wave functions as in eq. (24) then the center of mass co-ordinate still factors out as in eq. (31), provided that the mean position of the clusters $\boldsymbol{S}$ is the same in all the wave functions in the sum. The eigenvalue problem (26) will never lead to a spurious state provided this condition is satisfied. In practical problems it is convenient to take the mean position of the clusters at the origin of the co-ordinate system. This is even necessary if we wish to project eigenstates of angular momentum.

The separation of center of mass motion in this problem is analogous to the separation in the harmonic oscillator shell-model as discussed by ELLIOTT and SKYRME [22]. It occurs because the orbital wave functions in each cluster are Gaussian with the same radius parameter b.

9. – Projection of eigenstates of angular momentum and parity.

9·1. *Parity*. – If $\Phi(\beta)$ is a cluster wave function depending on the vectors $\beta = \boldsymbol{R}_1, ..., \boldsymbol{R}_N$ then we obtain the reflected wave function $P\Phi(\beta)$ by inverting the coordinates of every nucleon in the state,

$$\boldsymbol{r}_i \to -\boldsymbol{r}_i , \qquad i = 1, ..., 4N, \tag{32}$$

since the particle co-ordinates always occur in the combination $(\boldsymbol{r}_i - \boldsymbol{R}_j)^2$ where $\boldsymbol{R}_j$ is the center of some cluster, the transformation (32) is equivalent to the inversion

$$\boldsymbol{R}_j \to -\boldsymbol{R}_j , \qquad j = 1, ..., N,$$

of the centers of all the clusters. That is

$$P\Phi(\beta) = \Phi(-\beta) ,$$

where $-\beta$ stands for $(-\boldsymbol{R}_1, ..., -\boldsymbol{R}_N)$. If the centers of the clusters have inversion symmetry then $\beta = -\beta$ and the wave function $\Phi(\beta)$ has even parity.

When the cluster has no inversion symmetry we can project positive and negative parity components Φ^+ and Φ^-

$$\Phi^+ = \frac{1}{2\alpha_+} \left(\Phi(\beta) + \Phi(-\beta)\right) , \qquad \Phi^- = \frac{1}{2\alpha_-} \left(\Phi(\beta) - \Phi(-\beta)\right) ,$$

or

$$\Phi(\beta) = \alpha_+\Phi^+ + \alpha_-\Phi^-, \qquad \Phi(-\beta) = \alpha_+\Phi^+ - \alpha_-\Phi^-.$$

If Φ^+ and Φ^- are required to be normalized then

$$|\alpha_+|^2 + |\alpha_-|^2 = 1 .$$

In fact $|\alpha_+|^2$ and $|\alpha_-|^2$ are the proportions of positive and negative parity states in $\Phi(\beta)$. We have also that

$$|\alpha_+|^2 - |\alpha_-|^2 = \langle\Phi(\beta), \Phi(-\beta)\rangle . \tag{33}$$

Denoting $\langle\Phi^+, H\Phi^+\rangle$ and $\langle\Phi^-, H\Phi^-\rangle$ by E_+ and E_- respectively, then if H conserves parity

$$\langle\Phi(\beta), H\Phi(\beta)\rangle = |\alpha_+|^2 E_+ + |\alpha_-|^2 E_- . \tag{34}$$

Table IV gives some values of these quantities calculated for a tetrahedral configuration of ^{16}O with the interaction (17) (Majorana exchange component $M = -0.65$) for several values of the cluster separation d. The radius parameter of the clusters was taken to be $b = 1.61$ fermi ($\hbar\omega = 16$ MeV) and the binding energy of the spherical shell-model wave function (*i.e.* the limit as $d \to 0$) was 117.6 MeV. The energies are given in MeV. Also given are the projected energies of the 0^+ and 3^- states.

TABLE IV.

d	1 fermi	2 fermi	3 fermi
$\|\alpha_+\|^2$	0.78	0.55	0.50
$\|\alpha_-\|^2$	0.22	0.45	0.50
$\langle\Phi(\beta), H\Phi(\beta)\rangle$	115.5	109.6	99.9
E_+	118.6	112.4	100.1
E_-	104.4	105.9	99.4
E_{0^+}	119.7	123.1	119.1
E_{3^-}	104.4	108.0	104.9

After projecting angular momentum and parity the lowest-energy state has $d \neq 0$, that is it has tetrahedral deformation.

9·2. *Angular momentum projection.* – We project angular momentum eigenstates using the projection operator

$$P^J_{KM} = \int d\Omega\, \mathscr{D}^{+J}_{KM}(\Omega)\mathscr{R}(\Omega) , \tag{35}$$

$$\Phi^J_{KM}(\beta) = P^J_{KM}\Phi(\beta) , \tag{36}$$

where $R(\Omega)$ is a unitary rotation operator which rotates a wave function through Euler angles Ω. Two successive rotations Ω_1 and Ω_2 give the combined rotation $\Omega_2\Omega_1$

$$\mathscr{R}(\Omega_1)\mathscr{R}(\Omega_2)=\mathscr{R}(\Omega_2\Omega_1)\,. \tag{37}$$

The unitary rotation matrix is defined by

$$\mathscr{D}^J_{KM}(\Omega)=\langle JK|\mathscr{R}(\Omega)|JM\rangle\,,\qquad \mathscr{D}^{+J}_{KM}(\Omega)=\big(\mathscr{D}^J_{MK}(\Omega)\big)^*=\mathscr{D}^J_{KM}(\Omega^{-1})\,. \tag{38}$$

The operator relation (37) gives the matrix multiplication rule for the rotation matrices

$$\mathscr{D}^J_{KM}(\Omega_2\Omega_1)=\sum_Z \mathscr{D}^J_{KZ}(\Omega_1)\mathscr{D}^J_{ZM}(\Omega_2)\,,\qquad \mathscr{D}^{+J}_{KM}(\Omega_2\Omega_1)=\sum_Z \mathscr{D}^{+J}_{KZ}(\Omega_2)\mathscr{D}^{+J}_{ZM}(\Omega_1)\,. \tag{39}$$

These equations summarize some of the properties of the rotation matrices.

Using these properties we may prove the following relations for the projection operators (35):

$$\text{i)}\quad \mathscr{R}(\Omega)\,P^J_{KM}=\sum_{M'} P^J_{KM'}\mathscr{D}^J_{M'M}(\Omega)\,, \tag{40}$$

$$\text{ii)}\quad P^J_{KM}\mathscr{R}(\Omega)=\sum_{K'} \mathscr{D}^J_{KK'}(\Omega)P^J_{K'M}\,, \tag{41}$$

$$\text{iii)}\quad (P^J_{KM})^+P^{J'}_{K'M'}=\left(\frac{8\pi^2}{2J+1}\right)\delta_{JJ'}\delta_{MM'}P^J_{K'K}\,. \tag{42}$$

For example

$$\begin{aligned}\mathscr{R}(\Omega)P^J_{KM}&=\int \mathrm{d}\Omega'\,\mathscr{D}^{+J}_{KM}(\Omega')\mathscr{R}(\Omega'\Omega)=\\ &=\int \mathrm{d}\Omega''\,\mathscr{D}^{+J}_{KM}(\Omega''\Omega^{-1})\mathscr{R}(\Omega'')=\sum_{M'}P^J_{KM'}\mathscr{D}^{+J}_{M'M}(\Omega^{-1}) &&\text{from eq. (39)}\,,\\ &=\sum_{M'}P^J_{KM'}\mathscr{D}^J_{M'M}(\Omega) &&\text{from eq. (38)}\,.\end{aligned}$$

The proof of the relation iii) also requires the orthogonality condition for rotation matrices on integration over the Euler angles.

In projecting from a given intrinsic state $\Phi(\beta)$ we obtain $2J+1$ states $\Phi^J_{KM}(-J\leqslant K\leqslant J)$ with the same eigenvalues of J and M. Are all these $2J+1$ states, corresponding to different K values, linearly independent? Can it ever happen that for some J values $\Phi^J_{KM}=0$ for all K values? The answers to these questions depend on the symmetry of the intrinsic state $\Phi(\beta)$. In many cases the intrinsic state is unchanged for certain rotations $\{S_i\}$. These rotations would form a finite subgroup $\mathscr{G}$ of the full rotation group. We have

$$\mathscr{R}(S)\Phi(\beta)=\Phi(S\beta)\qquad\text{for } S \text{ in } \mathscr{G}. \tag{43}$$

We may easily find the consequences of this symmetry for the projected wave functions. For each S in $\mathcal{G}$ we have

$$\begin{aligned} \Phi^J_{KM} &= P^J_{KM}\Phi(\beta) = P^J_{KM}\mathcal{R}(S)\Phi(\beta) \qquad \text{from (43)}, \\ &= \sum_{K'} \mathcal{D}^J_{KK'}(S)\Phi^J_{K'M} \,. \end{aligned} \tag{44}$$

Suppose there are r linearly independent wave functions in the set Φ^J_{KM}, we may then express

$$\Phi^J_{KM} = \sum_{j=1}^{r} a_{Kj}\Phi^J_{jM} \,,$$

where the wave functions Φ^J_{jM} are orthogonal for different j. If we substitute into eq. (44) and use the orthogonality properties of the Φ^J_{jM} we find that the expansion coefficients satisfy relations similar to (44):

$$a_{Kj} = \sum_{K'} \mathcal{D}^J_{KK'}(S)a_{K'j} \qquad j = 1, \ldots, r \text{ and } S \text{ in } \mathcal{G} \,. \tag{45}$$

The rotation matrices $\mathcal{D}^J_{KM}(S)$ form an irreducible matrix representation of the full rotation group. $\mathcal{G}$ is a subgroup of the full rotation group, hence the rotation matrices form a representation, in general reducible, of this subgroup $\mathcal{G}$. The relations (45) imply that the representation by the matrices $\mathcal{D}^J_{KM}(S)$ must indeed be reducible and must contain the scalar representation of $\mathcal{G}$ at least r times. We may summarize this result in the following way:

If the intrinsic state $\Phi(\beta)$ is invariant under a finite group of rotations $\mathcal{G}$ then the number of linearly independent eigenstates of J and M which may be projected from $\Phi(\beta)$ is not greater than the number of times the scalar representation of $\mathcal{G}$ is contained in representation $\mathcal{D}^J$ of the full rotation group.

If this number is zero then no state with total angular momentum J can be projected from $\Phi(\beta)$.

Let n_0 be the number of times the scalar representation of $\mathcal{G}$ is contained in the representation $\mathcal{D}^J$ of the full rotation group. This number may be determined by the standard methods of the theory of finite groups and is given by the formula

$$n_0 = \frac{1}{g}\sum_{S} \chi^J(S) \,, \tag{46}$$

where the sum is taken over all elements S of the finite group $\mathcal{G}$ and $\chi^J(S) = \sum_K \mathcal{D}^J_{KK}(S)$ are group characters belonging to the representation $\mathcal{D}^J$. The order of the group is g.

In order to calculate energies of cluster states it is necessary to calculate matrix elements of the Hamiltonian with projected cluster wave functions.

If we introduce the matrices

$$H^J_{KK'} = \langle \Phi^J_{KM} | H | \Phi^J_{K'M} \rangle \,, \qquad B^J_{KK'} = \langle \Phi^J_{KM} | \Phi^J_{K'M} \rangle \,, \tag{47}$$

then the expectation value of the energy in the state (JKM) is

$$E^J_K = H^J_{KK} / B^J_{KK} \,. \tag{48}$$

The states Φ^J_{KM} are not orthogonal in K and if several K-values are important for a given J it may be necessary to replace the expectation values (48) by the eigenvalue problem

$$\sum_{K'} (H^J_{KK'} - E B^J_{KK'}) c_{K'} = 0 \,. \tag{49}$$

Writing the matrix elements (47) showing the projection operators P^J_{KM} explicitly we get

$$\begin{aligned} H^J_{KK'} &= \langle \Phi | (P^J_{KM})^+ H P^J_{K'M} | \Phi \rangle = \langle \Phi | H P^J_{K'K} | \Phi \rangle \frac{8\pi^2}{2J+1} = \\ &= \frac{8\pi^2}{2J+1} \int \mathrm{d}\Omega \, \mathscr{D}^{+J}_{K'K}(\Omega) \big(\Phi | H \mathscr{R}(\Omega) | \Phi \big) \,, \end{aligned} \tag{50}$$

with a similar expression for $B^J_{K'K}$. The projection method we use calculates the overlap matrix elements

$$\langle \Phi | H \mathscr{R}(\Omega) | \Phi \rangle \qquad \text{and} \qquad \langle \Phi | \mathscr{R}(\Omega) | \Phi \rangle \,,$$

numerically for certain values of Ω then evaluates $H^J_{KK'}$ and $B^J_{KK'}$ by a numerical integration. The cluster states we use are not axially symmetric and the intrinsic states $\Phi(\beta)$ do not have a definite value of K. As a result the integrations in (50) are over three variables α, β and γ. We avoid this difficulty by projecting from linear combinations of intrinsic states which already have an approximate axis of symmetry and definite values of K. The integration in (50) then reduces to

$$H^J_{KK'} = \frac{8\pi^2}{2J+1} \int \sin\beta \, \mathrm{d}\beta \, d^J_{KK'}(\beta) H_{KK'}(\beta) \,, \tag{51}$$

where

$$H_{KK'}(\beta) = \langle \Phi_{K'} | H \mathscr{R}(\beta) | \Phi_K \rangle \,.$$

In practical cases studied it turns out that the overlap matrix elements are very nearly represented by Gaussian functions

$$H_{KK'}(\beta) \simeq A \exp[-\alpha_1 \beta^2] \qquad \text{and} \qquad B_{KK'} \simeq \exp[-\alpha_2 \beta^2] \,. \tag{52}$$

Even in ^{12}C these Gaussian formulae are numerically accurate within about 5%, and for deformed states in ^{16}O they are much better. The energy and overlap matrices are equally well represented by formulae (52).

Numerical calculations made on the tetrahedral configuration of ^{16}O with Volkov force show that, after projection of angular momentum and parity, the tetrahedral shape is unstable for a Majorana exchange component $M > 0.6$.

Appendix

Properties of Slater-determinant wave functions.

A·1. *Some properties of determinants.* – Let $A = (a_{\alpha\beta})$ be an $n \times n$ matrix. The determinant of A is defined by

$$\det A = \sum \varepsilon(\alpha\beta \dots \delta) a_{1\alpha} a_{2\beta} \dots a_{n\delta} .$$

We can expand $\det A$ showing the matrix elements of the row α explicitly

$$\det A = \sum_{\beta} a_{\alpha\beta} c_{\alpha\beta} ,$$

where the coefficients $c_{\alpha\beta}$ depend on the matrix elements in other rows. The coefficients $c_{\alpha\beta}$ form an $n \times n$ matrix sometimes called the cofactor matrix. They have the property

$$\sum_{\beta} a_{\alpha\beta} c_{\alpha'\beta} = (\det A) \cdot \delta_{\alpha\alpha'} .$$

In other words if $\det A \neq 0$

$$c_{\alpha\beta} = (a^{-1})_{\beta\alpha} (\det A) . \tag{A.1}$$

The $(a^{-1})_{\beta\alpha}$ are components of the matrix A^{-1} which is the inverse of A.

The determinant may also be expanded showing the matrix elements of two rows α and β explicitly

$$\det A = \sum_{\gamma\delta} a_{\alpha\gamma} a_{\beta\delta} c(\alpha\beta, \gamma\delta) .$$

The coefficients $c(\alpha\beta, \gamma\delta)$ are some sort of generalized cofactors which depend on matrix elements in other rows and have the following property

$$\sum_{\gamma\delta} a_{\alpha\gamma} a_{\beta\delta} c(\alpha'\beta', \gamma\delta) = \det A[\delta(\alpha\alpha')\delta(\beta\beta') - \delta(\alpha\beta')\delta(\beta\alpha')] .$$

This equation expresses the property that a determinant vanishes if two rows are equal and changes sign if two rows α and β are exchanged. If follows that

$$c(\alpha\beta,\gamma\delta) = \det A\big((a^{-1})_{\gamma\alpha}(a^{-1})_{\delta\beta} - (a^{-1})_{\gamma\beta}(a^{-1})_{\delta\alpha}\big)\,, \tag{A.2}$$

if $\det A \neq 0$.

A·2. *Slater-determinant wave functions.* – Let $\Phi(x_1, \ldots, x_A)$ be a function of the co-ordinates of nucleons. (x_1 includes the spin and isobaric spin co-ordinates as well as the position vector of the nucleon.) The antisymmetrization operator $\mathscr{A}$ is defined by

$$\mathscr{A}\Phi(x_1, \ldots, x_A) = \frac{1}{A!}\sum \varepsilon(\alpha\beta \ldots \eta)\Phi(x_\alpha, x_\beta, \ldots, x_\eta)\,.$$

This operator is a projection *i.e.* $\mathscr{A}^2 = \mathscr{A}$.

Let $\varphi_1, \ldots, \varphi_A$ be a set of linearly independent single-particle wave functions and let φ_0 stand for the n-particle wave function

$$\Phi_0 = \varphi_1(x_1)\varphi_2(x_2) \ldots \varphi_A(x_A)\,.$$

The corresponding antisymmetrized Slater-determinant (S.D.) wave function is defined by

$$\Phi = N_\Phi \mathscr{A}\Phi_0\,, \tag{A.3}$$

where N_Φ is a positive normalization constant. The wave functions $\varphi_1, \ldots, \varphi_A$ need not be orthogonal.

Let $\varphi_1, \ldots, \varphi_A$ be a set of single-particle wave functions linearly independent, but not necessarily orthogonal and let $\psi_1, \ldots, \psi_A$ be another set formed from linear combination of the first set

$$\psi_\alpha = \sum_\beta A_{\alpha\beta}\varphi_\beta\,.$$

If $\Phi = \mathscr{A}(\varphi_1, \ldots, \varphi_A)$ and $\Psi = \mathscr{A}(\psi_1, \ldots, \psi_A)$ are the corresponding (unnormalized) S.D. wave functions then

$$\Psi = (\det A)\Phi\,,$$

by the law of multiplication of determinants. In other words a S.D. wave function is unchanged except for a numerical factor if a different choice of basis vectors is made.

The problems in this and some of the following Sections of the Appendix have been discussed in detail by Löwdin [22].

A·3. *The overlap of two Slater-determinant wave functions.* – Let $\varphi_1, \ldots, \varphi_A$ and $\psi_1, \ldots, \psi_A$ be two linearly independent sets of single particle wave functions. Let Φ and Ψ be the corresponding S.D. wave functions

$$\Phi = N_\Phi \mathscr{A}\Phi_0\,, \qquad \Psi = N_\Psi \mathscr{A}\Psi_0\,.$$

Then

$$\langle \Phi, \Psi \rangle = N_\Phi N_\Psi \langle \mathscr{A}\Phi_0, \mathscr{A}\Psi_0 \rangle = N_\Phi N_\Psi \langle \Phi_0, \mathscr{A}\Psi_0 \rangle . \tag{A.4}$$

If we write (A.4) out in full we get

$$\begin{aligned}\langle \Phi, \Psi \rangle &= \frac{1}{A!} N_\Phi N_\Psi \langle \varphi_1(1) \dots \varphi_n(n), \sum \varepsilon(\alpha\beta \dots \eta)\psi_\alpha(1) \dots \psi_\eta(n) \rangle = \\ &= \frac{1}{A!} N_\Phi N_\Psi \sum \varepsilon(\alpha\beta \dots \eta) \langle \varphi_1, \psi_\alpha \rangle \langle \varphi_2, \psi_\beta \rangle \dots \langle \varphi_n, \psi_\eta \rangle = \\ &= \frac{1}{A!} N_\Phi N_\Psi \det\{\langle \varphi_\alpha, \psi_\beta \rangle\} .\end{aligned} \tag{A.5}$$

The overlap of the A-particle S.D. wave functions is proportional to the determinant of the $A \times A$ matrix of overlaps of single-particle wave functions. Equation (A.5) may be used to determine the normalization constant N_Ψ by putting $\Phi = \Psi$ in (A.5)

$$\langle \Psi, \Psi \rangle = 1 = \frac{1}{A!} N_\Psi^2 \det\{\langle \psi_\alpha, \psi_\beta \rangle\} ,$$

or

$$N_\Psi = (A! \det\{\langle \psi_\alpha, \psi_\beta \rangle\})^{-\frac{1}{2}}. \tag{A.6}$$

Combining (A.5) and (A.6)

$$\langle \Phi, \Psi \rangle = \det\{\langle \varphi_\alpha, \psi_\beta \rangle\} / (\det\{\langle \varphi_\alpha, \varphi_\beta \rangle\} \det\{\langle \psi_\alpha, \psi_\beta \rangle\})^{-\frac{1}{2}}. \tag{A.7}$$

A'4. *Matrix elements of a one-body operator.* – Let $T = \sum_1^A t_\alpha$ where t_α acts only on the co-ordinates of the nucleon α

$$\begin{aligned}\langle \Phi, T\Phi \rangle = \langle \mathscr{A}\Phi_0, T\mathscr{A}\Psi_0 \rangle N_\Phi N_\Psi = N_\Phi N_\Psi \sum_\alpha \langle \Phi_0, t_\alpha \mathscr{A}\Psi_0 \rangle = \\ = N_\Phi N_\Psi \sum_\alpha \langle t_\alpha \Phi_0, \mathscr{A}\Psi_0 \rangle .\end{aligned} \tag{A.8}$$

The wave function $t_\alpha \Phi_0$ is obtained from Φ_0 by replacing the single-particle wave function $\varphi_\alpha(x_\alpha)$ by $t_\alpha \varphi_\alpha(x_\alpha)$. Hence the right-hand side of (A.8) may be evaluated using (A.5). It is only necessary to replace the matrix elements $\langle \varphi_\alpha, \psi_\beta \rangle$ in the α-th row of $\det \langle \varphi_\alpha, \psi_\beta \rangle$ by $\langle t_\alpha \varphi_\alpha, \psi_\beta \rangle = \langle \varphi_\alpha, t_\alpha \psi_\beta \rangle$. The modified determinant may be evaluated using the cofactor expansion. Hence the terms α in the sum in (A.8) must be

$$\sum \langle \varphi_\alpha, t\psi_\beta \rangle c_{\alpha\beta} ,$$

where $c_{\alpha\beta}$ is the cofactor of $\langle \varphi_\alpha, \psi_\beta \rangle$ in $\det \langle \varphi_\alpha, \psi_\beta \rangle$. Finally using (A.1) and

(A.5) we get

(A.9) $$\langle \Phi, T\Psi\rangle = \langle \Phi, \Psi\rangle \sum_{\alpha\beta} \langle \varphi_\alpha, t\psi_\beta\rangle (B^{-1})_{\beta\alpha} ,$$

where $B_{\alpha\beta} = \langle \varphi_\alpha, \psi_\beta\rangle$ and B^{-1} is the inverse of the matrix B. The wave functions $\varphi_1, \dots, \varphi_A$ and $\psi_1, \dots, \psi_A$ need have no special orthogonality properties for formula (A.9) to hold. If $\Phi = \Psi$ and the functions $\psi_1, \dots, \psi_A$ are orthonormal then the overlap matrix B is the unit matrix and

$$\langle \Psi, T\Psi\rangle = \sum_{\alpha=1}^{A} \langle \psi_\alpha, t\psi_\alpha\rangle .$$

The special case where the overlap matrix B is singular will be discussed later in Sect. **6** of this Appendix.

A.5. *Matrix elements of a two-body operator.* – Let $V = \sum_{\alpha<\beta} V_{\alpha\beta}$ where $V_{\alpha\beta}$ acts only on the co-ordinates x_α and x_β of the nucleons α and β. By an argument similar to that given in Sect. **4** of this Appendix

$$\langle \Phi, V\Psi\rangle = \tfrac{1}{2} N_\Phi N_\Psi \sum \langle \varphi_\alpha\varphi_\beta | V | \psi_\gamma\psi_\delta\rangle c(\alpha\beta, \gamma\delta) ,$$

where $c(\alpha\beta, \gamma\delta)$ are the generalized cofactors defined in eq. (A.1). Using eq. (A.2) we get

(A.10) $$\langle \Phi, V\Psi\rangle = \tfrac{1}{2}\langle \Phi, \Psi\rangle \sum \langle \varphi_\alpha\varphi_\beta | V | \psi_\gamma\psi_\delta\rangle [(B^{-1})_{\gamma\alpha}(B^{-1})_{\delta\beta} - (B^{-1})_{\gamma\beta}(B^{-1})_{\delta\alpha}] .$$

A.6. *Explicit discussion of spin and isobaric spin.* – We write the label $\alpha = (i, a)$ where i stands for an orbital and a for a spin-isobaric spin quantum number, and consider S.D. wave functions in which each orbital state is occupied by 4 nucleons.

The overlap matrix $4N \times 4N$ $(A = 4N)$

$$\langle \varphi_\alpha, \psi_\beta\rangle = \langle \varphi_{ia}, \psi_{jb}\rangle = \langle \varphi_i, \psi_j\rangle \delta_{ab} ,$$

splits up into 4 identical blocks each of which is an $N \times N$ orbital overlap matrix $\langle \varphi_i, \psi_j\rangle$. Hence

$$\det \langle \varphi_\alpha, \psi_\beta\rangle = (\det \langle \varphi_i, \psi_j\rangle)^4,$$

and

(A.11) $$\langle \Phi, \Psi\rangle = (\det \langle \varphi_i, \psi_j\rangle)^4 / (\det \langle \varphi_i, \varphi_j\rangle \det \langle \psi_i, \psi_j\rangle)^2.$$

To calculate the one-body matrix element in a case where t is independent of spin and isobaric spin we note that

$$B_{ia,jb} = \langle \varphi_{ia}, \psi_{jb}\rangle = \langle \varphi_i, \psi_j\rangle \delta_{ab} = B_{ij}\delta_{ab} .$$

Hence

$$B^{-1}_{ia,jb} = (B^{-1})_{ij}\delta_{ab} .$$

Substituting in eq. (A.9) we get

$$\text{(A.12)}\qquad \langle \Phi, T\Psi\rangle = \langle \Phi, \Psi\rangle \sum_{ijab} \langle \varphi_{ia}, t\psi_{jb}\rangle (B^{-1})_{ia,jb} = 4\langle \Phi, \Psi\rangle \sum_{ij} \langle \varphi_i, t\psi_j\rangle (B^{-1})_{ij} .$$

For the two-body operator with arbitrary spin-isospin dependence

$$\text{(A.13)}\qquad \langle \Phi, V\Psi\rangle = \tfrac{1}{2}\langle \Phi, \Psi\rangle \sum \langle \varphi_{ia}\varphi_{jb}|V|\psi_{ka'}\psi_{lb'}\rangle \cdot$$
$$\cdot[(B^{-1})_{ki}(B^{-1})_{lj}\delta(aa')\delta(bb') - (B^{-1})_{kj}(B^{-1})_{li}\delta(ab')\delta(ba')] .$$

If V is a central potential with spin dependence

$$V(r) = u(r)(W + BP_\sigma - HP_\tau - MP_\sigma P_\tau) ,$$

then

$$\text{(A.14)}\qquad \langle \Phi, V\Psi\rangle = \langle \Phi, \Psi\rangle \sum \langle \varphi_i\varphi_j|u|\psi_k\psi_l\rangle \cdot$$
$$\cdot \big(X_d(B^{-1})_{ki}(B^{-1})_{lj} + X_e(B^{-1})_{kj}(B^{-1})_{li}\big) = X_d V_d + X_e V_e ,$$

where

$$X_d = 8W + 4B - 4H - 2M , \qquad X_e = 8M + 4H - 4M - 2W .$$

In particular for $V(r) = u(r)\big((1-M) - MP_\sigma P_\tau\big)$

$$X_d = (8 - 10M) , \qquad X_e = 10M - 2 .$$

V_d and V_e are the direct and exchange matrix elements.

We still have to discuss the case when the orbital overlap matrix $\langle \varphi_i, \psi_j\rangle$ is singular *i.e.* when $\det\langle \varphi_i, \psi_j\rangle = 0$. In this case the inverse matrix B^{-1} is undefined, but the cofactors $c_{\alpha\beta}$ and $c(\alpha\beta, \gamma\delta)$ are all finite. Each $c_{\alpha\beta}$ contains a factor $(\det\langle \varphi_i, \psi_j\rangle)^3$ while each $c(\alpha\beta, \gamma\delta)$ contains at least a factor $(\det\langle \varphi_i, \psi_j\rangle)^2$. In other words $c_{\alpha\beta}$ and $c(\alpha\beta, \gamma\delta)$ become zero when $\det\langle \varphi_i, \psi_j\rangle = 0$ hence $\langle \Phi, T\Psi\rangle$ and $\langle \Phi, V\Psi\rangle$ also become zero in this limit.

REFERENCES

[1] J. A. Wheeler: *Phys. Rev.*, **52**, 1083 (1937).
[2] S. Edwards: *Proc. Cam. Phil. Soc.*, **48**, 652 (1952).
[3] K. Wildermuth and Th. Kanellopoulos: *Nucl. Phys.*, **9**, 449 (1958).
[4] Z. Matthies, V. G. Neudachin and Yu. F. Smirnov: *Žurn. Èksp. Teor. Fiz.*, **45**, 107 (1963); *Nucl. Phys.*, **49**, 97 (1963).
[5] H. Margenau: *Phys. Rev.*, **59**, 37 (1941).
[6] S. J. Biel: *Proc. Phys. Soc.*, A **70**, 866 (1957).
[7] W. Wefelmeier: *Naturwiss.*, **25**, 525 (1937).

[8] E. Teller and J. A. Wheeler: *Phys. Rev.*, **53**, 778 (1938).
[9] D. Dennison: *Phys. Rev.*, **57**, 454 (1940); **96**, 378 (1954).
[10] S. L. Kameny: *Phys. Rev.*, **103**, 358 (1956).
[11] J. M. Soper: *Phil. Mag.*, **2**, 1219 (1957).
[12] R. A. Ferrel and W. M. Visscher: *Phys. Rev.*, **104**, 475 (1956).
[13] V. Gillet: *Nucl. Phys.*, **51**, 410 (1964).
[14] L. Rosenfeld: *Nuclear Forces* (Amsterdam, 1948).
[15] J. P. E. Elliott: this volume, p. 128.
[16] S. A. Moskowski and B. L. Scott: *Nucl. Phys.*, **29**, 665 (1962).
[17] A. Kallio and K. Koltveit: *Nucl. Phys.*, **53**, 87 (1964).
[18] A. B. Volkov: *Phys. Lett.*, **12**, 118 (1964).
[19] J. Hayward and D. Thouless: to be published.
[20] D. L. Hill, J. A. Wheeler and J. J. Griffin: *Phys. Rev.*, **89**, 1102 (1952).
[21] R. Courant and D. Hilbert: *Methods of Mathematics Physics* (New York, 1953), p. 406; P. R. Halmos: *Finite-Dimensional Vector Spaces* (New York, 1958), p. 181.
[22] J. P. Elliott and T. H. R. Skyrme: *Nuovo Cimento*, **4**, 164 (1956).
[23] P. O. Löwdin: *Phys. Rev.*, **97**, 1490 (1955).

Multipole and Sum-Rule Methods in Spectroscopy (*).

J. B. French

Department of Physics and Astronomy, University of Rochester - Rochester, N. Y.

1. – Introduction.

Angular momentum is of obvious importance in nuclear-structure physics. On the one hand, this is shown by the mere existence of the nuclear shell model giving reasonable approximations for nuclear states; on the other hand we have only to think of such terms as « enhanced quadrupole transitions », « *p*-wave giant resonances » and « pairing + quadrupole interactions » all of which involve angular-momentum statements.

When we speak of « multipole methods » we mean certain techniques which pay full attention to the angular momenta carried by the quantities with which we deal. In fact it is advantageous to deal only with quantities which carry definite angular momenta, which, in other words, are *spherical tensors* of definite rank. At the same time we must deal with the antisymmetry requirements imposed by the Pauli principle. These are most easily taken account of by working with a second-quantized formalism, which in fact has also certain major advantages, not directly connected with antisymmetry, over a configuration-space representation. Thus we find ourselves dealing with *second-quantized spherical tensors* and all our formal discussion will be about the properties of such objects.

There are several reasons why it is worthwhile developing methods (they are really very simple) which treat angular momenta in a sophisticated way. For one thing, we would like to understand, without recourse to detailed calculation, what « part » of the internucleon interaction is responsible for a particular phenomenon; for phenomena described in multipole terms one has a natural expectation that the answer will come most easily if we make some sort of multipole expansion of the interaction. Beyond that we are often interested in really detailed analyses of complex nuclear systems. If this should involve us in large shell-model calculations, then such sophistication is almost

(*) Supported in part by the U. S. Atomic Energy Commission.

essential. This has become true in the past two or three years. Before that, computing facilities were themselves so limited that really large problems were ruled out anyway, while, for the smaller ones, elegant techniques were not necessary. As things stand now, this is no longer true. For example, if one wishes to deal with the $2\hbar\omega$ excitations of ^{16}O he will find himself with a system containing about 1500 states and an interaction Hamiltonian defined by almost 800 independent matrix elements. The dimensionalities for states of given J and T will range up to 150 and there will be as many as a dozen spurious states (those which treat the center of mass improperly) for a given (J, T) matrix. This is obviously a complicated problem and one may even ask why it is interesting to become involved in such a thing, especially since, for the most part, only a few dozen states of the system are of real interest in detail. The answer is that by considering such cases one may be able to learn something about the *general* properties of such excited systems, or alternatively may be able to check on the validity of various models proposed on the basis of experimental evidence or otherwise.

Granted then that really large calculations are worth-while (as long as a machine will do them), it is still true that the way of the future is not exclusively or even primarily by means of large computing programs. For the complexity of spectroscopic calculations increases so rapidly with the number of « active » particles (or holes) and orbits that very quickly they outrun the possibilities of any computers. Noting that almost all of the detailed information which one produces in a large calculation is useless anyway, one wonders whether he cannot calculate in a more direct way these things which are of real interest, such as the strengths, centroid energies and widths of various excitations of nuclei. Indeed it might even be possible to work backwards from experiment and decide what certain properties of an observed excitation tell us about the target and the interaction.

Good progress along this line can be made by the use of sum-rule methods. Conventional sum-rule methods have not, in the past, been applied very much, in part because they yield only a very limited amount of information. The « multipole sum-rule » methods which we shall use take full account of the angular momenta involved and yield a great deal more information. Note that the sum-rule methods are, in a sense, exactly opposite in spirit to the method of detailed shell-model calculations.

In these lectures we shall start with a review of the properties of spherical tensors and shall then be led to introduce the general definition of the « strength » of an excitation. We shall then discuss energy and angular moments of the « strength function » introduced, expressing the results in terms of integrals over the target state of certain operators. From the general nature of these target integrals we shall draw certain tentative conclusions about the proper way of comparing model calculations with experimental data.

In order to focus then on the more specific properties of the target integrals we shall give a formal account of the appropriate ways of representing the Hamiltonian and other operators and shall, *inter alia*, discuss such things as hole $\rightleftharpoons$ particle transforms and so on. One must remember that the centroid energy for a certain excitation must itself be a certain matrix element of the Hamiltonian, and, if we have in advance chosen the proper representation, then this matrix element should come into evidence immediately, giving us therefore some understanding of what is going on. Certain technical problems concerning the evaluation of commutators, vacuum-expectation values, and so on are discussed in an Appendix by Dr. L. S. Hsu who gives also Tables for some of these quantities.

We shall apply the results in some detail to excitations caused by adding a particle or a hole to a target state (single-nucleon transfer), and in less detail to hole-particle excitations. Certain questions concerning isobaric spin will be treated incidentally as they come up.

The sum-rule methods will then be our principal domain of interest in so far as applications are concerned, but we shall devote the last part of these lectures to the question of how to set up a formalism for really large spectroscopic calculations, and we shall describe one such program which is now in operation. We might mention that the sum-rule methods are of value here also, both in checking the accuracy of large calculations and in supplying major extensions of them.

Our principal purpose will be to indicate how calculations are made, and how one can hope to understand the general properties of simple nuclear excitations. We shall therefore not attempt to discuss the applications in any great detail. Also some of the applications represent work still in progress, as a result of which, some of our remarks will be speculative and our conclusions tentative.

2. – Notation and elementary results.

The Clebsch-Gordan coupling of angular momenta is given by

(2.1) $(a\times b)^c_m \equiv$ 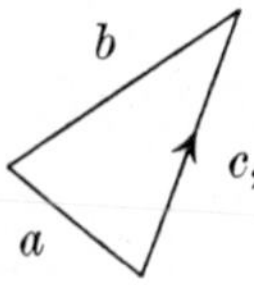 $c,\, m = \sum_{m'} C^{abc}_{m',m-m'}\, \psi^a_{m'}\, \psi^b_{m-m'}$,

where the C's (for which, whenever necessary, we would use the Condon-Shortley phases) have a large set of sum-rule and symmetry properties. Most of these we shall have no need of. We shall use

(2.2) 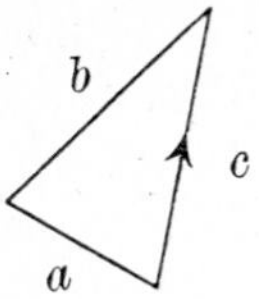 $= (-1)^{a+b-c}$ 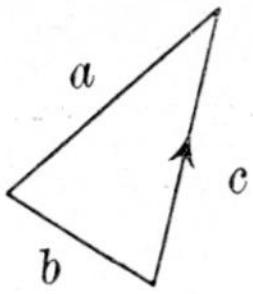 (as long as a, b commute)

(2.3) $$C^{aa0}_{m,-m} = [a]^{-\frac{1}{2}}(-1)^{a-m}; \qquad C^{aa0}_{-m,m} = [a]^{-\frac{1}{2}}(-1)^{a+m}.$$

We have here written

(2.4) $$(2a+1) = [a].$$

We shall also write

(2.5) $$\begin{cases} [ab\ldots] = [a][b]\ldots\,, \\ \left[\dfrac{ab}{c}\right] = \dfrac{[a][b]}{[c]}\,, \qquad \text{etc.} \end{cases}$$

For Racah recoupling of three angular momenta,

(2.6)

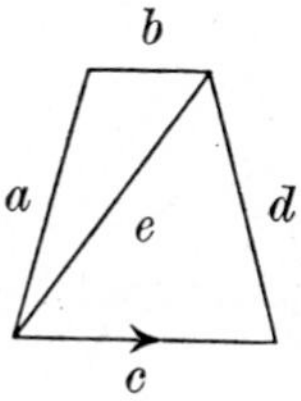 $= \sum_f U(abcd:ef)$ 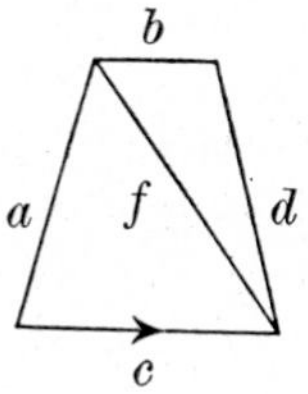 ,

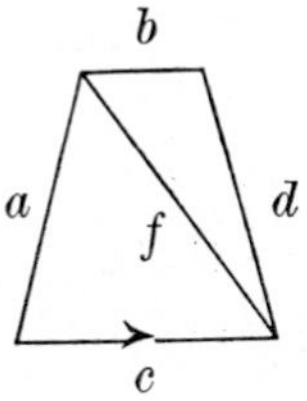 $= \sum_e U(abcd:ef)$ 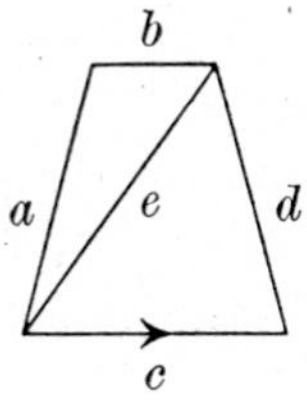 ,

and then

(2.7) $$\sum_e U(abcd:ef)\,U(abcd:ef') = \delta_{ff'}\,,$$

and similarly for the f sum. We have

(2.8) $$U(abcd:ef) = [ef]^{\frac{1}{2}}\,W(abcd:ef)\,.$$

The triangle properties of the U's are obvious while their various sum-rule and symmetry properties are of very little interest to us. If for example we encounter a reducible intermediate-parameter sum of a product of U functions, that is almost always because we have not taken full advantage of the geometry; a better procedure not needing the sum should have been found. Still, we shall occasionally use

$$\sum_{\lambda} (-1)^{-\lambda} U(abdc:e\lambda)\, U(acdb:f\lambda) = (-1)^{e+f-a-b-c-d}\, U(abcd:ef)\,, \tag{2.9}$$

$$\sum_{J} (-1)^{J} [J]^{\frac{1}{2}}\, U(abab:Jk) = (-1)^{a+b} [ab]^{\frac{1}{2}} \delta_{k0}\,, \tag{2.10}$$

$$\sum_{J} [J]^{\frac{1}{2}}\, U(abba:Jk) = [k]^{\frac{1}{2}}\,, \tag{2.11}$$

and the special values

$$U(aabb:of) = \left[\frac{f}{ab}\right]^{\frac{1}{2}} (-1)^{a+b-f}, \tag{2.12}$$

$$U(abab:f1) = \frac{\sqrt{3}[f]^{\frac{1}{2}}(-1)^{a+b-f}}{\sqrt{4a(a+1)[a]b(b+1)[b]}} \{f(f+1)-a(a+1)-b(b+1)\}. \tag{2.13}$$

Recoupling for complicated cases can always be done by means of eqs. (2.2), (2.6). The recoupling coefficients then may involve an irreducible summation over intermediate parameters and may define new symbols. We shall occasionally meet the *normalized* 9j-*symbol* defined by

(2.14)

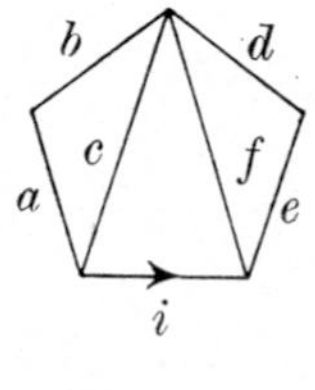

$$= \sum_{g,h} \begin{vmatrix} \overline{a \quad b \quad c} \\ d \quad e \quad f \\ g \quad h \quad i \end{vmatrix}$$

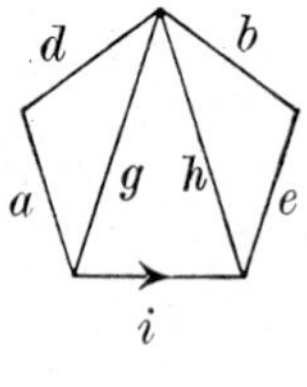

(if b, d commute),

a special case of which is

(2.15)

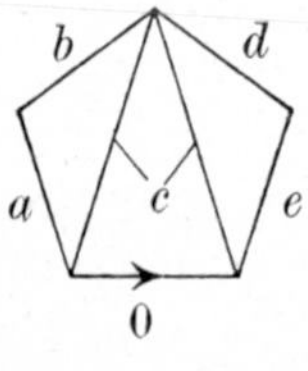

$$= \sum_{g} (-1)^{a+e-c-g}\, U(abde:cg)$$

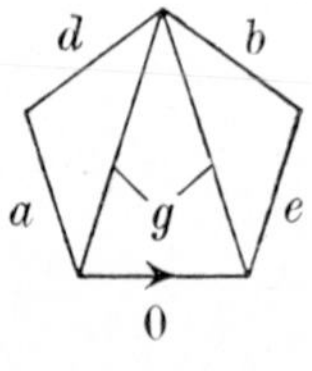

(if b, d commute) .

We shall often deal with direct-product vector spaces, (l, s), (j, t) etc. In order to write equations which may be interpreted according to any of these schemes it is advantageous to use a direct-product notation:

$$\begin{cases} J \quad \text{or} \quad J, T \quad \text{or} \quad L, S \quad \text{or} \quad L, S, T \Rightarrow \Gamma , \\ j \quad \text{or} \quad j, t \quad \text{or} \quad l, s \quad \text{or} \quad l, s, t \Rightarrow \varrho , \end{cases} \tag{2.16}$$

and then, in the jt case,

$$\begin{cases} (-1)^{\Gamma} \equiv (-1)^{J+T} \qquad \text{etc.}, \\ U(\Gamma\varrho\Gamma\varrho : \Gamma_1\nu) \equiv U(JjJj : J_1\nu_j)\, U(T\tfrac{1}{2}\, T\tfrac{1}{2} : T_1\nu_t) , \end{cases} \tag{2.17}$$

and so on for other cases.

The radial quantum number for the orbit will, for the most part, be understood. But occasionally we will have to introduce it explicitly as n_r. There will arise circumstances when two orbits are the same ($\varrho = \varrho'$), and others in which the orbit angular momenta are the same but not the radial quantum number (*e.g.* $1p_{\frac{3}{2}}$ and $2p_{\frac{3}{2}}$). To distinguish the two cases we introduce $\delta_{\varrho\varrho'}$ for the first and $\delta^{a.m.}_{\varrho\varrho'} \equiv \delta^{a}_{\varrho\varrho'}$ for the second. Thus

$$\delta_{\varrho\varrho'} = \delta^{a}_{\varrho\varrho'} \cdot \delta_{n_r n'_r} . \tag{2.18}$$

For wave functions (and for spherical tensors in general) we write the total angular momenta as superscripts, the z-component as a subscript, and the non-angular-momentum quantum numbers as subscripts or in a bracket, *viz.*

$$\psi^{\Gamma}_{x} , \qquad (\psi^{\Gamma}_{x})_{\mu} , \qquad \psi^{\Gamma}_{x}(n) , \qquad \psi^{\Gamma}(x) .$$

Very often the μ labelling will be omitted as indicated.

3. – Spherical tensors.

In this Section we shall review the *general* properties of spherical tensors, those which follow from the « over-all » tensorial ranks of the objects treated, without paying specific attention to their detailed intrinsic structure (part of which may in fact also be describable in tensorial terms). We shall assume knowledge of the most elementary results (some of which are given in Sect. **2**), and shall derive others, not all of which seem to be well known. We shall use the results to consider nuclear excitations in general terms, defining strengths for such excitations and developing certain sum rules, or moment equations, for them.

3·1. *Definition.* – To begin with, a set of quantities T^λ_μ, where $\mu = -\lambda$ $-\lambda+1, \dots +\lambda$, forms a spherical tensor $\boldsymbol{T}^\lambda$ with respect to an underlying co-ordinate system if the T^λ_μ transform under rotations of that system like the angular-momentum eigenfunctions ψ^λ_μ involving the same co-ordinates. It follows then that $\lambda =$ integer or $\frac{1}{2}$-integer, and of course we may be working in a direct-product space so that λ stands for a number of quantities, the ranks in the separate spaces. We shall understand in this case that, in a component of $\boldsymbol{T}^\lambda$, the individual μ-values in the separate spaces are also specified; thus T^λ_μ is defined in the so-called « m-representation » instead of a coupled representation. As an example the single-particle wave function $\psi^{nls}_{m_l m_s}$ for a particle with spin is a tensor of rank (l, s) in the $(\boldsymbol{r}, \boldsymbol{s})$ space, while the corresponding jj-coupling function $\psi^{nlsj}_{m_j}$ is a tensor in the $\boldsymbol{j}$ space, the l and s then describing the internal structure. The relationship between the two is best understood in terms of the vector spaces in which the tensors reside.

3·2. *Coupling of tensors.* – Tensors may be coupled according to the usual Clebsch-Gordan rules. We shall write coupled tensors as $(\boldsymbol{T}^\lambda \times \boldsymbol{U}^{\lambda'})^\nu$ and similarly for more complicated cases in which, if there are more than two tensors involved, we must also specify the internal couplings in some manner. For integral-rank tensors there is a conventionally defined *scalar product* whose normalization is different from that of the zero-coupled product. We have

$$(3.1)\qquad (\boldsymbol{T}^\lambda \cdot \boldsymbol{U}^\lambda) \equiv \sum_\mu (-1)^\mu T^\lambda_\mu U^\lambda_{-\mu} = (-1)^\lambda [\lambda]^{\frac{1}{2}} (\boldsymbol{T}^\lambda \times \boldsymbol{U}^\lambda)^0 \qquad (\lambda = \text{integer}).$$

A spherical tensor of rank 1 is equivalent to an ordinary Cartesian vector for, unlike in the case of higher rank, the 3-dimensional function space defined by a Cartesian vector is irreducible with respect to rotations. For combinations of vectors, we have, writing $\boldsymbol{T}^1 \equiv \boldsymbol{T}$,

$$(3.2)\qquad \begin{cases} -\sqrt{3}\,(\boldsymbol{T}^1 \times \boldsymbol{U}^1)^0 = (\boldsymbol{T}^1 \cdot \boldsymbol{U}^1) = (\boldsymbol{T} \cdot \boldsymbol{U})\,, \\[2ex] (\boldsymbol{T}^1 \times \boldsymbol{U}^1)^1 \equiv \dfrac{i}{\sqrt{2}} (\boldsymbol{T} \times \boldsymbol{U})\,, \\[2ex] (\boldsymbol{T}^1 \times \boldsymbol{U}^1)^2_0 = -\dfrac{1}{\sqrt{6}} \{(\boldsymbol{T} \cdot \boldsymbol{U}) - 3 T_z U_z\}, \end{cases}$$

where for rank 2 we write only the $\mu = 0$ component.

Finally observe that we can carry out recoupling of coupled tensors by the usual procedures. If the recoupling involves a change of order of the tensors we shall need to make use of the commutation rules.

3·3. *Commutators.* – For two tensors $\boldsymbol{T}^\lambda$ and $\boldsymbol{U}^{\lambda'}$ there are $[\lambda\lambda']$ separate commutators $[T^\lambda_\mu, U^{\lambda'}_{\mu'}]$. But the system is much simpler than that because, since a commutator involves products, we can deal with coupled operators and thereby automatically take account of the Clebsch-Gordan relationships which exist between products. Since $(\boldsymbol{T}^{\lambda}\times\boldsymbol{U}^{\lambda'})^{\nu}_{\alpha}$ for fixed λ, λ' spans the same space as $T^{\lambda}_{\mu}U^{\lambda'}_{\mu'}$ we can deal with the *tensorial* commutators (—) or anti-commutators (+)

$$[\boldsymbol{T}^{\lambda}, \boldsymbol{U}^{\lambda'}]^{\nu}_{\pm} \equiv (\boldsymbol{T}^{\lambda}\times\boldsymbol{U}^{\lambda'})^{\nu} \pm (-1)^{\lambda+\lambda'-\nu}(\boldsymbol{U}^{\lambda'}\times\boldsymbol{T}^{\lambda})^{\nu} . \tag{3.3}$$

In the case of the commutator we shall consistently omit the subscript (—), writing simply $[\boldsymbol{T}^{\lambda}, \boldsymbol{U}^{\lambda'}]^{\nu}$. Note the « geometrical » phase $(-1)^{\lambda+\lambda'-\nu}$ which always enters when we invert a coupling order. We now have to deal with only $[\lambda]$ or $[\lambda']$ (whichever is smaller) quantities rather than with $[\lambda\lambda']$ as in the uncoupled case.

We have an alternative definition of a tensor. Remembering that behaviour of an object under rotations can be studied by investigating the commutation relations of the object with the angular-momentum operators (the infinitesimal generators of a rotation) we have easily that $\boldsymbol{T}^k$ is a tensor of rank k (in a single space) if

$$[\boldsymbol{J}, \boldsymbol{T}^k]^l = -\delta_{lk}\sqrt{k(k+1)}\,\boldsymbol{T}^k \qquad \text{(for all } l\text{)}, \tag{3.4}$$

where $\boldsymbol{J}\equiv\boldsymbol{J}^1$ is the angular-momentum operator for the underlying co-ordinate system. The commutator of $\boldsymbol{J}\cdot\boldsymbol{J}$ with a tensor is of some interest; it will be found easily, on appropriate application of eq. (3.4) that

$$[\boldsymbol{J}\cdot\boldsymbol{J}, \boldsymbol{T}^k] = k(k+1)\boldsymbol{T}^k + 2\sqrt{k(k+1)}\,(\boldsymbol{T}^k\times\boldsymbol{J})^k. \tag{3.5}$$

We have written k here rather than λ to emphasize that the results are valid, as they are written, in a single vector space. If we deal with a direct-product space, for example (j, t), there are obvious extensions of eq. (3.4) involving either the vectors in the individual spaces $(\boldsymbol{J}, \boldsymbol{T})$ or the multiple vector $(\boldsymbol{JT})$; and similarly for eq. (3.5).

Consider the relationship of this to the usual wave-function result

$$J^2\Psi^J_M = J(J+1)\Psi^J_M . \tag{3.6}$$

The essential difference is that in the latter equation, we understand that J^2 acts *on* Ψ^J_M having no effect on any function standing to the right of Ψ^J_M. Equation (3.5) is the general operator result which emerges when this restriction is removed, just as eq. (3.4) is the generalization of

$$(\boldsymbol{J}\times\boldsymbol{\Psi}^J)^{\nu} = -\delta_{\nu J}\sqrt{J(J+1)}\,\boldsymbol{\Psi}^J,$$

which contains the usual $J_{\pm}$ and J_z equations.

We mention also an obvious but important result which follows immediately from the commutator definition of a tensor. If the co-ordinate space q_i is augmented to form the space Q_i then, as long as $\boldsymbol{T}^\lambda$ is independent of the new co-ordinates or behaves like a zero-rank tensor with respect to them, it is of rank λ with respect to rotations of the larger co-ordinate set Q_i. For example if particle i is one of the nucleons of a nucleus we have that the spin vector $\boldsymbol{s}(i)$ is a vector both with respect to rotations of the spin co-ordinates of the i-th particle and with respect to rotations of the entire nucleus.

3·4. *Adjoints.* – The adjoint operation appears in a somewhat different form when we deal with spherical tensors because of the appearance of the imaginary quantity i in the definition of the components (for a vector we have for example $F_{\pm 1} = \mp(1/\sqrt{2})(F_x \pm iF_y)$, $F_0 = F_z$). By the usual definition of the Hermitian adjoint one finds then that to a tensor $\boldsymbol{T}^\lambda$ we can associate the *Hermitian adjoint tensor* $\boldsymbol{T}^{(\dagger)\lambda}$ whose components are defined by

$$(T^{(\dagger)\lambda})_\mu = (-1)^\mu (T^\lambda_{-\mu})^\dagger . \tag{3.7}$$

We observe now that the Hermitian adjoint of T^λ_μ is not a (λ, μ) tensor (*i.e.* the μ-component of a tensor of rank λ) nor indeed, because of the μ-dependent phase, is it even a $(\lambda, -\mu)$ tensor.

For the $\frac{1}{2}$-integral-rank case the occurrence of $(-1)^\mu$ is awkward and to avoid this we introduce instead the *adjoint tensor* $\overline{\boldsymbol{T}}^\lambda$ which we shall use throughout for tensors of integral as well as $\frac{1}{2}$-integral rank. This is defined by

$$\overline{T}^\lambda_\mu = (-1)^{\mu-\lambda} (T^\lambda_{-\mu})^\dagger = (-1)^{-\lambda} (T^{(\dagger)\lambda})_\mu , \tag{3.8}$$

and it should be verified that the quantity so defined is indeed a (λ, μ) tensor. For the adjoint of the adjoint it follows easily that

$$\overline{\overline{\boldsymbol{T}}}^\lambda = (-1)^{2\lambda} \boldsymbol{T}^\lambda . \tag{3.9}$$

Observing that the angular-momentum eigenfunction ψ^Γ_μ is itself a (Γ, μ) tensor we see that we have automatically introduced the *adjoint wave function* $\overline{\psi}^\Gamma_\mu$ to replace $\psi^{\Gamma *}_\mu$ which is not a proper tensor. We will now be able to carry out angular-momentum-coupling operations just as freely with the $\overline{\psi}$ functions as with the ψ functions; a ψ^* function on the other hand should be converted to a $\overline{\psi}$ before coupling to other quantities.

For coupled tensors we find easily that

$$\overline{(\boldsymbol{T}^\lambda \times \boldsymbol{U}^{\lambda'})^\nu} = (-1)^{\lambda+\lambda'-\nu} (\overline{\boldsymbol{U}}^{\lambda'} \times \overline{\boldsymbol{T}}^\lambda)^\nu \to (\overline{\boldsymbol{T}}^\lambda \times \overline{\boldsymbol{U}}^{\lambda'})^\nu \qquad \text{if } \boldsymbol{T}^\lambda,\ \boldsymbol{U}^{\lambda'} \text{ commute.} \tag{3.10}$$

Once again observe the geometrical phase.

3'5. *Wave-function orthonormalization.* – Starting with the usual result, rewriting in terms of tensors and recoupling we have

$$\langle \psi^{\Gamma *}_{x\mu} \psi^{\Gamma}_{x\mu} \rangle = 1 = (-1)^{\Gamma+\mu} \langle \bar{\psi}^{\Gamma}_{x,-\mu} \psi^{\Gamma}_{x\mu} \rangle =$$

$$= (-1)^{\Gamma+\mu} \sum_{\Lambda} C^{\Gamma\Gamma\Lambda}_{-\mu,\mu} \langle (\bar{\boldsymbol{\psi}}^{\Gamma}_{x} \times \boldsymbol{\psi}^{\Gamma}_{x})^{\Lambda}_{0} \rangle = [\Gamma]^{-\frac{1}{2}} \langle (\bar{\boldsymbol{\psi}}^{\Gamma}_{x} \times \boldsymbol{\psi}^{\Gamma}_{x})^{0} \rangle ,$$

where the last result follows from the (obvious) fact that the integral over all its co-ordinates of a nonscalar tensor must vanish; inserting the value of the C-G coefficient with $\Lambda = 0$ gives the result. Making the obvious extension we have

$$\langle (\bar{\boldsymbol{\psi}}^{\Gamma}_{x} \times \boldsymbol{\psi}^{\Gamma'}_{x'})^{\Lambda} \rangle = \delta_{\Lambda 0} \cdot \delta_{xx'} \cdot \delta_{\Gamma\Gamma'} [\Gamma]^{\frac{1}{2}}, \tag{3.11}$$

as long as x denotes an orthogonal labelling.

3'6. *Operating on a wave-function with an operator.* – This process is of great importance to us since one of our primary objects is to consider excitations of nuclei which are formally produced by the action of some operator on the ground state of the target in question (there is of course nothing to prevent us from considering excitations founded on some state other than the ground state and this will have to be borne in mind). We have the standard results, which pay no particular attention to tensorial behaviour

$$\left\{ \begin{aligned} T\psi_{\alpha} &= \sum_{\beta} T_{\beta\alpha} \psi_{\beta} , \\ \psi^{*}_{\beta} T &= \sum_{\alpha} T_{\beta\alpha} \psi^{*}_{\alpha} , \\ T_{\beta\alpha} &= \langle \psi^{*}_{\beta} T \psi_{\alpha} \rangle . \end{aligned} \right. \tag{3.12}$$

What happens to these when all the quantities are tensors? To begin with, ordinary multiplication is to be replaced by vector coupling, as in $(\boldsymbol{T}^{\lambda} \times \boldsymbol{\psi}^{\Gamma}_{x})^{\Gamma_1}$. We can think of this as representing the excitation of the target state (x, Γ) to a system with a definite angular momentum Γ_1. For example, the $E1$ excitation ($\lambda = 1, 1$ in j, t representation) of the ^{15}N ground state ($J, T = \frac{1}{2}, \frac{1}{2}$) can lead to four different excitations with $J, T = \frac{1}{2}\frac{1}{2}, \frac{1}{2}\frac{3}{2}, \frac{3}{2}\frac{1}{2}$, and $\frac{3}{2}\frac{3}{2}$; we are then considering each of these separately.

The excitation function can be expanded in terms of all the states with fixed Γ_1 *and the expansion coefficient must be independent of all* μ*'s* (for otherwise the tensorial behaviour would not be correct). The coefficient will depend on $\boldsymbol{T}^{\lambda}$, x, Γ and the particular state in the expansion, say y, Γ_1, which we are considering. Then, inserting a phase and an extra factor for convenience, we write

(3.13)
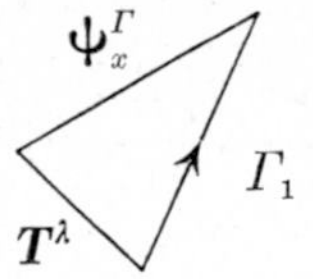

$$= \frac{(-1)^{\Gamma_1-\lambda-\Gamma}}{[\Gamma_1]^{\frac{1}{2}}} \sum_y \langle y\Gamma_1 \| \boldsymbol{T}^\lambda \| x\Gamma \rangle \Psi_y^{\Gamma_1}\,,$$

the adjoint (*) of which is (changing the labels appropriately)

(3.14)
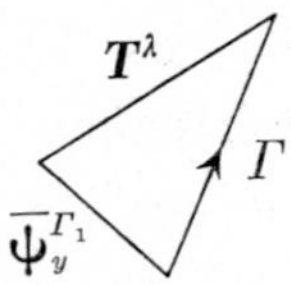

$$= \frac{(-1)^{\Gamma_1-\lambda-\Gamma}}{[\Gamma]^{\frac{1}{2}}} \sum_x \langle y\Gamma_1 \| \boldsymbol{T}^\lambda \| x\Gamma \rangle \overline{\Psi}_x^{\Gamma}\,.$$

The double-barred matrix element (d.b.m.e.) introduced here is identical with an already familiar object. Taking overlaps in eq. (3.13) we have

(3.15) $\langle \psi^{\Gamma_1 *}_{y\mu} |$
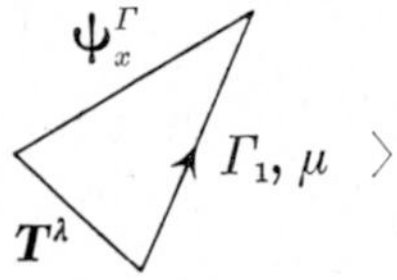

$$\rangle = \frac{(-1)^{\Gamma_1-\lambda-\Gamma}}{[\Gamma_1]^{\frac{1}{2}}} \langle y\Gamma_1 \| \boldsymbol{T}^\lambda \| x\Gamma \rangle\,.$$

But on decoupling the left-hand expression we get

$$\text{(3.16)} \qquad \sum_\alpha C^{\lambda\Gamma\Gamma_1}_{\alpha,\mu-\alpha} \langle \psi^{\Gamma_1 *}_{y\mu} T^\lambda_\alpha \psi^\Gamma_{x,\mu-\alpha} \rangle = \sum_\alpha (-1)^{\lambda+\Gamma-\Gamma_1} C^{\Gamma\lambda\Gamma_1}_{\mu-\alpha,\alpha} \cdot$$
$$\cdot\, C^{\Gamma\lambda\Gamma_1}_{\mu-\alpha,\alpha} [\Gamma_1]^{-\frac{1}{2}} \langle y\Gamma_1 \| \boldsymbol{T}^\lambda \| x\Gamma \rangle_{\text{Racah}} = \frac{(-1)^{\Gamma_1-\lambda-\Gamma}}{[\Gamma_1]^{\frac{1}{2}}} \langle y\Gamma_1 \| \boldsymbol{T}^\lambda \| x\Gamma \rangle_{\text{Racah}}\,,$$

where we have evaluated the integral by introducing Racah's d.b.m.e. as shown (inverting also the order of coupling in the first C.G. coefficient, thereby introducing a phase). The outcome of this painful operation (and any introduction of μ is painful) is to show that our d.b.m.e. is identical, in magnitude and phase, with the standard Racah d.b.m.e.

Going back now to eq. (3.15), making the transformation from ψ^* to $\overline{\psi}$ and recoupling the product, we find the pleasing results that

(3.17) $\langle y\Gamma_1 \| \boldsymbol{T}^\lambda \| x\Gamma \rangle = (-1)^{\Gamma_1-\lambda-\Gamma} \Big\langle$
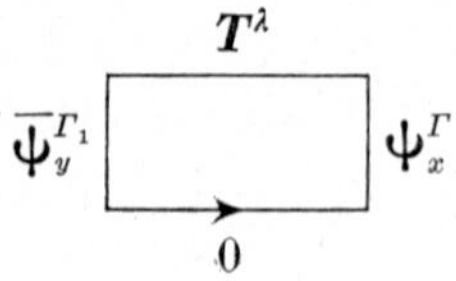

$\Big\rangle =$

$= \Big\langle$
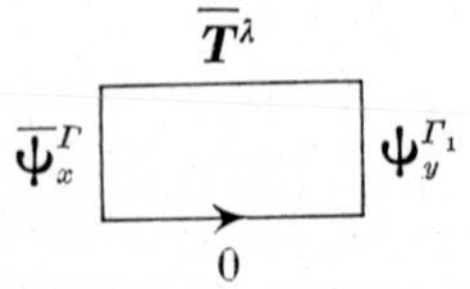

$\Big\rangle = (-1)^{\Gamma_1+\lambda-\Gamma} \langle x\Gamma \| \overline{\boldsymbol{T}}^\lambda \| y\Gamma_1 \rangle\,,$

(*) We may regard all the matrix elements which we shall meet as being real.

where the third form follows by taking the adjoint of the second. It should be noted that no internal coupling line need be shown in the coupled integrals, for, since the over-all angular momentum is zero, such an internal-coupling specification would be redundant.

In considering an operator acting on a wave function we have been forced to make a distinction between wave-function tensors and operator tensors (see the discussion following eq. (3.6)). In the final result the two kinds of tensors enter in the d.b.m.e. almost on the same footing. When later we think of the w.f. tensors as second-quantized operators which act on the vacuum, all the operators will be on exactly the same footing and the d.b.m.e. will then be, to within the phase shown, a *coupled vacuum expectation value*.

3·7. *Excitation strengths.* – Consider the excitation of the target leading to any of the final states shown. We need a satisfactory definition of the excitation strength which we shall call $\mathscr{G}$. It is pretty obvious that to within a possible statistical factor the strength must simply be the square of the d.b.m.e. But we verify it anyway. On summing over the final states and averaging over the initial ones we have for the probability, omitting all « external » factors,

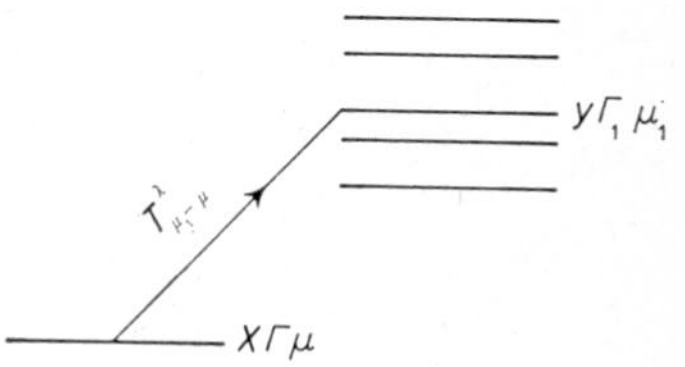

Fig. 1. – An excitation of the target (x, Γ) leading to a final state (y, Γ_1).

$$(3.18)\qquad [\Gamma]^{-1}\sum_{\mu\mu_1}\langle\psi^{\Gamma_1^*}_{y\mu_1}T^{\lambda}_{\mu_1-\mu}\psi^{\Gamma}_{x\mu}\rangle^2 = [\Gamma\Gamma_1]^{-1}\langle y\Gamma_1\|\boldsymbol{T}^{\lambda}\|x\Gamma\rangle^2\sum_{\mu\mu_1}(C^{\Gamma\lambda\Gamma_1}_{\mu,\mu_1-\mu})^2 = [\Gamma]^{-1}\langle y\Gamma_1\|\boldsymbol{T}^{\lambda}\|x\Gamma\rangle^2 .$$

For reasons which will become clear later (and are related to a $d\theta \to d\cos\theta$ transformation) we shall multiply this by $[\Gamma/\Gamma_1]$ in defining the strength $\mathscr{G}$ and write

$$(3.19)\qquad \mathscr{G}(x\Gamma\times\boldsymbol{T}^{\lambda}\to y\Gamma_1) = [\Gamma_1]^{-1}\sum_{\mu\mu_1}\langle\psi^{\Gamma_1^*}_{y\mu_1}T^{\lambda}_{\mu_1-\mu}\psi^{\Gamma}_{x\mu}\rangle^2 = [\Gamma_1]^{-1}\langle y\Gamma_1\|\boldsymbol{T}^{\lambda}\|x\Gamma\rangle^2 ,$$

where we have written the polarized matrix-element form, only in order to make contact with the usual procedure. For certain purposes it will be necessary for us to consider the reduced transition *amplitude* rather than the reduced *strength* (by « reduced » we imply of course that the μ-dependences have been divided out). Some examples of strengths are the so-called « spectroscopic factors » for single-nucleon transfer reactions, and the $BE2$ and similar quantities for electromagnetic processes. Except for the normalization these are identical with the strength $\mathscr{G}$ introduced above.

3·8. *Intermediate-state expansions; multipole sum rules.* – The essence of any sum rule is the intermediate-state expansion for the matrix element of a product of operators. The usual intermediate-state expansion is

$$\langle \psi_\alpha^* S T \psi_\beta \rangle = \sum_\gamma \langle \psi_\alpha^* S \psi_\gamma \rangle \langle \psi_\gamma^* T \psi_\beta \rangle \, . \tag{3.20}$$

What does this become when all the quantities involved are spherical tensors? We have immediately that

(3.21) $\langle x\Gamma \| (\boldsymbol{S}^\sigma \times \boldsymbol{T}^\lambda)^\nu \| x'\Gamma' \rangle = (-1)^{\Gamma-\nu-\Gamma'}$ 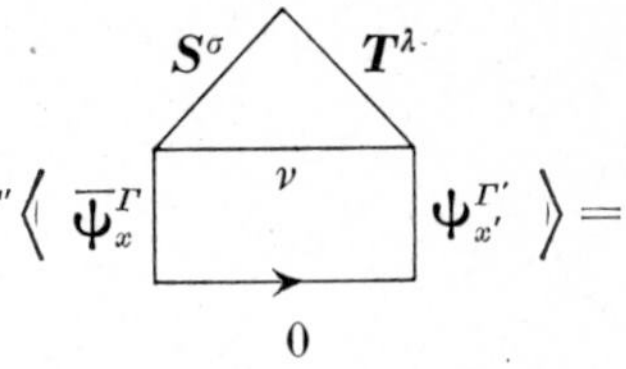 $=$

$= (-1)^{\Gamma-\nu-\Gamma'} \sum_{\Gamma_1} U(\Gamma\sigma\Gamma'\lambda : \Gamma_1\nu)$ 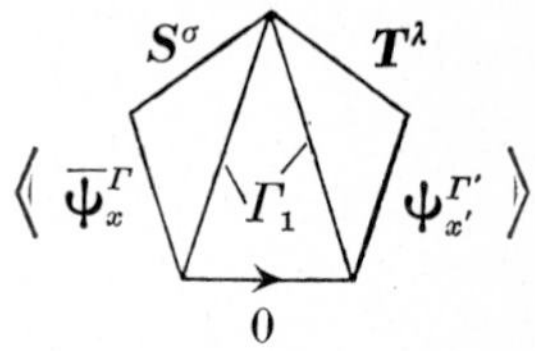 ,

where we have made a Racah recoupling. The last matrix element written appears as the scalar product of two (unnormalized) excitation states. But we have already given, in eqs. (3.13), (3.14), the expansion of each of these quantities in terms of the basis states $\Psi_y^{\Gamma_1}$ of the system and their adjoints. Using these expansions we have

$$\begin{aligned} &\langle x\Gamma \| (\boldsymbol{S}^\sigma \times \boldsymbol{T}^\lambda)^\nu \| x'\Gamma' \rangle = \\ &\qquad = (-1)^{\sigma+\lambda-\nu} \sum_{y\Gamma_1} [\Gamma_1]^{-\frac{1}{2}} U(\Gamma\sigma\Gamma'\lambda : \Gamma_1\nu) \langle x\Gamma \| \boldsymbol{S}^\sigma \| y\Gamma_1 \rangle \langle y\Gamma_1 \| \boldsymbol{T}^\lambda \| x'\Gamma' \rangle , \end{aligned} \tag{3.22}$$

and this is the equation which we have been seeking.

Note now the remarkable fact that, in sharp contrast to the « scalar » expansion, the multipole one can be partially inverted and we have

$$\begin{aligned} &\sum_y \langle x\Gamma \| \boldsymbol{S}^\sigma \| y\Gamma_1 \rangle \langle y\Gamma_1 \| \boldsymbol{T}^\lambda \| x'\Gamma' \rangle = \\ &\qquad = [\Gamma_1]^{\frac{1}{2}} \sum_\nu (-1)^{\sigma+\lambda-\nu} U(\Gamma\sigma\Gamma'\lambda : \Gamma_1\nu) \langle x\Gamma \| (\boldsymbol{S}^\sigma \times \boldsymbol{T}^\lambda)^\nu \| x'\Gamma' \rangle . \end{aligned} \tag{3.23}$$

We are interested primarily in the diagonal case. Taking $\Gamma = \Gamma'$, $x = x'$, $\sigma = \lambda$, $\boldsymbol{S}^\sigma = \overline{\boldsymbol{T}}{}^\lambda$ we find

$$\begin{aligned} &\sum_y \mathcal{G}(x\Gamma \times \boldsymbol{T}^\lambda \to y\Gamma_1) = (-1)^{\Gamma+\lambda-\Gamma_1} [\Gamma_1]^{-\frac{1}{2}} \cdot \\ &\qquad \cdot \sum_\nu (-1)^\nu U(\Gamma\lambda\Gamma\lambda : \Gamma_1\nu) \langle x\Gamma \| (\overline{\boldsymbol{T}}{}^\lambda \times \boldsymbol{T}^\lambda)^\nu \| x\Gamma \rangle , \end{aligned} \tag{3.24}$$

whose angular-momentum inverse is

$$(3.25)\qquad \langle x\Gamma \| (\overline{\boldsymbol{T}}^{\lambda}\times \boldsymbol{T}^{\lambda})^{\nu} \| x\Gamma\rangle = \\ = (-1)^{\Gamma+\lambda+\nu}\sum_{y\Gamma_1} U(\Gamma\lambda\Gamma\lambda:\Gamma_1\nu)(-1)^{-\Gamma_1}[\Gamma_1]^{\frac{1}{2}}\mathscr{G}(x\Gamma\times \boldsymbol{T}^{\lambda}\to y\Gamma_1)\,.$$

The whole point of a direct sum-rule analysis of strengths is to convert the measured quantities into « interior » information about the target state and the interaction. The multipole sum rules, here, which take account of the strengths *and* the angular momenta, do this to some extent. In fact, if there is only one state for each Γ_1 value the conversion is obviously complete with respect to the target information. We end up, in any case, with $[\lambda]$ or $[\Gamma]$ (whichever is smaller) pieces of information about the target state, though with nothing explicit about the interaction. This represents a considerable advance over the results produced by the nonmultipole sum rule, which gives only one piece of information. We shall see shortly how to go much further.

Besides the « direct sum-rule analysis » we are equally interested in the inverse problem, that of calculating strength distributions from a known or assumed Hamiltonian and ground-state properties. The formalism of course works either way. We remark also that the partial inversion of the sum rule, which applies for systems of arbitrary complexity, may be regarded as due to the existence of a group, the rotation group, underlying our definition of a tensor. If all the states and operators belong to irreducible representations of other groups further partial inversions are in principle possible.

3'9. *The « semiclassical » form for the sum-rule equations.* – Our basic equations can be written, without loss of precision, in a much more familiar form. If we are dealing with the diagonal case, not mixed in multipolarity, the final-state angular momentum Γ_1 may be thought of as defining an angle θ (in a direct-product space of course). We have

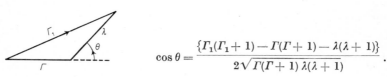

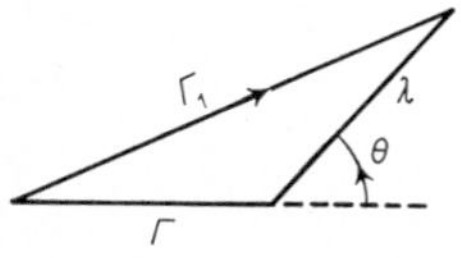

Fig. 2. – The coupling angle θ.

$$\cos\theta = \frac{\{\Gamma_1(\Gamma_1+1)-\Gamma(\Gamma+1)-\lambda(\lambda+1)\}}{2\sqrt{\Gamma(\Gamma+1)\,\lambda(\lambda+1)}}\,.$$

where the angle introduced has been familiar since the days of the Bohr model. Since Γ and λ are fixed, we can think of the strength as an angular function:

$$(3.26)\qquad \mathscr{G}(x\Gamma\times \boldsymbol{T}^{\lambda}\to y\Gamma_1) \Rightarrow \mathscr{G}_y(\theta)\,.$$

But we must remember that only certain values of θ ($[\Gamma]$ or $[\lambda]$ of them, whichever is smaller) are *observable.*

The situation is described schematically in Fig. 3 which shows strengths $\mathscr{G}$ (whose value is proportional to the length of the heavy line) for the final states reached in an excitation.

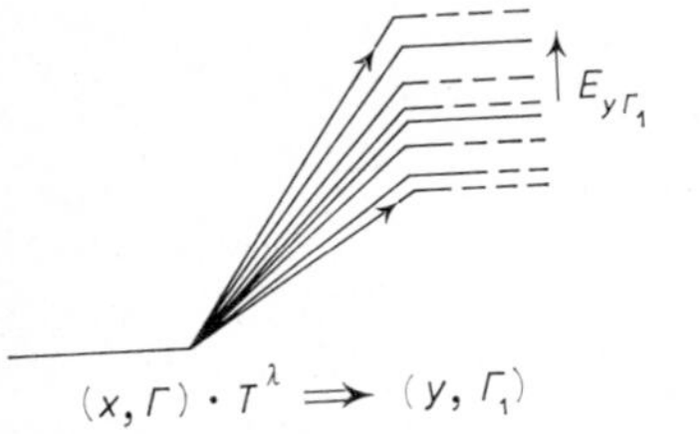

Fig. 3. – A schematic representation of the transition strengths. The final states have various angular momenta, and the strengths are proportional to the heavy lines drawn at each energy.

Replotting the strengths to show the way things vary with θ we get something like this:

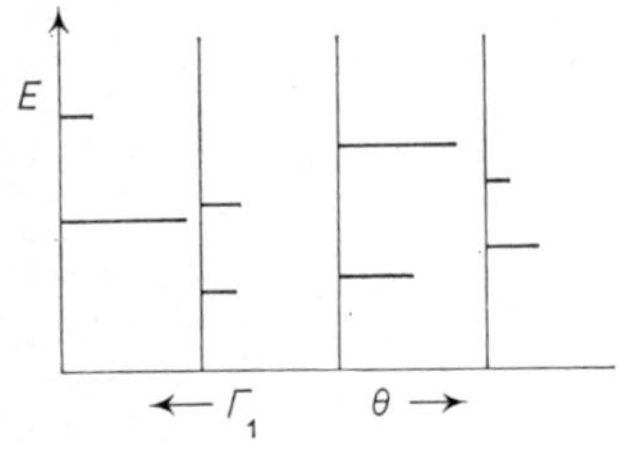

Fig. 4. – The transition strengths of Fig. 3 but plotted against the excitation energy and the coupling angle.

Figure 4 cannot be regarded as an angular distribution, for an energy level at one angle θ (value of Γ_1) is not related in a known way to a level at another value of θ. But we can convert Fig. 4 into a set of angular distributions by taking *energy moments.* Let

$$\mathscr{G}^{(m)}(\theta) = \sum_{y} \left(E_y(\theta)\right)^m \mathscr{G}_y(\theta) \,, \tag{3.27}$$

where of course $E_y(\theta)$ is simply $E_{y\Gamma_1}$. Then our knowledge about the excitation strengths is expressed in terms of the angularly dependent moment functions $\mathscr{G}^{(m)}(\theta)$. The $m=0$ function gives the variation of the total strength among the different values of Γ_1; the $m=1$ function does the same for the centroid energies, and the $m=2$ for the widths of the « giant resonances » associated with the excitation.

The natural thing to do now is to expand $\mathscr{G}^{(m)}(\theta)$ in terms of Legendre polynomials

$$\mathscr{G}^{(m)}(\theta) = \sum_{\nu} g^m(\nu) P_\nu(\cos\theta) \,, \tag{3.28}$$

and then the information appears in the coefficients $g^m(\nu)$. We can expect this expansion to be the mathematically significant one because of our agreement that all the states and operators which we encounter have a definite rank with respect to rotations.

What do we mean by a P_ν expansion when the angle θ takes only a discrete set of values? The answer to this question is well known. P_ν expansions and angular integrations are replaced by certain Racah transforms. The correspondence between the two techniques is summarized below.

Racah-Legendre correspondences (*)

$$(3.29)\quad \begin{cases} (a)\quad P_\nu(\cos\theta) \Rightarrow \left[\dfrac{\Gamma\lambda}{\Gamma_1\nu}\right]^{\frac{1}{2}}(-1)^{\Gamma+\lambda-\Gamma_1}U(\Gamma\lambda\Gamma\lambda:\Gamma_1\nu)\,, \\[2ex] (b)\quad \dfrac{1}{2}\displaystyle\int_{-1}^{1}\mathrm{d}\cos\theta \Rightarrow \dfrac{1}{[\Gamma\lambda]}\sum_{\Gamma_1}[\Gamma_1]\,, \\[2ex] \left.\begin{array}{l}(c)\quad \mathscr{G}(\theta)=\displaystyle\sum_\nu g(\nu)P_\nu(\cos\theta) \\[1ex] (d)\quad g(\nu)=\dfrac{[\nu]}{2}\displaystyle\int \mathrm{d}\cos\theta\,\mathscr{G}(\theta)P_\nu(\cos\theta)\end{array}\right\}\Rightarrow \\[2ex] \qquad\Rightarrow\begin{cases} \mathscr{G}(\Gamma_1)=\displaystyle\sum_\nu g(\nu)\left[\dfrac{\Gamma\lambda}{\Gamma_1\nu}\right]^{\frac{1}{2}}(-1)^{\Gamma+\lambda-\Gamma_1}U(\Gamma\lambda\Gamma\lambda:\Gamma_1\nu)\,, \\[2ex] g(\nu)=\displaystyle\sum_{\Gamma_1}\mathscr{G}(\Gamma_1)\left[\dfrac{\Gamma\lambda}{\Gamma_1\nu}\right]^{-\frac{1}{2}}(-1)^{\Gamma+\lambda-\Gamma_1}U(\Gamma\lambda\Gamma\lambda:\Gamma_1\nu)\,, \end{cases} \\[2ex] (e)\quad \left\{\begin{array}{ll}\text{If } g^{(+)}(\nu) & =(-1)^\nu g^{(-)}(\nu) \\ \text{then } \mathscr{G}^{(\pm)}(\theta) & =\mathscr{G}^{(\mp)}(\pi-\theta)\end{array}\right\}\Rightarrow \\[2ex] \qquad\Rightarrow\begin{cases} \text{If } g^{(+)}(\nu) =(-1)^\nu g^{(-)}(\nu)\,, \\[1ex] \text{then } \mathscr{G}^{(\pm)}(\Gamma_1)=\displaystyle\sum_{\Gamma_1'}\left[\dfrac{\Gamma_1'}{\Gamma_1}\right]^{\frac{1}{2}}U(\Gamma\lambda\lambda\Gamma:\Gamma_1\Gamma_1')\,\mathscr{G}^{(\mp)}(\Gamma_1')\,, \end{cases} \end{cases}$$

Note the appearance of the $[\Gamma_1/\Gamma]$ factor in the discrete equivalent of $\int\mathrm{d}\cos\theta$. It is because of this factor, as will be clear shortly, that we have found it convenient to define the strength as $[\Gamma/\Gamma_1]$ times the more natural expression (see eq. (3.19)). Equations (*c*) and (*d*) follow immediately from (*a*) and (*b*). The Racah correspondence given by (*e*) will be very important for us, when we consider the effects produced by certain hole$\rightleftharpoons$particle transformations; it can also be derived easily from (*a*) and (*b*) together with an elementary Racah sum rule.

(*) The factor $\frac{1}{2}$ appearing in $\int\mathrm{d}\cos\theta$ should strictly speaking be written as $[\frac{1}{2}]^{-1}$ since it enters in every member of a direct-product space. This is of particular consequence should we wish to integrate in some but not all of the angular spaces.

The P_ν-Racah correspondence is an identity for the case $\nu = 0, 1$, but otherwise only in the limit where all the angular momenta become indefinitely large. For our purposes (especially in the isospin space) this is not at all the case. But, as may easily be verified, there is none the less a complete one-to-one correspondence between the two systems of equations and, since the P_ν form is both easier to write and physically more transparent, we shall talk about the angular forms of the strength moments; for actual calculations however, we would use the Racah forms. The latter forms are of course more general since they work also in the off-diagonal cases in which the P_ν forms fail (being replaced by forms involving Jacobi polynomials).

Looking back now at our multipole sum rule eq. (3.24) we realize that

$$\sum_y \mathcal{G}(x\Gamma \times \boldsymbol{T}^\lambda \to y\Gamma_1) \equiv \sum_y \mathcal{G}_y(\theta) = \mathcal{G}^{(0)}(\theta) , \tag{3.30}$$

the zeroth energy moment of the strength. Rewriting the right-hand side of the same equation by means of the P_ν-Racah correspondence we have the result that

$$\mathcal{G}^{(0)}(\theta) = \sum_\nu (-1)^\nu \left[\frac{\nu}{\Gamma\lambda}\right]^{\frac{1}{2}} \langle x\Gamma \| (\overline{\boldsymbol{T}}^\lambda \times \boldsymbol{T}^\lambda)^\nu \| x\Gamma\rangle \cdot P_\nu(\cos\theta) . \tag{3.31}$$

To complete the job we must find the corresponding results for the m-th moment of the strength. But now looking back at the genesis of the multipole-sum-rule equation we see that, just as

$$\langle \psi_\alpha^* S(H)^m T\psi_\beta\rangle = \sum_\gamma \langle \psi_\alpha^* S\psi_\gamma\rangle \cdot (E_\gamma)^m \cdot \langle \psi_\gamma^* T\psi_\beta\rangle , \tag{3.32}$$

as long as the ψ_γ are eigenfunctions of H, so likewise we have

$$\begin{aligned}\sum_y \mathcal{G}(x\Gamma \times \boldsymbol{T}^\lambda \to y\Gamma_1)(E_{y\Gamma_1})^m = \\ = (-1)^{\Gamma+\lambda-\Gamma_1}[\Gamma_1]^{-\frac{1}{2}} \sum_\nu U(\Gamma\lambda\Gamma\lambda : \Gamma_1\nu)(-1)^\nu \langle x\Gamma \| (\overline{\boldsymbol{T}}^\lambda \times (H)^m \times \boldsymbol{T}^\lambda)^\nu \| x\Gamma\rangle ,\end{aligned} \tag{3.33}$$

the more civilized form of which is

$$\mathcal{G}^{(m)}(\theta) = \sum_\nu (-1)^\nu \left[\frac{\nu}{\Gamma\lambda}\right]^{\frac{1}{2}} \langle x\Gamma \| (\overline{\boldsymbol{T}}^\lambda \times (H)^m \times \boldsymbol{T}^\lambda)^\nu \| x\Gamma\rangle \cdot P_\nu(\cos\theta) , \tag{3.34}$$

which, with its inverse

$$\langle x\Gamma \| (\overline{\boldsymbol{T}}^\lambda \times (H)^m \times \boldsymbol{T}^\lambda)^\nu \| x\Gamma\rangle = \tfrac{1}{2}(-1)^\nu [\nu\Gamma\lambda]^{\frac{1}{2}} \int \mathcal{G}^m(\theta) \cdot P_\nu(\cos\theta)\, \mathrm{d}\cos\theta , \tag{3.35}$$

constitutes our basic equations. We stress that these equations are of general validity, for arbitrary excitation operators $\boldsymbol{T}^\lambda$ (of rank λ) and for target and final states of arbitrary complexity.

All of the low-order sum rules are of interest (as we shall see), but perhaps the most interesting is the linear-energy-weighted rule ($m=1$). This defines $\mathscr{E}(\theta)$, the *centroid energy* for the excitation (which we shall simply call the « *excitation energy* »), this being the center of gravity of the final-state energies for a given angular momentum Γ_1, defined with a weighting equal to the strength. We thus have

$$\mathscr{E}(\theta)=\frac{\mathscr{G}^{(1)}(\theta)}{\mathscr{G}^{(0)}(\theta)}\,. \tag{3.36}$$

Of course if we are dealing with a scalar target or a scalar excitation ($\Gamma=0$ or $\lambda=0$), $\mathscr{E}(\theta)\Rightarrow\mathscr{E}$, being in fact independent of θ (since $\nu=0$ only). But even when this is not the case we shall often be interested in the « *over-all* » or « *monopole* » *centroid*, defined by taking all the strength, paying no attention to the final-state angular momenta. It is easy to see that in both of these cases we have

$$\mathscr{E}=\frac{\int \mathrm{d}\cos\theta\cdot\mathscr{G}^{(1)}(\theta)}{\int \mathrm{d}\cos\theta\cdot\mathscr{G}^{(0)}(\theta)}=\frac{\langle x\Gamma\|(\overline{T}^{\lambda}\times H\times T^{\lambda})^{0}\|x\Gamma\rangle}{\langle x\Gamma\|(\overline{T}^{\lambda}\times T^{\lambda})^{0}\|x\Gamma\rangle}\,. \tag{3.37}$$

In some cases the monopole centroid $\mathscr{E}$ defined here is not the interesting one because the excitation mechanism itself introduces a dependence on the final-state angular momenta which is separate from that defined by the strength $\mathscr{G}(\theta)$. This happens particularly if we deal with systems and excitations which are partially polarized. For example if we excite a nucleus with a neutron excess by adding a further neutron we shall see only the state with $T_1=T+\frac{1}{2}$, the centroid of which we may call $\mathscr{E}(T_{1>})$; the centroid given by eq. (3.37) is on the other hand

$$\mathscr{E}=\frac{(T+1)}{[T]}\,\mathscr{E}(T_{1>})+\frac{T}{[T]}\,\mathscr{E}(T_{1<})\,,$$

which is a quite different thing. In this particular case, on the other hand, if we should use a p-n formalism (in which the isobaric spin is not an angular-momentum quantum number) then this question does not arise at all. We shall later consider the relationship between the two formalisms and then this matter will become much clearer. With regard to polarized sum rule problems in general, one should at the beginning, for example by the usual Clebsch-Gordan techniques, express things in terms of d.b.m.e. and then the theorems above apply.

In the completely unpolarized case there is of course no interference (in the transition strength) between excitations of different multipolarity but this is not true in the polarized case; besides that we may be interested in correlated excitations, such as for example in a γ-cascade, in which the intermediate states decay to a state different from the target state. The general eqs. (3.22), (3.23) (extended if necessary to deal with products of more than two operators) are adequate to deal with the more general case. Written in terms of the excitation *amplitudes* which we define as (see eq. (3.19))

$$\mathscr{G}^{\frac{1}{2}}(x\Gamma\times \boldsymbol{T}^{\lambda}\to y\Gamma_1)=[\Gamma_1]^{-\frac{1}{2}}\langle x\Gamma\|\overline{\boldsymbol{T}}^{\lambda}\|y\Gamma_1\rangle\,, \tag{3.38}$$

the general equation becomes

$$\sum_y \mathscr{G}^{\frac{1}{2}}(x\Gamma\times \boldsymbol{T}^{\lambda}\to y\Gamma_1)\,\mathscr{G}^{\frac{1}{2}}(x'\Gamma'\times \boldsymbol{U}^{\lambda'}\to y\Gamma_1)= \tag{3.39}$$
$$=\sum_\nu[\Gamma_1]^{-\frac{1}{2}}(-1)^{\Gamma_1-\Gamma'-\lambda+\nu}\,U(\Gamma\lambda\Gamma'\lambda':\Gamma_1\nu)\langle x\Gamma\|(\overline{\boldsymbol{T}}^{\lambda}\times\boldsymbol{U}^{\lambda'})^{\nu}\|x'\Gamma'\rangle\,.$$

Although there are now *two* angles, $\theta=\widehat{\Gamma\cdot\lambda}$, $\theta'=\widehat{\Gamma'\cdot\lambda'}$ one could probably establish a correspondence with the Legendre polynomial forms so that even the mixed-multipolarity cases nondiagonal in the target state could be described by the same equations as the simpler ones.

3·10. *Coupled systems.* – The basic sum rule of eq. (3.21) is quite general. Often however we wish to regard the states of the system as being made up of several distinct parts coupled together. By « distinct » we imply that the co-ordinates appearing in one part are independent of those appearing in another, the same separation of co-ordinates applying to all the functions with which we deal. The states in a p-n formalism are usually given in this way. For another example, think of the usual representation of a multi-shell wave-function, things here being slightly complicated by antisymmetry in the case of a configuration-space representation but not in a second-quantized one.

The question now is what special forms are assumed by the strength amplitude (eq. (3.38)) and by the target integrals, when the states are written in this way, and when the excitation operator works on only one of the components of the states or is a sum of such operators. The answers are given by completely well-known Racah theorems but we write the results and indicate how they can be derived without effort from the earlier ones. In point of fact it is often easier to rederive them in the needed form than to transcribe the standard results.

We have

$$\langle(\psi^{\Gamma_1'}_{x_1'}\times\psi^{\Gamma_2'}_{x_2'})^{\Gamma'}\|\boldsymbol{T}^{\lambda}\|(\psi^{\Gamma_1}_{x_1}\times\psi^{\Gamma_2}_{x_2})^{\Gamma}\rangle= \tag{3.40}$$
$$=(-1)^{\Gamma_2+\lambda-\Gamma_1-\Gamma'}\left[\frac{\Gamma\Gamma'}{\Gamma_2\,\lambda}\right]^{\frac{1}{2}}\delta_{x_2x_2'}\delta_{\Gamma_2\Gamma_2'}\,U(\Gamma_1'\Gamma'\Gamma_1\Gamma:\Gamma_2\lambda)\,\langle\psi^{\Gamma_1'}_{x_1'}\|\boldsymbol{T}^{\lambda}\|\psi^{\Gamma_1}_{x_1}\rangle,$$

if $\boldsymbol{T}^\lambda$ operates only on the co-ordinates of the first group. An obvious modification produces the result if $\boldsymbol{T}^\lambda$ operates with the second group instead of the first. The result is derived in a simple way by writing in the coupled-integral form (eq. (3.17)), then recoupling so that the inert functions stand together. The integrand then factors and the result emerges. This equation is useful for eliminating the inert group (whose influence survives only as a decoupling factor). It should be verified that the equation will still be valid when we interpret the ψ's as second-quantized operators which may either commute or anticommute.

In exactly the same way we have

$$(3.41)\qquad \langle(\psi^{\Gamma_1'}_{x_1'}\times\psi^{\Gamma_2'}_{x_2'})^{\Gamma'}\|(\boldsymbol{T}^\lambda\times\boldsymbol{U}^\omega)^\nu\|(\psi^{\Gamma_1}_{x_1}\times\psi^{\Gamma_2}_{x_2})^{\Gamma}\rangle = \\ = \left[\frac{\nu}{\lambda\omega}\right]^{\frac{1}{2}}\begin{Bmatrix}\Gamma_1' & \Gamma_2' & \Gamma' \\ \Gamma_1 & \Gamma_2 & \Gamma \\ \lambda & \omega & \nu\end{Bmatrix}\langle\psi^{\Gamma_1'}_{x_1'}\|\boldsymbol{T}^\lambda\|\psi^{\Gamma_1}_{x_1}\rangle\langle\psi^{\Gamma_2'}_{x_2'}\|\boldsymbol{U}^\omega\|\psi^{\Gamma_2}_{x_2}\rangle,$$

when $\boldsymbol{T}^\lambda$ operates on the first group and $\boldsymbol{U}^\omega$ on the second. A special case of this is

$$(3.42)\qquad \langle(\psi^{\Gamma_1'}_{x_1'}\times\psi^{\Gamma_2'}_{x_2'})^{\Gamma}\|(\boldsymbol{T}^\lambda\times\boldsymbol{U}^\lambda)^0\|(\psi^{\Gamma_1}_{x_1}\times\psi^{\Gamma_2}_{x_2})^{\Gamma}\rangle = \\ = (-1)^{\Gamma_1'+\Gamma_2-\Gamma-\lambda}[\lambda]^{-1}\,U(\Gamma_1'\Gamma_2'\Gamma_1\Gamma_2:\Gamma\lambda)\,\langle\psi^{\Gamma_1'}_{x_1'}\|\boldsymbol{T}^\lambda\|\psi^{\Gamma_1}_{x_1}\rangle\langle\psi^{\Gamma_2'}_{x_2'}\|\boldsymbol{U}^\lambda\|\psi^{\Gamma_2}_{x_2}\rangle\,.$$

If we are dealing with second-quantized fermion operators an extra phase $(-1)^{n_1(n_2-n_2')}$ appears in eqs. (3.42), (3.43).

For certain diagonal cases these results may also be written in spherical-harmonic form, and they may be applied explicitly to rewrite the strength equations for coupled systems. These things are left as exercises.

4. – General remarks about sum-rule methods.

Before considering the explicit representation of excitation operators, wave functions, and so on, we make a series of general remarks, some of which are trivial, concerning possible applications of the sum rules derived in the last Section.

4·1. *The scalar target case.* – For a scalar target ($\Gamma=0$) we necessarily have $\Gamma_1=\lambda$ and $\nu=0$ and thus only a monopole sum rule. There are then no significant angular-momentum considerations, and the multipole sum rules simply produce the conventional sum-rule results. We have here an example (for $\Gamma=0$ or more generally for $\Gamma<\lambda$ if we assume that the excitation operator is known) of the « decoupling loss of information ». There is an obvious advantage, *ceteris paribus*, in dealing with nonscalar targets.

4·2. *Non-energy-weighted sum rules* ($m=0$). – Since the target integrals do not contain H, these sum rules measure for us properties of the ground-state only, saying nothing *explicitly* about the Hamiltonian. This separation of information can be extremely useful.

4·3. *Inverse energy weighting.* – One might at first think that sum rules with negative m should enter on the same footing as those with positive m, but a little thought will show that this is not true. Inserting a reference energy E_0 we have $(\partial/\partial E_0)(H-E_0)^m=-m(H-E_0)^{m-1}$. Thus we note that the information involved in a sum rule has only a trivial dependence on E_0 as long as $m\geqslant 0$ since if we are investigating, for example, the $m=2$ rule, changing E_0 simply induces a multiple of the $m=1$ rule which we already know. For negative m, however the Taylor series is replaced by a Laurent series and to know things for a given negative m as a function of E_0 one must really know them for all negative m. The information content of an inverse energy-weighted-rule is very large and, as is obvious anyway, we are really dealing with Green's functions and with the complete solutions of the problem rather than with integrals of them. On the other hand the multipole decomposition of Green's functions, which we shall not consider, should turn out to be a useful device.

4·4. *Self-adjoint and nonself-adjoint excitations.* – An electromagnetic excitation operator is self-adjoint. Excitation by particle addition is not, the adjoint operation being that of removing a particle (or adding a hole). In this latter case we thus have two separate excitation processes, which have however closely related target integrals:

$$\langle\|(\overline{\boldsymbol{T}}^\lambda\times(H)^m\times\boldsymbol{T}^\lambda)^\nu\|\rangle,\qquad\langle\|(\boldsymbol{T}^\lambda\times(H)^m\times\overline{\boldsymbol{T}}^\lambda)^\nu\|\rangle,$$

and thus closely related strength moments. There are then certain generalized hole $\rightleftharpoons$ particle transform relationships between the moments, and these have some interesting consequences as we shall later see.

4·5. *Examples of observable excitation processes.* – Table I shows four important cases and gives some capsule comments about them, and the second-quantized representation of the operators. $\boldsymbol{A}^\varrho$ is the creation-operator tensor for the orbit ϱ while $\boldsymbol{B}^\varrho$ is the destruction-operator tensor (and as we shall see later $\boldsymbol{A}^\varrho = \overline{\boldsymbol{B}}^\varrho$).

TABLE I. – *Some observable excitation processes.*

Process	Operator	Comments
1. Single-nucleon transfer	$\boldsymbol{A}^\varrho$ or $\boldsymbol{B}^\varrho$	i) Almost completely known operator. ii) Not self-adjoint. iii) Uses DWBA. iv) Needs determination of l, j.
2. Electromagnetic excitation	$\sum_{\varrho,\varrho'} c_{\varrho\varrho'}(\boldsymbol{A}^\varrho \times \boldsymbol{B}^{\varrho'})^\lambda$	i) More complex than 1 but operator almost completely known. ii) Self-adjoint. iii) Uses e.m. theory. iv) Multipole order often not easily measurable.
3. Inelastic scattering	$\sum_{\varrho,\varrho'} d_{\varrho\varrho'}(\boldsymbol{A}^\varrho \times \boldsymbol{B}^{\varrho'})^\lambda$	i) Same structure as in 2 but coefficients depend on nuclear interaction. ii) Self-adjoint. iii) Uses DWBA. iv) Multipole order may be distinguishable by angular distribution. v) There are angle-dependent sum rules.
4. Two-nucleon transfer	$\sum_{\varrho,\varrho'} e_{\varrho\varrho'}(\boldsymbol{A}^\varrho \times \boldsymbol{A}^{\varrho'})^\lambda$ $\sum_{\varrho,\varrho'} f_{\varrho\varrho'}(\boldsymbol{B}^\varrho \times \boldsymbol{B}^{\varrho'})^\lambda$	i) Coefficients depend on light-particle wavefunctions; not well known. ii) Not self-adjoint. iii) Needs DWBA. iv) λ is often not easily distinguishable.

4·6. *Some excitation processes invented by theorists.* – There is nothing to prevent one from inventing an excitation and there is plenty of room for physical intuition in inventing excitations which are *interesting*, this usually implying that the excitation strength is large and that the width is small (the strength therefore being measurable) and that the excitation has some systematic behaviour throughout a region of the periodic Table. We mention only two cases.

An important example is the single-quasi-particle excitation (in the BCS sense). This has been investigated experimentally, in particular by carrying out stripping or pick-up experiments on even-even nuclei which can be regarded as BCS ground states. Then the monopole non-energy-weighted sum rule (in the sense of the p-n formalism) gives the v^2 parameters, while the monopole linear EWSR gives the so-called quasi-particle energy. As far as the parameters are concerned, it is important to understand (we shall see it in detail later but it has been known for many years) that the experiments really determine essentially model-independent occupation numbers, which are more important than BCS parameters. The same is true in fact for the quasi-particle energy; if one makes the assumption that the ground state has seniority zero but that it is not necessarily a BCS vacuum state (which is also of seniority zero but the correct-number part of which has the special form $(\varphi_0)^{n/2}$, where φ_0 is the wave function for a single pair distributed coherently over all the orbits), we can produce in fact a formally exact result which is somewhat like the approximate quasi-particle result.

Another important excitation, the two-phonon excitation, can be discussed either in terms of quasi-particles, where the first 2^+ (two-quasi-particle) state of an even nucleus is taken as the one-phonon excitation (simple), in terms of seniority (harder), or in terms of the shell model (very much harder). In the quasi-particle picture we have simply that the one-phonon excitation operator is $\sum_{\varrho\varrho'} C_{\varrho\varrho'}(\tilde{\boldsymbol{A}}^{\varrho}\times\tilde{\boldsymbol{A}}^{\varrho'})^2=\boldsymbol{Q}^2$ say, where $\tilde{\boldsymbol{A}}^{\varrho}$ creates a ϱ-quasi-particle. Then there are three two-phonon excitation operators $(\boldsymbol{Q}^2\times\boldsymbol{Q}^2)^k$ with $k=0, 2, 4$. Studying the three two-phonon strengths then (*e.g.* by evaluating the appropriate ground-state integrals) is what one must do in order to decide whether the two-phonon excitation is physically interesting.

4·7. *The use of sum rules in direct analysis of data.* – The direct analysis of data to produce values for certain integrals has already been done for the case of stripping and pick-up reactions using the non-energy-weighted sum-rules which are monopole in the j-space, and monopole or dipole in the t-space. These analyses lead, as we shall see, to measurements of neutron and proton occupancies of orbits in the target state. There is at present a fair body of such data which could be analysed with $m>0$ sum rules but such analyses have so far not really been done. Moreover, sum rules which are nonmonopole in j, and sum rules for other processes, have not so far been used at all in the direct way. Broadly speaking, the outlook is fairly good for single-nucleon-transfer reactions but rather bad for more complex processes, at least in so far as the nonmonopole moments are concerned.

4·8. *Other uses of sum rules.* – Whenever a ground-state wave function is available, and one knows the significant parts of the Hamiltonian for the system, one can calculate the target integrals and predict the results of experiments. This seems to be an extremely profitable activity. There are also some simple cases where one is prepared to make an assumption for the ground-state function which is essentially independent of the interaction. This could happen when the ground-state is isolated from the relevant excited states by an effective energy gap. In this case one can calculate the target integrals as *explicit functions* of the interaction parameters and thus really isolate what it is that is determined. Many shell-model calculations in particular make this simple ground-state assumption and the significant shell-model results can then often be derived by a trivial operation. An example would be the shell-model calculation of the $E1$ giant resonance on closed-shell nuclei where ground-state correlation effects are ignored. And of course we emphasize that the same methods can be used for nonclosed-shell nuclei. In very many cases of course, where we know a reasonably good ground-state wave function, the final-state wave functions may be far too complex for detailed calculation. As an example, while the ^{16}O $2\hbar\omega$ states are now susceptible to a standard shell-model analysis, the corresponding problem for ^{17}O is hopelessly out of range. Thus a *shell-model* calculation for particle giant resonances with an ^{16}O target (*i.e.* ^{16}O + nucleon) of the same « quality » as the ^{16}O calculations is impossible; but a sum-rule calculation of the properties of such a resonance is quite feasible. Thus sum rules may be used to extend greatly the range of possible calculations and, along the same line, in comparing the « essential » features of various models, in deciding on such things as how to truncate vector spaces, how to estimate the effects of configurations omitted in shell-model calculations, and so on.

4·9. *The sum-rule classification of strength data.* – As the multipole order ν increases, the sum-rule analysis, for fixed m, will decrease in accuracy, in exactly the same way as the accuracy decreases with increasing ν for the P_ν expansion of any angular function whose points have inaccuracies. We cannot *eliminate* this by doing better and better experiments, for there is also the inaccuracy in the reduction of the original data to produce strengths (as for example via a DWBA analysis). If ν_{max} is small enough, this may not be serious but otherwise it will be.

More important, the reliability decreases with increasing m for, as m increases, we pay more and more attention to the components of the strength which lie at higher energies, even far above the centroid. Components below a certain magnitude cannot be detected at all, but moreover there arise rather fundamental difficulties connected with the radial functions which enter into the excitation operator, and with radial correlations. Half-way between a $1f_{\frac{7}{2}}$ and a $2f_{\frac{7}{2}}$ particle giant resonance, what are we to assume for the radial quantum number?

Besides that there is a theoretical consideration. A sum rule for high m involves a target operator $(\overline{\boldsymbol{T}}^{\lambda} \times (H)^m \times \boldsymbol{T}^{\lambda})^{\nu}$ which would appear to be extremely sensitive to high-order correlations in the target. It would be naive to argue that we can thus measure such correlations. All experience has been that such an argument is wrong. Instead we would say that such operators make far too severe a demand on the model wave functions in terms of which we try to learn about nuclear structure and as a result they are without interest. This reinforces the argument that high m is uninteresting; at the same time it reminds us of a defect in model wave functions—they promise more in the way of particle correlations than they can really deliver.

It may be of course that we can, by sum rules, « use up » all the data which are available before things deteriorate; this could well happen if we are studying low-lying excitations, such things for example as the $f_{\frac{7}{2}}$ particle strength with $f_{\frac{7}{2}}$-shell targets (it would of course be meaningless to convert 10 pieces of data into 100 integrals by taking higher and higher m).

In the general case we must however expect that sum rules will deteriorate and become unusable as ν and m increase. We believe that this is not a flaw in the sum-rule method of analysis but that, on the contrary, exhibiting this behaviour is a major advantage of the sum-rule classification of data. The argument follows.

4·10. *On comparison of experiment and calculation.* – We have converted the energy and angular excitation spectrum into a set of target integrals defined by the parameters ν, m. Since a target integral $\langle x\Gamma \| (\bar{\boldsymbol{T}}^{\lambda} \times (H)^m \times \boldsymbol{T}^{\lambda})^{\nu} \| x\Gamma \rangle$ is given by a linear combination of all the excitation strengths we see that the (ν, m) classification is, in a real sense, the opposite of the point-by-point classification of the data in which the strengths for each level are considered separately. There arises now a vague and difficult but none the less important question. The question is: what is the proper way to compare experimental data with theoretical calculations? The data that we have in mind refer to strengths, energies and angular momenta, so that we exclude from consideration great masses of data that do not fall into these categories.

The conventional way of making a comparison has involved a « microscopic » fitting of the data. One calculates model wave functions and uses them to calculate those quantities which have been observed; then the comparison is made.

One major difficulty with this process is that it is hard to know what is a reasonable criterion for comparison. Suppose that a measurement finds two close levels which are fairly strong, while calculation gives only one which is very strong. Or suppose that measurement gives two levels, each of which is strong for one process and weak for another, while calculation gives two levels one of which is strong for both, the other being weak for both. Are we supposed to feel contented in either or both of these situations? There are obviously many more complex examples.

We are inclined to argue as follows. The sum-rule classification uses the same data as the « microscopic » level-by-level classification and therefore contains the same information. If the sum rules deteriorate as ν and m increase, this implies that the complete set of strength data in question contains both useful and useless elements; an attempt to fit all of it may lead one badly astray. And indeed if our point of view is the correct one an attempt to fit even *some* of the pieces of data may be the wrong thing. We would argue that the proper thing is to fit those combinations of the data represented by the low-order sum rules.

4'11. *The nature of sum rules.* – One often likes to think of sum rules as exact and one stresses that, as we shall sometimes do, by talking about « model-independent » sum rules. This actually does not seem to be the most profitable way of thinking, because a sum rule is useless unless the separate terms in the sum can place themselves in evidence in the appropriate experiments. This does not really happen with « exact » sum rules because a part of the strength will always be mixed into some kind of background, while another part may involve processes which are well outside our domain of interest (for example pion production at higher energies if we are studying the low-lying resonances in nuclear photodisintegration). Except then for imposing a lower limit on the total strength or the excitation energy, the exact sum rule is useless. If on the other hand we think of the sum rules as existing in the domain of models we may be much better off, for the model may give us a formal mechanism for eliminating the strength which we do not know how to deal with; for example with a harmonic-oscillator shell model the $E1$ photodisintegration involves only the $1\hbar\omega$ excitations. If the model sum rules turn out to be violated we conclude that the model must be extended and we have then a program for action.

5. – Explicit multipole representations.

5'1. *Introduction.* – So far the only property of the operators and wave functions involved which we have found necessary to specify is the over-all angular momentum. To make further progress we must specify something about their internal structure. We wish to do this however paying full attention to the tensorial nature of this structure, and this implies naturally that we shall describe it in terms of spherical orbits ϱ, or in other words that we shall use a shell-model *representation*. Just this fact does not at all imply however that we are restricting ourselves to conventional shell-model problems and abandoning the more general procedures.

We shall of course use a second-quantized formalism (*), and thus a compact way of describing our activities is to say that we are considering the properties

(*) In Sect. 5'11 we discuss the relationship between this and the configuration-space formalism.

of second-quantized spherical tensors. Besides all the minor and major advantages that arise from using second-quantization methods, there is an additional one which is of major importance in any kind of explicit generalized-spectroscopy calculations; that is the factoring of symmetrical n-body operators into parts depending on various orbits. Without this factoring, which has no visible counterpart in a non-second-quantized formalism, the explicit construction of a system for really complex spectroscopy would be immensely more difficult and, so far as one can now see, the really large calculations which are now beginning to be done would not be feasible.

5'2. *Creation and destruction tensors.* – Following the usual procedure of second-quantization, there underlies the whole formalism a complete set of single-particle functions ψ^{ϱ}_{μ} where of course ψ^{ϱ} is a tensor of rank ϱ. Then if A^{ϱ}_{μ} be the operator which makes a particle in orbit ϱ, we see by acting with $\boldsymbol{A}^{\varrho}$ on the (scalar) vacuum that $\boldsymbol{A}^{\varrho}$ is a tensor of the indicated rank. The destruction tensor $\boldsymbol{B}^{\varrho}$ is related to $\boldsymbol{A}^{\varrho}$ in that they are essentially adjoints of each other. Taking note of the result for the double adjoint, eq. (3.9), we can define

$$\boldsymbol{B}^{\varrho} = (-1)^{2\varrho}\overline{\boldsymbol{A}}^{\varrho}, \tag{5.1}$$

and then

$$\boldsymbol{A}^{\varrho} = \overline{\boldsymbol{B}}^{\varrho}. \tag{5.2}$$

The signature $(-1)^{2\varrho}$ depends on the representation (j, jt, etc.) but not otherwise on ϱ.

It now follows easily (see Sect. **3**) that the components of these tensors may be related to the conventional a, $a^{\dagger}$ operators by

$$A^{\varrho}_{\mu} = a^{\dagger}_{\varrho\mu}\,, \qquad B^{\varrho}_{\mu} = (-1)^{\varrho+\mu} a_{\varrho,-\mu}\,, \tag{5.3}$$

and then the standard commutation rules, transcribed in terms of the tensors, become

$$\left\{\begin{array}{l} [\boldsymbol{A}^{\varrho}, \boldsymbol{B}^{\varrho'}]^{\nu}_{+} \equiv (\boldsymbol{A}^{\varrho}\times \boldsymbol{B}^{\varrho'})^{\nu} + (-1)^{\varrho+\varrho'-\nu}(\boldsymbol{B}^{\varrho'}\times \boldsymbol{A}^{\varrho})^{\nu} = [\varrho]^{\frac{1}{2}}\delta_{\varrho\varrho'}\delta_{\nu 0}\,, \\ [\boldsymbol{A}^{\varrho}, \boldsymbol{A}^{\varrho'}]^{\nu}_{+} = 0 = [\boldsymbol{B}^{\varrho}, \boldsymbol{B}^{\varrho'}]^{\nu}_{+}\,, \\ (\boldsymbol{A}^{\varrho}\times \boldsymbol{A}^{\varrho})^{\Gamma} = 0 = (\boldsymbol{B}^{\varrho}\times \boldsymbol{B}^{\varrho})^{\Gamma} \quad \text{if} \quad (-1)^{2\varrho-\Gamma} = +1\,, \end{array}\right. \tag{5.4}$$

and the number operator, by the same procedure, becomes

$$n_{\text{op}} = \sum_{\varrho} n_{\text{op}}(\varrho) = \sum_{\varrho} [\varrho]^{\frac{1}{2}} (\boldsymbol{A}^{\varrho}\times \boldsymbol{B}^{\varrho})^{0}. \tag{5.5}$$

Note once again the geometrical phase which enters into the $\boldsymbol{A}^{\varrho}$, $\boldsymbol{B}^{\varrho'}$ anticommutators.

The fundamental d.b.m.e. for the $\boldsymbol{A}^\varrho$, $\boldsymbol{B}^\varrho$ operators are easily found to be

$$\langle\varrho\|\boldsymbol{A}^\varrho\|0\rangle = \langle 0\|\boldsymbol{B}^\varrho\|\varrho\rangle = [\varrho]^{\frac{1}{2}}, \tag{5.6}$$

where $|\varrho\rangle$ is the properly normalized one-particle state whose μ-component is simply $A^\varrho_\mu|0\rangle$.

Consider now the fact that creating a ϱ-particle is equivalent to destroying a ϱ-hole; thus we may regard $\boldsymbol{A}^\varrho$ as the *destruction* tensor for a ϱ-hole while $\boldsymbol{B}^\varrho$ is then essentially the hole *creation* tensor. Holes being also fermions, we wish to preserve the adjoint relationship and the commutation rules. It is easy to verify that we succeed in this by identifying

$$\boldsymbol{A}^\varrho \equiv \overline{\boldsymbol{B}}^\varrho = \boldsymbol{B}^\varrho(h)\,, \qquad (-1)^{2\varrho}\boldsymbol{B}^\varrho \equiv \overline{\boldsymbol{A}}^\varrho = \boldsymbol{A}^\varrho(h)\,, \tag{5.7}$$

the $n(\varrho)$ operator equation then becoming

$$n_{\text{op}}(\varrho) = [\varrho] - n_{\text{op}}(\varrho\text{-hole})\,, \tag{5.8}$$

as it obviously must. It might be noted that the hole $\rightleftharpoons$ particle transformation when carried out twice, does not necessarily give us back the original operators. We find instead that

$$\boldsymbol{A}^\varrho\{h(h)\} = (-1)^{2\varrho}\boldsymbol{A}^\varrho, \tag{5.9}$$

and similarly for $\boldsymbol{B}^\varrho$, a minus sign then entering when we use a nonisobaric-spin formalism.

In the p-n formalism (in which the protons and neutrons belong to separate fields), there are of course separate proton and neutron operators. Every operator of the proton system then *commutes* (not « anticommutes ») with every operator of the neutron system. We shall for the most part derive results for a single fermion field (which may of course involve protons and neutrons if we use an isobaric-spin formalism) and will later demonstrate by example the simple modifications needed for the p-n formalism.

5'3. *Single particle unit tensors and the expansion of a one-body operator.* – Considering now the more general operator $(\boldsymbol{A}^\varrho\times\boldsymbol{B}^{\varrho'})^\nu$, we note that this is the representation of a symmetrical one-body operator of rank ν which promotes a particle from orbit ϱ' to orbit ϱ. In one-body states its only nonvanishing matrix element is then $\langle\varrho\|(\boldsymbol{A}^\varrho\times\boldsymbol{B}^{\varrho'})^\nu\|\varrho'\rangle$. To evaluate this matrix element we use the intermediate-state expansion (eq. (3.22)). Since the only intermediate state is the vacuum, for which $\Gamma_1=0$ we have

$$\langle\varrho\|(\boldsymbol{A}^\varrho\times\boldsymbol{B}^{\varrho'})^\nu\|\varrho'\rangle = (-1)^{\varrho+\varrho'-\nu}\,U(\varrho\varrho\varrho'\varrho':0\nu)\langle\varrho\|\boldsymbol{A}^\varrho\|0\rangle\langle 0\|\boldsymbol{B}^{\varrho'}\|\varrho'\rangle\,. \tag{5.10}$$

Taking the vacuum-one-particle d.b.m.e. from eq. (5.6) we have then

$$\langle\varrho_1\|(\boldsymbol{A}^{\varrho}\times\boldsymbol{B}^{\varrho'})^{\nu}\|\varrho_2\rangle=[\nu]^{\frac{1}{2}}\delta_{\varrho_1\varrho}\delta_{\varrho_2\varrho'}\,,\tag{5.11}$$

from which, as discussed later in (Sect. **5**·11), we can infer that $[\nu]^{-\frac{1}{2}}(\boldsymbol{A}^{\varrho}\times\boldsymbol{B}^{\varrho'})^{\nu}$ is the second-quantized representation of the (symmetrical) single-particle unit tensor introduced long ago by RACAH. We have

$$\sum_i \boldsymbol{u}^{\nu}_{\varrho\varrho'}(i)\Rightarrow\mathcal{U}^{\nu}_{\varrho\varrho'}\equiv[\nu]^{-\frac{1}{2}}(\boldsymbol{A}^{\varrho}\times\boldsymbol{B}^{\varrho'})^{\nu},\tag{5.12}$$

and we note for this case the factoring of which we have spoken above.

It is clear that any symmetrical one-body operator of rank ν can be expanded as a (ϱ,ϱ') sum of these operators; specifically we have (where, in a particle-numbered representation, $\boldsymbol{T}^{\nu}=\sum_i \boldsymbol{t}^{\nu}(i)$) that

$$\boldsymbol{T}^{\nu}=\sum_{\varrho,\varrho'}\langle\varrho\|\boldsymbol{t}^{\nu}\|\varrho'\rangle\cdot\mathcal{U}^{\nu}_{\varrho\varrho'}\,,\tag{5.13}$$

and this is the general expansion of a one-body operator of rank ν (specifying the rank is of course no real restriction) in terms of the complete set of such operators $\mathcal{U}^{\nu}_{\varrho\varrho'}$. It is commonplace that an operator is specified once we know all its matrix elements in some representation. The expansion given here makes this entirely explicit for a one-body operator. The more general case comes later.

The number-operator equation given above is an example of this expansion; others, in a (jt) formalism, are

$$\tag{5.14}\left\{\begin{aligned}
&\boldsymbol{J}=\sum_{\varrho}\{j(j+1)[\varrho]\}^{\frac{1}{2}}\mathcal{U}^{10}_{\varrho\varrho}\,,\\
&\boldsymbol{T}=\frac{1}{2}\sum_{\varrho}\{3[\varrho]\}^{\frac{1}{2}}\mathcal{U}^{01}_{\varrho\varrho}\,,\\
&\sum_i \boldsymbol{j}(i)\boldsymbol{t}(i)=\frac{1}{2}\sum_{\varrho}\{3j(j+1)[\varrho]\}^{\frac{1}{2}}\mathcal{U}^{11}_{\varrho\varrho}\,,\\
&\frac{\boldsymbol{\mu}}{\mu_0}=\frac{1}{2}\sum_{\varrho}\left\{1+(g_{\text{n}}+g_{\text{p}}-1)\frac{(-1)^{l+\frac{1}{2}-j}}{[l]}\right\}\cdot\{j(j+1)[\varrho]\}^{\frac{1}{2}}\mathcal{U}^{10}_{\varrho\varrho}-\\
&\qquad-\frac{\sqrt{3}}{2}\sum_{\varrho}\left\{1-(g_{\text{n}}-g_{\text{p}}+1)\frac{(-1)^{l+\frac{1}{2}-j}}{[l]}\right\}\{j(j+1)[\varrho]\}^{\frac{1}{2}}\mathcal{U}^{11}_{\varrho\varrho}+\\
&\qquad\qquad+\text{terms off-diagonal in }\varrho\,,
\end{aligned}\right.$$

while in a j formalism we have *e.g.*

$$\boldsymbol{J}=\sum_{j}\{j(j+1)[j]\}^{\frac{1}{2}}\mathcal{U}^{1}_{jj}\,,\tag{5.15}$$

and, in an l, s, t representation, using harmonic-oscillator radial functions, we have for the center-of-mass co-ordinate of the nucleus

$$\boldsymbol{R} = 2\sum_{\substack{n'l'\\n,l}}\left\{-\sqrt{\frac{(l+1)(2n+2l+1)}{2\alpha}}\,\delta_{n'n}\delta_{l',l+1} - \sqrt{\frac{ln}{\alpha}}\,\delta_{n',n+1}\delta_{l',l-1} + \right. \tag{5.16}$$
$$\left. + \sqrt{\frac{(l+1)(n-1)}{\alpha}}\,\delta_{n',n-1}\delta_{l',l+1} + \sqrt{\frac{l(2n+2l-1)}{2\alpha}}\,\delta_{n'n}\delta_{l',l-1}\right\}\mathcal{U}^{100}_{n\,l;n'l'}\,,$$

where the radial quantum number (which we write here as n) corresponds to the orbit ordering $1s$, $1p$, $1d$, $2s$, ..., and the parameter α is defined by the Gaussian factor in the single-particle wave functions which is $\exp[-\frac{1}{2}\alpha r^2]$. For the center-of-mass momentum operator $\boldsymbol{P}$ multiply the first two terms in eq. (5.16) by $i\alpha$, the last two terms by $-i\alpha$, this last result following from the standard correspondence

$$\langle\varrho'\|\boldsymbol{p}\|\varrho\rangle = \pm i\alpha\langle\varrho'\|\boldsymbol{r}\|\varrho\rangle\,, \tag{5.17}$$

where the $(+)$ applies when ϱ' has a higher harmonic-oscillator energy than ϱ.

There are several ways in which we can think about the operators. From eq. (5.15) it is clear that we can regard $\{j(j+1)[j]\}^{\frac{1}{2}}\mathcal{U}^{1}_{jj}$ as the « partial angular-momentum operator », partial in the sense that it measures the contribution to the total angular momentum from the particles in the single orbit (n, l, j) (which as usual we abbreviate as j). Then the operators $\mathcal{U}^{\nu}_{\varrho\varrho'}$ may be thought of as the « partial multipole moment » operators of the system, the nondiagonal ones entering because, for example, a quadrupole-moment operator is not diagonal in orbit. The single-particle radial dependences are not contained in the operators, these entering instead in the one-body matrix elements which come into the expansion of a general one-body operator (only in the last example above is there a radial dependence). We shall see later how target matrix elements of the orbit-diagonal operators $\mathcal{U}^{\nu}_{\varrho\varrho}$ can be determined by experiment and shall discuss their relationship to the electromagnetic moments.

Alternatively the complete set of operators, $\mathcal{U}^{\nu}_{\varrho\varrho'}$, can be regarded as giving a spherical-orbit operator representation of the single-particle density matrix. Or again, using the hole-particle relationship we have

$$\mathcal{U}^{\nu}_{\varrho\varrho'} = (-1)^{2\varrho}[\nu]^{-\frac{1}{2}}(\boldsymbol{A}^{\varrho}\times\boldsymbol{A}^{\varrho'}(h))^{\nu}, \tag{5.18}$$

which for the case $\varrho\neq\varrho'$ indicates that $\mathcal{U}^{\nu}_{\varrho\varrho'}$ is the (unnormalized) elementary excitation operator for making a coupled hole-particle pair.

5·4. *Many-body state operators.* – Before developing the expansion of an operator of arbitrary complexity, we must consider the structure of many-body wave-functions. We may think of $\boldsymbol{A}^{\varrho}$ as being the one-body *state operator* in the sense that, when operating on the vacuum, it gives a normalized one-body state. Then generally to the wave function $\boldsymbol{\Psi}_x^\Gamma$ we can associate (*) $\boldsymbol{Z}_x^\Gamma$ by

$$\Psi_x^\Gamma = \boldsymbol{Z}_x^\Gamma \Psi_{\text{vac}} \,, \tag{5.19}$$

while to $\overline{\boldsymbol{\Psi}}_x^\Gamma$ there then corresponds $\overline{\boldsymbol{Z}}_x^\Gamma$. In this notation x will stand for all the quantum numbers except the over-all angular momenta, states which differ only in x being understood to be orthogonal; occasionally if we wish to stress the number of particles involved we may write such things as $\boldsymbol{Z}_x^\Gamma(n)$ or $\boldsymbol{Z}^\Gamma(n)$ or $\boldsymbol{Z}^\Gamma(\varrho^n)$. The operator $\boldsymbol{Z}^\Gamma$ is of course a tensor of rank Γ. $\boldsymbol{Z}^\Gamma(n)$ may be written as a linear combination of coupled products of n A-operators but for complex systems such an explicit form will not be convenient.

The orthonormalization equation for Ψ, eq. (3.11), now leads to

$$\langle(\overline{\boldsymbol{Z}}_x^\Gamma \times \boldsymbol{Z}_{x'}^{\Gamma'})^\Delta\rangle_0 = \delta_{xx'}\delta_{\Gamma\Gamma'}\delta_{\Delta 0}[\Gamma]^{\frac{1}{2}}, \tag{5.20}$$

while a d.b.m.e. for a tensor operator $\boldsymbol{P}^\nu$ becomes (eq. (3.16))

(5.21) $\langle \Psi_{x'}^{\Gamma'} \| \boldsymbol{P}^\nu \| \Psi_x^\Gamma \rangle = (-1)^{\Gamma'-\nu-\Gamma}$ 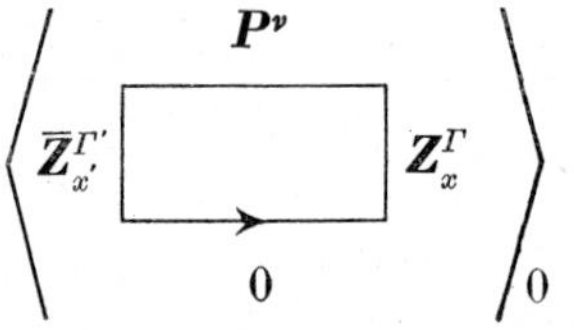 .

Here the symbol $\langle\,\rangle_0$ is to denote the expectation value in the vacuum state, *i.e.* the « *vacuum expectation value* » or *v.e.v.* The association, in this matrix element, of « wave functions » and « operators » on the same footing will be found to be of real importance.

For the one-particle case we have already agreed that $\boldsymbol{Z}^\varrho = \boldsymbol{A}^\varrho$ and thus $\overline{\boldsymbol{Z}}^\varrho = (-1)^{2\varrho}\boldsymbol{B}^\varrho$. For two equivalent particles we resolve a sign arbitrariness and then

$$\left\{\begin{aligned} \boldsymbol{Z}^\Gamma(\varrho^2) &= -\frac{1}{\sqrt{2}}(\boldsymbol{A}^\varrho \times \boldsymbol{A}^\varrho)^\Gamma, \\ \overline{\boldsymbol{Z}}^\Gamma(\varrho^2) &= +\frac{1}{\sqrt{2}}(\boldsymbol{B}^\varrho \times \boldsymbol{B}^\varrho)^\Gamma, \end{aligned}\right. \tag{5.22}$$

as we easily verify by evaluating the normalization v.e.v.

Because of the number of possible couplings and the complexities of the v.e.v. involved it is hardly practical to extend this direct method of constructing Z

(*) We use a different symbol for the state operator than for the wave function in order to avoid confusion when one wishes to use a configuration representation for Ψ. The state operator is not uniquely defined by (5.19) but if we agree also that for n particles its general form is $(A)^n$ the arbitrariness disappears.

operators for particles in the same shell to more than say three or perhaps four particles; instead one uses an inductive (or fractional-parentage) procedure.

Coupling together completely inequivalent groups (groups with no orbit in common) is simpler, for the state operator of one group, and its adjoint as well, essentially (*) commute with the operators for the other group. It is easy to see then that coupling of the state operators for two such inequivalent groups produces a properly normalized state operator, in sharp contrast to what happens when we couple equivalent state operators. Formally this comes about because the normalization v.e.v. in the first case factors into a product of two such, one for each group. If

$$\boldsymbol{Z}^{\Gamma} = (\boldsymbol{Z}^{\Gamma_1}_{x_1} \times \boldsymbol{Z}^{\Gamma_2}_{x_2})^{\Gamma} \quad \text{then} \quad \bar{\boldsymbol{Z}}^{\Gamma} = (-1)^{\Gamma_1+\Gamma_2-\Gamma} (\bar{\boldsymbol{Z}}^{\Gamma_2}_{x_2} \times \bar{\boldsymbol{Z}}^{\Gamma_1}_{x_1})^{\Gamma}$$

and

$$\langle (\bar{\boldsymbol{Z}}^{\Gamma} \times \boldsymbol{Z}^{\Gamma})^0 \rangle_0 = (-1)^{\Gamma_1+\Gamma_2-\Gamma}$$

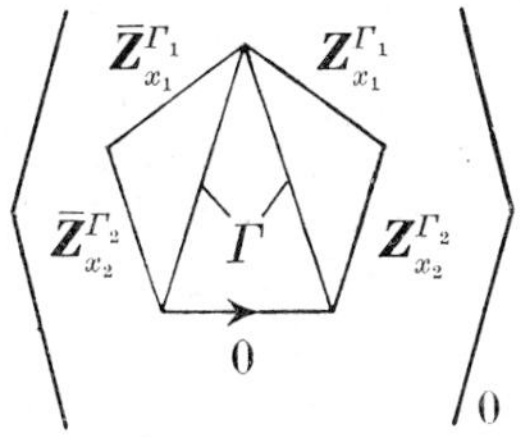

$$= (-1)^{\Gamma_1+\Gamma_2-\Gamma} \sum_{\lambda} U(\Gamma_2\Gamma_1\Gamma_2\Gamma_1 : \Gamma\lambda)$$

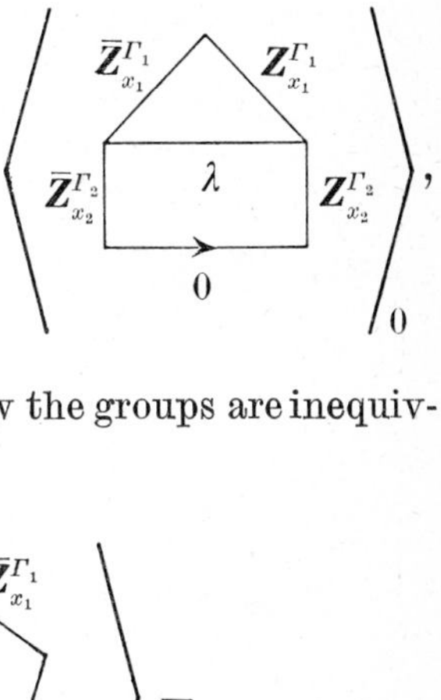

where we have made an elementary recoupling. If now the groups are inequivalent we have that

(5.23)

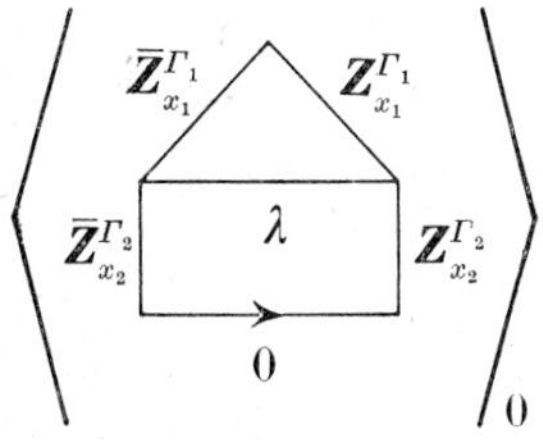

$$= (-1)^{\lambda}$$

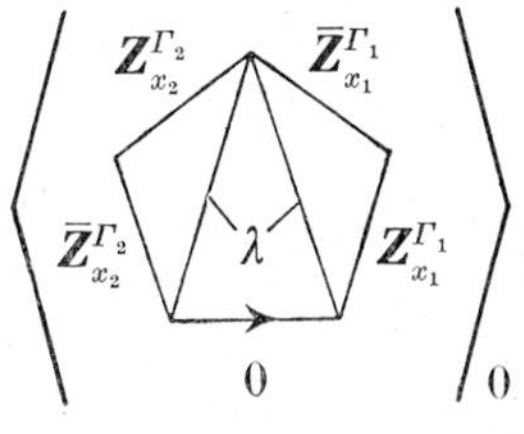

$$= \delta_{\lambda 0} \langle (\bar{\boldsymbol{Z}}^{\Gamma_2}_{x_2} \times \boldsymbol{Z}^{\Gamma_2}_{x_2})^0 \rangle_0 \cdot \langle (\bar{\boldsymbol{Z}}^{\Gamma_1}_{x_1} \times \boldsymbol{Z}^{\Gamma_1}_{x_1})^0 \rangle_0 = \delta_{\lambda 0} [\Gamma_1 \Gamma_2]^{\frac{1}{2}},$$

(*) By « essentially commutes » we mean either commutes or anticommutes according to the numbers of particles involved in the two groups. We shall sometimes drop the qualifying « essentially » and then will speak of « commuting » even though the appropriate operation may be anticommutation.

and then

$$\langle(\bar{Z}^{\Gamma}\times Z^{\Gamma})^{0}\rangle_{0}=[\Gamma]^{\frac{1}{2}}, \tag{5.24}$$

indicating that the state operator is properly normalized. We have written this rather trivial and obvious derivation as a prototype of a whole class of such derivations which rely on the factoring of the v.e.v. We have already encountered this factoring in Sect. **3**.

As a simple consequence we have for two particles in different orbits

$$\begin{cases} Z^{\Gamma}(\varrho_r,\varrho_s)\equiv Z^{\Gamma}(r,s)=-(A^{\varrho_r}\times A^{\varrho_s})^{\Gamma}. \\ \bar{Z}^{\Gamma}(\varrho_r,\varrho_s)\equiv \bar{Z}^{\Gamma}(r,s)=+(B^{\varrho_r}\times B^{\varrho_s})^{\Gamma}, \end{cases} \qquad (r\neq s), \tag{5.25}$$

and generally

$$\begin{cases} Z^{\Gamma}(r,s)=-\zeta_{rs}(A^{\varrho_r}\times A^{\varrho_s})^{\Gamma}, & \zeta_{rs}=1 \quad \text{if } r\neq s, \\ \bar{Z}^{\Gamma}(r,s)=+\zeta_{rs}(B^{\varrho_r}\times B^{\varrho_s})^{\Gamma}, & =1/\sqrt{2} \quad \text{if } r=s. \end{cases} \tag{5.26}$$

We introduce the necessary minus sign here in the state operator rather than its adjoint because, as will be shown later, a complete one-to-one correspondence between second-quantized calculations and conventional spectroscopic calculations can be maintained if we couple the *adjoint* operators in the same manner as the particle groups in the non-second-quantized procedure. This is of no importance to us here but we may as well maintain it.

Next we have for the commutators

$$(Z^{\Gamma}_{x}(n)\times Z^{\Gamma'}_{x'}(n'))^{\Lambda}-(-1)^{n\cdot n'+\Gamma+\Gamma'-\Lambda}(Z^{\Gamma'}_{x'}(n')\times Z^{\Gamma}_{x}(n))^{\Lambda}=0\,, \tag{5.27}$$

and similarly for two adjoint operators, where the $(-1)^{n\cdot n'}$ phase may be called the *Pauli phase*. In contrast, we have that the corresponding commutators for one Z and one $\bar{Z}$ operator do not in general vanish. When they do we may describe the two operators as being *inequivalent*, thereby generalizing the notion of inequivalence. If two operators have no orbit in common they are of course inequivalent but they also may be *partially inequivalent* (*i.e* with the commutators vanishing for some values of the coupling), or even *fully inequivalent*, because of their interior structure. The generalized definition, it should be noted, is representation-independent.

We turn now to the fractional-parentage method of representing the state operator for a complex system. Conventional spectroscopy in fact is dominated by the fractional-parentage method in which one calculates things by making a kind of Fourier expansion (expanding an n-particle state in terms of a particle coupled to the various $(n-1)$-particle states). For many purposes this is not at all the best way to proceed, but it is none the less an important one.

Consider first the single-particle fractional-parentage expansion. The operator $(\boldsymbol{B}^{\varrho}\times\boldsymbol{Z}_x^{\Gamma}(n))^{\Gamma_1}$ is an (unnormalized) $(n-1)$-particle state operator and may therefore be expanded in any complete set of such operators. From our general expansion of an excitation (eq. (3.13)) we have (where $+$ is for n odd)

$$(\boldsymbol{B}^{\varrho},\boldsymbol{Z}_x^{\Gamma}(n))_{\pm}^{\Gamma_1}=\frac{(-1)^{\Gamma_1-\varrho-\Gamma}}{[\Gamma_1]^{\frac{1}{2}}}\sum_y\langle n-1,\,y\Gamma_1\|\boldsymbol{B}^{\varrho}\|nx\Gamma\rangle\boldsymbol{Z}_y^{\Gamma_1}(n-1)\,. \tag{5.28}$$

This equation is clearly the general one-particle fractional-parentage expansion, written for states of arbitrary complexity. We can just as easily make an expansion in terms of the $(n+1)$-particle states and have then

$$(\boldsymbol{A}^{\varrho}\times\boldsymbol{Z}_x^{\Gamma}(n))^{\Gamma_1}=\frac{(-1)^{\Gamma_1-\varrho-\Gamma}}{[\Gamma_1]^{\frac{1}{2}}}\sum_y\langle n+1,\,y\Gamma_1\|\boldsymbol{A}^{\varrho}\|nx\Gamma\rangle\boldsymbol{Z}_y^{\Gamma_1}(n+1)\,. \tag{5.29}$$

Starting with eqs. (5.28), (5.29) one can, by simple coupling operations. construct further equations giving for example the expansion of hole-particle or two-particle excitations in terms of one-particle excitations. When one needs such things they are easy to produce and we shall not bother now to write them, One simple example however is

(5.30) $\quad(n_{\text{op}}(\varrho),\boldsymbol{Z}_x^{\Gamma}(n))=[\Gamma]^{-\frac{1}{2}}\sum_{y,\Gamma_1}\langle n-1,\,y\Gamma_1\|\boldsymbol{B}^{\varrho}\|nx\Gamma\rangle$ 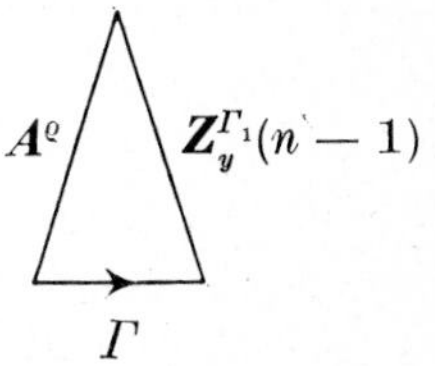 ,

from which one infers the following relationships between the usual fractional-parentage coefficients and the $\boldsymbol{A}^{\varrho}$ and $\boldsymbol{B}^{\varrho}$ d.b.m.e.:

(5.31) $\quad\langle nx\Gamma|n-1,\,y\Gamma_1+\varrho\rangle=\{n[\Gamma]\}^{-\frac{1}{2}}(-1)^{\Gamma_1+\varrho-\Gamma}\langle n-1,\,y\Gamma_1\|\boldsymbol{B}^{\varrho}\|nx\Gamma\rangle=$

$=\{n[\Gamma]\}^{-\frac{1}{2}}\langle nx\Gamma\|\boldsymbol{A}_{\varrho}\|n-1,\,y\Gamma_1\rangle=\dfrac{(-1)^{2\varrho}}{\sqrt{n[\Gamma]}}$ 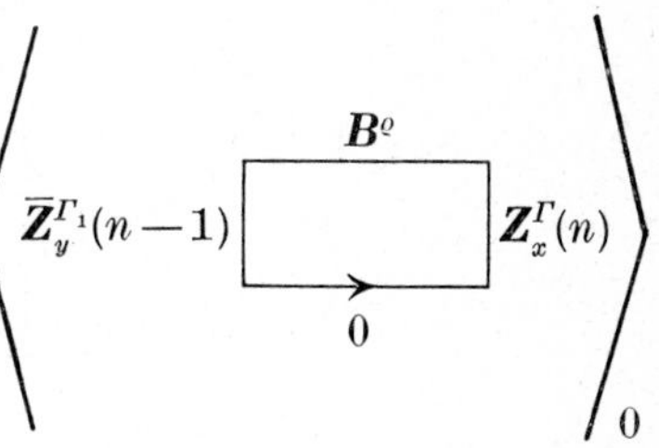 $=$

$=\dfrac{(-1)^{\Gamma_1+\varrho-\Gamma}}{\sqrt{n[\Gamma]}}$ 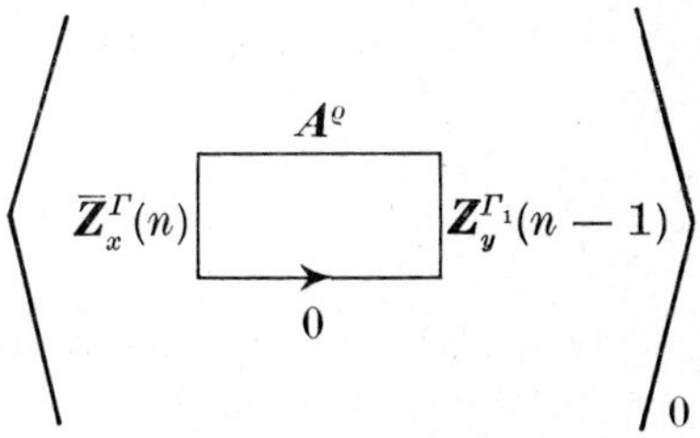 .

Hole-particle extensions of these results are given later (eq. (5.53)). A more rigorous derivation is outlined in Sect. 5'11.

There is no reason why we should restrict ourselves to one-particle fractional-parentage expansions. We leave it as an exercise to carry out the most general fractional-parentage expansion and to show in particular that, for the decomposition of a system into two fragments ($n \to n_1 + n_2$), the fractional-parentage coefficient is, to within an arbitrary phase,

$$\langle nx\Gamma|(n_1 y_1 \Gamma_1) + (n_2 y_2 \Gamma_2)\rangle = \left\{\frac{n_1!\, n_2!}{n![\Gamma]}\right\}^{\frac{1}{2}} \langle(\overline{\boldsymbol{Z}}^{\Gamma_2}_{y_2}(n_2) \times \overline{\boldsymbol{Z}}^{\Gamma_1}_{y_1}(n_1) \times \boldsymbol{Z}^{\Gamma}_{x}(n))^0\rangle_0 \,. \tag{5.32}$$

The n-dependent factors occur here, just as they do in eq. (5.31), because the fractional-parentage coefficient is conventionally defined in a physically unreasonable way, corresponding to separating off certain numbered particles.

5'5. *The expansion of a many-body operator* (*). – An n-body operator has the properties i) that its matrix elements vanish between states with $m < n$ particles, ii) that its matrix elements between m-particle states with $m > n$ are determined by its n-body matrix elements and iii) its general form may always be written as $(A)^n(B)^n$, taking of course appropriate couplings and appropriate linear combinations.

Without loss of generality we can assume that the n-body operator is a tensor of rank ν. Thus we can make the expansion (whose justification becomes evident as we proceed) in terms of « normalized » n-body operators

$$\boldsymbol{Q}^{\nu} = \sum_{\substack{\Lambda\Lambda' \\ yy'}} C^{\Lambda\Lambda'}_{yy'} (\boldsymbol{Z}^{\Lambda}_{y}(n) \times \overline{\boldsymbol{Z}}^{\Lambda'}_{y'}(n))^{\nu} \,, \tag{5.33}$$

where the summation is over the complete sets of *orthonormal* state operators $\boldsymbol{Z}^{\Lambda}_{y}(n)$ and $\overline{\boldsymbol{Z}}^{\Lambda'}_{y'}(n)$.

Taking matrix elements and using the result of eq. (5.21) we have

$$\langle nx\Gamma \| \boldsymbol{Q}^{\nu} \| nx'\Gamma' \rangle = \sum_{\substack{yy' \\ \Lambda\Lambda'}} (-1)^{\Gamma-\nu-\Gamma'} C^{\Lambda\Lambda'}_{yy'} \tag{5.34}$$

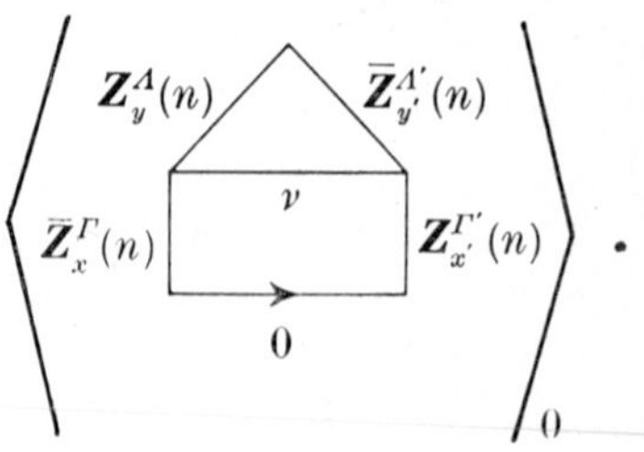

(*) By « many-body operator » we imply a number-conserving operator as distinct from a « many-body state operator ».

But now on carrying out the obvious recoupling in the right-hand integrand, we observe that the only intermediate state is the vacuum. Then, as in previous cases, the v.e.v. factors into two orthonormalization v.e.v.'s, giving a result $\delta_{xy}\delta_{x'y'}[\Gamma\Gamma']^{\frac{1}{2}}$. Thus we have

(5.35) $$C^{\Gamma\Gamma'}_{xx'} = (-1)^{2\Gamma'}[\nu]^{-\frac{1}{2}}\langle nx\Gamma\|\boldsymbol{Q}^\nu\|nx'\Gamma'\rangle\,,$$

the general expansion for an n-body operator of rank ν then becoming

(5.36) $$\boldsymbol{Q}^\nu = \sum_{\substack{xx'\\ \Gamma\Gamma'}}(-1)^{2\Gamma'}[\nu]^{-\frac{1}{2}}\langle nx\Gamma\|\boldsymbol{Q}^\nu\|nx'\Gamma'\rangle\big(\boldsymbol{Z}^\Gamma_x(n)\times\overline{\boldsymbol{Z}}^{\Gamma'}_{x'}(n)\big).$$

It is easily verified that for a one-body operator this equation gives back the result of eq. (5.13). We shall be especially concerned, in Sect. **5·7**, with the application of this theorem to the expansion of the general shell-model Hamiltonian. Note too that in an obvious sense the n-body operators $\big(\boldsymbol{Z}^\Gamma_x(n)\times\overline{\boldsymbol{Z}}^{\Gamma'}_{x'}(n)\big)^\nu$ form a set of orthonormal n-body interaction operators of rank ν.

5·6. *Hole ⇌ particle transforms.* – We have mentioned that holes and particles can be considered on the same footing and we have given the simple relationships between the fundamental particle and hole operators (eq. (5.7)). It is clear then that we can deal equally well with holes as with particles. However one often must be able to make h ⇌ p transformations at various stages of a calculation; or, on the other hand, we may wish to relate the properties of two systems which are connected by such a transform.

Writing the basic commutation rule (eq. (5.4)) as

(5.37) $$\mathcal{U}^\nu_{\varrho\varrho'} + (-1)^{\varrho-\varrho'-\nu}\mathcal{U}^\nu_{\varrho'\varrho}(h) = [\varrho]^{\frac{1}{2}}\delta_{\varrho\varrho'}\delta_{\nu 0}\,,$$

we can pretty well guess that, for a single shell, the n-particle d.b.m.e. for $\mathcal{U}^\nu_{\varrho\varrho}$ with $\nu\neq 0$ may be related to the corresponding n-hole d.b.m.e. by a sign $-(-1)^\nu$, provided that the wave-function phases are appropriately chosen. This is correct but not enough, for we wish to consider more complex operators and systems.

Suppose that we are considering the states for n particles distributed among N single-particle states. Realizing that the particle and hole operators for the system form two separate equivalent sets with separate vacua but with the same commutation rules, we can write that for any operator Q, a function of the various $\boldsymbol{A}$ and $\boldsymbol{B}$ operators, we have

(5.38) $$\langle Q(\boldsymbol{A},\boldsymbol{B})\rangle_0 = \langle Q\big(\boldsymbol{A}(h),\boldsymbol{B}(h)\big)\rangle_{0_h}\,,$$

where $|0_h\rangle$ is the hole vacuum. But now we can relate the two systems by observing that the vacuum for one is a state of the other; in particular, since the hole-vacuum is the particle-filled state, defined say by the state operator $\boldsymbol{Z}(f)$, and since the hole operators are the adjoints of the particle operators, we have

$$\langle Q(\boldsymbol{A}, \boldsymbol{B})\rangle_0 = \langle \boldsymbol{Z}^\dagger(f) Q(\overline{\boldsymbol{A}}, \boldsymbol{B}) \boldsymbol{Z}(f)\rangle_0 \,. \tag{5.39}$$

Consider now the particular case where Q is the integrand operator for a coupled matrix element, *i.e.*

$$Q(\boldsymbol{A}, \boldsymbol{B}) = (\overline{\boldsymbol{Z}}{}^{\Gamma}_{x}(n) \times K^{\lambda}(\boldsymbol{A}, \boldsymbol{B}) \times \boldsymbol{Z}^{\Gamma'}_{x'}(n'))_0 .$$

It is left as an exercise to show that

$$\left\{\begin{array}{l} \boldsymbol{Z}^{\Gamma}_{x}(n) \overset{\boldsymbol{A}\to\overline{\boldsymbol{A}}}{\Rightarrow} (-1)^{n(n-1)/2} \overline{\boldsymbol{Z}}{}^{\Gamma}_{x}(n) \,, \\ \overline{\boldsymbol{Z}}{}^{\Gamma}_{x}(n) \overset{\boldsymbol{B}\to\overline{\boldsymbol{B}}}{\Rightarrow} (-1)^{n(n-1)/2} \overline{\overline{\boldsymbol{Z}}}{}^{\Gamma}_{x}(n) = (-1)^{(n(n-1)/2)+2\Gamma} \boldsymbol{Z}^{\Gamma}_{x}(n) \,, \end{array}\right. \tag{5.40}$$

the $(-1)^{n(n-1)/2}$ phase being that required to invert the ordering of n anticommuting objects. Using these results we have

$$\begin{aligned} \langle (\overline{\boldsymbol{Z}}{}^{\Gamma}_{x}(n) \times \boldsymbol{K}^{\lambda}(\boldsymbol{A}, \boldsymbol{B}) \times \boldsymbol{Z}^{\Gamma'}_{x'}(n'))^0\rangle_0 = \\ = (-1)^{(n(n-1)/2)+(n'(n'-1)/2)+2\Gamma} \langle \overline{\boldsymbol{Z}}(f) (\boldsymbol{Z}^{\Gamma}_{x}(n) \times \boldsymbol{K}^{\lambda}(\overline{\boldsymbol{A}}, \overline{\boldsymbol{B}}) \times \overline{\boldsymbol{Z}}{}^{\Gamma'}_{x'}(n'))^0 \boldsymbol{Z}(f)\rangle_0 \,. \end{aligned} \tag{5.41}$$

We have here implicitly assumed that the vacuum state is scalar and we may as well assume that the same is true also for the filled state (though neither of these assumptions is really necessary). Then $\boldsymbol{Z}(f)$ is scalar and $\boldsymbol{Z}^\dagger(f) = \overline{\boldsymbol{Z}}(f)$.

If now we define the state complementary to $\boldsymbol{Z}^{\Gamma}_{x}$ by the equation

$$\boldsymbol{Z}^{\Gamma}_{x_c}|0\rangle = (-1)^{n(n-1)/2} \overline{\boldsymbol{Z}}{}^{\Gamma}_{x} \boldsymbol{Z}(f)|0\rangle \,, \tag{5.42}$$

whose adjoint is

$$\langle 0|\overline{\boldsymbol{Z}}{}^{\Gamma}_{x_c} = (-1)^{(n(n-1)/2)+2\Gamma} \langle 0|\overline{\boldsymbol{Z}}(f) \boldsymbol{Z}^{\Gamma}_{x} \,, \tag{5.43}$$

then we have simply

$$\langle (\overline{\boldsymbol{Z}}{}^{\Gamma}_{x}(n) \times \boldsymbol{K}^{\lambda}(\boldsymbol{A},\boldsymbol{B}) \times \boldsymbol{Z}^{\Gamma'}_{x'}(n'))^0\rangle_0 = \langle (\overline{\boldsymbol{Z}}{}^{\Gamma}_{x_c}(N-n) \times \boldsymbol{K}^{\lambda}(\overline{\boldsymbol{A}},\overline{\boldsymbol{B}}) \times \boldsymbol{Z}^{\Gamma'}_{x'_c}(N-n'))^0\rangle_0 , \tag{5.44}$$

where N is the degeneracy of the closed-shell system and directly from eq. (5.42) we see that the complement to an n-particle state has $(N-n)$ particles. Note that eqs. (5.42), (5.43) are not valid as operator equations, since $\boldsymbol{Z}(f)$ will destroy any state except the vacuum.

The relationship between a state and its complement is pretty clear from the defining equation but let us in any case explore it a little further. The operator

$$(\boldsymbol{Z}_x^\Gamma(N-n)\times\boldsymbol{Z}_{x_c'}^{\Gamma'}(n))^\Lambda,$$

trivially vanishes unless $\Gamma=\Gamma'$, $\Lambda=0$. It has only a single nonvanishing matrix element and this connects the vacuum with the closed-shell state. Thus

$$(\boldsymbol{Z}_x^\Gamma\times\boldsymbol{Z}_{x_c'}^\Gamma)^0|0\rangle = C_{xx'}|f\rangle,$$

where

$$C_{xx'}=\langle 0|\overline{\boldsymbol{Z}}(f)(\boldsymbol{Z}_x^\Gamma\times\boldsymbol{Z}_{x_c'}^\Gamma)^0|0\rangle=(-1)^{n(n-1)/2+2\Gamma}\langle 0|(\overline{\boldsymbol{Z}}_{x_c}^\Gamma\times\boldsymbol{Z}_{x_c'}^\Gamma)^0|0\rangle=(-1)^{n(n-1)/2+2\Gamma}[\Gamma]^{\frac{1}{2}}\delta_{xx'},$$

and thus

$$(5.45)\qquad (\boldsymbol{Z}_x^\Gamma(n)\times\boldsymbol{Z}_{x_c'}^{\Gamma'}(N-n))^\Lambda=\delta_{\Gamma\Gamma'}\delta_{\Lambda 0}\delta_{xx'}(-1)^{(n(n-1)/2)+2\Gamma}[\Gamma]^{\frac{1}{2}}\boldsymbol{Z}(f)\,,$$

which has an immediate interpretation that the single-particle states which are left empty by $\boldsymbol{Z}_x^\Gamma$ are filled by $\boldsymbol{Z}_{x_c}^\Gamma$ and vice versa, the two together then producing the closed-shell state.

To demonstrate this even more explicitly, we observe that in a representation in which every single-particle state is either filled or empty, a state α and its natural complements α_c are, in the sense of the discussion following eq. (5.27), completely inequivalent; *i.e.*

$$(5.46)\qquad Z_\alpha(n)Z_{\alpha_c}^\dagger(N-n)=(-1)^n Z_{\alpha_c}^\dagger(N-n)Z_\alpha(n)\,,$$

where $(-1)^{n(N-n)}=(-1)^n$ is the obvious Pauli phase. Besides that we have

$$(5.47)\qquad \begin{cases} Z_{\alpha_c}(N-n)Z_\beta(n)=(-1)^{(n(n-1)/2)+n}\delta_{\alpha\beta}Z(f)\,,\\ Z_\beta^\dagger(n)Z_{\alpha_c}^\dagger(N-n)=(-1)^{(n(n-1)/2)+n}\delta_{\alpha\beta}Z^\dagger(f)\,,\end{cases}$$

where the phase, just as before, is included for convenience. These equations allow us to define the complement in an arbitrary representation; to $Z_x=\sum_\alpha S_{x\alpha}Z_\alpha$ there corresponds $Z_{x_c}=\sum_\alpha S_{x\alpha}Z_{\alpha_c}(N-n)$. Thus we can convert to our original angular-momentum representation. Deriving first the result that

$$(5.48)\qquad \langle 0|Z^\dagger(f)Z_\alpha(n)=(-1)^{n(n-1)/2}\langle 0|Z_{\alpha_c}^\dagger(N-n)\,,$$

and then defining

$$(5.49)\qquad (Z_{x,-\mu}^\Gamma)_c=(-1)^{\Gamma-\mu}(Z_{x_c}^\Gamma)_\mu\,,$$

one produces very easily, having started with the simple representation with single-particle occupancies 0 or 1, the general coupled results given above. The details are left as an exercise.

The result of eq. (5.44) is of course valid when we are dealing with multishell wave-functions, the hole $\rightleftharpoons$ particle transformations being applied for all the shells. But it is equally valid, as may easily be seen, when we make h $\rightleftharpoons$ p transformations only for certain shells, the other remaining unchanged, and recognition of this enables one in fact to produce in a very simple way a number of results dealing with closed-shell, and shell-shell interactions and other things like that.

We have now, even for a single shell, defined two complete sets of state operators $\boldsymbol{Z}_x^\Gamma(n)$ and $\boldsymbol{Z}_{x_c}^\Gamma(n)$ for all n. This is rather awkward and we avoid it by using $\boldsymbol{Z}_x^\Gamma(n)$ for the lower $\frac{1}{2}$-shell and $\boldsymbol{Z}_{x_c}^\Gamma(n)$ for the upper half. A difficulty does arise at the $\frac{1}{2}$-shell, for then there is a division of the vector space for $n=N/2$ into states which are self-complementary and states which undergo a sign change under the h $\rightleftharpoons$ p transformation. An analytic solution for the classification is not available except for special cases (such as the seniority representation for j^n identical particles), but the classification can be made by considering the matrix elements of one-body even-rank tensors and making use of eq. (5.51) below, in an obvious way. Once the complements have been established for single shells, the multishell complements immediately follow.

As an example, consider the matrix elements of $\mathcal{U}_{rs}^\lambda$ under a h $\rightleftharpoons$ p transformation involving both orbits. We have

$$\mathcal{U}_{rs}^\lambda=[\lambda]^{-\frac{1}{2}}(\boldsymbol{A}^r\times\boldsymbol{B}^s)^\lambda \overset{\mathrm{h}\rightleftharpoons\mathrm{p}}{\Longrightarrow}[\lambda]^{-\frac{1}{2}}(\overline{\boldsymbol{A}}^r\times\overline{\boldsymbol{B}}^s)^\lambda=\delta_{\lambda 0}\delta_{rs}[r]^{\frac{1}{2}}-(-1)^{r-s-\lambda}\mathcal{U}_{sr}^\lambda\,, \tag{5.50}$$

and thus

$$\langle nx\Gamma\|\mathcal{U}_{rs}^\lambda\|nx'\Gamma'\rangle=\delta_{\lambda 0}\delta_{rs}\delta_{xx'}\delta_{\Gamma\Gamma'}[r\Gamma]^{\frac{1}{2}}-$$
$$-(-1)^{r-s-\lambda}\langle N-n,\,x_c\Gamma\|\mathcal{U}_{sr}^\lambda\|N-n,\,x_c'\Gamma'\rangle, \tag{5.51}$$

which, for the diagonal matrix element with $r=s$, becomes a famous result due originally to Racah

$$\langle nx\Gamma\|\mathcal{U}_{rr}^\lambda\|nx\Gamma\rangle=\delta_{\lambda 0}[r\Gamma]^{\frac{1}{2}}-(-1)^\lambda\langle N-n,\,x_c\Gamma\|\mathcal{U}_{rr}^\lambda\|N-n,\,x_c\Gamma\rangle\,. \tag{5.52}$$

Note the extremely important parity distinction between the behaviour of odd-rank and even-rank tensors.

As a further and also important example, we give the h $\rightleftharpoons$ p transform results for the $\boldsymbol{A}^\varrho$ operator, writing also the relationship between the $\boldsymbol{A}^\varrho$ matrix elements and the fractional-parentage coefficients. We have

$$(5.53)\qquad \langle nx\Gamma\|\boldsymbol{A}^{\varrho}\|n-1, x'\Gamma'\rangle = (-1)^{2\varrho}\langle N-n, x_c\Gamma\|\boldsymbol{B}^{\varrho}\|N-n+1, x'_c\Gamma'\rangle =$$
$$= (-1)^{\Gamma-\varrho-\Gamma'}\langle N-n+1, x'_c\Gamma'\|\boldsymbol{A}^{\varrho}\|N-n, x_c\Gamma\rangle =$$
$$= (-1)^{\Gamma-\varrho-\Gamma'}\langle n-1, x'\Gamma'\|\boldsymbol{B}^{\varrho}\|nx\Gamma\rangle = \sqrt{n[\Gamma]}\langle nx\Gamma|n-1, x'\Gamma'+\varrho\rangle =$$
$$= (-1)^{\Gamma-\varrho-\Gamma'}\sqrt{(N-n+1)[\Gamma']}\langle N-n+1, x'_c\Gamma'|N-n, x_c\Gamma+\varrho\rangle,$$

and, as in eq. (5.31), we can give these results also in v.e.v. form.

5·7. *The Hamiltonian expansion.* – We have given in a preceding Section the general expansion of an n-body operator in terms of a set of operators with the n-body matrix elements as coefficients. We now write this explicitly for the Hamiltonian operator and then recast the result into a variety of forms which will be of value to us.

If we assume, as usual, that the interaction between nucleons is given by a two-body scalar operator, we have that H is the sum of a one-body operator (the kinetic energy) and a two-body operator (the potential energy). Then we have that

$$(5.54)\qquad H = H^{(1)} + H^{(2)} = \sum_{r,s}\varepsilon_{rs}[r]^{\frac{1}{2}}(\boldsymbol{A}^r\times\boldsymbol{B}^s)^0 + \sum_{\substack{rstu\,:\,\Gamma\\ r\leq s\\ t\leq u}}[\Gamma]^{\frac{1}{2}}W^{\Gamma}_{rstu}(\boldsymbol{Z}^{\Gamma}(rs)\times\bar{\boldsymbol{Z}}^{\Gamma}(tu))^0,$$

where, as before,

$$(5.55)\qquad \boldsymbol{Z}^{\Gamma}(rs) = -\zeta_{rs}(\boldsymbol{A}^r\times\boldsymbol{A}^s)^{\Gamma},\qquad \zeta_{rs} = 1 \text{ if } r\neq s,\quad = 1/\sqrt{2} \text{ if } r=s.$$

Here the orbits are labelled by r, s, t, u and we understand them to be ordered in some definite fashion. In the second term we restrict the summation to avoid double counting. W^{Γ}_{rstu} is the (antisymmetrized) two-body matrix element $\langle rs|H|tu\rangle_{\Gamma}$ and as shown $\boldsymbol{Z}^{\Gamma}(r, s)$ is the two-particle state operator. We are using and will continue to use an abbreviated notation where $r\equiv\varrho_r$ and, for example, $[r]=[\varrho_r]$ and so on. The $[\Gamma]^{\frac{1}{2}}$ enters because W^{Γ} is defined as an ordinary matrix element not as a d.b.m.e.

The two-body matrix elements and the one-body parameters have the following obvious symmetry properties:

$$(5.56)\qquad \begin{cases} W^{\Gamma}_{rstu} = -(-1)^{r+s-\Gamma}W^{\Gamma}_{srtu} = -(-1)^{t+u-\Gamma}W^{\Gamma}_{rsut} = +(-1)^{r+s-t-u}W^{\Gamma}_{srut}\,, \\ \varepsilon_{rs} = \varepsilon_{sr}\,. \end{cases}$$

Let us now consider the matrix element of H between two states of arbitrary complexity. Our initial purpose will be to make a distinction between the roles of the closed shells and the « active orbits » and to indicate the nature of the single-particle energies. The results will be rather obvious (and of course are well known) but our derivations will give examples of useful formal manipulations.

We are considering $\langle\Psi H\Psi'\rangle$. Suppose that each state contains a certain set (the same set) of fully-closed orbits and some « active » nucleons distributed among the other orbits. We indicate the closed shells by $r<F$, say, and the active ones by $r>F$. The state operator for Ψ is now given by

$$(5.57)\qquad \bar{\boldsymbol{Z}}^{\Gamma}_{x}=\bar{\boldsymbol{Z}}^{0}(\text{c.s.})\times\bar{\boldsymbol{Z}}^{\Gamma}_{x}(\text{a})\qquad \begin{array}{l}\text{c.s.}\equiv\text{closed shells},\\ \text{a}\ \equiv\text{active},\end{array}$$

and similarly for Ψ'. We have now that

$$(5.58)\qquad H^{(1)}\equiv\sum_{r<F}[r]\varepsilon_r+\sum_{r,s>F}\varepsilon_{rs}[r]^{\frac{1}{2}}\mathcal{U}^{0}_{rs}\,,$$

where we have written $\varepsilon_{rr}\equiv\varepsilon_r$ and, in the second term, r, s can differ only in radial quantum number.

Now for $H^{(2)}$, writing separately the closed-shell and active-nucleon interactions and the interactions between them we have that

$$(5.59)\qquad H^{(2)}=\sum_{\substack{r\le s<F\\ \Gamma}}[\Gamma]^{\frac{1}{2}}W^{\Gamma}_{rsrs}(\boldsymbol{Z}^{\Gamma}(rs)\times\bar{\boldsymbol{Z}}^{\Gamma}(rs))^{0}+$$
$$+\sum_{\substack{r<F\\ s,u>F\\ \Gamma}}[\Gamma]^{\frac{1}{2}}W^{\Gamma}_{rsru}(\boldsymbol{Z}^{\Gamma}(rs)\times\bar{\boldsymbol{Z}}^{\Gamma}(ru))^{0}+\sum_{\substack{rstu>F\\ r\le s,t\le u\\ \Gamma}}[\Gamma]^{\frac{1}{2}}W^{\Gamma}_{rstu}(\boldsymbol{Z}^{\Gamma}(rs)\times\bar{\boldsymbol{Z}}^{\Gamma}(tu))^{0}\,.$$

But on recoupling we find that

$$(5.60)\qquad (\boldsymbol{Z}^{\Gamma}(rs)\times\bar{\boldsymbol{Z}}^{\Gamma}(tu))^{0}=\zeta_{rs}\zeta_{tu}\sum_{\nu}(-1)^{r+u-\Gamma-\nu}[\nu]\,U(rstu:\Gamma\nu)(\mathcal{U}^{\nu}_{rt}\times\mathcal{U}^{\nu}_{su})^{0}-$$
$$-\delta_{st}\zeta_{rs}\zeta_{us}(-1)^{r+s-\Gamma}\left[\frac{\Gamma}{r}\right]^{\frac{1}{2}}\mathcal{U}^{0}_{ru}\,.$$

It then follows easily that, for r, $s<F$ (and for allowed Γ if $r=s$),

$$(5.61)\qquad (\boldsymbol{Z}^{\Gamma}(rs)\times\bar{\boldsymbol{Z}}^{\Gamma}(rs))^{0}\equiv(\zeta_{rs})^{2}\frac{[\Gamma]^{\frac{1}{2}}}{[r]}\cdot n_{\text{op}}(r)\left\{\frac{n_{\text{op}}(s)}{[s]}+\delta_{rs}\right\},$$

and then the closed-shell energy becomes

$$(5.62)\qquad \sum_{\substack{r<s<F\\ \Gamma}}[\Gamma]W^{\Gamma}_{rsrs}+\sum_{\substack{r<F\\ \Gamma}}[\Gamma]W^{\Gamma}_{rrrr}+\sum_{r<F}[r]\varepsilon_r.$$

But the average interaction energy between a particle in orbit r and one in a distinct orbit s, is

$$\overline{W}_{rs} = [rs]^{-1} \sum_{\Gamma} [\Gamma] W^{\Gamma}_{rsrs} , \tag{5.63}$$

while for two particles in the same orbit

$$\overline{W}_{r} = \frac{2}{[r]\{[r]-1\}} \sum_{\Gamma} [\Gamma] W^{\Gamma}_{rrrr} . \tag{5.64}$$

Then for the energy of the closed shells we have the familiar results with an obvious interpretation

$$\sum_{r<F} [r]\varepsilon_r + \sum_{r<F} \frac{[r]\{[r]-1\}}{2} \overline{W}_r + \sum_{r<s<F} [rs]\overline{W}_{rs} , \tag{5.65}$$

and to the matrix element $\langle x\Gamma|H|x'\Gamma\rangle$ we get a contribution of this value if $x = x'$, otherwise of course zero. This part of the Hamiltonian behaves like a constant.

Turning now to the part of the Hamiltonian giving the interaction between the closed shells and the active particles, we note first that $H^{(1)}$ contributes nothing while, on using eq. (5.60), we have for $r < F$, s, $u > F$,

$$(\boldsymbol{Z}^{\Gamma}(rs) \times \bar{\boldsymbol{Z}}^{\Gamma}(ru))^0 \Rightarrow [\Gamma]^{\frac{1}{2}} \frac{n_{\text{op}}(r)}{[r]} \cdot \frac{\mathcal{U}^0_{su}}{[s]^{\frac{1}{2}}} = \frac{[\Gamma]^{\frac{1}{2}}}{[s]^{\frac{1}{2}}} \mathcal{U}^0_{su} , \tag{5.66}$$

and then this part of H becomes

$$\sum_{\substack{r<F \\ s,u>F \\ \Gamma}} [\Gamma] W^{\Gamma}_{rsru} \frac{\mathcal{U}^0_{su}}{[s]^{\frac{1}{2}}} = \sum_{\substack{r<F \\ s>F}} [r] \overline{W}_{rs} n_{\text{op}}(s) + \sum_{\substack{r<F \\ s,u>F \\ s\neq u \\ \Gamma}} [\Gamma] W^{\Gamma}_{rsru} \frac{\mathcal{U}^0_{su}}{[s]^{\frac{1}{2}}} , \tag{5.67}$$

which is an effective one-body interaction.

We have now

$$H \equiv E(\text{c.s.}) + \sum_{s>F} \varepsilon'_s n_{\text{op}}(s) + \sum_{\substack{s,u>F \\ s\neq u}} \varepsilon'_{su} [s]^{\frac{1}{2}} \mathcal{U}^0_{su} + H(\text{a}) , \tag{5.68}$$

where $E(\text{c.s.})$ is the energy of the closed shells, $H(\text{a})$ the interaction energy between the active particles, and the effective single-particle parameters are

$$\begin{cases} \varepsilon'_s = \varepsilon_s + \sum_{r<F} [r] \overline{W}_{rs} , \\ \varepsilon'_{su} = \varepsilon_{su} + [s]^{-1} \sum_{\substack{r<F \\ \Gamma}} [\Gamma] W^{\Gamma}_{rsru} . \end{cases} \tag{5.69}$$

There are a few points worth noting. It was mentioned earlier that the one-body interaction comes from the kinetic energy but we have seen that the one-body parameters are renormalized by the closed-shell interactions. But also in any shell-model calculations we must imagine that there are further renormalizations produced, for example, by the necessary truncation of the vector spaces and also due to the uncertainties in the (also renormalized) two-body interaction. And in the same way the closed-shell term E(c.s.), involving as it does both the one-body and two-body interactions, is a quantity whose real significance is not clear. One must conclude then that the Hamiltonian interaction being used in shell-model calculations no longer has a simple relationship to the original kinetic and potential terms, being instead an « effective » interaction whose parameters are to be determined in one of several *ad hoc* ways.

A subtle question arises with respect to the nondiagonal one-body term. If the major effect of the interaction of an active particle with the closed shells is to produce an effective one-body potential then if we use the « best » single-particle radial functions it should be that the nondiagonal kinetic-energy terms and the corresponding two-body terms cancel each other. With this argument, which is not precise because, for example, even which shells we should take as closed is not unambiguous (consider the hole representations used later), we are given a license simply to cancel off the off-diagonal $\mathcal{U}^0_{su}$ terms against the corresponding two-body terms.

Going back for a moment to the closed-shell energy term, it should none the less be remarked that simple deductions of such things as the average energy for a shell ($\overline{W}_r$) can be made by appropriate subtractions; *e.g.* from the energies of ^{40}Ca, ^{41}Ca, ^{48}Ca we can deduce an apparently reasonable value for the average identical-particle $(f_{\frac{7}{2}})^2$ energy, and similarly in a whole host of other cases. It is hard to have *a priori* feeling of how good this kind of « binding-energy-table » physics should be, but experience is that it makes out surprisingly well.

Let us turn now to the active-particle interactions given by $H^{(2)}$. We can distinguish several kinds of terms in $H^{(2)}$ and the distinctions for some purposes are important. The classification corresponding to this in fact applies to the entire $H^{(2)}$ so that for the moment we need not restrict ourselves to the active-particle part. We have:

5'7.1. Single-orbit interactions. $r=s=t=u$. The m.e. are exclusively inside a single shell. The internal energy of a closed shell comes from this interaction.

5'7.2. Pairing-type interactions. $r=s$, $t=u$, $r\neq t$. This interaction has matrix elements which promote a pair (*not necessarily zero-coupled*) from one orbit to another.

5·7.3. Multipole type (and excitation-type) interactions. $r = t$, $s = u$, $r \neq s$. Since by recoupling of $(\boldsymbol{Z}^\Gamma(rs)\times\overline{\boldsymbol{Z}}^\Gamma(rs))^0$ we get terms $(\mathcal{U}^\nu_{rr}\times\mathcal{U}^\nu_{ss})^0$ we see immediately that these « multipole » terms describe, in a way analogous to the classical case, the interactions between the multipole moments of the particles in one orbit and the moments of those in another. The interaction between closed shells is of this type (with $\nu = 0$), as is also the orbit-diagonal interaction between a particle and a closed shell. If on the other hand we recouple differently we can write this interaction as the scalar product of two *transition* moments, thus $(\mathcal{U}^\nu_{rs}\times\mathcal{U}^\nu_{sr})^0$. We shall sometimes describe this as being an « excitation-type » interaction. We must expect that this form will be significant in giving the energy of the $r \to s$ hole-particle excitation. Observe also that multipole and excitation-type interactions are *not* linearly independent since they both derive from the W^Γ_{rsrs} matrix elements.

5·7.4. Nondiagonal interactions. These are interactions not given above; they may involve 2, 3 or 4 distinct orbits. It will often happen however that there will be a natural « Fermi surface » for the nucleus considered (*e.g.* the s^4p^{12} state for ^{16}O) and that then the classification of orbits according as they are above or below the Fermi level will be more significant than the more detailed one based on equivalence. In this case we shall feel free to use the classification of interactions in a more general way, that which *e.g.* promotes a pair of p particles up to the (ds) shell being termed a pairing-type interaction.

The *matrix element form* of the interaction (eq. (5.54)) is such that the pairing-interaction parts are given in simple form. If, for example, $W^\Gamma_{rstu} = \delta_{\Gamma 0}\delta_{rs}\delta_{tu}[rs]^{\frac{1}{2}}$ in a j formalism, $H^{(2)}$ becomes simply the mixed-orbit identical-particle pairing operator. Let us rewrite the interaction in *multipole form* so that the multipole-interaction parts will be in simple form. We have, making a straightforward recoupling, and using eq. (5.60) that (*)

$$(5.70)\qquad H^{(2)} = -\sum_{\substack{rstu:\Gamma\\ r\leq s\\ t\leq u}} \zeta_{rs}\zeta_{tu}[\Gamma]^{\frac{1}{2}} W^\Gamma_{rstu}$$

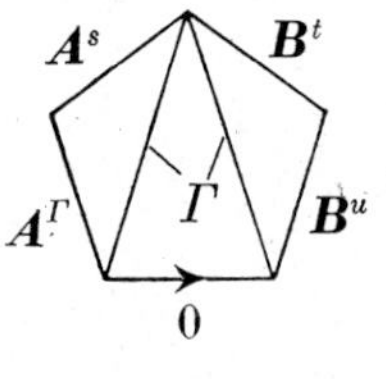

$$= \sum_{\substack{rstu:\nu\\ r\leq s\\ t\leq u}} \beta^\nu_{rtsu}\zeta_{rs}\zeta_{tu}[\nu](\mathcal{U}^\nu_{rt}\times\mathcal{U}^\nu_{su})^0 + \sum_{\substack{rsu\\ r\leq s, s\leq u}} \zeta_{rs}\zeta_{su}[s]^{\frac{1}{2}}\beta^0_{russ}\mathcal{U}^0_{ru}\,.$$

(*) There is no reason why we must transform the entire interaction in this way; it is often useful for some orbits, not for others. Also note that the restrictions $r \leqslant s$, $t \leqslant u$ may be replaced by $r \leqslant s$, $t \geqslant u$; it is easy to see that this is necessary if we wish to exhibit, for example, the two-orbit « excitation-type » interaction.

The multipole coefficients now are given by

$$\beta^{\nu}_{rtsu} = \sum_{\Gamma} (-1)^{r+u-\nu-\Gamma}\, U(rstu:\Gamma\nu)[\Gamma]^{\frac{1}{2}} W^{\Gamma}_{rstu}\,, \tag{5.71}$$

while the inverse equation is

$$[\Gamma]^{\frac{1}{2}} W^{\Gamma}_{rstu} = \sum_{\nu} (-1)^{r+u-\nu-\Gamma}\, U(rstu:\Gamma\nu)\beta^{\nu}_{rtsu}\,. \tag{5.72}$$

An awkward technical point must be noted concerning the (geometrical) $W^{\Gamma} \rightleftharpoons \beta^{\nu}$ transformation. Whenever we deal with parts of the interaction which involve two equivalent particles ($r = s$ or $t = u$), then formally W^{Γ}_{rstu} is not defined for all Γ because there are Pauli-forbidden states (with $(-1)^{2\varrho+\Gamma} = +1$). In the above we have simply agreed that $W^{\Gamma} = 0$ for all forbidden Γ. This does not affect $H^{(2)}$ at all because the $(\boldsymbol{AABB})$ operator itself vanishes for forbidden Γ, but it has the consequence that there are more β^{ν} parameters than physically significant W^{Γ} (the $(\mathcal{U}^{\nu}\times\mathcal{U}^{\nu})^0$ operators being not linearly independent). There is in fact an obvious class of transformations among the β^{ν} which leave $H^{(2)}$ invariant. A first consequence of this, very often ignored, is that there is no unique definition of a multipole spectrum or matrix involving equivalent nucleons; a pure quadrupole ϱ^2 spectrum can *e.g.* be reproduced by an interaction which has no quadrupole part at all. This ambiguity, which arises from a conflict between geometry and the Pauli principle must be continually borne in mind when we use the multipole (or the « excitation ») forms for H. It is particularly troublesome when we deal with the subject of linearly independent orthonormal interactions, which we shall briefly mention later.

Consider now the monopole interaction; then if we are not considering orbits with the same angular momenta but different radial quantum numbers, necessarily $r = t$ and $s = u$ and for $r \neq s$ we have

$$\beta^{0}_{rrss} = [rs]^{-\frac{1}{2}} \sum_{\Gamma} [\Gamma] W^{\Gamma}_{rsrs} = [rs]^{\frac{1}{2}} \overline{W}_{rs}\,, \tag{5.73}$$

the corresponding part of $H^{(2)}$ becoming

$$[rs]^{-\frac{1}{2}} \beta^{0}_{rrss} n_{\mathrm{op}}(r) n_{\mathrm{op}}(s) = \frac{\overline{W}_{rs}}{[rs]} n_{\mathrm{op}}(r) n_{\mathrm{op}}(s)\,, \qquad r \neq s\,. \tag{5.74}$$

The only contributing interaction between a closed shell and a nucleon in another orbit is then the monopole, but because of the constraints on the β^{ν} parameters, this would be a misleading statement about the self-energy of a closed shell. On the other hand it is easy to verify, from eq. (5.70), that the closed-shell energy is

(5.75) $$[r]\beta^0 = \tfrac{1}{2}[r]\{[r]-1\}\,\overline{W}_r\,,$$

in agreement with the result of eq. (5.65).

The monopole interactions, whichever way they are defined, have the property that they, to a large degree, are « summable »; in a representation in which the numbers of particles in a given orbit are specified, all the monopole m.e. may be written down at sight. If the representation specifies also the angular momenta of the particles in each orbit, the even-parity dipole interactions ($\nu = 1$ in a j formalism, (1, 0) and (0, 1) in jt) are also summable in the same way. We shall see later an application of this result.

When we have a pure multipole interaction (with a single nonvanishing multipole)

(5.76) $$\beta^{\nu}_{rtsu} = \beta\delta_{\nu\nu_0}\delta_{rt}\delta_{su}\,,$$

we can, recognizing an essentially classical situation of the interaction between two distributions, once again use the Racah-Legendre correspondence and, from the equation above for W^{Γ}_{rsrs}, we have for the two-body energies

(5.77) $$E^{\Gamma}(\nu_0) \sim P_{\nu_0}(\cos\varphi)\,,$$

where φ is defined in Fig. 5. As an example consider the situation shown in

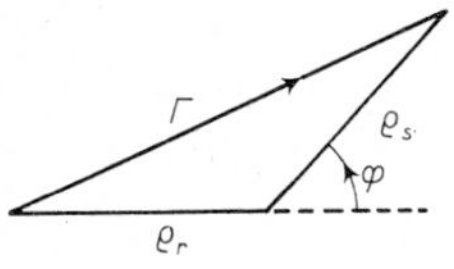

Fig. 5. – The internal coupling angle appropriate for multipole interactions.

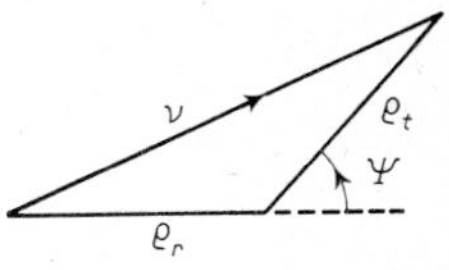

Fig. 6. – The internal coupling angle appropriate for pairing interactions.

Fig. 7, 8 for $(\frac{7}{2})^2$ in a nonisobaric-spin formalism; we might for example be thinking of the $f^2_{\frac{7}{2}}$ spectrum described in a p-n formalism so that there is no Pauli principle « interference » with the coupling geometry.

As a curiosity with some mathematical significance, note that for a pure pairing force ($r = s$, $t = u$) we can also introduce an angle as shown in Fig. 6, the roles of ν and Γ being now interchanged.

If now we have only a single component, *i.e.*

(5.78) $$W^{\Gamma}_{rstu} = W\delta_{\Gamma\Gamma_0}\delta_{rs}\delta_{tu}\,,$$

then

(5.79) $$\beta^{\nu}(\Gamma_0) \sim P_{\Gamma_0}(\cos\psi)\,.$$

We have discussed the Hamiltonian interaction entirely in a particle formalism but if one or more of the shells involved is almost filled it is of course

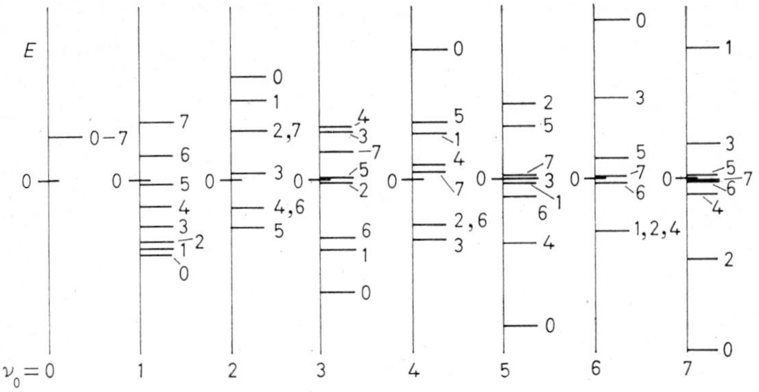

Fig. 7. – Multipole spectra for $(\frac{7}{2})^2$ in the p-n formalism. The quantity plotted, on the same scale for each ν_0 value and with $j=\frac{7}{2}$, is $E^J(\nu_0) = (-1)^{J+1}[J]^{-\frac{1}{2}}\,U(jjjj:\nu_0 J) \equiv [\nu_0]^{\frac{1}{2}}[j]^{-1}P_{\nu_0}(\cos\psi)$. These spectra are orthonormal in the sense that

$$\sum [J]E^J(\nu_0)E^J(\nu_0') \equiv \frac{[\nu_0]}{2}\int \mathrm{d}\cos\psi\, P_{\nu_0}(\cos\psi)\,P_{\nu_0'}(\cos\psi) = \delta_{\nu_0\nu_0'}.$$

more sensible to make $h \rightleftharpoons p$ transformations for these, via. eq. (5.44), taking the new Fermi level at the closure of the upper of these shells (at the same time of course one could eliminate the closed shells entirely by a $h \rightleftharpoons p$ transform). The general Hamiltonian now of course splits up into a number of different terms which do not all preserve the number of fermions. Classifications and transformations can be made in the same way as above, but it is hardly worth-while to write the general case, since in any given problem the procedures will be obvious. Besides that, if we deal with very simple situations (two-fermion states) we can always allow the calculation to make the appropriate transform for us; but this may not be satisfactory in more complex cases.

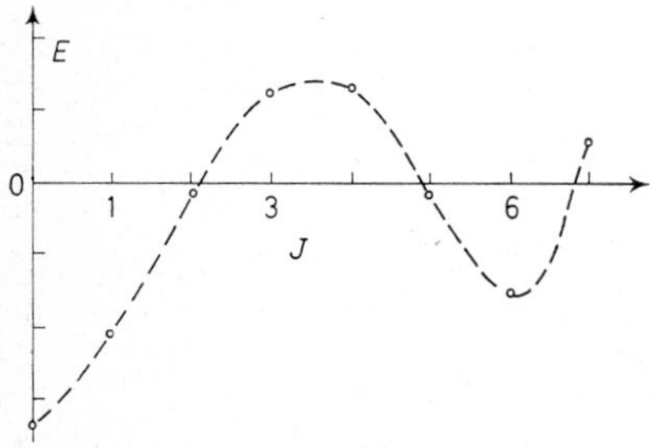

Fig. 8. – The octupole spectrum of Fig. 6 plotted linearly against J.

As an example, the result of which we shall need later, and a demonstration of the $h \rightleftharpoons p$ transformation, consider the matrix element of $H^{(2)}$ between two hole-particle states, say (k^{-1}, l) and (p^{-1}, q). Then using the orthogonality of the two-fermion state operators, we see that the $(\mathcal{U}\times\mathcal{U})^0$ part of $H^{(2)}$ which contributes to $\langle k^{-1}l|H^{(2)}|p^{-1}q\rangle_\Gamma$ is a multiple of $\big(\boldsymbol{Z}^\Gamma(k(h), l)\times\bar{\boldsymbol{Z}}^\Gamma(p(h), q)\big)^0$;

if the coefficient of this term in $H^{(2)}$ is D we see by the usual factoring that the matrix element has the value $[\Gamma]^{-\frac{1}{2}}D$. Since however

$$(5.80)\qquad \left(\boldsymbol{Z}^{\Gamma}(k(h), l) \times \bar{\boldsymbol{Z}}^{\Gamma}(p(h), q)\right)^0 = (-1)^{k-l-\Gamma}[\Gamma](\mathcal{U}^{\Gamma}_{lk} \times \mathcal{U}^{\Gamma}_{pq})^0,$$

we can, from eq. (5.70), identify $D = (-1)^{k-l-\Gamma}\beta^{\Gamma}_{lkpq}$ and, ignoring the single-fermion contribution (the $\mathcal{U}^0_{ru}$ term in eq. (5.70)), we have that

$$(5.81)\qquad \langle k^{-1}l|H^{(2)}|p^{-1}q\rangle_{\Gamma} = (-1)^{k-l-\Gamma}[\Gamma]^{-\frac{1}{2}}\beta^{\Gamma}_{lkpq}\,,$$

giving essentially an equality between a particle-particle excitation-type coefficient and a particle-hole matrix element. As an exercise it is suggested that the same quantity be derived using the matrix-element form of H.

5·8. *Isobaric spin and the* p-n *formalism.* – So far we have derived all results in a formalism using a single fermion field, which is appropriate when we use an isobaric-spin formalism or deal only with active identical particles. An alternative way of dealing with active protons and neutrons is to use two independent (commuting) fermion fields, one for each type of particle, and this we call the « p-n » formalism. In this formalism the isobaric-spin is not an angular-momentum-type quantum number and, except in certain simple cases, the basis states which one uses in calculations do not have good isobaric spin. Of course if we calculate eigenfunctions of a charge-independent Hamiltonian they will (barring a degeneracy) have good isobaric spin, but we may well have had to work in a larger vector space than if we should use a T formalism, and this may be troublesome.

Broadly speaking the p-n formalism is convenient whenever the isobaric spin is a redundant quantum number, or, for example, if we wish to incorporate, by a nonperturbative procedure, the effects of charge dependence in giving different radial functions for protons and neutrons. We shall see in Sect. **8** a use of the p-n formalism in solving a formal problem in spectroscopy (that of calculating fractional-parentage coefficients). It may also be convenient if we are studying specific effects of the p-n interaction and we shall see an example of that too. One should be careful about that however. If something is basically simpler in a T formalism it is hard to get excited about studying it in a p-n formalism. As an example of this the single-particle excitations produced by adding a proton to a target with a neutron excess are trivially described in a T formalism but are complicated, though with exotic names (« three-quasi-particle » and so on), in the p-n formalism. However if you like exotic names... .

From the strictly formal standpoint, all the manipulations that we have used so far can be carried out in the p-n formalism. The state operators are given as a proton operator coupled to a neutron operator $\left(\boldsymbol{Z}^{\Gamma_1}_{x_1}(\mathrm{p}) \times \boldsymbol{Z}^{\Gamma_2}_{x_2}(\mathrm{n})\right)^{\Gamma}$, or as a sum of such. The particle-conserving operators of the system can be written as a sum of proton and neutron operators along with n-p interaction operators which may be written in terms of tensor products of proton and neutron operators. Then the matrix elements of such operators can be written in terms of separate proton and neutron matrix elements along with decoupling factors. All the sum rules and so on given above can be transcribed into the p-n formalism; we leave this as an exercise.

One needs the form of the T^2 operator in the p-n case. Starting with a T formalism we have

$$\begin{cases} \boldsymbol{T} = \sum_i \boldsymbol{t}_i \,, \\ T^2 = \dfrac{3n}{4} + 2\sum_{i<j} \boldsymbol{t}_i \cdot \boldsymbol{t}_j = \dfrac{3n}{4} + \sum_{i<j}\left(H_{ij} - \dfrac{1}{2}\right), \end{cases} \tag{5.82}$$

where n is the total number of particles and H_{ij} the Heisenberg exchange operator, $\frac{1}{2}\{1 + 4\boldsymbol{t}_i \cdot \boldsymbol{t}_j\}$. Then rewriting in terms of the space-spin exchange operator P_{ij} $(\equiv -H_{ij})$ we have

$$T^2 = \frac{n(4-n)}{4} - \sum_{i<j} P_{ij} \,. \tag{5.83}$$

It is easy to see that this may be transcribed directly to the p-n formalism and, if we deal with n_1 protons and n_2 neutrons $(n_1 + n_2 = n)$, then

$$T^2 = \tfrac{1}{4}\{(n_1 - n_2)^2 + 2n\} - \sum P_{\mathrm{n,p}} \,, \tag{5.84}$$

where $P_{\mathrm{n,p}} \equiv$ an interchange of neutron and proton numbers.

As an elementary application consider the state produced by coupling a neutron group $j_2^{n_2}$ to a proton group $j_1^{n_1}$ where $j_2 \neq j_1$. Because of the complete inequivalence of the two groups $P_{\mathrm{n,p}}$ cannot contribute to the expectation value of T^2 which therefore becomes

$$\langle T^2 \rangle = \tfrac{1}{4}\{(n_1 - n_2)^2 + 2n\} \,. \tag{5.85}$$

For the case of a single neutron, this equation along with the normalization determines the isobaric-spin constitution of the coupled state and gives

$$j_1^{n_1} \times j_2 = \sqrt{\frac{n_1}{n_1+1}}\, \psi^{T=(n_1-1)/2} + \sqrt{\frac{1}{n_1+1}}\, \psi^{T=(n_1+1)/2} \,, \tag{5.86}$$

where the phases have been arbitrarily fixed. It may easily be verified that this is simply isobaric-spin Clebsch-Gordan coupling, but it is equally easy to see, though this is not always appreciated, that C-G coupling cannot be valid in general (when groups being coupled are not completely inequivalent).

To illustrate this point consider the coupling of a j-neutron to a zero-coupled proton group $(j^{n_1})_{J=0}$. Then observing that we can choose a representation in which $(j^{n_1})_{J=0} = ((j^{n_1-1})_{J=j} \times j)_0$ we find easily from eq. (5.84) that

$$\langle T^2 \rangle = \frac{1}{4}(n_1^2 + 3) - \frac{n_1}{[j]}, \tag{5.87}$$

and this then leads to the result

$$(j^{n_1})_{J=0} \times j = \sqrt{\frac{n_1}{n_1+1} \cdot \frac{2j+2}{[j]}}\, \psi^{T=(n_1-1)/2} + \sqrt{\frac{2j+1-n_1}{(n_1+1)[j]}}\, \psi^{T=(n_1+1)/2}. \tag{5.88}$$

We note a « blocking » effect which is not present in the C-G coupling of eq. (5.86).

It takes a little more work to do the same for the coupling of a zero-coupled neutron pair to an equivalent (j^{n_1}) proton group and the result depends on the seniority of the j^n group. For zero seniority we find

$$(j^{n_1})_{v=0} \times (j^2)_{J=0} = \sqrt{\frac{(2j+2)n_1}{(n_1+1)[j]}}\, \psi^{T=(n_1-2)/2} + \sqrt{\frac{2j+1-n_1}{(n_1+1)[j]}}\, \psi^{T=(n_1+2)/2}, \tag{5.89}$$

no component with $T = n_1/2$ appearing.

As another simple example consider the coupling of a closed neutron shell j^N ($N = [j]$) to a closed proton shell which is equivalent except for different radial functions (the difference being caused for example by Coulomb effects). Then from eq. (5.84) one finds easily that

$$\langle T^2 \rangle = N\{1 - \langle R_p R_n \rangle^2\}, \tag{5.90}$$

where $\langle R_p R_n \rangle$ is the radial overlap integral. If we assume as is reasonable that only the $T = 1$ admixture is of consequence then this equation gives directly the amount of the admixture (*).

There are a number of other elementary things worth mentioning. The isobaric-spin quantum number is of course redundant if we deal with identical particles only; but it is redundant also for states in which, ignoring shells closed for neutrons and protons both, any given orbit contains only identical neutrons or identical proton holes. These are states in which every orbit which contains protons is filled for neutrons. The lower states of heavier nuclei (with a neutron excess) are without doubt predominantly of the sort; as a consequence T is redundant (being equal to T_z) and the p-n formalism is convenient.

(*) This method has been used by S. Iwao and the present author to study isobaric-spin effects in heavy nuclei (unpublished, 1959).

If in such a case the active protons and neutrons separately may be regarded as belonging to unpolarizable odd groups (which in practice means a single particle or hole), the spectrum is produced by the n-p interaction. Expanding this as $\sum_\nu \gamma^\nu(\mathcal{U}^\nu(p)\times\mathcal{U}^\nu(n))^0$ we note first that the γ^ν can be determined from the experimental spectrum; in many cases where this has been done quadrupole n-p interactions are found to be dominant. Next note that there is a simple relationship between the spectra of two such systems which are identical except that one of the components of one system is the h$\rightleftharpoons$p complement of the corresponding component of the other. Then from eqs. (3.29*e*), (5.52) we have, ignoring the J-independent energies, that

$$E^{(1)}(\theta) = -E^{(2)}(\pi-\theta)\,, \tag{5.91}$$

which is the well-known Pandya theorem. An extension of this is given later.

Other elementary matters whose explicit working out we leave for exercises include: the isobaric-spin structure of systems composed of two identical groups; the behaviour of equivalent-particle groups under the neutron→neutron-hole transformation (think about the «isospin pairing» which shows up in the system $j(p)\times j^{-1}(n)$, and its relationship to eq. (5.79)), the transformation of wave-functions from a p-n to an isospin formalism and the inverse (harder!). A problem which is not so elementary is that of the isobaric-spin splitting of nuclear excitations (nonisoscalar ones of course), the questions here concerning the distribution of the strengths among the final isospins, and the isospin excitation spectrum. The general equations here are found by integrating, over $\cos\theta$, the general strength eq. (3.34).

We consider now how to separate the contributions to some process under consideration of the (p-n) interactions from the like-particle interactions. This is done automatically if we use the p-n formalism but because of the loss of the isospin quantum number this may not be a satisfactory representation. On the other hand the two-particle p-n state (separately numbered particles) is easily written as a combination of $T=0$ and $T=1$ states: we have

$$\Psi^J_{rs}(\mathrm{p},\mathrm{n}) = \frac{1}{\sqrt{2}\,\zeta_{rs}}\,(\Psi^{J,0}+\Psi^{J,1})\,, \tag{5.92}$$

and then we have for the matrix element of the p-n part of the interaction (as distinct from the like-particle part)

$$W^J_{rstu}(\mathrm{p},\mathrm{n}) = \frac{1}{2\,\zeta_{rs}\zeta_{tu}}\,\{W^{J,0}_{rstu}+W^{J,1}_{rstu}\}\,. \tag{5.93}$$

The point of this is that for any result expressed in terms of the two-body matrix elements W^Γ we have only to transform by

$$\left\{\begin{array}{l} W^{J,1}_{rstu} \to W^J_{rstu}(\text{like})\,, \\ W^{J,0}_{rstu} \to 2\zeta_{rs}\zeta_{tu} W^J_{rstu}(\text{p, n}) - W^J_{rstu}(\text{like})\,, \end{array}\right. \tag{5.94}$$

in order to examine the separate effects of the p-n and identical-particle interactions. If we wish we may also transform the Hamiltonian and then (in a *jt* representation)

$$\left\{\begin{array}{l} H^{(2)}(\text{like}) = \sum\limits_{\substack{rstu:J \\ r\leq s, t\leq u}} [J]^{\frac{1}{2}} W^J_{rstu}(\text{like})\{-(\boldsymbol{Z}^{J,0}(rs)\times\bar{\boldsymbol{Z}}^{J,0}(tu))^0 + \\ \qquad\qquad\qquad\qquad + \sqrt{3}(\boldsymbol{Z}^{J,1}(rs)\times\bar{\boldsymbol{Z}}^{J,1}(tu))^0\}\,, \\ H^{(2)}(\text{p-n}) = 2\sum\limits_{\substack{rstu:J \\ r\leq s, t\leq u}} \zeta_{rs}\zeta_{tu}[J]^{\frac{1}{2}} W^J_{rstu}(\text{p, n})(\boldsymbol{Z}^{J,0}(rs)\times\bar{\boldsymbol{Z}}^{J,0}(tu))^0, \end{array}\right. \tag{5.95}$$

these results, or their multipole counterparts, being useful if we wish to examine, by a sum-rule analysis, the contribution to a centroid energy or width from the p-n or like-particle parts of the interaction.

For the multipole forms of these equations we may use eq. (5.70) with appropriate multipole coefficients β^ν. We have from eq. (5.71), using

$$U(\tfrac{1}{2}\tfrac{1}{2}\tfrac{1}{2}\tfrac{1}{2};\, TT') = -\frac{1}{2}\,,\ \frac{\sqrt{3}}{2}\,,\ \frac{\sqrt{3}}{2}\,,\ +\frac{1}{2}$$

for $(T, T') = (0, 0)$, $(0, 1)$, $(1, 0)$ and $(1, 1)$ respectively, that

$$\left\{\begin{array}{l} \beta^{k,0}_{r\,su} = \sum\limits_J (-1)^{j_r+j_u-k-J} U(j_r j_t j_s j_u;\, kJ)[J]^{\frac{1}{2}} \left\{\dfrac{1}{2}(W^{J,0}_{rstu} + 3W^{J,1}_{rstu})\right\}, \\ \beta^{k,1}_{rtsu} = \sum\limits_J (-1)^{j_r+j_u-k-J} U(j_r j_t j_s j_u;\, kJ)[J]^{\frac{1}{2}} \left\{\dfrac{\sqrt{3}}{2}(W^{J,0}_{rstu} - W^{J,1}_{rstu})\right\}. \end{array}\right. \tag{5.96}$$

Writing these equations as

$$\left\{\begin{array}{l} \beta^{k,0} \equiv \dfrac{1}{2} W^{J,0} + \dfrac{3}{2} W^{J,1}, \\ \dfrac{1}{\sqrt{3}}\beta^{k,1} \equiv \dfrac{1}{2} W^{J,0} - \dfrac{1}{2} W^{J,1}, \end{array}\right. \tag{5.97}$$

we see that for $H^{(2)}$(p-n)

$$(5.98)\qquad \beta^{k,0}(\text{p-n}) = \frac{1}{\sqrt{3}}\beta^{k,1}(\text{p-n}) \equiv \zeta_{rs}\zeta_{tu}W^J(\text{pn}) = \frac{1}{2}(W^{J,0} + W^{J,1})\,,$$

which implies that, in the isospin formalism, the multipole coefficients for the p-n interaction (to be used in eq. (5.70) *et seq.*) are

$$(5.99)\qquad \beta^{k,0}_{rtsu}(\text{p, n}) = \frac{1}{\sqrt{3}}\beta^{k,1}_{rtsu}(\text{p, n}) = \frac{1}{2}\left\{\beta^{k,0}_{rtsu} + \frac{1}{\sqrt{3}}\beta^{k,1}_{rtsu}\right\},$$

while for the like-particle interactions we find, by the same procedure,

$$(5.100)\qquad \beta^{k,0}_{rtsu}(\text{like}) = -\frac{1}{\sqrt{3}}\beta^{k,1}_{rtsu}(\text{like}) = \frac{1}{2}\left\{\beta^{k,0}_{rtsu} - \frac{1}{\sqrt{3}}\beta^{k,1}_{rtsu}\right\},$$

and we can now write the explicit multipole form of the separate Hamiltonians. As a minor application consider the p-n contribution to the energy of a closed shell. Then, according to eq. (5.75) this is

$$(5.101)\qquad [\varrho]\beta^{0,0}(\text{p-n}) = \frac{[\varrho]}{2}\left(\beta^{0,0} + \frac{1}{\sqrt{3}}\beta^{0,1}\right) = \sum_J [J]\{W^{J,0} + W^{J,1}\}\,,$$

while the like-particle contributions are

$$(5.102)\qquad [\varrho]\beta^{0,0}(\text{like}) = \frac{[\varrho]}{2}\left(\beta^{0,0} - \frac{1}{\sqrt{3}}\beta^{0,1}\right) = 2\sum_J [J]W^{J,1}.$$

This elementary result could have been derived by writing separately the energies for a fully-closed shell (j, t representation) and for a closed identical-particle shell (j representation). Our example then is trivial but the general results, which enable us to examine p-n effects in an isospin representation, are not. They promise to be of considerable value.

Turning briefly now to the representation of operators in the p-n formalism we note first that unless the operator is available to us only in an isospin formalism, everything is simple. On the other hand, if the operator is isoscalar then it is not hard to see that we can make an immediate one-to-one correspondence (equality!) of its matrix elements in the two formalisms, so that there is no difficulty there either. Thus we can write, in the p-n formalism,

$$(5.103)\qquad H^{(2)}(\text{p, n}) = \sum_{rstu:J}[J]^{\frac{1}{2}}W^J_{rstu}(\text{p, n})\left(\boldsymbol{Z}^J_{rs}(\text{p, n}) \times \bar{\boldsymbol{Z}}^J_{tu}(\text{p, n})\right)^0,$$

where $r, t \equiv$ protons, $s, u \equiv$ neutrons, $W^J(\mathrm{p}, \mathrm{n})$ is related to the (J, T) matrix elements by eq. (5.93), and $\boldsymbol{Z}^J_{rs}(\mathrm{p}, \mathrm{n}) = (\boldsymbol{A}^r(\mathrm{p}) \times \boldsymbol{A}^s(\mathrm{n}))^J$. Starting from here we can write multipole forms, can consider hole $\rightleftharpoons$ particle transformations for protons (or neutrons) only, can compare the isospin and p-n formalism forms, and so on. These things are left for exercises.

One thing which we should write is a p-n form for T^2, more useful than the P_{np} form of eq. (5.83). Since P_{np}, the neutron-proton exchange operator, is an isoscalar two-body operator (eq. (5.83)), (which interchanges the *numbers*, not the labels, of a proton and neutron) we have

$$P_{\mathrm{np}}\psi_{rs}(\mathrm{p}, \mathrm{n}) = (-1)^{j_r+j_s-J}\psi_{sr}(\mathrm{p}, \mathrm{n}) \,, \tag{5.104}$$

and then its nonvanishing matrix elements are

$$\langle\psi_{sr}(\mathrm{p}, \mathrm{n})|P_{\mathrm{np}}|\psi_{rs}(\mathrm{p}, \mathrm{n})\rangle = (-1)^{j_r+j_s-J}. \tag{5.105}$$

Then the second-quantized matrix-element form of the operator $\sum P_{\mathrm{np}}$, separately symmetric in protons and neutrons, follows from eq. (5.103) and is (in a j representation)

$$\sum P_{\mathrm{np}} = \sum_{rs;J} [J]^{\frac{1}{2}}(-1)^{j_r+j_s-J}(\boldsymbol{Z}^J_{rs}(\mathrm{p}, \mathrm{n}) \times \overline{\boldsymbol{Z}}^J_{sr}(\mathrm{p}, \mathrm{n}))^0, \tag{5.106}$$

and this, coupled with the expression for T^2 (eq. (5.83)), gives us the matrix-element form of that operator in a p-n formalism. Transforming this to multipole form we have immediately that

$$\sum P_{\mathrm{np}} = \sum_{rs;k} (-1)^{j_r-j_s-k} [k]^{\frac{3}{2}} (\boldsymbol{\mathcal{U}}^k_{rs}(\mathrm{p}) \times \boldsymbol{\mathcal{U}}^k_{sr}(\mathrm{n}))^0, \tag{5.107}$$

and rewriting in scalar-product form (eq. (3.1)) this implies that for an (n_1-proton$+n_2$-neutron) system

$$T^2 = \tfrac{1}{4}\{(n_1 - n_2)^2 + 2(n_1 + n_2)\} - \sum_{rs;k} (-1)^{r-s}[k](\boldsymbol{\mathcal{U}}^k_{rs}(\mathrm{p}) \cdot \boldsymbol{\mathcal{U}}^k_{sr}(\mathrm{n})) \,, \tag{5.108}$$

a result which can be derived in many other ways, some simpler than the above.

The tensorial expansion of the exchange operator derived above, the two-particle form of which is

$$P_{12} = \sum_{rs;v} (-1)^{r-s}[v](\boldsymbol{u}^v_{rs}(1) \cdot \boldsymbol{u}^v_{sr}(2)) \,, \tag{5.109}$$

is of course of general validity, quite apart from any p-n considerations. It gives the generalization of the Dirac spin-exchange operator

$$B_{12} = \tfrac{1}{2}\{1 + \boldsymbol{\sigma}_1 \cdot \boldsymbol{\sigma}_2\}\,, \tag{5.110}$$

which is a special case of it.

5.9. *Averaging.* – We have several times talked about the very elementary problem of the average energy for two particles in the same or in different orbits. The energy of a closed shell is also an average since the ϱ^N vector space ($N=[\varrho]$) has only a single state. A much more general averaging problem, that of evaluating the average of a scalar operator over some naturally defined set of complex states is of some interest (there are also averagings involving nonscalar operators which we shall not mention). We might for example be interested in separating the Hamiltonian operator which acts in a certain vector space into a part which conserves some interesting quantity and a part which does not (symplectic or SU_3 symmetry for example). This separation requires that we have an appropriate orthonormalization criterion and for some purposes a reasonable one might be that the mean squared energy, $\overline{(H)^2}$, separate into two parts, one conserving and one nonconserving, with no cross-term between them. A more general procedure is to separate H into the maximum number of « orthogonal » parts using the same classification. As a very simple case the multipole separation of the two-body H is of this form: for example the multipole spectra plotted in Fig. 6 are orthogonal, satisfying

$$\sum_J [J]\, E^J(\nu)\, E^J(\nu') = 0 \qquad \text{if } \nu \neq \nu', \tag{5.111}$$

as is obvious from the P_ν correspondence.

Averaging then is interesting. As an introduction to it we *sketch* the solution to the problem of averaging an n-body *scalar* operator of otherwise arbitrary complexity over a mixed-configuration shell-model vector space for m particles. We insist that we carry out the averaging over *all* the states compatible with some assigned set of orbits, or over the smaller set of states in which a definite partition of the particles among the orbits is maintained; the reasonableness of this will become apparent on a little thought.

Given a scalar operator K, we first write it in normal form, using the techniques and results of the Appendix if the operator is very complicated. Then

$$K = \sum_{yy'\Lambda} \sum_{r=0}^{r_{\max}} d^{\Lambda}_{yy'}(r) \big(\boldsymbol{Z}_y(r) \times \overline{\boldsymbol{Z}}_{y'}(r)\big)^0, \tag{5.112}$$

where the coefficients $d^{\Lambda}(r)$ have already been given in terms of the r-particle matrix elements (eq. (5.36)). One now considers each of these terms separately, first making a particle-hole transformation (eqs. (5.40), (5.44)). Then, where N

is the degeneracy of the vector space,

$$(5.113) \quad \left\langle \begin{matrix} \mathbf{Z}_y^A(r) & & \bar{\mathbf{Z}}_{y'}^A(r) \\ & 0 & \\ \bar{\mathbf{Z}}_x^\Gamma(m) & & \mathbf{Z}_x^\Gamma(m) \\ & 0 & \end{matrix} \right\rangle_0 = (-1)^{2A} \left\langle \begin{matrix} \bar{\mathbf{Z}}_y^A(r) & & \mathbf{Z}_{y'}^A(r) \\ & 0 & \\ \bar{\mathbf{Z}}_{x_c}^\Gamma(N-m) & & \mathbf{Z}_{x_c}^\Gamma(N-m) \\ & 0 & \end{matrix} \right\rangle_0 =$$

$$= (-1)^{2A} \left\langle \begin{matrix} \bar{\mathbf{Z}}_{x_c}^\Gamma(N-m) & & \mathbf{Z}_{x_c}^\Gamma(N-m) \\ & 0 & \\ \bar{\mathbf{Z}}_y^A(r) & & \mathbf{Z}_{y'}^A(r) \\ & 0 & \end{matrix} \right\rangle_0$$

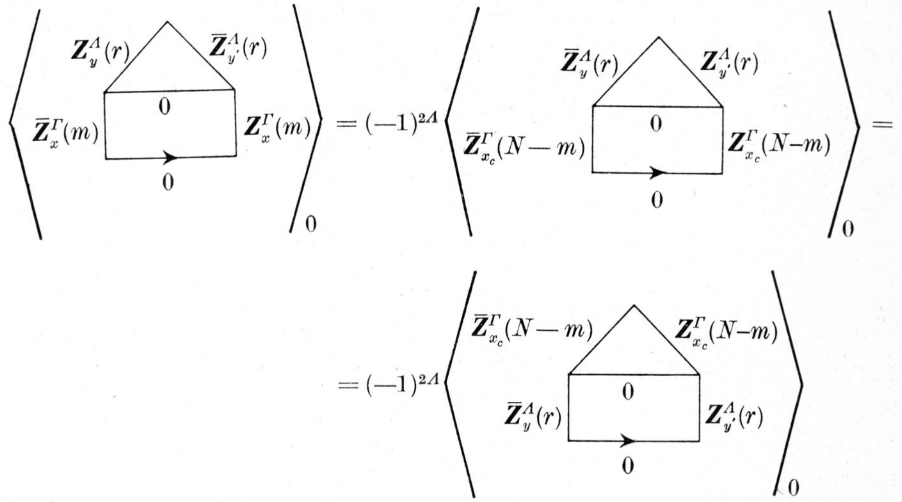

where, by a simple recoupling, we have written the matrix element as an $(N-m)$-hole operator in r-particle states. We have here made use of the fact that operators and wave-functions enter into the matrix element on the same footing, and of the hole-particle transformation, without which the recoupling would not have been feasible. Of course if it is simpler to write K in *antinormal* form $\left(\sim (\boldsymbol{B})^r (\boldsymbol{A})^r\right)$ then the h $\rightleftharpoons$ p transformation is not required.

But now to carry out the averaging we must perform the summation. The operator $\left(\bar{\mathbf{Z}}_{x_c}^\Gamma(N-m) \times \mathbf{Z}_{x_c}^\Gamma(N-m)\right)^0$ may be an extraordinarily complicated operator; but if we are dealing with a « complete » vector space, as defined above, a little thought will show that we must have

$$(5.114) \quad \sum_{x,\Gamma} [\Gamma]^{\frac{1}{2}} \ \bar{\mathbf{Z}}_x^\Gamma(s) \diagup \diagdown \mathbf{Z}_x^\Gamma(s) = \binom{N-n_{\mathrm{op}}}{s} \equiv \frac{(N-n_{\mathrm{op}})!}{s!(N-n_{\mathrm{op}}-s)!}$$

and then the problem is solved. We leave it as an exercise to work out, for example, the mean-squared energy for a complex system. It will be seen incidentally that only the total « weight » of the coefficients of given r in the expansion of eq. (5.112) need be known in order to evaluate the average.

There are many directions in which this kind of thing can be extended. An important one is to restrict the vector space over which the averaging is to be performed, which implies the construction of a more complex « averaging operator ». This has been done for « complete » vector spaces of given isobaric

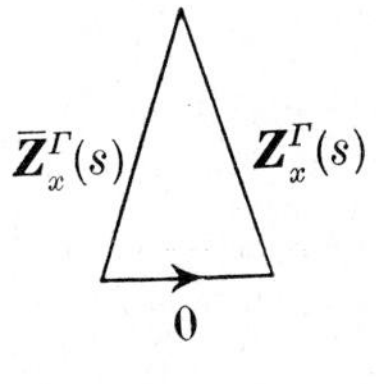

spin by Dr. H. BANERJEE and the author who have also made various applications of the averaging result.

5·10. *Miscellany.* – We touch lightly on a few topics which we are unable to discuss in any detail, the first being that of seniority and pairing. If we describe it in a j formalism, a zero-coupled pair for particles in a single orbit is a simple object, being scalar and moreover one which is known to be of great importance in nuclei. One is led to introduce the single-orbit interaction operator

$$(5.115)\qquad \begin{cases} G = [j] Z_0 \bar{Z}_0\,, \\ Z_0 = -\dfrac{1}{\sqrt{2}}(A^j \times A^j)^0\,, \qquad \bar{Z}_0 = \dfrac{1}{\sqrt{2}}(B^j \times B^j)^0\,, \end{cases}$$

whose only nonvanishing two-body matrix element is for the $J=0$ state. From the easily found commutation rules

$$(5.116)\qquad \begin{cases} [\bar{Z}_0, Z_0] = 1 - \dfrac{2}{[j]} n_{\text{op}}\,, \\ [n_{\text{op}}, Z_0] = 2Z_0\,, \qquad [n_{\text{op}}, \bar{Z}_0] = -2\bar{Z}_0\,, \\ [G, Z_0] = [j] Z_0 \left\{1 - \dfrac{2n_{\text{op}}}{[j]}\right\} = [j]\left\{1 - \dfrac{2}{[j]}(n_{\text{op}} - 2)\right\} Z_0\,, \\ [G, \bar{Z}_0] = -[j]\left\{1 - \dfrac{2}{[j]} n_{\text{op}}\right\} \bar{Z}_0 = -[j]\bar{Z}_0 \left\{1 - \dfrac{2}{[j]}(n_{\text{op}} - 2)\right\}, \end{cases}$$

and their extension using the general theorem of commutator algebra that

$$(5.117)\qquad [P, Q^m] = \sum_{s=0}^{m-1} Q^s [P, Q] Q^{m-s-1}\,,$$

we find that if $G\psi_n = g_n \psi_n$, then

$$(5.118)\qquad \begin{cases} G(Z_0)^p \psi_n = \left[g_n + p[j]\left\{1 - \dfrac{2}{[j]}(n + p - 1)\right\}\right] (Z_0)^p \psi_n\,, \\ G(\bar{Z}_0)^p \psi_n = \left[g_n - p[j]\left\{1 - \dfrac{2}{[j]}(n - p - 1)\right\}\right] (\bar{Z}_0)^p \psi_n\,. \end{cases}$$

These equations supply the basis for the seniority cataloguing of j^n states, due originally to RACAH, defining a set of related states $\psi(n, v)$, where $n = v$, $v+2, \ldots$ and $G\psi(v, v) = 0$. The core state then « has » no zero-coupled pairs, the higher states in the series have successively 1, 2, ... such pairs.

In order to find the normalization for $\psi(n, v)$ we consider the quantity $\bar{Z}_0^q Z_0^q$. By an obvious procedure one finds that

$$(5.119)\qquad \bar{Z}_0^q Z_0^q = \bar{Z}_0^{q-1} Z_0^{q-1} \left\{\frac{G}{[j]} + \left[1 - \frac{2}{[j]}(n_{\text{op}} - 1)\right] q - \frac{2}{[j]} q^2\right\},$$

and from this it follows easily that

$$\bar{Z}_0^q Z_0^q = \prod_{s=1}^{q} \left\{ \frac{G}{[j]} + \left[1 - \frac{2}{[j]}(n_{\text{op}} - 1)\right] s - \frac{2}{[j]} s^2 \right\}, \tag{5.120}$$

and then, when operating on states $\psi(v, v)$, for which $G = 0$, we have

$$\bar{Z}_0^{(n-v)/2} Z_0^{(n-v)/2} \Rightarrow \left(\frac{n-v}{2}\right)! \left(\frac{2}{[j]}\right)^{(n-v)/2} \frac{(([j]-2v)/2)!}{(([j]-v-n)/2)!}, \tag{5.121}$$

obviously supplying us with the desired normalization result. We now have an entirely explicit relationship between the members $\psi(n, v)$ of a set of seniority-related functions and the basic function of the set, $\psi(v, v)$. This can be exploited in a very simple way to yield values of matrix elements of various operators $\langle nv \| \boldsymbol{P}^\nu \| n'v' \rangle$ in terms of matrix elements in which no zero-coupled pairs appear. In short the zero-coupled pairs, being analytically trivial objects can be eliminated. These things we leave as exercises.

It is well known that these results can be extended without difficulty to the case where we have a number of degenerate orbits and where the pairing interaction operator is taken as $G = \sum_{r,s} [rs]^{\frac{1}{2}} Z_0(r) \bar{Z}_0(s)$, where $Z_0(r)$ is the pair creation operator (eq. (5.115)) for orbit r. The difficulties begin when the pairing operator is for a set of nondegenerate orbits (thus including a nontrivial one-body term) or when the relative contributions from various orbits to the two-body G no longer are proportional to $[rs]^{\frac{1}{2}}$ as above. The procedure which has been most used to handle the problem is that of carrying out a rotation in the $(\boldsymbol{A}^j, \boldsymbol{B}^j)$ space thereby introducing rotation parameters u_j^2, v_j^2 (with $u_j^2 + v_j^2 = 1$) and « quasi-particle » creation and destruction tensors. The h $\rightleftharpoons$ p transformation is a special case of this rotation. All the multipole techniques which we have used apply equally well in the quasi-particle space (and in fact also to the rotation in the operator space); in particular one can make good use of the results in the Appendix for handling relatively complex quasi-particle structures (though, if things get very complicated here, one should wonder whether quasi-particles are really the things to be using).

An alternative procedure, which for many purposes is almost as easy to use and which is liable to give more accurate results, is to use the many-orbit extensions of the seniority introduced above, approximations then being made by limiting the maximum seniority to be considered. For low-seniority states it is easy to evaluate the matrix elements of pertinent operators. One problem in this domain which seems at present quite interesting is the sum-rule analysis of excitations of low-seniority targets.

We have said nothing about groups. The infinitesimal operators of groups which contain our rotation group as a subgroup can be conveniently represented as single-particle spherical tensors, the Casimir operators for these groups then becoming a sum of scalar products of such tensors. Examples are the T^2 operator as given by eq. (5.108) and the pairing operator of eq. (5.115) whose multipole form will be found easily to involve odd-rank tensors only. (This last feature corresponds to the physical fact that an odd-rank operator cannot excite a zero-coupled j^2 pair since there is no odd-J state.) There are a large number of problems, interesting from the formal or physical standpoint, connected with these group properties but we cannot discuss them now.

Another topic which we are compelled to ignore is the study of specific interactions, paying attention for example to their multipole structure and more generally to their expansions in terms of orthonormal interactions, this being valuable in considering what type of interactions are responsible for what type of phenomena.

5·11. *Second quantizations vs. configuration-space techniques.* – In this Section we discuss briefly the relationship between the second-quantized and the configuration-space ways of doing things. The first point is that the entire second-quantized formalism follows from the introduction of the $\boldsymbol{A}^\varrho$ operator together with the provisos 1) that this operator should have m.e. only between states which are allowed by the Pauli principle and 2) that $A^\varrho_\mu \bar{A}^{\varrho'}_{\mu'}$ is a one-body operator. No reference at all need be made to representations (involving determinants and so on) in which particles are numbered. To carry out such a development (in which, for example, commutators are evaluated by means of the intermediate-state expansion) is left for an exercise.

On doing this we of course establish immediately a one-to-one correspondence between the representation of particle-conserving operators in the two schemes. Particle-nonconserving operators as such do not come into the configuration-space representations; we deal instead with their matrix elements which we label as c.f.p. and so on. The facts 1) that the matrix elements of such operators have much more complicated transformation properties than the operators themselves and 2) that certain geometrical factorings of more complex operators are not transparent in the configuration-space representations, are responsible for the relative complexity of calculations and manipulations in that representation. This complexity is such that many results are derived conventionally for special configurations and so on, which, with a more reasonable formalism, are derivable more easily and for more general cases; we shall see examples in the following Sections. However because a fair amount of work is still done in a configuration-space representation, and because we sometimes need to borrow results which have been so derived, it is worth-while to say a few things about the relationships between the two procedures.

Single-orbit unit tensor operators $\boldsymbol{u}^v_{\varrho\varrho}(i)$ and their symmetrical counterparts $\mathscr{U}^v_{\varrho\varrho} = \sum_i \boldsymbol{u}^v_{\varrho\varrho}(i)$ were introduced many years ago by RACAH; their extension to tensors nondiagonal in orbit, $\boldsymbol{u}^v_{\varrho\varrho'}$ and $\mathscr{U}^v_{\varrho\varrho'}$ is immediate. The general expansions of number-conserving operators in terms of such tensors is then immediate, as is also the combination rule

$$(5.122)\qquad (\boldsymbol{u}^{\nu}_{rs}(i)\times\boldsymbol{u}^{\nu'}_{tu}(i))^{\Omega}=\frac{\delta_{st}}{[s]^{\frac{1}{2}}}(-1)^{\nu+\nu'-\Omega}\,U(r\nu u\nu':s\Omega)\boldsymbol{u}^{\Omega}_{ru}(i),$$

which leads directly to the commutation rules given in the Appendix.

Explicit integro-differential representations for the unit tensor would probably be very difficult to produce and except for very special purposes not very interesting. On the other hand (using a j formalism for explicitness) $\boldsymbol{u}^{\nu}_{rr}$ is directly related to $(\boldsymbol{J}\times\boldsymbol{J}\times\boldsymbol{J}\,...)^{\nu}$ where there are ν factors in all, being obviously, to within a normalization factor, the projection of this latter oper ator into the (r, r) subspace. It is easy to show indeed that $\boldsymbol{u}^{\nu}_{rr}$ is the projection of

$$(5.123)\qquad \frac{(-1)^{\nu}}{\sqrt{\nu!}\,\{J(J+1)[J]\}^{\nu/2}\,Y_{112}\,Y_{213}\,Y_{314}\,...\,Y_{\nu-1,1\nu}}\underbrace{(\boldsymbol{J}\times\boldsymbol{J}\times\boldsymbol{J}\,...)^{\nu}}_{\nu\ \text{factors}},$$

where Y, symmetrical in the indices, is given by

$$(5.124)\qquad Y_{rst}=(-1)^{t}\,W(jrjs:jt)\,,$$

and has a variety of simple combination rules, such as

$$(5.125)\qquad Y_{n-2,1,n-1}\,Y_{n-1,1,n}=(-1)^{n+1}\sqrt{\frac{5}{[n-1]}}\,Y_{112}\,Y_{n-2,2,n}\,.$$

In eq. (5.124), W is the usual Racah coefficient. This explicit form can sometimes be of value. Such an explicit representation of the tensor nondiagonal in orbit, would be harder to produce.

A considerable amount of attention is paid to the question of « direct » *vs.* « exchange » contributions in calculating Hamiltonian matrix elements for complex systems. We have for example the standard result

$$(5.126)\qquad \langle\mathscr{A}(C_1\times C_2)|\sum_{i<j=1}^{n}H_{ij}|\mathscr{A}(C_1'\times C_2')\rangle=\delta_{C_2C_2'}\langle C_1|H|C_1'\rangle+\delta_{C_1C_1'}\langle C_2|H|C_2'\rangle+$$
$$+\langle(C_1\times C_2)|\sum_{i=1}^{n_1}\sum_{j=n_1+1}^{n}H_{ij}(1-P_{ij})|(C_1'\times C_2')\rangle\,,$$

where C_1 and C_2 are n_1- and n_2-particle separately-antisymmetrized normalized states which have no orbit in common; except in the first term, $C_1\equiv C_1(1,\,...\,n_1)$, $C_2\equiv C_2(n_1+1,\,...,\,n=n_1+n_2)$. On the other hand $\mathscr{A}(C_1\times C_2)$ has been antisymmetrized in all the particles and renormalized (without changing the phase of the $C_1(1,\,...,\,n_1)\times C_2(n_1+1,\,...,\,n)$ component); and similarly of course for C_1' and C_2'.

One is now tempted to consider the « direct » interaction involving H_{ij}, separately from the « exchange » interaction $H_{ij}P_{ij}$. But of course this is formally unnecessary for, if we parametrize H in terms of its matrix elements, it is clear that only the completely antisymmetrized elements can enter in any physical result. Thus one could, for example, ignore the exchange term entirely and recover the result by replacing the nonantisymmetrized matrix elements by the antisymmetrized ones. Or alternatively (and better) one could make a tensorial expansion of $H_{ij}(1-P_{ij})$, in which case the expansion coefficients automatically take account of the exchange contributions along with the direct ones. Two results, of interest if for some reason one wishes to study the formal relationship between various methods, are the tensorial expansion of the exchange operator (eq. (5.109)) and the result,

$$(5.127)\qquad \big(\boldsymbol{u}^{\nu}_{rs}(1)\cdot\boldsymbol{u}^{\nu}_{tu}(2)\big)P_{12} = \\ = (-1)^{r+t+s-u+\nu}\sum_{\Lambda}{}'(-1)^{-\Lambda}\left[\frac{\Lambda}{\nu}\right]^{\frac{1}{2}} U(rsut:\nu\Lambda)\big(\boldsymbol{u}^{\Lambda}_{ru}(1)\cdot\boldsymbol{u}^{\Lambda}_{ts}(2)\big)\,,$$

whose derivation, along with its nonscalar extension, we leave as an exercise.

From the strictly formal standpoint the separation into direct and exchange parts is not very interesting, but there are cases in which, on physical grounds, a separation is useful. Consider for example the W_{rsrs} Wigner interaction; the direct parts of this are necessarily of even rank, so that any process dependent on the odd-rank part necessarily depends on the exchange interaction. The second-quantization procedure automatically represents the two parts together, but they can be separated of course (in the coefficients, not in the operators) by using the direct or exchange matrix element instead of the antisymmetrized one.

Finally we need to establish the relationship (which we have already written down) between the fractional-parentage coefficients and the matrix elements of the $\boldsymbol{A}^{\varrho}$ operators. It is important that we get this right (phases and all!) because we can then immediately make a one-to-one correspondence between calculations made in the two representations.

We begin with the single-shell case. The c.f.p. expansion for ϱ^n is

$$(5.128)\qquad (\varrho^n)^{\Gamma}_x = \sum_{y\Gamma_1}\langle nx\Gamma|n-1,\, y\Gamma_1\rangle\,\big((\varrho^{n-1})^{\Gamma_1}_y\times\varrho(n)\big)^{\Gamma},$$

where the ϱ^n and ϱ^{n-1} states are antisymmetrized respectively in particles no. 1, ..., n and no. 1, ..., $(n-1)$. Consider now the matrix element of $\mathcal{U}^{\nu}_{\varrho\varrho}$ which by the usual fractional-parentage procedure becomes

$$(5.129)\qquad \langle nx\Gamma\|\mathcal{U}^{\nu}_{\varrho\varrho}\|nx'\Gamma'\rangle = \\ = n\sum_{y\Gamma_1}(-1)^{\Gamma_1+\nu-\varrho-\Gamma'}\left[\frac{\Gamma\Gamma'}{\Gamma_1\nu}\right]^{\frac{1}{2}} U(\Gamma\varrho\Gamma'\varrho:\Gamma_1\nu)\langle nx\Gamma|n-1,\, y\Gamma_1\rangle\langle nx'\Gamma'|n-1,\, y\Gamma_1\rangle\,.$$

In second quantization by the intermediate-state expansion method we find for the same element

$$(5.130)\qquad \sum_{y\Gamma_1}(-1)^{\Gamma_1+\nu-\varrho-\Gamma'}[\Gamma_1\nu]^{-\frac{1}{2}}U(\Gamma\varrho\Gamma'\varrho:\Gamma_1\nu)\cdot \\ \cdot\langle nx\Gamma\|A^{\varrho}\|n-1),\, y\Gamma_1\rangle\langle nx'\Gamma'\|A^{\varrho}\|n-1,\, y\Gamma_1\rangle\,.$$

We are now however free to make a decision about phases and doing this in the obvious way we have, for equivalent-particle states, the correspondence

$$(5.131)\qquad \langle nx\Gamma\|A^{\varrho}\|n-1,\, y\Gamma_1\rangle=\sqrt{n[\Gamma]}\langle nx\Gamma|n-1,\, y\Gamma_1\rangle\,.$$

Since particles equivalent in one representation are not necessarily so in another we suspect that this equation is valid in the most general case, and this is in fact true. But having established a phase correspondence between the configuration-space and second-quantized equivalent-particle states by means of this equation, we ask what becomes of this correspondence when we deal with more complex states, in particular with states made up of a number of coupled equivalent groups (which of course can describe the general situation). Consider the simple case of the separation of a particle ϱ' from a two-particle state $(\varrho\varrho')$ with $\varrho\neq\varrho'$. Then

$$(5.132)\qquad \Psi^{\Gamma}(\varrho\varrho')=\frac{1}{\sqrt{2}}\left\{\left(\varrho(1)\times\varrho'(2)\right)^{\Gamma}-\left(\varrho(2)\times\varrho'(1)\right)^{\Gamma}\right\},$$

and the c.f.p. is $+1/\sqrt{2}$. If now we take $\bar{Z}^{\Gamma}=(B^{\varrho}\times B^{\varrho'})^{\Gamma}$ so that

$$Z^{\Gamma}(\varrho\varrho')=(-1)^{\varrho+\varrho'-\Gamma}(A^{\varrho'}\times A^{\varrho})\,,$$

we have

$$(5.133)\qquad \langle\bar{Z}^{\Gamma}(\varrho\varrho')\|A^{\varrho'}\|Z^{\varrho}(\varrho)\rangle= \\ =(-1)^{\Gamma-\varrho'-\varrho}\langle(\bar{Z}^{\Gamma}(\varrho\varrho')\times A^{\varrho'}\times A^{\varrho})^{0}\rangle_0=\langle(\bar{Z}^{\Gamma}(\varrho\varrho')\times Z^{\Gamma}(\varrho\varrho'))^{0}\rangle_0=[\Gamma]^{\frac{1}{2}},$$

and thus we see that eq. (5.131) is satisfied for this simple case. The significant thing is that the *adjoint* state operator is coupled in the same order as the wave-function itself. It is almost obvious that this is true in general and we then have the correspondence (*): if

$$(5.134)\qquad \Psi=(\Psi_{x_1}^{\Gamma_1}\times\Psi_{x_2}^{\Gamma_2}\times\Psi_{x_3}^{\Gamma_3}\,...)^{\Gamma}\quad\text{then}\quad \bar{Z}=(\bar{Z}_{x_1}^{\Gamma_1}\times\bar{Z}_{x_2}^{\Gamma_2}\times\bar{Z}_{x_3}^{\Gamma_3}\,...)^{\Gamma}.$$

(*) The antisymmetrization of the coupled wave function is understood to be carried out in such a way that the overlap of the antisymmetrized state with the partially antisymmetrized state $\Psi_{x_1}^{\Gamma_1}(1\,...\,n_1)\times\Psi_{x_2}^{\Gamma_2}(n_1+1\,...\,n_1+n_2)\times...$ is positive (having in fact the value $\{n_1!n_2!\,.../(\sum n_i)!\}^{\frac{1}{2}}$). This is the usual sense in which a coupling order is specified in mixed-configuration spectroscopy.

This correspondence along with the c.f.p. correspondence of eq. (5.131) is all that we need to ensure that the results of configuration-space calculations will agree precisely (*i.e.* in phase) with the second-quantized ones.

A heuristic argument concerning the inversion implied by eq. (5.134) is that the configuration-space numbering conventionally runs from left to right, while the second-quantized « numbering » runs from right to left since with a product of $\boldsymbol{A}^{\varrho}$ operators the one on the right operates first on the vacuum. A rigorous formal proof of both eqs. (5.131), (5.134) can be given by using the coupled wave-function representation to evaluate the c.f.p. for separating off a particle from one of the groups, and then comparing the result with the corresponding v.e.v. This is left for an exercise.

As a final exercise consider that in evaluating the matrix element of a one-body operator (and similarly for more complex ones) one has, in the configuration-space representation, the choice of expressing the n-body matrix elements in terms of the $(n-1)$-body elements, or of evaluating them explicitly. The fractional-parentage expansion can be used for either purpose. Find the corresponding second-quantized results!

6. – Single-particle and single-hole excitations.

6·1. *General remarks.* – As the first major example of the application of multipole techniques we consider the analysis of excitations produced by adding a single particle or hole to a nucleus. If one does this by means of resonant reactions or by direct stripping or pick-up reactions, then, by the use of resonant-reaction theory or by DWBA analysis, one can extract with fair accuracy (say $\pm 20\,\%$ in good cases) the « spectroscopic factors » or transition strengths which are the quantities we need. There are, to be sure, many situations (*e.g.* (^{3}He, d) (α, t), etc.) in which the extraction of strengths from data is not as trustworthy as in the relatively simpler (d, p) reaction; it may be argued in fact that improving our understanding of these reactions and of direct reactions in general is at this time one of the things most badly needed for further progress in the study of nuclei. But that question is outside our domain and we shall refer to it again only because certain sum-rule results provide methods for testing the accuracy of the data $\rightarrow$ strengths reduction.

The closely related (p, 2p) reactions, while not at present giving measurements of single-level strengths, do provide excellent information about the excitation energies and the widths.

The various methods of applying sum rules discussed in Sect. **4** can be applied in the present case. As far as the direct analysis of data is concerned the experimentalist is faced with the problem of measuring strengths for a single transfer orbit, *i.e.* for a given n_r, l, j. The orbital angular momentum is easy but, except when one of the states involved has spin zero, the j value is in practice quite difficult, requiring some kind of polarization or correlation measurement. But there seems to be no good reason why methods for such measurements should not be developed in the future and, in the meantime, one can often *infer* the j-values from a general knowledge of the target and the final states; and of course for $l=0$ the question does not arise. The question of the radial quantum number, though usually ignored, is more difficult but, from the general standpoint of many-body problems, extremely interesting. It will certainly receive a great deal more attention in the future. Certain of the results which we shall derive will be of value in telling us about the inaccuracies, including those involving n_r and j, in the reduction of the data, and in giving us an over-all view of the accuracy.

If we are proceeding in the opposite direction (calculating strengths from target functions) there is of course no reason why we must restrict ourselves to a given j (or even a given n_r); we need only use the mixed-orbit strength functions for our analysis to be applicable to these cases.

We stress that our purpose in this Section, and in the following two as well, is not to attempt a complete review of the subjects but rather to indicate how the techniques developed above can be usefully applied.

6·2. *Non-energy-weighted* (NEW) *sum rules* ($m=0$). – If ϱ is the transfer orbit ($\varrho=n_r, l, j, t$, etc.) then $\lambda=\varrho$ and

$$(6.1)\qquad \left|\begin{array}{ll} \left.\begin{array}{l} \boldsymbol{T}^{\lambda}\Rightarrow \boldsymbol{A}^{\varrho} \\ \overline{\boldsymbol{T}}^{\lambda}\Rightarrow (-1)^{2\varrho}\boldsymbol{B}^{\varrho} \end{array}\right\} & \text{(adding a particle; +)}, \\ \left.\begin{array}{l} \boldsymbol{T}^{\lambda}\Rightarrow \boldsymbol{B}^{\varrho} \\ \overline{\boldsymbol{T}}^{\lambda}\Rightarrow \boldsymbol{A}^{\varrho} \end{array}\right\} & \text{(adding a hole; —)}, \end{array}\right.$$

and then by eqs. (3.19), (5.31), the strengths are related to the usual (*) « spectroscopic factors » $\mathscr{S}^{(\pm)}$, by

$$(6.2)\qquad \left|\begin{array}{l} \mathscr{G}^{(+)}=\mathscr{S}^{(+)}, \\ \mathscr{G}^{(-)}=\left[\dfrac{T}{T_1}\right]\mathscr{S}^{(-)}. \end{array}\right.$$

(*) It is best not to regard the spectroscopic factor as being the same in the isobaric-spin and (p-n) formalisms. Instead we have $(C)^2\mathscr{S}(T)=\mathscr{S}(p\text{-}n)$ where $(C)^2$ is the usual isobaric-spin coupling factor.

The equation for the nonenergy-weighted moment (3.31) now becomes

$$(6.3)\quad \begin{cases} \mathscr{G}^{(0,+)}(\theta) = \sum_\nu (-1)^{2\varrho-\nu} \left[\dfrac{\nu}{\Gamma\varrho}\right]^{\frac{1}{2}} \langle x\Gamma \| (\boldsymbol{B}^\varrho \times \boldsymbol{A}^\varrho)^\nu \| x\Gamma\rangle \cdot P_\nu(\cos\theta)\,, \\ \mathscr{G}^{(0,-)}(\theta) = \sum_\nu (-1)^\nu \left[\dfrac{\nu}{\Gamma\varrho}\right]^{\frac{1}{2}} \langle x\Gamma \| (\boldsymbol{A}^\varrho \times \boldsymbol{B}^\varrho)^\nu \| x\Gamma\rangle \cdot P_\nu(\cos\theta)\,. \end{cases}$$

Let us first combine these results and evaluate the combined target integrals by using the commutation rules (eq. (5.4)). Then remembering that

$$\langle x\Gamma \| 1 \| x\Gamma\rangle = [\Gamma]^{\frac{1}{2}}\,,$$

and using the P_ν results of eq. (3.29e) we have the very pleasing relationship that

$$(6.4)\qquad \mathscr{G}^{(0,\pm)}(\theta) = 1 - \mathscr{G}^{(0,\mp)}(\pi - \theta)\,,$$

the Racah form for which is

$$(6.5)\qquad \mathscr{G}^{(0,\pm)}(\Gamma_1) = 1 - \sum_{\Gamma_1'} \left[\frac{\Gamma_1'}{\Gamma_1}\right]^{\frac{1}{2}} U(\Gamma\varrho\varrho\Gamma : \Gamma_1\Gamma_1')\, \mathscr{G}^{(0,\mp)}(\Gamma_1')\,.$$

This equation is a direct transcription of the commutation rules. Considered in another way it gives a generalization of the statement that the number of (particles + holes) in an orbit is just the degeneracy of the orbit; indeed the $\nu = 0$ component of the equation, the only one if we have a scalar target, is just precisely this commonplace statement.

A simple consequence of this equation is that, if the target contains no ϱ particles $(\mathscr{G}^{(0,-)}(\theta) = 0)$ then necessarily the stripping strength is constant; this is a general statement of the so-called $(2J+1)$ rule. More to the point, the equation enables us to give a quantitative interpretation of departures from this rule and is of course valid even in the most general circumstances, when there is no reason to think of the elementary rule.

From the standpoint of the general classification of data (Sect. **4**) we have of course that, if $\mathscr{G}^{(0,+)}(\theta)$ has been already measured, then $\mathscr{G}^{(0,-)}(\theta)$ is redundant since it can be calculated from $\mathscr{G}^{(0,+)}(\theta)$; that is to say, the distribution among the different Γ_1 values of the strength for adding a particle determines completely the corresponding distribution for taking away a particle, this being true no matter how complex are the nuclear states involved.

At present the major use which one envisions for the equation is in testing the accuracy with which one can carry out the $\{$data $\to$ reduced data$\}$ reduction, *i.e.* in testing the accuracy of the DWBA analysis, since most strengths are found by analysis of direct-reaction experiments. So far, except for a few trivial applications of the monopole equation, no applications have been made of this sum rule but hopefully this will change before long.

Leaving now the relationship between adding a particle and a hole, let us consider each separately. The operator $(\boldsymbol{A}^{\varrho}\times\boldsymbol{B}^{\varrho})^{\nu}$ which enters is a one-body operator, of rank ν, which moves a particle around but only in the orbit ϱ. Except for normalization the operator is in fact simply the orbit-diagonal unit tensor operator which we have introduced via eq. (5.12). The $m=0$ strength equations are now

$$\text{(6.6)}\qquad \mathscr{G}^{(0,-)}(\theta)=1-\mathscr{G}^{(0,+)}(\pi-\theta)=\sum_{\nu}(-1)^{\nu}\frac{[\nu]}{[\Gamma\varrho]^{\frac{1}{2}}}\langle\|\mathscr{U}^{\nu}_{\varrho\varrho}\|\rangle\cdot P_{\nu}(\cos\theta)\,,$$

and, with the proviso discussed in Sect. **3** about the decreasing accuracy for higher m, we can therefore deduce from the $m=0$ moment, the reduced multipole moments of the system for the orbit involved in the transfer.

As a simple but important example consider the $\nu=0$ component of these equations. Then

$$\text{(6.7)}\qquad \frac{1}{2}\int \mathrm{d}\cos\theta\cdot\mathscr{G}^{(0,-)}(\theta)=1-\frac{1}{2}\int\mathrm{d}\cos\theta\cdot\mathscr{G}^{(0,+)}(\theta)=$$

$$=[\Gamma\varrho]^{\frac{1}{2}}\langle\|\mathscr{U}^{0}_{\varrho\varrho}\|\rangle=\frac{\langle n(\varrho)\rangle}{[\varrho]}=1-\frac{\langle n(\varrho_h)\rangle}{[\varrho]}\,,$$

where $\langle n(\varrho)\rangle$ and $\langle n(\varrho_h)\rangle$ are respectively the average number of ϱ-particles and ϱ-holes in the target, and we have used $[\varrho]^{\frac{1}{2}}\mathscr{U}^{0}_{\varrho\varrho}=n_{\text{op}}(\varrho)$ and $\langle\|1\|\rangle=[\Gamma]^{\frac{1}{2}}$. Rewriting in Racah form and with spectroscopic factors (eqs. (3.29), (6.2), (3.27)) tnis becomes

$$\text{(6.8)}\qquad \left\{\begin{aligned}&\sum_{\Gamma_1}\left[\frac{\Gamma_1}{\Gamma}\right]\mathscr{G}^{(0,-)}(\Gamma_1)\equiv\sum_{y\Gamma_1}\mathscr{S}^{(-)}_{y}(\Gamma_1)=\langle n(\varrho)\rangle\,,\\&\sum_{\Gamma_1}\left[\frac{\Gamma_1}{\Gamma}\right]\mathscr{G}^{(0,+)}(\Gamma_1)\equiv\sum_{y\Gamma_1}\left[\frac{\Gamma_1}{\Gamma}\right]\mathscr{S}^{(+)}_{y}(\Gamma_1)=\langle n(\varrho_h)\rangle\,,\end{aligned}\right.$$

where of course the h $\rightleftharpoons$ p relationship between the two results could have been inferred *a priori*.

We can interpret these (as always) in a p-n or in an isobaric-spin formalism. In the first we have for proton transfer (and similarly for neutron transfer),

$$\text{(6.9)}\qquad \left\{\begin{aligned}&\sum_{yJ_1}\mathscr{S}^{(-)}_{p}(y,J_1)=\langle\text{protons}\rangle_j\,,\\&\sum_{yJ_1}\left[\frac{J_1}{J}\right]\mathscr{S}^{(+)}_{p}(y,J_1)=\langle\text{proton holes}\rangle_j\,,\end{aligned}\right.$$

while in the second we have

$$(6.10)\quad \begin{cases} \sum_{yJ_1T_1} \mathscr{S}^{(-)}(yJ_1T_1) = \langle \text{nucleons} \rangle_j \,, \\ \sum_{yJ_1T_1} \left[\dfrac{J_1T_1}{JT}\right] \mathscr{S}^{(+)}(yJ_1T_1) = \langle \text{nucleon holes} \rangle_j \,. \end{cases}$$

It is left as an exercise to explain the relationship between these two sets of results (do not forget that the spectroscopic factors occurring are not the same in the two cases—see footnote following eq. (6.2)). It is clear that the separate proton and neutron results, implying as they do the separate results for the two final T_1-values, determine both the isoscalar and isovector monopole results, $\nu = (0, 0)$ and $\nu = (0, 1)$. These monopole equations are not new but only in the past year or so has any application beyond the simplest one been made. In this, SHERR and his collaborators have to a very good purpose, by separating pick-up strengths into groups with $T_1 = T \pm \frac{1}{2}$, made use of the two sum rules together.

In cases where we believe the target to have only a single active orbit, as may be sensible in the $f_{\frac{7}{2}}$ shell for example, the partial multipole moments (for $\nu \neq 0$) are in fact the total multipole moments of the system. In this case of course the $\nu = 1$ (or (1, 0) in the T-formalism) moment simply measures the J-values. We have then that the $\nu = 0$, $\nu = 1$ (or $\nu = (0, 0)$, (0, 1) and (1, 0)) moments all correspond to *redundant* information, and may therefore be used as « testing equations » to study the accuracy of the method used for extracting spectroscopic factors. And in such cases where the magnetic moment (a combination of the (1, 0) and (1, 1) moments) is known we can hopefully regard the (1, 1) partial moment as also redundant.

For a scalar target ($\Gamma = 0$) only the $\nu = 0$ target integrals are nonzero. This points up the fact that the moments being measured are not intrinsic moments (with respect to a symmetry axis of the nucleus) but rather moments with respect to axes fixed in space. In those cases then where $\Gamma < \varrho$ we have the usual *decoupling loss of information* mentioned earlier, which can only be avoided if, *e.g.* by considering such « correlated » reactions as (d, pγ), we impose a preferred axis on the system. Little consideration has yet been given to sum rules for these more complex reactions.

A final remark about the $\langle \| \mathscr{U}^{\nu}_{\varrho\varrho} \| \rangle$ quantities. These, the multipole generalizations of the orbit occupation numbers ($\nu = 0$), will automatically enter as parameters in any model of the nuclear states which goes beyond the simplest one in which maximal zero-coupled pairing is assumed. From another standpoint, as we have already said, they are coefficients in the spherical-orbit expansion of the general one-body nuclear density. That part of the single-body density which refers to particles in a single orbit is often discussed in terms of population moments $P(k)$. If, for a given orientation of the nucleus in space, the average populations of the m sublevel for the orbit j (we consider a j formalism) is $n(m)$ then the $P(k)$ are defined by

$$P(k) = \sum_{m=-j}^{+j} (m)^k n(m) , \tag{6.11}$$

and these contain the one-body information. But they vary in a complex fashion as the orientation in space is changed and on that account, except for problems involving aligned or polarized nuclei, are not convenient to use. We see that the $\langle \| \mathscr{U}^k_{jj} \| \rangle$ quantities then define a set of population moments with an invariant significance.

A final remark about the NEW sum rules is that, in a formal sense, they are complete in so far as the single-nucleon density is concerned. In other words, the multipole expansions of the single-particle strengths (both diagonal and nondiagonal in orbit) determine everything about the single-particle properties of the target.

This is in contrast to what one normally expects to find via an NEW sum rule: the extension comes about because of our incorporation of the angular momenta.

6'3. *Linear-energy-weighted* (LEW) *sum rules* ($m = 1$) (*). – The $m = 1$ sum-rule equations are

$$\begin{cases} \mathscr{G}^{(1,+)}(\theta) = \sum_\nu (-1)^{2\varrho-\nu} \left[\dfrac{\nu}{\Gamma\varrho}\right]^{\frac{1}{2}} \langle \| (\boldsymbol{B}^\varrho \times H \times \boldsymbol{A}^\varrho)^\nu \| \rangle P_\nu(\cos\theta) , \\ \mathscr{G}^{(1,-)}(\theta) = \sum_\nu (-1)^{\nu} \left[\dfrac{\nu}{\Gamma\varrho}\right]^{\frac{1}{2}} \langle \| (\boldsymbol{A}^\varrho \times H \times \boldsymbol{B}^\varrho)^\nu \| \rangle P_\nu(\cos\theta) , \end{cases} \tag{6.12}$$

and their essential role is in relating the (angle-dependent) excitation energies $\mathscr{E}(\theta)$, (eq. (3.36)), into information about the ground-state and the interaction. The figure shows the situation with which we are dealing:

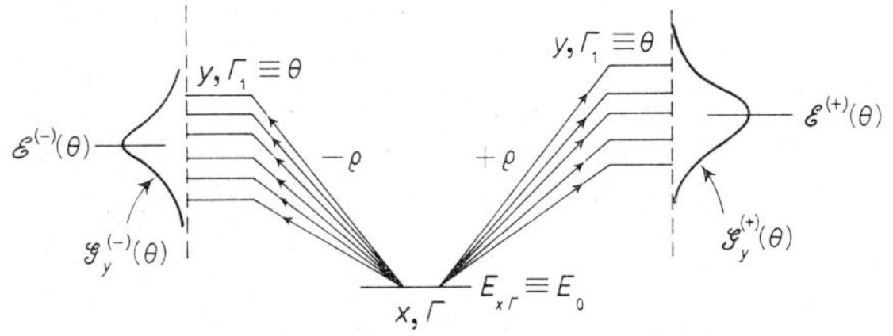

Fig. 9. – A schematic representation of the single-nucleon and single-hole strengths for the same target. If all the final levels shown have the same angular momenta the centroids are $\mathscr{E}^{(\pm)}(\theta)$ as indicated. If we consider levels of all angular momenta we get $\mathscr{E}^{(\pm)}$.

(*) The work of this Section has been done partly in collaboration with Dr. R. K. Bansal.

For the *over-all* excitation energy, $\mathscr{E}$, we have (eqs. (3.37), (6.7))

$$(6.13)\qquad \begin{cases} \mathscr{E}^{(+)} = \dfrac{\langle\|(\boldsymbol{B}^{\varrho}\times H\times \boldsymbol{A}^{\varrho})^{0}\|\rangle}{\langle\|(\boldsymbol{B}^{\varrho}\times \boldsymbol{A}^{\varrho})^{0}\|\rangle} = \dfrac{(-1)^{2\varrho}[\varrho]^{\frac{1}{2}}}{\langle n(\varrho_h)\rangle}\langle|(\boldsymbol{B}^{\varrho}\times H\times \boldsymbol{A}^{\varrho})^{0}|\rangle\,, \\[2ex] \mathscr{E}^{(-)} = \dfrac{\langle\|(\boldsymbol{A}^{\varrho}\times H\times \boldsymbol{B}^{\varrho})^{0}\|\rangle}{\langle\|(\boldsymbol{A}^{\varrho}\times \boldsymbol{B}^{\varrho})^{0}\|\rangle} = \dfrac{[\varrho]^{\frac{1}{2}}}{\langle n(\varrho)\rangle}\langle|(\boldsymbol{A}^{\varrho}\times H\times \boldsymbol{B}^{\varrho})^{0}|\rangle\,, \end{cases}$$

which are rather obvious results. Note that the right-hand integrals are single-barred matrix elements.

The target-integral operators in eqs. (6.12), (6.13) have three-body parts and are therefore complicated. However we can simplify things by using a commutator, writing then

$$(6.14)\qquad \begin{cases} (\boldsymbol{B}^{\varrho}\times H\times \boldsymbol{A}^{\varrho})^{\nu} = (\boldsymbol{B}^{\varrho}[H\boldsymbol{A}^{\varrho}])^{\nu} + (\boldsymbol{B}^{\varrho}\times \boldsymbol{A}^{\varrho})^{\nu}\, H\,, \\ (\boldsymbol{A}^{\varrho}\times H\times \boldsymbol{B}^{\varrho})^{\nu} = -\big([H\boldsymbol{A}^{\varrho}]\times \boldsymbol{B}^{\varrho}\big)^{\nu} + H(\boldsymbol{A}^{\varrho}\times \boldsymbol{B}^{\varrho})^{\nu}, \end{cases}$$

the advantage of this being that the complicated operators involving three-body parts are rewritten in terms of a simpler such operator and a two-body operator. Moreover if the ground-state be an eigenstate of H (as in principle it should be) the resultant three-body operator becomes effectively a simple one-body operator (*), a multiple indeed of the number operator for holes or particles in the transfer orbit.

Just as in the $m=0$ case, we first further simplify things by combining the particle and hole equations. Then

$$(6.15)\qquad (\boldsymbol{B}^{\varrho}\times H\boldsymbol{A}^{\varrho})^{\nu} - (-1)^{2\varrho-\nu}(\boldsymbol{A}^{\varrho}\times H\boldsymbol{B}^{\varrho})^{\nu} = \big(\boldsymbol{B}^{\varrho}\times[H\boldsymbol{A}^{\varrho}]\big)^{\nu} +$$
$$+ (-1)^{2\varrho-\nu}\big([H\boldsymbol{A}^{\varrho}]\times \boldsymbol{B}^{\varrho}\big)^{\nu} - (-1)^{2\varrho-\nu}[\nu]^{\frac{1}{2}}\{\mathscr{U}^{\nu}_{\varrho\varrho}H + H\mathscr{U}^{\nu}_{\varrho\varrho}\} + (-1)^{2\varrho}[\varrho]^{\frac{1}{2}}\delta_{\nu 0}H =$$
$$= (-1)^{2\varrho}\sum_{r,t}\beta^{\nu}_{r\,t\varrho\varrho}\zeta^{-1}_{r\varrho}\zeta^{-1}_{t\varrho}\mathscr{U}^{\nu}_{rt} - (-1)^{2\varrho-\nu}[\nu]^{\frac{1}{2}}\{\mathscr{U}^{\nu}_{\varrho\varrho}H + H\mathscr{U}^{\nu}_{\varrho\varrho}\} + (-1)^{2\varrho}[\varrho]^{\frac{1}{2}}\delta_{\nu 0}\{H+\varepsilon_{\varrho}\},$$

where the commutator has been evaluated by using the results in the Appendix, and where the Hamiltonian H and the multipole interaction parameter β^{ν} are given by eqs. (5.54), (5.71). Following the discussion centered around eq. (5.69) we have omitted the single-body terms nondiagonal in orbit and made a corresponding restriction on the two-particle H. As before

$$\zeta_{r\varrho} = 1 \quad \text{if} \quad r\neq\varrho\,, \qquad = \frac{1}{\sqrt{2}} \quad \text{if} \quad r=\varrho\,,$$

and we are using a hybrid, but obvious, notation for the orbits, the transfer orbit always being ϱ.

(*) When we speak of an n-body operator we will often mean that the most complex part is n-body, but there may be simpler parts.

Inserting this result into the $m=1$ moment expression we find, after some elementary transformations, that

$$(6.16)\quad \{\mathscr{G}^{(1,+)}(\pi-\theta)-\mathscr{G}^{(1,-)}(\theta)\}-E_0\{\mathscr{G}^{(0,+)}(\pi-\theta)-\mathscr{G}^{(0,-)}(\theta)\}=\sum_\nu F_\nu P_\nu(\cos\theta)+\varepsilon_\varrho,$$

which, rewritten in terms of the excitation energies by means of eq. (3.36), becomes

$$(6.17)\quad \big(\mathscr{E}^{(+)}(\pi-\theta)-E_0\big)\mathscr{G}^{(0,+)}(\pi-\theta)-\big(\mathscr{E}^{-}(\theta)-E_0\big)\mathscr{G}^{0,-}(\theta)=\sum_\nu F_\nu P_\nu(\cos\theta)+\varepsilon_\varrho.$$

In these expressions the quantity F_ν is given by

$$(6.18)\quad F_\nu=\sum_{r,t}\left[\frac{\nu}{\Gamma\varrho}\right]^{\frac{1}{2}}\beta^\nu_{rt\varrho\varrho}\zeta^{-1}_{r\varrho}\zeta^{-1}_{t\varrho}\langle x\Gamma\|\mathscr{U}^\nu_{rt}\|x\Gamma\rangle\,.$$

F_ν has a simple interpretation. It is essentially the ν-th multipole expansion coefficient for the interaction between a particle in an orbit ϱ and the nucleus in the target state. It takes full account of the complexities of the individual interactions and of the particle distributions in the target, no matter how complex these may be. We obviously have a need for such a quantity. At least for the interaction which is diagonal in the target orbit (*i.e.* $r=t$) the result for F_ν may also be written in spherical-harmonic form but this we leave as an exercise.

For the monopole case (monopole either because we have a scalar target or because we consider the « over-all » excitation energies of eq. (3.37)) we note first that we have (*) $\mathscr{U}^0_{rt}\sim\delta_{rt}n_{\text{op}}(r)$. Then using the $m=0$ monopole results of eq. (6.7), it follows from eq. (6.16) that

$$(6.19)\quad (\mathscr{E}^{(+)}-E_0)\frac{\langle n(\varrho_h)\rangle}{[\varrho]}-(\mathscr{E}^{(-)}-E_0)\frac{\langle n(\varrho)\rangle}{[\varrho]}=\varepsilon_\varrho+F_0\,.$$

But, using the results for average energies (eqs. (5.63), (5.64), (5.74), (5.75)) and understanding that $\overline{W}_{\varrho\varrho}\equiv\overline{W}_\varrho$, we have

$$(6.20)\quad \left\{\begin{aligned}&\beta^0_{rr\varrho\varrho}=(\zeta_{r\varrho})^2[\varrho r]^{\frac{1}{2}}\left\{1-\frac{\delta_{r\varrho}}{[\varrho]}\right\}\overline{W}_{r\varrho}\,,\\&F_0=\sum_r\langle n(r)\rangle\left\{1-\frac{\delta_{r\varrho}}{[\varrho]}\right\}\overline{W}_{r\varrho}\,,\end{aligned}\right.$$

(*) If the target has *active* orbits differing only in radial quantum number, this equivalence will not be strictly true unless we agree to extend our notion of the cancellation between the nondiagonal one-body terms and the corresponding $H^{(2)}$ terms to these orbits as well. But at present this point seems to be of little importance.

and finally the extremely useful result that

$$(6.21)\qquad (\mathscr{E}^{(+)}-E_0)\frac{\langle n(\varrho_h)\rangle}{[\varrho]}-(\mathscr{E}^{(-)}-E_0)\frac{\langle n(\varrho)\rangle}{[\varrho]}=\varepsilon_\varrho+\sum_r\langle n(r)\rangle\left\{1-\frac{\delta_{r\varrho}}{[\varrho]}\right\}\overline{W}_{r\varrho}\,,$$

where, as always, E_0 is the target energy.

We have here a relationship between the particle and hole monopole excitation energies, these being connected via the average orbit occupancies in the target and the average orbit-orbit interactions. The r sum is over all orbits but of course we can ignore the closed shells as long as we include in the single-particle energy, ε_ϱ, the contribution to the excitation energy which they produce. In fact, as we have discussed, there is an invariance of all such equations under the operation of omitting the two-particle interaction with closed shells, at the same time making the concomitant change in the single-particle parameter.

This monopole equation has a simple structure and could have been easily derived by elementary considerations. This seems to be hardly true however for the general case (eq. (6.17)). The importance of the latter result is that it extends the easily understandable monopole result to the most general case, being valid whether or not there are particles in the target equivalent to the transferred particle and independently of the complexity of the states involved, and giving of course also the « angular » structure. The « equivalence » extension is of some consequence because the methods of conventional spectroscopy always have great difficulty in handling such things as « weak coupling » of a partially equivalent particle.

The outcome of combining the $m=1$ particle and hole results is then to determine the target-particle interaction coefficients. For the case where the target has only a single active orbit and the particle transfer involves that same orbit, a determination of the $\beta^\nu_{\cdot}$ is of course equivalent to determining the two-body spectrum. But as we have mentioned earlier, there is a $\beta^\nu_{\cdot}$ redundancy in the one-orbit case which arises from the fact that there are twice as many β^ν values as two-body matrix elements, half of the latter which are allowed by the geometry being in fact excluded by the Pauli principle. This redundancy could then in principle be used for « testing » purposes.

We leave it as an exercise to write the $\nu=(0,1)$ equation which corresponds to eq. (6.21) and to work out the relationship between this result and the separate proton and neutron $\nu=0$ results.

Next consider what we can learn from the experimentally more accessible separate $m=1$ pick-up and stripping strengths. Using the results of the Appendix along with eqs. (6.12), (6.14) we find the following result:

$$(6.22)\qquad \mathscr{G}^{(1,-)}(\theta)=(E_0-\varepsilon_\varrho)\,\mathscr{G}^{(0,-)}(\pi-\theta)+\sum_\nu G_\nu P_\nu(\cos\theta)\,,$$

where the *two-body correlation* moment G_ν is given by

(6.23) $$G_\nu = \frac{(-1)^\nu}{[\varrho]}\left[\frac{\nu}{\Gamma}\right]^{\frac{1}{2}} \sum_{\substack{rst:\Lambda \\ r\leq s}} [\Lambda]^{\frac{1}{2}} W^{\Lambda}_{rst\varrho}\, \frac{\zeta_{rs}}{\zeta_{t\varrho}}\, \langle x\Gamma \| $$ 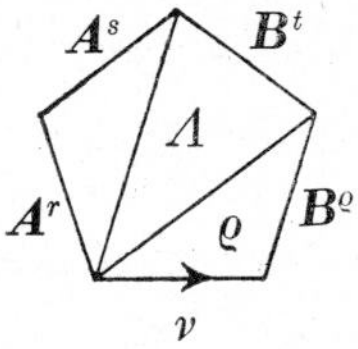

$$\| x\Gamma\rangle \, .$$

By means of eq. (6.16) relating $\mathscr{G}^{(1+)}$ and $\mathscr{G}^{(1-)}$, the $\mathscr{G}^{(1+)}$ function may also be written in the same way. The target integrals now involve the two-body correlation moments as indicated and therefore in principle tell us something about two-body correlations among the particles of the active shells (even though the process involved is a one-body process).

A very simple case arises if we can consider that the target has only a single active shell being described as $(\varrho^n)_{x\Gamma}$, and if we add an equivalent particle or hole to it. Then, ignoring for convenience the single-body energies (and therefore dealing with the single-orbit residual-interaction energies), we have

(6.24) $$G_0 = -\frac{2}{[\varrho]}\langle|H|\rangle = -\frac{2E_0}{[\varrho]},$$

and then the monopole excitation energy is

(6.25) $$\mathscr{E}^- = E_0 + \frac{G_0[\varrho]}{\langle n\rangle} = \frac{n-2}{n} E_0 \, ,$$

a result which could have been derived also by a direct use of the fact that, for a single-orbit Hamiltonian,

(6.26) $$(A^\varrho \times H \times B^\varrho)^0 = [\varrho]^{-\frac{1}{2}} H(n_{\mathrm{op}}(\varrho) - 2) \, .$$

Note also that good values for E_0 can often be found by consulting a Table of binding energies and making the natural subtractions.

A peculiar but not very important result is that the spectrum of the pick-up excitation energies produced by taking various ϱ^n states as targets (though they are not experimentally accessible as such) reproduces the ϱ^n level spectrum but with a modified scale factor. The $(n-2)/n$ factor is simply the relative number of pairs in the ϱ^{n-1} and ϱ^n nuclei. An elementary derivation of the result can be given via a fractional-parentage argument if we assume that all the states involved have only a single active orbit (though even this simple derivation does not seem to have been given until recently). But, as is general for sum-rule considerations, a simple assumption for the target state does not at all involve a similar assumption for the final states. The equation given is correct no matter how complex are the final states. This is an example of a very common phenomenon, that results derived in a restricted domain by conventional spectroscopy, have a natural generalization when derived by more sophisticated procedures.

The monopole excitation energy $\mathscr{E}^+$ for the target with a single active orbit can be derived the same way, for example by using

$$(6.27)\qquad (-1)^{2\varrho}[\varrho]^{\frac{1}{2}}(\boldsymbol{B}^{\varrho}\times H\times \boldsymbol{A}^{\varrho})^0 = H\{[\varrho]-n_{\mathrm{op}}(\varrho)-2\}+\frac{2}{[\varrho]}W(\text{c.s.})n_{\mathrm{op}}(\varrho)\,,$$

where $W(\text{c.s.})$ is the closed-shell energy (eq. (5.75)). Alternatively one could make a h$\rightleftharpoons$p transformation starting with the integral expressions for $\mathscr{E}^{\pm}$, eq. (3.37). We shall derive it instead directly from the $\mathscr{E}^-$ result, the purpose being to illustrate an important point about h$\rightleftharpoons$p transformations involving a two-body Hamiltonian. The point is that the *two-particle* operator H for a single shell when written in terms of holes has a two-hole part, a constant part (the closed-shell energy), but also a one-hole part implying a single-hole term. This follows formally from the structure of H, but more simply from the well-known fact (which would come easily by the method of Sect. **5**·9) that the average two-body energy for n particles is $\overline{W}(n)=\frac{1}{2}n(n-1)\overline{W}(2)$. Then, since for $n=N,\ N-1$ (where $N=[\varrho]$), $\overline{W}(n)=W(n)$, we identify the « vacuum energy » in the hole-picture as $\overline{W}(N)\equiv W(\text{c.s.})=\frac{1}{2}N(N-1)\overline{W}(2)$ and the single-hole energy as $\overline{W}(N-1)-\overline{W}(N)=-(N-1)\overline{W}(2)$. Using these results and remembering that, in the particle picture we have taken the vacuum and single-particle energies to be zero, we see that eq. (6.25) transforms into

$$(6.28)\qquad \{\mathscr{E}^+-W(N)+(N-1)\overline{W}(2)(N-n-1)\}= \\ =\frac{(N-n-2)}{(N-n)}\{E_0-W(N)+(N-1)\overline{W}(2)(N-n)\}\,,$$

and rewriting this we find for the excitation energy on a (ϱ^n) target

$$(6.29)\qquad \mathscr{E}^+=\frac{(N-n-2)}{(N-n)}E_0+\frac{(N-1)}{(N-n)}n\,\overline{W}(2)\,.$$

It should be verified that these special results for $\mathscr{E}^{\pm}$ are consistent with the general monopole result of eq. (6.21) which could of course have been used to derive one excitation energy from the other.

As an exercise and a minor illustration of these centroid results one might consider reactions starting with a seniority-zero or seniority-one target where the Hamiltonian is that of the identical-particle single-orbit pairing force, eq. (5.115). Then if $H=(A/N)\cdot G$, where now $N=[j]$, it will be found that (using a labelling (n, v)),

$$(6.30)\quad \begin{cases} \mathscr{G}^{+}(n, 0 \to n+1, 1) = \dfrac{N-n}{N}\,, \\ \mathscr{G}^{+}(n, 1 \to n+1, 0) = n+1\,, \\ \sum_{J_1} [J_1]\mathscr{G}^{+}(n, 1 \to n+1, 2;\, J_1) = (N+1)(N-n-1)\,, \\ \mathscr{G}^{-}(n, 0 \to n-1, 1) = \dfrac{n}{N}\,, \\ \mathscr{G}^{-}(n, 1 \to n-1, 0) = (N-n+1)\,, \\ \sum_{J_1} [J_1]\mathscr{G}^{-}(n, 1 \to n-1, 2;\, J_1) = (N+1)(n-1)\,. \end{cases}$$

The first of these follows from the observation that under a particle or hole addition $\delta v = \pm 1$ (prove it!), and the other results then follow from that, on making use of various general results given above. To give a demonstration of the centroid theorems one now needs to know the level energies which from eq. (5.118), are found to be

$$(6.31)\qquad E(n, v) = \frac{A}{2N}(n-v)(N-n-v+2)\,.$$

The pairing-interaction operator is the Casimir operator for a group (the symplectic group). The simple exercise above can serve as an introduction to the process of studying weighting not according to the energy but rather according to a group Casimir operator, the purpose of this being to study to what extent the symmetries implied by the group are maintained in the nuclear states.

Some interesting and useful extensions of the single-orbit results are to the mixed-orbit identical-particle cases where one makes the assumption, without doubt a very good one, that the target state is of definite (and low) mixed-orbit seniority. The often-favoured BCS assumption for the ground-state is a special case of this and experimental results on excitation energies have been interpreted in terms of the quasi-particle energies of the BCS theory (these interpretations then in fact not being completely consistent with the result of eq. (6.21)). It would seem that a more accurate and altogether better method of analysis would be by the direct use of the sum rules making the less restrictive low-seniority assumption for the target. In fact a study of various kinds of excitations of low-seniority systems would seem at present to be well worthwhile.

As a further elementary example, one could consider the single-orbit case but this time for mixed protons and neutrons considering in particular the isoscalar and isovector monopole results ($\nu=(0,0)$ and $(0,1)$ in a (jt) formalism), producing thereby the results for the isobaric-spin splitting of the single-particle and hole excitations of such targets. To go beyond this and study the multipole excitation energies of general systems requires of course the use of eqs. (6.22), (6.23).

Going in the opposite direction we consider now the particularly simple case of adding a completely inequivalent particle (or hole) to a target. Then $\langle n(\varrho)\rangle$ (or $\langle n(\varrho_h)\rangle$) $=0$. It is simpler to use the equations relating the pick-up and stripping excitations than the equations for the separate processes; since (in the particle case) there is no ϱ particle to remove we have that $\mathscr{G}^{(0,-)}(\theta)=\mathscr{G}^{(1,-)}(\theta)=0$ and then from eq. (6.4) $\mathscr{G}^{(0,+)}(\theta)=1$. Thus using equations (6.16), we find

$$\mathscr{E}^{+}(\theta)=E_0+\varepsilon_\varrho+\sum_\nu(-1)^\nu F_\nu P_\nu(\cos\theta)\,,\quad \text{(inequivalent-particle case)}, \tag{6.32}$$

and similarly for the pick-up case. Since however F_ν involves only multipole-interaction parameters of rank ν (*i.e.* β^ν) we have the result that *for the inequivalent-particle case a multipole interaction of a given rank produces an excitation spectrum of the same rank*; *i.e.*

$$\text{to } \beta^{\nu_0} \text{ there corresponds } \mathscr{E}^{+}(\theta)\sim P_{\nu_0}(\cos\theta)\,. \tag{6.33}$$

Let us consider the significance of this result. The simplest case of all is when we add an inequivalent particle to a completely nonpolarizable system; for example the system might have only a single active particle, say in the orbit $\varrho'\neq\varrho$, and the circumstances might be such that excitations of the inert particles can be ignored even when we add the ϱ particle. In this (weak coupling) situation, all the excitation strength at a given angle goes to a single state and, for a single-multipole interaction, we get a single-multipole excitation spectrum. Then clearly the excitation spectrum is identical with the appropriate part of the level spectrum. An example would involve adding a particle to the ground-state of ^{37}Cl, making the simplest assumption about the ^{37}Cl state.

Leaving this trivial case, suppose now that the system is polarizable, the target however still containing no ϱ particles. When we add the ϱ particle now, the strength at each angle becomes fragmented since the target does not maintain its identity in the final state. The energy spectrum of the final states now becomes more complex than in the weak coupling case, but according to eq. (6.32) the excitation spectrum, $\mathscr{E}^{+}(\theta)$, remains unaffected; the effects of the polarization show up in the *width* which develops at each angle (see Fig. 10). Equation (6.32) then enables us to « undo » the effects of the polarization produced by adding the particle.

We may say then that in this rather trivial case, the excitation spectra measure the « *multipole response* » of the system when it is disturbed by adding an inequivalent particle, this terminology being used in the standard sense of normal co-ordinates. But more important we have earlier isolated the function, namely

$$\{\mathscr{G}^{(1,+)}(\pi-\theta)-\mathscr{G}^{(1,-)}(\theta)\}$$

which measures the multipole response in the most general case; if for example all the forces are quadrupole, then no matter how complex things become, this function is a multiple of $P_2(\cos\theta)$. Presumably complex systems have many such functions corresponding, among other things, to different excitations, and these would appear to be important in drawing general conclusions about the system. One might ask whether there is such a function which involves no excitation strength at all, dealing instead with the level spectra; it would give a generalization of the spectrum result for the completely unpolarizable case mentioned above. A little thought will show that there cannot be such a function for any general case; and even if we assume that we are dealing say with pure ϱ^n states it seems difficult to produce one. But it would be physically not very interesting anyway, since strength distributions are, for the most part, more significant than level spectra.

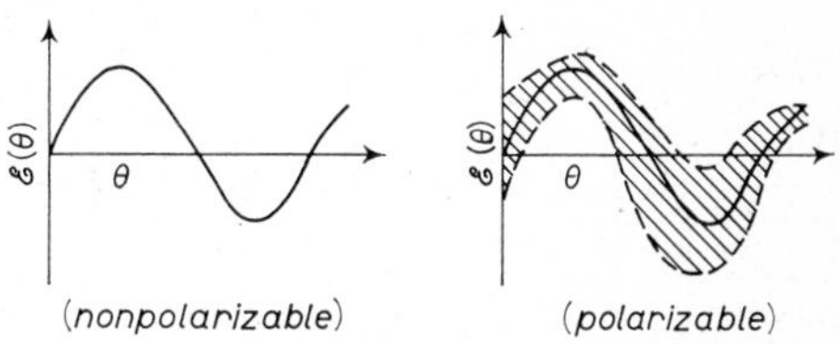

Fig. 10. – For an unpolarizable target the excitation spectrum is sharp at each angle. If the same target were polarizable the spectrum would be the same (as long as the transfer particle or hole is inequivalent) but at each angle there would be a width.

We mention now a couple of simple applications. The first involves the low-lying $d_{\frac{3}{2}}$ (and $s_{\frac{1}{2}}$) hole-states found a year or two ago at Argonne and Princeton by pick-up experiments on Ti isotopes. For a short time there was considerable interest in these because of their, at first sight surprisingly low, excitation energies, especially in some of the Sc isotopes. For even targets ($J=0$) the only « angular dependence » of the excitation energy is the two-point one in the isospin space while for odd targets, if we consider the *centroids* for the excitations of fixed T_1 $(=T\pm\frac{1}{2})$ we are left again with the same distribution, which is of course defined by $\nu=(0,0)$ and $(0,1)$ only. But if now we make the natural assumption that the target ground-states are describable as pure $f^n_{\frac{7}{2}}$, we are dealing with an inequivalent hole and then, by eq. (6.33), only interactions with $\nu=(0,0)$ and $(0,1)$ contribute to the excitation energies. Specifically the contributing interactions are, for a $d_{\frac{3}{2}}$ hole, defined by $\beta^{\nu}_{d_{\frac{3}{2}}d_{\frac{3}{2}}f_{\frac{7}{2}}f_{\frac{7}{2}}}$ with $\nu=(0\;0)$, $(0\;1)$.

These simple interactions being summable, in the sense of the discussion following eq. (5.75), it is simpler to write things in terms of the 1 and $\boldsymbol{t}_i\cdot\boldsymbol{t}_j$ operators rather than the corresponding unit tensors (as in eq. (5.70)). Then, the exchange effects being automatically included as in eq. (5.126), we have for the significant interaction

$$H_{ij}(1-P_{ij}) \equiv H_{ij}^{\text{Interaction}} = A + B\boldsymbol{t}_i\cdot\boldsymbol{t}_j\,. \tag{6.34}$$

Evaluating A, B in terms of the average two-body energy $\overline{E}(2)$ $(\equiv\overline{W}_{rs}$ of eq. (5.63)$)$ and $\overline{\Delta E}(2)=\overline{E^{T=1}}(2)-\overline{E^{T=0}}(2)$ we have for the $f_{\frac{7}{2}}^{n}$ target the intuitively obvious result that

$$H^{\text{Interaction}} = -n\overline{E}(2) + \overline{\Delta E}(2)\,\boldsymbol{T}\cdot\boldsymbol{t}\,, \tag{6.35}$$

where $\boldsymbol{T}$ is for the target, $\boldsymbol{t}$ for the hole and the minus sign in the $\overline{E}(2)$ term comes because we consider a hole, not a particle (Sect. **5**·6). The important thing to notice is that any interactions giving the same values for the two energy parameters will give the same excitation energies.

It turns out that with quite sensible values of the parameters the hole-state energies for many targets are quite well given. There are a number of other aspects of this problem into which however we cannot now go. The same kind of equation has been often used in the past in formally similar problems.

We mentioned earlier the Pandya result for the relationship between the energy spectra for a particle-particle and a corresponding particle-hole system, eq. (5.91). It should be clear now (the formal proof is left as an exercise) that the inequivalent-particle *excitation* spectra for two targets which are h $\rightleftharpoons$ p complements of each other are related by the same theorem. In the same way eq. (5.93) tells us for example that the average of the $T=0$ and $T=1$ $d_{\frac{3}{2}}$-$f_{\frac{7}{2}}$ energy spectra in ^{34}Cl (considered in terms of the simplest shell-model assignments) should reproduce the $d_{\frac{3}{2}}$-$f_{\frac{7}{2}}$ spectrum for ^{38}Cl. This result also has an excitation-spectrum extension. Find it!

Finally we repeat that excitation spectra are things of real interest. They do not of course contain all the information in the related energy spectra, and presumably not even all the useful information. One should therefore consider the spectrum of the widths and conceivably (but not probably) the spectra of some higher moments. But we are unable to consider these matters now.

7. – Single-particle-hole excitations (*).

7·1. *General remarks.* – This is a very large subject and we shall not attempt any kind of complete discussion or review. We shall discuss instead some rather simple cases in order to illustrate how reasonable calculations can be made and to point out certain interesting cases and some formal problems.

(*) Work reported in this Section was done with Dr. H. BANERJEE, who first derived the results given for excitation energies and widths.

We are considering the excitations produced by a one-body excitation operator $\boldsymbol{T}^\lambda$. The prominent cases are those of electromagnetic excitation and excitation by means of inelastic scattering of various projectiles, as indicated in Table I. As far as inelastic scattering is concerned, the choice of projectile is important in fixing in some cases the isospin rank of the excitation; inelastic scattering of deuterons or α-particles or other $T=0$ particles can involve only isoscalar interactions. The formal structure of the two-nucleon-transfer excitations is very similar to that of the h-p excitations, the main formal difference in fact being that one excitation is self-adjoint while the other is not. Remember that the excitations may be in a single shell, involving the orbit-diagonal $\mathcal{U}^\lambda_{\varrho\varrho}$; the « hole-particle » name applied to such excitations is rather misleading, but it has become so fashionable in the past few years (and a fashionable name is half the battle) that we cannot afford to do without it.

Except perhaps for the study of low-lying states, more and more of which is now being done, most hole-particle-excitation experiments do not lend themselves to a really detailed direct analysis and our emphasis therefore is necessarily directed more and more to a direct analysis of *monopole* excitation energies and widths (the angular distributions in the odd-target case being usually inaccessible) and otherwise to calculation of the excitation properties from an assumed ground-state and Hamiltonian. Such matters are of course of great theoretical interest quite apart from the analysis of reactions.

7'2. *Non-energy-weighted* (NEW) *sum rules* ($m=0$). – The excitation operator is given by

$$\boldsymbol{T}^\lambda = (-1)^\lambda \overline{\boldsymbol{T}^\lambda} = \sum_{r,s} q^\lambda_{rs} \mathcal{U}^\lambda_{rs}\,, \tag{7.1}$$

where the structure coefficients q^λ_{rs}, which, for a Hermitian excitation, satisfy

$$q^\lambda_{sr} = (-1)^{r-s} q^\lambda_{rs}\,, \tag{7.2}$$

may be calculated via eq. (5.13), if the explicit form of the operator is given. The operator which enters into the target integral (eq. (3.31)) is now

$$(\overline{\boldsymbol{T}^\lambda} \times \boldsymbol{T}^\lambda)^\nu = (-1)^\lambda \sum_{rstu} q^\lambda_{rs} q^\lambda_{tu} (\mathcal{U}^\lambda_{rs} \times \mathcal{U}^\lambda_{tu})^\nu, \tag{7.3}$$

which may of course be written in a number of other forms. In the general case then, the distribution of the strength determines (and is determined by) two-body target correlation moments as indicated. Rather than attempt to discuss these in any general way we consider only some cases which are especially simple because either the target state or the excitation is simple.

Consider an odd-parity excitation, in which case r, s in eq. (7.3) have opposite parity as also do t and u. Let us imagine that all the active orbits in the target have the same parity. The situation then is as shown:

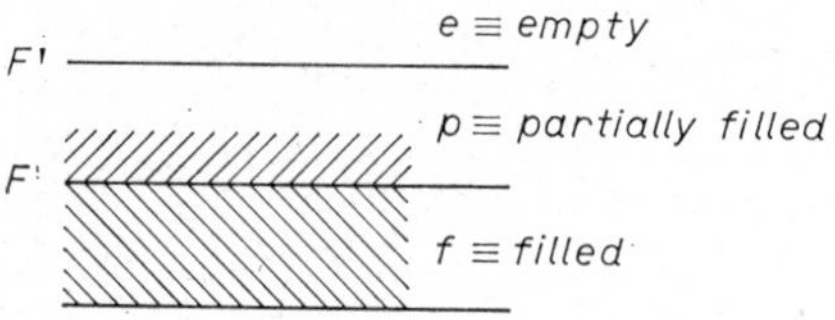

Fig. 11.

We further assume that $f \to e$ excitations can be ignored (formally we do this by putting the corresponding q_{rs} to zero). It will be recognized that the situation described here is that often assumed when one is dealing with hole-particle excitations. For example in p-shell photodisintegration, $f \equiv 1s$ shell, $p \equiv p$ shell, $e \equiv (1d, 2s)$ shell (orbits above this being ignored).

There are now two kinds of contributing transitions $(f \to p)$ and $(p \to e)$. For the first we have (in an obvious notation)

(7.4) $[\lambda](\mathcal{U}^\lambda \times \mathcal{U}^\lambda)^\nu \equiv$ 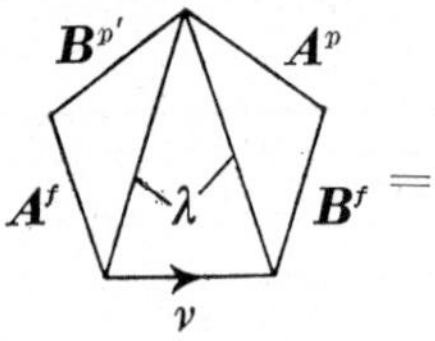 $= -(-1)^{p+f-\lambda}$ 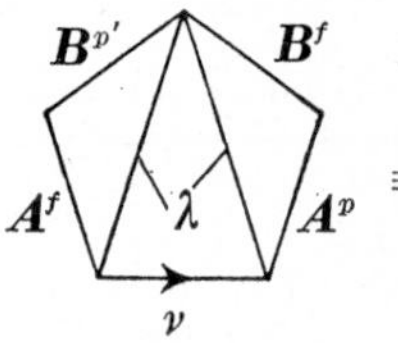 $\equiv$

$$\equiv (-1)^{p+f-\lambda} \begin{Bmatrix} f & p' & \lambda \\ f & p & \lambda \\ 0 & \nu & \nu \end{Bmatrix} [f]^{\frac{1}{2}}$$ 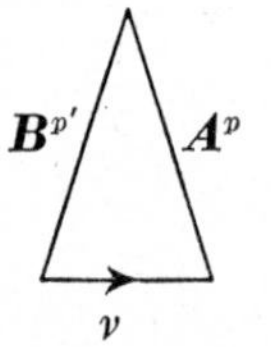 $$= (-1)^{p-p'-\nu} \frac{[\lambda]}{[f]^{\frac{1}{2}}} U(\lambda p \lambda p' : f\nu) \mathcal{U}^\nu_{p'p}(h)\,,$$

where we have made a recoupling, and have then used the facts that the partial system (f) can only support a *scalar* unit tensor and that then $(\boldsymbol{A}^f \times \boldsymbol{B}^f)^0 \equiv [f]^{\frac{1}{2}}$. The result follows on inserting the value for the degenerate $9j$-symbol and introducing the unit tensor for holes (eqs. (5.7), (5.12)),

$$(7.5) \qquad \mathcal{U}^\nu_{p'p}(h) = (-1)^{2\varrho}[\nu]^{-\frac{1}{2}}(\boldsymbol{B}^{p'} \times \boldsymbol{A}^p)^\nu = [p]^{\frac{1}{2}}\delta_{\nu 0}\delta_{pp'} - (-1)^{p-p'-\nu}\mathcal{U}^\nu_{pp'}\,.$$

For the $(p \to e)$ transitions we can use the same procedure or alternatively make a h $\rightleftharpoons$ p transformation in eq. (7.4), and then we find

$$(7.6) \qquad (\mathcal{U}^\lambda \times \mathcal{U}^\lambda)^\nu \equiv (\mathcal{U}^\lambda_{p'e} \times \mathcal{U}^\lambda_{ep}) \Rightarrow (-1)^\nu [e]^{-\frac{1}{2}} U(\lambda p \lambda p' : e\nu)\mathcal{U}^\nu_{p'p}\,.$$

Combining the two terms and using eqs. (7.5), (3.34) we have for the NEW strength function

$$\mathscr{G}^{(0)}(\theta) = \sum_{\nu} K_{\nu} P_{\nu}(\cos\theta)\,, \tag{7.7}$$

where

$$K_{\nu} = (-1)^{\lambda}\left[\frac{\nu}{\Gamma\lambda}\right]^{\frac{1}{2}}\Big\{\sum_{r>F'} - (-1)^{\nu}\sum_{r<F}\Big\}\sum_{p,p'}[r]^{-\frac{1}{2}} q^{\lambda}_{pr} q^{\lambda}_{rp'}\, U(\lambda p \lambda p' : r\nu)\langle x\Gamma \| \mathscr{U}^{\nu}_{pp'} \| x\Gamma\rangle + \\ + \delta_{\nu 0}[\lambda]^{-1} \sum_{\substack{p\\ r<F}} (q^{\lambda}_{pr})^{2}\,, \tag{7.8}$$

and in particular

$$K_{0} = \frac{1}{[\lambda]}\sum_{p}\left\{\sum_{r>F'}(q^{\lambda}_{pr})^{2}\frac{\langle n(p)\rangle}{[p]} + \sum_{r<F}(q^{\lambda}_{pr})^{2}\frac{\langle n(p_{h})\rangle}{[p]}\right\}. \tag{7.9}$$

As usual the structure of the monopole sum rule (by which we mean $\nu = 0$, *not* $\lambda = 0$) is simple and the equation could have been written without preliminary. We observe for example, in eq. (7.9), the enhancing effect of the active particles in so far as the $(p \to e)$ transitions are concerned and their inhibiting effect on the $(f \to p)$ transitions. On the other hand the structure of the nonmonopole equations is not quite transparent; it becomes much more so, at least for the single-active-shell case, if we introduce the «internal» angle $\varphi = \widehat{\boldsymbol{p}\cdot\boldsymbol{\lambda}}$ and then rewrite $\mathscr{G}^{(0)}(\theta)$ in terms of θ and an integral over φ; but that we leave as an exercise. Incidentally the $-(-1)^{\nu}$ phase distinguishing between the two kinds of transitions is precisely what we expect from the general h-p relationship.

It must be noted that the two-body correlation implied by the general target integral has disappeared and we are left with a target integral depending on a one-body moment only, this occurring of course because one of the shells involved in the transitions is always inert, being either filled or empty. It would seem that the detection of such correlations by non-energy-weighted sums is difficult; energy weighting on the other hand detects such correlations even for single-particle excitations (eqs. (6.22), (6.23)).

As easy applications of this result, which we leave as exercises, are the cases where the target has closed shells only or a single active particle or hole. It might be considered also whether there are any single-shell cases where the moments could be measured well enough by single-nucleon-transfer reactions to allow worth-while predictions concerning the hole-particle excitation.

We have in the above ruled out the possibility of excitations within the active shells $(p \to p)$ and thus, as indicated, the results are valid for negative-parity excitations. It is left as a formal exercise to derive the general results when this restriction is removed. These results, along with their energy-weighted extensions should serve in particular as the basis of a proper theory of « enhancements », in which one considers the circumstances under which the total strength leading from a particular state can become large, and the further circumstances under which much of it can be concentrated on a single other state. A fair amount is known about this subject but there does not seem to have been much systematic study.

7'3. *The linear energy-weighted sum rule* ($m=1$). – For brevity we restrict ourselves to considering the excitation of a closed-shell system (Fig. 12).

Then $\nu=0$ and the target integral becomes

$$\langle \| \bar{\boldsymbol{T}}^{\lambda} \times H \times \boldsymbol{T}^{\lambda})^{0} \| \rangle_{\text{c.s.}} = (-1)^{\lambda} \sum_{\substack{ef \\ e'f'}} q^{\lambda}_{f'e'} q^{\lambda}_{ef} \langle (\mathcal{U}^{\lambda}_{f'e'} \times H \times \mathcal{U}^{\lambda}_{ef})^{0} \rangle_{\text{c.s.}} . \tag{7.10}$$

The Hamiltonian now divides into three parts

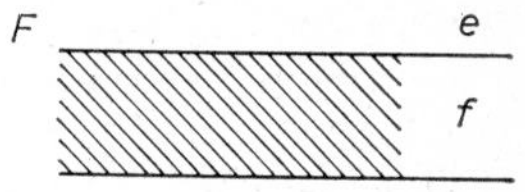

Fig. 12.

$$H = \sum_{s} \varepsilon''_{s} n_{\text{op}}(s) + \sum_{r,s} \beta^{0}_{rrss} (\zeta_{rs})^{2} n_{\text{op}}(s) + \tilde{H}^{(2)} \tag{7.11}$$

where $\tilde{H}^{(2)}$, the « multipole part » of $H^{(2)}$, is given by the $(\mathcal{U} \times \mathcal{U})$ term (*) in eq. (5.70), and, in the other terms, we have ruled out the possibility of active orbits of the same l, j but different n_r and of excitations involving such a pair (thus $\lambda \neq 0^{+}$). As usual we can replace by a constant those parts of H which involve only inert shells and then, combining the two single-particle terms,

$$H = \sum_{s} \varepsilon_{s} n_{\text{op}}(s) + \tilde{H}^{(2)}, \tag{7.12}$$

where we have not bothered to write the constant or to indicate that active shells only are to be considered.

Before proceeding we consider how the parameters of H are to be determined. Conventionally one does this by using H to calculate the energies of the systems, {closed shell} and {closed shell ± particle}, and then determines the ε_s parameters by equating these energies to the corresponding « observed » energies. Formally, when one does this the contributions of $H^{(2)}$, which are easily found by the methods used often above, must be considered and likewise the variation in the ε_s when the $H^{(2)}$ parameters are varied. From a physical standpoint this procedure is pretty crude. Even if there is a physical state corresponding « well enough » to the closed-shell system the single-particle and single-hole strengths need not be focussed on single levels. One can however identify the single-particle and hole states as excitation energies (as in Sect. **6**) and then place the burden of locating the centroid energies on the experimentalist. But if we are involved in a relatively « high-quality » calculation it will not be adequate to identify any physical state as closed shell. Under these circumstances one can proceed in a self-consistent way (for a given $H^{(2)}$) by assuming

(*) With the « excitation-type » summation restrictions, $r \leqslant s$, $t \geqslant u$.

a set of ε_s, then calculating the wave-function for the modified closed-shell state, and from that the particle and hole excitation energies, and thereby a new set of ε_s. Note here that although the system {modified closed shell $\pm$ nucleon} may be extremely complicated in detail the centroid calculation requires only a knowledge of the simpler system without the particle or hole.

Agreeing now that the parameters of H have been satisfactorily determined, we return to eq. (7.10). We shall need some of the simple results which flow from eqs. (5.7), (5.26) that

$$(7.13)\quad (\boldsymbol{A}^r\times\boldsymbol{B}^s)^\Gamma=[\Gamma]^{\frac{1}{2}}\mathscr{U}^\Gamma_{rs}=(\boldsymbol{B}^r(h)\times\boldsymbol{B}^s)^\Gamma=\bar{\boldsymbol{Z}}^\Gamma(r^{-1},s)=-(-1)^{r+s-\Gamma}\bar{\boldsymbol{Z}}^\Gamma(s,r^{-1})=$$
$$=(-1)^{2\varrho}(\boldsymbol{A}^r\times\boldsymbol{A}^s(h))^\Gamma=-(-1)^{2\varrho}\boldsymbol{Z}^\Gamma(r,s^{-1})=(-1)^{r-s-\Gamma}\boldsymbol{Z}^\Gamma(s^{-1},r)\qquad(r\neq s),$$

and then

$$(7.14)\quad \langle(\mathscr{U}^\lambda_{f'e'}\times H\times\mathscr{U}^\lambda_{ef})^0\rangle_{\text{c.s.}}=(-1)^{e-f-\lambda}[\lambda]^{-1}\langle(\bar{\boldsymbol{Z}}^\lambda(f'(h),e')\times H\times\boldsymbol{Z}^\lambda(f(h),e))^0\rangle_{\text{c.s.}}\,.$$

The evaluation of the single-particle matrix element is immediate and we have already evaluated the more complex one (eq. (5.81)). Thus we have that

$$(7.15)\quad \langle\|(\bar{\boldsymbol{T}}^\lambda\times H\times\boldsymbol{T}^\lambda)^0\|\rangle=$$
$$=\frac{1}{[\lambda]^{\frac{1}{2}}}\sum_{efe'f'}q^\lambda_{f'e'}q^\lambda_{ef}(-1)^{e-f}\{\delta_{ee'}\delta_{ff'}(\varepsilon_e-\varepsilon_f)+(-1)^{f'-e'-\lambda}[\lambda]^{-\frac{1}{2}}\beta^\lambda_{e'f'fe}\}\,,$$

and then for the centroid energy, via eqs. (3.37), (7.7), (7.9) (*), and using a symmetry property of the β^ν's, *viz.*

$$(7.16)\qquad \beta^\nu_{rtsu}=\beta^\nu_{surt}=(-1)^{r+t+s+u}\beta^\nu_{trus}=(-1)^{r+t+s+u}\beta^\nu_{ustr}\,,$$

we have the result

$$(7.17)\qquad \mathscr{E}^\lambda=\{\sum_{fe}(q^\lambda_{fe})^2\}^{-1}\cdot\left\{\sum_{fe}(q^\lambda_{fe})^2(\varepsilon_e-\varepsilon_f)+\frac{(-1)^\lambda}{[\lambda]^{\frac{1}{2}}}\sum_{efe'f'}q^\lambda_{f'e'}q^\lambda_{ef}\beta^\lambda_{f'e'ef}\right\}.$$

To make use of this completely explicit formula we need only evaluate the two-body coefficients β^λ (particle-hole matrix elements or combinations of two-body matrix elements), adequate programs for which exist for any explicit two-body interaction; and of course the excitation constants q^λ_{fe}. Then if we use for example a conventional interaction, {central + tensor + vector} with some definite radial forms, the excitation energies can be written as a linear function of the various strengths. And, as we have said many times, calculations may be made in various representations j, (j,t), (l,s), or (l,s,t).

(*) Or see ahead, eq. (7.26).

Note the important but *a priori* obvious fact that the energy of a λ-excitation depends only on the excitation-type coefficients β^λ; this however would not be true for the excitation of more complex systems. For the special case of a closed shell which we have considered, the results given are valid for even-parity as well as odd-parity excitations. And if we take the nucleus center-of-mass co-ordinate $\boldsymbol{R}$ to be the excitation operator, its structure coefficients being given in (l, s, t) by eq. (5.16), we calculate the energy of the dipole spurious state which should, with the natural zero of energy, itself turn out to be zero. With the closed-shell assumption, and with single-particle energies determined empirically as outlined above, it is well known that this does not in fact happen. If however we use the calculated spurious-state energy as defining the energy zero for the excitation then, for the important $E1$ case, we arrive at an interesting result.

On comparing the unit-tensor expansions for the operators $\boldsymbol{R} = \sum \boldsymbol{r}(i)$ and $\boldsymbol{RT} = \sum \boldsymbol{r}(i)\,\boldsymbol{t}(i)$ we find immediately that

$$q_{rs}^{1,0}(\boldsymbol{R}) = \frac{2}{\sqrt{3}}\, q_{rs}^{1,1}(\boldsymbol{RT})\,, \tag{7.18}$$

these of course being the only nonvanishing coefficients. We have written things in a (j, t) representation but the same result applies in (l, s, t) relating $q^{1,0,0}$ and $q^{1,0,1}$; and indeed the (l, s, t) representation is physically more reasonable in this case. It follows now from eqs. (7.17), (7.18) that the energy for an $E1$ excitation on a closed shell, measured with respect to the spurious-state zero, is

$$\mathscr{E}^{1,1} - \mathscr{E}^{1,0} = \frac{1}{\sqrt{3}} \Big\{\sum_{fe} (q_{fe}^{1,0})^2\Big\}^{-1} \left\{\sum_{\substack{ef\\ e'f'}} q_{f'e'}^{1,0} q_{ef}^{1,0} \left(\beta_{f'e'ef}^{1,0} + \frac{1}{\sqrt{3}}\, \beta_{f'e'ef}^{1,1}\right)\right\}. \tag{7.19}$$

But now referring back to our discussion of p-n interactions in an isospin formalism we see that the interaction constants here carry the signature of the p-n interaction (eq. (5.99)) and consequently

$$\mathscr{E}^{1,1} - \mathscr{E}^{1,0} = \frac{2}{\sqrt{3}} \Big\{\sum_{fe} (q_{fe}^{1,0})^2\Big\}^{-1} \Big\{\sum_{\substack{ef\\ e'f'}} q_{f'e'}^{1,0} q_{ef}^{1,0}\, \beta_{f'e'ef}^{1,0}(\text{p-n})\Big\}. \tag{7.20}$$

It should be recognized that this gives a « microscopic » derivation of the elementary Goldhaber-Teller treatment of the $E1$ giant resonance, the « spring constant » of that treatment being given here in terms of the p-n interaction constants. It is left as an exercise to derive the same result in the p-n formalism in which, as a matter of fact, one can see the relationship to the G-T treatment at every stage of the calculation (*).

(*) The above discussion of the $E1$ resonance is due to F. B. WANG and the present author. Miss WANG has considered also the width of the resonance and application of the same procedures to open-shell cases.

7·4. *Some aspects of self-consistency.* – One aspect of this, discussed above, is displayed by the fact that the calculated energies of the center-of mass spurious states do not come out correctly. This comes about because, having chosen a two-body interaction, one is determined to look after its deficiencies only by adjusting the parameters of the effective one-body interaction. A more general self-consistency problem arises in all calculations when the assumed ground state is not an eigenfunction of the assumed Hamiltonian. Consider for example the $(m=1)$ target integral for a self-adjoint excitation. Then with E_0 as the ground state energy,

$$(7.21)\qquad (\overline{\boldsymbol{T}}^{\lambda}\times(H-E_0)\times\boldsymbol{T}^{\lambda})^{\nu}=\tfrac{1}{2}\{(\overline{\boldsymbol{T}}^{\lambda}\times[H,\boldsymbol{T}^{\lambda}])^{\nu}-([H,\overline{\boldsymbol{T}}^{\lambda}]\times\boldsymbol{T}^{\lambda})^{\nu}\}+ \\ +\tfrac{1}{2}\{(\overline{\boldsymbol{T}}^{\lambda}\times\boldsymbol{T}^{\lambda})^{\nu}(H-E_0)+(H-E_0)(\overline{\boldsymbol{T}}^{\lambda}\times\boldsymbol{T}^{\lambda})^{\nu}\},$$

where the first term is a double commutator if $\boldsymbol{T}^{\lambda}$ is hermitian and ν is even. The self-consistency problem shows up in the second term whose target-expectation value is zero in an exact theory but which does not necessarily vanish in an approximate one. We will now arrive at two different results according as we do or do not eliminate this term before evaluating the target integrals with the *approximate* ground-state function. Formally of course one could arrive at any result whatever for the excitation energy by making use of this ambiguity but common sense imposes a limit on that kind of thing.

Another aspect of the same thing comes into evidence when we ask what value should be used for the ground-state energy in cases where $H\Psi_0\neq E_0\Psi_0$. In fact do we ever have a case in which the ground-state *is* an eigenstate of H_0?

The answer to the last question is of course « no » if we mean by H the true nuclear Hamiltonian. But in any calculation we make a severe truncation of the vector space and the question then is whether we can write a truncated Hamiltonian which « fits into » the truncated space, *i.e.* which has no matrix elements outside it. The H truncation is accomplished by simply omitting matrix elements which go to orbits outside the space. But if now the truncated H has pairing-type terms (see the classification in Sect. **5**), H cannot be fitted into a vector space in which the number of particles in an active orbit is limited. In calculations on closed-shell nuclei for example, if we allow only a single h-p excitation the resultant vector space does not supply a representation of an H with pairing terms. On the other hand in such shell-model calculations as those which have been recently done for Ni isotopes in which one considers all partitions of the particles among orbits we have the happier situation. In the first case we do not have a good definition of E_0 and there are many self-consistency problems; in the second we replace the nuclear problem by a mathematically significant truncated problem. The entire question of course is that of ground-state correlations whose importance was first stressed by FALLIEROS and FERRELL.

One might be tempted in applying the $m = 1$ sum rule to define E_0 by the condition that $\langle \| \overline{\boldsymbol{T}}^\lambda \times \boldsymbol{T}^\lambda)^\nu (H - E_0) \| \rangle = 0$, but the result is then dependent both on the excitation process and the multipole order, which is rather discouraging. Three other ways which one might consider are i) $\langle H \rangle_{\text{gr.}} = E_0$; ii) the zero is chosen so that the energy of the lowest observed state of the parity in question is fitted by the calculation; iii) for odd-parity excitations the zero is chosen so that the lowest center-of-mass spurious state comes out correctly. The second choice has often been made, the first seems rather more honest, the third has formal advantages in some cases as we have seen.

As far as sum-rule analyses are concerned the two questions are whether we can estimate the errors in the various strength functions due to improper treatment of ground-state correlations and whether we can make an improved calculation (always of course within the framework of a vector space defined by a finite set of orbits). We consider briefly only one of the ways in which one can attempt to solve these problems.

Perhaps a reasonable estimate of the error, in the excitation energy, for the closed-shell case comes by evaluating $\mathscr{E}$ in the two ways suggested by eq. (7.21), one where the left-hand-side expression is used in the target integral, the other (which we label $\tilde{\mathscr{E}}$) where the double-commutator expression is used. Then

$$\tilde{\mathscr{E}} - \mathscr{E} = -\frac{\langle \| (H - E_0)(\overline{\boldsymbol{T}}^\lambda \times \boldsymbol{T}^\lambda)^0 \| \rangle}{\langle \| (\overline{\boldsymbol{T}}^\lambda \times \boldsymbol{T}^\lambda)^0 \| \rangle}, \tag{7.22}$$

which we now evaluate with the approximate (closed-shell) ground-state and with E_0 taken as $\langle \text{c.s.} | H | \text{c.s.} \rangle$. Using the notation implied by Fig. 12 we see that we can ignore the E_0 term and take

$$\begin{aligned} (\overline{\boldsymbol{T}}^\lambda \times \boldsymbol{T}^\lambda)^0 &= (-1)^\lambda \sum_{f'e'ef} q^\lambda_{e'f'} q^\lambda_{ef} (\mathscr{U}^\lambda_{e'f'} \times \mathscr{U}^\lambda_{ef})^0 = \\ &= (-1)^\lambda [\lambda]^{-1} \sum_{f'e'fe:\Lambda} q^\lambda_{e'f'} q^\lambda_{ef} (-1)^{e'+f-\lambda-\Lambda} U(e'f'ef:\lambda\Lambda) \zeta^{-1}_{e'e} \zeta^{-1}_{f'f} (\boldsymbol{Z}^\Lambda(e', e) \times \overline{\boldsymbol{Z}}^\Lambda(f', f))^0, \end{aligned} \tag{7.23}$$

where we have recoupled (eq. (2.15)) to display the pairing and have then rewritten things in terms of normalized state operators (eq. (5.26)). We now recognize from eq. (5.54) that the only contributing part of H is

$$[\Lambda]^{\frac{1}{2}} W^\Lambda_{f'fe'e} (\boldsymbol{Z}^\Lambda(f', f) \times \overline{\boldsymbol{Z}}^\Lambda(e', e))^0,$$

and since, by a simple recoupling, it follows that

$$\langle (\boldsymbol{Z}^\Lambda(f', f) \times \overline{\boldsymbol{Z}}^\Lambda(e', e))^0 (\boldsymbol{Z}^\Lambda(e', e) \times \overline{\boldsymbol{Z}}^\Lambda(f', f))^0 \rangle_{\text{c.s.}} = 1, \tag{7.24}$$

we have the result that

$$\begin{aligned}(7.25)\qquad &\langle \text{c.s.}\|(H-E_0)(\bar{\boldsymbol{T}}^\lambda \times \boldsymbol{T}^\lambda)^0\|\text{c.s.}\rangle = \\ &= (-1)^\lambda[\lambda]^{-1} \sum_{f'e'fe;\Lambda} q^\lambda_{e'f'} q^\lambda_{ef} (-1)^{e'+f-\lambda-\Lambda} U(e'f'ef:\lambda\Lambda)\zeta^{-1}_{e'e}\zeta^{-1}_{f'f}[\Lambda]^{\frac{1}{2}} W^\Lambda_{f'fe'e} = \\ &= (-1)^\lambda[\lambda]^{-1} \sum_{f'e'fe} q^\lambda_{e'f'} q^\lambda_{ef} \zeta^{-1}_{e'e}\zeta^{-1}_{f'f}\beta^\lambda_{e'f'ef}\,,\end{aligned}$$

where in the last step we have used eq. (5.71).

Using the general strength eq. (3.34) along with eq. (7.9) we see that

$$(7.26)\qquad \langle \text{c.s.}\|(\bar{\boldsymbol{T}}^\lambda \times \boldsymbol{T}^\lambda)^0\|\text{c.s.}\rangle = [\lambda]^{-\frac{1}{2}} \sum_{e,f} (q^\lambda_{fe})^2,$$

and then, using the symmetry properties of q^λ and β^ν (eqs. (7.2), (7.16)), we find that

$$\begin{aligned}(7.27)\qquad \tilde{\mathscr{E}}^\lambda = &\{\sum_{fe}(q^\lambda_{fe})^2\}^{-1}\{\sum_{fe}(q^\lambda_{fe})^2(\varepsilon_e-\varepsilon_f) + \\ &+ (-1)^\lambda[\lambda]^{-\frac{1}{2}} \sum_{f'e'fe} q^\lambda_{f'e'} q^\lambda_{ef}[\beta^\lambda_{f'e'ef} - (-1)^{f-e}\zeta^{-1}_{ee'}\zeta^{-1}_{ff'}\beta^\lambda_{f'e'fe}]\}.\end{aligned}$$

The last term in the brackets represents the modification produced in the excitation energy by using the double-commutator procedure instead of the $\langle \text{c.s.}\|(\bar{\boldsymbol{T}}^\lambda \times H \times \boldsymbol{T}^\lambda)^0\|\text{c.s.}\rangle$ procedure which, it should be easy to see, gives the standard shell-model result. The correction term once again involves only a λ-part of the interaction but this time the λ-part of the pairing interaction. Such a term of course (which would for ^{16}O involve $p^2 \to (ds)^2$ excitations) is not encountered in the simple shell-model calculations. This added term is not small, being one to a few MeV for ^{16}O depending on the interaction (while the entire β^λ terms in eqs. (7.17), (7.27) are only 5 MeV or so, most of the excitation energy being supplied by the single-particle terms). It has to be remembered however that the double-commutator method does take some account (to what extent correctly is not clear) of pairing correlations in the ground-state and these should then have an effect on the single-particle energies. It might be better then to calculate these also by a double-commutator procedure.

One obvious way of exploring whether $\mathscr{E}^\lambda$ or $\tilde{\mathscr{E}}^\lambda$ gives a result closer to the truth is to take account of the ground-state correlations by a perturbation calculation. We are unable here to go into this matter but there is one technical aspect of the perturbation procedure which is worth emphasizing. If we include, as would be natural, the single-particle energy ($H^{(1)}$ of eq. (5.54)) in the unperturbed Hamiltonian, carrying out a perturbation with $H^{(2)}$, then, since $H^{(2)}$ is parametrized with respect to the single-particle orbits, it follows easily that all the corrections to the unperturbed wave-function which involve the same configuration can be represented by a single operator which acts on the unperturbed state. We then have an operator representation of the perturbed wave function which is much simpler than the corresponding matrix representation. To evaluate matrix elements of various operators in this representation we should then be prepared to evaluate vacuum expectation values following the procedures of the Appendix. The details are left for an exercise.

7'5. *The quadratic energy-weighted sum rule* ($m = 2$). – The $m = 2$ multipole sum rule determines the *dispersion* of the strength (or the square of the *width*) for given final-state angular momenta, according to the equation

$$\Delta(\theta) = \frac{\mathscr{G}^{(2)}(\theta)}{\mathscr{G}^{(0)}(\theta)} - \left(\frac{\mathscr{G}^{(1)}(\theta)}{\mathscr{G}^{(0)}(\theta)}\right)^2 = \frac{\mathscr{G}^{(2)}(\theta)}{\mathscr{G}^{(0)}(\theta)} - (\mathscr{E}(\theta))^2, \tag{7.28}$$

the corresponding monopole dispersion being

$$\Delta = \frac{\int \mathrm{d}\cos\theta \cdot \mathscr{G}^{(2)}(\theta)}{\int \mathrm{d}\cos\theta \cdot \mathscr{G}^{(0)}(\theta)} - (\mathscr{E})^2. \tag{7.29}$$

It must be noted that even if $\Delta(\theta) = 0$ it does not necessarily follow that $\Delta = 0$, for even if all the strength for each final angular momentum (Γ_1) goes to a single state, the energy of the state will usually vary with angular momentum. The trivial example is that of a weakly coupled particle. It is clear in fact that for nonscalar targets one can speak of a first-order ($m = 1$) « width » which is a true width if we care nothing about the angular momenta, but otherwise is not.

As a simple example of the calculation of a width for a hole-particle excitation let us consider Δ for the closed-shell case. We have (eqs. (3.34), (7.26))

$$\Delta^\lambda + (\mathscr{E}^\lambda)^2 = \frac{\langle \text{c.s.} \| (\overline{\boldsymbol{T}}^\lambda \times (H)^2 \times \boldsymbol{T}^\lambda)^0 \| \text{c.s.}\rangle}{\langle \text{c.s.} \| (\overline{\boldsymbol{T}}^\lambda \times \boldsymbol{T}^\lambda)^0 \| \text{c.s.}\rangle} = \tag{7.30}$$

$$= [\lambda]^{\frac{1}{2}} \{\sum_{ef} (q^\lambda_{ef})^2\}^{-1} \langle \text{c.s.} \| (\overline{\boldsymbol{T}}^\lambda \times (H)^2 \times \boldsymbol{T}^\lambda)^0 \| \text{c.s.}\rangle = \{\sum_{ef} (q^\lambda_{ef})^2\}^{-1} \sum_y \langle y\lambda \| H \boldsymbol{T}^\lambda \| \text{c.s.}\rangle^2,$$

where we have made an intermediate state expansion (eq. (3.22)) and used the adjoint eq. (3.17).

Just as in our evaluation of the excitation energy, we could now fiddle around with H commutators to produce different results. But apart from that, parts of H (the pairing parts!) which do not contribute to $\mathscr{E}^\lambda$ because they involve matrix elements which go outside the vector space being considered, do contribute to Δ^λ. (This does not happen of course if the vector space is large enough to « contain » H.) We content ourselves here with calculating the width which would be found in the usual shell-model calculation, which makes no use of the pairing parts of H. It follows then that y in the matrix element of eq. (7.30) defines a particle-hole state; *i.e.* $\boldsymbol{Z}_y^\lambda = \boldsymbol{Z}^\lambda(f'(h), e')$. Then since $\mathscr{U}_{ef}^\lambda = (-1)^{e-f-\lambda}[\lambda]^{-\frac{1}{2}}\boldsymbol{Z}^\lambda(f(h), e)$ by eq. (7.13) we have that

$$(7.31)\quad \langle y\lambda \| H\boldsymbol{T}^\lambda \| \text{c.s.}\rangle \Rightarrow [\lambda]^{-\frac{1}{2}} \sum_{e,f} q_{ef}^\lambda (-1)^{e-f-\lambda} \langle (\overline{\boldsymbol{Z}}^\lambda(f'(h), e') \times H \times \boldsymbol{Z}^\lambda(f(h), e))^0\rangle_0 =$$

$$= [\lambda]^{-\frac{1}{2}} \sum_{e,f} q_{ef}^\lambda (-1)^{e-f-\lambda} \langle f'(h), e' \| H \| f(h), e\rangle_\lambda =$$

$$= \sum_{e,f} q_{ef}^\lambda (-1)^{e-f-\lambda} \{(\varepsilon_e - \varepsilon_f)\delta_{ee'}\delta_{ff'} + (-1)^{f'-e'-\lambda}[\lambda]^{-\frac{1}{2}}\beta_{e'f'fe}^\lambda\},$$

where we have used the result of eq. (5.81). We thus have for the dispersion

$$(7.32)\quad \Delta^\lambda = \{\sum_{e,f} (q_{ef}^\lambda)^2\}^{-1} \sum_{e'f'} \left[q_{e'f'}^\lambda (\varepsilon_{e'} - \varepsilon_{f'}) + \frac{(-1)^\lambda}{[\lambda]^{\frac{1}{2}}} \sum_{ef} (-)^{e-f} q_{ef}^\lambda \beta_{e'f'fe}^\lambda \right]^2 - (\mathscr{E}^\lambda)^2 .$$

It should be observed that once again only the λ-excitation part of the two-body interaction contributes to the width. The extension of this « shell-model »-dispersion result to take account of the pairing parts of H has been given by BANERJEE who finds once again that only the λ-pairing part contributes. The derivation of the extended result is left for an exercise.

7·6. *Final remarks.* – The uncertainties and ambiguities referred to above are *not* in the sum rules but instead are inherent in the approximations made in reducing the nuclear problem to a soluble one. They are present for any kind of excitation including the single-particle or hole excitations of Sect. **6**. There appear now to be good ways of studying them.

Finally we stress that we have chosen to discuss only hole-particle excitations of closed-shell systems because of their comparative simplicity. But the general procedures which we have used coupled with the techniques and results of the Appendix enable us in fact to go much further than that in discussing such things as multi-hole-particle excitations and excitations of open-shell systems.

8. – Complex spectroscopy.

8·1. *General remarks.* – There are two reasons for being interested in complex spectroscopy (by which we mean standard shell-model spectroscopy applied to problems which are large enough that the most prosaic procedures are inadequate; an example would be the study of $2\hbar\omega$ states of ^{16}O mentioned in Sect. **1**). The reasons are: 1) in order to facilitate a direct detailed comparison between experiment and theory. We have earlier spoken about the difficulties of such comparisons and have suggested that sum-rule analyses may often be more pertinent (in that case extended shell-model calculations may be good for the ground-state); nevertheless, particularly when dealing with low-lying states there is still a good place for detailed comparisons. We envision that this activity will before long come to be regarded as an adjunct to experimental work, to be done by the experimentalist as part of his analysis. A good formalism, programmed for large computers, is needed to bring this about; 2) in order to study relationship between and the accuracy of various nuclear models. As things stand now most nuclear models are models of the shell-model and their validity is open to investigation by means of appropriate shell-model studies.

One must not be too optimistic about the use of large-scale computing. The course of standard shell-model spectroscopy throughout the 1950's was that calculations involving larger and larger shell-model vector spaces produced better and better agreement with experiment. This cannot really continue, for at the very core of such calculations there are some fundamental problems, in particular about the « effective » interaction to be used which cannot be settled within the framework of ordinary shell-model procedures. Indeed there is an indication that the attempt to understand nuclear data simply via larger and larger shell-model calculations may now be reaching a conclusion and a somewhat disappointing one at that; and it may be that there have been certain spurious elements in the past agreements between calculation and experiment, arising both from the freedom which the theorist has demanded in the effective interaction used and from the common insistence discussed in Sect. **4** of fitting the wrong kind of data.

With these precautionary remarks in mind we can proceed. We need a programmed formalism:

i) Which will be able to do complex calculations, limited only by the size of the vector spaces considered.

ii) The ingredients of which will be closely related to physically significant quantities. The various tensors with which we have been dealing satisfy this requirement, though when considering deformed states one might imagine a different set of basic ingredients.

iii) Should tolerate our increasing the size of the vector spaces considered without having to begin the entire calculation again.

iv) Should, insofar as that is compatible with ii), use mathematically significant ways of cataloguing states and operators. We think particularly here of any pertinent group (symplectic, SU_3, etc. which in fact fit very well into the tensor formalism). If the states belong at least fairly well to irreducible representations of a group the advantage of considering that group from the beginning is clear; but even if they do not, the mathematical advantages, in matrix-element evaluation and so on, might be of real consequence.

v) Should be able to handle input data expressed in various ways, and give the output in terms of physically significant forms.

8·2. *General multipole analysis.* – The scheme which we shall describe is based on a general multipole analysis for systems of interacting particles, and is a simple generalization of the procedure used, say, in classical electromagnetic theory. It is well known that the interaction between two nonoverlapping nonpolarizable charge distributions may be given in terms of a sum of scalar products of their electrostatic moments, and a simple extension does the same for two distributions which may overlap. If the systems are polarizable, things are more complicated and we find ourselves expanding the densities in some complete set of orthogonal functions and then finding, for example, a matrix equation for the coefficients. This of course is the scheme which we shall use for the problem in hand but we must deal with the wave-functions rather than the densities and recognize also that the moment operators are not necessarily number-conserving.

Given a set of states $\Phi^{\Gamma_1}_{x_1}$, for various Γ_1 and x_1, we can introduce a set of moment operators $\boldsymbol{Q}^{\nu}_{\alpha_1}(\mathrm{I})$, each with definite rank ν, the set to be adequate for dealing say with one- and two-body scalar interactions among the particles of the set, or between them and some other set (II) of particles. Then it will be seen easily that according to their $(\boldsymbol{A}^{\varrho}, \boldsymbol{B}^{\varrho})$ structures the operators $\boldsymbol{Q}^{\nu}$ have various forms as follows:

$$(8.1)\qquad \begin{cases} \boldsymbol{1};\ \boldsymbol{A}^r,\ \boldsymbol{B}^r; \quad (\boldsymbol{A}^r\times\boldsymbol{A}^s)^{\nu},\ (\boldsymbol{B}^r\times\boldsymbol{B}^s)^{\nu}; \quad (\boldsymbol{A}^r\times\boldsymbol{B}^s)^{\nu};\\ ((\boldsymbol{A}^r\times\boldsymbol{A}^s)^{\omega}\times\boldsymbol{B}^t)^{\nu},\ (\boldsymbol{A}^t\times(\boldsymbol{B}^r\times\boldsymbol{B}^s)^{\omega})^{\nu}; \quad ((\boldsymbol{A}^r\times\boldsymbol{A}^s)^{\omega}\times(\boldsymbol{B}^t\times\boldsymbol{B}^u)^{\omega})^{0}. \end{cases}$$

For each of these forms we must consider all the linearly independent orbit structures, allowing the orbit indices $r, s, \ldots$ to range over all the orbits which are found among the states. Suppose that we are now able to construct the various moment matrices

$$(8.2)\qquad Q^{\Gamma_1\nu\Gamma_1'}_{x_1\alpha_1x_1'}(\mathrm{I}) = \langle \Phi^{\Gamma_1}_{x_1} \| \boldsymbol{Q}^{\nu}_{\alpha_1}(\mathrm{I}) \| \Phi^{\Gamma_1'}_{x_1'} \rangle = (-1)^{\Gamma_1-\nu-\Gamma_1'} \langle (\overline{\boldsymbol{Z}}{}^{\Gamma_1}_{x_1} \times \boldsymbol{Q}^{\nu}_{\alpha_1}(\mathrm{I}) \times \boldsymbol{Z}^{\Gamma_1'}_{x_1'})^0 \rangle_0 \,.$$

In terms of these matrices we can now construct the Hamiltonian matrix for the $\Phi(\mathrm{I})$ system; this is trivial but, beyond that, if we consider an extended system (I+II), where system II has no orbits in common (*) with system I, we can do the same thing in terms of the separate moment matrices for the two partial systems.

(*) More precisely the two systems should be completely inequivalent in the sense of the discussion following eq. (5.27). One could generalize to partially or fully equivalent systems but this is not easy and is unnecessary for our purposes.

The proof is immediate. Consider for the combined system the two-particle H as given by eqs. (5.54) or (5.70). The parts of $H^{(2)}$ involving orbits not found in the combined system can be ignored; then each contributing term can be recoupled so that all the (I) operators stand to the left of the (II) operators, the coupled operators for each partial system having a definite rank ν. The corresponding operation for the one-body Hamiltonian is particularly simple, while no transformation at all is needed for the Hamiltonian of the separate systems. The outcome now is that

$$H \Rightarrow H(\mathrm{I}) + H(\mathrm{II}) + \sum_{\alpha_1\alpha_2\nu} M^{\nu}_{\alpha_1\alpha_2}\big(\boldsymbol{Q}^{\nu}_{\alpha_1}(\mathrm{I}) \times \boldsymbol{Q}^{\nu}_{\alpha_2}(\mathrm{II})\big)^0, \tag{8.3}$$

where $M^{\nu}_{\alpha_1\alpha_2}$ is (for the two-body interaction) a linear combination of the two-body matrix elements as given by the recoupling. The Hamiltonians for the separate groups produce a contribution

$$\delta_{\Gamma_1\Gamma_1'}\delta_{\Gamma_2\Gamma_2'}\{\delta_{x_2x_2'}\langle x_1\Gamma_1|H(\mathrm{I})|x_1'\Gamma_1'\rangle + \delta_{x_1x_1'}\langle x_2\Gamma_2|H(\mathrm{II})|x_2'\Gamma_2'\rangle\}\,,$$

while for the *interaction* Hamiltonian we use eq. (3.42) (and the note which follows it) and produce thereby the general multipole expansion.

We see at this stage that for a specified division of the orbits into two sets our program must be able to transform the Hamiltonian from the W^{Γ} form to the M^{ν} form; this is not very difficult. Also of course if we care to use as input an interaction expressed in configuration space the program must be able to parametrize this in terms of the orbits; it must in short contain a two-body-matrix-element program; that also causes no difficulty. It will be appreciated that if we have already solved the Hamiltonian problem for system (I) we may simply calculate its moments (and that may involve only a unitary transformation from the original basis set of system (I) to the « physical » set; but note that not all of the moment operators are number-conserving and thus we may have to consider solutions for the (I) system with various numbers of particles). We can now immediately produce the matrix for the extended case $\{(\mathrm{I})+\text{inequivalent particle}\}$; and if we have solved the problem for two separate complex systems we can combine them also. Some obvious approximations suggest themselves, in which we limit the number of « physical » states of the separate systems, say to those which are not highly excited or to those which are strongly coupled to the low states via the interaction moments. Detailed studies of this sort, of the mutual polarization of two systems, should be of some interest.

Our real concern at present is not in the interaction of two fully understood inequivalent systems, but rather in trying to understand a general complex system. Can we use the « extension » procedure for this purpose? Obviously we can if we think about a complex system as being composed of a set of equivalent-particle systems, something like $((\varrho_1^{n_1})\times(\varrho_2^{n_2})\times\ldots\times(\varrho_k^{n_k}))$. Then we can do the same thing as above though we must now be prepared for the fact that a single term in the Hamiltonian may give rise to an interaction between as many as four orbits at once; that aspect of the thing however causes very little trouble. But just as before we must remember that the pairing and non-diagonal parts of the interaction (in the sense of the classification preceding eq. (5.70)) do not preserve the occupation numbers n_i for the separate orbits. It will be better for us therefore to think about the complex system as being $(S_1\times S_2\times\ldots S_k)$, where S_i is the space of *all* the states for particles in the orbit ϱ_i. Then the interaction matrix may be given in terms of all the moment matrix elements for each separate shell and in this way we have achieved a complete decoupling of the complex system into its single-orbit parts, the form of the result being exactly analogous to the ordinary electrostatic result. Since the system Hamiltonian is number-preserving it follows of course that if we take *all* the states of every S_i as indicated we will be solving simultaneously a set of disjoint problems, one for each n; but we can instruct the program to consider only couplings in which the total number has the definite value of interest. Besides that we may, and often do, wish to restrict the possible numbers in various shells; it is easy to arrange this.

The formal equations are now very easy to write down and the structure of the whole thing should be very clear. The great importance of the second-quantization factoring of the operators should also be obvious. With the factoring everything becomes very simple; without it everything would be very difficult. There remains only the problem of constructing the single-shell moment matrices and that we now consider.

8·3. *Single-shell operators.* – By «single-shell» we imply «single-orbit» though there is in fact nothing whatever to prevent us from combining several orbits to make one shell (and this would be a good thing to do if we were to use an SU_3 scheme for cataloguing functions). By the same token we shall discuss things in jj coupling with an isospin formalism though there are obviously other possibilities. In fact it is quite feasible to discuss some orbits via one representation and other orbits via another.

The entire problem of calculating the single-shell matrix elements reduces to the single-shell single-particle fractional-parentage problem, for once we know the matrix elements of $\boldsymbol{A}^{\varrho}$ we find those for $\boldsymbol{B}^{\varrho}$ by taking adjoints (eq. (5.53)), while for the more complicated operators we can use the intermediate-state expansion (eq. (3.22)). And because of the hole$\rightleftharpoons$particle transform results (eq. (5.44) and the discussion prior to eq. (5.50)) it is adequate to consider the lower half-shell. There unfortunately does not exist any procedure for c.f.p. calculation which is both elegant and efficient and consequently we describe in configuration-space language a rather crude but fairly effective technique which has been used by J. N. GINOCCHIO and the present author.

A usual way to begin is to consider the coupling of a numbered particle (no. (n)) to an antisymmetrized $(n-1)$-particle basis function. The result is not antisymmetric in all particles and as a consequence the (n)-particle vector space formed in this way is in large part uninteresting, the physically interesting space being usually only a very small part of the total space. This has obvious major disadvantages. We can avoid these by using a p-n formalism to begin with, for the coupling of an antisymmetric proton state to an antisymmetric neutron state produces only physically allowable states (see Sect. **5**·8). Let us assume therefore that we have constructed the antisymmetric states $\psi^{J_1}_{x_1}(n_1)$ and $\psi^{J_2}_{x_2}(n_2)$ (which implies that we have their c.f.p. expansions), and consider the coupled states $(\psi^{J_1}_{x_1}(n_1)\times\psi^{J_2}_{x_2}(n_2))^J$. In order to produce, from these, states of good isobaric spin (though in the p-n formalism) we simply diagonalize T^2 as given by eqs. (5.84) or (5.108). Using the unit-tensor form we find easily that

$$(8.4)\quad \langle n_1x_1J_1;\, n_2x_2J_2|T^2|n_1x_1'J_1';\, n_2x_2'J_2'\rangle = \left\{\frac{n_1+n_2}{2}+\frac{(n_1-n_2)^2}{4}\right\}\delta_{x_1x_1'}\delta_{J_1J_1'}\delta_{x_2x_2'}\delta_{J_2J_2'} - $$
$$-(-1)^{J_1+J_2'-J}\sum_k\left[\frac{k}{J}\right]^{\frac{1}{2}} U(J_1J_2J_1'J_2':Jk)\langle n_1x_1J_1\|\mathcal{U}^k\|n_1x_1'J_1'\rangle\langle n_2x_2J_2\|\mathcal{U}^k\|n_2x_2'J_2'\rangle,$$

where the n_1- and n_2-particle matrices may be calculated via the assumed known c.f.p. expansions. A transformation which diagonalizes this matrix produces p-n formalism n-particle functions with good isobaric spin.

It is advantageous while carrying out this operation to consider also the symplectic symmetry of the states being produced, *i.e.* the way in which they transform under the operations of the symplectic group. The unit tensors $\mathcal{U}^k$ are such that their commutators are contained in the set, as follows easily from eq. (5.122). They are then the infinitesimal operators of a group (U_{2j+1}) and T^2 is essentially its Casimir operator. But from the same equation it follows that the odd-rank tensors form a group, the symplectic group Sp_{2j+1}. It is easy to show (we leave these things for exercises) that the symplectic Casimir operator may be taken as $G=2\sum_{k\,\text{odd}}[k](\mathcal{U}^k\cdot\mathcal{U}^k)$, that its eigenvalues in states of maximum T are $v(2j+3-v)$ where v is the seniority discussed briefly in **5**·10 and that its matrix representation in the p-n formalism is

$$(8.5)\quad \langle n_1x_1J_1;\, n_2x_2J_2|G|n_1x_1'J_1';\, n_2x_2'J_2'\rangle =$$
$$=\{v_1(2j+3-v_1)+v_2(2j+3-v_2)\}\delta_{x_1x_1'}\delta_{J_1J_1'}\delta_{x_2x_2'}\delta_{J_2J_2'}+$$
$$+4(-1)^{J_1+J_2'-J}\sum_{k\,\text{odd}}\left[\frac{k}{J}\right]^{\frac{1}{2}} U(J_1J_2J_1'J_2':Jk)\langle n_1x_1J_1\|\mathcal{U}^k\|n_1x_1'J_1'\rangle\langle n_2x_2J_2\|\mathcal{U}^k\|n_2x_2'J_2'\rangle.$$

It is understood here that the identical-particle groups have good seniority (and thus that $x_1 \equiv (v_1, \alpha_1)$ where α_1 is needed only if states of the same $n_1 J_1 v_1$ occur more than once).

T^2 and G commute and thus the transformation which simultaneously diagonalizes them produces states of good T and good symplectic symmetry. In the general case, where T is not necessarily maximum, it is well known that the irreducible representations of G are labelled by two quantum numbers (v, t), the eigenvalues of G being $\{(2j+2)v - \frac{1}{2}v(v-1) + \frac{3}{2}v - 2t(t+1)\}$; for T maximum we have $t = v/2$.

We have now the n-particle wave functions in the form

$$\Psi^{J,T}_{vt\alpha}(n) = \sum_{\substack{s_1 v_1 \alpha_1 J_1 \\ s_2 v_2 \alpha_2 J_2}} A^{J,T}_{s_1 v_1 \alpha_1 J_1; s_2 v_2 \alpha_2 J_2}(n) \left(\psi^{J_1,(T_1=n_1/2)}_{s_1 v_1 \alpha_1}(n_1) \times \psi^{J_2,(T_2=n_2/2)}_{s_2 v_2 \alpha_2}(n_2)\right)^J, \tag{8.6}$$

where the ψ functions are completely antisymmetric and although we apply a T label for Ψ we are still in the p-n formalism. The $A^{J,T}$ quantities themselves are a type of fractional-parentage coefficient but nonetheless eq. (8.6) does not give the usual isospin-formalism expansion which we are seeking. For example for the case $n_2 = 1$, $T = n/2 - \frac{1}{2}$, the usual expansion necessarily involves terms with $T_1 = n/2$ and $T_1 = n/2 - 1$, while eq. (8.6) contains only the first. The difference in the two expansions comes about because there does not exist, in the T formalism, a c.f.p. expansion in which *numbered* protons can be separated off from a state of definite T.

To complete the inductive procedure which we are obviously setting up we need to be able to calculate *isospin* c.f.p.'s using the p-n functions of eq. (8.6). One way to do this is by the direct conversion of the p-n functions into the T formalism. This has already been suggested as an exercise in Sect. **5.8**; it may be done by simply multiplying every $(n_1; n_2)$ function by $\left(\prod_{i=1}^{n_1} \omega_{-\frac{1}{2}}(i)\right) \cdot \left(\prod_{j=n_1+1}^{n} \omega_{+\frac{1}{2}}(j)\right)$ where ω_m is the single-particle isospin function, and then antisymmetrizing. Because of the orthogonality of the $\omega_{\pm\frac{1}{2}}$ functions the antisymmetrization causes no complication when one evaluates any matrix element and the whole operation becomes very simple; it is still left for an exercise. Alternatively one can infer the general relationship between the c.f.p. involving corresponding states in the two formalisms that

$$\sqrt{n_2}\langle n_1; n_2; JT | n_1; n_2 - 1; J_1 T_1 \rangle^{(p-n)} = \sqrt{n}\, C^{T_1 \frac{1}{2} T}_{T_{z_1}, \frac{1}{2}} \langle n; JT | n-1, J_1 T_1 \rangle^{(T)}, \tag{8.7}$$

where $2T_{z_1} = (n_2 - 1 - n_1)$. Assume now that the n- and $(n-1)$-particle functions are available in the form (8.6). We can easily evaluate the c.f.p. overlap in terms of the $n_2 \to (n_2 - 1)$ c.f.p. and by means of eq. (8.7) can then evaluate the isospin-formalism c.f.p.'s, special examples of which are the identical particle c.f.p.'s themselves.

All the ingredients for the c.f.p. calculation are now at hand. One starts with the $(n_1, n_2) = (1, 2)$ case, constructs and simultaneously diagonalizes the T^2 and G matrices, calculates from the resultant wave functions the c.f.p. overlap for $(n = 3) \to (n = 2)$ and from that the three-particle isospin-formalism c.f.p.'s. Then one proceeds step by step to the $(n_1, n_2) = (2, 2), (2, 3), (3, 3) \ldots$ cases, producing thereby the complete c.f.p.'s in the isospin symplectic-symmetry representation. If one is not interested in the c.f.p.'s for small T, as often happens, one simply omits the cases where $(n_2 - n_1)$ is small. The chain of activities outlined above has been programmed by J. N. GINOCCHIO and Mrs. J. RAYBURN at Oak Ridge National Laboratory and c.f.p. values thereby produced, from which all the necessary single-shell matrix elements can be calculated.

We have a few further remarks about the fractional-parentage problem. The procedure above is crude in many ways, one of which is that it takes no account of the Racah factoring of fractional-parentage coefficients (and other matrix elements) when the basis functions belong to « nested » groups. A way which does, and which is at the same time adequate for large shells and adaptable to programming, does not seem to have been produced. It seems possible however that the averaging procedure of Sect. **5·9** can be used to calculate some of the factors.

Finally it might be noted that the transform relationship which connects the single-particle and single-hole transfer strengths (eq. (6.4)) is a relationship between the squares of c.f.p.'s. A generalization of this transform, *viz.*,

$$(8.8)\quad \sum_y \langle x\Gamma \| \boldsymbol{P}^\lambda \| y\Gamma_1\rangle \langle y\Gamma_1 \| \boldsymbol{Q}^{\lambda'} \| x'\Gamma'\rangle = [\Gamma_1]^{\frac{1}{2}} \sum_\nu (-1)^{\lambda+\lambda'-\nu} U(\Gamma\lambda\Gamma'\lambda' : \Gamma_1\nu)[\boldsymbol{P}^\lambda \times \boldsymbol{Q}^{\lambda'}]_\pm \mp$$
$$\mp \sum_{y'_1\Gamma'_1} \left[\frac{\Gamma_1}{\Gamma'_1}\right]^{\frac{1}{2}} (-1)^{\Gamma_1+\Gamma'_1-\Gamma-\Gamma'} U(\Gamma\lambda\lambda'\Gamma' : \Gamma_1\Gamma'_1) \langle x\Gamma \| \boldsymbol{Q}^{\lambda'} \| y'_1\Gamma'_1\rangle \langle y'_1\Gamma'_1 \| \boldsymbol{P}^\lambda \| x'\Gamma'\rangle ,$$

whose derivation is left as an exercise, provides a class of phase-dependent relationships between the c.f.p.'s, and an extension along the lines of eq. (6.16) with a Casimir-operator weighting gives further relationships as well as the group-theoretical classification. It is not known however how complete is the set of equations thereby produced.

8·4. *Final remarks.* – The structure of the program based on the general multipole analysis should now be clear, as should also be the extent to which the structure meets the requirements outlined in Sect. **8·1**. The input information includes a specification of the orbits to be considered, the partitions of the particles among these orbits, the states of the resultant vector space to be included, and the interaction to be used. The interaction is appropriately parametrized and transformed into the general multipole form (eq. (8.3)). Then the Hamiltonian matrix is calculated in terms of the coefficients M^ν, making use of the single-shell matrix elements assumed to be available. Diagonalization produces the wave functions (in a single-shell symplectic-symmetry representation), and then by applying the unitary transform, which diagonalizes the Hamiltonian matrix, to the input moment matrices (or otherwise) one can produce in the « physical » representation the matrix of any tensor operator of interest, and thereby calculate the physically significant quantities. The program as constructed contains other features which we cannot now discuss, such as a method for handling the center-of-mass spurious-state problem. Various sum rules and averages which we have discussed in previous sections can be used to produce adequate checks on the results.

The very sophisticated planning and programming required to convert the logical structure outlined above into a working scheme for complex spectroscopic calculations have been done by Drs. E. C. HALBERT and J. B. MCGRORY of Oak Ridge National Laboratory and Dr. S. S. M. WONG of the University of Rochester.

9. – Conclusion.

Much of what we have discussed is very familiar and our discussion has sometimes been labored and pedantic; the usual apologies are offered. We have sought however to stress the treatment of excitation spectra (including the widths), and the proper treatment of angular momenta in nuclear problems (in order to avoid losing valuable information). These two things have been combined in the formalism of the multipole sum rules.

The procedures which we have used may be extended in several directions. It is probably worth-while extending the semi-classical forms to more complicated cases. It is certainly worth-while, and should in fact be extremely interesting, to introduce multipole Green's functions (corresponding to negative-m sum rules); a technical adjunct to this would be the use of Feynman techniques in spherical representation. It may be possible to extend the technique of seeking consistency in various formulations of the sum rules (which would be equivalent for an exact ground-state function) in order to bring the ground-state problem into the domain of the sum rules; it now stands outside. This may be accomplished by the use of perturbational and variational procedures, and perhaps also by applications of procedures such as RPA.

Among the important applications which we have at best only mentioned are the study of complex excitations (*e.g.* multi-hole-particle) in which perhaps which excitations are interesting could be determined by Hartree-Fock techniques, excitations of open-shell nuclei, and studies of more complex nuclear reactions, (d; p, γ) and things like that.

* * *

For many discussions, and in some cases for permission to make use of unpublished results, I am indebted to H. BANERJEE, R. K. BANSAL, J. N. GINOCCHIO, E. C. HALBERT, L. S. HSU, D. S. KOLTUN, J. B. McGRORY, F. B. WANG and S. S. M. WONG.

GENERAL REFERENCES

With few exceptions we have given references in the text only where we have referred to unpublished work. It is hardly feasible to give full references for other things because most of what we have done is of such a nature that it has probably been incidentally derived in the past by those who felt the need of it; our own first account of much of it is contained in unpublished notes for lectures at the University of Rochester during 1962-63. Following we give some general references useful to those who wish to pursue various questions which have been raised.

Standard references on angular momentum are: U. FANO and G. RACAH: *Irreducible Tensorial Sets* (New York, 1959); A. R. EDMONDS: *Angular Momentum in Quantum Mechanics* (Princeton, N. J., 1957); M. E. ROSE: *Elementary Theory of Angular Momentum* (New York, 1957); D. M. BRINK and G. R. SATCHLER: *Angular Momentum* (Oxford, 1962). For special insights, concerning the P_ν-Racah correspondences in particular, see the article by L. C. BIEDENHARN: in *Nuclear Spectroscopy*, F. AJZENBERG-SELOVE editor (New York, 1960); and Chapter 27 of *Group Theory* by E. P. WIGNER, translated by J. J. GRIFFIN (New York, 1959). Spectroscopy in configuration-space representation is reviewed in A. DE-SHALIT and I. TALMI: *Nuclear Shell Theory* (New York, 1963).

Multipole expansions of Hamiltonians are discussed, along with many other things, by M. BARANGER: *Phys. Rev.*, **120**, 957 (1960); and *Cargèse Lectures*, M. LÉVY, editor (New York, 1963). See also A. M. LANE: *Nuclear Theory* (New York, 1964); and B. MOTTELSON: *Lectures at Les Houches Summer School* (Paris, 1959), as well as other papers referred to in the last three references. Some formal discussions of sum rules are given by D. J. THOULESS: *The Quantum Mechanics of Many-Body Systems* (New York, 1961); and by W. BRENIG: in *Advances in Theoretical Physics*, K. A. BRUECKNER editor (New York, 1965). Thouless' book also contains a very clear discussion of Green's functions which would be of value in making the extension to multipole Green's functions; a more detailed account is given in *Methods of Quantum Field Theory in Statistical Physics* by A. A. ABRIKOSOV, L. P. GORKOV and I. E. DZYALOSHINSKI (New York, 1963). For diagrammatic techniques in spherical representation see F. DÖNAU and G. FLACH: *Nucl. Phys.*, **69**, 68 (1965).

For examples of the direct analysis of single-nucleon and hole excitations see for example M. H. MACFARLANE, B. J. RAZ, J. L. YNTEMA and B. ZEIDMAN: *Phys. Rev.*, **127**, 204 (1962); and B. L. COHEN, R. H. FULMER and A. L. McCARTHY: *Phys. Rev.*, **126**, 698 (1962). The experimental work on even-parity hole states in $f_{\frac{7}{2}}$-shell nuclei referred to in the text is reported by G. R. SATCHLER and J. L. YNTEMA: *Phys. Rev.*, **134**, B 976 (1964); and E. KASHY and Y. E. CONLON: *Phys. Rev.*, **135**, B 389 (1964). See also R. K. BANSAL and J. B. FRENCH: *Phys. Lett.*, **11**, 145 (1964); and J. B. FRENCH:

Proceedings of the Argonne Conference on Nuclear Spectroscopy with Direct Reactions, F. E. THROW editor (1964). The latter reference discusses other aspects of isobaric-spin phenomena also.

For electromagnetic sum rules and processes see, besides Brenig's article, J. S. LEVINGER: *Nuclear Photodisintegration* (Oxford, 1960); and E. G. FULLER and E. HAYWARD: *Nuclear Reactions*, vol. **2**; P. M. ENDT and P. B. SMITH editors (Amsterdam, 1962); as well as W. T. PINKSTON and G. R. SATCHLER: *Proceedings of the Kingston Conference*, D. A. BROMLEY and E. W. VOGT, editors (Toronto, 1960); and V. V. BALASHOV: *Sov. Phys. JETP*, **15**, 191 (1962). For more general aspects of hole-particle excitations see G. E. BROWN, J. A. EVANS and D. J. THOULESS: *Nucl. Phys.*, **24**, 1 (1961); and later papers by BROWN and by THOULESS. The early treatment of ground-state correlations referred to in the text is by S. FALLIEROS and R. A. FERRELL: *Phys. Rev.*, **116**, 660 (1959).

For discussions of group theory applied to spectroscopy see J. P. ELLIOTT: in *Selected Topics in Nuclear Theory* (Vienna, 1963); K. HELMERS: *Nucl. Phys.*, **23**, 594 (1961); K. T. HECHT: *Phys. Rev.*, **139**, B 794 (1965); and L. BIEDENHARN: *Lectures in Theoretical Physics*, vol. **5** (New York, 1963).

A more detailed account of complex spectroscopy, as discussed in Sect. **8** will be published later by E. C. HALBERT, J. B. McGRORY, S. S. M. WONG, and the present author. Programs for large-scale spectroscopy have been constructed and used by other groups, in particular by S. COHEN, R. D. LAWSON, M. H. MACFARLANE and M. SOGA at Argonne National Laboratory and by T. D. NEWTON at Chalk River, but it seems that detailed accounts have not been published.

Multi-particle-hole excitations have been discussed for light nuclei by W. H. BASSICHIS and G. RIPKA: *Phys. Lett.*, **15**, 323 (1965); I. KELSON: *Phys. Lett.*, **16**, 143 (1965) and G. E. BROWN and A. M. GREEN: (in press); see also I. KELSON and C. A. LEVINSON: *Phys. Rev.*, **134**, B 269 (1964). In our mention of the study of complex excitations by Hartree-Fock techniques we had in mind using the techniques and intuition of these authors to decide on the form of the excitation operator whose energy, width and so on are then to be determined by the sum-rule methods we have used above.

Appendix

Vacuum and Closed-Shell Expectation Values, Normal Forms and Commutators (*).

L. S. Hsu

Department of Physics and Astronomy, University of Rochester - Rochester, N. Y.

A·1. *General remarks.* – The methods used above and the sum-rule methods in particular, demand knowledge of several related entities, the vacuum expectation value, the closed-shell expectation value, the normal form of an operator, and the commutation relations between two operators. In principle, these can be obtained by repeated use of the basic commutation rule (eq. (5.4)), angular momentum recoupling (eqs. (2.2) and (2.6)) and the elementary hole-particle transformation (eq. (5.7)). The process of evaluating them can be accelerated by making use of commutation relations for operators made up of several basic (*i.e.* creation or destruction) operators (for example, see eqs. (A-5.1) to (A-5.8)). Both these processes may involve complicated intermediate operators. We have therefore generalized Wick's theorem to deal with operators in coupled form. With the definitions:

Normal Form. An operator is said to be in normal form if all the creation operators stand to the left of all the destruction operators.

Contraction. The contraction of two operators is obtained by bringing the two operators adjacent to each other by recoupling techniques assuming that all operators commute, and then replacing the two coupled operators by the vacuum expectation value.

Wick's theorem in coupled form states that a coupled operator made up of n basic operators can be decomposed into a sum of operators in normal form and involving $n, n-2, \ldots, 0, (1)$ basic operators; the terms involving $n-2m$ basic operators are obtained by making all possible combinations of m contractions, the remaining operators in each case being then brought to normal form by assuming that they all commute. The vacuum expectation value is then just the constant term in Wick's expansion. The closed-shell expectation value is obtained in the same way except that a hole-particle transformation on operators involving orbits below the closed shell is needed before applying

(*) Supported in part by the U. S. Atomic Energy Commission.

Wick's theorem. The commutator or anticommutator of two operators $\boldsymbol{P}^{\Gamma_1}$ and $\boldsymbol{Q}^{\Gamma_2}$ is obtained by summing the partial Wick's expansion of the operators $(\boldsymbol{P}^{\Gamma_1}\times\boldsymbol{Q}^{\Gamma_2})^{\Gamma}$ and $\mp(-1)^{\Gamma_1+\Gamma_2-\Gamma}(\boldsymbol{Q}^{\Gamma_2}\times\boldsymbol{P}^{\Gamma_1})^{\Gamma}$. The partial expansion contains only terms obtained by at least one contraction involving one operator each from $\boldsymbol{P}^{\Gamma_1}$ and $\boldsymbol{Q}^{\Gamma_2}$.

Making use of the above theorem, a computing program has been written to produce these quantities in analytical form. Some of the results are presented in this Appendix. With slight modifications, the program can produce numerical in addition to analytical answers.

The results are given in four sections. Each section starts with a set of numbered diagrams. In the equations which follow, a curly bracket $\{i\}$ stands for the Fig. i. In Sect. A·**4** where diagrams are needed in both sides of the equations, the diagrams are divided into two groups, those appearing in the left-hand side of the equations being given first. Instead of the U-coefficients used in the main text, we have used the Racah coefficients W. The two quantities are related by eq. (2.8). We have also introduced an exchange operator $E_{ab\Gamma}$ defined by

(A-1.1) $$E_{ab\Gamma}\,f(a,b,\Gamma)=f(a,b,\Gamma)-(-1)^{a+b-\Gamma}f(b,a,\Gamma)\,,$$

where $f(a,b,\Gamma)$ is an arbitrary function of a, b and Γ. It follows that, (for the case that a and b are identical) $E_{aa\Gamma}\equiv 2$ for allowed Γ and $E_{aa\Gamma}\equiv 0$ for forbidden Γ.

Section A·**2** gives the vacuum expectation values of operators involving up to eight basic operators. Certain more complicated vacuum expectation values can be obtained from the table if the operator involved can be separated into two or more groups in each of which the number of creation operators is the same as that of destruction operators. Then operating on the vacuum we encounter the vacuum again as an intermediate state, and then by the method of intermediate state sums (eq. (3.22)), the vacuum expectation value factors into several simple parts, which, hopefully, can be found in the Table.

For example, the vacuum expectation value

(A-1.2)

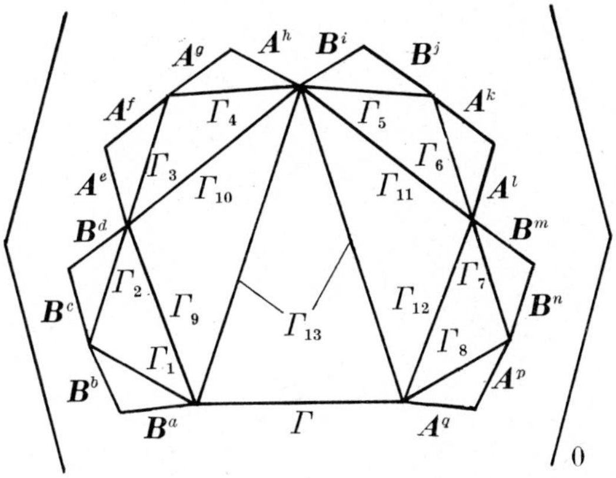

is not directly available from the Table, but can be easily evaluated by factoring into

(A-1.3) 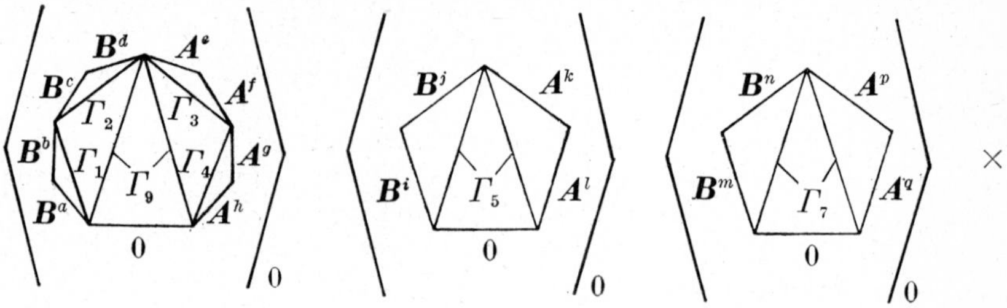

$$\times \delta_{\Gamma_5\Gamma_6}\delta_{\Gamma_7\Gamma_8}\delta_{\Gamma_9\Gamma_{10}}\delta_{\Gamma_{11}0}\delta_{\Gamma_{12}0}\delta_{\Gamma_{13}0}\,.$$

By the same token, operators involving less than eight basic operators are omitted if they can be factored easily. For example, the vacuum expectation value

(A-1.4) 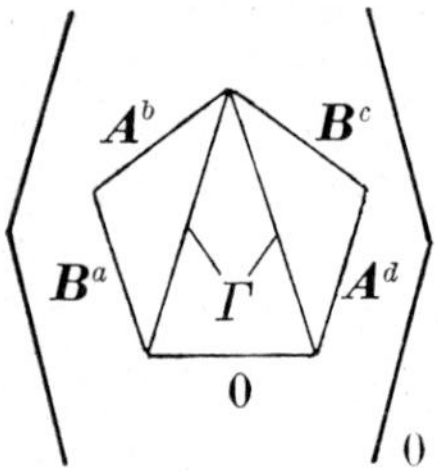

can be factored into

(A-1.5) 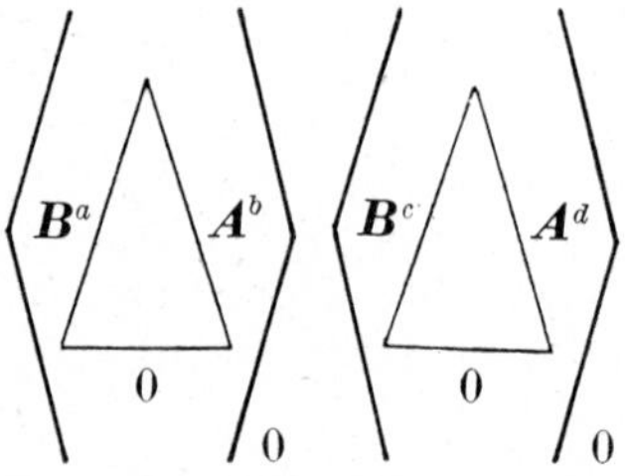 $\delta_{\Gamma 0}$,

and is thus omitted. The above examples are particularly simple. Actually a vacuum expectation value can be factored even if the intermediate state is a one-particle or one-hole state rather than vacuum, or more generally, it can be written as a simple sum of factors if the intermediate state is simple. Even in cases where the intermediate state is not simple, it might pay to make use of simple commutation relations to make it so. Expectation values involving the Hamiltonian are not included, they can be easily obtained from Sect. A.**3** by dropping terms referring to operators below the closed shell.

Section A.**3** gives closed-shell expectation values. In this Section we label orbits so that a, b, c, d, e, f, g, h refer to orbits above the closed shell while i, j, k, l, m, n, p, q refer to those below the closed shell. Since closed-shell expectation values not involving the Hamiltonian are derivable immediately by a hole-particle transformation on the results of Sect. A.**2**, all formulae in this Section involve the Hamiltonian. One can of course extract the expectation value for one particular term in the Hamiltonian by making all except one of the two-body matrix elements or single-particle energy parameters vanish.

Due to space limitation we have restricted ourselves to deal with excitations involving not more than two particles and two holes. For such simple excitations, the expectation value of the square of the Hamiltonian can be easily obtained by the method of intermediate-state sums, and is therefore omitted. For example

(A-1.6)

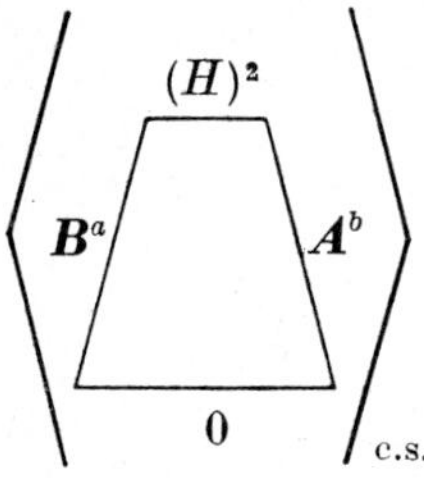

$$= \sum_c [ab]^{\frac{1}{2}} \left\{ \varepsilon_{ac}\delta_{ac}^{am} + \delta_{ac}\sum_p [p]\varepsilon_{pp} + \sum_p \left[\frac{p}{a}\right]^{\frac{1}{2}} \beta^0_{acpp} + \sum_{p\leq q} [pq]^{\frac{1}{2}} \beta^0_{ppqq}\delta_{ac} \right\} \left\{ \varepsilon_{bc}\delta_{bc}^{am} + \sum_p [p]\varepsilon_{pp}\delta_{bc} + \sum_p \left[\frac{p}{b}\right]^{\frac{1}{2}} \beta^0_{bcpp} + \sum_{p\leq q} [pq]^{\frac{1}{2}} \beta^0_{ppqq}\delta_{bc} \right\}.$$

Excitation operators are assumed to be in normal form. If they are not, one can use results in Sect. A˙**4** to put them in that form.

Section A˙**4** gives the normal form for operators involving not more than four basic operators. For operators made up of five or six basic operators, the vacuum expectation values given in Sect. A˙**2** enable one to get a partial Wick's expansion including terms involving less than three basic operators. For a complete expansion in such cases and for cases involving more complicated operators one would have to use the program specifically for the case at hand.

Section A˙**5** gives commutation relations, and normal forms for operators of the form $(\overline{\boldsymbol{T}}^{\Gamma_1}\times[H, \boldsymbol{T}^{\Gamma_2}])^{\Gamma}$ which are frequently encountered when using sum-rule methods. Anticommutation relations for such things as $[\boldsymbol{A}, \boldsymbol{ABB}]_+$ and so on are not given but the simpler ones could be easily derived from the results given in Sect. A˙**4**.

There are various ways to check the accuracy of the results. We can compare the vacuum expectation value with the leading term in the normal form. For example, eq. (A-2.2) is in agreement with the first term in eq. (A-4.11). Some results can be derived from others by means of hole-particle transformation or by taking adjoints (for example, eqs. (A-3.9) and (A-3.10)); and other procedures will suggest themselves.

All the results given have been derived by means of the programmed Wick's theorem. The program can successfully handle considerably more complicated cases but, as indicated above, there are far too many of them, and their analytic forms are too complicated, to make feasible any listing. Particular ones which are needed can be produced, but, as also indicated, *numerical* forms for the complicated ones (and often even for the simpler ones) might be more useful; with certain modifications the program can produce these too.

For cases which are extremely complicated a generalized fractional-parentage procedure might be advantageous for it could make use of quantities already evaluated. Suppose we are evaluating a v.e.v. which we can write in the form $\langle(\overline{\boldsymbol{Z}}{}^{\Gamma}_{x}(n)\times\boldsymbol{O}^{\lambda}\times\boldsymbol{Z}^{\Gamma}_{x'}(n'))^0\rangle_0$ (this is automatically the form if we are considering a d.b.m.e., but even in other cases it may be advantageous to consider things in this way). Then if we write $\boldsymbol{O}^{\lambda} = (\boldsymbol{Z}^{\Lambda}_{y}(m)\times\boldsymbol{O}^{\lambda'}\times\overline{\boldsymbol{Z}}{}^{\Lambda'}_{y'}(m'))^{\lambda}$ or as a sum of such terms we will, on recoupling, and making fractional-parentage expansions of $(\bar{\boldsymbol{Z}}_x^{\Gamma} \times \boldsymbol{Z}_y^{A})$ and $(\bar{\boldsymbol{Z}}_{y'}^{A^*} \times \boldsymbol{Z}_{x'}^{\Gamma})$ express the original v.e.v. as a fractional-parentage sum of v.e.v.'s involving the new operator $\boldsymbol{O}^{\lambda'}$. One clearly has a lot of freedom in carrying out this reduction and besides that there are alternative fractional-parentage procedures too as indicated at the end of Sect. **5**.

A·**2**. *Vacuum expectation values.*

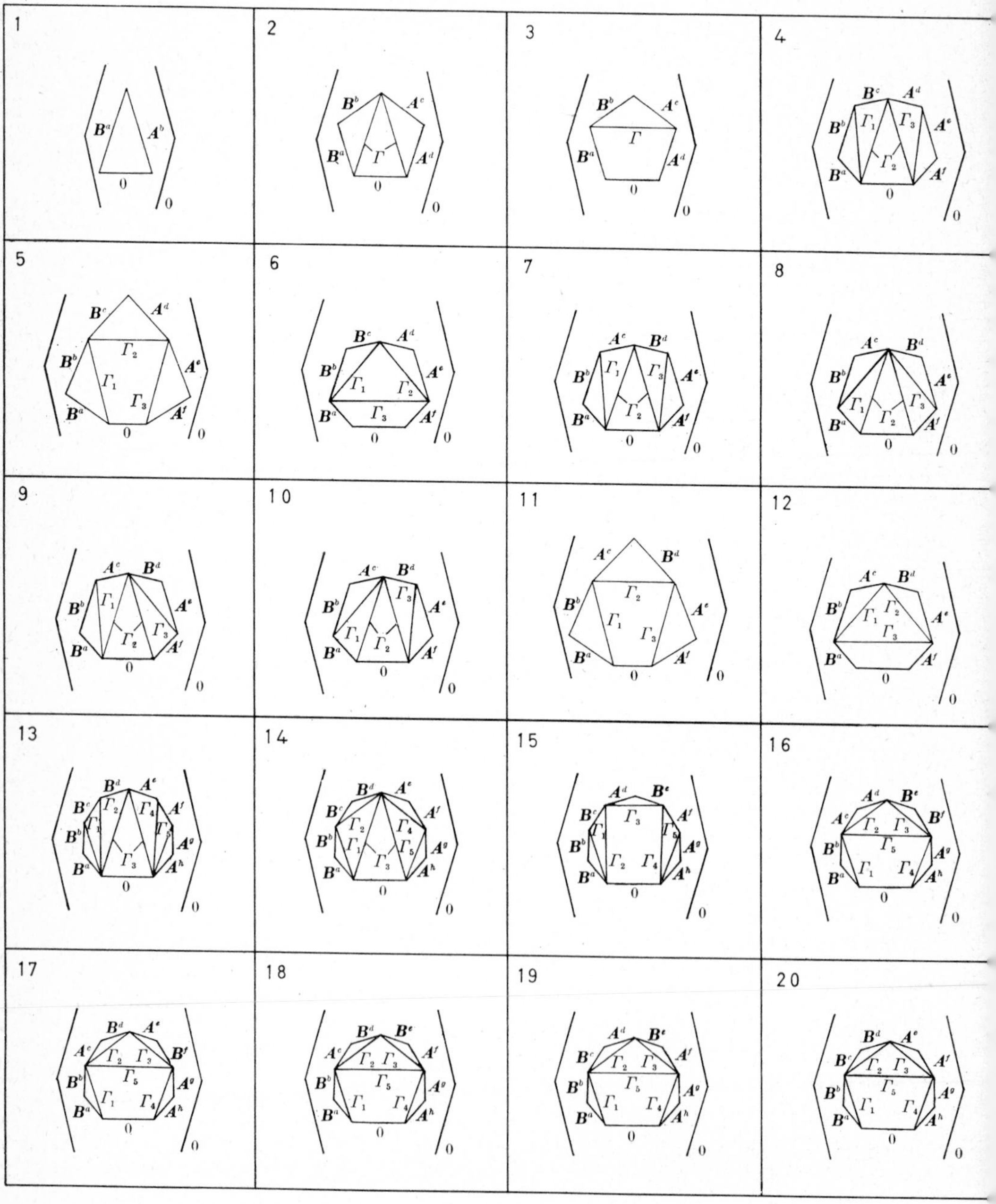

(A-2.1) $\{1\} = (-1)^{2a}[a]^{\frac{1}{2}}\delta_{ab}$,

(A-2.1) $\{2\} = -[\Gamma]^{\frac{1}{2}}E_{ab\Gamma}\delta_{ac}\delta_{bd}$,

(A-2.3) $\{3\} = -[\Gamma]^{\frac{1}{2}}\delta_{ac}\delta_{bd} + [ab]^{\frac{1}{2}}\delta_{ad}\delta_{bc}\delta_{\Gamma 0}$,

(A-2.4) $$\{4\} = -[\Gamma_1\Gamma_2\Gamma_3]^{\frac{1}{2}}E_{ab\Gamma_1}E_{ef\Gamma_3}(-1)^{b+\Gamma_1-\Gamma_2+\Gamma_3}W(\Gamma_3 ac\Gamma_1;\ \Gamma_2 b)\delta_{ad}\delta_{be}\delta_{cf} - (-1)^{c+\Gamma_1+\Gamma_2}[\Gamma_2]^{\frac{1}{2}}E_{ab\Gamma_1}\delta_{ae}\delta_{bf}\delta_{cd}\delta_{\Gamma_1\Gamma_3},$$

(A-2.5) $$\{5\} = -[\Gamma_1\Gamma_2\Gamma_3]^{\frac{1}{2}}E_{ab\Gamma_1}E_{ef\Gamma_3}(-1)^{a-c+\Gamma_2}W(ca\Gamma_3\Gamma_1;\ \Gamma_2 b)\delta_{ad}\delta_{be}\delta_{cf} - (-1)^{2c}[c\Gamma_1]^{\frac{1}{2}}E_{ab\Gamma_1}\delta_{ae}\delta_{bf}\delta_{cd}\delta_{\Gamma_1\Gamma_3}\delta_{\Gamma_2 0},$$

(A-2.6) $$\{6\} = -[\Gamma_1\Gamma_2\Gamma_3]^{\frac{1}{2}}E_{bc\Gamma_1}E_{de\Gamma_2}(-1)^{a-c+\Gamma_3}W(ca\Gamma_1\Gamma_2;\ \Gamma_3 b)\delta_{ad}\delta_{be}\delta_{cf} - (-1)^{2a}[a\Gamma_1]^{\frac{1}{2}}E_{bc\Gamma_1}\delta_{af}\delta_{bd}\delta_{ce}\delta_{\Gamma_1\Gamma_2}\delta_{\Gamma_3 0},$$

(A-2.7) $\{7\} = (-1)^{2c}[\Gamma_1\Gamma_3]^{\frac{1}{2}}E_{ab\Gamma_1}E_{ef\Gamma_3}[b]^{-\frac{1}{2}}\delta_{ac}\delta_{be}\delta_{df}\delta_{\Gamma_2 b}$,

(A-2.8) $$\{8\} = (-1)^{2a}\left\{\left[\frac{\Gamma_1\Gamma_3}{b}\right]^{\frac{1}{2}}\delta_{ac}\delta_{be}\delta_{df}\delta_{\Gamma_2 b} - [d\Gamma_1]^{\frac{1}{2}}\delta_{ac}\delta_{bf}\delta_{de}\delta_{\Gamma_2 f}\delta_{\Gamma_3 0} - [b\Gamma_3]^{\frac{1}{2}}\delta_{ae}\delta_{bc}\delta_{df}\delta_{\Gamma_2 a}\delta_{\Gamma_1 0} + [abd]^{\frac{1}{2}}\delta_{cf}\delta_{bc}\delta_{de}\delta_{\Gamma_2 a}\delta_{\Gamma_1 0}\delta_{\Gamma_3 0}\right\},$$

(A-2.9) $$\{9\} = (-1)^{2c}\{[\Gamma_1\Gamma_3]^{\frac{1}{2}}E_{ab\Gamma_1}[b]^{-\frac{1}{2}}\delta_{ac}\delta_{be}\delta_{df}\delta_{\Gamma_2 b} - [d\Gamma_1]^{\frac{1}{2}}E_{ab\Gamma_1}\delta_{ac}\delta_{bf}\delta_{de}\delta_{\Gamma_3 f}\delta_{\Gamma_3 0}\},$$

(A-2.10) $$\{10\} = (-1)^{2a}\left\{\left[\frac{\Gamma_1\Gamma_3}{b}\right]^{\frac{1}{2}}E_{ef\Gamma_3}\delta_{ac}\delta_{be}\delta_{df}\delta_{\Gamma_2 b} - [b\Gamma_3]^{\frac{1}{2}}E_{ef\Gamma_3}\delta_{ae}\delta_{bc}\delta_{df}\delta_{\Gamma_2 a}\delta_{\Gamma_1 0}\right\},$$

(A-2.11) $$\{11\} = (-1)^{2c}[\Gamma_1\Gamma_2\Gamma_3]^{\frac{1}{2}}E_{ab\Gamma_1}E_{ef\Gamma_3}W(\Gamma_1 a\Gamma_3 d;\ b\Gamma_2)\delta_{ac}\delta_{be}\delta_{df},$$

(A-2.12) $$\{12\} = (-1)^{2a}\{[\Gamma_1\Gamma_2\Gamma_3]^{\frac{1}{2}}W(a\Gamma_1 d\Gamma_2;\ b\Gamma_3)\delta_{ac}\delta_{be}\delta_{df} - [d\Gamma_1]^{\frac{1}{2}}\delta_{ac}\delta_{bf}\delta_{de}\delta_{\Gamma_1\Gamma_3}\delta_{\Gamma_2 0} - [b\Gamma_2]^{\frac{1}{2}}\delta_{ae}\delta_{bc}\delta_{df}\delta_{\Gamma_2\Gamma_3}\delta_{\Gamma_1 0} + [abd]^{\frac{1}{2}}\delta_{af}\delta_{bc}\delta_{de}\delta_{\Gamma_1 0}\delta_{\Gamma_2 0}\delta_{\Gamma_3 0}\},$$

(A-2.13) $$\{13\} = [\Gamma_1\Gamma_2\Gamma_3\Gamma_4\Gamma_5]^{\frac{1}{2}}E_{ab\Gamma_1}E_{gh\Gamma_5}\Big\{(-1)^{-b+\Gamma_1+\Gamma_3+\Gamma_4}W(\Gamma_1 a\Gamma_5\Gamma_4;\ b\Gamma_3)\cdot W(\Gamma_3\Gamma_1 dc;\ \Gamma_5\Gamma_2)\delta_{ae}\delta_{bf}\delta_{cg}\delta_{dh} - (-1)^{b+c+\Gamma_2+\Gamma_3+\Gamma_4}\begin{Bmatrix} d & \Gamma_5 & b \\ \Gamma_3 & \Gamma_4 & a \\ \Gamma_2 & c & \Gamma_1 \end{Bmatrix}\delta_{ae}\delta_{bg}\delta_{cf}\delta_{dh} + (-1)^{b-d+\Gamma_1+\Gamma_2+\Gamma_4}W(\Gamma_5 da\Gamma_3;\ \Gamma_4\Gamma_2)W(\Gamma_5 ac\Gamma_1;\ \Gamma_2 b)\delta_{ae}\delta_{bg}\delta_{ch}\delta_{df} +$$

$$+(-1)^{b-c+\Gamma_1+\Gamma_3+\Gamma_5} W(\Gamma_4 c d \Gamma_2;\, \Gamma_3\Gamma_1)\, W(\Gamma_5 a d \Gamma_1;\, \Gamma_4 b)\, \delta_{af}\delta_{bg}\delta_{ce}\delta_{dh}\Bigg\} +$$

$$+(-1)^{c+d+\Gamma_1+\Gamma_3}[\Gamma_2\Gamma_3\Gamma_4]^{\frac{1}{2}} W(\Gamma_4 c d \Gamma_2;\, \Gamma_3\Gamma_1) E_{ab\Gamma_1}\delta_{ag}\delta_{bh}\delta_{ce}\delta_{df}\delta_{\Gamma_1\Gamma_5} -$$

$$-(-1)^{c+d+\Gamma_1+\Gamma_3}[\Gamma_3]^{\frac{1}{2}} E_{ab\Gamma_1}\delta_{ag}\delta_{bh}\delta_{cf}\delta_{de}\delta_{\Gamma_1\Gamma_5}\delta_{\Gamma_2\Gamma_4} -$$

$$-[\Gamma_1\Gamma_3\Gamma_5]^{\frac{1}{2}} E_{ab\Gamma_1} E_{gh\Gamma_5}(-1)^{b-d+\Gamma_1+\Gamma_2+\Gamma_5} W(\Gamma_5 a c \Gamma_1;\, \Gamma_2 b)\delta_{af}\delta_{bg}\delta_{ch}\delta_{de}\delta_{\Gamma_2\Gamma_4},$$

$$\text{(A-2.14)}\quad \{14\} = [\Gamma_3]^{\frac{1}{2}} E_{ab\Gamma_1} E_{cd\Gamma_2}\{\delta_{ae}\delta_{bf}\delta_{cf}\delta_{dh}\delta_{\Gamma_1\Gamma_4}\delta_{\Gamma_2\Gamma_5} +$$

$$+(-1)^{\Gamma_1+\Gamma_2+\Gamma_3}\delta_{ag}\delta_{bh}\delta_{ce}\delta_{df}\delta_{\Gamma_1\Gamma_5}\delta_{\Gamma_2\Gamma_4}\} -$$

$$-E_{ab\Gamma_1}E_{cd\Gamma_2}E_{ef\Gamma_4}E_{gh\Gamma_5}[\Gamma_1\Gamma_2\Gamma_3\Gamma_4\Gamma_5]^{\frac{1}{2}} \begin{Bmatrix} b & \Gamma_1 & a \\ d & \Gamma_2 & c \\ \Gamma_5 & \Gamma_3 & \Gamma_4 \end{Bmatrix} \delta_{ae}\delta_{bg}\delta_{cf}\delta_{dh},$$

$$\text{(A-2.15)}\quad \{15\} = [\Gamma_1\Gamma_2\Gamma_3\Gamma_4\Gamma_5]^{\frac{1}{2}} E_{ab\Gamma_1} E_{gh\Gamma_5}\Bigg\{ - \begin{Bmatrix} e & c & \Gamma_5 \\ a & \Gamma_1 & b \\ \Gamma_3 & \Gamma_2 & \Gamma_4 \end{Bmatrix} \delta_{ad}\delta_{bf}\delta_{cg}\delta_{eh} +$$

$$+(-1)^{a-b+\Gamma_1} W(\Gamma_1\Gamma_2\Gamma_5\Gamma_4;\, c\Gamma_3)\, W(\Gamma_3\Gamma_1 e b;\, \Gamma_5 a)\delta_{ad}\delta_{bg}\delta_{cf}\delta_{eh} -$$

$$-(-1)^{b-e+\Gamma_1+\Gamma_2+\Gamma_4} W(\Gamma_2 a \Gamma_4 e;\, \Gamma_5\Gamma_3)\, W(\Gamma_5 a c \Gamma_1;\, \Gamma_2 b)\delta_{ad}\delta_{bg}\delta_{ch}\delta_{ef} -$$

$$-(-1)^{b-c+\Gamma_2+\Gamma_4+\Gamma_5} W(\Gamma_2 c \Gamma_4 e;\, \Gamma_1\Gamma_3)\, W(\Gamma_5 a e \Gamma_1;\, \Gamma_4 b)\delta_{af}\delta_{bg}\delta_{cd}\delta_{eh}\Bigg\} -$$

$$-(-1)^{c+e+\Gamma_2+\Gamma_4}[\Gamma_2\Gamma_3\Gamma_4]^{\frac{1}{2}} W(\Gamma_2 c \Gamma_4 e;\, \Gamma_1\Gamma_3) E_{ab\Gamma_1}\delta_{ag}\delta_{bh}\delta_{cd}\delta_{ef}\delta_{\Gamma_1\Gamma_5},$$

$$\text{(A-2.16)}\quad \{16\} = (-1)^{\Gamma_1+\Gamma_3+\Gamma_5}[\Gamma_5]^{\frac{1}{2}} E_{ab\Gamma_1} E_{ef\Gamma_3}\delta_{ac}\delta_{bd}\delta_{eg}\delta_{fh}\delta_{\Gamma_1\Gamma_2}\delta_{\Gamma_3\Gamma_4},$$

$$\text{(A-2.17)}\quad \{17\} = [\Gamma_1\Gamma_2\Gamma_3\Gamma_4\Gamma_5]^{\frac{1}{2}} E_{ab\Gamma_1} E_{gh\Gamma_4}\Bigg\{ -(-1)^{\Gamma_1+\Gamma_4+\Gamma_5} \begin{Bmatrix} \Gamma_1 & a & b \\ \Gamma_4 & d & f \\ \Gamma_5 & \Gamma_2 & \Gamma_3 \end{Bmatrix} \cdot$$

$$\cdot\, \delta_{ac}\delta_{be}\delta_{dg}\delta_{fh} + (-1)^{b+f+\Gamma_1+\Gamma_2+\Gamma_3} W(a\Gamma_2 f\Gamma_3;\, d\Gamma_5)\, W(\Gamma_5 a \Gamma_4 b;\, f\Gamma_1)\delta_{ac}\delta_{bg}\delta_{de}\delta_{fh}\Bigg\},$$

$$\text{(A-2.18)}\quad \{18\} = [\Gamma_1\Gamma_2\Gamma_3\Gamma_4\Gamma_5]^{\frac{1}{2}} E_{ab\Gamma_1} E_{gh\Gamma_4}\Bigg\{ (-1)^{a+d+\Gamma_2} \begin{Bmatrix} \Gamma_4 & d & e \\ \Gamma_1 & a & b \\ \Gamma_5 & \Gamma_2 & \Gamma_3 \end{Bmatrix} \cdot$$

$$\left.\cdot\,\delta_{ac}\delta_{bf}\delta_{dg}\delta_{eh} - (-1)^{b-d+\Gamma_1+\Gamma_2} W(a\Gamma_2 e\Gamma_3;\, d\Gamma_5)\, W(\Gamma_5 a\Gamma_4 b;\, e\Gamma_1)\,\delta_{ac}\delta_{bg}\delta_{df}\delta_{eh}\right\} +$$

$$+\,[e\Gamma_1\Gamma_2\Gamma_4]^{\frac{1}{2}} E_{ab\Gamma_1} E_{gh\Gamma_4} W(\Gamma_1 a\Gamma_4 d;\, b\Gamma_2)\,\delta_{ac}\delta_{bg}\delta_{dh}\delta_{ef}\delta_{\Gamma_2\Gamma_5}\delta_{\Gamma_3 0}\,,$$

$$\text{(A-2.19)}\quad \{19\} = [\Gamma_1\Gamma_2\Gamma_3\Gamma_4\Gamma_5]^{\frac{1}{2}} E_{ab\Gamma_1} E_{gh\Gamma_4}\left\{ -\begin{Bmatrix} \Gamma_4 & c & e \\ \Gamma_1 & a & b \\ \Gamma_5 & \Gamma_2 & \Gamma_3 \end{Bmatrix} \delta_{cg}\delta_{ad}\delta_{bf}\delta_{eh} + \right.$$

$$\left. + (-1)^{a+b+\Gamma_1} W(a\Gamma_2 e\Gamma_3;\, c\Gamma_5)\, W(\Gamma_5 a\Gamma_4 b;\, e\Gamma_1)\,\delta_{ad}\delta_{bg}\delta_{cf}\delta_{eh}\right\} -$$

$$-\,[e\Gamma_1\Gamma_2\Gamma_4]^{\frac{1}{2}} E_{ab\Gamma_1} E_{gh\Gamma_4} (-1)^{a+c+\Gamma_2} W(ca\Gamma_4\Gamma_1;\, \Gamma_2 b)\,\delta_{ad}\delta_{bg}\delta_{ch}\delta_{ef}\delta_{\Gamma_2\Gamma_5}\delta_{\Gamma_3 0} -$$

$$-\,[c\Gamma_1\Gamma_3\Gamma_4]^{\frac{1}{2}} E_{ab\Gamma_1} E_{gh\Gamma_4} (-1)^{a+e+\Gamma_3} W(ea\Gamma_4\Gamma_1;\, \Gamma_3 b)\,\delta_{af}\delta_{bg}\delta_{eh}\delta_{cd}\delta_{\Gamma_3\Gamma_5}\delta_{\Gamma_2 0} -$$

$$-\,[ce\Gamma_1]^{\frac{1}{2}} E_{ab\Gamma_1}\,\delta_{ag}\delta_{bh}\delta_{cd}\delta_{ef}\delta_{\Gamma_1\Gamma_4}\delta_{\Gamma_2 0}\delta_{\Gamma_3 0}\delta_{\Gamma_5 0}\,,$$

$$\text{(A-2.20)}\quad \{20\} = [\Gamma_5]^{\frac{1}{2}} E_{ab\Gamma_1} E_{cd\Gamma_2}\,\delta_{ae}\delta_{bf}\delta_{cg}\delta_{dh}\delta_{\Gamma_2\Gamma_4}\delta_{\Gamma_1\Gamma_3} -$$

$$-\,[\Gamma_1\Gamma_2\Gamma_3\Gamma_4\Gamma_5]^{\frac{1}{2}} E_{ab\Gamma_1} E_{cd\Gamma_2} E_{ef\Gamma_3} E_{gh\Gamma_4} W(d\Gamma_2 a\Gamma_3;\, c\Gamma_5)\, W(\Gamma_4 d\Gamma_1 a;\, b\Gamma_5)\,\cdot$$

$$\cdot\,\delta_{ae}\delta_{bg}\delta_{cf}\delta_{dh} + [\Gamma_1\Gamma_2]^{\frac{1}{2}} E_{ab\Gamma_1} E_{cd\Gamma_2}\,\delta_{ag}\delta_{bh}\delta_{ce}\delta_{df}\delta_{\Gamma_1\Gamma_4}\delta_{\Gamma_2\Gamma_3}\delta_{\Gamma_5 0}\,.$$

A·3. *Closed-shell expectation values.* – a, b, c, d, e, f, g, h refer to orbits above the closed shell while i, j, k, l, m, n, p, q refer to those below it. H is defined by eq. (5.54) and by eq. (5.71).

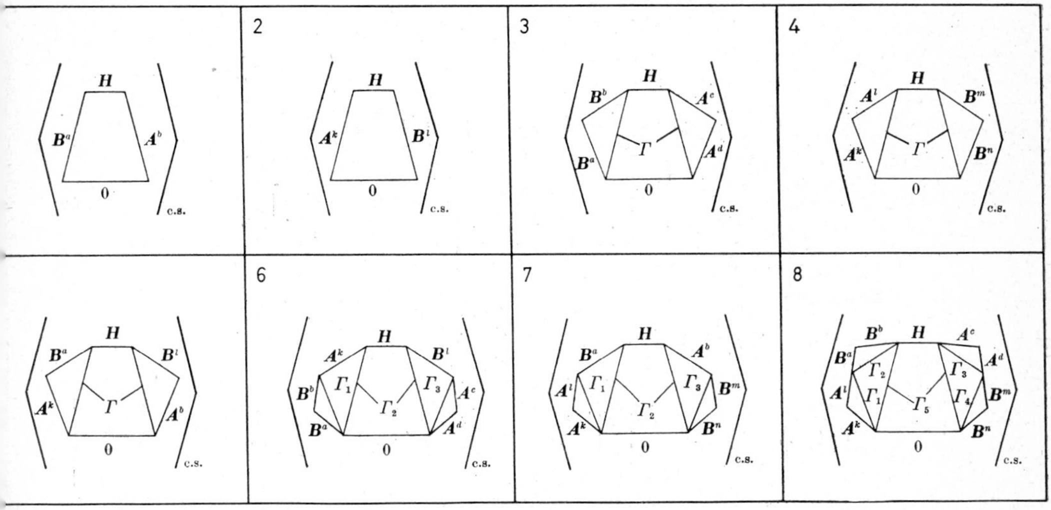

(A-3.1) $$\{1\} = (-1)^{2a}[a]^{\frac{1}{2}}\left\{\varepsilon_{ab}\delta^{am}_{ab} + \delta_{ab}\sum_{p}[p]\varepsilon_{pp} + \sum_{p}\left[\frac{p}{a}\right]^{\frac{1}{2}}\beta^{0}_{abpp} + \delta_{ab}\sum_{p\leq q}[pq]^{\frac{1}{2}}\beta^{0}_{ppqq}\right\},$$

(A-3.2) $$\{2\} = [k]^{\frac{1}{2}}\left\{-\varepsilon_{kl}\delta^{am}_{kl} + \delta_{kl}\sum_{p}[p]\varepsilon_{pp} - \sum_{p}\left[\frac{p}{k}\right]^{\frac{1}{2}}\zeta^{-1}_{pk}\zeta^{-1}_{pl}\beta^{0}_{lkpp} + \delta_{kl}\sum_{p\leq q}[pq]^{\frac{1}{2}}\beta^{0}_{ppqq}\right\},$$

(A-3.3) $$\{3\} = [\Gamma]^{\frac{1}{2}}\Big\{(-1)^{a+b+\Gamma}E_{ab\Gamma}E_{cd\Gamma}\varepsilon_{ad}\delta_{bc}\delta^{am}_{ad} - E_{ab\Gamma}\delta_{ac}\delta_{bd}\sum_{p}[p]\varepsilon_{pp} -$$
$$- \zeta^{-1}_{ab}\zeta^{-1}_{cd}W^{\Gamma}_{abcd} + (-1)^{a+b+\Gamma}E_{ab\Gamma}E_{cd\Gamma}\delta_{bc}\sum_{p}\left[\frac{p}{a}\right]^{\frac{1}{2}}\beta^{0}_{adpp} - E_{ab\Gamma}\delta_{ac}\delta_{bd}\sum_{p\leq q}[pq]^{\frac{1}{2}}\beta^{0}_{ppqq}\Big\},$$

(A-3.4) $$\{4\} = [\Gamma]^{\frac{1}{2}}\Big\{-(-1)^{k+l+\Gamma}E_{kl\Gamma}E_{mn\Gamma}\varepsilon_{nk}\delta_{lm}\delta^{am}_{nk} - E_{kl\Gamma}\delta_{km}\delta_{ln}\sum_{p}[p]\varepsilon_{pp} -$$
$$- \zeta^{-1}_{mn}\zeta^{-1}_{kl}W^{\Gamma}_{mnkl} - (-1)^{k+l+\Gamma}E_{kl\Gamma}E_{mn\Gamma}\delta_{lm}\sum_{p}\left[\frac{p}{k}\right]^{\frac{1}{2}}\zeta^{-1}_{pn}\zeta^{-1}_{pk}\beta^{0}_{nkpp} - E_{kl\Gamma}\delta_{km}\delta_{ln}\sum_{p\leq q}[pq]^{\frac{1}{2}}\beta^{0}_{ppqq}\Big\},$$

(A-3.5) $$\{5\} = (-1)^{2a}[\Gamma]^{\frac{1}{2}}\Big\{-\varepsilon_{ab}\delta_{kl}\delta^{am}_{ab} + \varepsilon_{kl}\delta_{ab}\delta^{am}_{kl} - \delta_{kl}\delta_{ab}\sum_{p}[p]\varepsilon_{pp} -$$
$$-(-1)^{a-k+\Gamma}[\Gamma]^{-\frac{1}{2}}\beta^{\Gamma}_{aklb} - \delta_{kl}\sum_{p}\left[\frac{p}{a}\right]^{\frac{1}{2}}\beta^{0}_{abpp} + \delta_{ab}\sum_{p}\left[\frac{p}{k}\right]^{\frac{1}{2}}\zeta^{-1}_{pk}\zeta^{-1}_{pl}\beta^{0}_{lkpp} - \delta_{kl}\delta_{ab}\sum_{p\leq q}[pq]^{\frac{1}{2}}\beta^{0}_{ppqq}\Big\},$$

(A-3.6) $$\{6\} = (-1)^{k+\Gamma_1-\Gamma_2}[\Gamma_2]^{\frac{1}{2}}\Big\{(-1)^{a+b+\Gamma_1}E_{ab\Gamma_1}E_{cd\Gamma_3}\varepsilon_{ad}\delta_{bc}\delta_{kl}\delta^{am}_{ad}\delta_{\Gamma_1\Gamma_3} +$$
$$+ \varepsilon_{kl}E_{ab\Gamma_1}\delta_{ac}\delta_{bd}\delta^{am}_{kl}\delta_{\Gamma_1\Gamma_3} - E_{ab\Gamma_1}\delta_{ac}\delta_{bd}\delta_{kl}\delta_{\Gamma_1\Gamma_3}\sum_{p}[p]\varepsilon_{pp} - \zeta^{-1}_{ab}\zeta^{-1}_{cd}W^{\Gamma_1}_{abcd}\delta_{kl}\delta_{\Gamma_1\Gamma_3} +$$
$$+ (-1)^{k+\Gamma_1+\Gamma_2}[\Gamma_1\Gamma_3]^{\frac{1}{2}}E_{ab\Gamma_1}E_{cd\Gamma_3}\delta_{bc}\sum_{\Omega}[\Omega]\begin{Bmatrix}\Omega & d & k\\ l & \Gamma_3 & \Gamma_2\\ a & b & \Gamma_1\end{Bmatrix}W^{\Omega}_{ladk} +$$
$$+ (-1)^{a+b+\Gamma_1}E_{ab\Gamma_1}E_{cd\Gamma_3}\delta_{bc}\delta_{kl}\delta_{\Gamma_1\Gamma_3}\sum_{p}\left[\frac{p}{a}\right]^{\frac{1}{2}}\beta^{0}_{adpp} +$$
$$+ E_{ab\Gamma_1}\delta_{ac}\delta_{bd}\delta_{\Gamma_1\Gamma_3}\sum_{p}\left[\frac{p}{k}\right]^{\frac{1}{2}}\zeta^{-1}_{pl}\zeta^{-1}_{pk}\beta^{0}_{lkpp} - E_{ab\Gamma_1}\delta_{ac}\delta_{bd}\delta_{kl}\delta_{\Gamma_1\Gamma_3}\sum_{p\leq q}[pq]^{\frac{1}{2}}\beta^{0}_{ppqq}\Big\},$$

$$\text{(A-3.7)}\qquad \{7\}=(-1)^{a+\Gamma_1+\Gamma_2}[\Gamma_2]^{\frac{1}{2}}\Bigg\{-\varepsilon_{ab}E_{kl\Gamma_1}\delta_{km}\delta_{ln}\delta_{ab}^{am}\delta_{\Gamma_1\Gamma_3}-$$

$$-(-1)^{k+l+\Gamma_1}E_{kl\Gamma_1}E_{mn\Gamma_3}\varepsilon_{nk}\delta_{lm}\delta_{ab}\delta_{nk}^{am}\delta_{\Gamma_1\Gamma_3}-$$

$$-E_{kl\Gamma_1}\delta_{km}\delta_{ln}\delta_{ab}\delta_{\Gamma_1\Gamma_3}\sum_p[p]\varepsilon_{pp}-\zeta_{mn}^{-1}\zeta_{kl}^{-1}W_{mnkl}^{\Gamma_1}\delta_{ab}\delta_{\Gamma_1\Gamma_3}+$$

$$+(-1)^{a+\Gamma_1+\Gamma_2}[\Gamma_1\Gamma_3]^{\frac{1}{2}}E_{kl\Gamma_1}E_{mn\Gamma_3}\delta_{lm}\sum_\Omega[\Omega]\begin{Bmatrix}n & a & \Omega\\ \Gamma_3 & \Gamma_2 & b\\ l & \Gamma_1 & k\end{Bmatrix}W_{nabk}^{\Omega}-$$

$$-E_{kl\Gamma_1}\delta_{km}\delta_{ln}\delta_{\Gamma_1\Gamma_3}\sum_p\begin{bmatrix}p\\a\end{bmatrix}^{\frac{1}{2}}\beta_{abpp}^0-(-1)^{k+l+\Gamma_1}E_{kl\Gamma_1}E_{mn\Gamma_3}\delta_{lm}\delta_{ab}\delta_{\Gamma_1\Gamma_3}\sum_p\begin{bmatrix}p\\k\end{bmatrix}^{\frac{1}{2}}\cdot$$

$$\cdot\zeta_{pn}^{-1}\zeta_{pk}^{-1}\beta_{nkpp}^0-E_{kl\Gamma_1}\delta_{km}\delta_{ln}\delta_{ab}\delta_{\Gamma_1\Gamma_3}\sum_{p\leq q}[pq]^{\frac{1}{2}}\beta_{ppqq}^0\Bigg\},$$

$$\text{(A-3.8)}\qquad \{8\}=(-1)^{\Gamma_1+\Gamma_2+\Gamma_5}[\Gamma_5]^{\frac{1}{2}}\Big\{-(-1)^{a+b+\Gamma_2}E_{kl\Gamma_1}E_{ab\Gamma_2}E_{cd\Gamma_3}\varepsilon_{ad}\delta_{km}\delta_{ln}\delta_{bc}\delta_{ad}^{am}+$$

$$+(-1)^{k+l+\Gamma_1}E_{kl\Gamma_1}E_{ab\Gamma_2}E_{mn\Gamma_4}\varepsilon_{nk}\delta_{lm}\delta_{ac}\delta_{bd}\delta_{kn}^{am}+E_{kl\Gamma_1}E_{ab\Gamma_2}\delta_{km}\delta_{ln}\delta_{ac}\delta_{bd}\sum_p[p]\varepsilon_{pp}-$$

$$-\zeta_{ab}^{-1}\zeta_{cd}^{-1}W_{abcd}^{\Gamma_2}E_{kl\Gamma_1}\delta_{km}\delta_{ln}+\zeta_{mn}^{-1}\zeta_{kl}^{-1}W_{mnkl}^{\Gamma_1}E_{ab\Gamma_2}\delta_{ac}\delta_{bd}-$$

$$-(-1)^{a+b+\Gamma_2}E_{kl\Gamma_1}E_{ab\Gamma_2}E_{cd\Gamma_3}\delta_{km}\delta_{ln}\delta_{bc}\sum_p\begin{bmatrix}p\\a\end{bmatrix}^{\frac{1}{2}}\beta_{adpp}^0+$$

$$+(-1)^{k+l+\Gamma_1}E_{kl\Gamma_1}E_{ab\Gamma_2}E_{mn\Gamma_4}\delta_{lm}\delta_{ac}\delta_{bd}\sum_p\begin{bmatrix}p\\k\end{bmatrix}^{\frac{1}{2}}\zeta_{pn}^{-1}\zeta_{pk}^{-1}\beta_{nkpp}^0+$$

$$+E_{kl\Gamma_1}E_{ab\Gamma_2}\delta_{km}\delta_{ln}\delta_{ac}\delta_{bd}\sum_{p\leq q}[pq]^{\frac{1}{2}}\beta_{ppqq}^0\Big\}\delta_{\Gamma_1\Gamma_4}\delta_{\Gamma_2\Gamma_3}-$$

$$-(-1)^{k+l+c+d+\Gamma_2+\Gamma_3+\Gamma_5}[\Gamma_1\Gamma_2\Gamma_3\Gamma_4\Gamma_5]^{\frac{1}{2}}E_{kl\Gamma_1}E_{ab\Gamma_2}E_{cd\Gamma_3}E_{mn\Gamma_4}\delta_{lm}\delta_{bc}\cdot$$

$$\cdot\sum_{\alpha\beta\Omega}[\alpha\beta\Omega]W(\Gamma_4kn\Gamma_1;\beta l)\begin{Bmatrix}\Gamma_1 & \Gamma_5 & \Gamma_2\\ n & \Omega & a\\ \beta & \alpha & b\end{Bmatrix}\begin{Bmatrix}\Gamma_4 & \Gamma_5 & \Gamma_3\\ k & \Omega & d\\ \beta & \alpha & b\end{Bmatrix}W_{andk}^{\Omega}\,.$$

A·4. *Normal form of operators.*

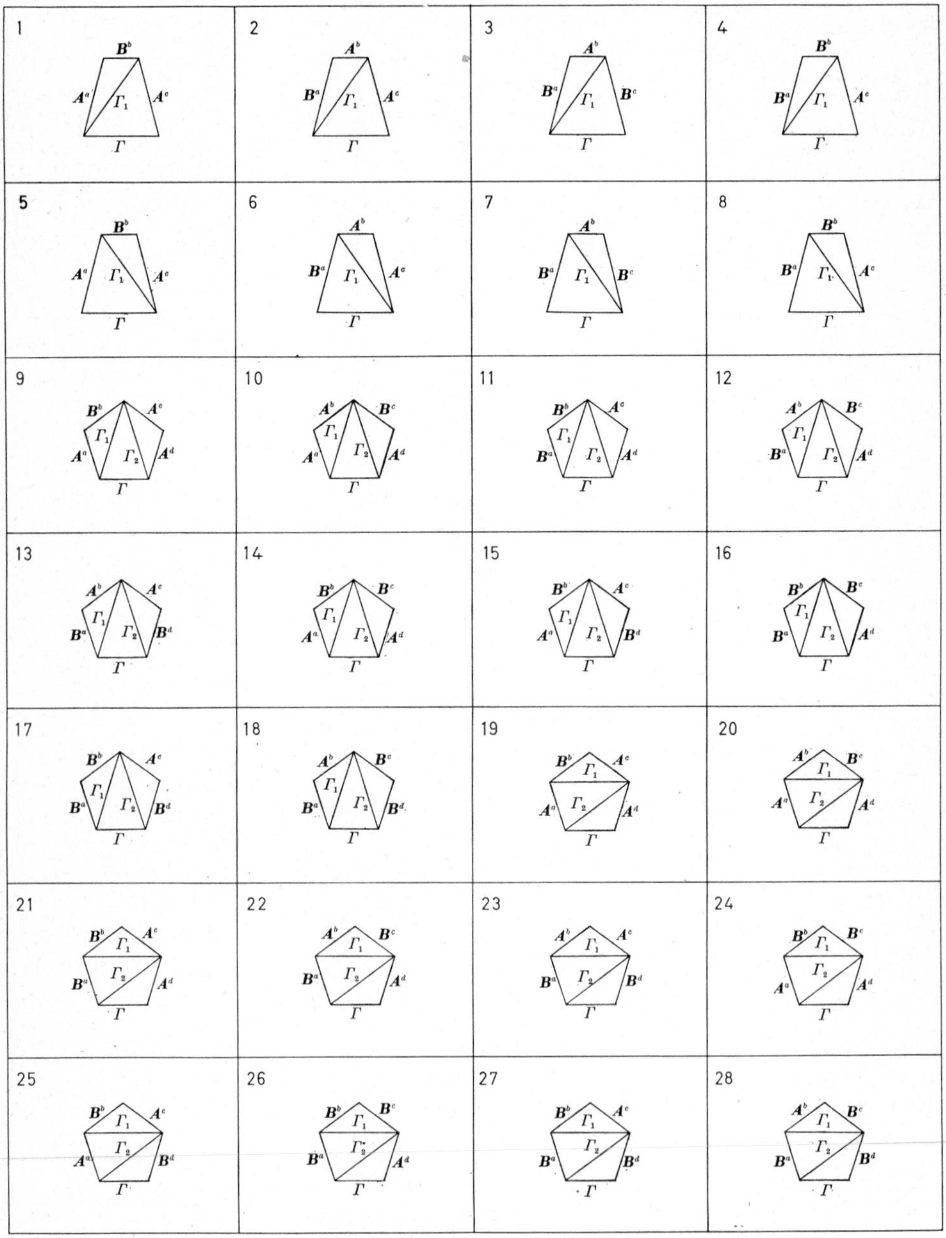

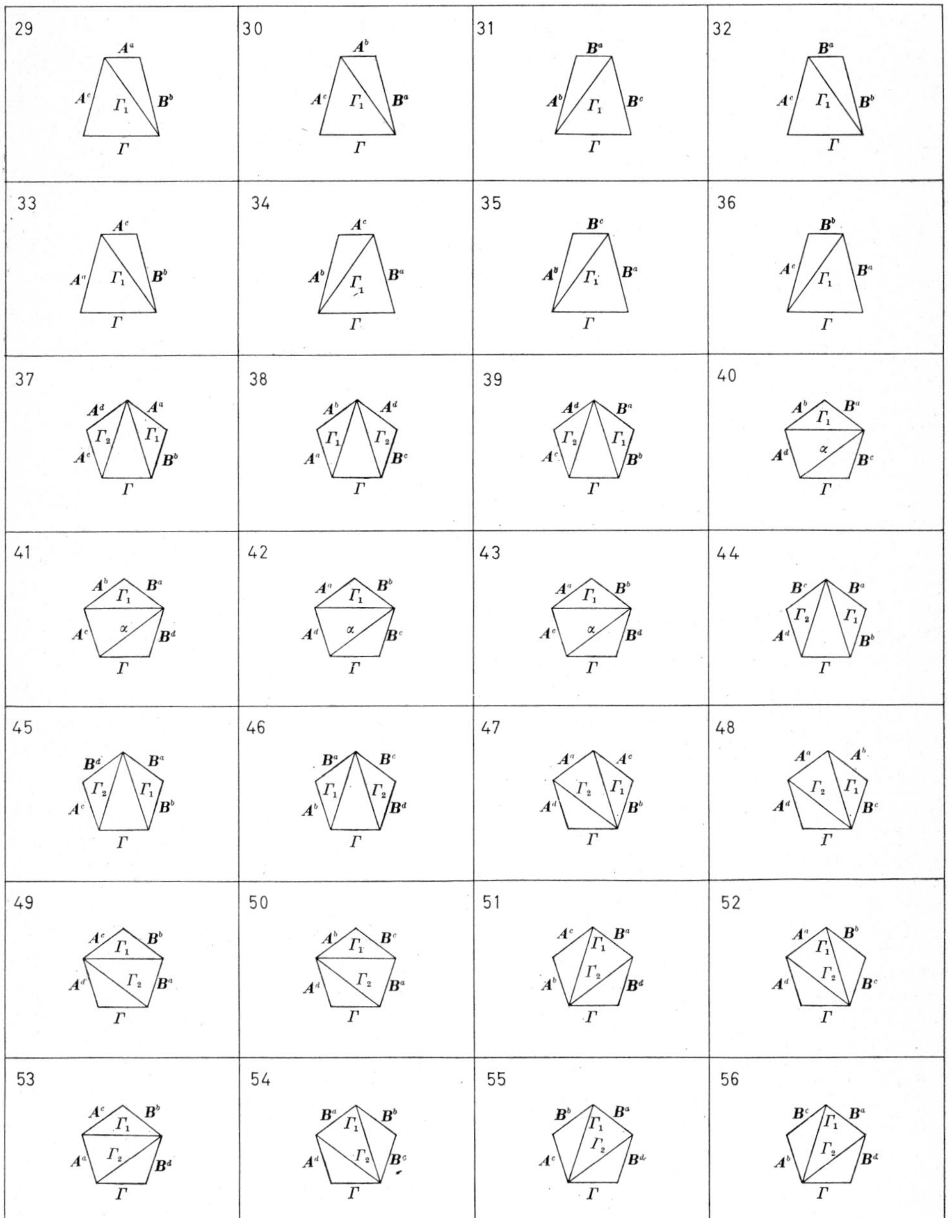
29
30
31
32
33
34
35
36
37
38
39
40
41
42
43
44
45
46
47
48
49
50
51
52
53
54
55
56

(A-4.1) $$\{1\} = (-1)^{a-b+\Gamma_1}\left[\frac{\Gamma_1}{a}\right]^{\frac{1}{2}}\delta_{bc}\delta_{\Gamma a}\boldsymbol{A}^a + (-1)^{c+\Gamma_1-\Gamma}\{29\}\,,$$

(A-4.2) $$\{2\} = (-1)^{2a}[a]^{\frac{1}{2}}\delta_{ab}\delta_{\Gamma c}\delta_{\Gamma_1 0}\boldsymbol{A}^c - (-1)^{2a}\left[\frac{\Gamma_1}{b}\right]^{\frac{1}{2}}\delta_{ac}\delta_{\Gamma b}\boldsymbol{A}^b - (-1)^{a+b+c-\Gamma}\{30\},$$

(A-4.3) $$\{3\} = (-1)^{2a}[a]^{\frac{1}{2}}\delta_{ab}\delta_{\Gamma c}\delta_{\Gamma_1 0}\boldsymbol{B}^c - (-1)^{a+b+\Gamma_1}\{31\}\,,$$

(A-4.4) $$\{4\} = (-1)^{a-b+\Gamma_1}E_{ab\Gamma_1}\left[\frac{\Gamma_1}{a}\right]^{\frac{1}{2}}\delta_{bc}\delta_{\Gamma a}\boldsymbol{B}^a + (-1)^{c+\Gamma_1-\Gamma}\{32\}\,,$$

(A-4.5) $$\{5\} = (-1)^{2a}[b]^{\frac{1}{2}}\delta_{bc}\delta_{\Gamma a}\delta_{\Gamma_1 0}\boldsymbol{A}^a - (-1)^{b+c-\Gamma_1}\{33\}\,,$$

(A-4.6) $$\{6\} = E_{bc\Gamma_1}(-1)^{a-c+\Gamma_1}\left[\frac{\Gamma_1}{c}\right]^{\frac{1}{2}}\delta_{ab}\delta_{\Gamma c}\boldsymbol{A}^c + (-1)^{a+\Gamma_1-\Gamma}\{34\}\,,$$

(A-4.7) $$\{7\} = (-1)^{a-c+\Gamma_1}\left[\frac{\Gamma_1}{c}\right]^{\frac{1}{2}}\delta_{ab}\delta_{\Gamma c}\boldsymbol{B}^c + (-1)^{a+\Gamma_1-\Gamma}\{35\}\,,$$

(A-4.8) $$\{8\} = -(-1)^{2a}\left[\frac{\Gamma_1}{b}\right]^{\frac{1}{2}}\delta_{ac}\delta_{\Gamma b}\boldsymbol{B}^b + (-1)^{2a}[b]^{\frac{1}{2}}\delta_{bc}\delta_{\Gamma a}\delta_{\Gamma_1 0}\boldsymbol{B}^a - $$
$$- (-1)^{a+b+c-\Gamma}\{36\}\,,$$

(A-4.9) $$\{9\} = (-1)^{a-b+\Gamma_1}[\Gamma_1\Gamma_2]^{\frac{1}{2}}E_{cd\Gamma_2}W(\Gamma_1 b\Gamma d;\, a\Gamma_2)\delta_{bc}(\boldsymbol{A}^a\times\boldsymbol{A}^d)^\Gamma +$$
$$+ (-1)^{\Gamma_1+\Gamma_2-\Gamma}\{37\}$$

(A-4.10) $$\{10\} = (-1)^{2a}[c]^{\frac{1}{2}}\delta_{cd}\delta_{\Gamma_1\Gamma}\delta_{\Gamma_2 0}(\boldsymbol{A}^a\times\boldsymbol{A}^b)^\Gamma - (-1)^{c+d-\Gamma_2}\{38\}\,,$$

(A-4.11) $$\{11\} = -[\Gamma_1]^{\frac{1}{2}}E_{ab\Gamma_1}\delta_{ac}\delta_{bd}\delta_{\Gamma_1\Gamma_2}\delta_{\Gamma 0} -$$
$$-[\Gamma_1\Gamma_2]^{\frac{1}{2}}E_{ab\Gamma_1}E_{cd\Gamma_2}(-1)^{b+d+\Gamma_1+\Gamma}W(\Gamma_1 b\Gamma d;\, a\Gamma_2)\delta_{bc}(\boldsymbol{A}^d\times\boldsymbol{B}^a)^\Gamma + (-1)^{\Gamma_1+\Gamma_2+\Gamma}\{39\}\,,$$

(A-4.12) $$\{12\} = -(-1)^{c-d+\Gamma_2}[a]^{\frac{1}{2}}\delta_{ab}\delta_{\Gamma\Gamma_2}\delta_{\Gamma_1 0}(\boldsymbol{A}^d\times\boldsymbol{B}^c)^\Gamma +$$
$$+ (-1)^{a-c+\Gamma_2}[\Gamma_1\Gamma_2]^{\frac{1}{2}}W(ca\Gamma\Gamma_1;\, \Gamma_2 b)\delta_{ad}(\boldsymbol{A}^b\times\boldsymbol{B}^c)^\Gamma -$$
$$- (-1)^{a-b+\Gamma_1}[c]^{\frac{1}{2}}\delta_{cd}\delta_{\Gamma_1\Gamma}\delta_{\Gamma_2 0}(\boldsymbol{A}^b\times\boldsymbol{B}^a)^\Gamma + [ac]^{\frac{1}{2}}\delta_{ab}\delta_{cd}\delta_{\Gamma_1 0}\delta_{\Gamma_2 0}\delta_{\Gamma 0} +$$
$$+ \sum_\alpha (-1)^{a+b+c+\alpha+\Gamma_2}[\alpha\Gamma_2]^{\frac{1}{2}}W(\Gamma_1 d\Gamma c;\, \alpha\Gamma_2)\,\{40\}\,,$$

(A-4.13) $$\{13\} = (-1)^{2a}[a]^{\frac{1}{2}}\delta_{ab}\delta_{\Gamma_2\Gamma}\delta_{\Gamma_1 0}(\boldsymbol{A}^c\times\boldsymbol{B}^d)^\Gamma -$$
$$-(-1)^{2a}[\Gamma_1\Gamma_2]^{\frac{1}{2}}W(\Gamma_1 a\Gamma d;\, b\Gamma_2)\delta_{ac}(\boldsymbol{A}^b\times\boldsymbol{B}^d)^\Gamma -$$
$$-\sum_\alpha (-1)^{a+b+c-\alpha}[\alpha\Gamma_2]^{\frac{1}{2}}W(\Gamma_1 c\Gamma d;\, \alpha\Gamma_2)\{41\}\,,$$

(A-4.14) $$\{14\} = (-1)^{2c}[c]^{\frac{1}{2}}\delta_{cd}\delta_{\Gamma_1\Gamma}\delta_{\Gamma_2 0}(\boldsymbol{A}^a\times\boldsymbol{B}^b)^\Gamma -$$
$$-(-1)^{a+c+\Gamma_1+\Gamma_2}[\Gamma_1\Gamma_2]^{\frac{1}{2}}W(cb\Gamma\Gamma_1;\, \Gamma_2 a)\delta_{bd}(\boldsymbol{A}^a\times\boldsymbol{B}^c)^\Gamma -$$
$$-\sum_\alpha (-1)^{c+\alpha+\Gamma_1+\Gamma_2}[\alpha\Gamma_2]^{\frac{1}{2}}W(\Gamma_1 d\Gamma c;\, \alpha\Gamma_2)\{42\}\,,$$

(A-4.15) $\{15\} = (-1)^{a-b+\Gamma_1}[\Gamma_1\Gamma_2]^{\frac{1}{2}} W(\Gamma_1 b\Gamma d;\, a\Gamma_2)\,\delta_{bc}(\boldsymbol{A}^a \times \boldsymbol{B}^d)^\Gamma +$
$+ \sum_\alpha (-1)^{c-\alpha+\Gamma_1}[\alpha\Gamma_2]^{\frac{1}{2}} W(\Gamma_1 c\Gamma d;\, \alpha\Gamma_2)\{43\}\,,$

(A-4.16) $\{16\} = (-1)^{2c}[c]^{\frac{1}{2}}\delta_{cd}\delta_{\Gamma_1\Gamma}\delta_{\Gamma_2 0}(\boldsymbol{B}^a \times \boldsymbol{B}^b)^\Gamma -$
$-(-1)^{a+c+\Gamma_1+\Gamma_2}[\Gamma_1\Gamma_2]^{\frac{1}{2}} E_{ab\Gamma_1} W(cb\Gamma\Gamma_1;\, \Gamma_2 a)\,\delta_{bd}(\boldsymbol{B}^a \times \boldsymbol{B}^c)^\Gamma - (-1)^{c+d+\Gamma+\Gamma_1}\{44\}\,,$

(A-4.17) $\{17\} = (-1)^{a-b+\Gamma_1}[\Gamma_1\Gamma_2]^{\frac{1}{2}} E_{ab\Gamma_1} W(\Gamma_1 b\Gamma d;\, a\Gamma_2)\,\delta_{bc}(\boldsymbol{B}^a \times \boldsymbol{B}^d)^\Gamma +$
$+ (-1)^{\Gamma_1+\Gamma_2+\Gamma}\{45\}\,,$

(A-4.18) $\{18\} = (-1)^{2a}[a]^{\frac{1}{2}}\delta_{ab}\delta_{\Gamma_2\Gamma}\delta_{\Gamma_1 0}(\boldsymbol{B}^c \times \boldsymbol{B}^d)^\Gamma - (-1)^{a+b+\Gamma_1}\{46\}\,,$

(A-4.19) $\{19\} = (-1)^{2b}[b]^{\frac{1}{2}}\delta_{bc}\delta_{\Gamma_2 a}\delta_{\Gamma_1 0}(\boldsymbol{A}^a \times \boldsymbol{A}^d)^\Gamma -$
$-(-1)^{c+\Gamma_1-\Gamma_2+\Gamma}[\Gamma_1\Gamma_2]^{\frac{1}{2}} W(cba\Gamma_2;\, \Gamma_1\Gamma)\,\delta_{bd}(\boldsymbol{A}^a \times \boldsymbol{A}^c)^\Gamma + (-1)^{b+c+d+\Gamma_1+\Gamma_2+\Gamma}\{47\}\,,$

(A-4.20) $\{20\} = (-1)^{c+\Gamma_2+\Gamma}[\Gamma_1\Gamma_2]^{\frac{1}{2}} W(ab\Gamma_2 c;\, \Gamma\Gamma_1)\,\delta_{cd}(\boldsymbol{A}^a \times \boldsymbol{A}^b)^\Gamma - (-1)^{d+\Gamma_2+\Gamma}\{48\},$

(A-4.21) $\{21\} = -[\Gamma_1]^{\frac{1}{2}}\delta_{ac}\delta_{bd}\delta_{\Gamma_2 b}\delta_{\Gamma 0} + [ab]^{\frac{1}{2}}\delta_{ad}\delta_{bc}\delta_{\Gamma_2 a}\delta_{\Gamma_1 0}\delta_{\Gamma 0} +$
$+ (-1)^{b-d+\Gamma}\left[\frac{\Gamma_1}{b}\right]^{\frac{1}{2}}\delta_{ac}\delta_{\Gamma_2 b}(\boldsymbol{A}^d \times \boldsymbol{B}^b)^\Gamma - (-1)^{b-c+\Gamma_1}\left[\frac{\Gamma_2}{\Gamma_1}\right]^{\frac{1}{2}}\delta_{ad}\,\delta_{\Gamma_1\Gamma}\,(\boldsymbol{A}^c \times \boldsymbol{B}^b)^\Gamma -$
$-(-1)^{a-d+\Gamma}[b]^{\frac{1}{2}}\delta_{bc}\delta_{\Gamma_2 a}\delta_{\Gamma_1 0}(\boldsymbol{A}^d \times \boldsymbol{B}^a)^\Gamma +$
$+ (-1)^{a+\Gamma_1+\Gamma_2}[\Gamma_1\Gamma_2]^{\frac{1}{2}} W(cba\Gamma_2;\, \Gamma_1\Gamma)\,\delta_{bd}(\boldsymbol{A}^c \times \boldsymbol{B}^a)^\Gamma + (-1)^{a+b+c+d+\Gamma}\{49\}\,,$

(A-4.22) $\{22\} = -(-1)^{a+d+\Gamma_1+\Gamma}\left[\frac{\Gamma_1}{c}\right]^{\frac{1}{2}}\delta_{ab}\delta_{\Gamma_2 c}(\boldsymbol{A}^d \times \boldsymbol{B}^c)^\Gamma +$
$+(-1)^{2a}\left[\frac{\Gamma_2}{\Gamma_1}\right]^{\frac{1}{2}}\delta_{ad}\delta_{\Gamma_1\Gamma}(\boldsymbol{A}^b \times \boldsymbol{B}^c)^\Gamma - (-1)^{a+b+c+\Gamma_2}[\Gamma_1\Gamma_2]^{\frac{1}{2}} W(ab\Gamma_2 c;\, \Gamma\Gamma_1)\,\delta_{cd}(\boldsymbol{A}^b \times \boldsymbol{B}^a)^\Gamma +$
$+ (-1)^{a+c-\Gamma_1}[\Gamma_1]^{\frac{1}{2}}\delta_{ab}\delta_{cd}\delta_{\Gamma_2 d}\delta_{\Gamma 0} - (-1)^{a+d+\Gamma_1+\Gamma}\{50\}\,,$

(A-4.23) $\{23\} = E_{bc\Gamma_1}(-1)^{a-c+\Gamma_1}\left[\frac{\Gamma_1}{c}\right]^{\frac{1}{2}}\delta_{ab}\delta_{\Gamma_2 c}(\boldsymbol{A}^c \times \boldsymbol{B}^d)^\Gamma + (-1)^{a+\Gamma_1-\Gamma_2}\{51\}\,,$

(A-4.24) $\{24\} = E_{bc\Gamma_1}(-1)^{c+\Gamma_2+\Gamma}[\Gamma_1\Gamma_2]^{\frac{1}{2}} W(ab\Gamma_2 c;\, \Gamma\Gamma_1)\,\delta_{cd}(\boldsymbol{A}^a \times \boldsymbol{B}^b)^\Gamma -$
$-(-1)^{d+\Gamma_2+\Gamma}\{52\}\,,$

(A-4.25) $\{25\} = (-1)^{2b}[b]^{\frac{1}{2}}\delta_{bc}\delta_{\Gamma_2 a}\delta_{\Gamma_1 0}(\boldsymbol{A}^a \times \boldsymbol{B}^d)^\Gamma - (-1)^{b+c+\Gamma_1}\{53\}\,,$

(A-4.26) $\{26\} = (-1)^{2a}\left[\frac{\Gamma_2}{\Gamma_1}\right]^{\frac{1}{2}}\delta_{ad}\delta_{\Gamma\Gamma_1}(\boldsymbol{B}^b \times \boldsymbol{B}^c)^\Gamma + [\Gamma_1\Gamma_2]^{\frac{1}{2}} E_{bc\Gamma_1}(-1)^{c+\Gamma_2+\Gamma}\cdot$
$\cdot W(ab\Gamma_2 c;\, \Gamma\Gamma_1)\,\delta_{cd}(\boldsymbol{B}^a \times \boldsymbol{B}^b)^\Gamma - (-1)^{d+\Gamma_2+\Gamma}\{54\}\,,$

(A-4.27) $\{27\} = -(-1)^{2a}\left[\frac{\Gamma_1}{b}\right]^{\frac{1}{2}}\delta_{ac}\delta_{\Gamma_2 b}(\boldsymbol{B}^b \times \boldsymbol{B}^d)^\Gamma +$
$+ (-1)^{2b}[b]^{\frac{1}{2}}\delta_{bc}\delta_{\Gamma_2 a}\delta_{\Gamma_1 0}(\boldsymbol{B}^a \times \boldsymbol{B}^d)^\Gamma - (-1)^{a+b+c-\Gamma_2}\{55\}\,,$

$$(\text{A-}4.28)\quad \{28\} = (-1)^{a-c+\Gamma_1}\left[\frac{\Gamma_1}{c}\right]^{\frac{1}{2}}\delta_{ab}\,\delta_{\Gamma_2 c}\,(\boldsymbol{B}^c\times\boldsymbol{B}^d)^{\Gamma} + (-1)^{a+\Gamma_1-\Gamma_2}\{56\}\,.$$

A·5. *Commutation relations.* – H is defined by eq. (5.54).

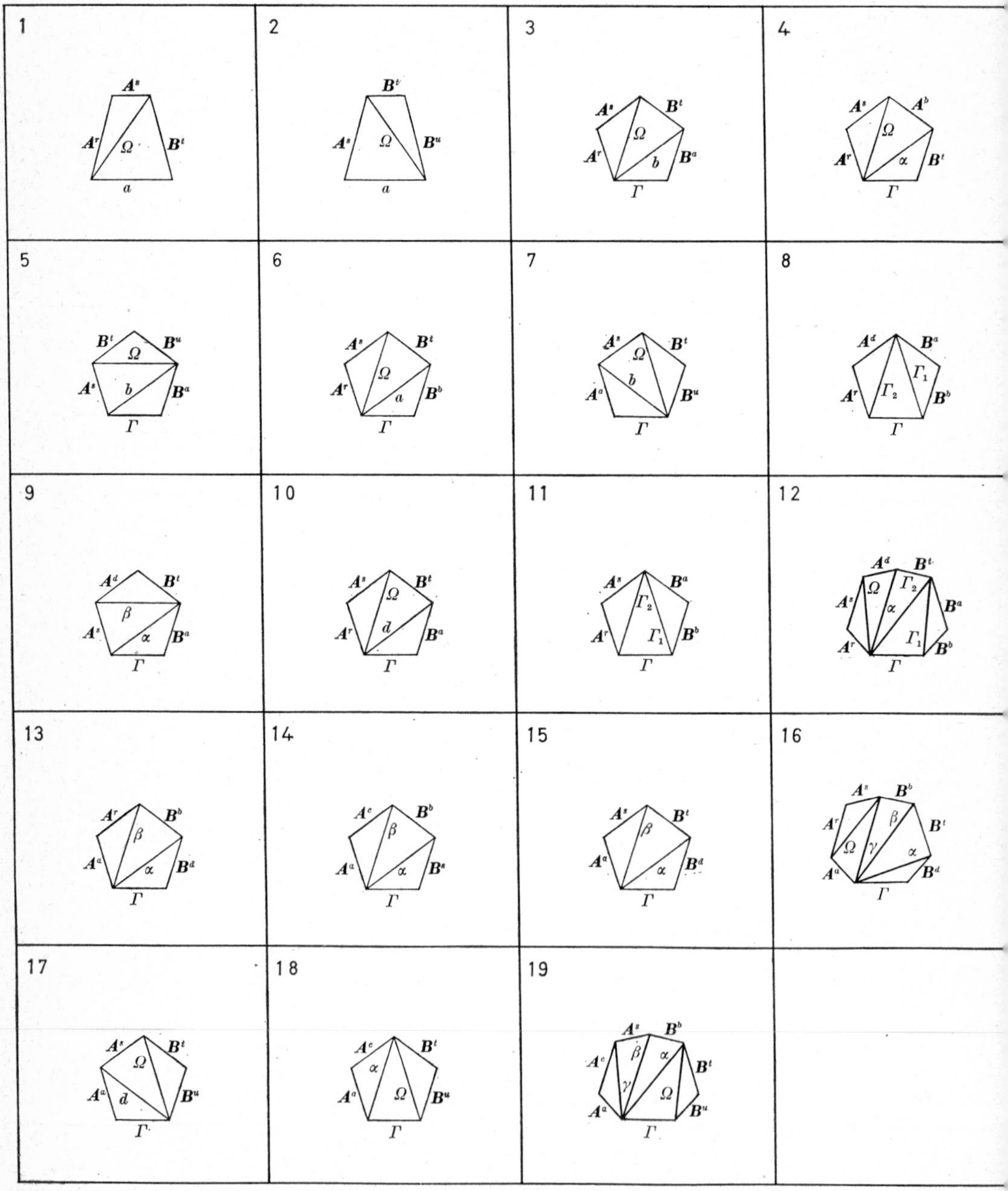

$$\text{(A-5.1)}\quad [(\boldsymbol{A}^a\times\boldsymbol{B}^b)^{\Gamma_1},\ \boldsymbol{A}^c]^\Gamma=(-1)^{a-b+\Gamma_1}\left[\frac{\Gamma_1}{a}\right]^{\frac{1}{2}}\delta_{bc}\delta_{\Gamma a}\boldsymbol{A}^a,$$

$$\text{(A-5.2)}\quad [(\boldsymbol{B}^a\times\boldsymbol{B}^b)^{\Gamma_1},\ \boldsymbol{A}^c]^\Gamma=(-1)^{a-b+\Gamma_1}E_{ab\Gamma_1}\left[\frac{\Gamma_1}{a}\right]^{\frac{1}{2}}\delta_{bc}\delta_{\Gamma a}\boldsymbol{B}^a,$$

$$\text{(A.5-3)}\quad [\boldsymbol{B}^a,\ (\boldsymbol{A}^b\times\boldsymbol{B}^c)^{\Gamma_1}]^\Gamma=(-1)^{a-c+\Gamma_1}\left[\frac{\Gamma_1}{c}\right]^{\frac{1}{2}}\delta_{ab}\delta_{\Gamma c}\boldsymbol{B}^c,$$

$$\text{(A-5.4)}\quad [\boldsymbol{B}^a,\ (\boldsymbol{A}^b\times\boldsymbol{A}^c)^{\Gamma_1}]^\Gamma=E_{bc\Gamma_1}(-1)^{a-c+\Gamma_1}\left[\frac{\Gamma_1}{c}\right]^{\frac{1}{2}}\delta_{ab}\delta_{\Gamma c}\boldsymbol{A}^c,$$

$$\text{(A-5.5)}\quad [(\boldsymbol{B}^a\times\boldsymbol{B}^b)^{\Gamma_1},\ (\boldsymbol{A}^c\times\boldsymbol{A}^d)^{\Gamma_2}]^\Gamma=-[\Gamma_1]^{\frac{1}{2}}E_{ab\Gamma_1}\delta_{ac}\delta_{bd}\delta_{\Gamma_1\Gamma_2}\delta_{\Gamma 0}-$$
$$-[\Gamma_1\Gamma_2]^{\frac{1}{2}}E_{ab\Gamma_1}E_{cd\Gamma_2}(-1)^{b+d+\Gamma_1+\Gamma}W(\Gamma_1 b\Gamma d;\ a\Gamma_2)\delta_{bc}(\boldsymbol{A}^d\times\boldsymbol{B}^a)^\Gamma,$$

$$\text{(A-5.6)}\quad [(\boldsymbol{A}^a\times\boldsymbol{B}^b)^{\Gamma_1},\ (\boldsymbol{A}^c\times\boldsymbol{A}^d)^{\Gamma_2}]^\Gamma=$$
$$=(-1)^{a-b+\Gamma_1}[\Gamma_1\Gamma_2]^{\frac{1}{2}}E_{cd\Gamma_2}W(\Gamma_1 b\Gamma d;\ a\Gamma_2)\delta_{bc}(\boldsymbol{A}^a\times\boldsymbol{A}^d)^\Gamma,$$

$$\text{(A-5.7)}\quad [(\boldsymbol{B}^a\times\boldsymbol{B}^b)^{\Gamma_1},\ (\boldsymbol{A}^c\times\boldsymbol{B}^d)^{\Gamma_2}]^\Gamma=(-1)^{a-b+\Gamma_1}[\Gamma_1\Gamma_2]^{\frac{1}{2}}\cdot$$
$$\cdot E_{ab\Gamma_1}W(\Gamma_1 b\Gamma d;\ a\Gamma_2)\delta_{bc}(\boldsymbol{B}^a\times\boldsymbol{B}^d)^\Gamma,$$

$$\text{(A-5.8)}\quad [(\boldsymbol{A}^a\times\boldsymbol{B}^b)^{\Gamma_1},\ (\boldsymbol{A}^c\times\boldsymbol{B}^d)^{\Gamma_2}]^\Gamma=(-1)^{a-b+\Gamma_1}[\Gamma_1\Gamma_2]^{\frac{1}{2}}W(\Gamma_1 b\Gamma d;\ a\Gamma_2)\cdot$$
$$\cdot\delta_{bc}(\boldsymbol{A}^a\times\boldsymbol{B}^d)^\Gamma-(-1)^{c-d+\Gamma_1+\Gamma}[\Gamma_1\Gamma_2]^{\frac{1}{2}}W(\Gamma_2 d\Gamma b;\ c\Gamma_1)\delta_{ad}(\boldsymbol{A}^c\times\boldsymbol{B}^b)^\Gamma,$$

$$\text{(A-5.9)}\quad [H,\boldsymbol{A}^a]=\sum_r\varepsilon_{ra}\delta^{am}_{ar}\boldsymbol{A}^r-\sum_{\substack{rst\Omega\\ r\le s}}\left[\frac{\Omega}{a}\right]^{\frac{1}{2}}\frac{\zeta_{rs}}{\zeta_{ta}}W^{\Omega}_{rsta}\{1\},$$

$$\text{(A-5.10)}\quad [H,\boldsymbol{B}^a]=-\sum_s\varepsilon_{as}\delta^{am}_{as}\boldsymbol{B}^s+\sum_{\substack{stu\Omega\\ t\le u}}\left[\frac{\Omega}{a}\right]^{\frac{1}{2}}\frac{\zeta_{tu}}{\zeta_{as}}W^{\Omega}_{astu}\{2\},$$

$$\text{(A-5.11)}\quad (\boldsymbol{B}^a\times[H,\boldsymbol{A}^b])^\Gamma=(-1)^{2a}[a]^{\frac{1}{2}}\varepsilon_{ab}\delta^{am}_{ab}\delta_{\Gamma 0}-(-1)^{a+b+\Gamma}\sum_r\varepsilon_{rb}\delta^{am}_{rb}(\boldsymbol{A}^r\times\boldsymbol{B}^a)^\Gamma+$$
$$+(-1)^{2a}\sum_{s,t}\zeta^{-1}_{as}\zeta^{-1}_{bt}[\Gamma]^{-\frac{1}{2}}\beta^{\Gamma}_{stab}(\boldsymbol{A}^s\times\boldsymbol{B}^t)^\Gamma+(-1)^{a+b+\Gamma}\sum_{\substack{rst\Omega\\ r\le s}}\left[\frac{\Omega}{b}\right]^{\frac{1}{2}}\frac{\zeta_{rs}}{\zeta_{tb}}W^{\Omega}_{rstb}\{3\},$$

$$\text{(A-5.12)}\quad [H,\ (\boldsymbol{A}^a\times\boldsymbol{A}^b)^\Gamma]=E_{ab\Gamma}\sum_r\varepsilon_{ra}\delta^{am}_{ra}(\boldsymbol{A}^r\times\boldsymbol{A}^b)^\Gamma+\sum_{\substack{rs\\ r\le s}}\frac{\zeta_{rs}}{\zeta_{ab}}W^{\Gamma}_{rsab}(\boldsymbol{A}^r\times\boldsymbol{A}^s)^\Gamma+$$
$$+E_{ab\Gamma}\sum_{\substack{rst\alpha\Omega\\ r\le s}}(-1)^{a+\alpha+\Omega+\Gamma}[\Omega\alpha]^{\frac{1}{2}}\frac{\zeta_{rs}}{\zeta_{ta}}W(\Gamma bt\Omega;\ a\alpha)W^{\Omega}_{rsta}\{4\},$$

$$\text{(A-5.13)}\quad [H,\ (\boldsymbol{B}^a\times\boldsymbol{B}^b)^\Gamma]=-E_{ab\Gamma}\sum_s\varepsilon_{bs}\delta^{am}_{bs}(\boldsymbol{B}^a\times\boldsymbol{B})^{s\Gamma}-\sum_{\substack{tu\\ t\le u}}\frac{\zeta_{tu}}{\zeta_{ab}}W^{\Gamma}_{abtu}(\boldsymbol{B}^t\times\boldsymbol{B}^u)^\Gamma-$$
$$-(-1)^{a+b+\Gamma}E_{ab\Gamma}\sum_{\substack{tus\Omega\\ t\le u}}\left[\frac{\Omega}{b}\right]^{\frac{1}{2}}\frac{\zeta_{tu}}{\zeta_{bs}}W^{\Omega}_{bstu}\{5\},$$

(A-5.14) $$[H,(\boldsymbol{A}^a\times\boldsymbol{B}^b)^\Gamma]=\sum_r \varepsilon_{ra}\delta_{ra}^{am}(\boldsymbol{A}^r\times\boldsymbol{B}^b)^\Gamma-\sum_r \varepsilon_{br}\delta_{br}^{am}(\boldsymbol{A}^a\times\boldsymbol{B}^r)^\Gamma-$$

$$-\sum_{\substack{rst\Omega\\ r\le s}}\frac{\zeta_{rs}}{\zeta_{at}}\left[\frac{\Omega}{a}\right]^{\frac12}W^{\Omega}_{rsta}\{6\}+\sum_{\substack{stu\Omega\\ t\le u}}\frac{\zeta_{tu}}{\zeta_{bs}}\left[\frac{\Omega}{b}\right]^{\frac12}W^{\Omega}_{bstu}\{7\},$$

(A-5.15) $$((\boldsymbol{B}^a\times\boldsymbol{B}^b)^{\Gamma_1}\times[H,(\boldsymbol{A}^c\times\boldsymbol{A}^d)^{\Gamma_2}])^\Gamma=$$

$$=(-1)^{a+b+\Gamma_1}[\Gamma_1]^{\frac12}E_{ab\Gamma_1}E_{cd\Gamma_2}\varepsilon_{ad}\delta_{bc}\delta_{ad}^{am}\delta_{\Gamma_1\Gamma_2}\delta_{\Gamma 0}-[\Gamma_1\Gamma_2]^{\frac12}E_{ab\Gamma_1}E_{cd\Gamma_2}(-1)^{b+d+\Gamma_1+\Gamma}\cdot$$

$$\cdot W(\Gamma_1 b\Gamma d;\,a\Gamma_2)\Big\{\delta_{bc}\sum_r\varepsilon_{rd}\delta_{rd}^{am}(\boldsymbol{A}^r\times\boldsymbol{B}^a)^\Gamma-\delta_{bc}^{am}\varepsilon_{bc}(\boldsymbol{A}^d\times\boldsymbol{B}^a)^\Gamma\Big\}+$$

$$+(-1)^{\Gamma_1+\Gamma_2+\Gamma}E_{cd\Gamma_2}\sum_r\varepsilon_{rc}\delta_{rc}^{am}\{8\}-[\Gamma_1]^{\frac12}\zeta_{ab}^{-1}\zeta_{cd}^{-1}W^{\Gamma_1}_{abcd}\delta_{\Gamma_1\Gamma_2}\delta_{\Gamma 0}+$$

$$+(-1)^{\Gamma_1+\Gamma_2+\Gamma}[\Gamma_1\Gamma_2]^{\frac12}E_{ab\Gamma_1}\sum_s\zeta_{bs}^{-1}\zeta_{cd}^{-1}W^{\Gamma_2}_{sbcd}W(\Gamma_1 b\Gamma s;\,a\Gamma_2)(\boldsymbol{A}^s\times\boldsymbol{B}^a)^\Gamma+$$

$$+(-1)^{a+b+\Gamma_1}\left[\frac{\Gamma_1\Gamma_2}{\Gamma}\right]^{\frac12}E_{ab\Gamma_1}E_{cd\Gamma_2}\sum_{s,t}\zeta_{as}^{-1}\zeta_{td}^{-1}W(\Gamma\Gamma_1 db;\,\Gamma_2 a)\beta^{\Gamma}_{adst}\delta_{bc}(\boldsymbol{A}^s\times\boldsymbol{B}^t)^\Gamma-$$

$$-(-1)^{c+d+\Gamma_1+\Gamma}[\Gamma_1\Gamma_2]^{\frac12}E_{cd\Gamma_2}\sum_t\zeta_{ab}^{-1}\zeta_{ct}^{-1}W(\Gamma_1 c\Gamma d;\,t\Gamma_2)W^{\Gamma_1}_{abtc}(\boldsymbol{A}^d\times\boldsymbol{B}^t)^\Gamma-$$

$$-E_{ab\Gamma_1}E_{cd\Gamma_2}\sum_{st\alpha\beta\Omega}(-1)^{b+c+d+\alpha+\Gamma_1+\Gamma_2+\Gamma}[\Omega][\Gamma_1\Gamma_2\alpha\beta]^{\frac12}W(b\alpha\Gamma_1\Gamma;\,\Gamma_2 a)\cdot$$

$$\cdot W(\Omega c\beta d;\,t\Gamma_2)W(b\Gamma_2 s\beta;\,\alpha\Omega)\zeta_{bs}^{-1}\zeta_{tc}^{-1}W^{\Omega}_{bstc}\{9\}+$$

$$+(-1)^{c+d+\Gamma_1+\Gamma}E_{ab\Gamma_1}E_{cd\Gamma_2}\sum_{\substack{rst\Omega\\ r\le s}}\left[\frac{\Gamma_1\Gamma_2\Omega}{d}\right]^{\frac12}\frac{\zeta_{rs}}{\zeta_{td}}W(bd\Gamma_1\Gamma;\,\Gamma_2 a)\delta_{bc}W^{\Omega}_{rsta}\{10\}+$$

$$+(-1)^{\Gamma_1+\Gamma_2+\Gamma}\sum_{\substack{rs\\ r\le s}}\frac{\zeta_{rs}}{\zeta_{cd}}W^{\Gamma_2}_{rscd}\{11\}+$$

$$+(-1)^{\Gamma_1+\Gamma_2+\Gamma}E_{cd\Gamma_2}\sum_{\substack{rst\Omega\\ r\le s}}[\Omega\alpha]^{\frac12}\frac{\zeta_{rs}}{\zeta_{ct}}W(\alpha dtc;\,\Omega\Gamma_2)W^{\Omega}_{rstc}\{12\},$$

(A-5.16) $$((\boldsymbol{A}^a\times\boldsymbol{B}^b)^{\Gamma_1}\times[H,(\boldsymbol{A}^c\times\boldsymbol{B}^d)^{\Gamma_2}])^\Gamma=(-1)^{a-b+\Gamma_1}[\Gamma_1\Gamma_2]^{\frac12}W(\Gamma_1 b\Gamma d;\,a\Gamma_2)\cdot$$

$$\cdot\Big\{\varepsilon_{bc}\delta_{bc}^{am}(\boldsymbol{A}^a\times\boldsymbol{B}^d)^\Gamma-\sum_s\varepsilon_{ds}\delta_{bc}\delta_{ds}^{am}(\boldsymbol{A}^a\times\boldsymbol{B}^s)^\Gamma\Big\}-\sum_{\alpha\beta}(-1)^{a+\Gamma_1+\alpha+\beta}[\Gamma_1\Gamma_2\alpha\beta]^{\frac12}\cdot$$

$$\cdot W(\Gamma_1 c\Gamma d;\,\alpha\Gamma_2)W(\alpha cba;\,\Gamma_1\beta)\Big\{\sum_r\varepsilon_{rc}\delta_{rc}^{am}\{13\}-\sum_s\varepsilon_{ds}\delta_{ds}^{am}\{14\}\Big\}-$$

$$-\sum_{st\Omega\alpha\beta}(-1)^{a+b+c+\Gamma_1+\Omega+\alpha+\beta}[\Omega][\Gamma_1\Gamma_2\alpha\beta]^{\frac12}\zeta_{bs}^{-1}\zeta_{tc}^{-1}W^{\Omega}_{bstc}W(\Gamma_1 b\beta s;\,a\Omega)\cdot$$

$$\cdot W(\beta t\Gamma_1 c;\,\alpha\Omega)W(\Gamma_1 c\Gamma d;\,\alpha\Gamma_2)\{15\}-$$

$$-\sum_{\substack{rst\Omega\alpha\beta\gamma\\ r\le s}}(-1)^{a-c+\Gamma_1+\Omega+\alpha+\gamma}[\Gamma_1\Gamma_2\Omega\alpha\beta\gamma]^{\frac12}W(\beta t\Gamma_1 c;\,\alpha\Omega)W(\Gamma_1 c\Gamma d;\,\alpha\Gamma_2)\cdot$$

$$\cdot W(a\Omega b\beta;\,\gamma\Gamma_1)\frac{\zeta_{rs}}{\zeta_{tc}}W^{\Omega}_{rstc}\{16\}+$$

$$+\sum_{\substack{stu\Omega\\ t\le u}}(-1)^{a-b+\Gamma_1}\left[\frac{\Gamma_1\Gamma_2\Omega}{d}\right]^{\frac{1}{2}}\frac{\zeta_{tu}}{\zeta_{ds}}W(\Gamma_1 b\Gamma d;\, a\Gamma_2)\,W^{\Omega}_{dstu}\delta_{bc}\{17\}+$$

$$+(-1)^{2a}\sum_{\substack{\alpha tu\Omega\\ t\le u}}[\Gamma_1\Gamma_2\alpha\Omega]^{\frac{1}{2}}\frac{\zeta_{tu}}{\zeta_{bd}}\begin{Bmatrix}\alpha & \Gamma & \Omega\\ c & \Gamma_2 & d\\ a & \Gamma_1 & b\end{Bmatrix}W^{\Omega}_{bdtu}\{18\}+$$

$$+\sum_{\substack{stu\Omega\\ \alpha\beta\gamma\lambda\\ t\le u}}(-1)^{a+d+\Gamma_1+\Omega+\lambda+\beta}[\lambda][\Omega\Gamma_1\Gamma_2\alpha\beta\gamma]^{\frac{1}{2}}\frac{\zeta_{tu}}{\zeta_{ds}}W(\Gamma_1 c\Gamma d;\,\lambda\Gamma_2)\cdot$$

$$\cdot W(\Gamma d\alpha s;\,\lambda\Omega)\,W(\lambda cba;\,\Gamma_1\gamma)\,W(\alpha sb\gamma;\,\lambda\beta)\,W^{\Omega}_{dstu}\{19\}\,.$$

An Introduction to the Many-Body Theory of Nuclear Reactions.

C. Bloch
Service de Physique Théorique, C.E.N. de Saclay - Gif-sur-Yvette

1. – Black-box and many-body theories of nuclear reactions.

It may be worth-while to start by a brief historical survey of the development of the theory of nuclear reactions. It is interesting in particular to compare it with the development of the theory of nuclear structure. This comparison actually shows very clearly, I think, the direction of development of the theory of nuclear reactions, at least in the near future.

The first phase of the development of the theories of nuclear structure and reactions was dominated by the idea that the detailed dynamics of internal nuclear motions is so hopelessly complicated that the only conclusions which can be reached should be deduced without any detailed consideration of internal dynamics. Typical of this attitude is the supermultiplet theory of Wigner, which follows simply from symmetry or invariance properties of the Hamiltonian. Incidentally the most recent developments on the internal symmetries of elementary particles are precisely again of the same kind. The same attitude—avoidance of any detailed dynamical description—leads to the « black-box » theories of nuclear reactions.

I shall not go here into any detail of these theories of nuclear reactions. It will be sufficient to recall the general idea. At an energy such that a nuclear system can break up into two or more fragments, the spectrum of the Hamiltonian is clearly continuous, and no stable excited state can exist. In the traditional forms of the black-box formulation, a fictitious closed system is defined by putting in all the open channels « mirrors » which prevent the system from breaking up. In more mathematical terms, one introduces boundary conditions in the various open channels. The resulting closed system has a discrete spectrum. Thus one may define a set of parameters: the energies of the levels and the values of the eigenfunctions at the boundaries in the various channels. Then it is possible to show that all reaction cross-sections can be expressed in terms of these parameters.

This is the so-called formal theory of nuclear reactions. It exists in various forms (KAPUR-PEIERLS, WIGNER-EISENBUD, ROSENFELD-HUMBLET [1, 2]) depending on the particular choice of the boundary conditions. Actually the most recent forms of the black-box formulation [2] avoid the introduction of artificial boundary conditions, and the definition of the set of characteristic parameters is achieved in a somewhat different way. The main success of this kind of theory is the derivation of the famous Breit-Wigner formulae, which show that under certain conditions and within appropriate limitations, the energies defined as eigenvalues of the system closed by the mirrors appear as resonance energies, and may be associated with the compound states of Bohr.

Without going any further into the black-box or formal theory of nuclear reactions, its main drawback appears immediately: the theory does not provide any means for computing the infinitely many parameters entering the expressions for the cross-sections. This was at first considered, on the contrary, as a great success of the theory: it was possible to say something about nuclear cross-sections without actually solving the complete dynamical problem.

The theory of nuclear structure has long passed that stage; the shell model and all its subsequent developments have shown that it is possible by an approximate but detailed description of the internal dynamics to predict fairly well many characteristic features of the ground state and first excited states of nuclei (energies, spins, parities, or transition matrix elements ...). It is therefore quite natural now to try to apply the same ideas to the systematic prediction of reaction cross-sections.

This is actually not a completely new point of view. The discovery of the success of the optical model for the prediction of averaged cross-sections stimulated investigations in this direction. In order to derive the optical model from the formal theory of nuclear reactions, it was necessary as shown by LANE, THOMAS and WIGNER [3] to introduce specific assumptions about some of the parameters appearing in this theory, namely the partial reduced widths. The « giant resonance » behaviour, assumed by LANE, THOMAS and WIGNER, can in turn be derived from a partial treatment of the dynamics of the nuclear reaction [4]. It is however typical that in these works, the argument was carefully arranged in such a way that the internal dynamics of the target nucleus could be ignored. The only interactions appearing explicitly are those of the incoming nucleon with the nucleons of the target nucleus. This of course introduces a dissymetry in the treatment of the two-body interactions, with the consequence that the antisymmetrization of the wave function (expressing the identity of the incoming nucleon with the nucleons inside the nucleus) is very hard to take into account. Clearly this difficulty can be removed only by a full treatment of the internal dynamical problem.

The ultimate purpose of the many-body theory of nuclear structure may be defined as the prediction of all quantities observed in nuclear reactions in terms of the nucleon-nucleon interactions, exclusively. We are of course very far yet from this ambitious aim, and the theory is actually in a much more preliminary state of development than the theory of nuclear structure.

The formulation of a complete many-body theory of nuclear reactions faces the difficulties of the theory of nuclear structure plus the difficulties due to the existence of several regions in the space representing the positions of the nucleons. In the internal region, all nucleons interact, but there are channel regions in which the system is split into two or more subsystems which do not interact with one another. For simplicity the channels involving more than two particles will be entirely omitted here. To be consistent, one must also exclude the channels consisting of a residual nucleus plus a composite particle (a deuteron for instance) since in a many-body formulation, the composite particle should be considered as a bound state of its constituents—and this raises the same kind of problems as the channels where the composite particle is broken into pieces.

The program defined here has been attacked already by quite a few authors [5] using different mathematical formalisms. The approach I shall describe here [6, 7] is most closely related to that used by FANO [8] in atomic problems. The central idea will be to try to be as straightforward as possible: simply write the Schrödinger equation in an appropriate basis. In this way, the theory of nuclear reactions will appear as nothing more than an extension of the method of diagonalization in a restricted configuration subspace used in nuclear structure problems; the new feature being the introduction of the continuous part of the single-particle spectrum. The general formalism will be described in Sect. **2** and **4**. It is based on the perhaps drastic simplification of ignoring all components of the wave function in which more than one nucleon is in a continuum state. No attempt will be made to give arguments trying to prove that the results or some of the results are actually more general than this assumption would seem to imply, although this could obviously be done in many cases at the expense of replacing well-defined mathematical objects by somewhat vague entities. Actually, the correct treatment of the configurations with two nucleons in the continuum (necessary for the consideration of deuterons) involves the complications of the three-body collision problem. This aspect of the theory will be totally ignored here.

On the other hand, the complete antisymmetrization of the wave function will be introduced at the beginning and rigorously kept through the calculations. There will also be no problem connected with a nuclear radius.

The general formalism can in principle be used as such for numerical calculations in simple cases (light nuclei, closed-shell nuclei, etc.). Some of the problems connected with numerical calculations as well as numerical tests on simple models will be discussed in Sect. **3** and **4**. A realistic calculation for ^{16}O done by RAYNAL and MELKANOFF will be reported in a seminar.

The standard problems of resonances due to compound levels are discussed in Sect. **5**. Finally, Sect. **6** is devoted to the cases where the situation is too complicated to be treated in full detail. The general formalism of Sect. **2** must then be further reduced along the lines suggested by the theories of the optical model, the direct interactions and more recently the so-called intermediate resonances. This may actually be done only by introducing further assumptions: weak coupling of certain classes of states, random distribution of matrix elements. Within the framework of a completely defined theory as we have here, it should be possible to test these assumptions against a complete treatment of a particular model. I do not think that this has been done as yet.

The mathematical machinery involved in such a formalism has already been used by many authors [5]. It may become very tedious. It is convenient to recognize that it is nothing but the « generalized algorithm of Gauss ». A symmetry theorem and other properties proved in the Appendix are then very useful for avoiding complicated operator manipulations.

Clearly many aspects of the problem will be entirely left out. Besides the complete omission of channels where more than one nucleon is emitted, a whole series of problems, which are not yet completely solved in the theory of nuclear structure, will not even be mentioned here: introduction of really self-consistent fields, treatment of deformed nuclear structures, degenerate shell-model problems etc.

2. – General formalism in a restricted configuration space.

In this Section we shall describe a particularly simple model of a nuclear reaction based on a restriction of the configuration space [6]. This will be defined by choosing a subspace in the eigenfunction space of the shell-model unperturbed Hamiltonian H_0. Besides this limitation, no further approximation will, in principle, be made. In particular, all functions will always be properly antisymmetrized, so that exchange collisions will be treated exactly. Of course, in practical calculations, it will often be necessary to truncate further the configuration space since with the present limitations its number of dimensions may still be tremendously large. This will be discussed further in Sect. **6**.

As usual, we rewrite the nuclear Hamiltonian in the form

$$H = H_0 + V\,, \tag{2.1}$$

where H_0 is an independent-particle Hamiltonian and V the residual interaction. We assume here that the single-particle potential included in H_0 has the proper behaviour at large distance. Let then φ_m, ε_m be the bound normalized eigenfunctions and energies in this potential, and $\varphi_{n,\varepsilon}$ the standing wave eigenfunctions of positive energy normalized according to

$$\int \varphi^*_{n,\varepsilon}\varphi_{n'\varepsilon'}\mathrm{d}\tau = \delta_{nn'}\delta(\varepsilon-\varepsilon') \,. \tag{2.2}$$

The behaviour of these functions for large r is of the form

$$\varphi_{n\varepsilon}(r) \sim \sqrt{\frac{2}{\pi\hbar v}}\,\frac{1}{r}\,Y_{lm}(\hat{r})\chi_\sigma \sin(kr+\delta_l - l\pi/2) \,, \tag{2.3}$$

for uncharged particles (with obvious notations). Here δ_l is the phase shift introduced by the one-body potential present in H_0, $v=\hbar k/M$ is the velocity. For charged particles, we have similarly

$$\varphi_{n\varepsilon}(r) \sim \sqrt{\frac{2}{\pi\hbar v}}\,\frac{1}{r}\,Y_{lm}(\hat{r})\chi_\sigma \sin(kr+\delta_l+\sigma_l - l\pi/2 - \gamma\log 2kr) \,, \tag{2.4}$$

where σ_l is the pure Coulomb phase shift and

$$\gamma = Ze^2/\hbar v \,.$$

The unperturbed eigenfunctions for the $A+1$ particle system are Slater-determinants of the φ_m and $\varphi_{n\varepsilon}$ We shall restrict the configuration space to states such that at most one particle is in the continuum. We have two kinds of states, *i.e.* two orthogonal subspaces 1 and 2 depending on whether all nucleons are in bound states or one is in a continuum state. We shall denote these states by

$$\begin{cases} 1) & |m_1;\, m_2;\, \dots;\, m_{A+1}) = |\alpha) \,, \\ 2) & |m_1;\, m_2;\, \dots;\, m_A;\, n,\, \varepsilon) = |\beta,\, \varepsilon) \,. \end{cases} \tag{2.5}$$

The unperturbed energies of these states will be denoted by E_α and $E_\beta+\varepsilon$, respectively.

The most general wave function within the limited configuration space considered here may be decomposed into a component $|1)$ in space 1 and a component $|2)$ in space 2:

$$\begin{cases} |\Psi) = |1) + |2) \,, \\ |1) = \sum_\alpha |\alpha)\, a(\alpha) \,, \\ |2) = \sum_\beta \int \mathrm{d}\varepsilon\, |\beta,\, \varepsilon)\, a(\beta,\, \varepsilon), \end{cases} \tag{2.6}$$

where $a(\alpha)$ and $a(\beta, \varepsilon)$ are characteristic amplitudes.

The residual interaction is of the form

$$V=\tfrac{1}{2}\sum_{ij}v_{ij}-\sum_{i}v_i\,, \tag{2.7}$$

where v_{ij} denotes the two-body interaction, v_i the shell-model potential already included in H_0. It may be decomposed into four submatrices corresponding to the subspaces 1 and 2:

$$V=\left|\begin{array}{c|c} V^{11} & V^{12} \\ \hline V^{21} & V^{22} \end{array}\right|. \tag{2.8}$$

The matrix elements of V^{22} require a special analysis. They read

$$(\beta\varepsilon|V|\beta'\varepsilon')=\int \mathrm{d}\tau_1\,\dots\,\mathrm{d}\tau_{A+1}\sum_{P}(-)^P\varphi^*_{m_1}(1)\,\dots\,\varphi^*_{m_A}(A)\varphi_{n\varepsilon}(A+1)\cdot \tag{2.9}$$
$$\cdot\Big(\sum_{ij}v_{ij}-\sum_{i}v_i\Big)\,\varphi_{m'_1}(P1)\,\dots\,\varphi_{m'_A}(PA)\varphi_{n'\varepsilon'}\{P(A+1)\}\,,$$

where the summation must be extended to all permutations P of the $A+1$ nucleons. The terms such that $P(A+1)=A+1$, $i\neq A+1$, $j\neq A+1$ have contributions containing a δ-function which may be written

$$\delta_{nn'}\delta(\varepsilon-\varepsilon')(\beta|V_r|\beta')\,, \tag{2.10}$$

where V_r denotes the part of V involving interactions between particles in bound states only, or in other words interactions of particles belonging to the residual nucleus resulting from the removal of the particle in the continuum state $n\varepsilon$. All other terms of (2.6) are continuous functions of ε and ε'. Thus

$$(\beta\varepsilon|V|\beta'\varepsilon')=\delta_{nn'}\delta(\varepsilon-\varepsilon')(\beta|V_r|\beta')+(\beta\varepsilon|V_d|\beta'\varepsilon')\,, \tag{2.11}$$

where the last term is the sum of the terms where the particle in the continuum either interacts and/or is exchanged with a particle in a bound state. The first term corresponds to a particle in the continuum which does not interact with the A residual particles. It will be convenient to write the separation (2.11) symbolically as

$$V^{22}=V^{22}_r+V^{22}_d\,. \tag{2.11'}$$

The matrix elements of V^{12} or V^{21} are all continuous functions of ε. Introducing now the expansion (2.6) into the Schrödinger equation, we obtain a system which may be written

$$(2.12)\qquad \begin{cases} (H^{11}-E)|1) + V^{12}|2) = 0\,, \\ V^{21}|1) + (H^{22}-E)|2) = 0\,, \end{cases}$$

or explicitly, using (2.11),

$$(2.13)\qquad \begin{cases} (E_\alpha - E)a(\alpha) + \sum\limits_{\alpha'} (\alpha|V|\alpha')a(\alpha') + \sum\limits_{\beta'} \int \mathrm{d}\varepsilon' (\alpha|V|\beta'\varepsilon')a(\beta'\varepsilon') = 0\,, \\ \sum\limits_{\alpha'} (\beta\varepsilon|V|\alpha')a(\alpha') + (E_\beta + \varepsilon - E)a(\beta, \varepsilon) + \sum\limits_{\beta'} (\beta|V_r|\beta')\, a(\beta', \varepsilon) + \\ \qquad\qquad + \sum\limits_{\beta'} \int \mathrm{d}\varepsilon' (\beta\varepsilon|V_d|\beta'\varepsilon')a(\beta'\varepsilon') = 0\,. \end{cases}$$

These equations contain all the information about the problem, except the boundary conditions. In a scattering problem, those depend on how the reaction was initiated. I shall not use the common procedure of constructing an integral equation containing at the same time the eqs. (2.13) and specific boundary conditions. It will be more convenient to discuss the general solution to the eqs. (2.13).

It is essential to study the singularities of the amplitudes $a(\beta, \varepsilon)$ since they determine the asymptotic behaviour of the wave functions at large distance and therefore the S-matrix and the cross-sections. The first and last terms of the second eq. (2.13) are regular functions of ε. Thus singularities of $a(\beta, \varepsilon)$ will occur for

$$(2.14)\qquad E - \varepsilon = E_\lambda\,,$$

where E_λ is an eigenvalue of the equation

$$(2.15)\qquad (E_\beta - E_\lambda)u_\lambda(\beta) + \sum_{\beta'} (\beta|V_r|\beta')u_\lambda(\beta') = 0\,,$$

corresponding to the two middle terms of the second eq. (2.13). This is actually the Schrödinger equation of the residual nucleus (of mass A), in the approximation corresponding to the reduced configuration space where all nucleons are confined to bound single-particle states. Thus λ denotes the various channels in which the system breaks up into one nucleon and a residual nucleus of mass A.

Let us assume that we have solved (2.15) and take the $u_\lambda(\beta)$ orthonormalized according to

$$(2.16)\qquad \sum_\beta u^*_\lambda(\beta)u_{\lambda'}(\beta) = \delta_{\lambda\lambda'}\,,$$

as a basis by writing

$$a(\beta, \varepsilon) = \sum_{\lambda} a(\lambda, \varepsilon) u_\lambda(\beta) . \tag{2.17}$$

Then (2.13) becomes

$$\left\{\begin{aligned} &(E_\alpha - E)a(\alpha) + \sum_{\alpha'} (\alpha|V|\alpha')a(\alpha') + \sum_{\lambda'} \int d\varepsilon' (\alpha|V|\lambda'\varepsilon')a(\lambda'\varepsilon') = 0 , \\ &(\varepsilon + E_\lambda - E)a(\lambda\varepsilon) + \sum_{\lambda'} \int d\varepsilon' (\lambda\varepsilon|V_d|\lambda'\varepsilon')a(\lambda'\varepsilon') + \sum_{\alpha'} (\lambda\varepsilon|V|\alpha')a(\alpha') = 0 , \end{aligned}\right. \tag{2.18}$$

where

$$(\lambda\varepsilon|V_d|\lambda'\varepsilon') = \sum_{\beta\beta'} u^*_\lambda(\beta) u_{\lambda'}(\beta')(\beta\varepsilon|V_d|\beta'\varepsilon') , \quad \text{etc.} \tag{2.19}$$

are the matrix elements computed for the « exact » (*i.e.* exact within the limited configuration space) wave functions of the residual nucleus:

$$|\lambda\varepsilon) = \sum_{\beta} |\beta\varepsilon) u_\lambda(\beta) . \tag{2.20}$$

Since these manipulations may appear somewhat abstract, it may be useful to illustrate them on a simple example. Consider three identical nucleons in the presence of an inert core creating a central potential. Let us assume that only 4 bound states φ_i $(i = 1, 2, 3, 4)$ and a continuum φ_ε are available to these nucleons. The indices β characterize the states of the residual system of 2 nucleons in the discrete states. Taking the Pauli principle into account, we have 6 values for β:

$$\beta = (1, 2) , \quad (1, 3) , \quad (1, 4) , \quad (2, 3) , \quad (2, 4) , \quad (3, 4);$$

in general

$$\beta = (i, j) , \quad i < j , \quad i, j = 1, 2, 3, 4 .$$

Similarly, we have 4 values of α corresponding to all possible occupations of the 4 discrete states by the 3 nucleons:

$$\alpha = (1, 2, 3) , \quad (1, 2, 4) , \quad (1, 3, 4) , \quad (2, 3, 4) . \tag{2.21}$$

The wave functions $|\beta)$ are the Slater determinants

$$|i, j) = \frac{1}{\sqrt{2}} \begin{vmatrix} \varphi_i(1) & \varphi_i(2) \\ \varphi_j(1) & \varphi_j(2) \end{vmatrix} \qquad (i, j = 1, 2, 3, 4). \tag{2.22}$$

The Schrödinger eq. (2.15) for the residual system reads now

$$(2.23)\qquad (\varepsilon_i+\varepsilon_j-E_\lambda)u_\lambda(ij)+\sum_{k\neq l=1}^{4}(ij|V|kl)\,u_\lambda(kl)=0\,,$$

where ε_i is the energy of the state i. The matrix elements of V are the usual Slater integrals

$$(2.24)\qquad (ij|V|kl)=\int\mathrm{d}\tau_1\mathrm{d}\tau_2\varphi_i^*(1)\varphi_j^*(2)\,V(1,2)[\varphi_k(1)\varphi_l(2)-\varphi_k(2)\varphi_l(1)]\,.$$

The eq. (2.23) is actually a matrix equation in the 6-dimensional space β. It has therefore 6 eigenvalues giving rise to 6 channels λ. Usually, angular momentum conservation will split the system (2.24) into simpler systems, but let us not go into such details. With each solution $u_\lambda(ij)$, we can now construct the wave function (2.20)

$$(2.25)\qquad |\lambda\varepsilon)=\sum_{ij}u_\lambda(ij)\,|ij\varepsilon)\,,$$

where $|ij\varepsilon)$ are the Slater determinants

$$(2.26)\qquad |ij\varepsilon)=\frac{1}{\sqrt{6}}\begin{vmatrix}\varphi_i(1) & \varphi_i(2) & \varphi_i(3)\\ \varphi_j(1) & \varphi_j(2) & \varphi_j(3)\\ \varphi_\varepsilon(1) & \varphi_\varepsilon(2) & \varphi_\varepsilon(3)\end{vmatrix}\,.$$

If we denote by

$$(2.27)\qquad \Psi_\lambda(12)=\sum_{ij}u_\lambda(ij)\,|ij)\,,$$

the 2-nucleon wave function of the residual nucleus in state λ, we see that (2.25) may be written

$$(2.28)\qquad |\lambda\varepsilon)=\frac{1}{\sqrt{3}}[\Psi_\lambda(1\,2)\varphi_\varepsilon(3)-\Psi_\lambda(1\,3)\varphi_\varepsilon(2)-\Psi_\lambda(3\,2)\varphi_\varepsilon(1)]\,.$$

Thus $|\lambda\varepsilon)$ appears as the normalized antisymmetrized product of the wave functions of the residual nucleus and of the nucleon in the continuum. This conclusion of course holds in all cases.

Let us now return to the general formalism. The second eq. (2.18) exhibits very clearly the singularities of $a(\lambda\varepsilon)$. The last two terms are regular functions of ε. Thus $a(\lambda\varepsilon)$ has at

$$(2.29)\qquad \varepsilon=\varepsilon_\lambda\equiv E-E_\lambda\,,$$

a singularity of the form

$$(2.30)\qquad \begin{cases} a(\lambda\varepsilon) = A_\lambda\, \delta(\varepsilon - \varepsilon_\lambda) + b(\lambda\varepsilon)\,, \\ b(\lambda\varepsilon) \sim \dfrac{B_\lambda}{\varepsilon - \varepsilon_\lambda} \qquad (\varepsilon \approx \varepsilon_\lambda)\,. \end{cases}$$

Clearly ε_λ defined by (2.29) is the channel energy *i.e.* the energy of an emitted particle leaving the residual nucleus in the state λ.

As a consequence of (2.30), the integrals in (2.18) involve singular integrands, and a convention is required to define their value at the pole of $b(\lambda\varepsilon)$. This convention may in principle be chosen arbitrarily. Two particularly convenient choices are:

$$(2.31)\qquad \begin{cases} 1)\ \text{replace } \varepsilon \text{ by } \varepsilon - i\eta \qquad (\eta \to +0)\,, \\ 2)\ \text{take the principal part.} \end{cases}$$

The first choice leads automatically to the outgoing-wave boundary condition corresponding to a scattering problem. The second choice, however, as we shall see has the advantage of introducing purely Hermitian matrices at every step, which is very convenient for numerical calculations.

Let us denote by $⨍$ the integral defined according to some convention. Separating the δ-function term in $a(\lambda\varepsilon)$, we may rewrite the Schrödinger equation in the form

$$(2.32)\qquad \begin{cases} (E_\alpha - E)a(\alpha) + \sum\limits_{\alpha'} (\alpha|V|\alpha')\,a(\alpha') + \sum\limits_{\lambda'} ⨍ \mathrm{d}\varepsilon' (\alpha|V|\lambda'\varepsilon')\,b(\lambda'\varepsilon') = \\ \qquad\qquad = -\sum\limits_{\lambda'} (\alpha|V|\lambda'\varepsilon_{\lambda'})\,A_{\lambda'}\,, \\ (\varepsilon + E_\lambda - E)\,b(\lambda\varepsilon) + \sum\limits_{\lambda'} ⨍ \mathrm{d}\varepsilon' (\lambda\varepsilon|V_d|\lambda'\varepsilon')\,b(\lambda'\varepsilon') + \\ \qquad\qquad + \sum\limits_{\alpha'} (\lambda\varepsilon|V|\alpha')\,a(\alpha') = -\sum\limits_{\lambda'} (\lambda\varepsilon|V_d|\lambda'\varepsilon_{\lambda'})\,A_{\lambda'}\,. \end{cases}$$

This system determines in principle all the amplitudes $a(\alpha)$ and $a(\lambda\varepsilon)$ in terms of the A_λ.

It will be useful to introduce a concise notation for (2.32). As in (2.6) we call again 1 the purely discrete subspace but we now divide the continuous subspace 2 into the *off-energy-shell* part ($\varepsilon \neq \varepsilon_\lambda$) which we continue to denote by 2 and the *energy-shell* part ($\varepsilon = \varepsilon_\lambda$) which we denote by 3. Thus we divide the wave function into 3 components belonging to these 3 subspaces, with the following notations:

$$(2.33)\qquad |\Psi) = |1) + |b) + |A)\,,$$

where

$$(2.34)\qquad \begin{cases} |1) = \sum\limits_{\alpha} |\alpha)\, a(\alpha)\,, \\ |b) = \sum\limits_{\lambda} \int \mathrm{d}\varepsilon\, |\lambda\varepsilon)\, b(\lambda\varepsilon)\,, \\ |A) = \sum\limits_{\lambda} |\lambda\varepsilon_\lambda)\, A_\lambda\,. \end{cases}$$

Note that the basic vectors in space 3 are labelled by the channel indices λ. The energy-shell space 3 may thus also be described as the *channel space*.

Now (2.32) may be written

$$(2.35)\qquad \begin{cases} (H^{11}-E)|1) + V^{12}|b) = -V^{13}|A)\,, \\ V^{21}|1) + (H^{22}-E)|b) = -V^{23}|A)\,, \end{cases}$$

where

$$(2.36)\qquad \begin{cases} (\alpha|H^{11}|\alpha') = E_\alpha \delta_{\alpha\alpha'} + (\alpha|V|\alpha')\,, \\ (\lambda\varepsilon|H^{22}|\lambda'\varepsilon') = (\varepsilon + E_\lambda)\delta_{\lambda\lambda'}\delta(\varepsilon-\varepsilon') + (\lambda\varepsilon|V_d|\lambda'\varepsilon')\,, \\ (\lambda\varepsilon|V^{23}|\lambda'\varepsilon_{\lambda'}) = (\lambda\varepsilon|V_d|\lambda'\varepsilon_{\lambda'})\,, \quad \text{etc.} \end{cases}$$

We are interested in expressing the amplitudes $|b)$ in terms of the $|A)$. Thus we solve the first eq. (2.35) for $|1)$:

$$(2.37)\qquad |1) = \frac{1}{E-H^{11}}\,[V^{12}|b) + V^{13}|A)]\,,$$

and substitute into the second equation. This yields

$$(2.38)\qquad \left[H^{22} + V^{21}\frac{1}{E-H^{11}}V^{12} - E\right]|b) = -\left[V^{23} + V^{21}\frac{1}{E-H^{11}}V^{13}\right]|A)\,.$$

This equation may be written more simply in terms of an effective potential acting in the continuous spaces 2, 3 and resulting from the elimination of space 1. The process of successive elimination will play a very important role in what follows. It is therefore useful to introduce appropriate notations which are summarized in the Appendix. Thus it is convenient to write

$$(2.39)\qquad V^{ij}_{(1)} = V^{ij} + V^{i1}\frac{1}{E-H^{11}}V^{1j} \qquad (i,\, j = 2,\, 3)\,,$$

where the subscript (1) reminds that subspace 1 has been eliminated. Similarly we define the effective Hamiltonian resulting from the elimination of subspace 1 by

$$H^{22}_{(1)} = H^{22} + V^{21}\frac{1}{E-H^{11}}V^{12} = H^{22}_0 + V^{22}_{(1)} . \tag{2.40}$$

We may now rewrite (2.38) as

$$(H^{22}_{(1)} - E)|b) = -V^{23}_{(1)}|A) . \tag{2.41}$$

Thus

$$|b) = \frac{1}{E-H^{22}_{(1)}}V^{23}_{(1)}|A) . \tag{2.42}$$

The coefficients B_λ giving the residue of $b(\lambda\varepsilon)$ at the pole $\varepsilon = \varepsilon_\lambda$ (see (2.30)) may be obtained from the second eq. (2.32) by setting $\varepsilon = \varepsilon_\lambda$. This gives

$$B_\lambda = -\sum_{\lambda'}\int d\varepsilon'(\lambda\varepsilon_\lambda|V_d|\lambda'\varepsilon')b(\lambda'\varepsilon') - \sum_{\alpha'}(\lambda\varepsilon_\lambda|V|\alpha')a(\alpha') - \sum_{\lambda'}(\lambda\varepsilon_\lambda|V_d|\lambda'\varepsilon_{\lambda'})A_{\lambda'}, \tag{2.43}$$

or symbolically

$$|B) = -V^{31}|1) - V^{32}|b) - V^{33}|A) . \tag{2.44}$$

Substitution into (2.44) of (2.37) and (2.42) yields

$$|B) = -K|A) , \tag{2.45}$$

where

$$K = V^{33}_{(1)} + V^{32}_{(1)}\frac{1}{E-H^{22}_{(1)}}V^{23}_{(1)} = V^{33}_{(12)} . \tag{2.46}$$

The symbol $V^{33}_{(12)}$ denotes the effective potential after elimination of subspaces 1 and 2. In (2.46) it is defined (compare with (2.39)) by eliminating subspace 2 after 1 has been eliminated. It is fairly obvious, and it is shown in the Appendix that the order of elimination of the subspaces is irrelevant. Thus

$$V^{33}_{(12)} = V^{33}_{(21)} .$$

It should be remembered that the inversion of $E - H^{22}_{(1)}$ occurring in (2.42) and (2.46) is a singular operation. It implies a convention which does not appear explicitly in the symbolic relations. Thus (2.42) actually stands for the solution of the equation

$$(\varepsilon + E_\lambda - E)b(\lambda\varepsilon) + \sum_{\lambda'}\int d\varepsilon'(\lambda\varepsilon|V_{(1)}|\lambda'\varepsilon')b(\lambda'\varepsilon') = \sum_{\lambda'}(\lambda\varepsilon|V_{(1)}|\lambda'\varepsilon_{\lambda'})A_{\lambda'} , \tag{2.47}$$

where the singular integral in the left-hand side should be computed according to a specified convention as discussed above.

So much for the resolution of the Schrödinger equation. We now turn to another aspect of the problem: the relation between the A_λ, B_λ and the asymptotic form of the wave functions at large distance. This will lead to the relation between the matrix K defined by (2.46) and the S-matrix.

The form of the basic function φ_ε for large r was given in (2.3) and (2.4). In channel λ, the wave function describing the incoming or outgoing particle is of the form

$$\int \mathrm{d}\varepsilon a(\lambda\varepsilon)\varphi_\varepsilon(r) = A_\lambda \varphi_{\varepsilon_\lambda}(r) + \fint \mathrm{d}\varepsilon b(\lambda\varepsilon)\varphi_\varepsilon(r)\,. \tag{2.48}$$

The value of the second term for large r is determined entirely by the neighbourhood of the singularity of $b(\lambda, \varepsilon)$; *i.e.* for $\varepsilon \approx \varepsilon_\lambda$. It depends on the convention chosen for integration at this singularity. It is easy to show that for $r \to \infty$, and the two conventions (2.31)

$$\left\{\begin{aligned} &\fint \mathrm{d}\varepsilon b(\lambda\varepsilon)\varphi_\varepsilon(r) \sim B_\lambda \int \frac{\mathrm{d}\varepsilon}{\varepsilon - \varepsilon_\lambda - i\eta}\,\varphi_\varepsilon(r) \sim \\ &\qquad\qquad \sim \pi B_\lambda \xi_\lambda \exp[i(k_\lambda r + \delta_\lambda - l\pi/2) \qquad (i\eta)\,, \\ &\text{or} \\ &\fint \mathrm{d}\varepsilon b(\lambda\varepsilon)\varphi_\varepsilon(r) \sim B_\lambda \mathscr{P}\int \frac{\mathrm{d}\varepsilon}{\varepsilon - \varepsilon_\lambda}\,\varphi_\varepsilon(r) \sim \pi B_\lambda \xi_\lambda \cos(k_\lambda r + \delta_\lambda - l\pi/2) \quad (\mathscr{P})\,, \end{aligned}\right. \tag{2.49}$$

where we have introduced the notation

$$\xi_\lambda = \sqrt{\frac{2}{\pi\hbar v_\lambda}}\,\frac{1}{r}\,Y_{lm}(\hat{r})\chi_\sigma\,, \tag{2.50}$$

for the various factors occurring in $\varphi_\varepsilon(r)$. The expressions (2.38) hold for uncharged particles. For charged particles, the argument of the exponential or the cosine contains the additional Coulomb phase shift

$$\sigma_l - \gamma \log 2kr\,. \tag{2.51}$$

The wave functions in the various channels may be decomposed into incoming and outgoing waves with amplitudes $a_\lambda^{(-)}$ and $a_\lambda^{(+)}$:

$$\xi_\lambda\{a_\lambda^{(-)} \exp[-i(k_\lambda r - l\pi/2)] - a_\lambda^{(+)} \exp[i(k_\lambda r - l\pi/2)]\}\,. \tag{2.52}$$

The S-matrix gives the outgoing amplitudes in terms of the incoming amplitudes according to

$$a_\lambda^{(+)} = \sum_\mu (\lambda|S|\mu)\, a_\mu^{(-)} . \tag{2.53}$$

Finally the cross-sections are given in terms of the S-matrix in a well-known manner which needs not be recalled here.

From (2.48) and (2.49) we obtain for the wave function in channel λ at large distance

$$(2.54)\quad \begin{cases} \xi_\lambda[A_\lambda \sin(k_\lambda r + \delta_\lambda - l\pi/2) + \pi B_\lambda \exp[i(k_\lambda r + \delta_\lambda - l\pi/2)]] & (i\eta), \\ \text{or} \\ \xi_\lambda[A_\lambda \sin(k_\lambda r + \delta_\lambda - l\pi/2) + \pi B_\lambda \cos(k_\lambda r + \delta_\lambda - l\pi/2)] & (\mathscr{P}). \end{cases}$$

Identification of these expressions with (2.52) yields

$$(2.55)\quad \begin{cases} 2ia_\lambda^{(-)} = A_\lambda \exp[-i\delta_\lambda]\,, \qquad 2ia_\lambda^{(+)} = (A_\lambda + 2i\pi B_\lambda)\exp[i\delta_\lambda] & (i\eta), \\ \text{or} \\ 2ia_\lambda^{(-)} = (A_\lambda - i\pi B_\lambda)\exp[-i\delta_\lambda]\,, \quad 2ia_\lambda^{(+)} = (A_\lambda + i\pi B_\lambda)\exp[i\delta_\lambda] & (\mathscr{P}), \end{cases}$$

for the two integration conventions (2.31). For charged particles, the phase shift (2.51) should be added in the expressions (2.54), but the relations (2.55) remain unchanged.

The relation between S and K follows now from (2.45), (2.53) and (2.55) by elimination of all amplitudes. One obtains for the two conventions:

$$S = e^{i\delta}\bar{S}e^{i\delta}, \tag{2.56}$$

where

$$\bar{S} = 1 - 2i\pi K \qquad (i\eta), \tag{2.57}$$

or

$$\bar{S} = \frac{1 - i\pi K}{1 + i\pi K} \qquad (\mathscr{P}). \tag{2.58}$$

In (2.56) δ denotes a diagonal matrix of the channel space 3 with elements equal to the shell-model potential phase shifts δ_λ. Explicitly, (2.56) means

$$(\lambda|S|\mu) = (\lambda|\bar{S}|\mu)\exp[i(\delta_\lambda + \delta_\mu)] .$$

The relations (2.57) and (2.58) are matrix relations in the channel space 3.

It is seen that the $i\eta$ convention leads to a much simpler relation between S and K. With the principal-part convention, the relation (2.58) yields always a unitary S-matrix for every approximate K. In this case, the matrix K is known as the reactance matrix.

It may be useful here to summarize the properties of the partial Hamiltonians introduced so far (see Fig. 1).

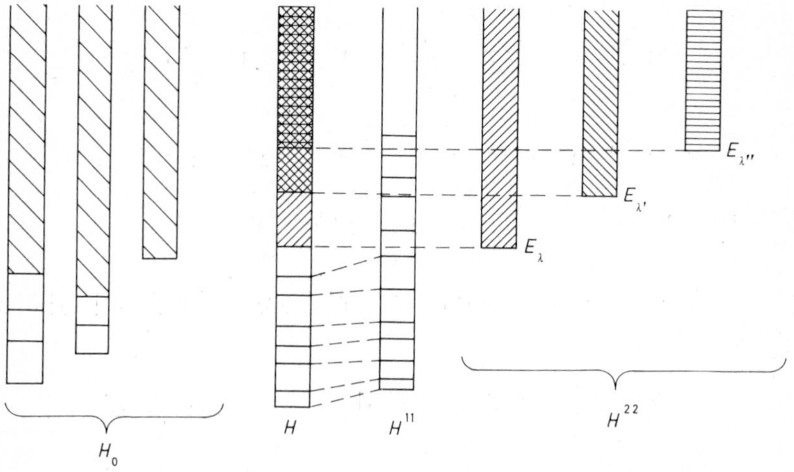

Fig. 1. – The spectrum of the various partial Hamiltonians.

1) The spectrum of the unperturbed Hamiltonian H_0 in the restricted configuration space considered here is a superposition of partially discrete and partially continuous subspectra.

2) The exact Hamiltonian H has a discrete spectrum plus a continuous spectrum which is actually a superposition of various continuous subspectra starting each at the energy E_λ of a level of the residual nucleus obtained by removing one nucleon.

3) The restriction H^{11} of H to the purely discrete vector space 1 has a purely discrete spectrum. Its lowest eigenstates are in principle very close to those of the exact Hamiltonian H, since the effect of the continuum should be small far below the threshold of H.

4) The operator H^{22}, restriction of H to the purely continuous vector space 2 has essentially a continuous spectrum identical with that of H. If the interaction V_d^{22} is sufficiently strong, discrete levels may appear below the continuum. They do not, however, play an essential role.

3. – Numerical treatment of continuous spectra.

In a numerical calculation based on the formulation of Sect. **2**, the integration over the continuous variable ε must naturally be replaced by a discrete summation. Thus the integral equations become systems of linear equations, for which standard methods apply. The dimension of the linear systems is proportional to the number of intervals. It is therefore necessary for practical reasons to keep the number of intervals to a minimum. This suggests the use of elaborate integration methods such that a good accuracy may be obtained with a relatively small number of points. I would like to describe briefly here a number of possibilities, although they have not yet been all completely tested in practice.

Let me first recall the very well-known standard method for numerical integration. The starting point is the Lagrange interpolation formula for a given set of points $\varepsilon_1, \varepsilon_2, \ldots, \varepsilon_N$:

$$\hat{f}(\varepsilon) = \sum_n f(\varepsilon_n) \frac{\varphi(\varepsilon)}{(\varepsilon - \varepsilon_n)\varphi'(\varepsilon_n)}, \tag{3.1}$$

where

$$\varphi(\varepsilon) \equiv (\varepsilon - \varepsilon_1)(\varepsilon - \varepsilon_2) \ldots (\varepsilon - \varepsilon_N). \tag{3.2}$$

The expression (3.1) is clearly a polynomial of degree $N-1$ equal to $f(\varepsilon_n)$ for $\varepsilon = \varepsilon_n$ $(n = 1, 2, \ldots, N)$. An N-point integration formula is then obtained by integrating the polynomial (3.1). The simplest choice is to take equally spaced points with ε_1 and ε_N at the boundaries of the interval of the integration. One obtains then the so-called Newton-Cotes integration formula and the weights A_n may be found in Tables [9] up to a high value of N. For $N = 2$ the general formula becomes the trapeze formula, for $N = 3$ the Simpson formula, etc.

These formulae may be applied in two ways. By taking N sufficiently large one may apply the integration formula to the full interval at once. It is on the other hand possible to divide the full interval into smaller ones and apply an integration formula with a small N to each interval separately.

For our problem, two modifications must be introduced because:

1) we have an infinite interval;

2) the integrand has a simple pole at a known energy ε_λ.

In an infinite interval, the polynomial (3.1) cannot be used since its integral diverges. We may then introduce a weight function $w(\varepsilon)$ decreasing for $\varepsilon \to \infty$ as much as possible at the same rate as the integrand (this is not a very precise statement!), and such that

$$\int^{+\infty} \varepsilon^{N-1} w(\varepsilon) \mathrm{d}\varepsilon < \infty .$$

We apply then the Lagrange interpolation formula to $f(\varepsilon)/w(\varepsilon)$. This yields

$$\hat{f}(\varepsilon) = w(\varepsilon) \sum_n f(\varepsilon_n) \frac{\varphi(\varepsilon)}{w(\varepsilon_n)(\varepsilon-\varepsilon_n)\varphi'(\varepsilon_n)} . \tag{3.3}$$

By integration we obtain the N-point formula

$$\int f(\varepsilon) \mathrm{d}\varepsilon \approx \sum_{n=1}^{N} A_n f(\varepsilon_n) , \tag{3.4}$$

where

$$A_n = \int \frac{w(\varepsilon)\varphi(\varepsilon)\mathrm{d}\varepsilon}{w(\varepsilon_n)(\varepsilon-\varepsilon_n)\varphi'(\varepsilon_n)} . \tag{3.5}$$

The integration formula (3.4) is clearly exact if $f(\varepsilon)$ is the product of $w(\varepsilon)$ by an arbitrary polynomial of degree up to $N-1$.

The simplest choice for $w(\varepsilon)$ is

$$\begin{cases} w(\varepsilon) = 1 , & 0 < \varepsilon < \mathscr{E}_m , \\ w(\varepsilon) = 0 , & \varepsilon > \mathscr{E}_m . \end{cases} \tag{3.6}$$

Let us now consider an integrand $f(\varepsilon)$ having a simple pole at ε_λ and try to evaluate the principal part of its integral. The most obvious procedure consists in placing ε_λ, by an appropriate choice of the total energy E, in the middle of an interval ε_n, ε_{n+1} and in evaluating separately the integrals from 0 to ε_n and ε_{n+1} to $+\infty$. This however is not a very consistent method. Moreover it is not convenient if one wishes to keep the points $\varepsilon_1, \ldots, \varepsilon_N$ fixed (this avoids the complete recalculation of all matrix elements for each value of E), since the number of possible values of E is then only $N-1$. This may not be sufficient if the cross-section is rapidly varying.

A more satisfactory procedure [10] consists in subtracting the pole term from $f(\varepsilon)$ and applying the standard integration formula to the difference. The residue at the pole is not known, but it may be evaluated by applying the interpolation formula (3.3) to the function $(\varepsilon-\varepsilon_\lambda)f(\varepsilon)$ for $\varepsilon = \varepsilon_\lambda$. This gives

$$r = (\varepsilon-\varepsilon_\lambda)f(\varepsilon)\big|_{\varepsilon=\varepsilon_\lambda} \approx -\sum_n f(\varepsilon_n) \frac{w(\varepsilon_\lambda)\varphi(\varepsilon_\lambda)}{w(\varepsilon_n)\varphi'(\varepsilon_n)} . \tag{3.7}$$

Applying now the integration formula (3.4) to the function

$$f(\varepsilon)-r\frac{w(\varepsilon)}{w(\varepsilon_\lambda)(\varepsilon-\varepsilon_\lambda)}\,,$$

we get

$$\text{(3.8)}\qquad \int f(\varepsilon)\,\mathrm{d}\varepsilon \approx \frac{r}{w(\varepsilon_\lambda)}\int\frac{w(\varepsilon)\,\mathrm{d}\varepsilon}{\varepsilon-\varepsilon_\lambda}+\sum_n A_n\left[f(\varepsilon_n)-r\frac{w(\varepsilon_n)}{(\varepsilon_n-\varepsilon_\lambda)w(\varepsilon_\lambda)}\right]\approx$$

$$\approx\sum_n f(\varepsilon_n)\left[A_n-\frac{\varphi(\varepsilon_\lambda)}{w(\varepsilon_n)\varphi'(\varepsilon_n)}\left(\int\frac{w(\varepsilon)\,\mathrm{d}\varepsilon}{\varepsilon-\varepsilon_\lambda}-\sum_m A_m\frac{w(\varepsilon_m)}{\varepsilon_m-\varepsilon_\lambda}\right)\right].$$

Thus we obtain an integration formula which may be applied no matter where ε_λ stands with respect to the points ε_n. In particular, it is easy to check that the coefficient of $f(\varepsilon_n)$ goes to zero if $\varepsilon_\lambda\to\varepsilon_n$. The formula (3.8) is exact if $f(\varepsilon)$ is the product of $w(\varepsilon)$ by the sum of a simple pole term at ε_λ and a polynomial of degree up to $N-2$. For simple forms of $w(\varepsilon)$, the integral in (3.8) may be calculated exactly. For instance, for (3.6), one obtains

$$\text{(3.9)}\qquad \int\frac{w(\varepsilon)\,\mathrm{d}\varepsilon}{\varepsilon-\varepsilon_\lambda}=\int_0^{\mathscr{E}_m}\frac{\mathrm{d}\varepsilon}{\varepsilon-\varepsilon_\lambda}=\log\frac{\mathscr{E}_m-\varepsilon_\lambda}{\varepsilon_\lambda}\,.$$

As mentioned already above, these integration formulae may be applied either directly to the full integration interval with a sufficiently large N, or after division of the full interval into smaller ones to each small interval separately with a small N. In the latter case, the corrected formulae (3.8) need be applied only to the interval which contains the pole ε_λ. The second method is probably better since for large N (actually $N\geqslant 8$ for the Newton-Cotes formula) some of the coefficients A_n are negative and actually oscillations appear: some coefficients become very large, some positive and some negative. This is certainly very bad from the computational point of view.

I would like finally to mention the possibility of extending the Gauss-integration formulae to functions having a simple pole, in very much the same way as the Newton-Cotes formulae. The idea of the method of Gauss is to choose the points $\varepsilon_1, \varepsilon_2, \ldots, \varepsilon_N$ in the best possible way (instead of taking them equally spaced) in order to obtain integration formulae which are exact for the product of $w(\varepsilon)$ by polynomials of degree as high as possible. With N points, the highest possible degree is $2N-1$, and this gives extremely good integration formulae. The coefficients A_n are always positive. They are tabulated as well as the positions of the points up to high values of N and for several weight functions $w(\varepsilon)$.

The correction of the Gauss integration formulae for including a pole may be done in two ways. The first method yields a formula which is exact for the product of $w(\varepsilon)$ by the sum of a pole term at ε_λ and an arbitrary polynomial of degree up to $2N-2$. It has however the drawback that the points $\varepsilon_1, ..., \varepsilon_N$ are not the standard tabulated ones. Moreover they vary when ε_λ changes and have to be recomputed as zeros of a certain polynomial for each value of ε_λ. The second method uses the standard fixed points; it is exact for products of $w(\varepsilon)$ by the sum of a pole term at ε_λ and arbitrary polynomials of degree up to $2N-1$ *except* one polynomial of degree $N-1$. Since these methods have not yet been tested, I shall not say any more about them.

The possibility of calculations along these lines has been tested by GILLET [7] by applying the method to the scattering of an S-wave neutron by a square-well potential. The unperturbed Hamiltonian H_0 was the kinetic energy, and V was the square well of depth v and radius R. The basic states are then the standing free waves:

$$\varphi_\varepsilon(r) = \sqrt{\frac{2}{\pi k}}\,\frac{1}{r}\sin kr\,.$$

The matrix elements of V are equal to

$$(\varepsilon|V|\varepsilon') = \frac{v}{\pi\sqrt{kk'}}\left[\frac{\sin(k-k')R}{k-k'} - \frac{\sin(k+k')R}{k+k'}\right],$$

with

$$k=\sqrt{2M\varepsilon}\,, \qquad k'=\sqrt{2M\varepsilon'}.$$

The matrix K reduces to a pure number which is actually equal to

$$K = -\frac{1}{\pi}\operatorname{tg}\delta\,, \tag{3.10}$$

where δ is the phase shift produced by the potential. The exact value of δ

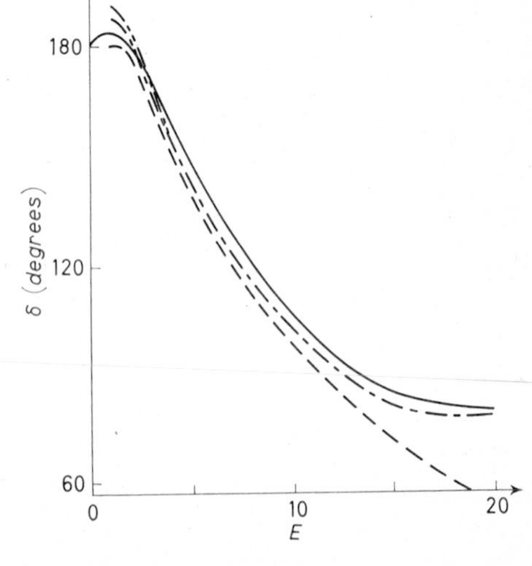

Fig. 2. – The s-phase shifts for a square well potential of depth $v=-10$ and radius $R=1$ ($\hbar=m=1$). The exact solution represented by the solid line is compared to the results of the formalism of Sect. **2** for various maximum energies $\mathscr{E}_m$ of the restricted configuration space. A constant discrete energy interval $\Delta=1$ is used. ——— $\mathscr{E}_m=25$, $\Delta=1$; —·—·— $\mathscr{E}_m=50$, $\Delta=1$; —··—··— $\mathscr{E}_m=100$, $\Delta=1$.

is given by an elementary calculation. It was compared with (3.10) where K is given by the expressions of Sect. **2**, using the principal part convention. In the first calculations reported on Figs. 2-4 none of the elaborate integration methods discussed above was used. The integrals over ε were computed by the trapeze method, placing $\varepsilon_\lambda = E$ in the middle of one of the elementary intervals. The weight function (3.6) was used. The purpose of this computational experiment was to test the effect of the maximum energy $\mathscr{E}_m$ and of the elementary energy interval Δ. Figure 2 gives the influence of $\mathscr{E}_m$. For a fixed $\Delta = 1$ ($\hbar = M = 1$), the maximum energy $\mathscr{E}_m$ is set equal to 25, 50, 100. No significant difference appears between 50 and 100. This shows that a rather limited configuration space yields a reasonably accurate solution. At low energy, the variation of the phase shift is rapid due to a resonance, and requires a smaller integration step (see Fig. 3). The reduction of the integration step brings improvement up to $\Delta = 0.5$; the curves $\Delta = 0.5$ and $\Delta = 0.33$ are indistinguishable.

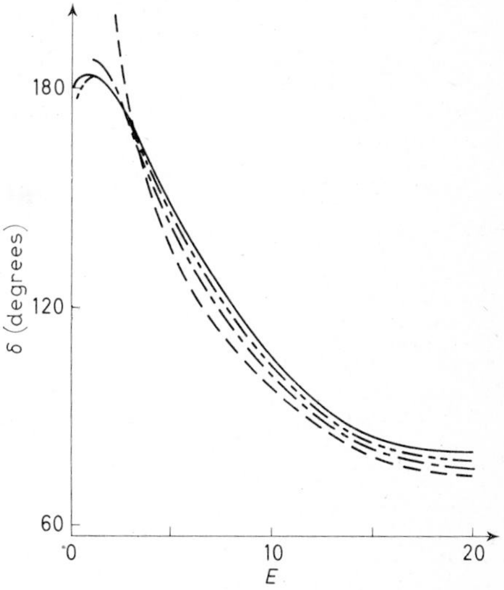

Fig.3. – Influence of the size Δ of the integration step on the accuracy of the solutions (the exact solution is given by the solid line), $v = -10$, $R = 1$. ——— $\mathscr{E}_m = 50$, $\Delta = 2$; —·—·— $\mathscr{E}_m = 50$, $\Delta = 1$; —··—··— $\mathscr{E}_m = 50$, $\Delta = 0.5$ and 0.33.

Figure 4 shows that the inaccuracy of the solutions grows only moderately when the potential depth v increases to give rise to 1 or 2 bound states.

These results are encouraging particularly in view of the fact that better integration methods should allow a reduction of the number of points for the same accuracy. The possibility of using a small number of points and

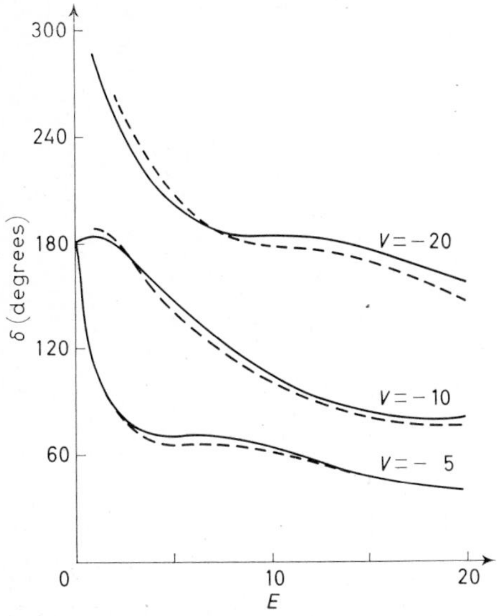

Fig. 4. – Influence of the depth v of the potential on the accuracy of the solution. The radius of the well is $R = 1$, $\mathscr{E}_m = 50$. The exact solutions are given by the solid curves.

therefore of keeping the dimension of matrices to reasonable values is, of course, the crucial point. It seems that the amplitudes $a(\lambda\varepsilon)$ are usually slowly varying with energy. It is interesting to note that even if the cross-section shows a narrow peak as a function of E due to a compound state, this does not mean that for each E the $a(\lambda\varepsilon)$ may not be slowly varying functions of ε. There is however an exception. When the shell-model potential has a narrow virtual state (due to a high potential barrier, a d-wave for instance) the $a(\lambda\varepsilon)$ are rapidly varying when ε is in the neighbourhood of the energy of that state [10]. It may then become necessary to take locally a smaller elementary energy interval.

4. – Photonuclear reactions.

The cross-sections of photonuclear reactions can be studied along the same line as the reactions involving the absorption and emission of a nucleon. Let us derive the expression of the total cross-section for absorption of a γ ray. According to the golden rule, the transition rate per unit of time for the absorption of a photon is given by

$$\frac{2\pi}{\hbar}\sum_n \varrho_n(E_f)|\langle n, E_f|Q|i)|^2, \tag{4.1}$$

where $|i)$ is the ground-state wave function, Q the electromagnetic-transition operator, $|n, E_f\rangle$ a complete system of states orthonormalized in a large box and having the final energy $E_f = E_i + \hbar\omega$; $\varrho_n(E_f)$ is the density of these states

$$\langle n, E_f | n', E'_f\rangle = \delta_{nn'}\,\delta_{E_f E'_f}\,. \tag{4.2}$$

Here n stands for all quantum numbers other than the energy.

The methods described in other lectures allow in principle to write down approximate expressions for the ground-state wave function $|i)$, which will therefore not be discussed any further here.

The final states $|nE_f\rangle$, on the other hand, belong to the continuum and the standard methods do not apply immediately. We shall discuss the description of these states in terms of the truncated configuration space introduced in Sect. **2**. General expansions of the wave functions of the system at a given energy were derived there in terms of arbitrary amplitudes A_λ. These amplitudes are determined in a collision problem by the initial conditions, *i.e.* by incoming waves. In order to apply directly (4.1) we should find a set of amplitudes A_λ^n defining a set of wave functions $|nE_f\rangle$ properly orthonormalized in the large box. Actually, it is simpler to reformulate the problem in a somewhat different form.

We notice that for the total absorption cross-section, the system of final states $|nE_f\rangle$ enters (4.1) only through an expression which may be written in terms of a δ-function:

(4.3) $$\sum_n \varrho_n(E_f)|n, E_f\rangle\langle n, E_f| = \delta(H - E_f) ,$$

where H is the Hamiltonian of the system and E_f is the final energy.

Let us now consider a set of states $|n, E_f)$ orthonormalized according to a δ-function of the energy:

(4.4) $$(n, E_f|n', E_f') = \delta_{nn'}\delta(E_f - E_f') .$$

In terms of these wave functions, we may rewrite (4.3) as

$$\sum_n \varrho_n(E_f)|n, E_f\rangle\langle n, E_f| = \sum_n |n, E_f)(n, E_f| ,$$

and the golden rule becomes

(4.5) $$\frac{2\pi}{\hbar}\sum_n |(n, E_f|Q|i)|^2 .$$

Our problem is therefore now to determine a system of wave functions orthonormalized according to (4.4). In the continuous spectrum, the normalization depends only on the asymptotic values at large distance in the various channels. This is because we are interested only in the coefficient of $\delta(E_f - E_f')$ in the scalar product. Any finite region of space gives a finite contribution and may therefore be disregarded in this calculation. Let us consider two eigenfunctions of energies E_f and E_f' having in the various channels λ incoming and outgoing amplitudes $a_\lambda^{(-)}$, $a_\lambda^{(+)}$, $a_\lambda^{(-)\prime}$, $a_\lambda^{(+)\prime}$, according to (2.52). We can then write for $E_f' \to E_f$

$$(n, E_f|n', E_f') \sim \sum_\lambda \frac{2}{\pi\hbar v_\lambda^{\frac{1}{2}} v_\lambda'^{\frac{1}{2}}} \int^{+\infty} dr\{a_\lambda^{(-)*}a_\lambda^{(-)\prime}\exp[i(k_\lambda - k_\lambda')r] +$$

$$+ a_\lambda^{(+)*}a_\lambda^{(+)\prime}\exp[-i(k_\lambda - k_\lambda')r]\} \sim \sum_\lambda \frac{2}{\pi\hbar v_\lambda^{\frac{1}{2}} v_\lambda'^{\frac{1}{2}}}\left[\frac{a_\lambda^{(-)*}a_\lambda^{(-)\prime}}{k_\lambda - k_\lambda' + i\eta} + \frac{a_\lambda^{(+)*}a_\lambda^{(+)\prime}}{k_\lambda' - k_\lambda + i\eta}\right] ,$$

where η is an infinitely small positive number. This may be written

$$(n, E_f|n', E_f') \sim \frac{2i}{\pi}\sum_\lambda \left[\frac{a_\lambda^{(-)*}a_\lambda^{(-)\prime}}{E_f - E_f' + i\eta} + \frac{a_\lambda^{(+)*}a_\lambda^{(+)\prime}}{E_f' - E_f + i\eta}\right] .$$

As a consequence of the unitarity of the S-matrix

$$\sum_\lambda a_\lambda^{(+)*}a^{(+)\prime} = \sum_\lambda a_\lambda^{(-)*}a_\lambda^{(-)\prime} .$$

Thus

$$(n, E_f|n', E'_f) \sim \frac{2i}{\pi}\left[\frac{1}{E_f - E'_f + i\eta} + \frac{1}{E'_f - E_f + i\eta}\right] \sum_\lambda a_\lambda^{(-)*} a_\lambda^{(-)\prime} = \\ = 4\delta(E_f - E'_f) \sum_\lambda a_\lambda^{(-)*} a_\lambda^{(-)\prime} .$$

We see finally that the orthonormalization condition (4.4) requires for two wave functions of the same energy:

$$\text{(4.6)} \qquad \sum_\lambda a_\lambda^{(-)*} a_\lambda^{(-)\prime} = \tfrac{1}{4}\delta_{nn'} .$$

This may be expressed in terms of the A_λ by using (2.55):

$$\text{(4.7)} \qquad \begin{cases} \sum_\lambda A_\lambda^* A'_\lambda = \delta_{nn'} , & (i\eta), \\ \sum_\lambda (A_\lambda^* A'_\lambda + \pi^2 B_\lambda^* B'_\lambda) = \sum_{\lambda\mu} A_\lambda^*(\lambda|1 + \pi^2 K^2|\mu) A'_\mu = \delta_{nn'} , & (\mathscr{P}), \end{cases}$$

where we have used the relation (2.45) between the A_λ and B_λ.

The construction of a complete system of vectors $A_\lambda^{(n)}$ satisfying one of the conditions (4.7) is now a standard problem. Actually one does not need to do this explicitly since the only combination through which these vectors enter the cross-section formula is

$$\text{(4.8)} \qquad \sum_n A_\lambda^{(n)*} A_\mu^{(n)} = \begin{cases} \delta_{\lambda\mu} & (i\eta), \\ \text{or} \\ = \left(\lambda \left| \dfrac{1}{1 + \pi^2 K^2} \right| \mu\right) & (\mathscr{P}), \end{cases}$$

for the two possible integration conventions.

Let us now return to the explicit construction of the wave function for given A_λ. Its expansion is given by (2.33), where the amplitudes $|1)$ and $|b)$ are obtained in terms of $|A)$ by solving the system (2.35). The solution may be expressed in several equivalent forms, as discussed in the Appendix. We obtain in general

$$\text{(4.9)} \qquad |\Psi) = \mathcal{O}|A) ,$$

where, if we use for instance (A.22) for $|2) = |b)$ and (A.23) for $|1)$

$$\text{(4.10)} \qquad \mathcal{O} = 1 + \frac{1}{E - H_{(2)}^{11}} V_{(2)}^{13} + \frac{1}{E - H_{(1)}^{22}} V_{(1)}^{23} .$$

According to (4.8) the total transition rate (4.1) becomes, for the two integration conventions,

$$(4.11)\qquad \begin{cases} \dfrac{2\pi}{\hbar}(i|Q\mathcal{O}P_3\mathcal{O}^+Q|i) = \dfrac{2\pi}{\hbar}\sum\limits_{\lambda}|(i|Q\mathcal{O}|\lambda\varepsilon_\lambda)|^2 & (i\eta), \\ \dfrac{2\pi}{\hbar}(i|Q\mathcal{O}\dfrac{1}{1+\pi^2K^2}\mathcal{O}^+Q|i) & (\mathscr{P}), \end{cases}$$

where P_3 is the projection operator over the space 3 of the vectors $|A)$.

In a continuation of the work reported at the end of Sect. **3**, GILLET investigated numerically a very simplified model of γ-ray absorption by a nucleus [7]. The model is constructed in such a way as to include two channels and one quasi-bound state (*i.e.* a state in space 1). All wave functions are neutron s-waves. The target is a closed-shell nucleus. The channels consist of a hole coupled with an unbound particle in finite square wells of depth 40 MeV and 60 MeV for channels 1 and 2, respectively. In addition, a quasi-bound particle-hole state at 12 MeV above the threshold for particle emission is included in some calculations. These values as well as all the other constants of the model are chosen of the order of magnitude of actual nuclear data. The precise values are of course quite arbitrary. The radius of the various wells was taken equal to π fermi. The residual two-body force responsible for configuration mixing is a zero-range central force of strength 3 MeV fermi^{-2}. For simplicity, the electromagnetic transition operator is taken of the monopole type. Three different intensities Q_1, Q_2 and Q_B are used for the transitions from ground state to the particle-hole configurations associated with channel 1, channel 2 and the quasi-bound state.

All matrix elements in this model are very simple to evaluate, but they retain nevertheless the characteristic behaviour as functions of the unbound-particle energies which would be found in a more realistic calculation.

The range of the continuous variables ε associated with the two channels is limited to a maximum energy $\mathscr{E}_m$ and divided into equal steps Δ. The numerical calculation was done using again the principal-part convention.

A convergence test on the value of Δ shows that although the cross-section may vary quite rapidly with energy, the step Δ can be chosen quite large (up to 1.5 MeV!). This is due to the fact that the matrix elements, as well as the amplitudes $a_\lambda(\varepsilon)$ are actually slowly varying functions of ε. As for the maximum energy $\mathscr{E}_m$, a value of 31 MeV gives satisfactory results for the K-matrix up to 13 MeV. However, the convergence of the energy integrals which enter the calculation of the transition rate is not so rapid.

The results are summarized on Fig. 5.

a) The dashed curves of Fig. 5.I and 5.II correspond to the presence of the two channels with their nuclear zero-range coupling, but the quasi-bound state is omitted. The intensities Q_1 and Q_2 are set equal. The transition rate T shows no rapid variation. The dashed curve of Fig. 5.III corresponds to the *same nuclear wave functions*, but Q_1 is set equal to zero to simulate the effect of a continuum which mixes in the wave function through nuclear interactions, but has no direct transition matrix element. This only affects the magnitude of the transition rate, but not its variation with energy.

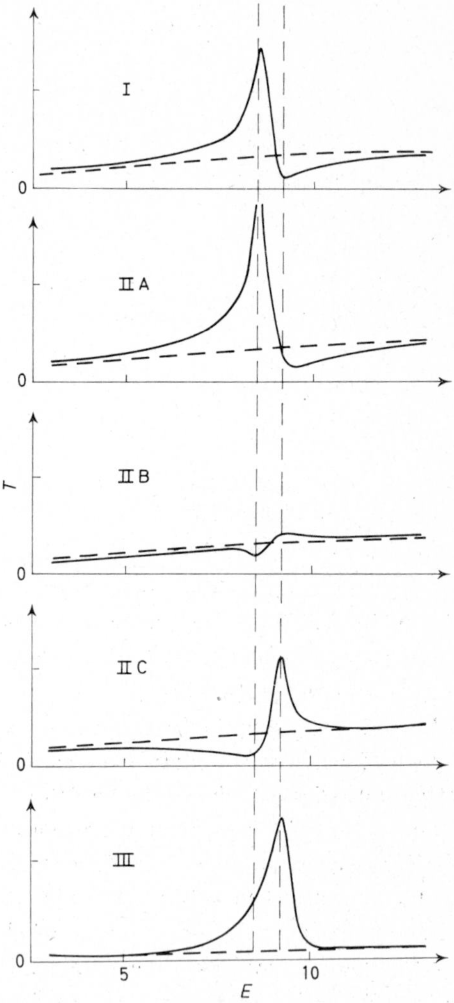

Fig. 5. – The transition rate in arbitrary units as a function of the energy E (in MeV) for various parameters of the model involving two channels and one quasi-bound state.

b) The solid curves of Fig. 5.I, II and III, correspond to the *same nuclear wave functions* including both channels and the bound state mixed by the zero-range interaction. They differ only by the values of Q_B. In Fig. 5.I where $Q_B = 0$, $Q_1 = Q_2 = 1$, the quasi-bound state has no direct transition matrix element. It gives rise nevertheless to a characteristic interference pattern of a resonance coherent with a background. Such an effect is typical of the *strong coupling* of the quasi-bound state with the continuous configurations through the nuclear interaction. The order of magnitude of the coupling is shown by the width of the peaks and dips. In actual cases, a quasi-bound compound state without direct-transition matrix element should be at least of the 2 particle-2 hole type. The expected width of the resulting peaks and dips would be much smaller, namely of the order of magnitude of the residual-force matrix elements between a 2p-2h configuration and an unbound 1p-1h configuration (*i.e.* from about 100 keV for light nuclei to 50 keV for heavy nuclei).

In Fig. 5.II A, B and C, the values of Q_B are 0.03, -0.10 and -0.14

respectively ($Q_1 = Q_2 = 1$). Although the wave functions are unchanged in all three figures, the magnitude of the peak in the transition rate is modified (it may even vanish), and its position is shifted in energy. This behaviour is due to interference effects between the contributions of the continua and of the quasi-bound state.

In Fig. 5.III, $Q_B^{\bar{}} = -0.14$ as in 5.II C, but $Q_1 = 0$. Thus one continuum has no direct transition matrix element; that of the other continuum is much smaller than that of the quasi-bound state. The interference is hardly visible and an almost symmetric peak with no dip is obtained.

The analytic investigation of quasi-bound state will be presented in the next Section. We shall see that the existence of interferences, even in the absence of direct transition to the quasi-bound state can be predicted analytically. The main purpose of Gillet's calculation was to test the possibility of a numerical analysis of such problems. A realistic calculation of the giant resonance in ^{16}O along the same lines has been done at UCLA by M. MELKANOFF, J. RAYNAL and S. SAWADA. It will be reported in a seminar by M. MELKANOFF.

5. – Resonances.

Resonances in the cross-sections are associated with compound nucleus levels. These are, of course, automatically included into the exact expressions given in previous Sections. If we wish, however, to derive approximate analytic expressions which exhibit the behaviour of a resonance, we are led to distinguish two kinds of resonances.

The first type of compound states is provided by the eigenstates of H^{11} which lie in the continuum. These are discrete bound states, but their coupling with continuum states through the interaction V will produce an energy shift and introduce a width. If the coupling is weak, the wave function for such a state may be pictured as consisting essentially of the bound eigenstate of H^{11} plus some small components in the open channels.

On the other hand, the single-particle wave functions in the continuum have virtual levels which may be relatively narrow particularly if there is a large potential barrier. These single-particle virtual levels will show up in the cross-sections as resonances of a second kind, in which the wave function consists mainly of an unbound particle in a virtual state and an almost unperturbed residual nucleus.

The resonances of the first kind correspond to the usual picture of a compound nucleus, whereas the second kind corresponds more to a giant-resonance behaviour. In an actual situation, the two kinds may of course be superimposed and interferences will take place.

It is easy to study the behaviour of the cross-sections in the neighbourhood of a level of H^{11}, and thus to derive the equivalent of the one-level Breit-Wigner expressions. With only a small additional care in writing the equations, it is actually easy to derive the many-level formulae.

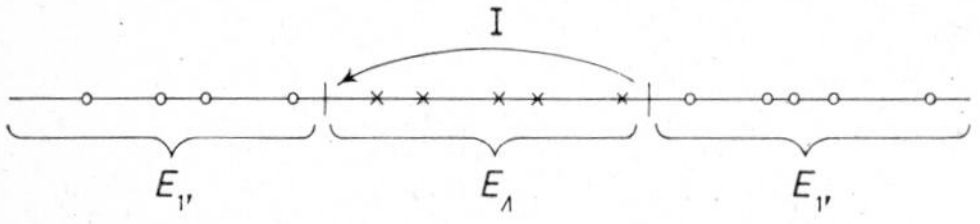

Fig. 6. – Energy levels of H^{11}.

Let us therefore consider (Fig. 6) the set of eigenvalues E_Λ of H^{11} contained in some energy interval I. The eigenfunctions associated with the E_Λ span a subspace which we shall denote by (Λ). The other eigenvalues $E_{1'}$, span an orthogonal subspace say $(1')$. An arbitrary eigenfunction of the complete Hamiltonian may now be split into four components:

$$|\Psi) = |\Lambda) + |1') + |b) + |A)\,, \tag{5.1}$$

instead of 3 as in (2.33). We must then replace (2.35) by

$$\begin{cases} (H^{\Lambda\Lambda} - E)|\Lambda) + V^{\Lambda 2}|b) = -V^{\Lambda 3}|A)\,, \\ (H^{1'1'} - E)|1') + V^{1'2}|b) = -V^{1'3}|A)\,, \\ V^{2\Lambda}|\Lambda) + V^{21'}|1') + (H^{22} - E)|b) = -V^{23}|A)\,. \end{cases} \tag{5.2}$$

Note that (*)

$$H^{\Lambda 1'} = H^{1'\Lambda} = 0\,, \tag{5.3}$$

as a consequence of the definition of the subspaces Λ and $1'$ of 1 by eigenfunctions of H^{11}.

The only difference between (5.2) and (2.35) is the splitting of 1 into $1'$ and Λ. The elimination procedure requires therefore an additional step, but the result may be written in complete analogy with (2.46):

$$K = V^{33}_{(1'2\Lambda)}\,. \tag{5.4}$$

From the Appendix we know that the order of the eliminations given by the lower subscripts is irrelevant. For obtaining explicitly the dependence associated with the states Λ, it is most convenient to perform the elimination of Λ last. Thus we write

$$K = V^{33}_{(1'2)} + V^{3\Lambda}_{(1'2)} \frac{1}{E - H^{\Lambda\Lambda}_{(1'2)}} V^{\Lambda 3}_{(1'2)}\,, \tag{5.5}$$

(*) It should be pointed out that $H_0^{1'\Lambda}$ and $H_0^{\Lambda 1'}$ do not in general vanish. Thus in (5.10) for i or $j = \Lambda$ it is necessary to use $H^{i1'}$ or $H^{1'i}$ instead of the usual $V^{i1'}$ or $V^{1'i}$.

where

$$H^{AA}_{(1'2)} = H^{AA} + V^{A2}\frac{1}{E - H^{22}_{(1')}}V^{2A}, \tag{5.6}$$

and

$$V^{ij}_{(1'2)} = V^{ij}_{(1')} + V^{i2}_{(1')}\frac{1}{E - H^{22}_{(1')}}V^{2j}_{(1')} \qquad (i, j = A, 3). \tag{5.7}$$

Here we have taken into account that

$$H^{AA}_{(1')} = H^{AA}, \qquad V^{A2}_{(1')} = V^{A2}, \qquad V^{2A}_{(1')} = V^{2A}, \tag{5.8}$$

as a consequence of (5.3). Finally, the quantities with lower index $1'$ are given by

$$H^{22}_{(1')} = H^{22} + V^{21'}\frac{1}{E - H^{1'1'}}V^{1'2} \tag{5.9}$$

and

$$V^{ij}_{(1')} = H^{ij} + V^{i1'}\frac{1}{E - H^{1'1'}}H^{1'j} \qquad (i, j = A, 2, 3). \tag{5.10}$$

The idea of the one- or many-level formula is that the levels $1'$ are sufficiently far from the considered energy interval that they do not give any rapidly varying denominator in (5.9) and (5.10). Similarly the energy interval is supposed to be sufficiently small that all quantities associated with the continuum 2 vary very little. Thus all quantities with lower indices $1'$ or $1'$ and 2 are slowly varying, and the only rapid variation of K comes from the denominators appearing in (5.5).

From K we must still derive the S-matrix. This is particularly simple with the $i\eta$ convention, according to (2.56) and (2.57). Then

$$\bar{S} = 1 - 2i\pi V^{33}_{(1'2)} - 2i\pi V^{3A}_{(1'2)}\frac{1}{E - H^{AA}_{(1'2)}}V^{A3}_{(1'2)}, \tag{5.11}$$

where

$$H^{AA}_{(1'2)} = H^{AA} + V^{A2}\frac{1}{E - H^{22}_{(1')} + i\eta}V^{2A}. \tag{5.12}$$

Similarly, in (5.7) E must be replaced in the denominator by $E + i\eta$.

The interpretation of (5.11) and (5.12) is particularly simple in the one-level case. Then H^{AA} is a pure number

$$H^{AA} = E_A + \Delta E_A - i\Gamma_A/2, \tag{5.13}$$

where the level shift ΔE_Λ and the width Γ_Λ are given by

(5.14)
$$\begin{cases} \Delta E_\Lambda = V^{\Lambda 2} \dfrac{\mathscr{P}}{E - H^{22}_{(1')}} V^{2\Lambda}, \\[2ex] \Gamma_\Lambda = 2\pi V^{\Lambda 2} \delta(E - H^{22}_{(1')}) V^{2\Lambda}. \end{cases}$$

In the expression for ΔE_Λ, $\mathscr{P}$ stands for the principal part.

Let us now define a vector of the channel space 3 by writing

(5.15)
$$\sqrt{2\pi}\, V^{\Lambda 3}_{(1'2)} = \boldsymbol{G}_\Lambda,$$

where the factor $\sqrt{2\pi}$ is introduced to conform to the standard notations. We obtain then the usual Breit-Wigner one-level formula:

(5.16)
$$\bar{S} = 1 - 2i\pi V^{33}_{(1'2)} - i\, \frac{\boldsymbol{G}^*_\Lambda \times \boldsymbol{G}_\Lambda}{E - E_\Lambda - \Delta E_\Lambda + i\Gamma_\Lambda/2}.$$

The first term in this expression gives the potential scattering, the second term is the resonant amplitude.

Explicitly, the partial-width amplitudes defined by (5.15) are given by

(5.17)
$$G^\lambda_\Lambda = \sqrt{2\pi}\,(\Lambda|V_{(1'2)}|\lambda\varepsilon_\lambda) = \sqrt{2\pi}\,\Big(\Lambda\Big|V + V\, \frac{P_2}{E - H^{22}_{(1')} + i\eta}\, V_{(1')}\Big|\lambda\varepsilon_\lambda\Big).$$

Here P_2 is the projection operator over the subspace 2. We have used the relations (5.7) with $i = \Lambda$, $j = 3$ and

(5.18)
$$V^{\Lambda 3}_{(1')} = V^{\Lambda 3},$$

which follows from (5.3) (compare with (5.8)).

In order to obtain a more explicit form of the total width Γ_Λ, we shall express the δ-function occurring in (5.14) in the same way as (4.3) in Sect. **4**. Thus we must look for a system of solutions of

(5.19)
$$H^{22}_{(1')}|nE) = E|nE),$$

orthonormalized as

(5.20)
$$(nE|n'E') = \delta_{nn'} \cdot \delta(E - E').$$

The same argument as in Sect. **4** yields, using the $i\eta$ convention,

(5.21)
$$|nE) = \sum_\lambda \mathcal{O}|\lambda\varepsilon_\lambda) A^{(n)}_\lambda,$$

where

$$\mathcal{O} = 1 + \frac{1}{E - H^{22}_{(1')} + i\eta} V^{23}_{(1')} \tag{5.22}$$

and the $A^{(n)}_\lambda$ are the components of any set of vectors orthonormalized according to

$$\sum_\lambda A^{(n)*}_\lambda A^{(n')}_\lambda = \delta_{nn'} . \tag{5.23}$$

The reduced width (5.14) takes then the form

$$\Gamma_\Lambda = 2\pi \sum_n |(\Lambda|V|nE)|^2. \tag{5.24}$$

As a particular solution of (5.23), we may choose

$$A^{(n)}_\lambda = \delta^n_\lambda = \begin{cases} 1 & \text{if } n = \lambda , \\ 0 & \text{if } n \neq \lambda . \end{cases}$$

Then (5.24) becomes, taking into account (5.21) and (5.22),

$$\Gamma_\Lambda = 2\pi \sum_\lambda \left| (\Lambda|V\left[1 + \frac{1}{E - H^{22}_{(1')} + i\eta} V^{23}_{(1')}\right] |\lambda\varepsilon_\lambda) \right|^2 ,$$

and by comparing with the expression (5.17) of the partial width amplitudes, we obtain the usual relation

$$\Gamma_\Lambda = \sum_\lambda |G^\lambda_\Lambda|^2. \tag{5.25}$$

This could also be derived from the unitarity condition of (5.16).

It should be noted that (5.17) and (5.25) give a way to calculate the widths occurring in the Breit-Wigner formula provided one knows the wave functions of the compound state $|\Lambda)$ and of the residual nucleus corresponding to the various channels.

It should be remembered that the G_Λ as well as ΔE_λ and Γ_Λ are energy-dependent. Thus the expression (5.16) will really exhibit a resonance of width Γ_Λ only if the variation of these quantities is small over an energy range of the order of Γ_Λ.

It is finally interesting to note that the usual penetration factor (and the associated reduced partial widths) do not appear explicitly in this formulation. The effects of potential barriers are implicitly introduced by the single-particle functions $\varphi_{n\varepsilon}(r)$ occurring in $|\lambda\varepsilon_\lambda)$. These functions are normalized at infinity. On the other hand, the main contributions to the integrals in (5.17) come from the internal region. The ratio of the functions $\varphi_{n\varepsilon}(r)$ in the internal and external regions depends precisely on the penetration of the potential barriers. It is, of course, an advantage not to have to introduce explicitly the penetration factors which depend on a nuclear radius and are therefore not well defined.

In the many-level case, $H^{\Lambda\Lambda}_{(1'2)}$ is a matrix and the inversion implied in (5.11) is no longer trivial. For a small number of levels it may still be carried out explicitly. For a large number of levels, it is possible to introduce statistical assumptions. This yields the Breit-Wigner many-level formula as in the standard formal theories of nuclear reactions.

The same type of problems may be treated in very much the same way in the case of γ-ray absorption. Let us use for simplicity the expression (4.11) with the $i\eta$ convention. The operator $\mathcal{O}$ is obtained from the solution (A.21) for a system with $n=3$ subspaces: Λ, $1'$, 2. In order to exhibit the rapid dependence introduced by the states of subspace Λ, we perform the elimination of Λ as the last step. Using the order $1'$, 2, Λ, we obtain readily

$$\mathcal{O} = \mathscr{A}^3 + \mathscr{A}^\Lambda \frac{1}{E - H^{\Lambda\Lambda}_{(1'2)}} V^{\Lambda 3}_{(1'2)}\,, \tag{5.26}$$

where, for $i = 3, \Lambda$,

$$\mathscr{A}^i = 1 + \frac{1}{E - H^{1'1'}} V^{1'2} \frac{1}{E - H^{22}_{(1')} + i\eta} V^{2i}_{(1')} + \frac{1}{E - H^{1'1'}} H^{1'i} + \\ + \frac{1}{E - H^{22}_{(1')} + i\eta} V^{2i}_{(1')}\,. \tag{5.27}$$

The operators $\mathscr{A}^3$ and $\mathscr{A}^\Lambda$ are slowly varying with energy; the rapid variations come only from the factor $1/(E - H^{\Lambda\Lambda}_{(1'2)})$ in (5.26). Substitution of (5.26) into the first expression (4.11) gives for the transition rate

$$\frac{2\pi}{\hbar} \sum_\lambda \left| (i|Q \left[\mathscr{A}^3 + \mathscr{A}^\Lambda \frac{1}{E - H^{\Lambda\Lambda}_{(1'2)}} V_{(1'2)} \right] |\lambda\varepsilon_\lambda) \right|^2 . \tag{5.28}$$

The term in $\mathscr{A}^3$ gives a nonresonant amplitude, whereas the term in $\mathscr{A}^\Lambda$ gives a resonant term. These amplitudes add coherently, and the resonances will therefore have the same characteristic aspect as in elastic scattering. This appears very clearly on Fig. 5.

6. – Optical model, giant resonances, intermediate resonances.

6·1. *Introduction.* – The method described so far gives a satisfactory description when the number of shell-model configurations around the energy under consideration is not too large. It is then in principle conceivable to take them all into account. At higher energy, particularly in heavy nuclei, this becomes meaningless. Fortunately, many experimental results have shown that in such cases it often turns out that a relatively small number of particular simple states of the system play a dominant role. The remaining states may produce rapid fluctuations of the cross-sections—a fine structure which may be disregarded at first, or perhaps treated in a statistical way. If the density of these complicated states is high, the fluctuations which they produce may average out. The cross-sections will then be smooth and differ rather little from the predictions obtained from considering only the simple states. Most of the difference may be accounted for by the introduction of a complex potential representing the damping of the simple states, *i.e.* their dissolution into more complicated states.

A typical example of such a situation is provided by the single-particle resonances appearing in neutron elastic-scattering cross-sections. In medium or heavy nuclei, an incoming neutron of a few MeV can give rise to many compound states. It turns out, however, that the states equal simply to the product of the ground-state wave function of the target nucleus by single-particle wave functions of the incoming nucleon in the average shell-model potential play the dominant role. The effect of the other possible nuclear states is very well described, at least as regards the smooth part of the cross-sections, by including an additional complex potential.

WEISSKOPF [11] has recently extended this optical-model picture by considering more systematically the formation of compound states in the shell-model description. Let us take, for simplicity, a closed-shell nucleus whose ground-state wave function may be well represented by a single Slater determinant,

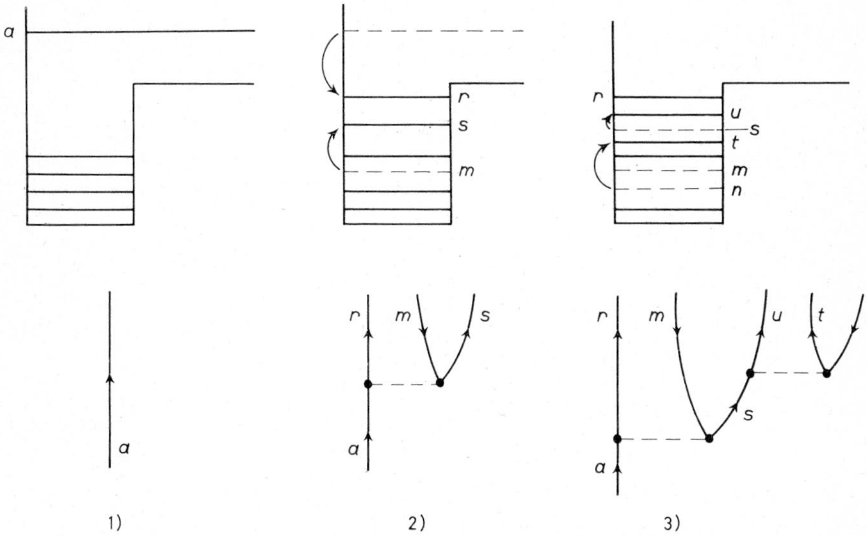

Fig. 7. – Formation of a compound state by successive interactions in the collision of a nucleon with a closed-shell nucleus.

bombarded by a nucleon. It is convenient to take the target ground-state wave function as reference state in a Feynman-diagram representation. In the first step (the only one which is treated in detail in the optical model) the wave function is simply a product of the ground-state wave function and the incoming wave function distorted by the shell-model potential. In Feynman-diagram language, this is a one-particle configuration (Fig. 7.1). In the second step towards the formation of a compound state, the two-body interaction will act: the incoming nucleon will go over to another single particle state, and a nucleon from the target will be excited to some empty single-particle state (Fig. 7.2). A 2 particle-1 hole configuration is thus produced. Further two-body interactions will produce more and more complicated configurations: 3p-2h, 4p-3h, ... In the optical model, all steps beyond the 1-particle configuration are treated only in a statistical manner in terms of a complex potential.

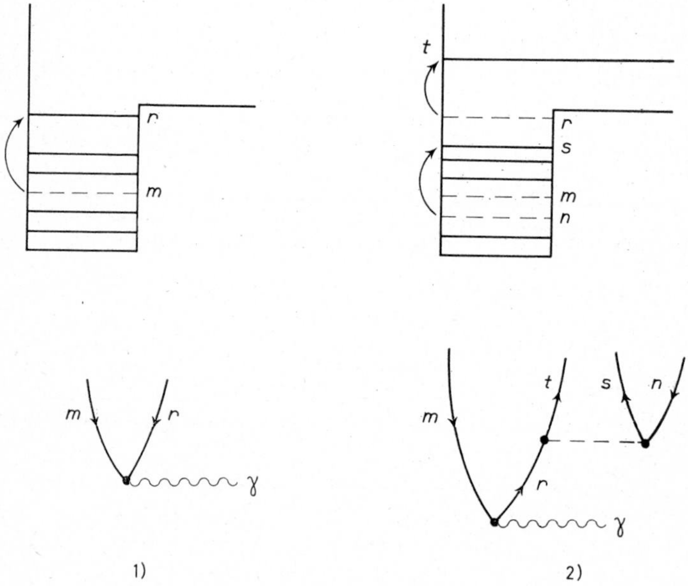

Fig. 8. – Formation of a compound state by successive interactions after the absorption of a γ-ray by a closed-shell nucleus.

In very much the same way, the absorption of a γ-ray by a closed-shell nucleus may be pictured as a succession of steps involving 1p-1h configurations, then 2p-2h configurations, and so on (Fig. 8).

This introduces the important idea of a *hierarchy of configurations*. Clearly, more and more complicated configurations have higher and higher energies.

Thus at a given energy, configurations up to a certain order of complication only can be of importance.

It is naturally essential to discuss the effect of the coupling between configurations due to the nuclear interactions. Usually, the coupling is stronger between configurations of the same order in the hierarchy than between configurations of a different order. It is then reasonable to treat exactly the interactions between configurations up to a certain type, and to treat only statistically their interactions with more complicated configurations. The interactions within configurations of a given type may produce very drastic effects. For instance, in the case of γ-ray absorption, the interactions between 1p-1h configurations give rise to a coherent state of considerably modified energy, which is responsible for the giant photonuclear resonance. It is naturally these states resulting from the diagonalization of the Hamiltonian within the subspace of a certain kind of configurations which play an important role in the cross-sections, rather than the basic configurations themselves.

The coupling of such a state with more complicated configurations, when treated statistically will give rise to a broadening of the state, corresponding to a decrease of its lifetime through dissolution into more complicated configurations. Clearly this broadening should not be so large as to make all states of the same family overlap in such a way that the resulting structure is completely averaged out. This introduces a limitation to the possibility of observing the resonances associated with a certain kind of states.

Finally, another important factor in the observability of a certain state is the magnitude of its coupling with the incoming or outgoing channels. For instance, the coherent 1p-1h state mentioned above has a very large $E1$ transition matrix element which explains the magnitude of its contribution to photonuclear reaction cross-sections.

It is now possible to give a more precise definition of a dominant state (or « doorway state » in the terminology of FESHBACH *et al.*, or « dangerous state » in the terminology of MIGDAL). It is a wave function which has the property of being relatively strongly coupled to the channels of the reaction, but relatively weakly coupled to the other wave functions of the system. It must be sufficiently isolated from other states having the same properties in order to give rise to a relatively isolated peak in the cross-section. These states are of course not exact eigenstates of the Hamiltonian. They are, however, usually defined as eigenstates of the restriction of the Hamiltonian to a sufficiently small subspace to give rise to a numerically soluble eigenvalue problem. Since the dominant states must be weakly coupled to other states, they are approximate eigenstates of the complete Hamiltonian.

It is interesting to notice that there is a kind of continuity between light and heavy nuclei concerning simple states. In light nuclei, these simple states are really the compound states. In heavy nuclei, the compound states are, so to say, much deeper, but the simple states should remain apparent as a gross structure of cross-sections.

6·2. *Classification of subspaces.* – These ideas may easily be discussed within the framework introduced in the previous Sections. The neglect of three- and more-body channels although it is not so justified when the energy increases, does not prevent the discussion of such typically many-body aspects of the theory.

The amount of formal machinery exhibited below is perhaps excessive in comparison with what has actually been achieved with it. It may nevertheless help to clarify the concepts involved in this kind of discussion.

The introduction of a hierarchy amounts to dividing the subspaces 1, 2, 3 of Sect. **2** (see eq. (2.33)) into smaller subspaces which we shall denote n', n'' and n''', respectively with $n = 0, 1, 2, \dots$. In this notation, n stands for the hierarchic rank, the number of dashes recalls the particular subspace, 1, 2 or 3. Thus,

$$|1) = \sum_n |n') , \qquad |b) = \sum_n |n'') , \qquad |A) = \sum_n |n''') . \tag{6.1}$$

The meaning of n may depend on the problem. In the simplest case of a closed-shell nucleus bombarded by a nucleon, already mentioned above, (n) will denote the subspace of the $n+1$ particle-n hole configurations. In the case of the γ-ray absorption by a closed-shell nucleus, n will denote the subspace of the n particle-n hole configurations. Some value of n may also be used to denote a particular state belonging to one of these subspaces. For instance, the coherent dipole state, superposition of 1p-1h configurations, could be considered as one of the subspaces n. Thus there exists a considerable flexibility in the choice of a hierarchy appropriate to each particular situation.

The components of $|1)$ into subspaces of given rank may be written (compare with (2.6))

$$|n') = \sum_{\alpha \in (n)} |\alpha) a(\alpha) , \tag{6.2}$$

where the summation is extended only to the configurations of rank n, as indicated by the symbol $\alpha \in (n)$.

The decomposition of $|A)$ into hierarchic components is a little less obvious. It requires the substitution into the expansion (2.34) of the decomposition (2.20) of $|\lambda\varepsilon)$ into components $|\beta\varepsilon)$ having a natural hierarchy: in the case of a closed shell target nucleus, $|\beta\varepsilon)$ is of rank n when β is a n particle-n hole configuration. Thus we have

$$|n''') = \sum_{\beta \in (n)} \sum_{\lambda} |\beta\varepsilon_\lambda) u_\lambda(\beta) A_\lambda . \tag{6.3}$$

Similarly, the hierarchic components of $|b)$ read

$$|n'') = \sum_{\beta\in(n)} \sum_{\lambda} \mathop{\int\!\!\!\!\!\!\sum} \mathrm{d}\varepsilon |\beta\varepsilon) u_\lambda(\beta) b(\lambda\varepsilon) , \tag{6.4}$$

$$= \sum_{\beta\in(n)} \mathop{\int\!\!\!\!\!\!\sum} \mathrm{d}\varepsilon |\beta\varepsilon) b(\beta\varepsilon) . \tag{6.5}$$

In the second form of this decomposition, we have introduced the components of $|b)$ in the basis β according to (2.17):

$$b(\beta\varepsilon) = \sum_{\lambda} b(\lambda\varepsilon) u_\lambda(\beta) . \tag{6.6}$$

It should of course be remembered that the $b(\beta\varepsilon)$ have singularities at all ε_λ whereas each $b(\lambda\varepsilon)$ has only one singularity at $\varepsilon = \varepsilon_\lambda$.

It may be added that for the ground state and the first excited states of the residual nucleus, configuration mixing is much less important than for the compound states described by the subspace 1. Thus it is possible, in first approximation to represent the states of the residual nucleus by pure shell-model configurations. The ground state then has the pure hierarchic rank 0.

The justification for the introduction of a hierarchy of configurations lies in the fact that although configurations of the same rank may be strongly coupled together, the interactions between configurations of different rank are weak and occur mainly when the ranks differ by one unit only. When the rank is defined by the number of particles and holes, two-body interactions couple configurations with a difference of rank up to two, but its seems that in most cases the dominant couplings occur when the difference is only one. All of this should be considered only as qualitative indications. It does not seem that the experience gained so far in the evaluation of matrix elements has been sufficient to exhibit reliable general rules. Anyway, we shall assume, as an example that all matrix elements other than

$$V^{(n)(n+1)}, \qquad V^{(n)(n)}, \qquad V^{(n+1)(n)}, \tag{6.7}$$

may be neglected.

The system of eq. (2.35), when hierarchy is introduced, reads then

$$\begin{cases} \sum_m [(H-E)^{n'm'}|m') + V^{n'm''}|m'')] = -\sum_m V^{n'm'''}|m''') , \\ \sum_m [V^{n''m'}|m') + (H-E)^{n''m''}|m'')] = -\sum_m V^{n''m'''}|m''') . \end{cases} \tag{6.8}$$

Substitution of (6.3) and (6.4) or (6.5) into these equations yields a system of linear equations for the amplitudes $a(\alpha)$ and $b(\lambda\varepsilon)$ or $b(\beta\varepsilon)$. In (6.8) the summations over m are extended only to three values:

$$m = n - 1\,, \quad n\,, \quad n + 1\,.$$

In order to take full advantage of the vanishing of matrix elements due to hierarchy, it is convenient to treat together the components of subspaces 1 and 2 having the same hierarchic rank. Thus we shall consider the total component of the wave function, off the energy shell and of rank n, and denote it simply by

$$|n) = |n') + |n'')\,. \tag{6.9}$$

The eq. (6.8) may then be rewritten in the simpler form

$$(H^{nn} - E)|n) + \sum_{m=n\pm1} V^{nm}|m) = -\sum_{m=n-1}^{n+1} V^{nm'''}|m''')\,. \tag{6.10}$$

Such a system could be treated numerically for specific problems. For a general discussion, we may again use the algorithm described in the Appendix. The problem here is the elimination of all hierarchic components $|n)$ of space $1+2$ and the evaluation of the matrix elements of the resulting $V_{(A\dots0)}$ between states of the subspaces $|n''')$ corresponding to the energy shell. Indeed, according to (2.46), (2.20), (6.1) and (6.3) the elements of the matrix K are given by

$$(\mu|K|\lambda) = (\mu\varepsilon_\mu|V_{(A\dots0)}|\lambda\varepsilon_\lambda) = \sum_{\beta,\gamma} (\gamma\varepsilon_\mu|V_{(A\dots0)}|\beta\varepsilon_\lambda)\, u_\mu^*(\gamma)\, u_\lambda(\beta)\,. \tag{6.11}$$

The matrix elements occurring in the right-hand side are precisely those of $V_{(A\dots0)}$ between states $|n''')$. Symbolically we must therefore evaluate

$$V_{(A\dots0)}^{n'''m'''}\,. \tag{6.12}$$

This may be done systematically by using recursion relations of the type (A.9) or (2.39 and 40).

6'3. *Average cross-sections.* – When cross-sections fluctuate rapidly due to the presence of many compound-nucleus resonances, it is interesting to eliminate this fine structure and to extract the gross structure by considering the cross-sections averaged over some energy interval I:

$$\bar{\sigma}(E) = \frac{1}{I}\int\limits_{E-I/2}^{E+I/2} \sigma(E')\,\mathrm{d}E'\,.$$

Actually it is even more interesting to separate this cross-section in two terms.

The first term is obtained by averaging the S-matrix itself:

$$\bar{S}(E) = \frac{1}{I} \int_{E-I/2}^{E+I/2} S(E')\,\mathrm{d}E' .$$

The average cross-section is proportional to the average of the square of S-matrix elements:

$$\bar{\sigma}(E) \sim \overline{|S|^2} .$$

It may be written

$$\bar{\sigma} = \sigma_i + \sigma_r ,$$

where

$$\sigma_i \sim |\bar{S}|^2 ,$$

$$\sigma_r \sim \overline{|S|^2} - |\bar{S}|^2 .$$

This would be entirely artificial if WEISSKOPF had not given the interpretation of σ_i and σ_r: σ_i is the instantaneous reaction cross-section, σ_r is the compound-reaction cross-section. Thus it is natural to expect a theory describing only the first steps of a reaction to reproduce only σ_i. Compound states are narrow and therefore long-lived: they contribute only to σ_r. Of course, σ_i is not really an instantaneous cross-section. If refers to the part of a wave packet which has only a small delay, of the order of

$$\tau \sim \hbar / I .$$

Thus by varying I, one may investigate various delays and therefore by taking I smaller and smaller observe further and further steps towards the formation of compound nuclear states. This is the idea of intermediate resonances [12]. With a very large I, one should observe only the ordinary giant resonances. By reducing I finer resonances should appear. There could perhaps exist several such structures before the ultimate compound nuclear states appear.

The calculation of σ_i, *i.e.* of $\bar{S}(E)$ is considerably simplified by an old remark of THOMAS [1]. As a consequence of the analyticity of $S(E)$ for ordinary values of the energy (that is, not at a threshold), it is easy to see that

$$\bar{S}(E) = S(E + i\Delta) , \tag{6.13}$$

where Δ is a positive quantity of the order of magnitude of I. Since the S-matrix has poles below the real axis at energies

$$E_s - i\Gamma_s/2 ,$$

where E_s are the compound nuclear levels, it is clear that going above the real axis according to (6.13) gives a smoother and smoother function when Δ increases. The problem of intermediate structures is therefore to investigate if several successive structures appear when Δ goes to zero, starting from a sufficiently large value. I do not think that the answer to this question is known as yet in general.

6·4. *Theory of intermediate resonances* [12]. – In order to exhibit resonances associated with dominant states, we should evaluate the quantities (6.12) by treating exactly all subspaces containing the configurations giving rise to the dominant state and leading to it with large transition amplitudes from initial and final states. The other configurations should on the other hand be treated statistically. For showing the general mechanism of this procedure, let us group together all subspaces to be treated exactly into (d stands for « direct »)

$$|d) = |0) + |1) + \dots + |q) , \tag{6.14}$$

and those to be treated statistically into (c stands for « compound »)

$$|c) = |q+1) + |q+2) + \dots + |A) . \tag{6.15}$$

The components (6.14) correspond to the direct, or relatively direct part of the reaction; (6.15) to the compound part. With this new notation, (6.12) reads

$$V^{n'''m'''}_{(cd)} .$$

Let us now use again the elimination formula, eliminating (d) after (c). With the $i\eta$ convention we have (when E is replaced by $E+i\Delta$, η is replaced by Δ)

$$V^{n'''m'''}_{(cd)} = V^{n'''m'''}_{(c)} + V^{n'''d}_{(c)} \frac{1}{E - H_0^{dd} - V^{dd}_{(c)} + i\eta} V^{dm'''}_{(c)} \tag{6.16}$$

and

$$V^{ij}_{(c)} = V^{ij} + V^{ic} \frac{1}{E - H_0^{cc} - V^{cc} + i\eta} V^{cj} , \qquad (i, j = n''', m''', d). \tag{6.17}$$

Simplifications occur as a consequence of the hierarchic selection rule of V for

$$n''' \leqslant q - 1 , \qquad m''' \leqslant q - 1 . \tag{6.18}$$

If one neglects for simplicity the components in the initial and final states of rank higher than $q-1$, then

$$V^{n'''c} = V^{cm'''} = 0 ,$$

and (6.16) reduces to

$$V_{(cd)}^{n'''m'''} = V^{n'''m'''} + V^{n'''d} \frac{1}{E - H_0^{dd} - V_{(c)}^{dd} + i\eta} V^{dm'''}, \tag{6.19}$$

$$V_{(c)}^{dd} = V^{dd} + V^{dc} \frac{1}{E - H_0^{cc} - V^{cc} + i\eta} V^{cd}. \tag{6.20}$$

Again, as a consequence of selection rules on the rank, the coupling V^{dc} between spaces (d) and (c) occurs only between the components of rank q and $q+1$. Thus in space (d), the interactions of the various configurations are the straightforward two-body interactions, except for the configurations of highest rank q which may dissolve into compound states.

So far all relations are purely formal. *The essential approximation now is to treat the coupling of* (d) *with compound states*, represented by the last term of (6.20), *in a statistical way*. Here we shall begin to step on very much less solid ground.

First of all, we may want to investigate the qualitative nature of the approximation. The restricted Hamiltonian $H^{cc} = H_0^{cc} + V^{cc}$ has been truncated only of a relatively small number of its dimensions. It has still very many eigenvalues, practically of the same density as the complete Hamiltonian. Let us denote by

$$|s) \qquad \text{and} \qquad E_s + i\Gamma_s/2\,,$$

the eigenstates and eigenvalues of H^{cc}. They have a width since space (c) includes part of the continuum space (2) of Sect. **2**. This allows the direct escape of a nucleon from a state of space (c). We may then write

$$V_{(c)}^{dd} = V^{dd} + \sum_s \frac{V^{dc}|s)(s|V^{cd}}{E - E_s + i\Gamma_s/2}\,. \tag{6.21}$$

If the widths Γ are not large with respect to the level spacing D, this will show a succession of peaks, as a function of E. However, if we replace E by $E + i\Delta$, with $\Delta \gg D$, the denominator becomes a smooth function of E_s and E. If the widths are such that $\Gamma_s \gg D$, this happens already for $\Delta = 0$. In any case, (6.21) is then a smooth function of E, and an averaging of the matrix elements over s takes place. It becomes reasonable to assume that the signs of the matrix elements of V between a given state $|q)$ of (d) and successive states $|s)$ are randomly distributed. This is particularly justified because the state $|q)$ is relatively simple whereas the states $|s)$ are very complicated: they are of the same complication as compound states. Under this assumption, the nondiagonal elements of the second term of (6.21) become negligible. The diagonal terms for a state $|q)$ of $|d)$ are approximately equal to

$$(6.22)\qquad W_q \approx \sum_s \frac{|(q|V|s)|^2}{E-E_s+i\Gamma_s/2} \approx \frac{|(q|V|s)|^2_{\mathrm{Av}}}{D}\int\frac{\mathrm{d}E_s}{E-E_s+i\Gamma_s/2} = -\frac{i\pi}{D}|(q|V|s)|^2_{\mathrm{Av}}\,.$$

The result is therefore that the configurations $|q)$ of the highest rank treated exactly are undergoing an additional imaginary potential, representing the dissolution of the state into more complicated configurations.

This argument is an exact transposition of that used a long time ago to justify the optical model [4]. It reduces to the old argument if one takes for (d) only the subspace $|0)$ of the 1-particle configurations.

The expression (6.22) does not yield easily numerical values since the states $|s)$ cannot be determined without solving the full Schrödinger equation. Numerical estimates so far, have been made by considering the first step of the dissolution of $|q)$, *i.e.* the transition to a state $|q+1)$.

It is easy to write formal expressions describing all the successive steps of the formation of the compound state. Returning to more explicit notations, we may write the effective Hamiltonian for the configurations $|q)$ in the form

$$H^{qq}_{(A\ldots q+1)}\,.$$

We can then apply the elimination formulae. It is easy to see that considerable simplifications occur when the elimination is carried out in the hierarchic order, starting from the highest rank: $A, A-1, \ldots, q+1$. The formulae reduce then to the relation

$$(6.23)\qquad H^{qq}_{(A\ldots q+1)} = H^{qq} + V^{q,q+1}\frac{1}{E-H^{q+1,q+1}_{(A\ldots q+2)}+i\eta}V^{q+1,q},$$

and to similar ones obtained by replacing q by $q+1, q+2, \ldots, A-1$.

Danos and Greiner [13] have recently made a numerical estimate of the damping of the giant dipole resonance in heavy nuclei by neglecting all steps of the dissolution beyond the first one. The dipole state is an eigenstate in the 1p-1h configuration space ($q=1$ with the present notations). The damping results from the formation of 2p-2h states ($q=2$) as a first step. If all further steps are omitted, the relation (6.23) with $q=1$ is replaced by

$$(6.24)\qquad H^{11}_{(A\ldots 2)} = H^{11} + V^{12}\frac{1}{E-H^{22}+i\eta}V^{21}\,.$$

Of course, interactions between the 2 particles and 2 holes are neglected: H^{22} is replaced by H^{22}_0. For $A\approx 200$, there are hundreds of 2p-2h configurations at the energy of the giant resonance. These states have a width due to particle emission, as mentioned above. It turns out to be sufficiently large to make the levels overlap. Thus there is no need to introduce a Δ even if one takes into account only the first step; (6.24) is smooth right away. This means that for $A \approx 200$ it is out of question to observe a structure due to 2p-2h states superimposed on the giant resonance. The value obtained for the imaginary potential W is $0.25\ \text{MeV} \leqslant W \leqslant 1.25\ \text{MeV}$. The uncertainty in this value comes mostly from the uncertainty in the strength of the interaction.

Experimental evidence concerning the existence of intermediate structure in photonuclear reactions is discussed in a seminar by Dr. E. HAYWARD.

6·5. *Diagram representation.* – It may be worth while finally to mention that the relations of the type (6.23) have a very simple interpretation in terms of Feynman diagrams [14] (Fig. 9). With the present notation, the one-particle propagator (Fig. 9*a*) reads

$$\frac{1}{E - H^{00}_{(A...1)}}\,. \tag{6.25}$$

As is well known, the diagrams of Fig. 8*a* may be analysed into proper parts (Fig. 9*b*), corresponding to the mass operator which reads with the present notations $V^{00}_{(A...1)}$. We recall that

$$H^{00}_{(A...1)} = H^{00}_{0} + V^{00}_{(A...1)}\,. \tag{6.26}$$

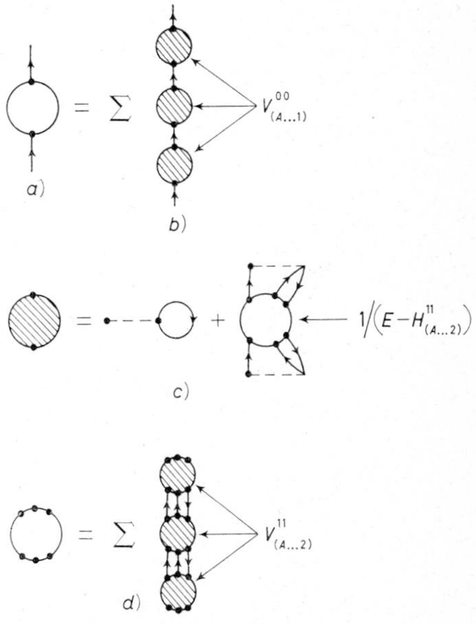

Fig. 9. – Feynman-diagram representation of the elimination formulae.

In a proper self-energy diagram, the intermediate states contain necessarily more than one particle, and therefore the simplest possible intermediate states are the 2p-1h states. The diagrams for $V^{00}_{(A...1)}$ may be decomposed according to Fig. 9*c* into a direct diagram involving no 2p-1h state and the sum of all diagrams involving 2p-1h states. This is described by the relation

$$V^{00}_{(A...1)} = V^{00} + V^{01}\frac{1}{E - H^{11}_{(A...2)}}V^{10}, \tag{6.27}$$

which is exactly equivalent to (6.23) for $q = 0$. Now the 2p-1h propagator

$$\frac{1}{E - H^{11}_{(A...2)}}, \tag{6.28}$$

may again be decomposed into proper parts, where proper means here that no intermediate state contains less than three particles and two holes (Fig. 9*d*). This decomposition introduces then the 2p-1h mass operator $V^{11}_{(A...2)}$ such that

$$H^{11}_{(A...2)} = H^{11}_0 + V^{11}_{(A...2)} \,. \tag{6.29}$$

Such diagram interpretations may be generalized in an obvious way:

$$V^{qq}_{(A...q+1)} \,,$$

represents the sum of all proper diagrams having initial and final states of rank q ($q+1$ particles and q holes, for instance) and intermediate states of rank A, $A+1$,..., $q+1$.

Appendix

The generalized algorithm of Gauss.

A.1. – We consider here a linear system of equations of the type used throughout these lectures. It is convenient to introduce the more symmetrical notations:

$$\begin{cases} M^{ij} = H^{ij} & (i \neq j), \\ M^{ii} = H^{ii} - E \,. \end{cases} \tag{A.1}$$

The linear system to be studied reads then

$$\sum_{j=1}^{n+1} M^{ij}|j) = 0 \qquad (i = 1, 2, ..., n), \tag{A.2}$$

where the $|j)$ are vectors belonging each to a separate vector space, the M^{ij} are (generally rectangular) matrices. We suppose that $|n+1)$ is a given vector. The eqs. (A.2) then determine $|1)$, $|2)$, ..., $|n)$ uniquely, if one disregards exceptional sets of matrices M^{ij}.

The method used above for solving such a system is the so-called generalized algorithm of Gauss. It consists in solving the equation $i = 1$ (assuming that $\det M^{11} \neq 0$)

$$|1) = -\frac{1}{M^{11}} \sum_{j=2}^{n+1} M^{1j}|j) \tag{A.3}$$

and substituting into the equations $i = 2, 3, ..., n$. The system is then replaced by

$$\text{(A.4)} \qquad \sum_{j=1}^{n+1} M^{1j}|j) = 0\,, \qquad \sum_{j=2}^{n+1} M^{ij}_{(1)}|j) = 0\,, \qquad (i = 2, 3, \ldots, n),$$

where

$$\text{(A.5)} \qquad M^{ij}_{(1)} = M^{ij} - M^{i1}\frac{1}{M^{11}}M^{1j}.$$

The same process may be repeated. The next step gives

$$\text{(A.6)} \qquad \sum_{j=1}^{n+1} M^{1j}|j) = 0\,, \quad \sum_{j=2}^{n+1} M^{2j}_{(1)}|j) = 0\,, \quad \sum_{j=3}^{n+1} M^{ij}_{(12)}|j) = 0\,, \quad (i = 3, \ldots, n),$$

where

$$\text{(A.7)} \qquad M^{ij}_{(12)} = M^{ij}_{(1)} - M^{i2}_{(1)}\frac{1}{M^{22}_{(1)}}M^{2j}_{(1)}\,.$$

More generally, one obtains after k such steps

$$\text{(A.8)} \qquad \sum_{j=1}^{n+1} M^{1j}|j) = 0\,, \quad \sum_{j=2}^{n+1} M^{2j}_{(1)}|j) = 0\,, \quad \ldots, \quad \sum_{j=k+1}^{n+1} M^{ij}_{(12\ldots k)}|j) = 0$$
$$(i = k+1, k+2, \ldots, n),$$

where the $M^{ij}_{(12\ldots k)}$ are defined by the recursion relations

$$\text{(A.9)} \qquad M^{ij}_{(12\ldots k)} = M^{ij}_{(12\ldots k-1)} - M^{ik}_{(12\ldots k-1)}\frac{1}{M^{kk}_{(12\ldots k-1)}}M^{kj}_{(12\ldots k-1)}\,.$$

In this derivation, it is naturally assumed that

$$\text{(A.10)} \qquad \det M^{11} \neq 0\,, \qquad \det M^{22}_{(1)} \neq 0\,, \quad \ldots, \quad \det M^{kk}_{(12\ldots k-1)} \neq 0\,.$$

A.2. – The successive elimination of the vectors $|1), |2), \ldots, |k)$ could naturally be performed in a different order. We have then:

Symmetry theorem. – The matrices $M^{ij}_{(123\ldots k)}$ are invariant under permutation of the lower indices:

$$\text{(A.11)} \qquad M^{ij}_{(123\ldots k)} = M^{ij}_{(213\ldots k)} = M^{ij}_{(231\ldots k)} = \ldots\,.$$

Proof. It is clearly sufficient to prove the symmetry property for the permutation of two successive indices, which may be assumed to be the last indices on the right, and even to be the only indices. Thus we should prove that

$$\text{(A.12)} \qquad M^{ij}_{(12)} = M^{ij}_{(21)}\,.$$

The linear system

$$\sum_{j=3}^{n+1} M^{ij}_{(12)}|j) = 0 , \qquad \sum_{j=3}^{n+1} M^{ij}_{(21)}|j) = 0 , \tag{A.13}$$

results from

$$\sum_{j=1}^{n+1} M^{ij}|j) = 0 , \tag{A.14}$$

by elimination of $|1)$ and $|2)$ in two different manners: either $|1)$ is eliminated first by solving the eq. (A.14) $i=1$ and then $|2)$ by solving the equation $i=2$, or these operations are performed in the other order. This amounts to solving in two different ways the equations

$$\begin{cases} M^{11}|1) + M^{12}|2) = -\sum_{j=3}^{n+1} M^{1j}|j) , \\ M^{21}|1) + M^{22}|2) = -\sum_{j=3}^{n+1} M^{2j}|j) , \end{cases} \tag{A.15}$$

and substituting the resulting expressions for $|1)$ and $|2)$ into the equations

$$\sum_{j=1}^{n+1} M^{ij}|j) = 0 \qquad (i = 3, 4, \ldots, n+1). \tag{A.16}$$

The solution of a system such as (A.15) is unique if one disregards exceptional values of the coefficients. Thus the expressions for $|1)$ and $|2)$ obtained by solving the first equation for $|1)$, substituting into the second equation and solving then for $|2)$, or by doing the operations in reverse order are identical. This may of course be checked directly by an elementary though tedious calculation. It follows that the two systems (A.13) resulting from substitution of these expressions into (A.16) are identical and this proves the symmetry relation (A.12).

A.3. – Let us finally express the complete solution of the linear system. We assume that the elimination has been performed in a given order, say the natural order. The reduced system of equations obtained by performing entirely the elimination outlined above reads

$$\sum_{j=1}^{n+1} N^{ij}|j) = 0 \qquad (i = 1, 2, \ldots, n), \tag{A.17}$$

where we have introduced the notation

$$N^{ij} = M^{ij}_{(123\ldots i-1)} \qquad (i<j). \tag{A.18}$$

These equations are easily solved one after the other in the order

$i = n,\ n-1,\ n-2,\ \dots$. The equation $i = n$ gives

$$|n) = -\frac{1}{N^{nn}} N^{n,n+1} |n+1) \,.$$

By substituting this into the equation $i = n-1$, and solving it for $|n-1)$, one obtains

$$|n-1) = \left[-\frac{1}{N^{n-1,n-1}} N^{n-1,n+1} + \frac{1}{N^{n-1,n-1}} N^{n-1,n} \frac{1}{N^{n,n}} N^{n,n+1}\right] |n+1) \,.$$

Continuation of the same procedure yields the general expression

$$\text{(A.19)} \qquad |i) = \sum_{p=0}^{n-i} \sum_{i_1,\dots,i_p} (-)^{p+1} \frac{1}{N^{i,i}} N^{i,i_1} \frac{1}{N^{i_1,i_1}} N^{i_1,i_2} \frac{1}{N^{i_2,i_2}} \dots N^{i_p,n+1} |n+1) \,,$$

where the summation is extended to all $i_1, i_2, \dots, i_p$ such that

$$\text{(A.20)} \qquad i < i_1 < i_2 < \dots < i_p < n+1 \,.$$

Returning to the original notations, the expression (A.19) takes the final form

$$\text{(A.21)} \qquad |i) = \sum_{i<i_1<\dots<i_p<n+1} \frac{1}{E - H^{ii}_{(12\dots i-1)}} V^{ii_1}_{(12\dots i-1)} \frac{1}{E - H^{i_1 i_1}_{(12\dots i_1-1)}} \cdot V^{i_1 i_2}_{(12\dots i_2-1)} \frac{1}{E - H^{i_2 i_2}_{(12\dots i_2-1)}} \cdots V^{i_p n+1}_{(12\dots i_p-1)} |n+1) \,.$$

The mode of resolution used here is basically associated with a particular ordering of the indices $1, 2, \dots, n$ labelling the various vector spaces. The solution, however, is unique and therefore independent of the ordering. This shows the existence of a large number of identities obtained by equating the expressions (A.20), (A.21) for different orders.

As an example, let us take the case $n = 2$. With the natural order 1, 2 we obtain

$$\text{(A.22)} \qquad \begin{cases} |1) = \left[\dfrac{1}{E - H^{11}} V^{13} + \dfrac{1}{E - H^{11}} V^{12} \dfrac{1}{E - H^{22}_{(1)}} V^{23}_{(1)}\right] |3) \,, \\[2ex] |2) = \left[\dfrac{1}{E - H^{22}_{(1)}} V^{23}_{(1)} |3) \,. \end{cases}$$

With the reversed order 2, 1, the same solution reads

$$\text{(A.23)} \qquad \begin{cases} |1) = \dfrac{1}{E - H^{11}_{(2)}} V^{13}_{(2)} |3) \,, \\[2ex] |2) = \left[\dfrac{1}{E - H^{22}} V^{23} + \dfrac{1}{E - H^{22}} V^{21} \dfrac{1}{E - H^{11}_{(2)}} V^{13}_{(2)}\right] |3) \,. \end{cases}$$

Thus we have the identity

$$\text{(A.24)}\qquad \frac{1}{E-H^{11}}V^{13}+\frac{1}{E-H^{11}}V^{12}\frac{1}{E-H^{22}_{(1)}}V^{23}_{(1)}\equiv\frac{1}{E-H^{11}_{(2)}}V^{13}_{(2)}\,,$$

and a similar one obtained by permutation of 1 and 2.

A.4. – It may be useful to indicate the connection of this formalism with perturbation theory, particularly in view of comparing it with other formulations. In perturbation theory, taking the diagonal part H^{ii} as unperturbed Hamiltonian and the off-diagonal elements V^{ij} as perturbation, the solution to the linear system (A.2) reads

$$\text{(A.25)}\qquad |i)=\sum_{i_1,\dots,i_p}\frac{1}{E-H^{ii}}V^{ii_1}\frac{1}{E-H^{i_1i_1}}V^{i_1i_2}\frac{1}{E-H^{i_2i_2}}\dots V^{i_pn+1}|n+1)\,,$$

where the summation is now extended to *all* combinations of $i_1, \dots, i_p$.

The various terms of this expansion may be represented by diagrams indicating the successive transitions between vector spaces: $n+1\to i_p\to\dots\to i_1\to i$. On Fig. 10 the subspaces have been symbolized by horizontal dashed lines, the elements V^{ij} by vertical lines and the factors $1/(E-H^{ii})$ by dots. The expansion (A.25) is then represented by all lines going from $|n+1)$ to $|i)$ through any number of intermediate vector spaces.

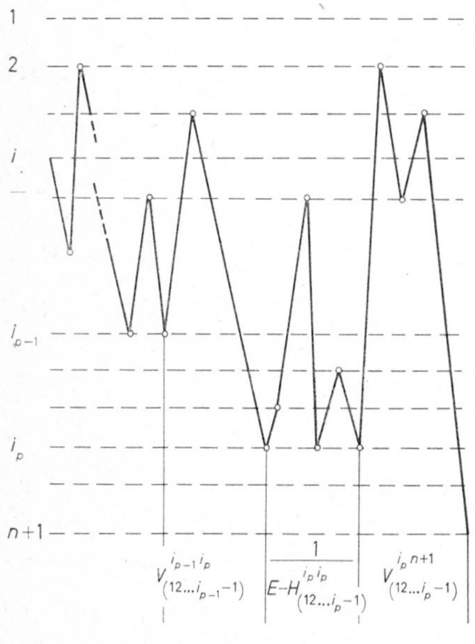

Fig. 10. – Perturbation expression of the elimination formulae.

It is easy to check that $V^{ij}_{(kl\dots)}$ is given by the sum of the terms associated with all lines starting at j and ending at i (no dots at the ends) and going through $k, l, \dots$ any number of times. Similarly, $1/(E-H^{ii}_{(kl\dots)})$ is the sum of all lines starting and ending at i (with dots at the ends) and going through $k, l, \dots$ any number of times. This interpretation is clearly equivalent to the generating relation (A.9).

The diagram interpretation of the expression (A.21) is indicated on Fig. 10. The lines representing the vector spaces $1, 2, \dots, n+1$ are drawn from top to bottom in the order chosen for the elimination. The line going from $n+1$ to i is decomposed in an unambiguous way as follows. Call i_p the horizontal line carrying the lowest dots on the diagram. Follow now the line $n+1$ towards i. The section between $n+1$ and the first dot at i_p (dot at i_p excluded) corresponds to a term of $V^{i_pn+1}_{(12\dots i_p-1)}$. The section between the first and last dots at i_p (dots included) corresponds to a term of $1/(E-H^{i_pi_p}_{(12\dots i_p-1)})$. Note that the first and last dots at i_p may be identical, in other words there may be a unique dot at i_p. Consider now the remaining section of the line from i_p to i and locate the lowest dots, which are say on the horizontal line $i_p - 1$. Again, the section from the last dot at i_p to the first one at $i_p - 1$ (dots excluded) corresponds to a term of $V^{i_{p-1}i_p}_{(12\ldots i_{p-1}-1)}$, whereas the section between the first and last dots at i_{p-1} (dots included) corresponds to a term of $1/(E - H^{i_{p-1}i_{p-1}}_{(12\ldots i_{p-1}-1)})$; and so on. This process reconstructs the expression (A.21) term by term, and it is clear that the summation over $i_1, i_2, \ldots, i_p$ reproduces the entire expansion (A.25).

REFERENCES

[1] See the review article by A. M. Lane and R. C. Thomas: *Rev. Mod. Phys.*, **30**, 257 (1958).

[2] J. Humblet and L. Rosenfeld: *Nucl. Phys.*, **26**, 529 (1961); L. Rosenfeld: *Nucl. Phys.*, **26**, 594 (1961); J. Humblet: *Nucl. Phys.*, **31**, 544 (1962); **50**, 1 (1964); **57**, 386 (1964); **58**, 1 (1964); C. Mahaux: *Nucl. Phys.*, **67**, 358 (1965); **68**, 481 (1965).

[3] A. M. Lane, R. G. Thomas and E. P. Wigner: *Phys. Rev.*, **98**, 693 (1955).

[4] C. Bloch: *Nucl. Phys.*, **3**, 137 (1957); **4**, 503 (1957).

[5] H. Feshbach: *Ann. of Phys.*, **5**, 357 (1958); **19**, 287 (1962); C. Shakin: *Ann. of Phys.*, **22**, 54 (1963); R. Lemmer and C. M. Shakin: *Ann. of Phys.*, **27**, 13 (1964); J. E. Young: *Nucl Phys.*, **34**, 476 (1962); and in the press; *Proc. S.I.F.*, Course XXIII (New York, London, 1961); A. Agodi and E. Eberle: *Nuovo Cimento*, **28**, 718 (1960); L. Fonda and R. G. Newton: *Ann. of Phys.*, **10**, 490 (1960); W. M. MacDonald: *Nucl. Phys.*, **54**, 393 (1964); **56**, 636, 647 (1964).

[6] C. Bloch and V. Gillet: *Phys. Lett.*, **16**, 62 (1965).

[7] V. Gillet and C. Bloch: *Phys. Lett.*, **18**, 58 (1965).

[8] U. Fano: *Phys. Rev.*, **124**, 1866 (1961); and in the press; U. Fano and F. Prats: *Proc. Nat. Acad. Sci. India*, *AXXXIII* (1963), p. 553.

[9] Zdeněk Kopal: *Numerical Analysis* (London, 1961).

[10] J. Raynal: private communication.

[11] V. F. Weisskopf: *Phys. Today*, **14**, 18 (1961).

[12] K. Izumo: *Progr. Theor. Phys.*, **26**, 807 (1961); B. Block and H. Feshbach: *Ann. of Phys.*, **23**, 47 (1963); A. K. Kerman, L. S. Rodberg and J. E. Young: *Phys. Rev. Lett.*, **11**, 422 (1963); B. Block and A. Lande: *Phys. Rev. Lett.*, **12**, 334 (1964). The first appearance of the idea is found in K. A. Brueckner, R. J. Eden and N. C. Francis: *Phys. Rev.*, **100**, 891 (1955).

[13] M. Danos and W. Greiner: *Phys. Rev.*, **138**, B 877 (1965).

[14] C. Bloch: *Congr. Int. de Phys. Nucl. Paris* (1964).

The Seniority $v=0$ and $v=1$ Approximation in the Spectra of the Ni Isotopes.

N. AUERBACH

Weizmann Institute of Science, Department of Nuclear Physics - Rehovoth

1. – Introduction.

We consider the spectra of the Ni isotopes within the framework of the shell model, using the method of effective interactions introduced by TALMI [1, 2] for theoretical interpretation of nuclear spectra. The basic assumptions of this method are the following:

1) The residual interaction is a two-body interaction only.

2) The radial parts of the single-particle wave functions are the same for all particles in a certain shell (or subshell), independent of the number of particles in this shell (subshell).

Under these assumptions the energies in n-particle configurations can be expressed in terms of the energies of two-particle configurations. These two-particle energies, as well as the single-particle energies are considered as free parameters. We look for a set of values of these parameters which will reproduce the experimental energies as accurately as possible. This procedure is meaningful if the number of experimentally determined energies is considerably bigger than the number of parameters.

Good agreement between calculated and experimental energies shows that the assumptions made in the theory are justified, namely that the choice of configurations, spin and parity assignments of the different energy levels taken into account are correct. The main limitation of the described method is the fact that not in all the cases enough experimental data are available.

The number of parameters is increased drastically when configuration mixing is included. For this reason the effective interaction calculations were applied mainly in those regions where the pure j-j coupling is a good approximation. In general, the large number of off-diagonal matrix elements connecting different configurations and, on the other hand, the limited number of experimental energies made such kind of calculations impossible.

Only in relatively simple cases, where the number of off-diagonal matrix elements is small, was this method applied with great success [3, 4].

One of the regions where it is necessary to introduce configuration mixing in order to explain the observed spectra is the region of the nickel isotopes.

Recently, experiments on these nuclei were performed which make possible an effective interaction calculation under certain assumptions.

In the nickel isotopes ${}^{N+n}_{Z}\mathrm{Ni}$, where $Z = N = 28$ (closed shells), the extra n neutrons may occupy the $2p_{\frac{3}{2}}$, $1f_{\frac{5}{2}}$, $2p_{\frac{1}{2}}$ and $1g_{\frac{9}{2}}$ orbits.

In the previous calculations, different approximation methods and phenomenological forces were employed and in most of the cases these isotopes were considered to be nuclei whose spectrum is vibrational in character. Most analyses were concerned with energy spacings rather than with total energies. In the present analysis the total energies of these nuclei are studied using effective interactions. The ground and first excited $J = 0^+$ states for even A isotopes and the lowest $J = \frac{1}{2}^-$, $\frac{3}{2}^-$ and $\frac{5}{2}^-$ states of the odd isotopes are calculated. Two basic assumptions are made in this calculation. First, it is assumed that the states which were taken into account can be approximately given by states of seniority $v = 0$ (for even A) and $v = 1$ (for odd A). (The seniority here is simply the number of nucleons that are not coupled into $J = 0$ pairs.)

The $J = 0^+$ states are thus expressed as linear combinations of the

$$|p_{\frac{3}{2}}^{n_1}(J_1 = 0,\ v_1 = 0) f_{\frac{5}{2}}^{n_2}(J_2 = 0,\ v_2 = 0) p_{\frac{1}{2}}^{2}(J_3 = 0,\ v_3 = 0) J = 0\rangle$$

wave functions, while the $J = \frac{1}{2}^-$, $\frac{3}{2}^-$, $\frac{5}{2}^-$ states are linear combinations of the

$$|p_{\frac{3}{2}}^{n_1}(J_1 = 0,\ v_1 = 0) f_{\frac{5}{2}}^{n_2}(J_2 = 0,\ v_2 = 0) p_{\frac{1}{2}} J = \tfrac{1}{2}\rangle\,,$$

$$|p_{\frac{3}{2}}^{n_1}(J_1 = \tfrac{3}{2},\ v_1 = 1) f_{\frac{5}{2}}^{n_2}(J_2 = 0,\ v_2 = 0) p_{\frac{1}{2}}^{n_3}(J_3 = 0,\ v_3 = 0) J = \tfrac{3}{2}\rangle$$

and

$$|p_{\frac{3}{2}}^{n_1}(J_1 = 0, v_1 = 0)\ f_{\frac{5}{2}}^{n_2}(J_2 = \tfrac{5}{2},\ v_2 = 1) p_{\frac{1}{2}}^{n_3}(J_3 = 0,\ v_3 = 0) J = \tfrac{5}{2}\rangle$$

states respectively. States of higher seniority *e.g.* $v = 4$ in the case of $J = 0^+$, $v = 3$ and $v = 5$ in the case of $J = \frac{1}{2}^-$, $\frac{3}{2}^-$ and $\frac{5}{2}^-$ are omitted. It is assumed that these states lie higher than the low-seniority states and are weakly coupled to them. (Recent calculations of COHEN, LAWSON, MACFARLANE and SOGA give credence to this assumption for the $J = 0^+$ states in even-A nickel isotopes).

The second basic assumption lies in considering only the $2p_{\frac{3}{2}}$, $1f_{\frac{5}{2}}$ and $2p_{\frac{1}{2}}$ orbits for the extra neutrons. The contributions of the configurations containing the $1g_{\frac{9}{2}}$ orbit are not taken into account because of the rather large separation between the $p_{\frac{3}{2}}$, $f_{\frac{5}{2}}$, $p_{\frac{1}{2}}$ and $g_{\frac{9}{2}}$ single-particle levels.

Configurations containing an even number of $g_{\frac{9}{2}}$ neutrons lie high and are assumed to contribute only slightly to the states considered. Those configurations which contain one $g_{\frac{9}{2}}$ neutron may be lower in energy. However, they cannot combine with the other configurations because of the opposite parities.

The validity of the assumptions is demonstrated by the good agreement between calculated and observed spectra. The total energies of the levels considered are reproduced very accurately, the average deviations being less than 0.1 MeV. The effective two-body matrix elements determined from the calculation have reasonable values. In spite of strong configuration mixing which occurs in the nickel isotopes the matrix elements of the effective interaction obtained, resemble very much the ones known from the calculations in other regions where pure j-j coupling is a much better approximation [2].

The calculation presented here cannot bear *directly* on the character of the first excited $J=2^+$ states in ^{58}Ni, ^{60}Ni and ^{62}Ni. These states have seniority of at least two. These and the analogous 2^+ states in the Sn and Pb isotopes have for a long time been considered to be collective, one-phonon, vibrational states. (Such states are also found in some nuclei with neutrons and protons in open shells, such as Cd, Te.) In these nuclei a triplet with spins $J=0^+$, 2^+, 4^+ is frequently observed.

The energy of the center of mass of this triplet is found to be twice the energy of the first excited $J=2^+$ state. The members of the triplet are usually considered as two-phonon vibrational states obtained by coupling two one-phonon states of the first excited $J=2^+$ state [5].

In the case of the Sn isotopes the number of the nucleons taking part in the collective states is at least ten. The situation for the Ni isotopes is somewhat less clear because such « collective » states appear even when there are only two or four neutrons in the open shell. A possible explanation could be that additional particles, arising from particle-hole excitations from the $f_{\frac{7}{2}}$ shell, contribute to the formation of the one-phonon state.

Such particle-hole excitations would necessarily contribute to the two-phonon states. Thus, if the 0^+, 2^+, 4^+ triplet observed in the nickel isotopes is to be considered as a two-phonon state obtained by coupling two one-phonon states, it must contain such particle-hole excitations from the $f_{\frac{7}{2}}$ shell. Moreover two-phonon states have large admixtures of seniority-four components. In spite of this, the calculated energies of the first excited $J=0^+$ states agree very well with the experimental values. This indicates that the observed triplet ($J=0^+$, 2^+, 4^+) in the Ni isotopes (or at least the $J=0^+$ member of it) is *not a two-phonon state* (*).

(*) Recent experiments give credence to this statement (as was pointed out by Prof. J. French).

2. – Method of calculation.

As mentioned above the total energies of the levels are considered in this analysis. The total energy of the level is the binding energy of the nucleus minus the height of the level above the ground state and is taken in this calculation relative to the binding energy of the ^{56}Ni inert core.

The number of experimental data available for our calculation is twenty one (Table I, columns 1 and 2). These energies can be expressed in terms of the

TABLE I. – *Calculated and experimental total energies (relative to* ^{56}Ni) *in* MeV.

Nucleus	Level	Experimental	Calculated
$^{57}_{28}Ni_{29}$	$\frac{3}{2}^-$ (g.s.)	10.25	10.17
$^{58}_{28}Ni_{30}$	0^+ (g.s.)	22.45	22.44
	0^+ (2.77)	19.68	19.72
$^{59}_{28}Ni_{31}$	$\frac{3}{2}^-$ (g.s.)	31.45	31.38
	$\frac{5}{2}^-$ (0.34)	31.11	31.12
	$\frac{1}{2}^-$ (0.47)	30.98	30.86
$^{60}_{28}Ni_{32}$	0^+ (g.s.)	42.84	42.83
	0^+ (2.29)	40.55	40.50
$^{61}_{28}Ni_{33}$	$\frac{3}{2}^-$ (g.s.)	50.66	50.56
	$\frac{5}{2}^-$ (0.07)	50.59	50.57
	$\frac{1}{2}^-$ (0.28)	50.38	50.48
$^{62}_{28}Ni_{34}$	0^+ (g.s.)	61.25	61.29
	0^+ (2.05)	59.20	59.20
$^{63}_{28}Ni_{35}$	$\frac{1}{2}^-$ (g.s.)	68.09	68.11
	$\frac{5}{2}^-$ (0.09)	68.00	68.17
	$\frac{3}{2}^-$ (0.16)	67.93	67.96
$^{64}_{28}Ni_{36}$	0^+ (g.s.)	77.76	77.73
$^{65}_{28}Ni_{37}$	$\frac{5}{2}^-$ (g.s.)	83.89	83.88
	$\frac{1}{2}^-$ (0.06)	83.83	83.82
	$\frac{3}{2}^-$ (0.32)	83.57	83.66
$^{66}_{28}Ni_{38}$	0^+ (g.s.)	92.85	92.72
σ		0.109	

following theoretical parameters:

$$1)\ a_{\frac{3}{2}} = \frac{5\langle \tfrac{3}{2}^2 J=2|V|\tfrac{3}{2}^2 J=2\rangle - \langle \tfrac{3}{2}^2 J=0|V|\tfrac{3}{2}^2 J=0\rangle}{4},$$

$$2)\ b_{\frac{3}{2}} = \tfrac{5}{4}\left(\langle \tfrac{3}{2}^2 J=0|V|\tfrac{3}{2}^2 J=0\rangle - \langle \tfrac{3}{2}^2 J=2|V|\tfrac{3}{2}^2 J=2\rangle\right),$$

$$3)\ a_{\frac{5}{2}} = \frac{7\bar{V}_2 - \langle \tfrac{5}{2}^2 J=0|V|\tfrac{5}{2}^2 J=0\rangle}{6},$$

$$4)\ b_{\frac{5}{2}} = \tfrac{7}{6}\left(\langle \tfrac{5}{2}^2 J=0|V|\tfrac{5}{2}^2 J=0\rangle - \bar{V}_2\right),$$

where

$$\bar{V}_2 = \frac{5\langle \tfrac{5}{2}^2 J=2|V|\tfrac{5}{2}^2 J=2\rangle + 9\langle \tfrac{5}{2}^2 J=4|V|\tfrac{5}{2}^2 J=4\rangle}{14},$$

$$5)\ W_{\frac{5}{2}\frac{3}{2}} = \frac{2\sum_{J=1}^{4}(2J+1)\langle \tfrac{5}{2}\tfrac{3}{2}J|V|\tfrac{5}{2}\tfrac{3}{2}J\rangle}{\sum_{J=1}^{4}(2J+1)}$$

(this is the interaction energy of a $f_{\frac{5}{2}}$ or $p_{\frac{3}{2}}$ neutron with a pair of $p_{\frac{3}{2}}$ or $f_{\frac{5}{2}}$ neutrons coupled to $J=0$),

$$6)\ W_{\frac{5}{2}\frac{1}{2}} = \frac{2\left(5\langle \tfrac{5}{2}\tfrac{1}{2}J=2|V|\tfrac{5}{2}\tfrac{1}{2}J=2\rangle + 7\langle \tfrac{5}{2}\tfrac{1}{2}J=3|V|\tfrac{5}{2}\tfrac{1}{2}J=3\rangle\right)}{12},$$

$$7)\ W_{\frac{3}{2}\frac{1}{2}} = \frac{2\left(3\langle \tfrac{3}{2}\tfrac{1}{2}J=1|V|\tfrac{3}{2}\tfrac{1}{2}J=1\rangle + 5\langle \tfrac{3}{2}\tfrac{1}{2}J=2|V|\tfrac{3}{2}\tfrac{1}{2}J=2\rangle\right)}{8}$$

($W_{\frac{5}{2}\frac{1}{2}}$ and $W_{\frac{3}{2}\frac{1}{2}}$ have a meaning similar to that of $W_{\frac{5}{2}\frac{3}{2}}$),

$$8)\quad V(p_{\frac{1}{2}}^2) = \langle \tfrac{1}{2}^2 J=0|V|\tfrac{1}{2}^2 J=0\rangle,$$

$$9)\quad V_{\frac{5}{2}\frac{3}{2}} = \langle \tfrac{5}{2}^2 J=0|V|\tfrac{3}{2}^2 J=0\rangle,$$

$$10)\quad V_{\frac{5}{2}\frac{1}{2}} = \langle \tfrac{5}{2}^2 J=0|V|\tfrac{1}{2}^2 J=0\rangle,$$

$$11)\quad V_{\frac{3}{2}\frac{1}{2}} = \langle \tfrac{3}{2}^2 J=0|V|\tfrac{1}{2}^2 J=0\rangle,$$

12) $C_{\frac{3}{2}}$ the single-particle energy of the $2p_{\frac{3}{2}}$ neutron. The total single-particle energies of the $1f_{\frac{5}{2}}$ and $2p_{\frac{1}{2}}$ states are not considered to be independent parameters. Their values were taken from the recently measured spectrum of ^{57}Ni:

$$\text{B.E.}(1f_{\frac{5}{2}}) = C_{\frac{3}{2}} - 0.78\,, \qquad \text{B.E.}(2p_{\frac{1}{2}}) = C_{\frac{3}{2}} - 1.08\,.$$

The diagonal matrix element

$$V = \langle p_{\frac{3}{2}}^{n_1} f_{\frac{5}{2}}^{n_2} p_{\frac{1}{2}}^{n_3} J, v|\sum V|p_{\frac{3}{2}}^{n_1} f_{\frac{5}{2}}^{n_2} p_{\frac{1}{2}}^{n_3} J, v\rangle$$

for $v=0$ or 1 can be expressed in terms of the defined parameters:

$$(1)\qquad V=\frac{n_1(n_1-1)}{2}\,a_{\frac{3}{2}}+\left[\frac{n_1}{2}\right]b_{\frac{3}{2}}+\frac{n_2(n_2-1)}{2}\,a_{\frac{5}{2}}+\left[\frac{n_2}{2}\right]b_{\frac{5}{2}}+$$

$$+\left[\frac{n_3}{2}\right]V(p_{\frac{1}{2}}^2)+\frac{1}{2}\,n_1n_2W_{\frac{3}{2}\frac{5}{2}}+\frac{1}{2}\,n_2n_3W_{\frac{5}{2}\frac{1}{2}}+\frac{1}{2}\,n_1n_3W_{\frac{3}{2}\frac{1}{2}}\,,$$

where

$$\left[\frac{n}{2}\right]=\begin{cases}\dfrac{n}{2} & n \text{ even},\\[2mm] \dfrac{n-1}{2} & n \text{ odd}.\end{cases}$$

The nondiagonal matrix element involved in our calculation is reduced to the following form:

$$V^{(1)}=\langle j_1^{n_1}(J_1,v_1)\,j_2^{n_2}(J_2,v_2)J|\sum V|j_1^{n_1-2}(J_1,v_1)\,j_2^{n_2+2}(J_2,v_2)J\rangle\,,$$

v_1, v_2 are 0 or 1 and $v_1+v_2=0$ or 1.

Using standard shell-model techniques [6] we obtain

$$(2)\qquad V^{(1)}=\frac{1}{2}\sqrt{\frac{(n_1-v_1)(2j_1+3-n_1-v_1)(n_2+2-v_2)(2j_2+1-n_2-v_2)}{(2j_1+1)(2j_2+1)}}\,\cdot$$

$$\cdot\langle j_1^2J=0|V_{12}|j_2^2J=0\rangle\,.$$

With these expressions for the matrix elements (1), (2) the interaction matrices were constructed in terms of the parameters defined above.

Values of these parameters which reproduce the experimental data as accurately as possible were found by a least-square fit.

3. – Results and discussion.

The experimental energies and those calculated, with the 12 parameters are shown in the second and third column of Table I. The good agreement between the experimental and calculated energies is shown by the small value of the root mean square deviation, which is equal to 0.109 MeV. (The root mean square deviation is defined by

$$\sigma=\sqrt{\frac{\sum_j\,(E_j^{\text{exp}}-E_j^{\text{calc}})^2}{n-k}}\,,$$

where n is the number of experimental energies and k the number of parameters.)

The spacing between the two $J=0^+$ states in ^{58}Ni, ^{60}Ni and ^{62}Ni are reproduced very accurately. The experimental spacings are 2.77, 2.29 and 2.05 while the calculated ones are 2.71, 2.33 and 2.09 respectively (Fig. 1). In Fig. 1

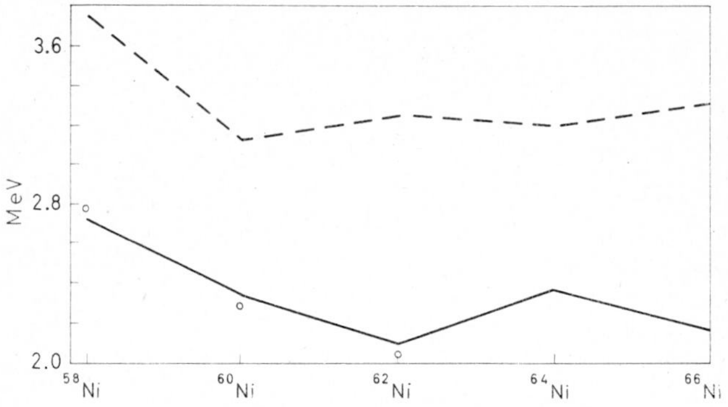

Fig. 1. – The positions of the first (solid line) and second (dashed) excited $J=0^+$ levels relative to the experimental ground-state energies. The circles indicate experimental values.

are shown the predicted first excited $J=0^+$ states for ^{64}Ni and ^{66}Ni, as well as the predicted second excited $J=0^+$ levels in all the even-A nickel isotopes. In the energy range of 1 MeV to 4 MeV above the first excited $J=0^+$ level other $J=0^+$ states are predicted by the calculation. It is rather difficult to rely on the predicted positions because certainly in this energy region the $1g_{\frac{9}{2}}$ neutron configurations start to contribute. Also 0^+ states with higher seniority may appear in this region.

Figure 2 shows the calculated and observed spectra of the odd-A isotopes

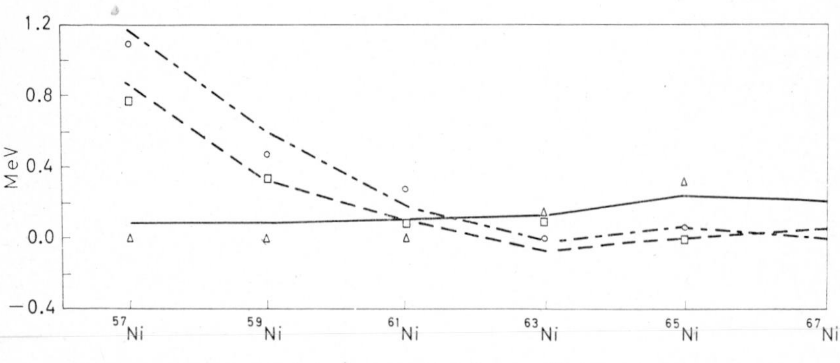

Fig. 2. – The positions of the lowest $J=\frac{1}{2}^-$, $\frac{3}{2}^-$ and $\frac{5}{2}^-$ levels relative to the experimental ground states. The calculated $\frac{3}{2}^-$ levels are connected by the solid line and the experimental ones are indicated by triangles. The dashed line and squares indicate calculated and experimental $\frac{5}{2}^-$ levels. The dash-dotted line connects the calculated $\frac{1}{2}^-$ levels whose experimental values are given by circles.

of Ni. The calculation gives the correct behavior of the levels as a function of A.

In ^{67}Ni not much is known experimentally. Recently the β-decay of ^{67}Ni to ^{67}Cu was studied. The measured end-point energy was (4.1 ± 0.3) MeV. Using the known binding energy of ^{67}Cu we can use this result to deduce the binding energy of ^{67}Ni, which turns out to be 98.05. This is in good agreement with the present calculation, which predicts a value 97.80 MeV for the $J = \frac{1}{2}^-$ ground state in ^{67}Ni. Other predicted levels in ^{67}Ni are shown in Fig. 2. Apart from the $J = \frac{1}{2}^-, \frac{3}{2}^-$ and $\frac{5}{2}^-$ $(v = 1)$ states which are included in the least-square fit, our calculation predicts additional $v = 1$ levels, which for all the nickel isotopes are well separated from the low-lying group. Their heights turn out to be not smaller than 1.7 MeV above the ground states of the various odd-A isotopes.

In all the odd nickel isotopes additional low-lying $J = \frac{1}{2}^-, \frac{3}{2}^-, \frac{5}{2}^-$ were measured. These seem to be low-lying seniority three states such as

$$|j^k(0)p_{\frac{3}{2}}^2(2)f_{\frac{5}{2}}J = \tfrac{1}{2}^-, \tfrac{3}{2}^-, \tfrac{5}{2}^-\rangle\,,$$

$$|j^k(0)f_{\frac{5}{2}}^2(2)p_{\frac{3}{2}}J = \tfrac{1}{2}^-, \tfrac{3}{2}^-, \tfrac{5}{2}^-\rangle\,, \qquad |j^k(0)f_{\frac{5}{2}}^3(\tfrac{3}{2})J = \tfrac{3}{2}^-\rangle$$

$$|j^k(0)p_{\frac{3}{2}}^2(2)p_{\frac{1}{2}}J = \tfrac{3}{2}^-, \tfrac{5}{2}^-\rangle$$

and

$$|j^k(0)\,f_{\frac{5}{2}}^2(2)p_{\frac{1}{2}}J = \tfrac{3}{2}^-, \tfrac{5}{2}^-\rangle$$

(or linear combinations of them).

In fact such low-lying seniority-three states occur in other regions. (For example the states $1d_{\frac{5}{2}}^3(\frac{3}{2}, v = 3)$ in ^{19}O, $2d_{\frac{5}{2}}^3(\frac{3}{2}, v = 3)$ in ^{93}Zr and $1g_{\frac{9}{2}}^3(\frac{7}{2}, v = 3)$ in ^{91}Nb are very close to the corresponding seniority-one states [2, 4]).

However, the good agreement between the calculated and experimental energies for odd-A nuclei indicates that if such states exist in the Ni isotopes they interact weakly with the seniority-one $(v = 1)$ states.

In the second column of Table II are given the values of the parameters obtained in this analysis. Also are shown the statistical errors of these parameters determined by the least-square fit. The parameters with small errors were obviously well determined. Those possessing large errors, in particular the $V(p_{\frac{1}{2}}^2)$ parameter, were not determined very accurately and one can try to fix some of them from other calculations. The mutual interaction of two $2p_{\frac{1}{2}}$ *protons* is known from the calculations performed in the Zr region [4]. The value of this parameter obtained there is 0.56 MeV. If we neglect the polarization effects of the different cores the following relation should be valid:

$$\langle 2p_{\frac{1}{2}}^2 J = 0|\,V_{\text{n}}\,|2p_{\frac{1}{2}}^2 J = 0\rangle = \langle 2p_{\frac{1}{2}}^2 J = 0\,|V_{\text{p}}|2p_{\frac{1}{2}}^2 J = 0\rangle + \left\langle 2p_{\frac{1}{2}}^2 J = 0\left|\frac{e^2}{r_{12}}\right|2p_{\frac{1}{2}}^2 J = 0\right\rangle .$$

The last term represents the Coulomb interaction energy of the two protons. Taking harmonic-oscillator wave functions for the single protons we were able to calculate this term. The calculated value is 0.2 MeV and hence

$$\langle 2p_{\frac{1}{2}}^2 J=0 | V_{\text{n}} | 2p_{\frac{1}{2}}^2 J=0 \rangle = 0.76 \text{ MeV} .$$

This value is close to the one obtained in our calculations for the Ni isotopes, the difference being only 0.13 MeV.

TABLE II. – *Single neutron energies and matrix elements of the effective interaction (in* MeV). The errors indicated are based on the least-square fit. In case II the matrix element $\langle 2p_{\frac{1}{2}}^2 J=0|V|2p_{\frac{1}{2}}^2 J=0\rangle$ has the fixed value 0.76 MeV.

Parameters	Case I	Case II
$a_{\frac{3}{2}}$	-0.53 ± 0.16	-0.52 ± 0.15
$b_{\frac{3}{2}}$	1.45 ± 0.55	1.42 ± 0.45
$a_{\frac{5}{2}}$	-0.36 ± 0.12	-0.35 ± 0.10
$b_{\frac{5}{2}}$	2.10 ± 0.37	2.08 ± 0.33
$W_{\frac{5}{2}\frac{3}{2}}$	-0.58 ± 0.15	-0.59 ± 0.10
$W_{\frac{5}{2}\frac{1}{2}}$	-0.56 ± 0.18	-0.56 ± 0.18
$W_{\frac{3}{2}\frac{1}{2}}$	-0.18 ± 0.50	-0.12 ± 0.19
$V(p_{\frac{1}{2}}^2)$	0.89 ± 1.05	0.76
$V_{\frac{5}{2}\frac{3}{2}}$	1.12 ± 0.19	1.10 ± 0.12
$V_{\frac{5}{2}\frac{1}{2}}$	0.56 ± 0.37	0.60 ± 0.25
$V_{\frac{3}{2}\frac{1}{2}}$	0.97 ± 0.60	1.03 ± 0.10
$C_{\frac{3}{2}}$	10.17 ± 0.08	10.17 ± 0.07

In Table II (column three) are shown the values of the parameters resulting from a calculation where $V(p_{\frac{1}{2}}^2)$ was fixed to be 0.76. (This calculation will be referred to as case II, while the previous one as case I.) The parameters are changed only slightly while the statistical errors are now considerably smaller. The calculated energies are almost the same as in the previous calculation.

Pairing-force calculations of the Ni isotopes have been carried out by KISSLINGER and SORENSEN [7] and by KERMAN *et al.* [8]. The former assumed a B.C.S. ground-state wave function, while the latter diagonalized the pairing interaction for different numbers of particles. A calculation analogous to the one of KERMAN *et al.* was carried out by us. For the matrix elements

$$\langle j_1 j_2 J | V_{12} | j_1' j_2' J \rangle$$

the expression

$$G \times \sqrt{(2j_1+1)(2j_1'+1)} \times \delta_{J0} \delta_{j_1 j_2} \delta_{j_1' j_1'}$$

was used and G was treated as a free parameter. As before, the $2p_{\frac{3}{2}}$ single-particle energy was also considered to be an independent parameter. The results were in poor agreement with the experimental data. The r.m.s. deviation was now about 1.1 MeV. This poor agreement is not surprising. In the pairing calculations the interactions between particles in different orbits are set to be zero. These interactions, represented in our previous calculations by $W_{\frac{5}{2}\frac{3}{2}}$, $W_{\frac{5}{2}\frac{1}{2}}$ and $W_{\frac{3}{2}\frac{1}{2}}$, are there rather well determined and not negligibly small (except $W_{\frac{3}{2}\frac{1}{2}}$).

4. – Summary.

Let us now summarize the main properties of the effective-interaction matrix elements deduced from the present calculations (Tables II and III) and the general conclusions about the character of the spectra of the Ni isotopes drawn from these calculations.

TABLE III. – *Values of some matrix elements of the effective interaction (in* MeV).

Matrix element	Value
$\langle \frac{3}{2}^2 J=0 \vert V \vert \frac{3}{2}^2 J=0 \rangle$	0.92
$\langle \frac{3}{2}^2 J=2 \vert V \vert \frac{3}{2}^2 J=2 \rangle$	-0.24
$\langle \frac{3}{2}^2 J=0 \vert V \vert \frac{3}{2}^2 J=0 \rangle - \langle \frac{3}{2}^2 J=2 \vert V \vert \frac{3}{2}^2 J=2 \rangle$	1.16
$\langle \frac{5}{2}^2 J=0 \vert V \vert \frac{5}{2}^2 J=0 \rangle$	1.74
$\bar{V}_2$	-0.06
$\langle \frac{5}{2}^2 J=0 \vert V \vert \frac{5}{2}^2 J=0 \rangle - \bar{V}_2$	1.80
$\langle \frac{5}{2}^2 J=0 \vert V \vert \frac{3}{2}^2 J=0 \rangle$	1.12

1) The a and b of the $2p_{\frac{3}{2}}$ and $1f_{\frac{5}{2}}$ neutrons have the same features as the analogous parameters in other regions [2, 4].

The coefficients $a_{\frac{3}{2}}$ and $a_{\frac{5}{2}}$, which determine the behavior of the mass parabola at large n, are small and repulsive, while the pairing terms $b_{\frac{3}{2}}$ and $b_{\frac{5}{2}}$ are large and attractive. Also $V(p_{\frac{1}{2}}^2)$ is attractive.

2) The interaction energies of pairs of nonequivalent particles are all repulsive, as has been observed in other regions [2, 4].

3) The nondiagonal matrix element $V_{\frac{5}{2}\frac{3}{2}} = \langle \frac{5}{2}^2 J=0 \vert V \vert \frac{3}{2}^2 J=0 \rangle$ is quite large compared to the diagonal ones, giving rise to large configuration mixing. Attempts to fit the experimental data by putting this matrix element equal to zero were quite unsatisfactory.

It is clear that the $V_{\frac{5}{2}\frac{3}{2}}$ matrix element plays an essential role in the spectra of the Ni isotopes.

The following main conclusions can be drawn from the analysis presented here:

a) It is enough to consider only the $p_{\frac{3}{2}}$, $f_{\frac{5}{2}}$ and $p_{\frac{1}{2}}$ orbits in order to reproduce the energies of the low-lying states of the Ni isotopes.

b) It is remarkable that configurations which contain the $2p_{\frac{1}{2}}$ orbit seem to play an important role in producing the spectra of the Ni isotopes. In particular, the $|j_1^{n_1}(0)j_2^{n_2}(0)p_{\frac{1}{2}}^2(0)J=0\rangle$ components in the excited $J=0^+$ states in ^{60}Ni and ^{62}Ni are quite large. Attempts to fit the experimental data including only configurations of the $p_{\frac{3}{2}}$ and $f_{\frac{5}{2}}$ orbits were quite unsatisfactory. The agreement was much worse than that obtained in the three-orbit calculation.

c) It is necessary to introduce configurations mixing in order to explain the spectra of the Ni isotopes.

d) The ground states and first excited $J=0^+$ states of the even nickel isotopes are reproduced very well with wave functions of seniority $v=0$. This implies that the first excited $J=0^+$ state *is not a two-phonon state.*

e) The low-lying states of odd Ni isotopes have large seniority $v=1$ components.

f) The approximation of a pure pairing interaction is not satisfactory when the total energies of the Ni isotopes are considered.

* * *

I would like to thank Prof. I. TALMI for his constant guidance throughout this investigation.

REFERENCES

[1] I. TALMI and I. UNNA: *Ann. Rev. Nucl. Sci.*, **10**, 353 (1960).
[2] I. TALMI: *Rev. Mod. Phys.*, **34**, 704 (1962).
[3] I. TALMI and I. UNNA: *Nucl. Phys.*, **19**, 225 (1960).
[4] N. AUERBACH and I. TALMI: *Nucl. Phys.*, **64**, 458 (1965).
[5] A. KERMAN and C. SHAKIN: *Phys. Lett.*, **1**, 151 (1962).
[6] A. DE-SHALIT and I. TALMI: *Nuclear Shell Theory* (New York, 1963).
[7] L. KISSLINGER and R. SORENSEN: *Rev. Mod. Phys.*, **35**, 853 (1963).
[8] A. KERMAN, R. LAWSON and M. MACFARLANE: *Phys. Rev.*, **124**, 162 (1961).

Application of the Hartree-Fock Method to the *s*-*d* Shell.

J. BAR-TOUV

Weizmann Institute of Science, Department of Nuclear Physics - Rehovoth

1. – Introduction.

It is the purpose of this lecture to discuss the application of the Hartree-Fock method to nuclei in the *s*-*d* shell carried out in the Weizmann Institute jointly by LEVINSON, KELSON and myself [1-3].

The Hartree-Fock method consists of finding the single-particle determinantal wave function Ψ minimizing the expectation value of the Hamiltonian, that is

$$\delta\langle\Psi|H|\Psi\rangle = 0 \,. \tag{1}$$

The trial N-particle wave function in second-quantization notation is written as

$$\Psi = a_1^\dagger a_2^\dagger \ldots a_N^\dagger|0\rangle \tag{2}$$

and the fact that we are dealing with Fermi-Dirac particles is taken into account by the appropriate anticommutation relations. The variation is done by considering a special class of variations which preserve the norm of Ψ to first order. The varied Ψ' is written as

$$\Psi' = \Psi + \eta a_\sigma^\dagger a_\lambda \Psi \,, \tag{3}$$

η infinitesimal parameter, λ occupied state, and σ unoccupied state. With such variation one gets from the variational equation (1) the Brillouin's theorem

$$\langle\Psi|a_\lambda^\dagger a_\sigma H|\Psi\rangle = 0 \,. \tag{4}$$

This theorem implies that the many-body Hamiltonian has no matrix elements between the state Ψ and the singly excited state obtained from Ψ

by promoting one particle from an occupied orbital to an unoccupied one. In other words, the Hartree-Fock solutions which we are going to get will be stable against one-particle excitations.

Substituting the many-body Hamiltonian, written in the form

$$H = \sum_{\alpha\beta} T_{\alpha\beta} a_\alpha^\dagger a_\beta + \tfrac{1}{2} \sum_{\alpha\beta\gamma\delta} \langle\alpha\beta|V|\gamma\delta\rangle a_\beta^\dagger a_\alpha^\dagger a_\gamma a_\delta \tag{5}$$

into Brillouin's theorem (4) and using anticommutation relation of the creation and annihilation operators, we pass to the self-consistency equivalent problem of finding the single-particle occupied states $\{\lambda\}$ which are eigenfunctions of the Hartree-Fock one-body Hamiltonian which in turn depends on the states $\{\lambda\}$ through

$$\langle\alpha|h|\beta\rangle = \langle\alpha|T|\beta\rangle + \sum_{\lambda=1}^{N} \langle\alpha\lambda|V_A|\beta\lambda\rangle\,, \tag{6}$$

where

$$\langle\alpha\lambda|V_A|\beta\lambda\rangle = \langle\alpha\lambda|V|\beta\lambda\rangle - \langle\alpha\lambda|V|\lambda\beta\rangle\,. \tag{7}$$

A determinantal wave function made up of these states gives a stationary point for the expectation value of the Hamiltonian. In general, there will be several stationary points out of which we choose the one which gives minimum to $\langle H\rangle$.

2. – Application to the s-d shell.

The general solution of the self-consistency problem is quite difficult. When applied to nuclei in the s-d shell the problem is greatly simplified under the following set of conditions:

a) *Existence of an* ^{16}O *intert core.*

b) The self-consistency space is limited to the *s-d shell only* and the radial functions are those of the spherical harmonic oscillator.

c) *Angular variation only*, that is in general any state $|\alpha\rangle$ is represented as a linear combination of the twelve functions of the s-d space ($j = \frac{1}{2}; \frac{3}{2}; \frac{5}{2}$)

$$|\alpha\rangle = \sum_{j,m} C_m^{j,\alpha} |jm\rangle \tag{8}$$

and the coefficients $C_m^{j,\alpha}$ are the parameters over which the variation is performed.

d) *Fourfold degeneracy*, that is each level is filled by two protons and two neutrons with their spins up and down. This results in taking the sum in eq. (6) over configurations of $4n$ nucleons.

e) *Occupation weighting.* For treating configurations not containing $4n$ nucleons, an occupation number $\theta(\lambda)$ multiplies the interactions in occupied configurations. When θ goes from zero to unity for a certain state, the occupation of that state grows from zero to four nucleons. This process involves an averaging effect over protons and neutrons. Therefore only nuclei with equal number of protons and neutrons are treated. The reason for such an averaging process is that dealing with configurations not containing $4n$ nucleons one looses the time-reversal invariance of the Hartree-Fock Hamiltonian and the variational parameters $C_m^{j,\alpha}$ may not be real anymore.

f) The one-body part T, in the Hamiltonian, is a sum of harmonic-oscillator energy (h.o.), $\boldsymbol{l}^2$ and $\boldsymbol{l}\cdot\boldsymbol{s}$ forces,

$$T = E_{\text{h.o.}} + \alpha_{l^2}\boldsymbol{l}^2 + \alpha_{l\cdot s}\boldsymbol{l}\cdot\boldsymbol{s}\,. \tag{9}$$

g) The two-body interaction is of the general form:

$$V_{ij} = V_c(r_{ij})\{W + MP^r + BP^\sigma + HP^\tau\}\,. \tag{10}$$

$V_c(r_{ij})$ is a Yukawa or Gaussian potential with certain choice of range and strength parameters.

3. – Characterization of the Hartree-Fock solutions.

Starting with different choices for the variational parameters one gets convergence of the iteration process to several different local minima, the number of which grows when increasing the number of occupied states. The distinction between these different Hartree-Fock solutions is done by the following quantities:

A) *Total energy*:

$$E_0 = \langle \Psi_0|H|\Psi_0\rangle = \sum_\lambda T_{\lambda\lambda} + \tfrac{1}{2}\sum_{\lambda\mu}\langle\lambda\mu|V_A|\lambda\mu\rangle\,. \tag{11}$$

B) *Energy of the system in an excited state.* The wave function for the excited one-particle state is given by

$$\Psi_\lambda^\sigma = a_\sigma^\dagger a_\lambda \Psi_0 \tag{12}$$

and the energy for exciting one particle is

$$\delta E_{\lambda\sigma} = \langle\Psi_\lambda^\sigma|H|\Psi_\lambda^\sigma\rangle - \langle\Psi_0|H|\Psi_0\rangle = \varepsilon_\sigma - \varepsilon_\lambda - \langle\lambda\sigma|V_A|\lambda\sigma\rangle\,, \tag{13}$$

where ε_σ and ε_λ are the Hartree-Fock single-particle energies.

C) Intrinsic quadrupoles.

$$\langle\Psi_0|\hat{Q}_\mu|\Psi_0\rangle = \sum_\lambda \sqrt{\frac{4\pi}{5}}\,\langle\lambda|r^2 Y_{2\mu}|\lambda\rangle\,. \tag{14}$$

D) The moment-of-inertia tensor. The moment-of-inertia tensor $\mathscr{J}$ is defined through

$$\langle\Psi(\omega)|H|\Psi(\omega)\rangle - E_0 = \tfrac{1}{2}\omega\cdot\mathscr{J}\cdot\omega\,, \tag{15}$$

where $\Psi(\omega)$ is the determinantal wave function which minimizes the expectation value of H under the subsidiary condition that $\langle J_x\rangle$, $\langle J_y\rangle$, $\langle J_z\rangle$ have prescribed values. The solution of the new restricted self-consistency problem is obtained by the Lagrange multipliers method. Three Lagrange multipliers ω_x, ω_y, ω_z are introduced and $\Psi(\omega)$ is found such that

$$\delta\langle\Psi(\omega)|H - \boldsymbol{\omega}\cdot\boldsymbol{J}|\Psi(\omega)\rangle = 0\,. \tag{16}$$

The equivalent self-consistency equations for $h(\omega)$ are

$$\langle\alpha|h(\omega)|\beta\rangle = \langle\alpha|T|\beta\rangle + \sum_{\lambda(\omega)}\langle\alpha\lambda(\omega)|V_A|\beta\lambda(\omega)\rangle - \langle\alpha|\boldsymbol{\omega}\cdot\boldsymbol{J}|\beta\rangle \tag{17}$$

and

$$h(\omega)|\lambda(\omega)\rangle = \varepsilon_{\lambda(\omega)}|\lambda(\omega)\rangle\,. \tag{18}$$

The approximation that we make in solving these equations is the one used in deriving the Inglis [4] cranking formula, namely, we neglect the effect of the two-body interactions and take simply

$$h(\omega) = h(0) - \boldsymbol{\omega}\cdot\boldsymbol{J}\,,$$

then in first order perturbation we get for $\mathscr{J}_{\alpha\beta}$:

$$\mathscr{J}_{\alpha\beta} = \sum_{\sigma,\lambda}\frac{\langle\lambda|J_\alpha|\sigma\rangle\langle\sigma|J_\beta|\lambda\rangle + \langle\lambda|J_\beta|\sigma\rangle\langle\sigma|J_\alpha|\lambda\rangle}{\varepsilon_\sigma - \varepsilon_\lambda} \tag{19}$$

with λ running over occupied, and σ over unoccupied states.

4. – Axially symmetric deformed orbitals.

We will study the systematics in the Hartree-Fock spectra of the s-d shell by incorporating the axial-symmetry assumption to the set of conditions given in Sect. 2. In general, symmetry properties, demanded for the Hartree-

Fock Hamiltonian may be introduced into it by properly restricting the set $\{\lambda\}$; if a certain operator Ω leaves the set invariant,

$$\Omega\{\lambda\} = \{\lambda\}\,, \tag{20}$$

and it also commutes with H,

$$[H, \Omega] = 0\,, \tag{21}$$

it will clearly also commute with h,

$$[h, \Omega] = 0\,. \tag{22}$$

In the case of an axially symmetric self-consistent field the trial single-particle states are taken as eigenstates of j_z, that is

$$|\lambda, k\rangle = \sum_j C_k^{j,\lambda}|jk\rangle\,, \tag{23}$$

k is the projection of j along the z-axis. For the axially-symmetric case the characterizing quantities are

$$E_0,\quad \delta E_{\lambda\sigma},\quad \langle Q_0\rangle \qquad \text{and} \qquad \mathscr{J}_{xx} = \mathscr{J}_{yy} = 2\sum_{\lambda,\sigma}\frac{|\langle\sigma|J_x|\lambda\rangle|^2}{\varepsilon_\sigma - \varepsilon_\lambda}\,. \tag{24}$$

Figure 1 shows the axially symmetric Hartree-Fock spectra for the nuclei in the s-d shell. The two-body force in deriving these spectra is of Yukawa shape with range 1.37 fermi strength 50 MeV and Rosenfeld mixture. In the single-body part $\alpha_{l^2} = 0$ and $\alpha_{l\cdot s} = 2.8$ MeV.

The main feature of these spectra is the occurrence of an energy gap between occupied and unoccupied states. We also find that the self-consistent single-particle level is depressed as its occupation number increases. These level depressions reflect the pairing properties of the two-body interactions both in the $T = 0$ and $T = 1$ isospin states. The consequent effect on the Inglis formula is to increase the important energy denominators and thereby to obtain an agreement with the experimental moments of inertia. Another feature of the spectra shown in this figure is the different structure of the single-particle spectra of systems in the first half of the shell and in the second half. The single-particle level reordering reflects itself in the change from positive quadrupole moments in the first half to negative values in the second half of the shell.

It is of great interest to compare the self-consistent deformed orbitals with those of the Mottelson-Nilsson [5] model. In this model the nucleons are assumed to be moving in an axially symmetric deformed harmonic-oscillator

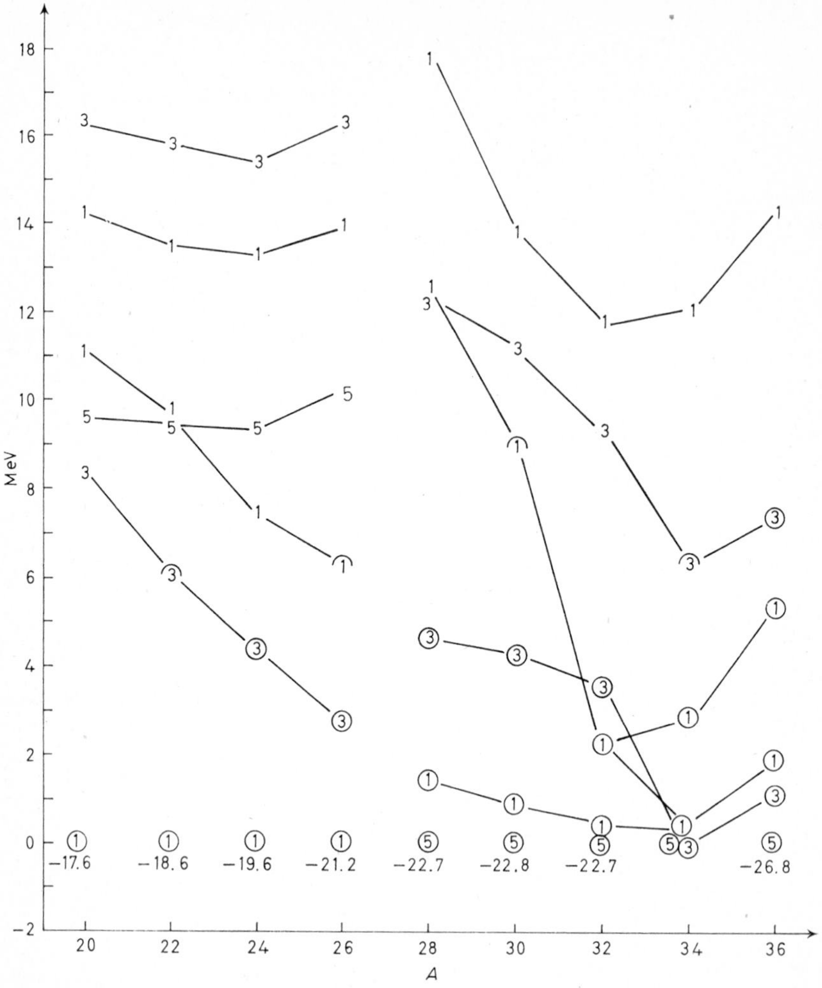

Fig. 1. – Single-particle Hartree-Fock spectra in *s-d* shell. Lowest axially symmetric solutions. Rosenfeld mixture, $V_0 = -50$ MeV, $d_{\frac{5}{2}} = -7.0$, $d_{\frac{3}{2}} = 0$, $s_{\frac{1}{2}} = -4.2$.

well. The set of wave functions and energies is obtained by diagonalizing the one-body Hamiltonian in a spherical shell-model representation.

In Fig. 2 the variation of the single-particle spectra of ^{24}Mg with the strength of the two-body force is plotted.

The resemblance to the Nilsson curve (which is a function of η) is striking.

In Fig. 3 comparison between the self-consistent spectra of ^{20}Ne and ^{24}Mg with the suitable Nilsson spectra is done. In the Nilsson spectra one finds no special separation between occupied and unoccupied states. The level depression mentioned before is completely neglected in the Nilsson model, therefore moments of inertia calculated with Nilsson wave functions and

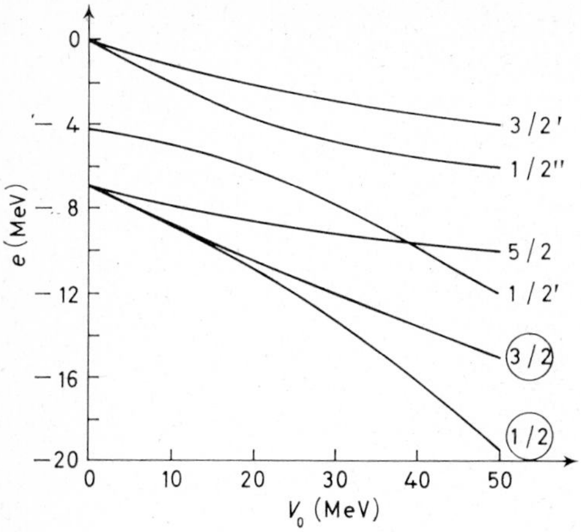

energies fall far above the experimental values and in fact coincide with the rigid-body values.

Figure 4 is a plot of y *vs.* x of the occupied $k=\frac{1}{2}$ state in ^{20}Ne defined by

$$(25)\quad |k=\tfrac{1}{2}\rangle = x|\tfrac{5}{2},\tfrac{1}{2}\rangle - y|\tfrac{3}{2},\tfrac{1}{2}\rangle + z|\tfrac{1}{2},\tfrac{1}{2}\rangle .$$

Fig. 2. – Single-particle self-consistent energies, for ^{24}Mg, as a function of the strength of the two-body interaction, V_0.

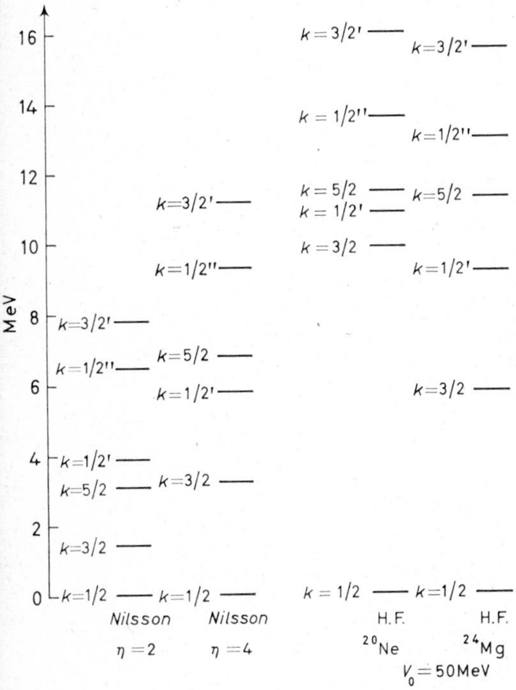

Fig. 3.

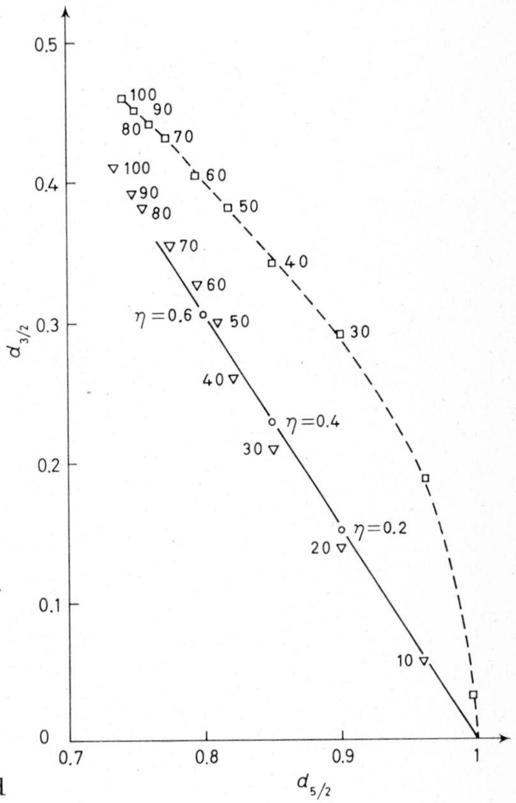

Fig. 4. – Plot of x *vs.* y for ^{20}Ne ($|k=\frac{1}{2}\rangle = x|\frac{5}{2},\frac{1}{2}\rangle - y|\frac{3}{2},\frac{1}{2}\rangle + |z\frac{1}{2},\frac{1}{2}\rangle$: ○ Nilsson, ▽ pure Wigner force, □ Rosenfeld mixture.

The Nilsson line is exactly reproduced by solving the self-consistency problem with a pure Wigner force. The moment of inertia coincides with the rigid-body value also for this force, and in fact it can be shown that a velocity-independent potential will always give with the cranking formula the rigid-body value [6]. Only when a velocity-dependent part is included in the two-body force one can deviate from the Nilsson line and get the correct moment of inertia [7]. Such case is shown also in this figure by the curved line belonging to the self-consistent solution with the Rosenfeld mixture.

5. – Axially asymmetric deformed states.

In looking for asymmetry regions in the s-d shell all the conditions of Sect. 2 are retained apart from the axial-symmetry restriction. In the present treatment each level is chosen in the form

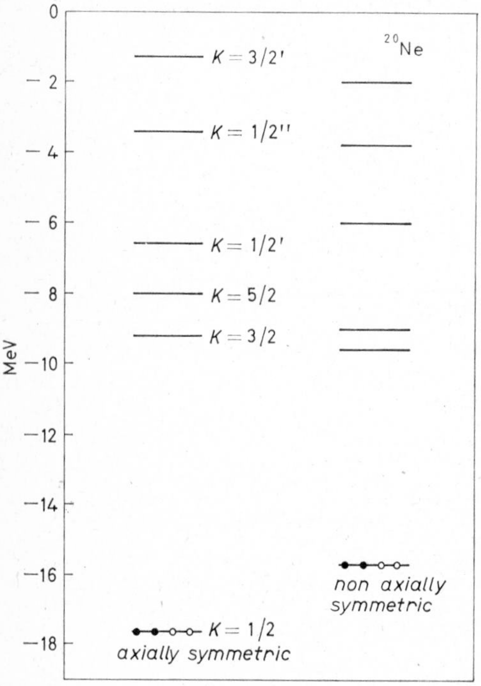

Fig. 5.

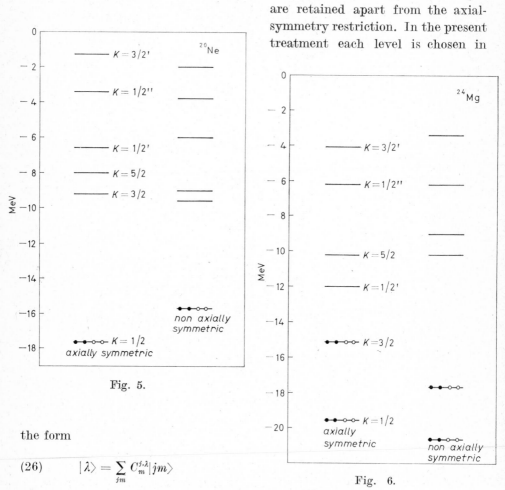

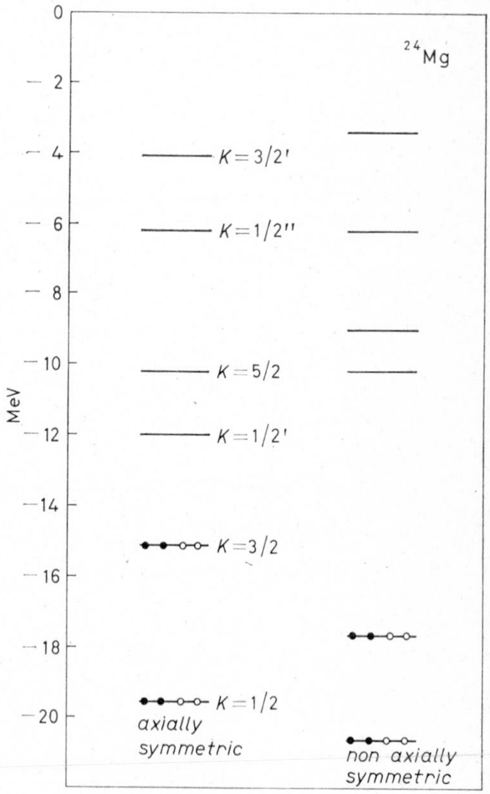

Fig. 6.

$$|\lambda\rangle = \sum_{jm} C_m^{j,\lambda} |jm\rangle \tag{26}$$

with $C_m^{j,\lambda}$ vanishing unless $m - \frac{1}{2}$ is even. Thus the summation in (10) goes over the states $d^{\frac{5}{2}}_{\frac{5}{2}}$, $d^{\frac{5}{2}}_{\frac{1}{2}}$, $d^{\frac{3}{2}}_{\frac{1}{2}}$, $s^{\frac{1}{2}}_{\frac{1}{2}}$, $d^{\frac{5}{2}}_{-\frac{3}{2}}$, $d^{\frac{3}{2}}_{-\frac{3}{2}}$ These states $|\lambda\rangle$ are invariant under rotations through π radians about the z-axis:

$$R_z(\pi)|\lambda\rangle = \pm i|\lambda\rangle \,. \tag{27}$$

The physical meaning of these restrictions on the intrinsic structure is that the nucleus may assume an ellipsoidal shape with x, y, z being the principal axes. The three principal moments of inertia $\mathscr{J}_{xx}$, $\mathscr{J}_{yy}$ and $\mathscr{J}_{zz}$ are determined by eq. (19). The extra freedom allowed to the intrinsic state by removing the restriction of axial symmetry results in a rearrangement of the single-particle levels. Therefore we generally find competition between the lowest axially symmetric and axially asymmetric intrinsic states. Two such typical situations are illustrated in Fig. 5 and 6.

In this figures a comparison between the single-particle spectra for the axially symmetric and axially asymmetric cases in ^{20}Ne and ^{24}Mg is done. The force parameters are $V_0 = 50$ MeV, $\alpha_{l \cdot s} = 2.8$ MeV with the Rosenfeld mixture.

Figure 7 gives the lowest Hartree-Fock solution for even-even nuclei in the shell. By allowing possible asymmetry the energy gap between occupied

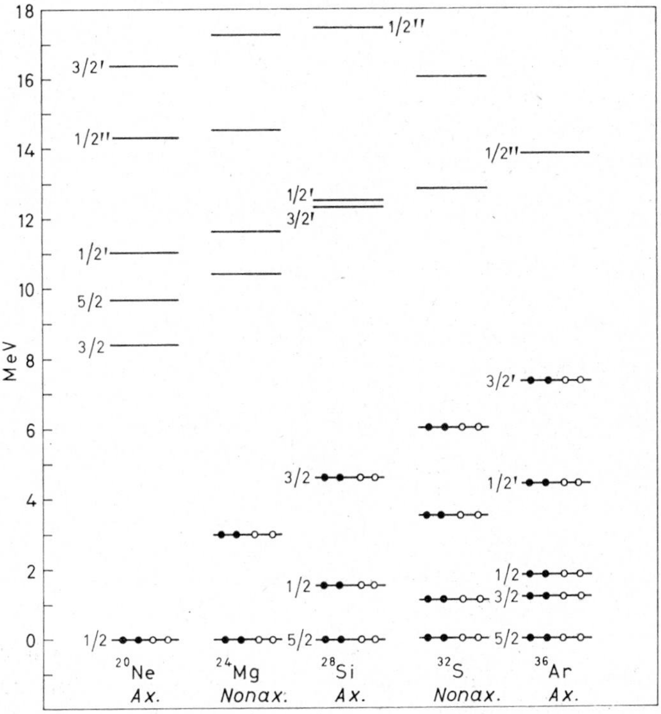

Fig. 7. – Lowest Hartree-Fock single-particle spectra in the s-d shell. Rosenfeld mixture, $V_0 = -50$ MeV, $d_{\frac{5}{2}} = -7.0$, $d_{\frac{3}{2}} = 0$, $s_{\frac{1}{2}} = -4.2$.

and unoccupied states is established for all cases. Two regions of axial asymmetry are found around ^{24}Mg and ^{32}S.

In Fig. 8 the moment-of-inertia parameters are plotted as function of mass number. The Nilsson spectrum values, the previous axially symmetric results for ^{24}Mg and ^{32}S and the average experimental values are shown. In the two asymmetry regions it is found that

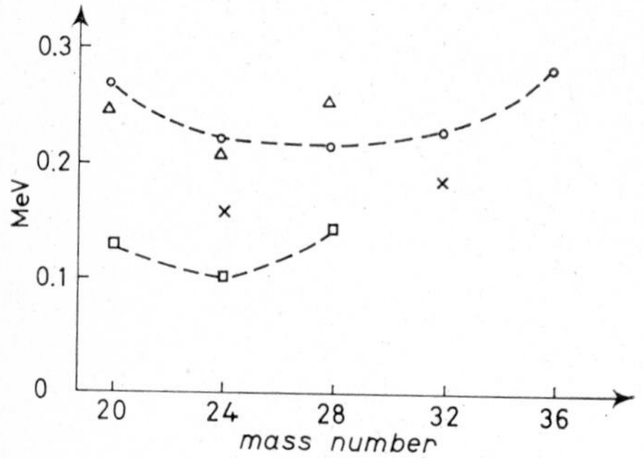

Fig. 8. – ○ present results, × former axially symmetric results, □ Nilsson spectrum results, △ average experimental values.

$$(28) \qquad \mathscr{I}_{xx} \approx \mathscr{I}_{yy} \qquad \text{and} \qquad \mathscr{I}_{zz} < \mathscr{I}_{xx} \,.$$

Thus the ground-state rotational band may still be approximated by a pure rotator with

$$(29) \qquad \mathscr{I} = \tfrac{1}{2}(\mathscr{I}_{xx} + \mathscr{I}_{yy}) \,.$$

It is of interest to compare the three moments of inertia of the self-consistent solutions with those of the irrotational model of BOHR and MOTTELSON [8]. Their parameters β and γ were used by DAVYDOV and FILIPPOV [9] to get energies of an even-even asymmetric rotator. There we have

$$(30) \qquad \mathscr{I}_\alpha = 4B\beta^2 \sin^2(\gamma - \tfrac{2}{3}\pi\alpha) \,, \qquad \alpha = 1, 2, 3 \,.$$

The extent to which one can fit the three moments of inertia of the self-consistent spectra with the two parameters β and γ is shown in Fig. 9 by the crosses. This enables us to judge the applicability of the Davydov and Filippov treatment in the *s-d* region.

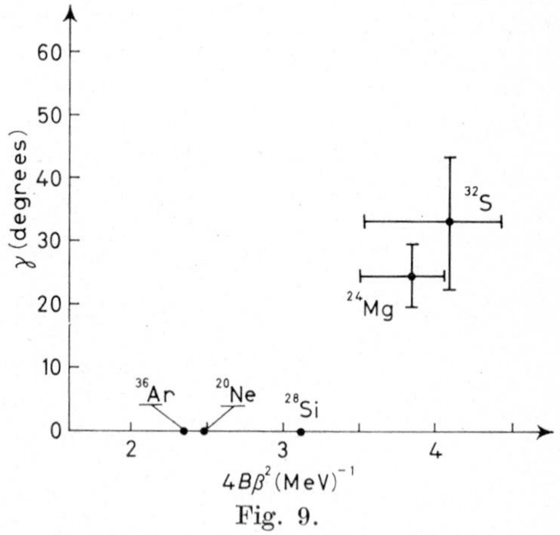

Fig. 9.

We conclude from this investigation of the systematics in the Hartree-Fock spectra of the *s-d* shell that the self-consistency method is an improved prescription for determining the appropriate deformed orbitals needed to describe the behavior of the nuclei in the shell.

REFERENCES

[1] I. Kelson: *Phys. Rev.*, **132**, 2189 (1963).
[2] I. Kelson and C. A. Levinson: *Phys. Rev.*, **134**, B 269 (1964).
[3] J. Bar-Touv and I. Kelson: *Phys. Rev.*, **138**, B 1035 (1965).
[4] D. R. Inglis: *Phys. Rev.*, **96**, 1059 (1954).
[5] S. G. Nilsson: *Kgl. Danske Videnskab. Selskab, Mat. Fys. Medd.*, **29**, No. 16 (1965).
[6] R. M. Rockmore: *Phys. Rev.*, **116**, 469 (1959).
[7] J. Bar-Touv and C. A. Levinson: to be published.
[8] A. Bohr and B. R. Motellson: *Kgl. Danske Viedenskab. Selskab, Mat. Fys. Medd.*, **27**, No. 16 (1953).
[9] A. S. Davidov and G. F. Filippov: *Nucl. Phys.*, **8**, 237 (1958).

Parity-Mixing in Spherical Nuclei.

K. BLEULER
Institute of Theoretical Nuclear Physics - Bonn

1. – Introduction and survey.

The first aim of this lecture is to give the mathematical reasons for a relative strong parity-mixing of the single-particle states in heavier spherical nuclear structures. This means the occurrence of characteristic admixtures of opposite-parity states due to special spin-dependent terms in the empirical nucleon-nucleon interaction (OPEP, $\boldsymbol{\sigma}_1 \cdot \boldsymbol{\sigma}_2$ term; compare Sect. **2** and Sect. **4**). Our main point is to observe that our effect *cannot* be treated merely by ordinary perturbation theory because of the existence of constructive interferences of all orders (Sect. **3**). We use instead a variation principle and we obtain in a natural way a generalized Hartree-Fock system (Sect. **5**). It contains a new type of wave functions and it leads at an intermediate stage to over-all states which violate parity conservation. We might therefore speak of a « collective parity deformation ». On the other hand, all 2-body forces we use are, of course, parity conserving and thus our complete nuclear state will again correspond to a sharp parity. For this reason we have to use a final projection which has a strong formal analogy to the well-known case of deformed nuclei (Sect. **6**). What remains might be visualized as a rather intensive parity exchange in between individual nucleons which appears quite natural also from the view point of the pion exchange. (The pseudoscalar character of the corresponding field plays a decisive role in this connection.)

In a second part we discuss the consequences on empirical properties (Sect. **7**). In fact our new state function which differs essentially from the conventional form yields a natural interpretation of several characteristic nuclear data: the position of the magnetic moments in between the Schmidt lines, a displacement of the single-particle levels which in effect is very similar to the action of a strong $\boldsymbol{l}\cdot\boldsymbol{\sigma}$ term, and finally, the polarization of scattered nucleons which again corresponds to the effect of an $\boldsymbol{l}\cdot\boldsymbol{\sigma}$ term. It seems, therefore, that the well-known difficulty of the strength of the spin-orbit coupling (in relation to the $\boldsymbol{L}\cdot\boldsymbol{S}$ term in the 2-body potential, which appears to be too weak) is overcome in a natural way. In addition the more detailed behaviour of magnetic moments becomes understandable.

2. – The basis of the calculations.

We give here an outline of our calculations in a somewhat simplified framework. We assume first the existence of a phenomenological spherical potential of the Wood-Saxon type (*). (For simplicity we omit completely the conventional $\boldsymbol{l}\cdot\boldsymbol{\sigma}$ term although it will be included in a later stage of our work.) The corresponding single-particle wave-functions (using conventional notations) then read

$$\varphi_{jlm_j} = R_l(r)P_{jlm_j}(\theta\varphi S) . \tag{1}$$

They exhibit the well-known degeneracy.

We now add the OPEP as an additional direct interaction (for simplicity we deal here only with one kind of nucleons):

$$T_{12} = -g^2(\text{grad}_1\,\boldsymbol{\sigma}_1)(\text{grad}_2\,\boldsymbol{\sigma}_2)\cdot\frac{\exp[-\mu r_{12}]}{r_{12}} . \tag{2}$$

This potential is very suitable for mathematical computations but we use also interaction terms of the $\boldsymbol{\sigma}_1\cdot\boldsymbol{\sigma}_2$ type which produce a similar parity-mixing effect in our calculations. A cut-off as well as the $\tau_1\tau_2$ operator have been included in the general case.

3. – Intuitive reason for the parity mixing.

We now consider the special properties of the OPEP according to (2); in fact we may write

$$T_{12} \approx (\boldsymbol{\sigma}_1\,\boldsymbol{r}_{12})(\boldsymbol{\sigma}_2\,\boldsymbol{r}_{12})f(r_{12}) . \tag{3}$$

An expansion starting from the centre yields as a first term the expression

$$T^0_{12} \approx (\boldsymbol{\sigma}_1\boldsymbol{r}^0_1)(\boldsymbol{\sigma}_2\boldsymbol{r}^0_2) , \tag{4}$$

where $\boldsymbol{r}^0_1$ and $\boldsymbol{r}^0_2$ represent the unit vectors pointing from the centre of the spherical potential to particle 1 and particle 2, respectively. We first consider

(*) M. BEINER: *Thesis* (Bonn, 1964); a best-fit potential has been determined from empirical data.

this term from the viewpoint of perturbation theory, the unperturbed system being formed by the wave-functions (1). The main point is that the single-particle operators $(\boldsymbol{\sigma r}^0)$ are just reversing the parities of these states:

(5) $$(\boldsymbol{\sigma r}^0) \equiv P_{\text{op}}\,, \qquad (\boldsymbol{\sigma r}^0)^2 = I\,.$$

We therefore have the following characteristic diagrams:

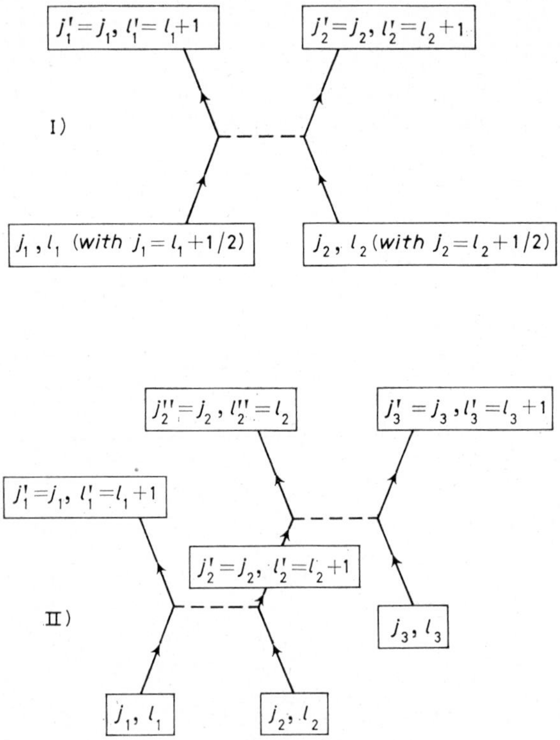

Fig. 1.

In the general case (in abbreviated notation):

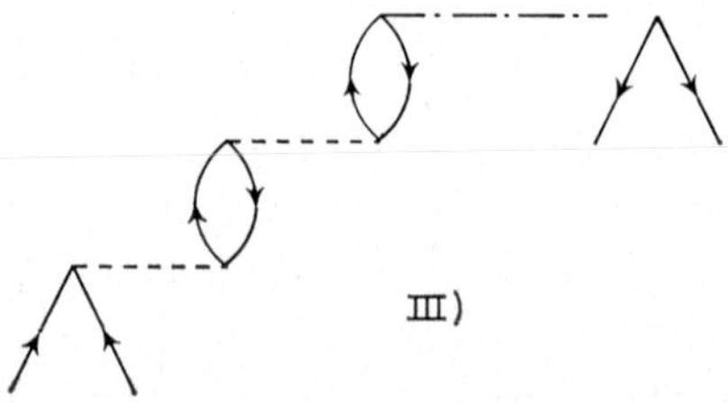

Fig. 2.

It is now important to observe that all diagrams of type I add up constructively (same signs) whereas also the diagrams of type II (and more general ones according to III) give a constructive interference with the former ones. This second effect is related to the sign of the OPEP in (2) which is characteristic for the pion exchange.

It is clear that all these diagrams exhibit a simultaneous change of parity for all pairs of particles. Therefore, it might be conjectured that a relatively strong mixing occurs, in principle due to the summation of certain characteristic diagrams.

4. – Generalized Hartree-Fock approximation.

In view of this fact it seems now quite natural to assume a parity mixing of the single-particle states from the outset of the calculations and to determine its strength with the help of a variational principle: this leads us to a new generalization of the Hartree-Fock method; instead of using a Slater determinant built on single-particle functions with fixed parity (and fixed j for the spherical case) we now use in this determinant parity-mixed states:

$$\Psi_{im_j} = f_{jlm_j} + g_{j\,l+1\,m_j} \qquad \text{(for } j = l + \tfrac{1}{2}\text{)}. \tag{6}$$

Again, we minimize the expectation value of the energy with respect to a state determined by the new Slater determinant which still belongs to a spherical structure if all subshells are assumed to be filled:

$$\Phi = \underset{\text{(antisym.)}}{A} \; \Pi_{\text{(Prod.)}} \dots (f_{jl} + g_{j\,l+1}) \dots . \tag{7}$$

Here, in principle, the variation of the radial functions of both states (f *and* g) must be considered. In our practical calculations we kept the f's fixed; they were determined from a Wood-Saxon potential and the g's were developed with respect to the excited states φ_n of this potential:

$$g_{jl+1\,m_j} = \sum_n \xi_j^{(n)} \varphi_{n\,jl+1\,m_j} . \tag{8}$$

The Fourier coefficients $\xi^{(n)}$ were then considered as variational parameters in the framework of a Ritz principle.

5. – The parity-mixing part in the Hartree-Fock potential (H.F. potential).

In this generalized scheme the H.F. self-consistent equations now contain as a consequence of (2) and (6) a relatively large spin-dependent additional term inducing a parity-mixing:

(9) $$\left(T_{\text{kin}} + V + (\operatorname{grad} W \cdot \boldsymbol{\sigma})\right)\Psi = E\Psi .$$

V and W are in principle to be determined from all 2-body forces and the Slater determinant (7) formed with the parity-mixed states (9). V might be of a rather complicated structure if the exchange terms are included, but we have checked that these contributions are relatively small (*). In a first approximation we use (for closed subshells) the phenomenological Wood-Saxon potential for V.

The second term in (9) is now due to the parity admixture *and* the direct (nonexchange) part of the OPEP. It is important to observe that every closed subshell ($m_j = -j,\ -j+1 \dots +j$) contributes in a simple and characteristic way to W:

(10) $$W(\boldsymbol{x}) = -g^2 \sum_j (\nabla^2 - \mu^2)^{-1} \operatorname{grad} \boldsymbol{\rho}_j(\boldsymbol{x}) \quad (^{**})$$

with

(11) $$\boldsymbol{\rho}_j(\boldsymbol{x}) = \sum_{(m_j=-j,\dots+j)} \left(\Psi_{jm_j}(\boldsymbol{x})\boldsymbol{\sigma}\Psi_{jm_j}(\boldsymbol{x})\right)$$

($\boldsymbol{\rho}(\boldsymbol{x})$ represents the so-called spin sum and includes the summation over all spin indices). The $\boldsymbol{\rho}_j(\boldsymbol{x})$ are (pseudo-) vector fields with spherical symmetry:

(12) $$\boldsymbol{\rho}_j(\boldsymbol{x}) = \boldsymbol{x} f_j(r) , \qquad \left(r = |\boldsymbol{x}|\right).$$

(This can be shown easily with group-theoretical methods: the summation over *all* m's is decisive.) If the Ψ's were now to have a *fixed* parity we would immediately see from (11)

(13) $$\boldsymbol{\rho}(\boldsymbol{x}) = +\boldsymbol{\rho}(-\boldsymbol{x}) ,$$

but we also conclude from (12)

$$\boldsymbol{\rho}(\boldsymbol{x}) = -\boldsymbol{\rho}(-\boldsymbol{x})$$

and it is clear that $\boldsymbol{\rho}$ *vanishes* in this case (***).

On the other hand we obtain for the characteristic cross-terms in expression (11) for the parity-*mixed* case:

(14) $$\boldsymbol{\rho}_j(\boldsymbol{x}) = \sum_{m_j} \left(f_{jlm_j}(\boldsymbol{x})\boldsymbol{\sigma} g_{j\,l+1\,m_j}(\boldsymbol{x})\right) = -\varrho(-\boldsymbol{x})$$

(*) J. MÜLLER, in collaboration with the author: to be published.

(**) Using the abbreviation $(\nabla^2 - \mu^2)^{-1}$ for the Green function of the Yukawa field.

(***) This shows that the main contribution from the OPEP just cancels out in closed subshells if we had a *fixed* parity!

and it can be seen that we have now a nonzero (mainly additive) result for $\boldsymbol{\rho}$. It is thus clear that the W-term in (9) is just due to the admixture. On the other hand this term *inforces* the parity mixing! In other words: it is realized that OPEP is by now « allowed to act » and that it determines the parity-mixing in a self-consistent way. (One might also infer from this argument that the effect depends critically on the strength of the coupling constant g^2 (*).) It is also easily seen that the $(\boldsymbol{\sigma}_1 \cdot \boldsymbol{\sigma}_2)$ term acts in very much the same way.

6. – The final projection.

So far even our complete H.F. wave function (7) has no fixed parity either but it is now important to observe that our solution exhibits a characteristic degeneracy. In fact the « mirror-function »

$$\Phi' = A\Pi \dots (f_{jl} - g_{j\,l+1}) \dots \equiv P_0 \Phi \text{ (**)} , \tag{15}$$

which leads to

$$W' = -W , \qquad V' = +V , \tag{16}$$

corresponds exactly to the same total H.F. energy and satisfies the same relations of consistency.

We therefore introduce the two new (projected) total state-functions Ψ^+ and Ψ^-:

$$\Psi^+ = \Phi + \Phi' , \qquad \Psi^- = \Phi - \Phi' . \tag{17}$$

It is immediately clear that these states *do* correspond to a well-defined (but opposite) parity and they represent the final result of our generalized H.F. method. The energies for the two states are different and it can be checked that Ψ^+ always corresponds to the stronger binding. The energy difference, however, decreases rather rapidly with increasing A. For heavy nuclei it is therefore important to estimate this difference with the help of a more refined approximation: we use the BCS method which yields a few MeV (***). On the other hand, it has also been checked that the OPEP with the empirical coupling constant from pion scattering is in the case of heavier nuclei large enough to induce an appreciable mixing ($\xi^{(n)} \approx 0.2$).

At this stage it is worth-while to develop our total wave-functions $\Psi^\pm$ with respect to the original fixed-parity single-particle states f and g (abbre-

---

(*) This fact has been shown explicitly by J. Müller.

(**) P_0 represents apart from a *sign* the parity operator.

(***) I am indebted to Dr. Becchi (Genova) for enlightening discussions on this point.

viated notation):

$$(18)\quad \begin{cases} \Psi^+ = (A\Pi f \dots f \dots) + \sum (A\Pi f \dots \underbrace{g \dots g}_{\substack{\text{(2 factors}\\ \text{of opposite parity)}}} \dots) + \\ \qquad\qquad + \sum (A\Pi f \dots \underbrace{g \dots g \dots g \dots g}_{\text{(4 factors of opposite parity)}} \dots)\,, \\ \Psi^- = (A\Pi f \dots \underbrace{g}_{\text{(1 factor)}} \dots) + \sum (A\Pi f \dots \underbrace{g \dots g \dots g}_{\text{(3 factors)}} \dots)\,. \end{cases}$$

We thus have a linear combination of Slater determinants, every one corresponding to a well-defined parity. The first one in the Ψ^+ function is just the ground state of the conventional shell structure and it is immediately seen that all the following ones correspond exactly to the perturbation diagrams of Sect. **2**. Thus we have, to a certain extent, summed up these different graphs. In addition, the first term in Ψ^- represents just an excited shell-structure state with opposite parity; the corresponding infinite series of admixtures have the consequence of lowering this state appreciably.

In this (developed) form it seems rather difficult to carry out explicit computations because the high orders seem to give the main contributions (at least in the case of heavier nuclei). On the other hand, many characteristic nuclear properties are already determined in a reasonable approximation from the unprojected functions Φ (7) which are given in closed, explicit form.

In this connection we have a very close formal analogy to the theory of deformed nuclei. There, Slater determinants built on states *without* a fixed j (but so far fixed parity) are considered. Again, there appears a (infinite) degeneracy and a final projection is used yielding thus the rotational states which now correspond to our typical opposite-parity state. This relatively low-lying state could therefore be interpreted as a « collective parity-oscillation ».

Finally, it should be mentioned that our H.F. eqs. (9) and (10) have also a rather intuitive signification in the framework of a semiclassical meson theory for the pion: (10) represents the production of the field by the sources, whereas (9) contains the action of the average field on the nucleons (*).

7. – Survey of the numerical results.

So far two kinds of explicit calculations have been carried out: a restricted number of $\xi^{(n)}$'s according to (8) were used as variational parameters in order

---

(*) This was actually the viewpoint of the first publications of the author with Ch. Terreau (HPA 1957) and the thesis under the auspices of the author by J.-P. Amiet (HPA 1960).

to obtain an estimate of the magnitude. This approximate solution was then used as the starting point of a self-consistent determination for the g's (and hence the W) going back and forth in between eqs. (9) and (10). So far the potential $V(r)$ was not varied in this procedure; it was chosen from suitable phenomenological properties. (A rough check of its approximate self-consistency has, however, been made.) The results thus obtained correspond to $\xi^{(n)}$-values which range from 0.1 to 0.3 (*) in the realm of heavier nuclei. The potential $W(r)$ has been determined for a large number of spherical nuclei and the corresponding characteristic functions are then constantly used in all practical applications of our theory:

A) *The magnetic moments.* – We first construct the state function (17) for the $(2N+1)$-particle case with the help of the corresponding function for $2N$ nucleons. We obtain a rather intuitive result:

$$\Psi_{2N+1} = \Psi^{+}_{2N} f_{jl} + \Psi^{-}_{2N} g_{j\,l+1}\,, \tag{19}$$

where f and g $(f+g=\psi)$ represent the state of the last unpaired particle. Ψ^{+} and Ψ^{-} correspond to spin 0, Ψ_{2N+1} has the assignment $J=j$ and a fixed parity determined from the parity of l.

Thus, we obtained a natural generalization of ordinary shell structure, which shows very explicitly the parity mixing of the single-particle states, whereas the total state retains its well-defined parity.

The magnetic moments corresponding to the separate functions f and g lie, of course, on the Schmidt lines and it is therefore immediately clear that our mixing-parameter ξ determines directly the position in between the two lines:

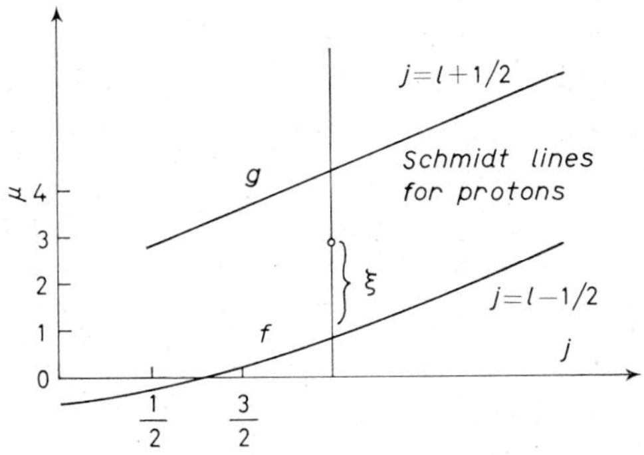

Fig. 3.

(*) J. Müller: to be published.

According to Müller's (*) calculations these values just account for the discrepancies so far encountered for the nuclei near the closed shells (or subshells).

B) *The scattering.* – The eq. (19) may also be used in a somewhat generalized sense for the higher excited states of the last particles which lie already in the continuum. We still take (for heavy nuclei) the same function for W as for the ground state, but we take the energy difference E_0 between the two core states Ψ^+ and Ψ^- into account. We then obtain the following system for the two parts f and g of the wave function Ψ of the last particle (disregarding for simplicity the conventional $(\boldsymbol{l}\cdot\boldsymbol{\sigma})$-term):

$$(20)\qquad \begin{cases} Vf + (\text{grad}\, W\boldsymbol{\sigma})\, g = Ef\,, \\ Vg + (\text{grad}\, W\boldsymbol{\sigma})\, f = (E - E_0)\, g\,. \end{cases}$$

It is quite interesting to realize that this system also yields the well-known polarization effect characterized by the operator

$$(21)\qquad ([\boldsymbol{k}_{\text{inc}} \times \boldsymbol{k}_{\text{scat}}]\cdot\boldsymbol{\sigma})\,.$$

D. SCHÜTTE (**) obtained very reasonable results, again with the same functions $W(r)$ for various nuclei ($E_0 \approx 3$ to 8 MeV). On the other hand this theory predicts also a relatively strong inelastic-scattering channel which is due to the core excitation $\Psi^+ \rightarrow \Psi^-$. The corresponding intensities and polarizations are directly related to the elastic channel and an experimental check of this new channel therefore appears most interesting (***).

For the moment there are only rather scarse indications for the new (*.*) Ψ^- level which is difficult to see in nuclear spectroscopy. The inelastic-scattering process seems to be by far the most adequate process to find this level.

C) *Spin-orbit splitting.* – The occurence of the new term (grad $W\boldsymbol{\sigma}$) in the single-particle Hamiltonian also induces a very peculiar shift of the single-particle levels with respect to the former, conventional case. Again, we use the same $W(r)$ and we assume that the final projection will *not* alter the relative distances of these levels appreciably (.*.). (A similar situation occurs in the theory of deformed nuclei; for the lowest levels the projection $\Psi^+ = \Phi + \Phi'$

(*) To be published.

(**) Work to be published.

(***) Dr. SCHÜTTE made explicit calculations; he obtains a very large polarization effect for this case.

(*.*) J. MÜLLER found so far about 5 levels distributed over the complete periodic table which might correspond to the Ψ^- state.

(.*.) The question of stability (energy increase) has also been studied at the author's Institute by J.-P. AMIET and P. HUGUENIN (N. Ph., 1963).

must be used.) The displacements may now—using again eq. (9)—be visualized from the following sketch (at left the degenerate single-particle levels without ($\boldsymbol{l\sigma}$) term in the potential V alone; at the right-hand side after the introduction of the new additional term (grad $W\boldsymbol{\sigma}$):

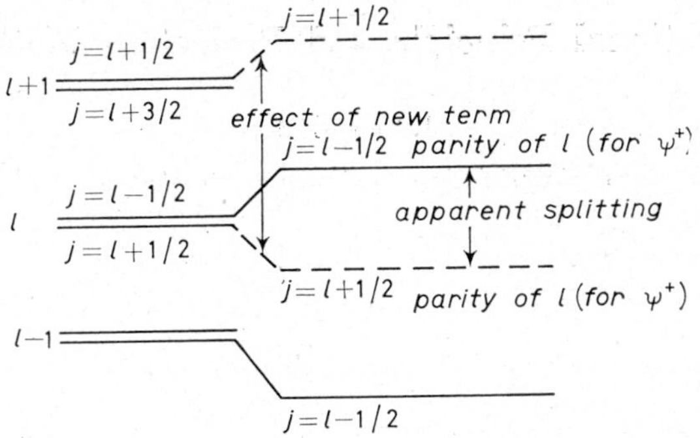

Fig. 4.

At the left side we have the natural succession of levels due to the centrifugal potential. The effect of a relatively *strong* W term is a rather intense linear combination of states with the *same* j but opposite parity and, therefore, in general an *increase* of the relative distance of these levels. Considering in addition the assignments of the total state after the projection with the positive sign (Ψ^+) it is seen that the new pattern of levels exactly corresponds to the vell-known effect of an *apparent* ($\boldsymbol{l\sigma}$) term, just with the sign used in nuclear structure. It is a rather striking fact that the same function W used before gives already a large part of the empirically observed splitting. In addition there appears (through the values for W) a direct relation between the magnetic moments and the apparent spin-orbit splitting which can be directly checked in the realm of heavy nuclei near closed shells.

Thus the well-known difficulty with the intensity of the empirical ($\boldsymbol{L}\cdot\boldsymbol{S}$) term in the 2-body potential (giving a too small direct ($\boldsymbol{l\sigma}$) term in the shell structure) appears to be removed (*). At the same time we have another example of the mathematical fact that it may be suitable to violate in the trial-functions of a variation principle the elementary symmetries of the problem. (Angular symmetry in the case of deformed nuclei.) In our case it might be suitable (light nuclei) to introduce the projection before the variation is actually carried out (**). A more detailed publication of this work is under way.

(*) There is a formal similarity to the work of Prof. A. B. Migdal (*Nucl. Phys.*, **57**, 29 (1964)). I am also very thankful to him for a most interesting discussion on this subject.

(**) Dr. B. H. Brandow, with whom I had many interesting discussions, will consider this question in more details.

Variational Principle and Projection Method.

J. Yoccoz

Université de Strasbourg - Strasbourg

Introduction.

When the projection method was first used in 1956 [1] in order to calculate the moments of inertia of the strongly deformed nuclei, a major objection was that, when applied in a similar way to the center-of-mass problem, the total mass does not come out correctly. The calculations were made with shell-model wave functions for the particles, but the use of Hartree-Fock ones does not improve the results very much, and that was the reason why Peierls and Thouless [2] proposed their double-projection formalism.

What we attempt to show is that, when the variational principle is used after projection, the results are correct in the case of the center-of-mass motion, and we will go then to the rotational λ case and see what are the consequences.

1. – Center-of-mass motion.

Suppose we have a Slater determinant $\Phi(\boldsymbol{r})$ built with N (number of particles) individual wave functions $u_i(\boldsymbol{r})$, which we may assume orthonormalized. As the Hamiltonian is translation-invariant, a translated Slater determinant $\Phi(\boldsymbol{r}-\boldsymbol{R})$ will give the same energy, and we are so led to introduce the following linear combination:

$$\Psi(\boldsymbol{r}) = \int g(\boldsymbol{R})\Phi(\boldsymbol{r}-\boldsymbol{R})\,\mathrm{d}\boldsymbol{R}\,.$$

If we want to describe a physical state, with total linear momentum $\hbar\boldsymbol{k}$, we have to choose $g(\boldsymbol{R}) = \exp[i\boldsymbol{k}\cdot\boldsymbol{R}]$. Ψ will be then an eigenfunction of the total linear momentum operator, with eigenvalue $\hbar\boldsymbol{k}$. The variational principle will then be applied to

$$\psi_k = \int \exp[i\boldsymbol{k}\cdot\boldsymbol{R}]\Phi_{(k)}(\boldsymbol{r}-\boldsymbol{R})\,\mathrm{d}\boldsymbol{R}\,,$$

where the notation $\Phi_{(\boldsymbol{k})}(\boldsymbol{r})$ implies that the individual wave functions $u_i(\boldsymbol{r}, \boldsymbol{k})$ (which will be varied) depend a priori on the N particles condition we have imposed on the total linear momentum.

The variational principle reads then

$$\delta I_k = \delta \int \mathrm{d}\boldsymbol{a} \exp[i\boldsymbol{k}\cdot\boldsymbol{a}] \langle \Phi_{\boldsymbol{k}}(\boldsymbol{r}) | H - E(\boldsymbol{k}) | \Phi_{\boldsymbol{k}}(\boldsymbol{r}-\boldsymbol{a}) \rangle = 0 , \tag{1}$$

$\langle\ \rangle$ implies that integration over $\boldsymbol{r}$ is carried out. For $\boldsymbol{k}=0$ we have

$$\delta I_0 = \delta \int \mathrm{d}\boldsymbol{a} \langle \Phi_0(\boldsymbol{r}) | H - E(0) | \Phi_0(\boldsymbol{r}-\boldsymbol{a}) \rangle = 0 . \tag{2}$$

It is easy to show that (1) can be reduced to (2) with the following transformation

$$u_i(\boldsymbol{r}, \boldsymbol{k}) = u_i(\boldsymbol{r}, 0) \exp[i\boldsymbol{k}\cdot\boldsymbol{r}/N],$$

so that

$$\Phi_{(\boldsymbol{k})}(\boldsymbol{r}) = \exp[i\boldsymbol{k}\cdot\boldsymbol{X}]\Phi_0(\boldsymbol{r}) \qquad \left(\boldsymbol{X} = \frac{1}{N}\sum_{i=1}^{N} \boldsymbol{r}_i\right)$$

and

$$E(\boldsymbol{k}) = E(0) + \frac{\hbar^2 k^2}{2NM} .$$

In fact, then,

$$\langle \Phi_{(\boldsymbol{k})}(\boldsymbol{r}) | \Phi_{(\boldsymbol{k})}(\boldsymbol{r}-\boldsymbol{a}) \rangle = \exp[-i\boldsymbol{k}\cdot\boldsymbol{a}] \langle \Phi_0(\boldsymbol{r}) | \Phi_0(\boldsymbol{r}-\boldsymbol{a}) \rangle ,$$

$$\langle \Phi_{)\boldsymbol{k})}(\boldsymbol{r}) | H | \Phi_{(\boldsymbol{k})}(\boldsymbol{r}-\boldsymbol{a}) \rangle = \exp[-i\boldsymbol{k}\cdot\boldsymbol{a}] \langle \Phi_0(\boldsymbol{r}) | H + \frac{\hbar^2 k^2}{2NM} | \Phi_0(\boldsymbol{r}-\boldsymbol{a}) \rangle .$$

So the Hartree-Fock problem for $\boldsymbol{k} \neq 0$ reduces to the Hartree-Fock problem for $\boldsymbol{k}=0$ and the total mass λ comes out correctly.

We will now investigate (2). We shall introduce the following quantities

$[N(\boldsymbol{a})]$ matrix of elements $N_{ij}(\boldsymbol{a}) = \langle u_i(\boldsymbol{r}) | u_j(\boldsymbol{r}-\boldsymbol{a}) \rangle$,

$$N(\boldsymbol{a}) = \det[N(\boldsymbol{a})] = \langle \Phi_0(\boldsymbol{r}) | \Phi_0(\boldsymbol{r}-\boldsymbol{a}) \rangle ,$$

$$[n(\boldsymbol{a})] = [N(\boldsymbol{a})]^{-1} ,$$

$$\langle \Phi_0(\boldsymbol{r}) | H | \Phi_0(\boldsymbol{r}-\boldsymbol{a}) \rangle = N(\boldsymbol{a}) h(\boldsymbol{a}) ,$$

$$h(\boldsymbol{a}) = \sum_i \langle u_i(\boldsymbol{r}) | t | \tilde{u}_i(\boldsymbol{r}, \boldsymbol{a}) \rangle + \\ + \tfrac{1}{2} \sum_{i,j} [\langle u_i(\boldsymbol{r}) u_j(\boldsymbol{r}) | V(\boldsymbol{r}, \boldsymbol{r}') | \tilde{u}_i(\boldsymbol{r}', \boldsymbol{a}) \tilde{u}_j(\boldsymbol{r}', \boldsymbol{a}) \rangle - \text{exchange}] .$$

The $\tilde{u}_i(\boldsymbol{r}, \boldsymbol{a})$ are *a set of functions orthonormal to the set* u_i *for every* $\boldsymbol{a}$, and are defined in terms of the u_i by

$$\tilde{u}_i(\boldsymbol{r}, \boldsymbol{a}) = \sum_{\substack{\text{occupied}\\ \text{states}}} u_j(\boldsymbol{r}-\boldsymbol{a}) n_{ji}(\boldsymbol{a}) ,$$

$$\langle u_j(\boldsymbol{r}), \tilde{u}_i(\boldsymbol{r}, \boldsymbol{a})\rangle = \delta_{ij} \qquad (i, j \text{ occupied states}).$$

Then (2) gives

$$\int N(\boldsymbol{a})\,\mathrm{d}\boldsymbol{a}[t\,\tilde{u}_i(\boldsymbol{r}, \boldsymbol{a}) + \sum_j \langle u_j|V|\tilde{u}_j\rangle \tilde{u}_i - \langle u_j|V|\tilde{u}_i\rangle \tilde{u}_j - \varepsilon_{ij}\tilde{u}_j] = 0 , \tag{3}$$

where t is the single-particle kinetic-energy operator

$$\langle u_j|V|\tilde{u}_j\rangle = \int \mathrm{d}\boldsymbol{r}'\langle u_j(\boldsymbol{r}')|V(\boldsymbol{r}, \boldsymbol{r}')|\tilde{u}_j(\boldsymbol{r}', \boldsymbol{a})\rangle$$

and

$$\varepsilon_{ij}(\boldsymbol{a}) = \langle u_j|t|\tilde{u}_i\rangle + \sum_k [\langle u_j u_k|V|\tilde{u}_i\,\tilde{u}_k\rangle - \text{exchange}] + \delta_{ij}[E_0 - h(\boldsymbol{a})] .$$

In any case

$$E_0 = \int N(\boldsymbol{a})h(\boldsymbol{a})\,\mathrm{d}\boldsymbol{a} \Big/ \int N(\boldsymbol{a})\,\mathrm{d}\boldsymbol{a} .$$

We shall try to solve (3) by a kind of perturbation method in respect to the ordinary Hartree-Fock equations, using the fact that $N(\boldsymbol{a})$ is a strongly peaked function around $\boldsymbol{a}=0$. For simplification we shall consider only a translation along a definite axis, $0x$ for example. We will suppose that parity is a good quantum number for Φ and therefore for Ψ. $N(a)$ is then a real, even function of a. We will introduce

$$u_i = u_i^0 + \Gamma u_i^{(1)} + \Gamma^2 u_i^{(2)} + \dots ,$$

where Γ is the width of the function $N_0(a) = \langle\Phi_0^0(\boldsymbol{r})|\Phi_0^0(\boldsymbol{r}-\boldsymbol{a})\rangle$, Φ_0^0 being built with the functions u_i^0. Γ decreases essentially like $1/N$ when the number N of particles increases.

Then

$$\int N(a)a^{2p}\,\mathrm{d}a \Big/ \int N(a)\,\mathrm{d}a = \lambda_p \Gamma^p$$

where λ_p is a shape-dependent numerical factor of order unity. (3) can be written symbolically

$$\int N(a)F(u, a)\,\mathrm{d}a = 0 .$$

Developing

$$F(u, a) = \sum_{\mu \text{ even}} F_\mu(u) a^\mu ,$$

$$N(a) = N_0(a)[1 + v_2 a^2 + \dots] ,$$

$$F_\mu(u) = F_\mu^0(u^0) + \Gamma F_\mu^{(1)}(u^{(0)}, u^{(1)}) + \dots] ,$$

we have

$$(4) \qquad F_0^0(u^0) + \Gamma[F_0^1(u^0, u^{(1)}) + \lambda_1[F_2^{(0)}(u^0) + v_2 F_0^0(u^0)]] + \Gamma^2[\dots] + \dots = 0 .$$

$$(5) \qquad F_0^{(0)}(u^0) = 0$$

are simply the ordinary Hartree-Fock equations. The $u^{(1)}$ are determined by

$$(6) \qquad F_0^{(1)}(u^0, u^{(1)}) + \lambda_1 F_2^0(u^0) = 0 .$$

When the complete basis determined by (5) is used, (6) can be solved by a (infinite) matrix inversion.

When $\boldsymbol{k} \neq 0$, $N(a)$ is no longer an even function, (6) becomes

$$(7) \qquad F_0^1(u^0, u^{(1)}) + \lambda_1[F_2^0(u^0) + ikF_1^0(u^0)] = 0 .$$

A part of the correction $n^{(1)}$ is proportional to k and when introduced in the calculation of the energy gives a contribution in k^2, and therefore a modification of the translational constant. That, we believe, is the reason why the old projection method was not able to give the correct mass.

To have an idea of the importance of the center-of-mass motion upon the determination of the self-consistent solutions, one may remark that, if the potential energy is little affected by this motion, the kinetic energy is decreased by 25 % in the case of ^{4}He and 4 % in the case of ^{16}O. The strongest influence will be on the radius of the self-consistent solutions.

2. – Rotational motion.

We have developed to some length the rather academic case of the translational motion, because one way to generalize to the rotational motion is just to go through the same kind of calculations.

We shall consider only even-even nuclei, axial symmetry and impose on the Slater determinant (which will depend on the quantum number J) the following conditions $K = 0$, $\exp[iJ_z\gamma]\Phi_J = \Phi_J$. Then

$$\psi_J^M = \int Y_J^{*M}(\beta, \alpha) \exp[+iJ_z\alpha] \exp[+iJ_y\beta] \Phi_J(\boldsymbol{r}, \boldsymbol{\sigma})$$

can be a physical state, projected out of the intrinsic state Φ.

The same procedure gives

$$\int_0^{\pi/2} P_J(\cos\beta)\,\mathrm{d}(\cos\beta) N_J(\beta)\big[t\,\tilde{u}_i(\mathbf{r},\boldsymbol{\sigma};\beta) + \sum_j \langle u_j|V|\tilde{u}_j\rangle\,\tilde{u}_i - \langle u_j|V|\tilde{u}_i\rangle\,\tilde{u}_j - \varepsilon_{ij}\tilde{u}_j(\mathbf{r},\boldsymbol{\sigma},\beta)\big] = 0\,, \tag{8}$$

where as before $N_J(\beta) = \langle \Phi_J(\mathbf{r},\boldsymbol{\sigma})|\exp[+iJ_y\beta]|\Phi_J(\mathbf{r},\boldsymbol{\sigma})\rangle$ λ and the set $\tilde{u}_i(\mathbf{r},\boldsymbol{\sigma};\beta)$, orthonormal to the set u_i for every β, is defined by

$$\tilde{u}_i(\mathbf{r},\boldsymbol{\sigma};\beta) = \sum_{\substack{\text{(occupied}\\ \text{states)}}} \exp[+ij_y\beta]u_j(\mathbf{r},\boldsymbol{\sigma})n_{ji}(\beta)\,.$$

$n_{ij}(\beta)$ is the matrix element of the inverse of $[N(\beta)]$.

We will apply to (8) the same perturbation approach as to (3). The width Γ is now a strongly depending function of the deformation and the filling of the shells. A good idea of Γ is given by $\Gamma = 2/\langle\Phi|J_y^2|\Phi\rangle$ and is, in the rare-earth region, of order 1/50.

Developing everything in respect to β, but $N(\beta)\,\mathrm{d}(\cos\beta)$ we get

$$F_0^0(u^0) + \Gamma\left[F_0^1(u^0, u^{(1)}) + \lambda_1\left[F_2^0(u^0) + \left[\gamma_2 - \frac{J(J+1)}{4}\right]F_0^0(u^0)\right]\right] + \Gamma^2[\ldots] + \ldots = 0\,. \tag{9}$$

In (9), Γ refers to the width of $N_0(\beta)$, computed with the u^0. γ_2 takes care of the difference between $N_0(\beta)$ and $N(\beta)$ to this order in Γ and λ_p is defined by

$$\lambda_p\Gamma^p = \int_0^{\pi/2} N_0(\beta)\,\mathrm{d}(\cos\beta)\,\beta^{2p} \bigg/ \int_0^{\pi/2} N_0(\beta)\,\mathrm{d}(\cos\beta)\,.$$

$$F_0^0(u^0) = 0 \tag{10}$$

are the ordinary H.F. equations. The first-order correction, defined by

$$F_0^1(u^0, u^{(1)}) + \lambda_1 F_2^0(u^0) = 0\,, \tag{11}$$

does not depend upon J.

Up to second order in Γ the energy is given by

$$E_J = E_0 + \lambda_1\Gamma E_2 + \lambda_2\Gamma^2 E_4 + J(J+1)\frac{\Gamma^2}{4}E_2[\lambda_2^2 - \lambda_1]\,,$$

$E_0 = \langle\Phi_0|H|\Phi_0\rangle$ is the ordinary H.F. energy,

$E_2 = \frac{1}{2}[\langle\Phi_0|J_y^2|\Phi_0\rangle\langle\Phi_0|H|\Phi_0\rangle - \langle\Phi_0|J_y^2 H|\Phi_0\rangle]\,.$

When the Gaussian form $\exp[-\beta^2/\Gamma]$ is assumed for $N_0(\beta)$, which is a very good approximation,

$$E_J \simeq E_0 - A\langle \boldsymbol{J}^2\rangle + AJ(J+1)\,.$$

A is the rotational constant of the spectrum of the band.

The J-depending corrections to the u^0 appear only in the second order of Γ and modify the energy in the Γ^4 terms. If we believe in the Γ development, these corrections are negligible, but in the higher part of the spectra, and therefore the old formula for the moment of inertia is still valid when H.F. solutions are used for the individual wave functions.

If the moment of inertia is correctly given by the projection method, (11) is essentially equivalent to the minimization of $E_0 - A\langle \boldsymbol{J}^2\rangle$ (terms of Γ^2 being neglected). This is to be compared with the Skyrme Levinson method [3]. In the latter, A, the rotational constant is determined either empirically or by a new condition. Here, A is itself a functional of the u.

The term $-A\langle \boldsymbol{J}^2\rangle$ is of order 2 MeV in the rare-earth region, which is negligible in respect to the total binding energy, but, as this term is strongly depending upon the deformation, we believe that it has some importance in the determination of the energy curves as functions of the shape of the self-consistent field.

Some calculations have been carried out, for ^{12}C, in the following sense. Assume that the u are harmonic-well wave functions, with the two *parameters* $a_\parallel$ and $a_\perp$ characteristic lengths of the well along and perpendicular to the symmetry axis. Assume that we have a two body interaction of Gaussian form, range $b = 2$ fermi depth 44 MeV and Ferrel-Vissher mixture. If a spherical shape is imposed, we have for the binding energy $B = 85$ MeV, and $a_\parallel = a_\perp = 1.54$ fermi. By variation after projection, we get a binding energy $B = 98$ MeV and $a_\parallel = 1.15$ fermi, $a_\perp = 1.70$ fermi. The 2^+ level has an excitation energy of 4.3 MeV and $a_\parallel = 1.20$ fermi, $a_\perp = 1.68$ fermi. The 4^+ level is at 12 MeV, and $a_\parallel = 1.4$ fermi, $a_\perp = 1.6$ fermi.

The deformation decreases when J increases, a surprising fact which can be understood within the method, but for which we have no physical explanation. The equilibrium deformation is strongly modified whether we minimize in respect to the parameters before or after projection. All these results must be taken as illustration, because they seem to depend upon the two-body forces we have used.

We shall now drop the condition: a single Slater determinant with $K = 0$ is projected. Instead we shall write

$$\psi_J^M = \sum_K a_k \int \mathscr{D}^{J*}_{MK}(\alpha\beta\gamma)\exp[+iJ_z\alpha]\exp[+iJ_y\beta]\exp[+iJ_z\gamma]\Phi_k\,.$$

We will still impose $\exp[iJ_y\pi]\Phi_0=\Phi_0$ on the leading term, and define the respective phases of Φ_K and Φ_{-K} $(K>0)$ by

$$\exp[iJ_y\pi]\Phi_K=\Phi_{-K}\,.$$

Then, if we consider the terms $(K\neq 0)$ coupled with the leading part $(K=0)$, the total wave function we project is of the form

$$\Phi_0+a_2[\Phi_2+\Phi_{-2}]+a_4[\Phi_{-4}+\Phi_4]+\ldots+a_1[\Phi_1-\Phi_{-1}]+a_3[\Phi_3-\Phi_{-3}]+\ldots$$

and so has no definite behavior in respect to rotation of π around an axis perpendicular to the symmetry axis.

$\langle\Phi_0|H$ or $1|\exp[-iJ_y\beta]\Phi_K\rangle$ is of order β^K when $K\to 0$ as well as $d^J_{0K}(\beta)$.

So the coupling terms between the $K=0$ and $K=1$ parts are of order Γ, between $K=0$ and $K=2$ of order Γ^2 and so on.

To second order in Γ in the expression of the energy, only the coupling between the $K=0$ and the $K=1$ band may play a role, and may modify the value of the moment of inertia (actually, the coupling term is proportional to $\sqrt{J(J+1)}\Gamma$, and may contribute to the energy with the required form $J(J+1)\Gamma^2$).

Unhappily, little is known about $K=1$ bands in the rare-earth region. It may be observed that the mixing between $K=0$ and $K=2$ is of order Γ^2, that is 10^{-3}, which is a correct order of magnitude.

3. – Summary.

It is shown that when the variational principle is applied to the projected wave function, the function we project being a priori dependent on the additional constraints we impose on the physical state, there is no difficulty about the total mass in the center-of-mass problem. The same kind of calculations leads to no modification of the old formula for the moments of inertia, if we keep the condition $K=0$. But we have to look for mixing between the $K=0$ and $K=1$ band. For some problems, the modification of the Hartree-Fock equations may be important.

REFERENCES

[1] R. E. Peierls and J. Yoccoz: *Proc. Phys. Soc.*, A **70**, 381 (1957); J. Yoccoz: *Proc. Phys. Soc.*, A **70**, 388 (1957).

[2] R. E. Peierls and D. J. Thouless: *Nucl. Phys.*, **38**, 154 (1962).

[3] T. Skyrme: *Proc. Phys. Soc.*, A **70**, 433 (1957); C. A. Levinson: *Phys. Rev.*, **132** 2184 (1963).

Neutron-Proton Pairing Correlations and a Generalized Bogoliubov Transformation.

P. CAMIZ

Istituto di Fisica dell'Università - Roma
Istituto Nazionale di Fisica Nucleare - Sezione di Roma

Introduction.

I will report here some results of a work done by JEAN, COVELLO and myself [1, 2].

The purpose of this work is to develop a method for treating a charge-independent pairing force in a completely symmetrical way, by means of a linear transformation of the Bogoliubov-Valatin kind, which mixes together not only particles and holes of the same kind, but also different particles.

Two kinds of difficulties arise when treating this problem: first, if one deals with a system containing many j values, although belonging to the same major shell, one has to solve a very complicated set of coupled equations which can be solved only numerically by long computational work; second, when mixing neutron and proton operators as well as creation and annihilation operators, not only are the particle numbers (actually the proton and neutron numbers) not conserved, but the total isospin T and its third component T_z are no longer good quantum numbers; so it is necessary to introduce more Lagrangian multipliers in order to adjust the average values of these quantities to the actual values.

Let me give just an outline of the general method for the multi-j-case: let

$$\mathscr{H} = \sum_{jmt} (\varepsilon_{jt} - \lambda_t) c^\dagger_{jmt} c_{jmt} + \tfrac{1}{4} \sum_{jmt} (12|V|34) c^\dagger_1 c^\dagger_2 c_4 c_3 \tag{1}$$

be the shell-model spherically symmetric Hamiltonian where t is the z-component of isospin,

$$(12|V|34) = - G\delta_{-m_1, m_2}\delta_{-m_3, m_4} s_{m_1} s_{m_3} (\delta_{t_1 t_3}\delta_{t_2 t_4} + \delta_{t_1 t_4}\delta_{t_2 t_3}) \tag{2}$$

be a charge-independent pairing interaction and $s_m = (-1)^{j-m}$.

This interaction is effective only in pairs of nucleons coupled to $J=0$, $T=1$.

Following BARANGER [3] we define a new set of operators

$$\eta^{\dagger}_{jm\tau} = \sum_t u_{jt\tau} c^{\dagger}_{jmt} + s_{jm} v_{jt\tau} c_{j-mt} \,, \qquad \tau = 1, 2 . \tag{3}$$

By imposing anticommutation rules to the η's one obtains some orthogonality relations relying the u's and the v's.

Writing down $\mathscr{H}$ in terms of normal products of $\eta^{\dagger}$'s and η's one obtains the usual separation

$$\mathscr{H} = H_{00} + H_{11} + H_{20} + H_{22} + H_{31} + H_{40} .$$

Disregarding the terms containing 4-operators and making the 2-operator terms vanish except for the diagonal ones, *i.e.* the ones containing $\eta^{\dagger}_{jm\tau}\eta_{jm\tau}$ one obtains a set of equations, which, together with the orthogonality conditions and the constraints on the average values of N_{π} and N_{ν} in the quasi-particle vacuum, determines completely the parameters of the transformation u's and v's and the chemical potentials λ_{π} and λ_{ν}. If one defines a quasi-particle vacuum by $|\tilde{0}\rangle = \prod_{\text{all } \alpha} \eta_{\alpha}|0\rangle$, H_{00} represents the vacuum energy and H_{11} represents the quasi-particle energy.

It can be easily seen that, if one omits the mixing term in the pairing interaction, the equations reduce themselves to the ordinary Bogoliubov equations for the pairing between identical particles. Work is now in progress at Orsay for solving the set of equations for a multi-j problem.

1. – Single-j case.

For the single-j case the equations become much simpler; moreover, it is possible to choose a particular representation of the transformation parameters which make the equations solvable analytically. To be precise let us rewrite the transformation in the following way; introducing $\alpha^{\dagger}$ and $\beta^{\dagger}$ for the quasi-particle creation operators:

$$\begin{cases} \alpha^{\dagger}_m = u_{\pi} c^{\dagger}_{\pi m} + u_{\nu} c^{\dagger}_{\nu m} + s_m v_{\pi} c_{\pi-m} + s_m v_{\nu} c_{\nu-m} \,, \\ \beta^{\dagger}_m = w_{\pi} c^{\dagger}_{\pi m} + w_{\nu} c^{\dagger}_{\nu m} + s_m z_{\pi} c_{\pi-m} + s_m z_{\nu} c_{\nu-m} \,, \end{cases} \tag{4}$$

the orthogonality conditions read now

$$\begin{cases} \sum_{t=\pi,\nu} (u_t^2 + v_t^2) = \sum_{t=\pi,\nu} (w_t^2 + z_t^2) = 1 \,, \\ \sum_{t=\pi,\nu} (u_t w_t + v_t z_t) = \sum_{t=\pi,\nu} (u_t z_t - v_t w_t) = 0 . \end{cases} \tag{5}$$

One can define a density matrix ϱ and a pairing tensor K

$$(6)\qquad \begin{cases} \varrho(mt, m't') = \langle\tilde{0}|c^\dagger_{mt}c_{m't'}|\tilde{0}\rangle = \delta_{mm'}(v_t v_{t'} + z_t z_{t'}) , \\ K(mt, m't') = \langle\tilde{0}|c_{mt}c_{m't'}|\tilde{0}\rangle = -\, s_{jm}\delta_{m,-m'}(u_t v_{t'} + w_t z_{t'}) , \end{cases}$$

and by means of ϱ and K the Hartree potential

$$\Gamma_{t_1 t_3} = \Gamma_{t_3 t_1} = -\, G\{\delta_{t_1 t_3} \sum_t \varrho_{tt} + \varrho_{t_1 t_3}\}$$

and the pairing potential

$$\Delta_{t_1 t_2} = \Delta_{t_2 t_1} = -\, 2\Omega G K_{t_1 t_2} ,$$

where

$$(7)\qquad \Omega = \frac{2j+1}{2} .$$

One can write the vacuum energy as

$$(8)\qquad H_{00} = 2\Omega\{\sum_t (\varepsilon_t - \lambda_t)\varrho_{tt} + \tfrac{1}{2} \sum_{tt'} (\varrho_{tt'}\Gamma_{tt'} + K_{tt'}\Delta_{tt'})\} .$$

The elimination of the dangerous terms in the quasi-particle Hamiltonian is equivalent to the minimum problem on H_{00}: so one has to solve $\delta H_{00} = 0$ for variations of the u's etc. which are compatible with the orthogonality relations (5). But one can observe that, following a theorem by BLOCH and MESSIAH [4], that the most general linear transformation can be reduced to a product of three particular transformations; in this case the transformation (4) can be rewritten in matrix form:

$$(9)\qquad \begin{pmatrix} \alpha^\dagger_m \\ \beta^\dagger_m \\ \alpha_{-m} \\ \beta_{-m} \end{pmatrix} =$$

$$= \begin{pmatrix} \cos\psi & \sin\psi & 0 & 0 \\ -\sin\psi & \cos\psi & 0 & 0 \\ 0 & 0 & \cos\psi & \sin\psi \\ 0 & 0 & -\sin\psi & \cos\psi \end{pmatrix} \begin{pmatrix} \cos\alpha & 0 & s_m \sin\alpha & 0 \\ 0 & \cos\beta & 0 & s_m \sin\beta \\ s_{-m}\sin\alpha & 0 & \cos\alpha & 0 \\ 0 & s_{-m}\sin\beta & 0 & \cos\beta \end{pmatrix} \cdot$$

$$\cdot \begin{pmatrix} \cos\varphi & \sin\varphi & 0 & 0 \\ -\sin\varphi & \cos\varphi & 0 & 0 \\ 0 & 0 & \cos\varphi & \sin\varphi \\ 0 & 0 & -\sin\varphi & \cos\varphi \end{pmatrix} \begin{pmatrix} c^\dagger_{\pi m} \\ c^\dagger_{\nu m} \\ c_{\pi -m} \\ c_{\nu -m} \end{pmatrix} .$$

The first matrix from the right produces a rotation of an angle φ around the z-axis in isospin space, the second one makes two Bogoliubov transformations on the new particle basis, mixing each particle with the corresponding hole, the third makes another simple rotation of an angle ψ in this quasi-particle basis. One can easily verify that the density matrix, the pairing tensor, and average values of N, T_z, T^2, H, have simple expressions in terms of the angles φ, α, β, ψ. In particular:

$$(10)\qquad \begin{cases} \langle\tilde{0}|N|\tilde{0}\rangle = 2\Omega(\sin^2\alpha + \sin^2\beta)\,, \\ \langle\tilde{0}|T_z|\tilde{0}\rangle = -\,\Omega\cos 2\varphi(\sin^2\alpha - \sin^2\beta)\,, \\ \langle\tilde{0}|T^2|\tilde{0}\rangle = \Omega^2(\sin^2\alpha - \sin^2\beta)^2 + 2\Omega[(\sin^2\alpha + \sin^2\beta) - \frac{1}{2}(\sin^2\alpha + \sin^2\beta)^2]\,. \end{cases}$$

The minimum problem for H_{00} does not need supplementary conditions because α, β, φ and ψ are independent parameters, so one has to solve

$$(11)\qquad \frac{\partial H_{00}}{\partial\alpha} = \frac{\partial H_{00}}{\partial\beta} = \frac{\partial H_{00}}{\partial\varphi} = \frac{\partial H_{00}}{\partial\psi} = 0\,.$$

It turns out that $\partial H_{00}/\partial\psi \equiv 0$, so that ψ has to be determined by the condition that H_{11} be diagonal in the single-quasi-particle space, and the result is $\sin 2\psi = 0$: one can conclude that for a pairing interaction the third transformation can be neglected. The three remaining equations, after some manipulations become

$$(12)\qquad \begin{cases} 0 = \sin 2\varphi(\sin^2\alpha - \sin^2\beta)[\tilde{\varepsilon}_- + G\cos 2\varphi(\sin^2\alpha - \sin^2\beta)]\,, \\ 0 = \sin 2\alpha[\tilde{\varepsilon}_+ + \cos 2\varphi\,\tilde{\varepsilon}_- - G\sin^2 2\varphi(\sin^2\alpha - \sin^2\beta) - 2G\Omega\cos\alpha]\,, \\ 0 = \sin 2\beta[\tilde{\varepsilon}_+ - \cos 2\varphi\,\tilde{\varepsilon}_- + G\sin^2 2\varphi(\sin^2\alpha - \sin^2\beta) - 2G\Omega\cos\beta]\,, \end{cases}$$

together with the constraints

$$\sin^2\alpha + \sin^2\beta = \frac{N}{2\Omega}\,,$$

$$(\sin^2\alpha - \sin^2\beta)\cos 2\varphi = -\frac{T_z}{\Omega}\,,$$

where $\tilde{\varepsilon}_\pm = \tilde{\varepsilon}_\pi \pm \tilde{\varepsilon}_\nu$ and

$$\tilde{\varepsilon}_t = \varepsilon_t - \frac{GN_t}{\Omega} - \frac{GN_{t'}}{2\Omega} - \lambda_t\,, \qquad t \neq t'\,.$$

There are some solutions which correspond to a particular choice of N and T_z, and which leave some unknown undetermined: we disregard them and consider only the solutions which completely determine the transformation (apart from phase factors) and the chemical potentials λ's.

A first solution, which we call A, is given by (*)

$$(13)\quad \begin{cases} \sin 2\varphi = 0\,, \qquad \sin^2\alpha = \dfrac{N_\pi}{2\Omega}\,, \qquad \sin^2\beta = \dfrac{N_\nu}{2\Omega}\,, \\ \tilde{\varepsilon}_+ = 2G\Omega\left(1-\dfrac{N}{2\Omega}\right), \qquad \tilde{\varepsilon}_- = GT_z\,, \qquad \langle\tilde{0}|T^2|\tilde{0}\rangle = T_z^2 + N\left(1-\dfrac{N}{4\Omega}\right), \\ E^{(A)} = \varepsilon N - \dfrac{G}{2\Omega}\left(\dfrac{3}{4}N^2 + T_z^2\right) + G\left(\dfrac{N^2}{4} + T_z^2\right) - G\Omega N\,. \end{cases}$$

One sees immediately from (9) that this solution corresponds to 2 ordinary Bogoliubov transformations acting separately upon neutrons and protons and that

$$|\tilde{0}\rangle = |\tilde{0}_p\rangle\cdot|\tilde{0}_n\rangle\,.$$

Another solution, which we call B is given by

$$(14)\quad \begin{cases} \sin 2\alpha = 0 \;\; (\sin 2\beta = 0 \;\text{ gives a similar solution, just interchanging the two quasi-particles})\,, \\ \sin^2\alpha = 0\,, \qquad \sin^2\beta = \dfrac{N}{2\Omega}\,, \qquad \cos 2\varphi = \dfrac{2T_z}{N}\,, \\ \tilde{\varepsilon}_- = \dfrac{GT_z}{\Omega}\,, \qquad \tilde{\varepsilon}_+ = G\left\{2\sin^2\alpha(2\Omega-1) + 2\Omega\left(1-\dfrac{N}{\Omega}\right) + \dfrac{N}{2\Omega}\right\}, \\ \langle\tilde{0}|T^2|\tilde{0}\rangle = \left(\dfrac{N}{2}\right)^2 + N\left(1-\dfrac{N}{4\Omega}\right), \\ E_0^{(B)} = \varepsilon N - \dfrac{G}{2\Omega}N^2 + \dfrac{G}{2}N^2 - G\Omega N\,, \qquad N<2\Omega. \end{cases}$$

If $N>2\Omega$ one has to choose $\sin^2\alpha = 1$ but the main features of the solution are the same. One can see that the solution A corresponds to a lower value for the ground-state energy, in fact

$$E_0^{(B)} - E_0^{(A)} = G\left(1-\frac{1}{2\Omega}\right)\left(\frac{N^2}{4} - T_z^2\right) \geqslant 0\,,$$

where the $=$ sign holds when $T_z = N/2$, that is only one kind of nucleons is present in $|\tilde{0}\rangle$. Looking at the average value of T^2 one sees also that for A it attains the minimum value allowed by the transformation, while in B the maximum value of T^2 is reached. If one compares the energies $E_0^{(A)}$ and $E_0^{(B)}$ with the exact ones given by EDMONDS and FLOWERS [5] in terms of seniority v

(*) Here and in the following the superscripts (A), (B), (C) will be used to indicate a quantity referred to solutions A, B, C.

and reduced isospin t

$$(15)\qquad E(N,\,T,\,v,\,t)=\varepsilon N-G\left\{\left[N\left(\Omega+\frac{3}{2}-\frac{N}{4}\right)-T(T+1)\right]-\right.$$
$$\left.-\left[v\left(\Omega+\frac{3}{2}-\frac{v}{4}\right)-t(t+1)\right]\right\},$$

putting in (15) $t=v=0$ and $T=|T_z|$ for $E_0^{(A)}$ and $T=N/2$ for $E_0^{(B)}$, one finds

$$E(N,|T_z|,0,0)=\varepsilon N-G\left(\frac{3}{2}N-|T_z|\right)+G\left(\frac{N^2}{4}+T_z^2\right)-G\Omega N,$$

$$E\left(N,\frac{N}{2},0,0\right)=\varepsilon N-GN+\frac{G}{2}N^2-G\Omega N,$$

which agree with (13) and (14) in the terms of higher oder in Ω. The fact that in the two solutions considered $\langle\tilde{0}|T^2|\tilde{0}\rangle$ is confined to the two extreme values compatible with the transformation is a very strong limitation; one can gain some freedom for the T-values introducing a third Lagrangian multiplier λ_T and solving the variational problem

$$(16)\qquad \delta\langle\tilde{0}|(H-\lambda_\pi N_\pi-\lambda_\nu N_\nu-\lambda_T T^2)|\tilde{0}\rangle=0$$

with the constraint $\langle\tilde{0}|T^2|\tilde{0}\rangle=T(T+1)$.

Now only one general solution C is obtained

$$(17)\qquad \left\{\begin{aligned}
&\sin^2\alpha=\frac{N}{4\Omega}+\frac{R}{2\Omega},\qquad \sin^2\beta=\frac{N}{4\Omega}-\frac{R}{2\Omega},\\
&\cos 2\varphi=-\frac{T_z}{R},\qquad \sin 2\psi=0,\\
&R=\sqrt{T(T+1)-N\left(1-\frac{N}{4\Omega}\right)},\\
&\tilde{\varepsilon}_-=\frac{GT_z}{\Omega},\qquad \varepsilon_+=2G\left(\Omega+1-\frac{1}{2\Omega}\right)\left(1-\frac{N}{2\Omega}\right),\\
&\lambda_T=G\left(1-\frac{1}{2\Omega}\right),\\
&E_0^{(C)}=\varepsilon N-\frac{GN^2}{8\Omega^2}+\frac{GN}{2\Omega}-\frac{GN^2}{8\Omega}-\frac{G}{2\Omega}T(T+1)-\\
&-GN+\frac{GN^2}{4}+GT(T+1)-GN\Omega,
\end{aligned}\right.$$

which again agrees with the exact formula (15) in the large-Ω limit. It can be observed that this solution goes into the A (or B) as far as α, β, φ, E_0 values are concerned if one takes for $\langle\tilde{0}|T^2|\tilde{0}\rangle$ the value corresponding to the solution A (or B).

2. – Excited states.

The quasi-particle energies, given by H_{11} are

$$\begin{cases} E_\alpha^{(A)} = E_\beta^{(A)} = G\Omega\,, & \\ E_\alpha^{(B)} = G\Omega\left[1-\dfrac{N}{\Omega}\left(1-\dfrac{1}{2\Omega}\right)\right], & E_\beta^{(B)} = G\Omega\,, \qquad \text{if } N<2\Omega, \\ E_\alpha^{(B)} = G\Omega\left[1-\dfrac{4\Omega-N}{\Omega}\left(1-\dfrac{1}{2\Omega}\right)\right], & E_\beta^{(B)} = G\Omega\,, \qquad \text{if } N>2\Omega, \\ E_\alpha^{(C)} = E_\beta^{(C)} = G\Omega+\dfrac{G}{4}\left(1-\dfrac{1}{2\Omega}\right). & \end{cases}$$

One can remark that in the seniority scheme the relation

$$E(NT21)-E(NT00) = 2G\Omega \tag{18}$$

holds.

In our formulation all the two quasi-particle states of solution A satisfy exactly this relation, in solution B only the $\beta\beta$ state can correspond to the $v=2$, $t=1$ state, while the 2α or $\alpha\beta$ states have an energy which becomes negative for $N>\Omega$; finally in solution C the symmetry between quasi-particles is restored and the relation (18) is satisfied in the large-Ω limit.

It would be interesting to study the stability of the different solutions and to make use of projection procedures in order to obtain eigenstates of T and N; moreover an analysis of the symmetry properties of the vacuum and of the excited states would give some information about the possibility of making a comparison with actual nuclei. Work is in progress in these directions.

Note added in proof.

In a recent letter (P. Camiz: *Nuovo Cimento*, **40**, 1220 (1965)) is shown that solution A is always stable, solution B is an unstable one, whereas solution C is stable provided $(T_z/R)^2<(1/12)\left[14\Omega-7/\Omega-4-\sqrt{(14\Omega-7/\Omega-4)^2-24(\Omega-\frac{1}{2}-1/2\Omega)}\right]$.

REFERENCES

[1] P. Camiz, A. Covello and M. Jean: *Nuovo Cimento*, **36**, 663 (1965).
[2] P. Camiz, A. Covello and M. Jean: *Nuovo Cimento*, **42**, B, 199 (1966).
[3] M. Baranger: *Phys. Rev.*, **122**, 992 (1961).
[4] C. Bloch and A. Messiah: *Nucl. Phys.*, **39**, 95 (1962).
[5] A. R. Edmonds and B. H. Flowers: *Proc. Roy. Soc.*, A **214**, 515 (1952).

Short-Range Correlations in Nuclei.

J. DA PROVIDENCIA
Laboratorio de Fisica, Universidade de Coimbra

1. – Hartree-Fock methods for systems with singular interactions.

1·1. *General considerations.* – It is usually admitted that the nuclear two-body interaction has the shape represented in Fig. 1 and it is also usually believed that this interaction induces in the wave-function of nuclei the two-body correlations having a healing distance d which are also represented in Fig. 1. We assume therefore that any two particles in a nucleus will be strongly correlated to each other only when the distance between them is smaller than d. The method which will be presented for introducing short-range correlations in the model wave function enables us to apply Hartree-Fock techniques to systems containing singular interactions. We will follow a work which has been carried out jointly by SHAKIN and myself [1] and was based on a suggestion of VILLARS [2]. We begin by describing how the type of correlations we want to consider may be taken into account by means of a unitary operator which transforms Slater determinants Φ into correlated wave functions $\tilde{\Phi}$ behaving like Φ for interparticle distances greater than d. Following VILLARS we write

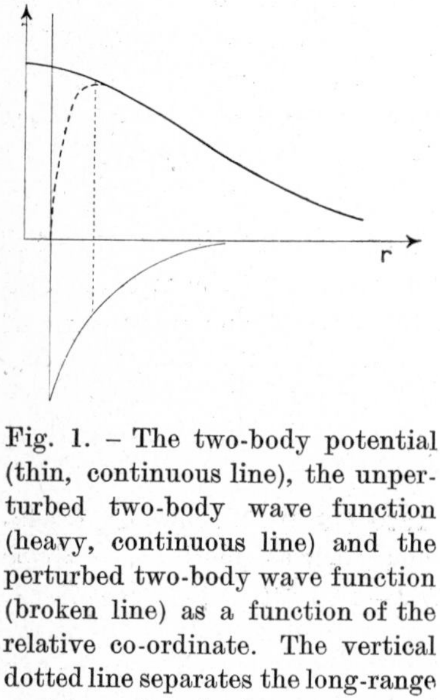

Fig. 1. – The two-body potential (thin, continuous line), the unperturbed two-body wave function (heavy, continuous line) and the perturbed two-body wave function (broken line) as a function of the relative co-ordinate. The vertical dotted line separates the long-range part from the short-range part of the two-body interaction.

$$\tilde{\Phi} = e^{iS}\Phi\,, \tag{1}$$

where S is a two-body, Hermitian operator

$$S = \frac{1}{2} \sum_{\alpha\beta\gamma\delta} s_{\alpha\beta,\gamma\delta} c_\alpha^\dagger c_\beta^\dagger c_\delta c_\gamma \,, \tag{2}$$

$c_\alpha^\dagger$ and c_α being the creation and annihilation operators of the single-particle state $\varphi_\alpha(x)$. Obviously the operator $\exp[iS]$ (and therefore, the operator S) will become completely defined after it has been defined in the subspace of two particles. For instance, in the subspace of three particles we will have simply

$$\exp[iS] = \exp[i(s_{12} + s_{13} + s_{23})] \,.$$

We define the operator $\exp[iS]$ in the subspace of two particles by means of a correspondence between uncorrelated state-vectors $|\alpha\beta\rangle$ and state vectors $|\widetilde{\alpha\beta}\rangle$ containing the type of distortion in the relative co-ordinate which we want to take into account and have shown in Fig. 1. We will have, therefore, in the subspace of two particles

$$\exp[iS] = \sum_{\alpha<\beta} |\widetilde{\alpha\beta}\rangle\langle\alpha\beta| \,, \tag{3}$$

the precise definition of the vectors $|\alpha\beta\rangle$ being according to the equation

$$|\alpha\beta \ldots \gamma\rangle = c_\alpha^\dagger c_\beta^\dagger \ldots c_\gamma^\dagger |0\rangle \,, \tag{4}$$

where $|0\rangle$ is the absolute vacuum.

Instead of calculating matrix elements of an operator H between correlated wave functions it will be more convenient to calculate matrix elements of a transformed operator $\widetilde{H}$ between Slater determinants. It is well known that we will have

$$\langle\widetilde{\Phi}|H|\widetilde{\Phi}'\rangle = \langle\Phi|\widetilde{H}|\Phi'\rangle$$

if we define

$$\widetilde{H} = \exp[-iS] H \exp[iS] \,. \tag{5}$$

1·2. *The transformed operator.* – The operator $\widetilde{H}$ contains in general 1-body, 2-body, 3-body, ... terms. It is a simple matter to calculate them [1, 2]. We write

$$\widetilde{H} = \widetilde{H}^{(1)} + \widetilde{H}^{(2)} + \widetilde{H}^{(3)} + \ldots = \tag{6}$$

$$= \sum_{\alpha\beta} \tilde{h}^{(1)}_{\alpha,\beta} c_\alpha^\dagger c_\beta + \frac{1}{2!} \sum_{\alpha\beta\gamma\delta} \tilde{h}^{(2)}_{\alpha\beta,\gamma\delta} c_\alpha^\dagger c_\beta^\dagger c_\delta c_\gamma + \frac{1}{3!} \sum_{\alpha\beta\gamma\lambda\mu\nu} \tilde{h}^{(3)}_{\alpha\beta\gamma,\lambda\mu\nu} c_\alpha^\dagger c_\beta^\dagger c_\gamma^\dagger c_\nu c_\mu c_\lambda + \ldots \,.$$

Now we remark that if we have a n-body operator $0^{(n)}$ and m-body wave functions $\Phi^{(m)}$ and $\Psi^{(m)}$, then

$$\langle \Phi^{(m)} | 0^{(n)} | \Psi^{(m)} \rangle = \begin{cases} 0 \text{ if } n > m\,, \\ \text{something if } n < m. \end{cases}$$

This remark enables us to calculate in succession the different parts of the operator $\widetilde{H}$. Starting from the one-body part we can write

$$\langle \alpha | \widetilde{H} | \beta \rangle = \langle \alpha | \widetilde{H}^{(1)} | \beta \rangle\,, \tag{7}$$

$$\langle \alpha | H | \beta \rangle = \langle \alpha | H^{(1)} | \beta \rangle\,. \tag{8}$$

Now, because S is a two-body operator it gives zero on a one-body wave function so that we may drop the tilde over the H on the left-hand side of eq. (7). We have, finally

$$\widetilde{H}^{(1)} = H^{(1)}\,. \tag{9}$$

Up to now we have said nothing about the operator H, but now we will take it to be the Hamiltonian. Therefore, its one-body part $H^{(1)}$ is just the kinetic energy

$$H^{(1)} = T = \sum_{\alpha\beta} t_{\alpha,\beta} c^{\dagger}_{\alpha} c_{\beta} \tag{10}$$

and its two-body part $H^{(2)}$ is the potential energy

$$H^{(2)} = V = \tfrac{1}{2} \sum_{\alpha\beta\gamma\delta} v_{\alpha\beta,\gamma\delta} c^{\dagger}_{\alpha} c^{\dagger}_{\beta} c_{\delta} c_{\gamma}\,. \tag{11}$$

Of course, the results we obtain will be also valid for operators having only a one-body part. We may now write eq. (9) in the form

$$\widetilde{h}^{(1)}_{\alpha,\beta} = t_{\alpha,\beta}\,. \tag{12}$$

In order to find the two-body part of H we just have to calculate $\langle \alpha\beta | \widetilde{H} | \gamma\delta \rangle$. Indeed we have

$$\langle \alpha\beta | \widetilde{H} | \gamma\delta \rangle = \langle \alpha\beta | \widetilde{H}^{(1)} | \gamma\delta \rangle + \langle \alpha\beta | \widetilde{H}^{(2)} | \gamma\delta \rangle\,. \tag{13}$$

This equation is readily solved with respect to $\widetilde{H}^{(2)}$. We obtain easily the following result [2],

$$\widetilde{h}^{(2)A}_{\alpha\beta,\gamma\delta} = \langle \widetilde{\alpha\beta} | t_1 + t_2 + v_{12} | \widetilde{\gamma\delta} \rangle - \langle \alpha\beta | t_1 + t_2 | \gamma\delta \rangle\,, \tag{14}$$

where the superscript A stands for antisymmetrized. The three-body part of $\widetilde{H}$ is calculated in the same way

$$(15)\qquad \langle\alpha\beta\gamma|\widetilde{H}|\lambda\mu\nu\rangle = \langle\widetilde{\alpha\beta\gamma}|H|\widetilde{\lambda\mu\nu}\rangle =$$
$$= \langle\alpha\beta\gamma|\widetilde{H}^{(1)}|\lambda\mu\nu\rangle + \langle\alpha\beta\gamma|\widetilde{H}^{(2)}|\lambda\mu\nu\rangle + \langle\alpha\beta\gamma|\widetilde{H}^{(3)}|\lambda\mu\nu\rangle\,.$$

1·3. *Diagrams.* – We are left with the problem of calculating quantities like

$$\langle\widetilde{\alpha\beta\,...\,\gamma}|H|\widetilde{\lambda\mu\,...\,\nu}\rangle\,.$$

For that it is convenient to develop a graphical technique [1] which will enable us to relate such quantities to matrix elements of H and S. We draw diagrams like the one which is represented in Fig. 2 and contributes to the quantity $\langle\alpha\beta\gamma\,...\,\delta|\cdot\exp[-iS]H\exp[iS]|\lambda\mu\nu\,...\,\omega\rangle$. The upper sequence of points labelled $\alpha, \beta, \gamma, ..., \delta$ corresponds to the bra$\langle\alpha\beta\gamma\,...\,\delta|$. The lower sequence of points labelled $\lambda, \mu, \nu, ..., \omega$ corresponds to the ket $|\lambda\mu\nu\,...\,\omega\rangle$. The wiggly line over the horizontal dashed line corresponds to a matrix element of the two-body interaction (for the kinetic energy we would use just one point). The horizontal lines, which we call s-lines, represent matrix elements of the operator S. They correspond to the expansion of the operators $\exp[-iS]$ or $\exp[iS]$ according to whether they stand above or below the horizontal dashed line. The vertical upgoing lines are contraction lines. There is no time-dependent factor associated with them. As a consequence of the unitarity nature of the transformation we are considering, it may be shown that we need not include diagrams containing s-lines which may be separated from the wiggly line without breaking contraction lines. Each one of the different n-body parts of $\widetilde{H}$ has also a simple graphical representation. It is simply represented by a diagram containing no contraction lines free of s- or wiggly lines. In Fig. 3 we show a diagram which contributes to $h^{(3)A}_{\alpha\beta\gamma,\lambda\mu\nu}$.

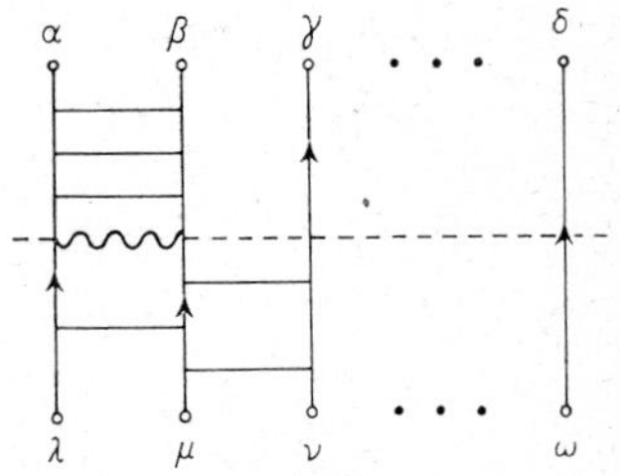

Fig. 2. – A diagram contributing to the matrix element
$\langle\widetilde{\alpha\beta\gamma\,...\,\delta}|H|\widetilde{\lambda\mu\nu\,...\,\omega}\rangle =$
$= \langle\alpha\beta\gamma\,...\,\delta|e^{-iS}He^{iS}|\lambda\mu\nu\,...\,\omega\rangle.$

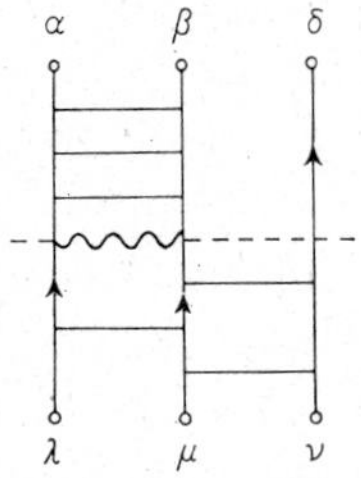

Fig. 3. – A diagram contributing to the matrix element $\langle\widetilde{\alpha\beta\gamma}|H|\widetilde{\lambda\mu\nu}\rangle =$
$= \langle\alpha\beta\gamma|e^{-iS}He^{iS}|\lambda\mu\nu\rangle$.

1·4. *The Hartree-Fock and r.p.a. equations.* – The transformed operator $\widetilde{H}$ which we have obtained is amenable to the treatment which has been developed in the lectures of Prof. VILLARS [3]. The Hartree-Fock equations become now [4]

$$t_{\alpha,\beta} + U^{\text{eff}}_{\alpha,\beta} = \lambda_\alpha \delta_{\alpha,\beta} , \tag{16}$$

where

$$U^{\text{eff}}_{\alpha,\beta} = \sum_\gamma \tilde{h}^{(2)\text{A}}_{\alpha\gamma,\beta\gamma} n_\gamma + \frac{1}{2!} \sum_{\gamma\delta} \tilde{h}^{(3)\text{A}}_{\alpha\gamma\delta,\beta\gamma\delta} n_\gamma n_\delta \tag{17}$$

with

$$\begin{cases} n_\gamma = 1 & \text{if } \gamma \leqslant N , \\ n_\gamma = 0 & \text{if } \gamma > N . \end{cases} \tag{18}$$

The equations for the eigenmodes of small amplitude vibrations (r.p.a.) become now [4]

$$(\omega + \lambda_\alpha - \lambda_\beta)\psi_{\alpha\beta} = (n_\alpha - n_\beta) \sum_{\gamma\delta} V^{\text{eff}}_{\alpha\gamma,\beta\delta} \psi_{\delta\gamma} , \tag{19}$$

where

$$V^{\text{eff}}_{\alpha\gamma,\beta\delta} = \tilde{h}^{(2)\text{A}}_{\alpha\gamma,\beta\delta} + \sum \tilde{h}^{(3)\text{A}}_{\alpha\gamma\lambda,\beta\delta\lambda} n_\lambda . \tag{20}$$

1·5. *Treatment of the three-body clusters.* – The expressions for U^{eff} and V^{eff} simplify a great deal because we may neglect in $\tilde{H}^{(3)}$ the kinetic energy and the short-range part of the 2-body interaction, their contribution to the binding energy being extremely small [1]. In $\tilde{H}^{(3)}$ we will keep only the dominant terms and so we will neglect diagrams containing correlations between more than one pair of particles. The contributions of $\tilde{H}^{(3)}$ to U^{eff} and V^{eff} contain summations over some indices. We make the further approximation of keeping only those diagrams in which one of the indices which is summed over corresponds to a contraction line free of s-lines, as shown in Fig. 4. It may be expected that the diagrams neglected on this basis would tend to cancel each other because they contribute with random signs. Finally we may express the contributions of the three-body clusters in terms of the correlated two-body state vectors $|\widetilde{\alpha\beta}\rangle$. We have simply

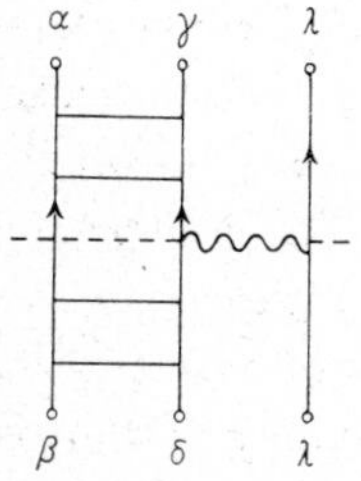

Fig. 4. – A diagram contributing to $\langle\widetilde{\alpha\gamma}|U_1^l + U_2^l|\widetilde{\beta\delta}\rangle - \langle\alpha\gamma|U_1^l + U_2^l|\beta\delta\rangle$.

$$\sum_\lambda \tilde{h}^{(3)\text{A}}_{\alpha\gamma\lambda,\beta\delta\lambda} n_\lambda = \langle\widetilde{\alpha\gamma}|\, U_1^l + U_2^l|\widetilde{\beta\delta}\rangle - \langle\alpha\gamma|\, U_1^l + U_2^l|\beta\delta\rangle , \tag{21}$$

$$\frac{1}{2!} \sum_{\gamma\lambda} \tilde{h}^{(3)}_{\alpha\gamma\lambda,\beta\gamma\lambda} n_\gamma n_\lambda = \sum_\lambda \{\langle\widetilde{\alpha\gamma}|\, U_1^l + U_2^l|\widetilde{\beta\gamma}\rangle - \langle\alpha\gamma|\, U_1^l + U_2^l|\beta\gamma\rangle\} n_\gamma . \tag{22}$$

If we consider Fig. 4, eq. (21) becomes obvious and eq. (22) is also easily derived. With the help of eqs. (21) and (22) we see that eqs. (16) and (19) become identical with those which we would obtain if, instead of starting from the Hamiltonian $\tilde{H}$, we had considered an effective Hamiltonian H^{eff} such that [1]

$$H^{\text{eff}} = \sum_{\alpha\beta} t_{\alpha,\beta} c_\alpha^\dagger c_\beta + \tfrac{1}{4} \sum_{\alpha\beta\gamma\delta} \{\langle \widetilde{\alpha\beta} | t_1 + U_1^l + t_2 + U_2^l + v_{12} | \widetilde{\gamma\delta} \rangle - \langle \alpha\beta | t_1 + U_1^l + t_2 + U_2^l | \gamma\delta \rangle\} c_\alpha^\dagger c_\beta^\dagger c_\delta c_\gamma \,. \tag{23}$$

Up to now we have left the shape of the two-body correlation undetermined. If we fix it by making use of the Moszkowski-Scott method the effective interaction simplifies and reduces essentially to the long-range part of the two-body force [1]. We are therefore led in a simple manner to the Kallio-Kolltweit force [5], but there are still some correction terms left over.

1·6. *Effective transition operators.* – We have seen that a one-body operator is transformed by $\exp[iS]$ as follows

$$\tilde{D} = \exp[-iS] D \exp[iS] = \sum_{\alpha\beta} d_{\alpha,\beta} c_\alpha^\dagger c_\beta + \tfrac{1}{4} \sum_{\alpha\beta\gamma\delta} \tilde{d}^{(2)\text{A}}_{\alpha\beta,\gamma\delta} c_\alpha^\dagger c_\beta^\dagger c_\delta c_\gamma \,, \tag{24}$$

where

$$\tilde{d}^{(2)\text{A}}_{\alpha\beta,\gamma\delta} = \langle \widetilde{\alpha\beta} | d_1 + d_2 | \widetilde{\gamma\delta} \rangle - \langle \alpha\beta | d_1 + d_2 | \gamma\delta \rangle \,. \tag{25}$$

The transformed operators $\tilde{D}$ lead to effective transition operators, which are to be used, for instance, in the r.p.a. [4], and are defined as follows

$$d^{\text{eff}}_{\alpha,\beta} = d_{\alpha,\beta} + \sum_\lambda \tilde{d}^{(2)\text{A}}_{\alpha\lambda,\beta\lambda} n_\lambda \,. \tag{26}$$

It has been shown [1] that for calculating transition rates involving real photons, $d^{\text{eff}}_{\alpha,\beta}$ is well approximated by $d_{\alpha,\beta}$, the uncorrelated operator. However, for processes involving a high-momentum transfer, the correction terms become important [6], because then the correlation structure of the wave function should begin to be seen.

2. – Two-body correlations induced by the long-range part of the interaction.

We have shown how we could convert a Hamiltonian containing a hard-core interaction into an effective Hamiltonian which was regular. However, the regularized interaction is still capable of inducing important correlations which, nevertheless, should be treated on a different footing from the very-short-range correlations which we have been considering. For instance, it seems very difficult and it may even be impossible to reproduce the correlations arising from the long-range part of the force by a correlation function. The correlation effects have therefore to be calculated by perturbation methods.

In the r.p.a. the amplitude for exciting a one-quasi-boson state $|r\}$ by means of a particle-hole operator $c_\sigma^\dagger c_\alpha$ is represented by the diagram in Fig. 5 and is given by

$$\{r|c_\sigma^\dagger c_\alpha|0\} = \psi_{\alpha\sigma}^{(r)}\,, \tag{27}$$

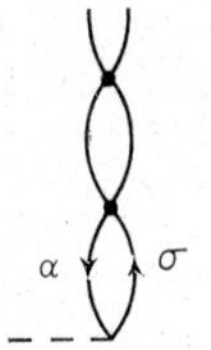

Fig. 5. – A diagram representing the r.p.a. transition amplitude.

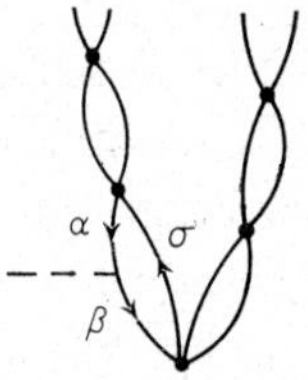

Fig. 6. – A diagram representing the amplitude for excitation of two quasi-bosons.

where $|0\}$ is the quasi-boson vacuum and the amplitudes $\psi_{\alpha\sigma}^{(r)}$ are given by eq. (19). Due to the ground-state correlations, we may consider also the production of two real quasi-bosons, as is represented in Fig. 6. The amplitude for exciting a two quasi-boson state is given by

$$\{rs|c_\beta^\dagger c_\alpha|0\} = \sum_\sigma (\psi_{\alpha\sigma}^{(r)}\psi_{\sigma\beta}^{(s)} + \psi_{\alpha\sigma}^{(s)}\psi_{\sigma\beta}^{(r)})\cdot(1-n_\alpha-n_\beta)\,. \tag{28}$$

The excitation of two quasi-boson states leads, of course, to the appearance of some strength at an energy higher than the one quasi-boson resonance. But the strength appearing at a higher energy should be subtracted from the strength of the low-energy state. In order to take into account this effect we have to calculate correlation corrections to eq. (27), essentially by including in our calculation diagrams like those shown in Fig. 7, which have a structure similar to the structure of the correlation term in eq. (26) (see eq. (25)).

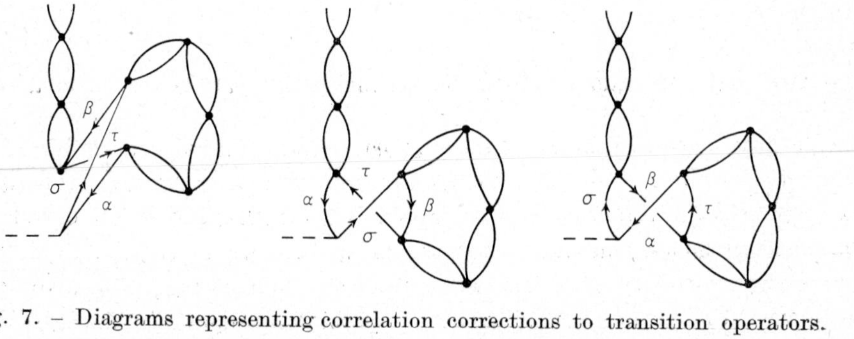

Fig. 7. – Diagrams representing correlation corrections to transition operators.

The correlation corrections to eq. (27) are simply given by

$$(29)\qquad \Delta\{r|c_\sigma^\dagger c_\alpha|0\} = -\sum_{\beta\tau s}\left(\psi_{\tau\beta}^{(r)}\psi_{\tau\alpha}^{(s)*}\psi_{\beta\sigma}^{(s)} + \tfrac{1}{2}\psi_{\alpha\tau}^{(r)}\psi_{\sigma\beta}^{(s)*}\psi_{\tau\beta}^{(s)} + \tfrac{1}{2}\psi_{\beta\sigma}^{(r)}\psi_{\tau\alpha}^{(s)*}\psi_{\tau\beta}^{(s)}\right).$$

If we consider the corrected transition amplitudes for the excitation of a one quasi-boson state, together with the transition amplitudes for the excitation of two quasi-boson states we arrive at an interesting extension of the well-known Thouless theorem for the sum rule, in which the expectation value of the double commutator $[D,[H,D]]$ in the Hartree-Fock ground-state becomes replaced by the expectation value of the same quantity in the quasi-boson vacuum [7]. This shows that the approximation we are considering is a conserving one and guarantees that the extra strength we get at higher energies will be subtracted at lower energies.

REFERENCES

[1] J. DA PROVIDENCIA and C. M. SHAKIN: *Ann. of Phys.*, **30**, 95 (1964).
[2] F. VILLARS: *Proceedings S.I.F.*, Course XXIII (New York, London, 1963).
[3] F. VILLARS: this volume, p. 1.
[4] J. DA PROVIDENCIA and C. M. SHAKIN: *Nucl. Phys.*, **65**, 75 (1965).
[5] A. KALLIO and K. KOLLTWEIT: *Nucl. Phys.*, **53**, 87 (1964).
[6] J. DA PROVIDENCIA and C. M. SHAKIN: *Nucl. Phys.*, **65**, 54 (1965).
[7] J. DA PROVIDENCIA: *Nucl. Phys.*, to be published.

Linked-Cluster Expansions for Open-Shell Nuclei.

B. H. BRANDOW (*)

The Niels Bohr Institute, University of Copenhagen - Copenhagen

1. – Introduction.

I would like to preface this talk by some remarks about the general research program which the present work belongs to. This is to extend the Brueckner-Bethe-Goldstone theory of nuclear matter to problems of actual nuclei. Our hope is that this may eventually provide a sound logical justification for the shell model, and also that practical methods of computation can be developed for the effective two-body interaction and for the shell-model potential.

Now there are many pessimists who say that this program is doomed to failure. Their critisisms are serious, and deserve careful attention. It is claimed that: *a*) The convergence of the Goldstone expansion is not sufficiently well established. *b*) The Goldstone expansion is unsuitable for nuclei with open shells. *c*) The task of doing accurate calculations with self-consistent shell-model orbitals is impossibly difficult. A few years ago there was much validity to all of these criticisms, but today the situation is quite different. We shall discuss computational methods in another seminar here. In a moment we shall discuss the required extension of the Goldstone diagrammatic formalism. First, though, let us look at the problems of convergence.

Many theoreticians have objected to the use of the Goldstone expansion on the grounds that nuclear matter may be a superfluid. None seriously believes that this is important quantitatively, but nevertheless this remains an important question of principle. At the end of this seminar we shall indicate how superfluidity can be treated, in a completely nonsingular fashion, *within* the same framework as the Goldstone expansion.

Another important question concerns the existence of a « small parameter »

(*) National Science Foundation Postdoctoral Fellow.

to characterize the rate of convergence. Indeed there *is* such a small parameter, namely

$$(1) \qquad \varkappa \equiv \varrho \int |\zeta(\boldsymbol{r})|^2 \mathrm{d}\tau \, .$$

Here ϱ is the density of nuclear matter, and $\zeta \equiv \varphi - \psi$ (Bethe-Goldstone wave function) is the « wound » in the two-body wave function caused by the strong repulsive core. In nuclear matter this $\varkappa$ turns out to be of order 10 %. That this is indeed the long-sought small parameter is not surprising—essentially the same quantity appears in the Jastrow method. A really convincing demonstration was not found until a year ago, when BETHE [1] solved the problem of three-body correlations to *all* orders of perturbation theory by means of the Faddeev equations. The solution has a rather surprising feature. It turns out that the Goldstone diagrams for three-body clusters actually form a divergent series. To get reasonable results one is forced to do a partial summation, in this case by direct solution of the Faddeev equations. The net effect is then found to be very small. (Actually much smaller than (1) would suggest, due to a close cancellation between attraction and repulsion). The lesson is that it is not enough to simply sum the upgoing ladders of singular potential interactions to form a new expansion in terms of two-body Brueckner matrices. Additional summations are required for three-body clusters, for four-body clusters, etc. Only then does one obtain an expansion in powers of $\varkappa$. The problem of calculating « all the right diagrams » is still far from trivial, but it is also far from being hopeless.

We turn now to the extensions of Goldstone's linked-cluster formalism which are needed for applications of nuclear matter theory to actual shell-model calculations. Let us make a table of the things we would like to have linked expansions for: energies, wave-functions, expectation values of a general operator, and shell-model transition amplitudes.

	E	Ψ	$\langle \mathcal{O} \rangle$	$\langle \alpha \vert \mathcal{O} \vert \beta \rangle$
nondegenerate case	Goldstone	Hugenholtz	Thouless	—
degenerate case	Bloch and Horowitz	—	—	—
degenerate case, completely linked	(Morita)	—	—	—

(Morita's name is in brackets here, because his derivation [2] is incomplete.) This table shows that about half of these linked expansions have already been published. It is worth-while to point this out, because, with the exception of Goldstone's famous result [3], these other expansions have not received the publicity they deserve. We have succeeded in completing this table, so there is now a « complete set » of mathematical tools to relate the Brueckner theory to the shell model [4]. Furthermore, we have derived or rederived all of these expansions by a new method which seems to us to be more simple and direct than previous derivations.

We shall concentrate here on the energy expansions of GOLDSTONE [3], BLOCH and HOROWITZ [5], and MORITA [2]. But first we would like to just mention the Hugenholtz and Thouless results. Goldstone's paper contains a recipe for the total wave function, but he did not reduce this to the simplest form possible. HUGENHOLTZ [6] has shown that

$$\Psi = \exp\left[\sum_r W_r\right]\Phi_0 . \tag{2}$$

The argument of the exponential is the sum of all « linked but open » diagrams, with particle-hole pairs emerging from the top. Each W_r is actually an operator since it has creation (annihilation) operators attached to each of its external particle (hole) lines. Thouless' prescription [7] for the ground-state expectation value of a general operator is that one should calculate all the closed, linked, Goldstone-like diagrams in which the special operator appears just once. The leading terms in the expansions for one and two-body operators are illustrated in Fig. 1.

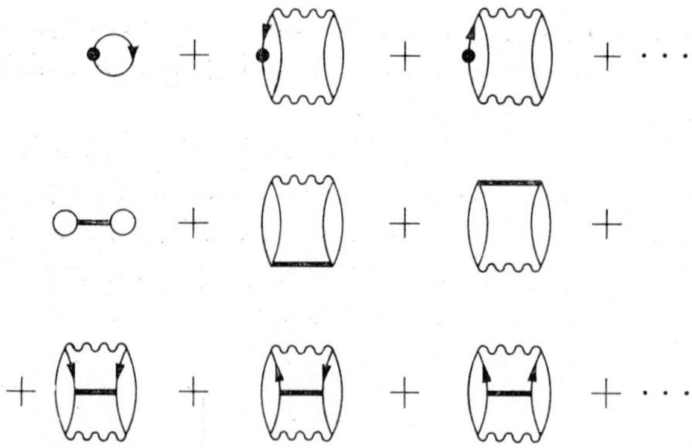

Fig. 1. – Leading terms in the Thouless expansions [7] for expectation values of one and two-body operators.

2. – General method. Degenerate perturbation theory.

The present method is closely related to Brueckner's original study of linked clusters [8]. Let's review what BRUECKNER did. He took the familiar Raleigh-Schrödinger perturbation series, and carefully examined the first few terms. After some algebraic manipulations with the energy denominators, he was able to show that the « unlinked » terms in each order of perturbation theory all cancel each other. This was not a general proof, only a term-by-term confirmation (eventually carried out to sixth order). The first general proof was given by GOLDSTONE, as you all know. Nevertheless, Brueckner's approach still has much appeal, by virtue of being so direct and elementary. We have extended this analysis to all orders of perturbation theory, by means of two tricks. First, we start with the Brillouin-Wigner form of perturbation theory, since this has a much simpler formal structure than the Raleigh-Schrödinger series. Secondly, we use the so-called factorization theorem [9, 10]. This expresses the required energy-denominator identities in a simple and general form.

To unify the discussion we begin with the degenerate case, considering the nondegenerate case as a special example. The degenerate form of Brillouin-Wigner perturbation theory is both simple and elegant, and we are surprised that this has never attracted much attention. (For earlier discussions of open-shell nuclei which are closely related, see [11, 12, 13].) Consider the expansion of the complete wave function in some complete basis; in this case the set of Slater determinants defined by an unperturbed shell-model Hamiltonian $H_0 = T + V_{\text{SM}}$:

$$\Psi = \sum_i a_i \Phi_i \, . \tag{3}$$

The basic idea is to split this sum into two parts

$$\Psi = \sum_{i \in D} + \sum_{i \notin D} , \tag{4}$$

where we have split off d of the lowest-lying eigenstates Φ_i to define a d-dimensional « quasi-degenerate » subspace D. Our shell-model wave function will be the « degenerate projection » of Ψ,

$$\Psi_0 = P\Psi = \sum_{i \in D} a_i \Phi_i \, . \tag{5}$$

The final result is that we must diagonalize a d-dimensional secular equation

$$[H_0 + \mathscr{V} - EI]_D A = 0 \, , \tag{6}$$

where A is the column vector of the a_i's in (5). The effective interaction matrix $\mathscr{V}$ is the solution of an integral equation,

$$\mathscr{V} = V + V \frac{Q}{E - H_0} \mathscr{V} , \tag{7}$$

where Q is the projection off the subspace D. Solving this equation by iteration leads to an expansion of Brillouin-Wigner form.

Note that the division (4) into two kinds of states Φ_i is rigorously preserved in this formulation. Degenerate states are treated by solving a secular problem, while the nondegenerate states simply renormalize the lowest-order interaction $V = v_{12} - V_{\text{SM}}$. But there is a price to pay for this simple form. The effective interaction $\mathscr{V}$ depends implicitly on the eigenvalue we wish to calculate. One consequence is that our shell-model wave functions (the A's) are generally not precisely orthogonal. This is probably a negligible effect quantitatively, for most applications, but it does complicate the analysis somewhat.

3. – The Goldstone expansion.

When the subspace D consists of only one state, Φ_0, (6) and (7) reduce to the usual Brillouin-Wigner expansion

$$(8) \qquad \Delta E = E - E_0 = \langle \Phi_0 | \mathscr{V} | \Phi_0 \rangle =$$

$$= \langle \Phi_0 | V + V \frac{Q}{E - H_0} V + V \frac{Q}{E - H_0} V \frac{Q}{E - H_0} V + \dots | \Phi_0 \rangle .$$

We apply this to a closed-shell nucleus, representing the various terms by means of diagrams as shown in Fig. 2.

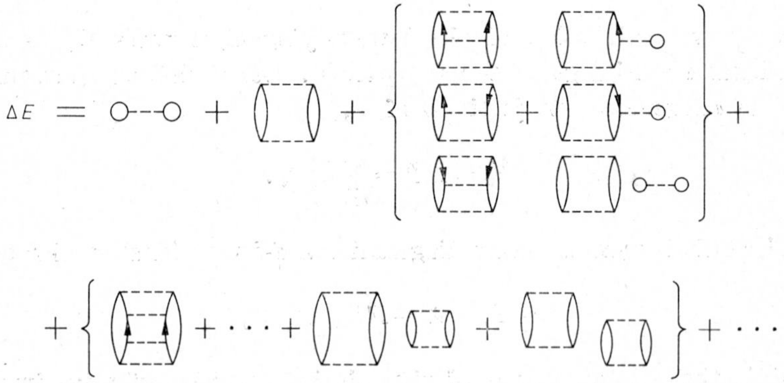

Fig. 2. – Diagrams for the Brillouin-Wigner expansion. Note the occurrence of unlinked terms.

The Brillouin-Wigner energy denominators are

$$(9) \qquad e_{\text{BW}} = E - H_0 = E_0 + \Delta E - H_0 ,$$

which in the present case means

$$e_{\mathrm{BW}} = \Delta E + \sum(\text{all downgoing line energies}) - \\ - \sum(\text{all upgoing line energies})\,. \tag{10}$$

We now replace these by denominators of Goldstone form,

$$e_{\mathrm{G}} = E_0 - H_0 = \sum(\text{all downgoing line energies}) - \\ - \sum(\text{all upgoing line energies})\,, \tag{11}$$

by expanding out ΔE. Each BW denominator is replaced by a geometric series,

$$\frac{1}{e_{\mathrm{BW}}} = \frac{1}{e_{\mathrm{G}}} + \frac{1}{e_{\mathrm{G}}}(-\Delta E)\frac{1}{e_{\mathrm{G}}} + \frac{1}{e_{\mathrm{G}}}(-\Delta E)\frac{1}{e_{\mathrm{G}}}(-\Delta E)\frac{1}{e_{\mathrm{G}}} + \dots\,. \tag{12}$$

Figure 3 illustrates how we represent this diagrammatically.

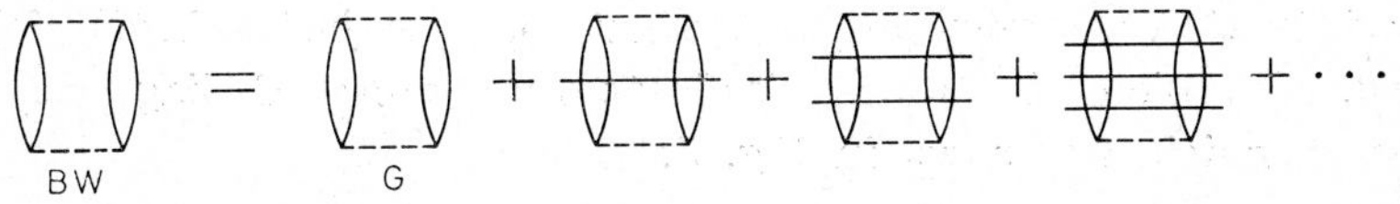

Fig. 3. – Application of the expansion (12) to the second-order graph in Fig. 2. The solid horizontal bars indicate « insertions » of $(-\Delta E)$.

When this is done to every denominator in the original BW expansion, Fig. 2, we find that the diagrams with $(-\Delta E)$ insertions identically cancel those with unlinked parts. The only remaining diagrams are those of Goldstone. For a simple illustration, consider the second diagram on the right-hand side of Fig. 3. Replace the ΔE factor by the new expansion in terms of Goldstone denominators. The result is shown in Fig. 4.

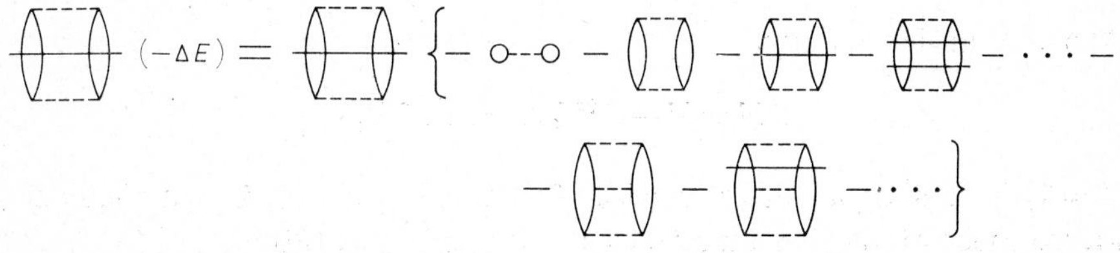

Fig. 4. – Diagrammatic expansion of the second term on the right-hand side of Fig. 3, using the expansion obtained by applying (12) to Fig. 2.

Note that the first term to the right in Fig. 4 just cancels against the simplest of the unlinked terms in Fig. 2. It is easy to show that this type of cancellation is quite general. The proof is included here in Appendix A.

4. – The Bloch-Horowitz expansion.

For the degenerate case, the first steps are to choose the subspace D, and to find a suitable diagrammatic representation for the matrix elements of the effective interaction

$$\mathscr{V}_{ij} = \langle \Phi_i | \mathscr{V} | \Phi_j \rangle \qquad (i, j \in D). \tag{13}$$

Bloch and Horowitz consider a nucleus with $A = N + n$ particles. The quasi-degenerate Φ_i's are those Slater determinants where the N core particles all occupy a corresponding set of N core orbitals, while the remaining n valence particles are distributed among a certain set of valence orbitals. To specify a particular one of these Φ_i's it is clear enough to know which n of the valence orbitals are occupied. This suggests a diagram convention with n external lines representing the valence particles. The occupied N-particle core is treated as a reference, or « vacuum », state, just as in the Goldstone expansion. Iteration of (7) then leads to four types of diagrams, simple examples of which are shown in Fig. 5.

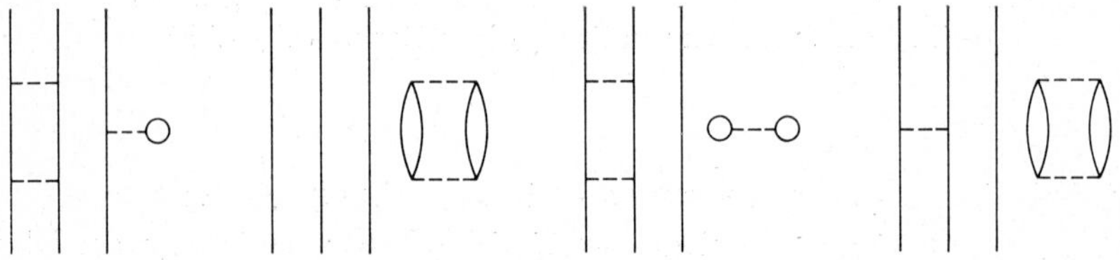

Fig. 5. – Examples of the four types of diagrams generated by eq. (7). *a*) is a valence diagram and *b*) is a core diagram; *c*) and *d*) are cross terms to be eliminated by a cancellation argument similar to that in Appendix A. Note that the valence diagrams need not be completely linked.

The interaction energy,

$$\Delta E \equiv E - A^{\dagger} H_0 A = A^{\dagger} \mathscr{V} A \,, \tag{14}$$

($A^{\dagger}A = 1$) is now assumed to consist of two parts, a core interaction energy and a valence interaction energy. To make this separation,

$$\Delta E = \Delta E_C + \Delta E_V \,, \tag{15}$$

well-defined, we require that ΔE_C be the interaction energy of the ground state of the $\mathcal{N}$-particle nucleus (presumably doubly-magic) obtained by *physically removing* the N valence particles. We expand ΔE_C out of *all* the energy denominators, and we furthermore remove ΔE_V from *some* of the denominators. An analysis similar to that in Appendix A then shows that all cross terms such as *c*) and *d*) of Fig. 5 are eliminated. This reduces $\mathscr{V}$ to the much simpler form

$$\mathscr{V} = \mathscr{V}_V + I\Delta E_C \,. \tag{16}$$

The unit matrix I comes from the noninteracting valence lines in Fig. 5 *b*), while ΔE_C is simply given by the Goldstone expansion for the $\mathcal{N}$-body core, calculated as if the valence particles did not exist. The valence part of the effective interaction, $\mathscr{V}_V$, is the sum of all valence diagrams such as Fig. 5 *a*). These contain no disconnected « vacuum fluctuations » of the core.

Some care is needed to determine the appropriate denominators for these $\mathscr{V}_V$ diagrams. The correct recipe for these « valence denominators » is

$$\begin{aligned} e_V = E - H_0 - \Delta E_C = A^\dagger(H_{0V} + \mathscr{V}_V)A\, + \\ + \sum(\text{down-going line energies}) - \sum(\text{up-going line energies}) \,. \end{aligned} \tag{17}$$

Here we have introduced the valence part of H_0, *i.e.* just that part of H_0 containing the valence orbitals. Thus

$$H_0 A = (H_{0V} + E_{0C})A \,, \tag{18}$$

where E_{0C} is the sum of the unperturbed core orbital energies. It is also convenient to define a « total valence energy »,

$$E_V \equiv E - E_{0C} - \Delta E_C \,. \tag{19}$$

Substituting (16), (18), and (19) into (6), we arrive at the very important Bloch-Horowitz result (*)

$$[H_{0V} + \mathscr{V}_V - E_V I]_D A = 0 \,. \tag{20}$$

Note that all core quantities have been eliminated from this « shell-model secular equation ». For spectral calculations there are no core terms to consider. To convert the resulting total valence energies E_V into total energies E, one must add the total core energy, $E_C \equiv E_{0C} + \Delta E_C$. But this is trivial, since E_C is just the true physical energy of the $\mathcal{N}$-particle core nucleus.

Some simple valence diagrams are shown in Fig. 6.

(*) This result was obtained independently by B. D. DAY (*Ph. D. Thesis*, Cornell University, 1964, unpublished) by essentially the same methods as used by Bloch-Horowitz. I am indebted to Dr. DAY for some helpful discussions.

Diagram *a*) shows that the leading term in the effective two-body interaction is the Brueckner reaction matrix, as has been known for many years [11, 12]. Diagram *b*) is the corresponding « Hartree-Fock » contribution [14] to the shell-model potential acting on the valence particles. Diagram *c*) is a correction to *a*) arising from core polarization [11]. This might be regarded as « exchange of a virtual core phonon ». This illustrates the fact that the Bloch-Horowitz secular equation (20) has only eliminated the *static* features of the core. All *dynamical* core effects will be included in the valence interaction $\mathscr{V}_V$.

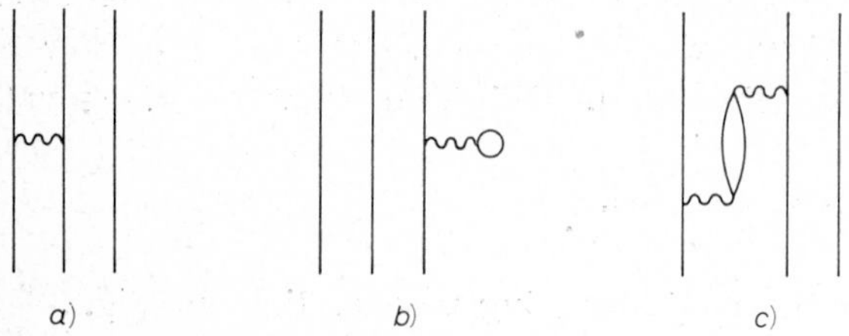

Fig. 6. – Some simple valence diagrams. *a*) The Brueckner matrix contribution to the effective two-body interaction. *b*) The corresponding « Hartree-Fock » part of the shell-model potential. *c*) A « core polarization » correction to *a*).

5. – Completely linked valence expansion.

It might appear from this discussion that the Bloch-Horowitz expansion provides a completely satisfactory formal framework for the shell model. This is not quite true. We have seen already in Fig. 5 *a*) that the valence diagrams need not be completely linked. Furthermore, the valence denominators (17) all contain the valence part ΔE_V of the interaction energy. In short, the Bloch-Horowitz expansion treats the core by means of the completely linked Goldstone expansion, but the valence part of the system is still handled by a form of Brillouin-Wigner perturbation theory. In a moment we will show that $\mathscr{V}_V$ can be completely reduced to an expansion of Goldstone form. But first we would like to explain why this is important for practical applications.

The unlinked valence term in Fig. 5 *a*) can of course be eliminated by a proper choice of the V_{SM} appearing in H_0. But consider the four-valence-particle diagram of Fig. 7 *a*). In the Bloch-Horowitz formulation, this must be considered part of the effective four-body interaction shown in Fig. 7 *b*). Now consider the following « gedanken » situation. Suppose we use this expansion to calculate the effective interactions to be used in an extremely ambitious « random phase » calculation of ^{208}Pb, where all 208 particles are allowed to participate in collective oscillations. In this application there are no closed (meaning *always* closed) shells at all, thus there is no « core » and no ΔE_C. (Remember that the number of external valence lines must be the same for all the matrix elements $(\mathscr{V}_V)_{ij}$.) The valence interaction energy will then have the same order of magnitude as the total binding energy of ^{208}Pb. When this enormous energy is included in the valence denominators (17) which occur within the Brueckner matrix elements of Fig. 6 *a*), the character of the resulting two-body interaction becomes drastically altered. Of course this is compensated by the occurrence of an enormous number of spurious 4-body, 6-body, ... 208-body interactions, but these render the shell-model calculation quite impossible. A completely linked expansion of $\mathscr{V}_V$ is needed to demonstrate that the effective two-body interaction, and the higher-order cluster corrections to this, are insensitive to the manner of division between core and valence particles. This problem was first attacked by MORITA [2]. His derivation of the linked valence expansion is, however, incomplete.

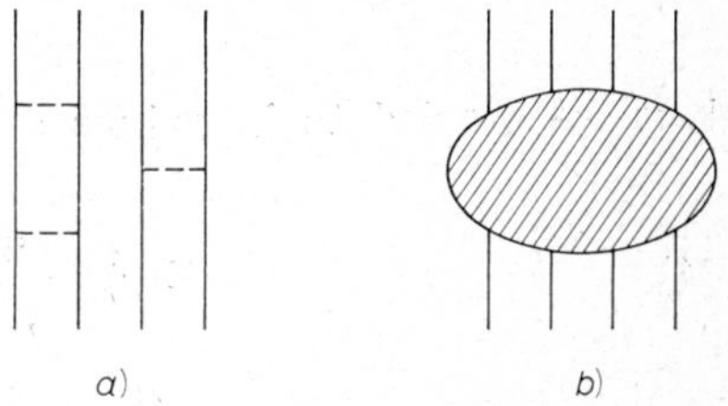

Fig. 7. – *a*) A reducible diagram in the Bloch-Horowitz expansion of $\mathscr{V}_V$. Their formulation treats this as a part of the effective four-body interaction *b*).

Notice that the matrix $\mathscr{V}$ becomes Hermitian when the E appearing in eq. (7) is held fixed. We set E equal to one of the desired eigenvalues, say E_α, and solve the *Hermitian* secular problem

$$[H_0 + \mathscr{V}(E_\alpha) - IE_\beta^{(\alpha)}]A_\beta^{(\alpha)} = 0 \tag{21}$$

to obtain a set of d eigenvectors $A_\beta^{(\alpha)}$ which are now *strictly orthogonal*. (For $\beta \neq \alpha$, the $E_\beta^{(\alpha)}$'s and $A_\beta^{(\alpha)}$'s have no physical significance.) Furthermore, we shall assume strict degeneracy. This reduces H_0 to a constant diagonal matrix, with the result that $\mathscr{V}(E_\alpha)$ is now *diagonal* in the $A_\beta^{(\alpha)}$ basis. (The assumption of exact degeneracy is not really a restriction. At the end of the derivation we add a one-body operator, V_1, to the perturbation V, where V_1 simply removes the degeneracy by shifting the unperturbed valence-orbital energies. The terms with V_1 are easily summed out, converting the result for exact degeneracy into a quasi-degenerate expansion of just the same form.)

When this expansion has been rearranged into the Bloch-Horowitz form, as outlined above, we take $\mathscr{V}_V$ and expand $\Delta E_{V\alpha}$ out of *all* its energy denominators. The resulting diagrams are grouped according to the number of their $(-\Delta E_{V\alpha})$ insertions,

$$\mathscr{V}(\Delta E_{V\alpha}) = \sum_{r=0}^{\infty} \mathscr{V}_V^{(r)}[-\Delta E_{V\alpha}]^r = \sum_{r=0}^{\infty} \mathscr{V}_V^{(r)}[-A_\alpha^+ \mathscr{V}_V(\Delta E_{V\alpha})A_\alpha]^r . \tag{22}$$

When this expansion is applied to the desired eigenvector $A_\alpha = A_\alpha^{(\alpha)}$, the diagonal property of $\mathscr{V}_V(\Delta E_{V\alpha})$ permits a simplification,

$$\mathscr{V}_V(\Delta E_{V\alpha})A_\alpha = \sum_{r=0}^{\infty} \mathscr{V}_V^{(r)}[-\mathscr{V}_V(\Delta E_{V\alpha})]^r A_\alpha \,. \tag{23}$$

Thus we are led to introduce a *new* matrix

$$\mathscr{W}_1(\alpha) \equiv \sum_{r=0}^{\infty} \mathscr{V}_V^{(r)}[-\mathscr{V}_V(\Delta E_{V\alpha})]^r \,, \tag{24}$$

whose set of eigensolutions includes the desired $\Delta E_{V\alpha}$ and A_α. By similar reasoning we can introduce an infinite sequence of matrices

$$\mathscr{W}_n(\alpha) \equiv \sum_{r=0}^{\infty} \mathscr{V}_V^{(r)}[-\mathscr{W}_{n-1}(\alpha)]^r \,, \tag{25}$$

which all share this property. The limiting form $\mathscr{W}_\infty$ (which no longer depends on α) defines a degenerate analogue of the Raleigh-Schrödinger series. « Inserted parts » which occur in this expansion are then taken « off the energy shell » by the procedure described in Appendix A. At this stage all diagrams which are not completely linked will cancel each other, leaving one with the true degenerate analogue of the Goldstone expansion.

To see how this works diagrammatically, consider the i, j matrix element of the $r = 1$ term in (24), namely

$$-\sum_{i'} [\mathscr{V}_V^{(1)}]_{ii'} [\mathscr{V}_V(\Delta E_{V\alpha})]_{i'j}. \tag{26}$$

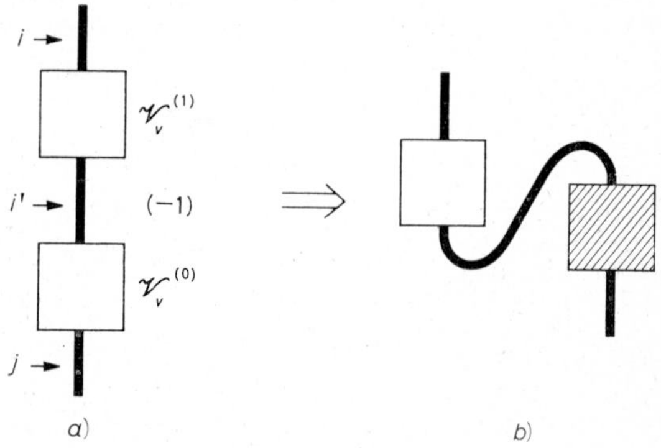

Fig. 8. – Diagrammatic representation of the $-[\mathscr{V}_V^{(1)}\mathscr{V}_V^{(0)}]_{ij}$ term in $\mathscr{W}_\infty$.

The analogous term in $\mathscr{W}_\infty$ will have $\mathscr{V}_V(\Delta E_{V\alpha})$ replaced by $\mathscr{V}_V^{(0)}$, so we now make this substitution. The result is illustrated in Fig. 8 *a*), where the set of n external valence lines is symbolized by a single heavy line. In diagram *b*) we have i) replaced $\mathscr{V}_V^{(1)}$ by a particular diagram in its perturbation expansion, ii) « folded » the middle line to bring the *top* of all the perturbation diagrams in $\mathscr{V}_V^{(0)}$ to the level where the $(-\Delta E_{V\alpha})$ was removed from the $\mathscr{V}_V^{(1)}$ diagram, iii) summed over the index i' and associated the factor (-1) with the folding operation, and iv) shaded $\mathscr{V}_V^{(0)}$ to indicate that it has been taken

« off the energy shell » (Raleigh-Schrödinger denominators replaced by Goldstone denominators) as described in Appendix A. Figure 9 illustrates two third-order perturbation terms contained in Fig. 8.

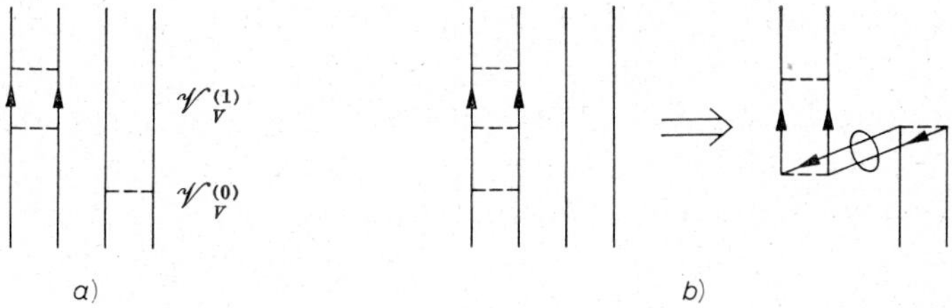

Fig. 9. – Two third-order terms in the perturbation expansion of Fig. 8. Term *a*) cancels diagram 7*a*). Term *b*) is the analogue of an exclusion-violating term in the Goldstone expansion.

Diagram 9 *a*) cancels the unlinked diagram 7 *a*). Diagram 9 *b*) is one of the « left over » terms of this expansion. These all correspond, in a one-to-one manner, with the « exclusion-violating » terms of the Goldstone series. (Consider the special nondegenerate case where the number of valence particles is just equal to the number of valence orbitals.) The completely noninteracting valence lines in 9 *b*) may be ignored. These carry no useful information because, just as in the Goldstone expansion, one must ignore exclusion in intermediate states. This also applies to the degenerate states *between* successive $\mathscr{V}_V^{(r)}$ terms. A loop has been drawn around the two « folded » valence lines in 9 *b*) to distinguish them from holes in the core. (Note that the expansion of $\mathscr{V}_V^{(0)}$ contains a term of the same form as the right-hand side of 9 *b*), but there the downgoing lines both represent holes in the core.) In the present case the downgoing lines are summed over all valence orbitals, and together they carry only a single factor of (-1). The complete rules for this expansion are given in Appendix B.

This formulation works equally well when there are n' « valence holes » in the core, in addition to the n valence particles; $A = N + n - n'$. Each Bloch-Horowitz diagram then has n' *downgoing* external lines in addition to its n upgoing external lines. Rules for the corresponding linked expansion are also given in Appendix B.

We would like to close with two final comments. First, the $\mathscr{V}_V$ matrix for a single valence particle is essentially the same as the self-energy or mass operator of a particle whose energy is real. The perturbation expansion which is usually given for this operator is of a character intermediate between the Bloch-Horowitz form and the present « completely linked » form, but their mathematical equivalence is easily demonstrated.

Finally, we believe that the present expansion offers a formally satisfactory method for treating the superfluidity of nuclear matter *within* the same framework as the Goldstone expansion, and *without* the occurrence of any singularities. The trick is to begin with a sample of nuclear matter whose density is high enough to ensure that its ground state is normal. One then adds enough valence holes to bring the over-all density down to the desired value. The effective two-body (hole-hole) interaction terms in $\mathscr{V}_V$ are evaluated to define a BCS-type residual Hamiltonian, which is then diagonalized by the standard BCS methods. This approach should enable one to give a formal expression of the physical notion that the superfluidity of nuclear matter is the limiting form of the pairing phenomenon in asymptotically large nuclei. We have not attempted to carry out this program.

Appendix A

General proof of cancellation.

To go beyond the simple example of cancellation illustrated in Fig. 4, we must introduce the *factorization theorem*. Consider the Goldstone-type denominators associated with the two different unlinked fourth-order diagrams shown in Fig. 2. Let e_L and e_R be the Goldstone denominators appropriate for the left-hand and right-hand unlinked parts, each considered separately. Then the complete energy-denominator products for these two diagrams are

$$\frac{1}{e_L}\cdot\frac{1}{e_L+e_R}\cdot\frac{1}{e_L} \tag{A.1}$$

and

$$\frac{1}{e_L}\cdot\frac{1}{e_L+e_R}\cdot\frac{1}{e_R}. \tag{A.2}$$

The sum of these two terms is simply $(e_L e_R e_L)^{-1}$, which corresponds to the negative of the second diagram on the right-hand side of Fig. 4. Now let us rephrase what we have just done. The denominators of the last-mentioned graph are of Raleigh-Schrödinger form, since the second-order « insertion » is « on the energy shell ». In other words, the denominator of the insertion part is not affected by the rest of the diagram to which it belongs. We have just shown that the Raleigh-Schrödinger diagram is equivalent to a sum of diagrams with Goldstone-type denominators, where the insertion part is « off the energy shell ». The latter diagrams are characterized as follows. The *top* of the inserted part is placed at the same intermediate-state level as the $(-\Delta E)$ insertion (the horizontal bar) which it represents. The remainder of the insertion is then allowed to assume all possible relative « time » orderings with respect to the lower part of the original diagram.

The factorization theorem [9, 10] is a purely algebraic identity which shows that this prescription is valid for diagrams of arbitrary complexity.

We are now ready for the general proof of cancellation between $(-\Delta E)$'s and unlinked parts. The first step is to apply the expansion (12) to all denominators of the original Brillouin-Wigner series, Fig. 1. The resulting terms have the form shown in Fig. 2. Now some definitions: The *principal part* of a diagram is that linked part which contains the topmost interaction of the entire diagram. Let us imagine that we have simply erased the principal part off a general diagram. The remains then consist of a number of *time blocks*, separated vertically by blank spaces corresponding (in the absence of the principal part) to the initial state Φ_0. These time blocks can consist either of isolated horizontal bars, or of *overlapping groups*. An overlapping group consists of one or more linked parts which overlap vertically, such that Φ_0 does not occur anywhere as an intermediate state. Any horizontal bars which intersect this group are considered part of the group. This analysis is applied to a typical diagram in Fig. 10.

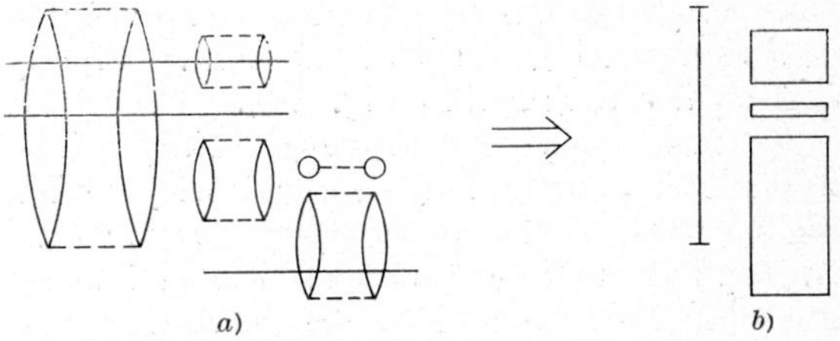

Fig. 10. – Analysis of a typical diagram into a principal part, shown as a vertical line, and several time blocks, shown as rectangles.

Consider a diagram with $n \geqslant 1$ time blocks, where the *lowest* of these time blocks is simply an isolated $(-\Delta E)$ insertion. Replace this insertion by the complete set of diagrams for ΔE as in Fig. 4. Now use the factorization theorem to take the inserted parts «off the energy shell», as described above. The result will be to cancel off all diagrams with the same principal part and the same first $n-1$ time blocks, but with an n-th time block consisting of an overlapping group extending downwards from the level where the $(-\Delta E)$ was. This cancellation is illustrated schematically in Fig. 11.

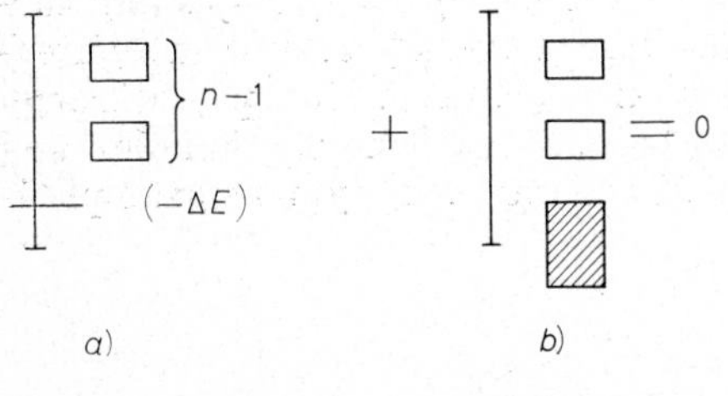

Fig. 11. – Illustration of the general cancellation between $(-\Delta E)$ insertions and unlinked parts. The shaded rectangle stands for all overlapping groups extending downwards from the level of $(-\Delta E)$.

Finally, note that every term in the complete expansion, obtained by applying (12) to Fig. 2, is either just a principal part, or else it fits into one of the categories *a*), *b*) shown in Fig. 11. The only terms that survive are the principal parts, which is just Goldstone's result.

Appendix B

Diagram rules for the linked valence expansion.

The following set of rules is complete and unambiguous. There are many details to keep track of, and it will be very helpful to consider both the «unfolded» and the «folded» form of each diagram.

1) *Topology*. – The most general diagram can be constructed as follows: Draw an arbitrary number $(f+1)$ of Bloch-Horowitz–type « interaction blocks », meaning diagrams such as Figs. 6 *a*) and 7 *a*), with no unlinked core parts and no many-body intermediate states Φ_i falling within the degenerate subspace. Arrange these blocks in a vertical column, and connect up the external valence lines between successive blocks to form an unfolded diagram like Fig. 8 *a*). Now discard all diagrams which are not completely connected (Fig. 9 *a*)), and erase any completely noninteracting valence lines (Fig. 9 *b*)). Draw a loop around each set of valence lines passing between successive blocks. The $(f+1)$ blocks are thus connected by f « bundles » of valence lines. (These loops are to prevent confusion between folded valence lines and downgoing lines representing holes in the core.) Finally, « fold » each of these bundles to form a diagram like Fig. 8 *b*).

To make this last step very clear, think of drawing the diagram of the previous step on a long vertical strip of paper and then making a zig-zag fold between each successive pair of blocks. Each fold should coincide with the topmost and bottommost interactions of the neighbouring blocks. The interactions of each block can have any relative time order with respect to those in other blocks, subject to two restrictions:

i) *The top interaction of each block must occur above the bottom of the previous block.* Neighbouring blocks must either overlap or completely overshoot each other.

ii) *The topmost interaction of the final folded diagram must be identical with the topmost interaction of the original unfolded diagram.* All diagrams satisfying these criteria must be considered.

The final folded diagrams can be drawn most neatly by i) displacing successive blocks horizontally to avoid any horizontal overlap, and ii) straightening out each folded valence line. External valence lines which pass through one or more blocks without interacting can be removed from the bundles and allowed to leave the diagram by the most direct route. A typical example is shown in Fig. 12.

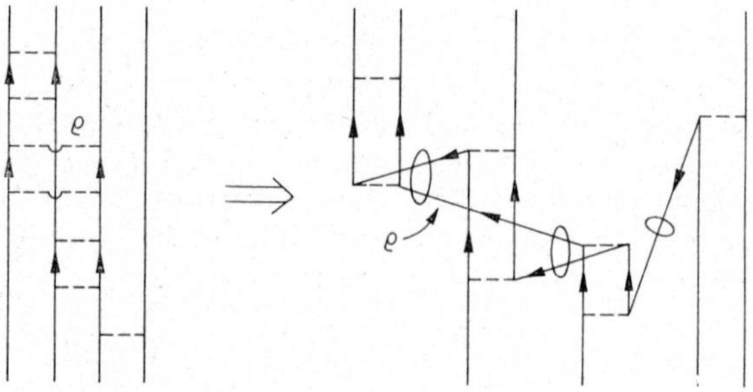

Fig. 12. – Representation of a typical folded diagram with four blocks $(f=3)$.

2) *Weighting factors*. – Consider the *unfolded* form of each diagram. From each « exchange group » of diagrams (diagrams which transform into each other when direct matrix elements of v_{12} are replaced by exchange elements, or vice versa), select just one member (the choice can be quite

arbitrary) and discard all the others. Considering all the v interactions in this diagram to be « direct », replace each element $\langle ab|v|cd\rangle$ by a « direct minus exchange » element, $\langle ab|v|cd - dc\rangle$. (This is equivalent to a « dot » diagram of HUGENHOLTZ [6]. We retain the dashed-line representation of v to avoid ambiguity of the over-all sign factor.) Now include a factor of $\frac{1}{2}$ for each « equivalent pair » of lines. An equivalent pair consists of two lines which i) both start at the same interaction, ii) both end at the same interaction, and iii) both go in the same direction. This rule applies to the folded valence lines between interaction blocks, as well as to lines within a single block.

3) *Over-all sign factor.* – It is necessary to have a consistent set of phases for the shell-model determinants Φ_i, $i \in D$. This is done by choosing a standard order for the entire set of valence orbitals. Now consider the *unfolded* diagram. Pull the *ends* of the external valence lines across each other to bring their labels into standard order. Do this at both the top and the bottom of the diagram. Then draw two horizontal « bending bars », one *above* the topmost interaction and one *below* the bottommost interaction. Finally, close the diagram by bending each external line through 180° around its bending bar, and connecting the opposite ends together. Standard ordering must be preserved here; the « first » line at the top must be joined to the « first » line at the bottom, etc. The sign factor is now $(-1)^{l+h+f}$, where l is the number of closed loops and h the *total* number of down-going line segments. Closure lines count as down-going segments, as well as holes in the core. The bending bars are necessary to insure the correct sign for certain «exchangelike» diagrams such as the example in Fig. 13.

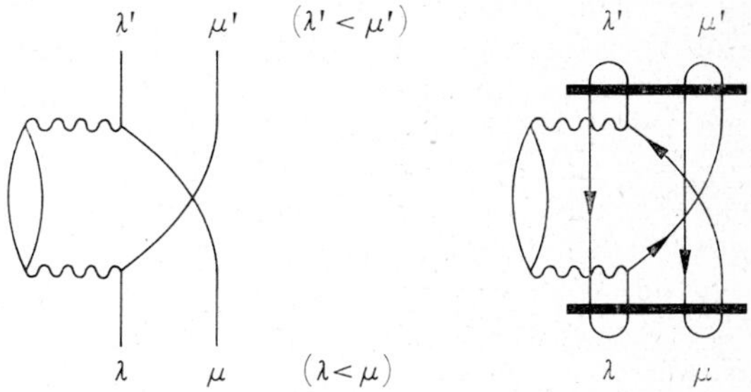

Fig. 13. – Example of an « exchangelike » diagram which requires the use of « bending bars » to determine the correct sign. The closed loop $\lambda\mu'\mu\lambda'$ counts as « two holes and one loop », giving an over-all sign factor of (-1).

4) *Energy denominators.* – Take the *folded* diagram and « close » it as in the previous step. The closure lines each carry two labels, one from the top and one from the bottom of the original diagram. Now erase the labels which came from the top of the open diagram, keeping only the *bottom* labels. The energy denominators are then given by the Goldstone prescription, eq. (11). (Note that the folded valence line labelled ϱ in Fig. 12 is upgoing, while the other folded lines are downgoing. The closure lines are also downgoing.)

5) *Sums over states.* – Within each block: sum each up-going line over all valence orbitals and over all the higher-lying « intermediate » orbitals. Sum each down-going line over all core orbitals. Between blocks: sum each folded valence line over all valence orbitals. Each summation is to be done independently, without regard to exclusion, except for one restriction. The many-body intermediate states Φ_i *within* each block must all be nondegenerate, thus within each block there must be at least one particle excited out of a core

orbital (thereby creating a hole) and/or at least one particle excited into an intermediate orbital. In case a degenerate state would result from two particles of an equivalent pair both occupying valence orbitals, the factor of $\frac{1}{2}$ can be retained if both of the allowed combinations « valence plus intermediate » and « intermediate plus valence » are included.

6) *Rules for valence holes.* – The general method also applies when the system contains n' « valence holes » in the core, in addition to n valence particles beyond the core; $A = N + n - n'$. The valence holes are represented by *downgoing* external valence lines whose labels are distributed among a subset of the core orbitals called *valence hole orbitals.* The above rules are modified as follows: *Topology*: Completely noninteracting valence hole lines may be ignored, otherwise no change. *Weighting factors*: No change. *Overall sign factor*: The set of valence hole orbitals must also be given a standard order, and this must be observed when closing the diagram. The recipe is still $(-1)^{l+h+f}$, but now one must also count the closure line segments which run outwards from the outermost interactions to the « bending bars ». For example, suppose that the four external lines in the left-hand diagram of Fig. 13 were valence holes instead of valence particles. The closed form of this diagram would then have a total of *five* downgoing line segments, giving an overall sign of (-1). *Energy denominators*: No change. *Sums over states*: Within each block the downgoing lines are summed over all valence hole orbitals as well as over the remaining core orbitals. This rule is again qualified by the requirement of no degenerate intermediate states. Between blocks each folded valence hole line is summed over all valence hole orbitals.

* * *

I am grateful to Prof. C. BLOCH for suggesting a clarification of these rules.

REFERENCES

[1] H. A. BETHE: *Phys. Rev.*, **138**, B 804 (1965).
[2] T. MORITA: *Progr. Theor. Phys.*, **29**, 351 (1963).
[3] J. GOLDSTONE: *Proc. Roy. Soc.*, A **239**, 267 (1957).
[4] B. BRANDOW: to appear in *Rev. Mod. Phys.*
[5] C. BLOCH and J. HOROWITZ: *Nucl. Phys.*, **8**, 91 (1958).
[6] N. H. HUGENHOLTZ: *Physica*, **23**, 481 (1957).
[7] D. J. THOULESS: *The Quantum Mechanics of Many-Body Systems* (New York, 1961), p. 47. See also A. E. GLASSGOLD, W. HECKROTTE and K. M. WATSON: *Phys. Rev.*, **115**, 1374 (1959).
[8] K. A. BRUECKNER: *Phys. Rev.*, **100**, 36 (1955).
[9] L. M. FRANTZ and R. L. MILLS: *Nucl. Phys.*, **15**, 16 (1960).
[10] H. A. BETHE, B. H. BRANDOW and A. G. PETSCHEK: *Phys. Rev.*, **129**, 225 (1963) (Appendix B).
[11] K. A. BRUECKNER, R. J. EDEN and N. C. FRANCIS: *Phys. Rev.*, **99**, 76 (1955).
[12] H. A. BETHE: *Phys. Rev.*, **103**, 1353 (1956).
[13] J. F. DAWSON, I. TALMI and J. D. WALECKA: *Ann. of. Phys.*, **18**, 339 (1962).
[14] K. A. BRUECKNER, J. L. GAMMEL and H. WEITZNER: *Phys. Rev.*, **110**, 431 (1958); B. H. BRANDOW: *Comptes Rendus du Congrès International de Physique Nucléaire*, Vol. **2** (Paris, 1964), p. 295.

Mixture of Deformed and Spherical States in the Oxygen Region.

G. E. Brown

Princeton University - Princeton, N. J.

Introduction.

Evidence for low-lying deformed states in the oxygen and calcium regions has been accumulating. Firstly, the number of low-lying states is just too large for the spherical shell model. Secondly, various transition probabilities turn out to be orders of magnitude larger than in the usual shell model description.

In this seminar I wish to give a short summary of work carried on at Princeton together with A. M. Green, aimed at giving a description of the low-lying even-parity states in the oxygen region.

1. – Spectra of ^{16}O.

In Fig. 1 I show an old compilation of experimental data which shows rather clearly the existence of rotational bands in the excited states of ^{16}O.

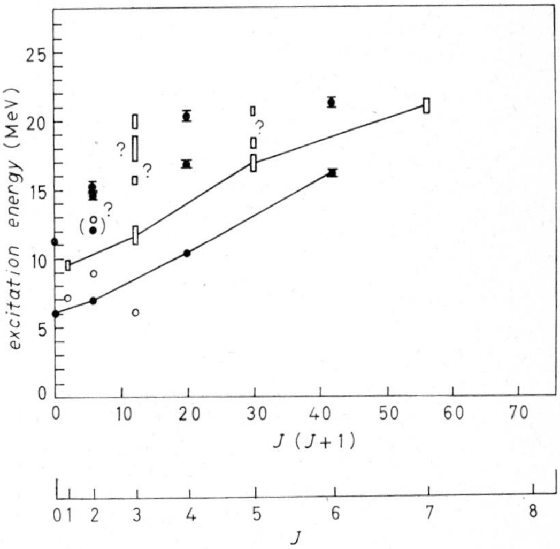

Fig. 1. – Various levels in ^{16}O. • positive-parity level, less than 100 keV width; ⧫ positive-parity level, width as shown; ○ negative-parity level, less than 100 keV width; ▯ negative-parity level, width as shown.

Out of these many levels, I wish to consider in detail three 0^+ and two 2^+ levels, as shown in Fig. 2. The excited 0^+ and 2^+ levels form the lowest two members of two rotational bands here. The sizable $BE(2)$ (~ one single-particle unit) between the 6.92 2^+ state and the ground state indicates considerable mixing between deformed and ground state.

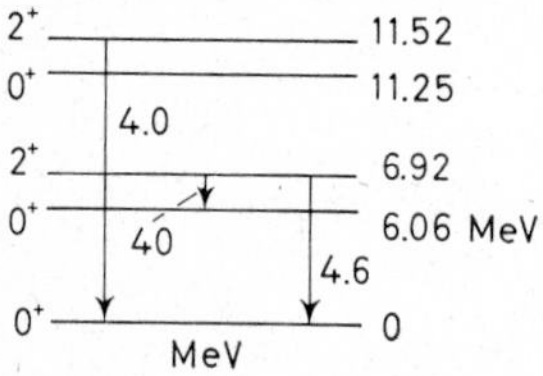

Fig. 2. – Low-lying 0^+ and 2^+ levels in ^{16}O. $BE(2)$'s in units of e^2 fermi^4 are given.

How can one have such low-lying deformed states? To see this, let us look at the Nilsson diagram, Fig. 3, which shows how levels move as the potential well is deformed. For a large prolate (cigar-shaped) deformation, particular $\frac{1}{2}^+$ and $\frac{1}{2}^-$ levels move together, and it costs relatively little energy to excite two particles from one to the other, as shown. In fact, it seems to cost even less energy to excite four particles [2].

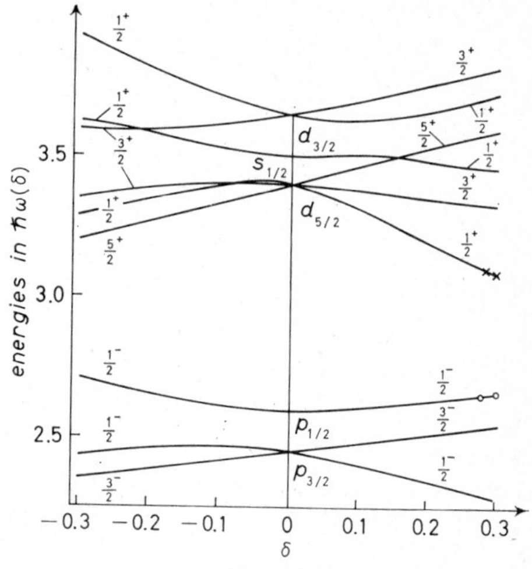

Fig. 3.

Using the Kallio-Kolltveit force (one which fits two-body scattering), we calculated matrix elements between the $0p0h$, $2p2h$, and $4p4h$ states. Deformations of $\beta = 0$, 0.3, and 0.5 were assumed for these. We obtained the following results:

$$\psi(0_1^+, 0\ \text{MeV}) = 0.87\ (0p0h) + 0.47\ (2p2h) + 0.13\ (4p4h)\ ,$$

$$\psi(0_2^+, 6.06) = -0.26\ (0p0h) + 0.23\ (2p2h) + 0.94\ (4p4h)\ ,$$

$$\psi(0_3^+, 11.25) = -0.41\ (0p0h) + 0.85\ (2p2h) - 0.32\ (4p4h)\ ,$$

where unperturbed energies were

$$E_{\text{unpert}}(0p0h) = 2.3\ \text{MeV}\ ,$$

$$E_{\text{unpert}}(2p2h) = 8.5\ ,$$

$$E_{\text{unpert}}(4p4h) = 6.5\ ,$$

and for the 2^+ states

$$\psi(2_1^+,\ 6.92\ \text{MeV}) = 0.38\ (2p2h) + 0.92\ (4p4h)\ ,$$
$$\psi(2_3^+,\ 11.52\ \text{MeV}) = 0.92\ (2p2h) - 0.38\ (4p4h)\ .$$

These arose from matrix elements

$$([0p0h]^{J=0}|V|[2p2h]^{J=0}) = -\ 4.3\ \text{MeV}\ ,$$
$$([2p2h]^{J=0}|V|[4p4h]^{J=0}) = -\ 1.8\ \text{MeV}\ ,$$
$$([2p2h]^{J=2}|V|[2p2h]^{J=2}) = -\ 1.6\ \text{MeV}\ ,$$

calculated from the Kallio-Kolltveit potential with allowance for cut-down for lack of core overlap (a factor of $\frac{3}{4}$ in the first matrix element).

These wave functions give rise to the following $BE(2)$'s

	Experiment
$B(E2,\ 2_1^+ \to 0_1^+) = 5.3\ e^2\ \text{fermi}^4\ ,$	$(4.6 \pm 1.0)\ e^2\ \text{fermi}^4\ ,$
$B(E2,\ 2_3^+ \to 0_1^+) = 3.3\ ,$	$4.0 \pm 0.5\ ,$
$B(E2,\ 2_1^+ \to 0_2^+) = 103\ ,$	$40\ ,$

and for the transition from the 10.36 MeV 4^+ level

$$B(E2,\ 4_1^+ \to 2_1^+) = 152\ , \qquad 117\ e^2\ \text{fermi}^4\ .$$

The over-all agreement is seen to be quite good.

2. – Other oxygen isotopes.

The situation in ^{17}O is quite complicated, because of the coupling of the odd neutron with the deformed states, and the single-particle strength, especially that from $d_{\frac{3}{2}}$, splits up into many levels. Whereas the ground state of ^{16}O was pushed down 2.3 MeV by interaction with deformed states in our calculations, that of ^{17}O is pushed down ~ 3.1 MeV. If these are correct, then the « shell-model » binding energy of a $1d_{\frac{5}{2}}$ neutron should be taken as 0.8 MeV less than the empirical difference in ^{17}O and ^{16}O binding energies, 0.8 MeV of that difference coming from the different mixing of deformed states.

In ^{18}O, the deformed state shown in Fig. 4, was mixed into low-lying two-particle states by ENGELAND and by FEDERMAN and TALMI [3]. This mixing was necessary for many reasons, which I covered in my talk at the Paris Conference last summer. The mixing with this collective state pushes the ground state down only ~ 0.6 MeV, but there are much larger matrix elements to other deformed states, such as the one shown in Fig. 5. Although the deformed state comes at ~ 9 MeV, the matrix element between it and two-particle ground state is ~ 3 MeV, so that it lowers the ground state

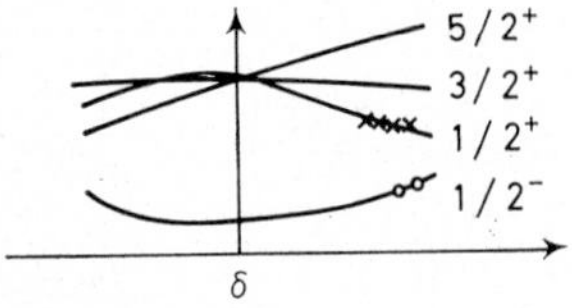

Fig. 4. – Schematic picture, using the Nilsson diagram, of the deformed state first introduced in ^{18}O.

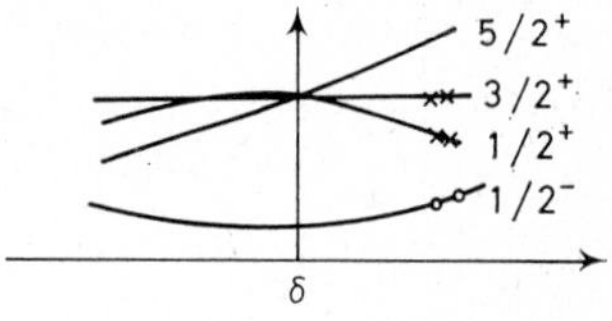

Fig. 5. – One of the deformed states with large matrix elements to the spherical ground state.

~ 1 MeV. (The reason that this matrix element is so large is with the two « passive » neutrons in the $\frac{3}{2}^+$ orbit, where they have a large overlap with those in the spherical two-particle state of ^{18}O, either neutrons or protons can be promoted from the $\frac{1}{2}^-$ to $\frac{1}{2}^+$ orbit, whereas in the state of Fig. 4, only protons of opposite spin can be promoted. One gains a factor of $\sqrt{6}$ from this.)

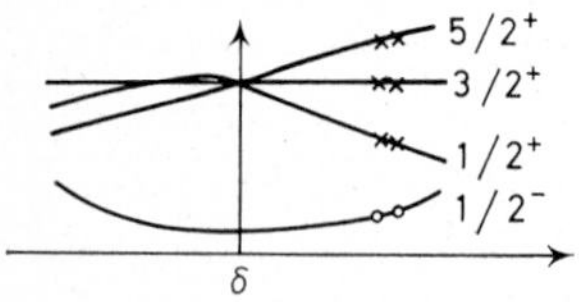

Fig. 6. – Schematic picture of deformed state in ^{20}O which has the largest matrix element to the ground state.

Although our calculations are not complete for ^{18}O, it looks as if the ground state is lowered about the same amount as that of ^{17}O and ^{16}O. At this stage, one might be tempted to say that all ground states are lowered about the same amount and that, therefore, effects from this would drop out if one took differences.

This does not seem to be so. In ^{20}O, for example, the deformed state connected to ground with largest matrix element is that shown in Fig. 6. The matrix element here is less than in ^{18}O, however, because of the lower overlap of the four « passive » particles with spherical four-particle state, and the effect on the energy will be less because of the higher energy of the state due to the two particles in the $\frac{5}{2}^+$ orbit.

The apparent configuration energy of ^{20}O, as obtained by Talmi and collaborators and others, is

$$CE(^{20}\text{O}) = BE(^{20}\text{O}) - 4[BE(^{17}\text{O}) - BE(^{16}\text{O})] - BE(^{16}\text{O}) \,, \tag{1}$$

the $4[BE(^{17}\text{O}) - BE(^{16}\text{O})]$ being the single-particle binding energies of the four $d_{\frac{5}{2}}$ particles.

If, on the other hand, we wish to separate out collective effects in order to see what energies forces used with the spherical shell model should produce, we find

$$CE(^{20}O) = CE(^{20}O) + \Delta(^{16}O) - \Delta(^{20}O) + 4[\Delta(^{17}O) - \Delta(^{16}O)]\,, \tag{2}$$

where the Δ's are the changes in energy by admixture of deformed configurations. In our case, $\Delta(^{16}O) > \Delta(^{20}O)$ and $\Delta(^{17}O) > \Delta(^{16}O)$.

TALMI, working with the configuration energies analogous to that of eq. (1), has emphasized that effective forces in nuclei must have terms which give repulsive contributions to the energies as one adds more neutrons. We see from eq. (2) that the configuration energy which should be produced in the spherical shell model seems to be larger than that obtained empirically, the repulsion (raising of ground-state energy) coming from the lower amount of admixture of deformed states.

In other words, the apparently repulsive terms in the binding energy come, in our picture, partly from the greater lowering of the ground state of ^{17}O than that of ^{16}O (giving the term with coefficient 4 in eq. (2)) and partly from the fact that collective states mix less with the ground states when more neutrons are present. In other words, as one adds more (like) particles, the nucleus becomes more nearly spherical, a general feature which, as TALMI has pointed out repeatedly, is demanded by empirical data.

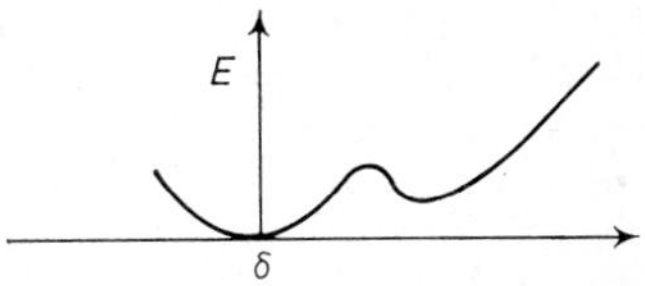

Fig. 7. – Typical curve of energy *vs.* deformation for a « spherical » nucleus.

In closing, I would like to remark that these phenomena, which I have spelled out in detail for the oxygen region, are not special in this region, but there are good indications that the admixtures of deformed states are important in most supposedly spherical nuclei. In particular, curves of energy *vs.* deformation probably look like that shown in Fig. 7, the dip on the right-hand side coming at the point where the state obtained by lifting particles out of the core comes at a lower energy than the deformed ground state. If this is so, vibrations will be extremely anharmonic to the extent that there is tunnelling through to the second minimum, and our usual (harmonic) picture of quadrupole oscillations must be changed.

REFERENCES

[1] T. ENGELAND: *Nucl. Phys.*, to be published.
[2] W. H. BASSICHIS and G. RIPKA: *Phys. Lett.*, **15**, 320 (1965); P. FEDERMAN and I. TALMI: private communication.
[3] P. FEDERMAN and I. TALMI: *Phys. Lett.*, **15**, 165 (1965).

Octupole Vibrations in Heavy, Even-Even Spherical Nuclei.

C. J. VEJE

The Niels Bohr Institute, University of Copenhagen - Copenhagen

Professor GILLET has asked me, before entering into the description of the octupoles, to mention briefly some calculations which have been performed recently in Copenhagen by B. SÖRENSEN to study the influence of possible improvements of the simple quasi-boson treatment of the 2^+ vibrations.

I am very sorry that I am not able to describe these calculations in detail.

Let me remind you of the situation in the $A \sim 120 \div 140$ region, as it was found by KISSLINGER and SØRENSEN. If you follow the energy of the lowest 2^+ excitation for a group of isotopes, beginning with the neutron number $N = 82$ and going downwards in A (keeping Z fixed), you find that the RPA calculation with pairing + quadrupole-quadrupole force gives a much too rapid decrease in energy. This is independent of whether you choose your quadrupole force constant to fit the lowest or the highest of the experimental 2^+ energies.

It also appears impossible to obtain a reasonable fit by the use of the same force constant for the $Z = 50$ nuclei as for the other ones.

You might suppose that these difficulties arise mainly from the restriction of the two-quasi-particle space to the excitations inside the partly filled shells. From a rough calculation which we have performed, taking all two-quasi-particle excitations into account, we learned, however, that this is not the case.

It was then a near lying possibility to introduce the ideas of Ikeda. He suggested to improve the RPA by taking into account that the creation and destruction operators for the vibrations do not exactly obey quasi-boson commutation relations (cf. Prof. Gillet's lectures, pp. 63ff.).

He introduced into the formulae explicitly the quasi-particle number operators $N(j, m)$, approximating them by their ground-state expectation values. The method has been further explored and developed by SÖRENSEN. (It is mainly a question of at which stage you linearize your equations, and how many terms you include.) The idea is essentially to solve the equations without taking $N(j, m)$ into account, then to find $\langle N(j, m) \rangle$ and insert it into your equations, find a new value of $\langle N(j, m)\rangle$, and so on. The iteration converges quite rapidly, until you reach asymptotic values of $\langle N(j, m)\rangle$ in the region $0.3 \div 0.4$, which happens for the lightest isotopes with Z just above 50. For the cases where the asymptotic value is 0.5, the whole treatment breaks down.

By the above-mentioned procedure the role of the two-quasi-particle excitations with lowest energy is diminished, sometimes by 30 % in the amplitudes, and the agreement with experimental energies and B-values becomes really nice. (In the Ikeda approach the resulting, collective energy E is always kept above a certain limit E(min).) Perhaps it is even too nice, since some effects, which may be of major importance, are neglected.

The main deficiences may be the following ones:

1) No dynamic anharmonicities are taken into account, although some of the nuclei considered are very near to (or even have) nonspherical equilibrium shape.

2) Only the expectation value of $N(j, m)$ is considered. Because of the vibrational character of the excitations, the fluctuations in $N(j, m)$ are expected to be large, and it may be important to include them.

Now, I shall turn to the description of the octupole vibrations, but first I must apologize for not being very concise. I did not expect to give a seminar here, and therefore I brought no tables or figures concerning my work.

The modes, which we are going to consider, are supposed to be related to harmonic vibrations in the general nuclear field.

We expect the interaction between a nucleon i and the relevant part of the field to be of the form $\sum_\mu f(r_i) Y_{3\mu}(i) F^*_{3\mu}$, where the operator $F_{3\mu}$ which is a spherical tensor, represents the nuclear field. The radial dependence $f(r_i)$ is not very well established. Since the low energetic collective vibrations which we primarily are going to consider are expected largely to be surface effects, $f(r_i)$ is assumed to weight the nuclear surface region quite heavily. A possible choice for f would be the radial derivative of a Saxon-Wood potential. For simplicity reasons, we just use $f(r_i) = r_i^3$. By this choice, all the radial matrix elements, connecting levels which differ by one in the principal quantum number N, are of the same order of magnitude even when squared, and thus no cancellation takes part. For the $\Delta N = 3$ matrix elements the fluctuations are greater, and in average the squares are half as great as for $\Delta N = 1$.

The interaction between the particles through the octupole part of the nuclear field is now simulated by taking into account the annihilation term (the field-producing part) of the following:

$$H(\text{long range}) \sim \sum_\mu \sum_i r_i^3 Y_{3\mu}(i) \sum_j r_j^3 Y^*_{3\mu}(j) \varkappa(i, j) \,.$$

The coupling constant $\varkappa$ is supposed to be an invariant under rotations in isospin space. By decomposition

$$\varkappa(i,j)=\varkappa_0+4\varkappa_1\boldsymbol{t}(i)\cdot\boldsymbol{t}(j)\;,$$

where $\boldsymbol{t}(i)$ and $\boldsymbol{t}(j)$ are the isospins of particles i and j; $\varkappa_0$ is the $\tau=0$ or isoscalar part of the interaction constant, $\varkappa_1$ is the $\tau=1$ or isovector part. We use the convention

$$t_0(i)=\begin{cases}\;\;\frac{1}{2}\text{ for protons,}\\-\frac{1}{2}\text{ for neutrons,}\end{cases}$$

where t_0 is the z-component or the $\nu=0$ spherical tensor component of t.

Since only the annihilation term is considered (and since by the excitation we keep inside the even-even nucleus) just $\varkappa_0+4\varkappa_1 t_0(i)t_0(j)$ survives in $\varkappa$. The $\varkappa_1 t_1(i)t_{-1}(j)$ term is relevant, *e.g.* in charge-exchange processes like (p, n), where we go to the neighbouring odd-odd nucleus and simultaneously excite a 3^- vibration.

Only little information is available concerning the magnitude of $\varkappa_1/\varkappa_0$. It is expected to be negative (repulsive $\tau=1$ interaction), since this will push the $\tau=1$ or B_1 strength (see below) upwards as is the case for the giant dipole. If we, in a rough approximation, take over the isospin dependence from the central nuclear field (as it manifests itself in the Weizsäcker formula and, perhaps less certain, also in the real part of the potential, used in optical-model calculations) or if we assume the force, which is responsible for our interaction to be of approximate Serber type, we get $\varkappa_1\simeq-0.5\varkappa_0$.

The results for the calculation of the low-energy, collective states are not very sensitive to the value of $\varkappa_1$, whereas this one is decisive for the energy distribution of the B_1 strength which is defined below. Calculations have been made, using $\varkappa_1=0$, $\varkappa_1=-0.5\varkappa_0$ and $\varkappa_1=-2\varkappa_0$. In the second case, the long-range proton-proton force is three times weaker than the neutron-proton one, which is quite a remarkable difference. In the third case, they even have opposite signs. The total Hamiltonian is now

$$H=H(\text{shell model})+H(\text{pairing})+H(\text{long range})\;,$$

where the first term describes particles moving independently in a shell-model potential, and the second one introduces pairing between particles with the same t_0. Only nuclei with neutrons and protons filling up different shells (or subshells) are considered.

In the simple picture of noninteracting particles in a pure harmonic-oscillator shell-model potential you can form 3^- excitations by lifting a particle either one or three shells. Using a more realistic shell-model potential and including pairing, you get a spectrum which consists of a group of lines ($60 \div 90$) of energy around $\hbar\omega_0$ and another group around $3\hbar\omega_0$ (ω_0 is the frequency in the harmonic oscillator) plus some few ($2 \div 4$) low-energetic lines from excitations inside the partly filled shells (*e.g.* in the $50 \div 82$ shell the two quasi-particle excitations $(h_{11/2}d_{5/2})_{3^-}$ and $(h_{11/2}g_{7/2})_{3^-}$). This is illustrated in Fig. 1.

It is thus essential for the features in the lowest part of the spectrum that the spin-orbit splitting sends one level like $h_{11/2}$ down to the shell below with opposite parity.

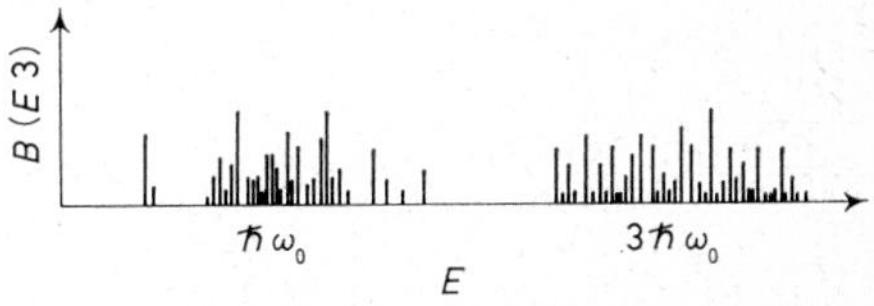

Fig. 1. – Rough sketch of the 3^- spectrum in some typical case, when H (long range) is not included.

In the calculation the shell-model single-particle energies were obtained from a simple nuclear potential, except for the partly filled shells. For these ones the energies were taken from the results of stripping and pick-up experiments or from KISSLINGER and SØRENSEN.

The resulting spectrum for the total Hamiltonian is found using the quasi-boson approximation. If $\varkappa_1 = 0$ or $\varkappa_0 = 0$, we are back to the cases treated by Prof. GILLET (p. 43). A rough sketch of the spectrum in a typical example is given in Fig. 2. In the low-energetic part, two strong lines of approximate $\tau = 0$ character (B_0 always greater than $10B_1$, see below) appear. In the highest-energetic part, there is (for $\varkappa_1 = -0.5\varkappa_0$) some, not very pronounced, tendency towards concentrating some $\tau = 1$ strength. In between there are many weak lines, often of mixed isospin character. It is worth-while to note that in the present model no strong lines are formed in the gap between the $\hbar\omega_0$ and $3\hbar\omega_0$ excitations.

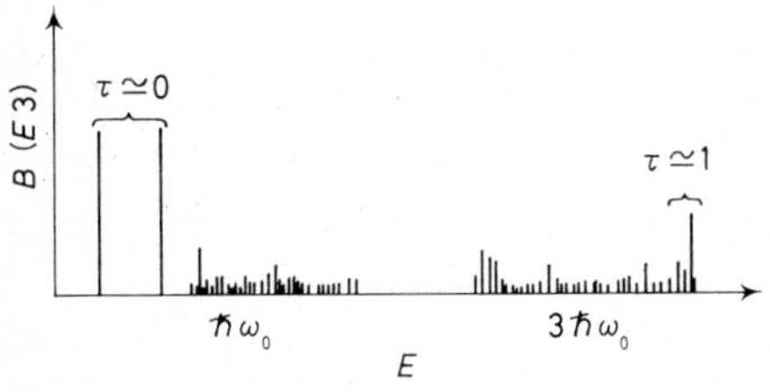

Fig. 2. – The resulting spectrum in the same case as Fig. 1, when H (long range) is taken into account ($\varkappa_1 = -0.5\varkappa_0$).

The isospin structure of the excitations may be conveniently described by B_0 and B_1, the squares of the reduced matrix elements between the ground state and the state in question, of the following operators:

$$M(\tau = 0;\, \lambda = 3, \mu) = \tfrac{1}{2} \sum_i r_i^3 Y_{3\mu}(i)$$

and

$$M(\tau = 1, \nu = 0;\, \lambda = 3, \mu) = \sum_i r_i^3 Y_{3\mu}(i)\, t_0(i)$$

summing over all the particles i. The quantities τ, ν describe the tensor character of the operators in isospace.

When

$$B_1 \equiv |\langle 3^-, \alpha \| M(\tau = 1, \nu = 0; \lambda = 3, \mu) \| 0 \rangle|^2 = 0$$

the state $|3^-, \alpha\rangle$ is formed by equal amounts of neutron and proton excitations, and by definition $\tau = 0$. ($|0\rangle$ is the ground state.) We note the difference between τ and T, the isospin of the states. When working on the ground state $|\beta, T = T_1, T_0 = -T_1\rangle$ with a $\tau = 0$ operator, we are sure to come back to the same isospin (it is easily seen that the lowest-energetic particle-hole excitations are pure $\tau = 0$), while $\tau = 1, \nu = 0$ excitation operators may also give rise to states

$$|\delta, T_1 + 1, -T_1\rangle .$$

These last ones are isobaric analogues to states $|\delta, T_1 + 1, -T_1 - 1\rangle$, fully aligned in isospin space, and shall not be discussed here. When we want the excited state to have a good $T = T_1$, we must construct it by vector coupling of τ and T_1. The 3^- state thus contains a part which consists of a $\tau = 1$, $\nu = -1$ excitation based on $|\beta, T_1, -T_1 + 1\rangle$, the isobaric analogue to the ground state in our nucleus.

When $T_1 \gg 1$, as is the case for the heavy nuclei, this part is small because of the vector coupling coefficient, and we do not take it into account.

Since B_0 treats protons and neutrons on the same footing, you just measure the B_0 or $\tau = 0$ part when exciting the oscillation by inelastic α or deuteron scattering (particles with $T = 0$). In electromagnetic processes you measure $B(E3)$, which is related to B_0 and B_1 by

$$B(E3) = e^2(\sqrt{B_0} \pm \sqrt{B_1})^2 .$$

Because of the interference term between $\sqrt{B_0}$ and $\sqrt{B_1}$, $B(E3)$ and B_0 may differ by a factor of two, even when B_1/B_0 is small. For the two low-energetic, strong, resulting states, described above, the relative strength may thus be very dependent on the excitation process in which you measure it.

When using inelastic scattering of $T \neq 0$ particles as *e.g.* neutrons or protons, B_0 and B_1 are measured in some mixture, unless the relevant interaction is isospin-independent. By excitations of different 3^- states in some nucleus we may, when using projectiles with different T, obtain information on this isospin dependence.

Another possibility may be to excite 3^- states in inelastic nucleon scattering and study the ratio of the probabilities for isospin-flip to nonisospin-flip of the nucleon.

In the calculation the results of which will be published in detail elsewhere (*Mat. Fys. Medd., Dan. Vid. Selsk.*), the stable, spherical even-even nuclei between Ni and Pb were considered. No concept of effective charge was introduced. In the major part, only the ten resulting states of lowest energy were found and the $\Delta N = 3$ two-quasi-particle excitations were concentrated in $3\hbar\omega_0$. If these last ones were left out, $B(E3)$ for the low-energy, strong states was diminished by roughly 50 %.

The agreement with the experimental energies is quite satisfactory, using a $\varkappa_0$ value which varies smoothly with A, approximately as $A^{8/3}$. In almost all cases the $B(E3)$ values lie between the experimental figures and 30 % below. The influence of the shell-model single-particle energies on the results is rather strong.

The predicted higher lying, strong line (in general around (4÷5) MeV) has not yet been studied experimentally. Preliminary results from an experiment by FARAGGI *et al.*, using inelastic α scattering, seem to indicate the existence in the Sn isotopes of some 3^- strength around 5 MeV.

For the lowest 3^- state in ^{208}Pb we may compare our results with those obtained by GILLET and coworkers, restricting themselves to the subspace of $\hbar\omega_0$ excitations and using a « realistic » force. For the 20 most low-energetic neutron or proton two-quasi-particle excitations, the amplitudes X and Y as defined by Prof. GILLET (p. 43) came out with the same sign in the two calculations, except for one case.

For the proton excitations the amplitudes are systematically about 30 % smaller in our calculation, while the neutron amplitudes are systematically some per cent greater. This is found using $\varkappa_1 = 0$. When $\varkappa_1 \neq 0$ is introduced, this discrepancy is greatly diminished since more proton motion is mixed into the low mode.

We are thus able, by a short calculation (computing time for the lowest 10 resulting 3^- states (3÷4) minutes on a GIER computing machine) to reproduce quite well the energy and wave function found by GILLET *et al.* by a much more refined and tedious method, and the agreement with the experimental energy and B-value is completely satisfactory.

This might perhaps give some slight justification of our assumptions.

Effective Forces in Nuclei.

G. E. Brown
Princeton University - Princeton, N. J.

Introduction.

Calculation of the two-body force in nuclei from the force between two free nucleons is obviously of great interest. In particular, it facilitates a better description of nuclear states in terms of configurations; often one has employed quite the wrong configurations but brought the final states to the empirical energies by juggling the many parameters in the usual effective forces. Also, one feels that nuclear physics is rather « sloppy » if one has to introduce new forces to describe each new phenomenon, many of these having nothing in common with forces used to analyse nucleon-nucleon scattering.

We shall show that the connection between the free-space nucleon-nucleon force and that in nuclei is a simple one, and that, furthermore, the effective force we calculate seems to have the necessary characteristics to explain known nuclear phenomena.

1. – Development.

Complications entering into the interaction of two particles in the nucleus stem from:

1) The hard core in the interaction.

2) Effects from the noninteracting (passive) particles through the Pauli principle.

3) Changes in the energies of the interacting particles stemming from the presence of the other particles (self-energy interactions) and higher-order interaction (three-body clusters, etc.).

The way to handle the hard core has been known for a long time. It is known that an infinite core causes no difficulty in the two-particle problem—one simply solves the Schrödinger equation, the wave function starting from zero at the edge of the core. BRUECKNER has introduced a technique having similar consequences into nuclear physics; one solves a t-matrix equation, which effectively means working with wave functions with strong two-body correlations in them. The t-matrix is called a G-matrix in nuclear physics, and the equation is

$$(1)\qquad (k_1k_2|G|k_3k_4) = (k_1k_2|V|k_3k_4) - \sum_{\substack{k_5,k_6\\ \text{over unoc-}\\ \text{cupied states}}} \frac{(k_1k_2|V|k_5k_6)(k_5k_6|G|k_3k_4)}{\varepsilon_5+\varepsilon_6-\varepsilon_3-\varepsilon_4},$$

where the k's label shell-model states. By taking the first term on the right-hand side as first approximation for G and iterating one sees that G contains effects of V to all order. This G-matrix differs from the free-particle t-matrix in two ways:

1) the sum over intermediate states is restricted by the Pauli principle,

2) the energy denominators ε_3, ε_4, etc. are not necessarily free-particle energies, because of the presence of the other particles.

As regards point 2), it has been known for years that the initial-state energies ε_3, ε_4 should be taken as the shell-model energies. In Brueckner theory, the energies ε_5 and ε_6 are to be computed self-consistently (and off the energy shell). However, BETHE has shown that the effect of inclusion of three-body clusters is to almost cancel the one-body potential energies introduced this way, so that it is much more accurate to take ε_5 and ε_6 as just kinetic energies and k_5 and k_6 as free-particle states (plane waves). This simplifies the procedure considerably.

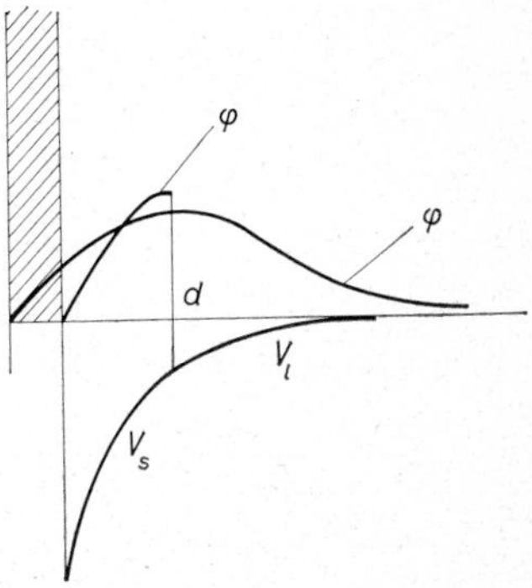

Fig. 1. – Illustration of the Moszkowski-Scott cut-off procedure.

Let us now consider two particles in shell-model orbitals, described by harmonic-oscillator functions. With such functions, one can transform to relative and centre-of-mass co-ordinates. Let us now consider a function of relative motion which, for simplicity, we take to be a $1s$ function, and call it φ. If two free particles collide, the wave function must start from zero, and we call it ψ. At some point d the logarithmic derivatives of ψ and φ become equal, and we use this point to divide the potential into long- and short-range parts.

MOSZKOWSKI and SCOTT have given an expansion for V in terms of G_s

and V_l, where G_s is the G-matrix which results from V_s. This is

$$G = G_s + V_l - 2G_s \frac{Q}{e} V_l - V_l \frac{Q}{e} V_l + \dots, \tag{2}$$

where Q represents the Pauli operator and e the energy denominator. Now, the point is that V_s is so strong that the Pauli principle is unimportant in calculating G_s. Furthermore, our definition of V_s is just such that it produces no net effect, the attraction just balancing the repulsion. Thus, G_s gives only negligible matrix elements, and the effective force is V_l plus correction terms. These correction terms are only large in the case of tensor forces, and one knows how to handle them (T. T. S. KUO and G. E. BROWN: *Phys. Lett.*, **18**, 54 (1965)). For simplicity, we shall restrict our considerations to central forces.

Rather than use the full complexity of modern forces, we discuss the Kallio-Kolltveit force

$$\begin{cases} V = V_S + V_T\,, \qquad V_S = V_T = \infty\,, & r < c\,, \\ V_S = -\,331\ \text{MeV}\exp[-2.4\ \text{fermi}^{-1}\,r]\,, & \\ V_T = -\,425\ \text{MeV}\exp[-2.52\ \text{fermi}^{-1}\,r]\,, & r > c\,, \end{cases} \tag{3}$$

which is assumed to operate only in relative S-states. The separation distances in oxygen are

$$d_S = 1.025\ \text{fermi}\,, \qquad d_T = 0.925\ \text{fermi}\,,$$

and vary slowly with increasing A, so that it is sufficient for most purposes to use these.

Our effective force is then V_l, the parts of V_S and V_T outside the separation distance. To these should be added a slightly renormalized tensor force, and odd-state interactions, but these are small and tend to average out for most phenomena.

Rather than go into more detail about the definition of the force, I will indicate typical phenomena which have been calculated with such forces.

1) Two-body spectra. In Fig. 2 the spectrum of ^{42}Sc, calculated by ZAMICK and BERTSCH at Princeton is shown.

In the theoretical results, tensor force and core polarization (calculated with the KK force) has been included. All two-particle states in the $2p$, $1f$ shell were included in the diagonalization.

ENGELAND (*Nucl. Phys.* (1964)) has calculated the spectrum of ^{20}Ne with the Kallio-Kolltveit forces and obtains about as good results as other people varying parameters with phenomenological forces. KUO has calculated vibrational spectra in the Sn isotopes, and finds that the KK forces give quite a good description. Also, spectra of ^{16}O, ^{18}O, ^{206}Pb, ^{210}Po have been calculated

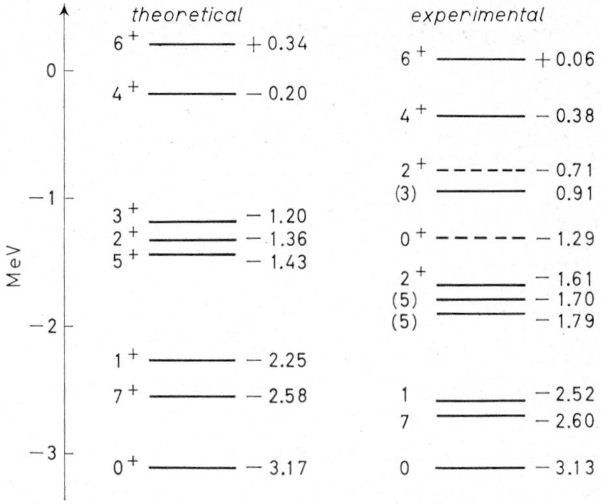

Fig. 2.

and in each case the fit to experiment is about as good as with the best phenomenological forces, each chosen to fit just the one region considered.

Finally, we note that the pairing matrix elements are about what are required. (A. KALLIO: *Ann. Acad. Sci. Fenn. Series* A, **6**, 163 (1964).)

Theory of the Effective Interaction.

B. H. BRANDOW (*)

The Niels Bohr Institute, University of Copenhagen - Copenhagen

1. – Introduction.

Our main concern here will be the calculation of the Brueckner reaction matrix elements for shell-model orbitals. This is the leading term in the linked-cluster expansion for the effective interaction between valence particles. The higher-order terms are also being investigated. Those which involve high excitation energies, corresponding to short-range correlations between three or more particles, belong to the natural domain of nuclear-matter theory. Bethe's discussion of three-body correlations [1] gives us good reason to believe that these terms are very small, probably negligible. On the other hand, the correction terms which involve low excitations, say a few tens of MeV or less, will overlap somewhat with the natural domain of shell-model configuration mixing. An important example is the phenomenon of core polarization, or « exchange of virtual core phonons » in the language of random phase theory. Several people are investigating this effect, but the subject is still in its infancy. Going further down the energy scale, to just a few MeV, we encounter all the well-known configuration problems of ordinary shell-model calculations. If one's configuration space is too small, or if the calculation methods (pairing, RPA, SU_3, etc.) are not sufficiently accurate, then of course one cannot expect good results from a « realistic » force. ELLIOTT has given an example of this in his lectures here, where he found that the omission of the higher configurations of pairing theory had led him to deduce an effective force with an unrealistic $L \cdot S$ component. BROWN has also pointed out the difficulties of an honest comparison between realistic forces and nuclear data. But these should be overcome as more is learned about the specific effects of the various components found in the theoretical interaction.

(*) National Science Foundation Postdoctoral Fellow.

We shall first discuss the available methods for calculating the matrix elements in infinite nuclear matter. This should provide some feeling for the various parameters which enter in these calculations. We then examine some geometrical features of actual shell-model orbitals. We shall see that one can take over the methods of nuclear-matter theory in a simple and direct way. This is an excellent approximation if one is careful enough in choosing appropriate values for the various parameters. Finally, we discuss some features of the interaction which emerges from this theory.

2. – Calculation methods for infinite nuclear matter.

Brueckner's reaction matrix equation is, in Bethe's notation,

$$G_N = v - v\frac{Q}{e_N}G_N \tag{1}$$

(N for nuclear matter), where

$$\begin{cases} \langle ab|\dfrac{Q}{e_N}|a'b'\rangle = \dfrac{\delta_{aa'}\delta_{bb'}}{E_a^N + E_b^N - E_m^N - E_n^N}\,, & k_a,\quad k_b > k_F\\ & k_m,\quad k_n < k_F\\ \qquad = 0\,, & k_a \text{ or } k_b < k_F\,. \end{cases} \tag{2}$$

To convert this into co-ordinate space, we note that

$$G_N = v\Omega_N\,, \tag{3}$$

where Ω_N is a wave operator that replaces the uncorrelated wavefunction for the relative motion of the pair $\boldsymbol{m}$, $\boldsymbol{n}$ by a correlated wavefunction

$$\psi_N = \Omega_N\phi\,. \tag{4}$$

The desired matrix element is then

$$\langle\phi|G_N|\phi\rangle = \langle\phi|v|\psi_N\rangle\,. \tag{5}$$

Dividing (1) on the left by v, and multiplying on the right by ϕ, we arrive at the Bethe-Goldstone equation,

$$\psi_N(\boldsymbol{r}) = \varphi(\boldsymbol{r}) - \int \Gamma(\boldsymbol{r}, \boldsymbol{r}')v(\boldsymbol{r}')\psi_N(\boldsymbol{r}')\,\mathrm{d}^3\boldsymbol{r}'\,, \tag{6}$$

where

$$\Gamma(\boldsymbol{r}, \boldsymbol{r}') = \int\limits_{k_a,\,k_b>k_F} \frac{\exp[i\boldsymbol{k}_{ab}\cdot(\boldsymbol{r}-\boldsymbol{r}')]}{E_a^N + E_b^N - E_m^N - E_n^N}\frac{\mathrm{d}^3\boldsymbol{k}_{ab}}{(2\pi)^3}\,. \tag{7}$$

This is a Schrödinger-like equation for the relative motion of particles m and n. It differs from the usual Schrödinger equation in two respects. First, the energies $E_i^N = \hbar^2 k_i^2/2M + U(k_i)$ contain self-consistent potential terms, as determined by an extension of Hartree-Fock theory. Secondly, antisymmetry requires that both of the intermediate states, a and b, must be outside the Fermi sea. The hard core forces us to solve this equation in co-ordinate space, where the physical interpretation is also quite clear. Unfortunately, the propagator Q/e_N becomes a nonlocal integral operator in co-ordinate space. Several methods have been developed to deal with this complication. Equation (6) is separable in partial waves (not exactly, but to an excellent approximation [2, 3]) and this forms the starting point in all treatments.

Brueckner and Gammel [4] attack the integral equation head on. For each partial wave, u_L, they replace the continuum $0 < r < \infty$ by a discrete set of points within the range of v. The corresponding radial Green's function, $\Gamma_L(r, r')$, is evaluated for all pairs of points, and u_L is then obtained by diagonalizing a finite matrix. A computer is necessary at all stages, so this method does not offer much physical insight. But, in principle, this method is capable of unlimited accuracy.

The Moszkowski-Scott separation method and the Bethe reference-spectrum method are both based on the same formal identity. In both cases one begins by calculating a more simple reaction matrix

$$\text{(8)} \qquad \begin{cases} G_A = v_A - v_A P_A G_A \\ \quad\; = v_A \Omega_A \,, \end{cases}$$

$$\text{(9)} \qquad \Omega_A = 1 - P_A v_A \Omega_A ,$$

(A is for approximate.) The propagator P_A consists of some projection operator (with boundary conditions implied), and an energy denominator defined by some approximation to the self-consistent single-particle energy spectrum. This G_A is then related to the desired G_N by the general identity [5]

$$\text{(10)} \qquad G_N = G_A + \Omega_A^\dagger (v - v_A) \Omega_N + G_A^\dagger \left(P_A - \frac{Q}{e_N} \right) G_N \,.$$

One can therefore treat the difference $G_N - G_A$ by perturbation methods.

Moszkowski and Scott [6] take P_A to be the « free » propagator, $P_F = 1/e_F$, which describes the ordinary scattering of two particles in otherwise free space. All potential energies are ignored; e_F is simply the difference of the kinetic energies. This alone would give a very poor approximation to ψ_N. In ordinary scattering, ψ differs significantly from ϕ even at large distances, while ψ_N rapidly approaches ϕ beyond the range of the force. To simulate this important

« healing » property of ψ_N, *M.S.* consider just the « short-range » part of v,

$$\text{(11)} \qquad \begin{cases} v_A \to v_S = v\,, & r < d, \\ \qquad\;\; = 0\,, & r > d. \end{cases}$$

Their « separation distance » d is chosen (individually for each partial wave and for each value of the relative momentum k_{mn}) such that v_s produces no phase shift. Thus v_s includes just enough of the short-range attraction to compensate for the core repulsion. They then treat both the long-range potential, $v_l \equiv v - v_s$, and the propagator difference, $(1/e_F) - (Q/e_N)$, as « small » quantities. Through second order, their expansion is

$$\text{(12)} \qquad G_N = G_s + v_l - v_l \frac{Q}{e_N} v_l - 2v_l \frac{Q}{e_N} G_s + G_s^\dagger \left(\frac{1}{e_F} - \frac{Q}{e_N}\right) G_s\,.$$

Their physical motivation is that v_s is strong and short-ranged, and mainly induces transitions to states outside the Fermi sea. This makes the correction for the exclusion principle quite small. On the other hand, v_l is comparatively weak and long-ranged, and it mainly tries to induce transitions to states within the Fermi sea. These transitions are forbidden by exclusion, so the higher-order terms in v_l are very small. For $^1S_0$ states (no tensor force) the largest single correction term is around 10% (repulsive). This comes from the difference between e_N and e_F, in other words from the omission of the self-consistent potential energies. But this correction is greatly reduced if one replaces the free propagator $1/e_F$ by the reference propagator $1/e_R$, as discussed below. BETHE [5] has called this the « modified M.S. separation method ». (The first-order term G_s in (12) is identically zero when the free propagator is used. With the reference propagator, it is -10% to -15% of the total G_N, both for $^1S_0$ and $^3S_1$ states.)

The basic idea of Bethe's reference-spectrum method [5] is to look for a propagator P_A which is as close as possible to the true one, Q/e_N, subject to the condition that the wave eq. (9) is still easily soluble. The most general energy denominator which is still easy to work with is of the form $(\alpha + \beta k_{ab}^2) \to \to (\alpha - \beta\nabla^2)$. Thus BETHE was led to introduce an approximate « reference spectrum » for the intermediate states,

$$\text{(13)} \qquad E_a^R = A + Bk_a^2 = A + \hbar^2 k_a^2 / 2Mm^*\,.$$

Fortunately, it is possible to treat the « starting energy » $E_m^N + E_n^N$ exactly. The reference propagator $P_R = 1/e_R$ is then given by

$$\text{(14)} \qquad e_R = E_a^R + E_b^R - (E_m^N + E_n^N) = (\hbar^2/Mm^*)(k_{ab}^2 - k_{mn}^2) + 2A - (A_m + A_n)\,,$$

where

(15) $$A_m \equiv E_m^N - \hbar^2 k_m^2 / 2Mm^* .$$

Defining

(16) $$\gamma_{mn}^2 = (\Delta_m + \Delta_n) k_F^2 - k_{mn}^2 ,$$

(17) $$\Delta_m = (Mm^*/\hbar^2 k_F^2)(A - A_m) ,$$

we arrive at the final form

(18) $$e_R = (\hbar^2/Mm^*)(k_{ab}^2 + \gamma_{mn}^2) \to (\hbar^2/Mm^*)(\gamma_{mn}^2 - \nabla^2) .$$

These relations are illustrated in Fig. 1. The two parameters, A and m^*, are adjusted to give the best fit to E_a^N over the important region of k_a's

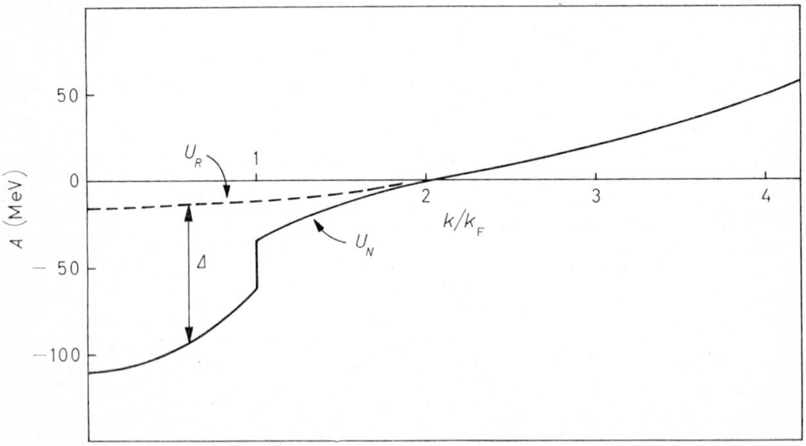

Fig. 1. – Spectrum of self-consistent potential energies for nuclear matter. $U_N(k) = E_N(k) - (\hbar^2 k^2/2M)$. U_R is the reference-spectrum approximation for U_N.

($k_a > k_F$ of course) as determined by eq. (27). In recent investigations, $0.9 < m^* \leqslant 1.0$, and $A \approx -15$ MeV. Typical average values for Δ are 0.6 to 0.7. (These uncertainties will be resolved by more careful calculations of the three-body clusters [1], including effects of the tensor force.) Note that γ^2 is positive, which means that e_R never vanishes and there is no pole in P_R to worry about. In co-ordinate space this means that there is no outgoing scattered wave, so « healing » is assured even without the M.S. separation (11).

The resulting « reference spectrum equation »

(19) $$(\nabla^2 - \gamma_{mn}^2)\zeta_R = -(Mm^*/\hbar^2) v \psi_R ,$$

(20) $$\zeta_R \equiv \phi - \psi_R ,$$

is almost the same as the ordinary Schrödinger equation. In terms of partial waves

$$\left.\begin{matrix}\phi\\ \psi\\ \zeta\end{matrix}\right\} = (k_{mn}r)^{-1}\sum_L (2L+1)\,i^L P_L(\hat{k}_{mn}\cdot\hat{r})\left\{\begin{matrix}\mathscr{J}_L\\ u_L\\ \chi_L\end{matrix}\right. , \tag{21}$$

$$\mathscr{J}_L(x) \equiv xj\ (x)\ , \tag{22}$$

$$\chi_L = \mathscr{J}_L - u\ \ , \tag{23}$$

this becomes

$$\left(\frac{\mathrm{d}^2}{\mathrm{d}r^2} - \frac{L(L+1)}{r^2} - \gamma_{mn}^2\right)\chi_L = -\,(Mm^*/\hbar^2)v_L u_L\,. \tag{24}$$

The qualitative behaviour of u_L is quite obvious. Consider the $^1S_0$ state. If there were no potential beyond the hard core the distortion would decay exponentially,

$$\chi_0 \sim \exp[-\gamma r]\,, \tag{25}$$

showing that u_0 rapidly approaches $\mathscr{J}_0 = \sin k_{mn}r$. (In nuclear matter, $\gamma_{mn}^{-1}\sim 0.7$ fermi.) The effect of the attractive potential is to pull u_0 inwards, making it « overshoot » $\mathscr{J}_0$ by around 10% at $r = 1.5$ fermi. Beyond this point, v is so weak that u_0 again « heals » exponentially. A typical wave function is shown in Fig. 2.

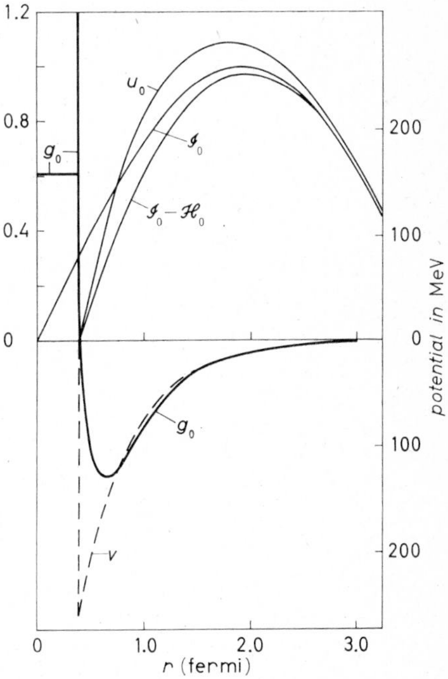

Fig. 2. – Typical $^1S_0$ wavefunctions (based on Fig. 12 of ref. [5]). $\mathscr{J}_0 = \sin k_{mn}r$ is the unperturbed wavefunction, $\mathscr{J}_0 - \mathscr{H}_0$ is the reference wavefunction for the case of no attraction beyond the hard core, and u_0 is the complete reference wavefunction. The corresponding effective interaction, g_0, is also shown. This has a delta-function repulsion at the surface of the hard core, and a finite repulsion inside, as explained in ref. [8]. Note that $g_0 \approx v$ for $r \gtrsim 1$ fermi, in agreement with the separation method. (See eq. (48) for the modification of this statement when a tensor force is present, as in $^3S_1$.)

The propagator correction term is

$$(26)\qquad \langle\phi|G_N - G_R|\phi\rangle = \langle\phi|G_R^\dagger\left(\frac{1}{e_R}-\frac{Q}{e_N}\right)G_N|\phi\rangle\,,$$

according to (10). We replace G_N by G_R, and use

$$(27)\qquad \frac{1}{e_R}\,G_R|\phi\rangle = (1-\Omega_R)|\phi\rangle = |\zeta_R\rangle$$

to put this in the form

$$(28)\qquad \langle\zeta_R|e_R\left(\frac{1}{e_R}-\frac{Q}{e_N}\right)e_R|\zeta_R\rangle = \int\frac{\mathrm{d}^3\boldsymbol{k}}{(2\pi)^3}\,|\langle\boldsymbol{k}|\zeta_R\rangle|^2\langle\boldsymbol{k}|e_R^2\left(\frac{1}{e_R}-\frac{Q}{e_N}\right)|\boldsymbol{k}\rangle\,.$$

In practice, of course, this is done separately for each partial wave. The weight of the Fourier transform comes mainly above $k=1.5k_F$. (The hard core, of radius c, leads to k_{ab}'s of order $\pi/2c\sim 2.5k_F$.) In this region $e_R\approx e_N$ (see Fig. 1), so the « spectral » part ($k>k_F$) of (28) is a very small correction, of order 1%. The « Pauli correction » ($k<k_F$) is also small, both because the core repulsion and outer attraction tend to cancel for low k, and because the large γ^2 in (18) further suppresses the low Fourier components, simulating the exclusion effect quite well. This is only a 5% correction for $^1S_0$ states, but the tensor force makes this considerably larger ($\sim$15%) in the $^3S_1$ states.

Let us take a closer look at the « healing » property of ψ_N. Exclusion is ultimately responsible for this, since it eliminates the low Fourier components which would have to describe any long-range distortions. The reference-spectrum method demonstrates that the jump Δ in the single-particle spectrum also contributes strongly to the healing. We can understand how these effects combine by considering $Q/e_N\approx Q/e_R=[1-(1-Q)]/e_R$. In co-ordinate space, $(1-Q)$ becomes the integral operator $(k_F^3/2\pi^2)x^{-1}j_1(x)$, $x=k_F|\boldsymbol{r}-\boldsymbol{r}'|$. The resulting corrections to the exponential healing of ζ_R have the asymptotic form

$$(29)\qquad \chi_L\to(a_L/r)\cos(k_F r+\eta_L)\,,$$

which should be compared with

$$(30)\qquad \mathscr{J}_L\to\sin[k_{mn}r-\tfrac{1}{2}L(L+1)\pi]\,.$$

One consequence of Q is that $\langle\zeta_N|\phi\rangle\equiv 0$. This indicates that ψ_N must contain a certain amount of overshoot to compensate for the hole made by the hard core. The a_L's in (29) are actually quite small, since γ^2 holds the overshoot of ζ_R rather firmly in check. The small excess of overshoot, which overestimates the attraction in (5), is compensated by the « Pauli correction » in (28). On the other hand, the separation method completely suppresses this overshoot. This is then supplied by the second-order terms, $-v_l(Q/e_N)(v_l+2G_s)$.

For $^1S_0$ states (pure central force) the separation and R.S. methods both err by about the same amount (5 %) in lowest order. In second order both are capable of high accuracy, better than 1 %. The separation method has the advantage of extreme simplicity for approximate calculations; the long-range potential v_l, evaluated in first Born approximation, gives one around 105 % of the exact G_N matrix element. BROWN has emphasized the convenience of this method for shell-model calculations.

The tensor force causes considerable complication in $^3S_1$ states. Its long-range part induces transitions from $^3S_1$ to $^3D_1$, which, in contrast to a central force, are relatively unaffected by the exclusion principle. Thus for $^3S_1$ states the « small » quantity, corresponding to the v_l of $^1S_0$ states, is now $v_{lc}-v_{lT}(Q/e_N)v_{lT}$(*). For accuracy comparable to that of the second-order expression (12) for $^1S_0$ states, one should now go to fourth order. Another problem is that the « interference » term, $-2v_l(Q/e_N)G_s$, which was only a 5 % correction for $^1S_0$ states, is now around 25 % of G_N. (The separation distance is chosen to give a close cancellation between attraction and repulsion for the central part of v_s. There is no such cancellation for the tensor part of v_s.) KUO and BROWN [7] have developed a convenient method for handling these complications. The accuracy of their separation treatment is difficult to ascertain, however. We think it should be possible to achieve an accuracy of 2 % by simply calculating the first two terms, G_R and (28), of the reference spectrum method. The next term, $G_R^\dagger(\delta P)\, G_R(\delta P)G_R$, should give an accuracy of around 0.3 %, since this is essentially a geometric series with a decrement of around 0.15. The propagator correction is a « smaller » and « simpler » expansion parameter than the long-range part of the tensor force. This reference spectrum method also works for states which have a net repulsion, ($^1P_1$, $^3P_1$, $^3D_1$), where separation does not apply.

3. – Reaction matrix in nuclei (**).

We wish to emphasize two points in this Section. First, that the Brueckner theory gives a well-defined effective interaction, and secondly that this can be calculated to high accuracy by a simple extension of the above methods [8].

One would like to express the shell-model matrix elements

$$\langle m'n'|G|mn\rangle = \iint d^3\boldsymbol{r}_1\, d^3\boldsymbol{r}_2 \varphi^*_{m'}(\boldsymbol{r}_1)\varphi^*_{n'}(\boldsymbol{r}_2)v(\boldsymbol{r}_{12})\Psi_{mn}(\boldsymbol{r}_1, \boldsymbol{r}_2)\,, \tag{31}$$

(*) Based on a study of the tensor force by E. J. IRWIN [2].

(**) The formulation in this section owes much to the work of B. D. DAY [9]. Discussions with Prof. H. A. BETHE and Dr. C. W. WONG have also been very helpful.

in the form

$$\iint d^3\boldsymbol{r}_1\, d^3\boldsymbol{r}_2 \varphi^*_{m'}(\boldsymbol{r}_1)\varphi^*_{n'}(\boldsymbol{r}_2) g_{mn}(\boldsymbol{r}_1, \boldsymbol{r}_2)\varphi_m(\boldsymbol{r}_1)\varphi_n(\boldsymbol{r}_2) . \tag{32}$$

Except for the problem of nodes occurring in

$$\Phi_{mn}(\boldsymbol{r}_1, \boldsymbol{r}_2) \equiv \varphi_m(\boldsymbol{r}_1)\varphi_n(\boldsymbol{r}_2) , \tag{33}$$

this could certainly be done by requiring that

$$g_{mn} = v\Psi_{mn}/\Phi_{mn} . \tag{34}$$

This indicates that we could consider g_{mn} to be a local function of $\boldsymbol{r}_1$ and $\boldsymbol{r}_2$, but it would then have an extremely complicated form. It is actually much more convenient to replace (34) by an equivalent nonlocal expression.

The correlated wave function Ψ_{mn} is determined by the Bethe-Goldstone equation for the *finite* system,

$$\zeta_{mn}(\boldsymbol{r}_1, \boldsymbol{r}_2) \equiv \Phi_{mn} - \Psi_{mn} = \sum_{a,b>A} \frac{\phi_a(\boldsymbol{r}_1)\phi_b(\boldsymbol{r}_2)\langle ab|v|\Psi_{mn}\rangle}{E^N_a + E^N_b - E^N_m - E^N_n} . \tag{35}$$

Referring to Fig. 1, we see that the effective shell-model potential acting on the intermediate orbitals ϕ_a, ϕ_b is quite weak, especially in comparison to their kinetic energies. This suggests a kind of W.K.B. approximation. We combine this with the reference spectrum idea, replacing E^N_a by

$$E^R_a = A(\boldsymbol{R}) - [\hbar^2/2Mm^*(\boldsymbol{R})]\nabla^2_1 . \tag{36}$$

Thanks to the « healing » phenomenon, *i.e.* the fact that ζ vanishes for large $\boldsymbol{r} = \boldsymbol{r}_1 - \boldsymbol{r}_2$, we shall only need to approximate the behavior of $\phi_a(\boldsymbol{r}_1)$ and $\phi_b(\boldsymbol{r}_2)$ within the neighborhood of their center-of-mass point $\boldsymbol{R} = \frac{1}{2}(\boldsymbol{r}_1 + \boldsymbol{r}_2)$. This allows us to use $\boldsymbol{R}$, instead of $\boldsymbol{r}_1$, in $A(\boldsymbol{R})$ and $m^*(\boldsymbol{R})$. (Brown has pointed out that A and m^* are at present indistinguishable from 0 and 1, respectively. Nevertheless, we shall retain these parameters until Bethe's 3-body cluster analysis [1] has been completed.) The « reference » energy denominator is therefore

$$e_R = (2A - E^N_m - E^N_n) - (\hbar^2/2Mm^*)(\nabla^2_1 + \nabla^2_2) . \tag{37}$$

Ignoring exclusion, and using closure to avoid problems of normalization and density of states, we arrive at the reference spectrum equation for a finite geometry,

$$[\nabla^2_r + \tfrac{1}{4}\nabla^2_R - \gamma'^2_{mn}(\boldsymbol{R})]\zeta_{mn}(\boldsymbol{r}, \boldsymbol{R}) = -[Mm^*(\boldsymbol{R})/\hbar^2]v(\boldsymbol{r})\Psi_{mn}(\boldsymbol{r}, \boldsymbol{R}) . \tag{38}$$

This equation was first introduced by DAY [9], in his study of the nuclear surface.

We shall assume a partial-wave analysis of the relative motion, centered about the point $\boldsymbol{R}$,

$$\left.\begin{matrix}\Phi_{mn}\\ \Psi_{mn}\\ \zeta_{mn}\end{matrix}\right\} \to [r k_{mn}(\boldsymbol{R})]^{-1} \sum_{LM} a_L^M(\boldsymbol{R})\, Y_L^M(\hat{r}) \left\{\begin{matrix}\varphi_L^M(r, \boldsymbol{R})\\ u_L^M(r, \boldsymbol{R})\\ \chi_L^M(r, \boldsymbol{R})\,.\end{matrix}\right. \tag{39}$$

In general this need only be a « gedanken » analysis, though of course it can be done analytically with oscillator orbitals. The main problem, now, is to determine a suitable effective relative momentum $k_{mn}(\boldsymbol{R})$, and similarly for the center-of-mass motion. With oscillator orbitals, the W.K.B. idea can be applied individually to each Talmi-Moshinsky component

$$\phi_{nlm}(\boldsymbol{r})\Phi_{NLM}(\boldsymbol{R})\,, \tag{40}$$

whereby

$$k_{mn}^2(nlm) = -\,(\nabla_r^2\phi_{nlm})/\phi_{nlm}\big|_{r=0}\,. \tag{41}$$

Similarly, we introduce

$$\gamma_{mn}^2(\boldsymbol{R}, NLM) = \gamma_{mn}'^2(\boldsymbol{R}) - \tfrac{1}{4}[\nabla_R^2\Phi_{NLM}(\boldsymbol{R})]/\Phi_{NLM}(\boldsymbol{R})\,, \tag{42}$$

which completes the reduction of (38) into radial equations of the form (24). In short, we have replaced the « global » Bethe-Goldstone eq. (35) by a set of « local » partial-wave reference equations.

One can solve these radial equations by extending the W.K.B. approach still further. Each $\varphi_L^M(r, \boldsymbol{R})$ is replaced by the Bessel function $\mathscr{J}_L[rk_{mn}(\boldsymbol{R})]$ which is « tangent » to it at $r=0$. The equations are now *exactly* the same as for infinite nuclear matter. Their solutions give us the partial-wave effective interactions

$$g_L \equiv v_L u_L/\mathscr{J}_L = v_L(1-\chi_L/\mathscr{J}_L)\,. \tag{43}$$

The ${}^1S_0$ interaction, g_0, is illustrated in Fig. 2.

It turns out that this W.K.B. method works extremely well for oscillator orbitals. Typical oscillator radial functions for relative motion are compared with their « tangential » Bessel functions in Fig. 3. (This figure is from KALLIO [10], who has used a similar argument in connection with his separation method.) Note that the approximation is truly excellent within the region of strong v, where χ_L is large. This is all one really needs, since, thanks to « healing », the difference between u_L^M/φ_L^M and $u_L/\mathscr{J}_L$ should be negligible even at large r. The error from $\varphi_L^M \neq \mathscr{J}_L$ is divided out when one uses (43).

Note that there are, in general, several Talmi-Moshinsky components (40) for each set of angular indices $lmLM$. For example, $\phi_{1p}(\boldsymbol{r}_1)\phi_{1p}(\boldsymbol{r}_2)$ contains

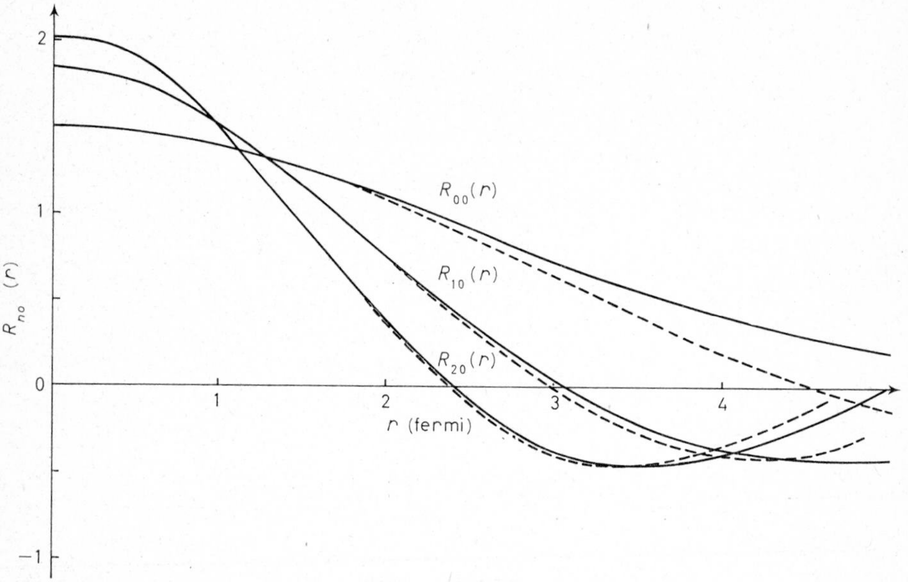

Fig. 3. – Typical oscillator radial functions R_{nl} for S-state relative motion (solid lines), compared with their « tangential » Bessel functions $j_0(kr)$ (broken lines). The excellent agreement, for $r \leqslant 2$ fermi, shows that the W.K.B. approximation of eqs. (41)-(43) is well justified. Here $\hbar\omega \approx 14$ MeV, corresponding to a pair of particles in the s-d shell. This figure is taken from ref. [10].

both $\phi_{1s}(\boldsymbol{r})\Phi_{2s}(\boldsymbol{R})$ and $\phi_{2s}(\boldsymbol{r})\Phi_{1s}(\boldsymbol{R})$. The $\boldsymbol{R}$ dependence of g induces a weak coupling between these components (*). The same problem occurs with more realistic single-particle orbitals. In extending our W.K.B. approach, we find that each φ_L^M should, quite generally, be approximated by a superposition of *four* $\mathscr{J}_L$'s, each with a different effective $k(\boldsymbol{R})$ (**). In principle, one should compute a separate g_L for each k component, but this must clearly be equivalent to the use of a single average k. (We note that (43) is only weakly k-dependent.) We determine a suitable « local average » by making simple modifications of (41) and (42) [8]. These new recipes do not depend on having done the expansion (39) explicitly. This allows us to avoid (39)

(*) This has been investigated by C. W. Wong (*Ph. D. Thesis*, Harvard, 1965, to be published). See also ref. [9].

(**) Similar considerations may be found in ref. [9].

by using a projection technique, replacing the local expression (34) by

$$(44)\qquad \langle\hat{r}|g_{mn}(r,\boldsymbol{R})|\hat{r}'\rangle = \\ = \sum_{LM} Y_L^M(\hat{r})g_L(r,\boldsymbol{R})Y_L^{M*}(\hat{r}') = (4\pi)^{-1}\sum_L (2L+1)g_L(r,\boldsymbol{R})P_L(\hat{r}\cdot\hat{r}')\,.$$

This is our final result. It differs from Brueckner's «local density» approximation [11] in three respects. *a*) The «starting energies» $E_m^N + E_n^N$ are treated exactly. *b*) The average over center-of-mass momenta (see (42)) can be handled more realistically. *c*) The radial nonlocality [*i.e.* $g_L(r, r', \boldsymbol{R})$] of Brueckner's expression, which corresponds to a projection treatment (analogous to (44)) for the mixture of local relative momenta $k(\boldsymbol{R})$, has been replaced by an explicit procedure for finding an appropriate «local average» k.

The propagator correction (28) is not negligible. To compute this, one should use a «local» exclusion operator corresponding to the local nuclear density $\varrho(\boldsymbol{R})$. The arguments of this Section are equally relevant if one prefers to use a separation method [7, 10, 13]. This is simply an alternative way of solving the «local» radial equations, and for handling the propagator correction. (The Brueckner-Gammel method [4] could also be used to solve these «local» radial equations. Now that the geometrical problems are better understood, it would not be necessary to use approximations as drastic as the «local-density» assumption of ref. [11].) For many applications this formalism can undoubtedly be simplified, by further averaging of parameters, etc., but this can only be decided after a thorough investigation. Our aim has been to develop a general method which can also be used for self-consistent calculations [12, 13].

4. – General features of realistic forces.

We consider some prominent features of the g discussed above. One should bear in mind that core polarizations may alter some of the details of the final effective interaction.

4·1. *Exchange, velocity dependence, and saturation.* – Several of the effective forces used in shell-model calculations have had their exchange mixtures adjusted to give saturation. Brueckner theory says that there are actually *three* different things that contribute to saturation: *a*) exchange mixture, in this case a *weak* repulsion from the spin average over P states; *b*) a strong velocity dependence of the matrix elements, due to the short-range repulsion in g; *c*) an over-all density dependence of g [11-14]. It is sometimes claimed that realistic forces do not have a strong enough Majorana exchange component, but the «evidence» here comes largely from the neglect of *b*) and *c*). PANDYA [15] has found some empirical evidence that this strong momentum dependence actually exists in nuclei. The $\boldsymbol{R}$-dependences of $\langle k_{mn}(\boldsymbol{R})\rangle_{av}$ and $\gamma_{mn}(\boldsymbol{R})$ both act to create the impression of an additional strong density dependence, over and above the true density dependence which contributes to saturation; they considerably enhance the effect of g in the nuclear surface [9].

4·2. *The tensor force.* – The tensor force couples ${}^3S_1$ and ${}^3D_1$ waves, just as in the deuteron. Thus we should think of the v and Ω of (3) as being 2×2 matrices, and make the replacements

(45*a*)
$$\mathscr{J}_0 \to \begin{pmatrix} \mathscr{J}_0 \\ 0 \end{pmatrix},$$

(45*b*)
$$u_0 \to \begin{pmatrix} u_0^{(0)} \\ u_2^{(0)} \end{pmatrix}.$$

Consider the matrix element

(46)
$$\langle {}^3S_1|G|{}^3S_1\rangle = \langle {}^3S_1|v\Omega|{}^3S_1\rangle .$$

Here Ω represents the instruction « solve the Bethe-Goldstone equation with the boundary condition that ψ_N contains only an S-wave ($\mathscr{J}_0$) at large radii ». The result for (46) is

(47)
$$(4\pi/k_{mn}^2)\int_0^\infty \mathscr{J}_0(v_{00}u_0^{(0)} + v_{02}u_2^{(0)})\,\mathrm{d}r = (4\pi/k_{mn}^2)\int_0^\infty \mathscr{J}_0 g \mathscr{J}_0\,\mathrm{d}r .$$

Now a tensor force cannot couple ${}^3S_1$ to ${}^3S_1$, in lowest order, only a central force can do that, so the effective central force must be

(48)
$$g_C = (v_{00}u_0^{(0)} + v_{02}u_2^{(0)})/\mathscr{J}_0 ,$$

instead of (43). Reasoning similarly, we deduce from $\langle {}^3D_1|G|{}^3S_1\rangle$ that the effective tensor force must be

(49)
$$g_T = (v_{02}u_0^{(0)} + v_{22}u_2^{(0)})/\sqrt{8}\mathscr{J}_0 .$$

One finds that the « subsidiary wave » $u_2^{(0)}$ is extremely important for g_C, accounting for about 2/3 of the total ${}^3S_1$ attraction (*). On the other hand $u_2^{(0)}$ makes only a small ($\lesssim 10\%$) contribution to g_T^* (*). Similar arguments apply to other partial waves [4, 5, 11].

(*) C. W. WONG: private communication.

What can one say at present about the effects of the tensor force in nuclei? *a*) It increases the over-all density dependence of g somewhat, contributing to saturation [4-6, 13]. *b*) It strongly renormalizes the effective central force in triplet states. *c*) The effective tensor force g_T should induce strong ground-state correlations, in the sense of random phase theory, by the mechanism BLEULER has described (*). These correlations may be the source of much of the observed $\boldsymbol{l}\cdot\boldsymbol{\sigma}$ splitting of the single-particle levels, and they should also influence the magnetic moments. *d*) Certain unnatural-parity states, such as the 0^- states of ^{16}O, are largely determined by g_T [16].

4·3. *The spin-orbit force.* – The proton-proton scattering data clearly indicate a strong $\boldsymbol{L}\cdot\boldsymbol{S}$ term in triplet-odd states, although the neutron-proton data are less clear about this in triplet-even states. To study its effect in nuclei, one should remember to use g_{LS}, as determined by arguments [11] analogous to (46)-(49). Only one systematic effect has been identified so far; it gives rise to a significant fraction of the observed $\boldsymbol{l}\cdot\boldsymbol{\sigma}$ splitting [11, 12]. Elliott's recent effective-force analysis suggests that g_{LS} may also have other systematic effects.

4·4. *The quadratic spin-orbit force.* – General invariance arguments [17] allow v to have a quadratic spin-orbit component

$$Q \equiv \tfrac{1}{2}[(\boldsymbol{\sigma}_1\cdot\boldsymbol{L})(\boldsymbol{\sigma}_2\cdot\boldsymbol{L}) + (\boldsymbol{\sigma}_2\cdot\boldsymbol{L})(\boldsymbol{\sigma}_1\cdot\boldsymbol{L})] = \tag{50}$$
$$= 2(\boldsymbol{L}\cdot\boldsymbol{S})^2 + \boldsymbol{L}\cdot\boldsymbol{S} - L^2 = (\boldsymbol{L}\cdot\boldsymbol{S})^2 - \delta_{L,J}L^2 = (1-2\delta_{L,J})L^2 - \boldsymbol{L}\cdot\boldsymbol{S}\,,$$

in addition to the familiar central, tensor, and $\boldsymbol{L}\cdot\boldsymbol{S}$ types of spin dependence. In fact the nonstatic corrections to OPEP are known to contain a term of the form [17]

$$L_{12} \equiv \boldsymbol{\sigma}_1\cdot\boldsymbol{\sigma}_2 L^2 - Q = (\boldsymbol{\sigma}_1\cdot\boldsymbol{\sigma}_2 - 1 + 2\delta_{L,J})L^2 + \boldsymbol{L}\cdot\boldsymbol{S}\,. \tag{51}$$

The $\boldsymbol{L}\cdot\boldsymbol{S}$ in the bottom lines of (50) and (51) is not very interesting, from a phenomenological standpoint, since v contains independent $\boldsymbol{L}\cdot\boldsymbol{S}$ terms. The interesting features are the $L(L+1)$ dependence and the new kind of spin dependence represented by $\delta_{L,J}$. The $^1D_2$, $^3D_2$, and $^3D_3$ phase shifts seem to require $\delta_{L,J}L(L+1)$ terms in the even states of v (note that neither Q nor L_{12} vanishes when $S=0$), and there is also some evidence [18] for an $L(L+1)$-dependent central force in the triplet-odd states. It is important to realize that Q and L_{12} both contain « central » and $\boldsymbol{L}\cdot\boldsymbol{S}$ components. (We refer to the fact that these expressions do not vanish when they are averaged, with relative weight $2J+1$, over the various J values for a given L. This « central » average occurs in

(*) I would like to thank Prof. BLEULER for several discussions.

the first Born approximation for the potential energy of nuclear matter.) The Q or L_{12} terms must not be overlooked when doing calculations with modern potentials [19], because, regardless of how realistic they may turn out to be, they now represent part of the « true » central and $\boldsymbol{L}\cdot\boldsymbol{S}$ character of v. It would be helpful to separate out their $\boldsymbol{L}\cdot\boldsymbol{S}$ force and $L(L+1)$-dependent central force parts by a kind of Schmidt orthogonalization process, analogous to the way one separates OPEP into tensor and $\boldsymbol{\sigma}_1\cdot\boldsymbol{\sigma}_2$ components.

Finally, a word of consolation about the present ambiguities in v. The G-matrix is intermediate in character between the observed phase shifts and the « true » potential v, so there should be less uncertainty in G than there is in v. The remaining uncertainty in G is of interest in nuclear-matter theory, but it is probably not very significant for shell-model calculations.

REFERENCES

[1] H. A. Bethe: *Paris Conference*, vol. **1** (1964), p. 101; *Phys. Rev.*, **138**, B 804 (1965).
[2] E. J. Irwin: *Ph. D. Thesis* (Cornell, 1963), unpublished.
[3] G. E. Brown, G. I. Schappert and C. W. Wong: *Nucl. Phys.*, **56**, 191 (1964).
[4] K. A. Brueckner and J. L. Gammel: *Phys. Rev.*, **109**, 1023 (1958).
[5] H. A. Bethe, B. H. Brandow and A. G. Petschek: *Phys. Rev.*, **129**, 225 (1963).
[6] S. A. Moszkowski and B. L. Scott: *Ann. Phys.*, **11**, 65 (1960); **14**, 107 (1961).
[7] T. T. S. Kuo and G. E. Brown: *Phys. Lett.*, **18**, 54 (1965).
[8] B. H. Brandow: *Phys. Lett.*, **4**, 8; 152 (1963); *Ph. D. Thesis*, Cornell University (1964), to be published; *Paris Conference*, vol. **2** (1964), p. 295.
[9] B. D. Day: *Phys. Rev.*, **136**, B 1594 (1964).
[10] A. Kallio: *Phys. Lett.*, **18**, 51 (1965).
[11] K. A. Brueckner, J. L. Gammel and H. Weitzner: *Phys. Rev.*, **110**, 431 (1958).
[12] K. A. Brueckner, A. M. Lockett and M. Rotenberg: *Phys. Rev.*, **121**, 255 (1961); K. S. Masterson jr. and A. M. Lockett: *Phys. Rev.*, **129**, 776 (1963).
[13] H. S. Köhler: *Nucl. Phys.*, **32**, 661 (1962); *Phys. Rev.*, **137**, B 1145; **138**, B 831 (1965).
[14] K. A. Brueckner and D. T. Goldman: *Phys. Rev.*, **116**, 424 (1959).
[15] S. P. Pandya: *Nucl. Phys.*, **43**, 636 (1963).
[16] A. M. Green, A. Kallio and K. Kolltveit: *Phys. Lett.*, **14**, 142 (1965). See also Fig. 24 of Gillet's lectures, this volume, p. 43.
[17] S. Okubo and R. E. Marshak: *Ann. of Phys.*, **4**, 166 (1958); N. Hoshizaki and S. Machida: *Progr. Theor. Phys.*, **24**, 1325 (1960).
[18] R. Tamagaki, M. Wada and W. Watari: *Progr. Theor. Phys.*, **33**, 55 (1965).
[19] T. Hamada: *Progr. Theor. Phys.*, **24**, 1033 (1960); **25**, 247 (1961); T. Hamada and I. D. Johnston: *Nucl. Phys.*, **34**, 382 (1962); K. E. Lassila, M. H. Hull jr., H. M. Ruppel, F. A. McDonald and G. Breit: *Phys. Rev.*, **126**, 881 (1962).

Calculation of the Total Photonuclear Cross-Section for ^{16}O.

M. A. MELKANOFF

Department of Engineering, University of California - Los Angeles, Cal.

1. – Introduction.

Calculations of the giant resonance in ^{16}O disagree with experiment in two respects: the calculated strength is generally too large by a factor of about four, and the theoretical curves do not exhibit the marked structure which characterizes the experimental curve. The computations do not include *a*) a correct treatment of the continuum (finite-well effects), *b*) short-range correlations, and *c*) higher-order configurations. The excessive calculated strength may be attributed to *a*) and *b*) above, and the lack of structure to *c*). The present calculation which was carried out by RAYNAL, SAWADA and myself includes a correct treatment of the continuum through the use of a realistic real Saxon-Wood potential well. So far we have only considered the effects of 1 particle-1 hole excitations. Calculations which include 2 particle-2 hole excitations are in progress.

2. – Configurational states.

We start from a Hartree-Fock picture; since we are interested in the 1^- $T=1$ state of ^{16}O, the hole states are $p_{\frac{3}{2}}$ and $p_{\frac{1}{2}}$ while the particle states are $s_{\frac{1}{2}}$, $d_{\frac{3}{2}}$ and $d_{\frac{5}{2}}$.

The single-particle states are given by

$$H_0\varphi_i = \varepsilon_i\varphi_i\,, \tag{1}$$

where

$$H_0 = p^2/2m + V_i^{\text{opt}}$$

and V_i^{opt} is the potential of a *real* Saxon-Wood potential well including spin-orbit. For the bound single-particle energies ($\varepsilon_i < 0$) we use the binding energies of neutron bound states. The $d_{\frac{3}{2}}$ state turns out to be unbound with a resonance at 0.93 MeV. The bound single-particle wave functions are taken as

$$\varphi_i(\boldsymbol{r}) \equiv \varphi_n^{jlm}(\boldsymbol{r}) = c_n \frac{R_{nl}(r)}{r} \mathcal{Y}_l^{jm},$$

where the normalization constant c_n is determined so that

$$\int \varphi_i^* \varphi_i \, \mathrm{d}^3 r = \delta_{ij} .$$

The unbound single-particle states are given by

$$\varphi_i(\boldsymbol{r}) \equiv \varphi_k^{jlm}(\boldsymbol{r}) = \sqrt{\frac{2m}{\hbar^2 \pi k}} \frac{R_{kl}}{r} \mathcal{Y}_l^{mj}$$

with the asymptotic form

$$R_{kl}(r) \underset{r\to\infty}{\longrightarrow} \sin\left(kr - \frac{l\pi}{2} + \delta_i\right),$$

where δ_i is the phase shift due to the optical-model potential. The normalization constant is chosen such that

$$\int \varphi_k^{jlm*} \varphi_k^{jlm} \, \mathrm{d}^3 r = \delta_{ll'} \delta_{jj'} \delta_{mm'} \delta(\varepsilon - \varepsilon') .$$

The radial wave functions $R_{nl}(r)$ and $R_{kl}(r)$ are obtained from numerical solutions of eq. (1) for negative and positive energies. Configurational states describing a particle-hole pair will be described by mixing bound and unbound single-particle functions. The spectra of the zero-order particle-hole configurations are shown in Fig. 1. We note the presence of a bound state for

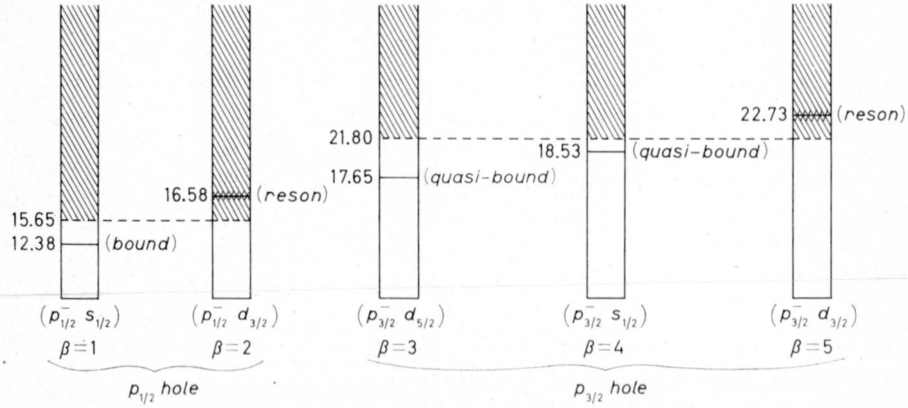

Fig. 1. – Spectra of the zero-order particle-hole configurations for ^{16}O.

the $(p^{-}s_{\frac{1}{2}})$ configuration at 12.38 MeV, and of two quasi-bound states for the configurations $(p_{\frac{3}{2}}^{-}d_{\frac{5}{2}})$ and $(p_{\frac{3}{2}}^{-}s_{\frac{1}{2}})$ at 17.65 and 18.53 MeV, respectively. These latter states are characterized by the fact that although they are bound their excitation energy exceeds the threshold energy for particle emission, thus they couple strongly with neighboring continuum states. The resonance states which are actually rather narrow ($\sim$ 200 keV) will also couple with the continuum and may produce large peaks in the total cross-section.

3. – Solution of the basic equations.

The Schrödinger equation for the total system is

$$H\Psi_E = E\Psi_E , \qquad H = H' + V ,$$

where H' is that part of the Hamiltonian which has eigenfunctions $|\alpha)$ which denote bound (or quasi-bound) particle-hole configurations in which all 16 particles are bound, and $|\beta\varepsilon)$ which denote unbound particle-hole configurations in which 15 particles are bound and one is unbound with energy $\varepsilon_{\mathrm{p}} = \varepsilon - \varepsilon_{\mathrm{h}}(\beta)$. Thus H' is diagonal while the residual interaction V can have both diagonal and nondiagonal elements. Now we may write

$$\Psi_E = \sum_{\alpha} a(\alpha)|\alpha) + \sum_{\beta}\int a(\beta\varepsilon)|\beta\varepsilon)\,\mathrm{d}\varepsilon ,$$

where the amplitudes $a(\alpha)$ and $a(\beta\varepsilon)$ are obtained from eq. (2.13) derived by BLOCH (*):

$$(E_\alpha - E)a(\alpha) + \sum_{\alpha'} (\alpha|V|\alpha')\,a(\alpha') + \sum_{\beta'}\int \mathrm{d}\varepsilon'(\alpha|V|\beta'\varepsilon')a(\beta'\varepsilon') = 0 ,$$

$$(E_\beta + \varepsilon - E)a(\beta\varepsilon) + \sum_{\alpha'} (\beta\varepsilon|V|\alpha')a(\alpha') + \sum_{\beta'}\int \mathrm{d}\varepsilon'(\beta\varepsilon|V|\beta'\varepsilon')a(\beta'\varepsilon') = 0 .$$

We can follow the treatment given by BLOCH except that in the 1 particle-1 hole case the λ's are identical with the β, *i.e.* the residual nucleus is described by a pure state. Removing the singularity by the principal part method and replacing the integrals by discrete sums with proper weight assignment we finally obtain

$$(2a) \qquad \sum_{j\beta'}\left\{\frac{\varepsilon_i - E}{\omega_{i\beta}}\,\delta_{ij}\delta_{\beta\beta'} + (\beta\varepsilon_i|V|\beta'\varepsilon_j)\right\}x_{j\beta'} + \sum_{\beta'}(\beta\varepsilon_i|V|\beta'E)X_{\beta'} = 0$$

(*) See lecture of Prof. C. BLOCH in this volume, p. 394.

and « on the energy shell »

$$(2b)\qquad \sum_{j\beta'} (\beta E|V|\beta'\varepsilon_j)\, x_{j\beta'} + \sum_{\beta'} (\beta E|V|\beta' E)\, X_{\beta'} = -B_\beta\,,$$

where

$$x_{j\beta'} = \omega_{\beta i} a(\beta\varepsilon_i)\,, \qquad X_\beta = A_\beta + c_\beta B_\beta\,,$$

ω's being weights assigned to the point according to the interpolation and

$$c = \ln\left(\frac{b-E}{E-a}\right) - \sum_r \frac{\omega_r}{\varepsilon_r - E}\,,$$

b and a being the upper and lower limits of the principal-part integrals. The variables X_β provide a relationship between the vectors A and B from which we should be able to extract the reaction matrix K which BLOCH showed to be given by

$$B = -KA\,.$$

Indeed, writing

$$X_\beta = -\sum_\beta N_{\beta\beta'} B_{\beta'}$$

and applying the previous definition of X_β

$$A_\beta = \sum_{\beta'} M_{\beta\beta'} B_{\beta'}\,,$$

where

$$M_{\beta\beta'} = -(N_{\beta\beta'} + c_\beta \delta_{\beta\beta'}) B_{\beta'}$$

and

$$M^{-1} = K\,.$$

Now eqs. (2) have as many independent solutions as there are β channels, and for

$$15.65 \leqslant E \leqslant 21.8\,, \quad \beta = 1 \text{ or } 2 \text{ (cf. Fig. 1)}$$

$$\text{for } E \geqslant 21.8\,, \quad \beta = 1, 2, 3, 4 \text{ or } 5.$$

In order to obtain the correct solution we may proceed as follows: in eq. (2), assume

$$B_\beta = 1 \qquad \text{for } \beta = \lambda,$$

$$= 0 \qquad \text{for } \beta \neq \lambda,$$

where λ takes on the successive values 1, 2 for $15.65 \leqslant E < 21.8$ and 1 through 5 for $E \geqslant 21.8$. The two or five solutions thus obtained, $\Psi^{\lambda}_{\beta}(E)$ are not properly normalized, nor do they have the proper asymptotic behavior. The desired solutions are obtained as linear combinations of the Ψ's,

$$\Phi^{\nu}_{\beta}(E) = \sum_{\lambda} N^{\nu}_{\lambda} \Psi^{\lambda}_{\beta}(E)\,, \qquad \nu = 1, 2 \text{ or } 1 \text{ to } 5,$$

where

$$\left(\Phi^{\nu *}(E),\, \Phi^{\nu'}(E')\right) = \delta_{\nu\nu'}\delta(E - E')$$

and $\Phi^{\nu}_{\beta}(E)$ have the asymptotic behavior of an incident plus an outgoing wave. These requirements lead to

$$N^{\nu}_{\lambda} = \exp\left[i\delta^{0}_{\nu}\right] \sum_{s} \frac{u^{s}_{\nu} u^{s}_{\lambda}}{\pi + i m_{s}}\,,$$

where u^{s} is the eigenvector of M corresponding to the eigenvalue m_{s} (of which there are 2 or 5). Finally the amplitude of the photonuclear cross-section is given by

$$f^{\nu} = \sum_{\beta} \int \mathrm{d}\varepsilon \left(\Phi^{\nu}_{\beta}(\varepsilon) | J | 0\right) = \sum_{\lambda} N^{\nu}_{\lambda} \sum_{\beta} \left\{ \sum_{i} x^{\lambda}_{i\beta} (\beta\varepsilon_{i} | J | 0) + X^{\lambda}_{\beta} (\beta E | J | 0) \right\}\,,$$

the total cross-section is then

$$\sigma_{T} = \sum_{\nu} |f^{\nu}|^{2}\,,$$

while the partial cross-sections are

$$\sigma_{p\frac{1}{2}} = |f^{1}|^{2} + |f^{2}|^{2}\,,$$
$$\sigma_{p\frac{3}{2}} = |f^{3}|^{2} + |f^{4}|^{2} + |f^{5}|^{2}\,.$$

The one-body operator J is given by

$$J \sim j_{1}\left(\frac{E}{\hbar c}\, r\right),$$

thus,

$$(\beta\varepsilon_{i} | J | 0) = G_{\beta} \int \mathrm{d}r\, j_{1}\left(\frac{E}{\hbar c}\, r\right) R_{\mathrm{p}_{\beta}}(\varepsilon_{i}, r) R_{\mathrm{h}_{\beta}}(r)\,,$$

where G is a geometrical factor corresponding to angular integrations, and which also depends upon the assumed nucleon-nucleon force, $R_{\mathrm{p}_{\beta}}$ is the radial wave function for a particle of energy $\varepsilon_{i} - \varepsilon_{\mathrm{h}_{\beta}}$ and $R_{\mathrm{h}_{\beta}}$ is the radial wave function for a hole. Both of these are obtained in the real optical potential V^{opt}_{i}.

4. – Review of the calculational procedure.

4·1. *Calculation of the necessary radial particle and hole wave functions.* – These are standard optical-model calculations with the proper choice of a real reasonable optical-model potential yielding the proper bound spectrum and resonance state.

4·2. *Computation of the 2-body matrix elements* $(\beta\varepsilon|V|\beta'\varepsilon')$. – These matrix elements are obtained as the sum of direct and exchange terms described as follows.

a) Exchange term

$$\int \varphi_{\mathrm{p}_\beta}(\varepsilon \boldsymbol{r}_2)\varphi_{\mathrm{h}_{\beta'}}(\boldsymbol{r}_1)V(\boldsymbol{r}_1,\,\boldsymbol{r}_2)\varphi_{\mathrm{p}_{\beta'}}(\varepsilon'\boldsymbol{r}_1)\varphi_{\mathrm{h}_\beta}(\boldsymbol{r}_2)\,\mathrm{d}r_1\,\mathrm{d}r_2\,.$$

b) Direct term:

$$\int \varphi_{\mathrm{p}_\beta}(\varepsilon \boldsymbol{r}_1)\varphi_{\mathrm{h}_\beta}(\boldsymbol{r}_2)V(\boldsymbol{r}_1,\,\boldsymbol{r}_2)\varphi_{\mathrm{p}_{\beta'}}(\varepsilon'\boldsymbol{r}_1)\varphi_{\mathrm{h}_{\beta'}}(\boldsymbol{r}_2)\,\mathrm{d}r_1\,\mathrm{d}r_2\,.$$

The diagrams are as shown below

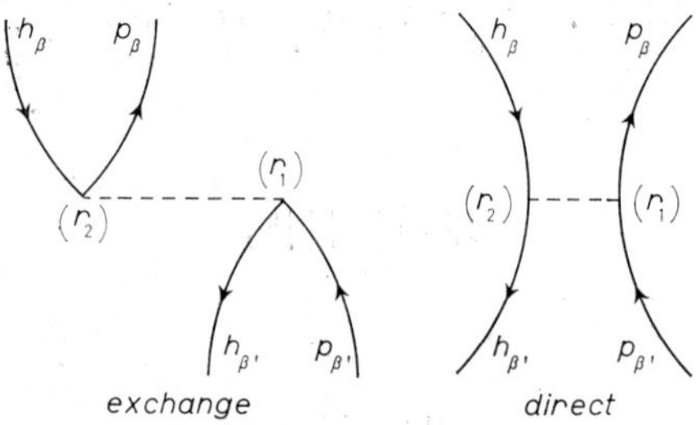

4·3. *Solutions of the basic equations.* – This procedure must be carried out for each value of E:

a) Proper choice of interpolation according to the value of E and calculation of necessary weights.

b) Inversion of the matrix yielding x and X.

c) Calculation of eigenvalues and eigenvectors of M.

d) Calculation of normalization matrix N. [Steps *b*) and *c*) must be repeated for each possible λ.]

e) Interpolation (if necessary) of 2-body matrix coefficients.

f) Computation of one-body matrix coefficients.

g) Computation of transition amplitudes and cross-sections.

5. – Preliminary results.

Preliminary results of our calculation are shown in Fig. 2. A number of comments are in order:

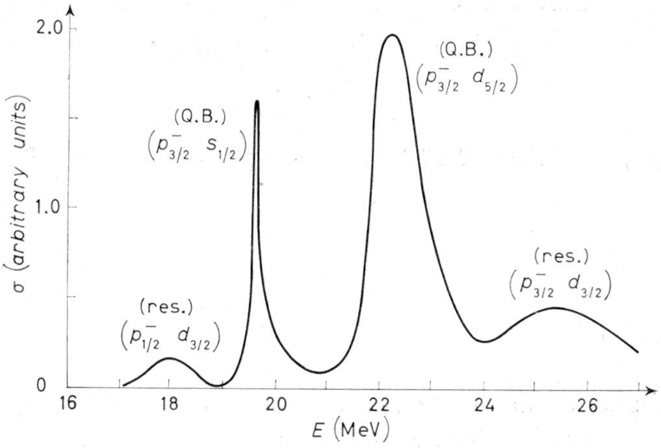

Fig. 2. – Preliminary results of total photonuclear cross-sections for ^{16}O. The peaks primarily due to the quasi-bound (Q.B.) and the resonance (Res) states are indicated on the figure. The cross-section is given in arbitrary units as the calculations were not normalized.

1) The positions of the peaks are about the same as those obtained in previous calculations; this confirms the idea that these positions are not too sensitive to the presence of the continuum.

2) Widths appear automatically as a result of the off-diagonal two-body matrix elements, whose diagonal elements are of the order of 2 to 4 MeV. Interactions between the quasi-bound states and the continua yield peaks which are about 2 MeV wide. On the other hand interactions between resonances (which are only 200 keV wide) and the continua broadens the peaks to 2 to 3 MeV.

3) The general structure of the curve matches fairly well the experimental data.

4) The relative height of the fourth peak is much too small.

The next step in the calculation will be to introduce 2 particle-2 hole excitations. Although these configurations cannot be excited directly by the γ-rays, their effect is felt by configuration mixing with the 1 particle-1hole states.

The Effective Two-Body Interaction in Nuclear Direct Reactions.

G. Schiffrer

Istituto di Fisica dell'Università - Catania

1. – Introduction.

It is well known that the cross-section for a nuclear reaction can be split, under definite physical conditions which often occur in practice, in the sum of two terms, representing the direct and the compound nucleus part, respectively. Since here the interest is mainly in the former, we refer to the formal definition of a direct reaction, which has been given by several authors, quoting the one by Agodi [1], who emphasizes the concept of « effective interaction operator » for a direct reaction. The direct transition amplitude, defined as the average over an energy interval I of the exact transition amplitude, can be written as the matrix element of a complicated effective-interaction operator between states representing the target and optical scattering in the initial state, and the residual nucleus and optical scattering in the final state. This means that the distorted-wave theory is exact, provided we know the effective-interaction operator. From this point of view, the importance of studying the properties of this operator is apparent.

In practice, one usually assumes weak coupling, so that one is led to the distorted-wave Born approximation (DWBA), whose amplitude connecting initial and final channel is given by [1]

$$T_{fi}^{\mathrm{DWBA}} = \langle \varphi_f^{(-)} | (V_i - P_i V_i P_i) | \varphi_i^{(+)} \rangle \, , \tag{1}$$

where $V_i = H - H_i$ is the interaction in channel i, P_i is the projection operator on channel i and $|\varphi_i^{(+)}\rangle$, $\langle\varphi_f^{(-)}|$ are the previously described states, where the $(+)$ and $(-)$ indicate, in the usual way, the boundary conditions of outgoing and incoming waves in the optical wave functions at infinity. Assuming then the shell model for the target and residual states, the approximate effective interaction in (1) for the reaction A(a, b)B (a, b nucleons) is exactly equal [1] to the residual interaction of spectroscopic calculations for the nucleus (a+A), starting from the shell model for the zero-order wave functions. Since the contribution of the second term in eq. (1) is negligible, we can assume that our effective interaction has the same general form as the one used by Prof. GILLET [2] in his calculations, *i.e.*

$$V_i = U_0 \sum_j f(\mu|\boldsymbol{r}_j - \boldsymbol{r}_i|)(W + MP_{\text{M}}^{ij} + BP_{\text{B}}^{ij} + HP_{\text{H}}^{ij}), \tag{2}$$

where P_{M}^{ij}, P_{B}^{ij} and P_{H}^{ij} are the Majorana, Bartlett and Heisenberg operators. With the convention $W+M+B+H=1$, U_0 is the triplet even potential strength. Here the radial dependence is assumed to be given by

$$f(\mu r) = \exp[-\mu r]/\mu r = U(r)/U_0 .$$

From the theoretical analysis of experimental data on direct reactions we can obtain informations on three main problems:

a) the nucleon-nucleus scattering (optical potential),

b) the properties of nuclear states,

c) the effective two-body interaction.

While the first two problems have received much attention in the past years, the third one has been often treated in a very crude approximation, assuming that the two-body interaction is given by a spin-independent δ-potential. This approximation has been shown to be very poor in (n, p) reactions [3], while it works better in (d, p) reactions [4]. Spin-independent finite-range interactions have been considered in refs. [3-5].

In Sect. **2** the finite-range and exchange effects of the interaction (2) are discussed, assuming the DWBA. In Sect. **3** a method is proposed, which would allow the determination of the parameters of eq. (2) in (n, p) reactions on doubly magic nuclei.

2. – Finite-range and exchange effects.

We want to show in this Section why a δ-potential is expected to give better results for (d, p) than for (nucleon, nucleon) reactions, discussing some properties of DWBA amplitudes with the interaction (2).

In transitions to the lowest residual states we can further assume that only the target nucleons in the last subshell participate to the reaction. In the case of (nucleon, nucleon) reactions the DWBA amplitudes can then be written as a linear combination of the two integrals:

$$D=\int\langle \boldsymbol{k}_f^{(-)}|\boldsymbol{r}_1\rangle\langle b_f|\boldsymbol{r}_2\rangle\, U(|\boldsymbol{r}_1-\boldsymbol{r}_2|)\langle \boldsymbol{r}_2|b_i\rangle\langle \boldsymbol{r}_1|\boldsymbol{k}_i^{(+)}\rangle\, \mathrm{d}^3r_1\,\mathrm{d}^3r_2\,, \tag{3}$$

$$E=\int\langle \boldsymbol{k}_f^{(-)}|\boldsymbol{r}_1\rangle\langle b_f|\boldsymbol{r}_2\rangle\, U(|\boldsymbol{r}_1-\boldsymbol{r}_2|)\langle \boldsymbol{r}_1|b_i\rangle\langle \boldsymbol{r}_2|\boldsymbol{k}_i^{(+)}\rangle\, \mathrm{d}^3r_1\,\mathrm{d}^3r_2\,, \tag{4}$$

where $\langle \boldsymbol{r}|\boldsymbol{k}_i^{(+)}\rangle$ and $\langle \boldsymbol{k}_f^{(-)}|\boldsymbol{r}\rangle$ are optical-model wave functions and $\langle \boldsymbol{r}|b_i\rangle$, $\langle \boldsymbol{r}|b_f\rangle$ single-particle bound-state wave functions. Expressions (3) and (4) will be referred to hereafter as direct (D) and exchange (E) integrals, although in a (n, p) reaction E corresponds to the nonexchange part of the interaction.

The bound-state wave functions have a definite orbital angular momentum, say λ_i and λ_f; expanding all functions contained in eqs. (3) and (4) in spherical harmonics, the quantum number L, resulting from expanding the interaction, must obey the conditions

$$\left.\begin{aligned} |\lambda_i-\lambda_f|\leqslant L\leqslant \lambda_i+\lambda_f\,,\\ |l_i-l_f|\leqslant L\leqslant l_i+l_f\,,\end{aligned}\right\}\ \text{in } D, \tag{5}$$

$$\left.\begin{aligned} |l_i-\lambda_f|\leqslant L\leqslant l_i+\lambda_f\,,\\ |l_f-\lambda_i|\leqslant L\leqslant l_f+\lambda_i\,,\end{aligned}\right\}\ \text{in } E, \tag{6}$$

where l_i and l_f are the angular momenta of the optical wave functions. In most cases conditions (5) restrict L to smaller values than conditions (6), since λ_i and λ_f are usually small and l_i, l_f are limited by $l_i \lesssim k_iR$, $l_f \lesssim k_fR$. Therefore, the high-angular momentum components will usually contribute less to eq. (4) than to (3), since in (4) they are associated with higher-L components, which are known to be less important in a finite-range force than those with smaller L. Smaller angular momenta correspond, in the average, to smaller radial coordinates, so that in the E integral the surface contribution is relatively smaller than in D; the zero-range integrals are, in this sense, intermediate between E and D, as can be argued from the properties of eqs. (7-10) and seen from Fig. 1 and Table I. In the angular distributions

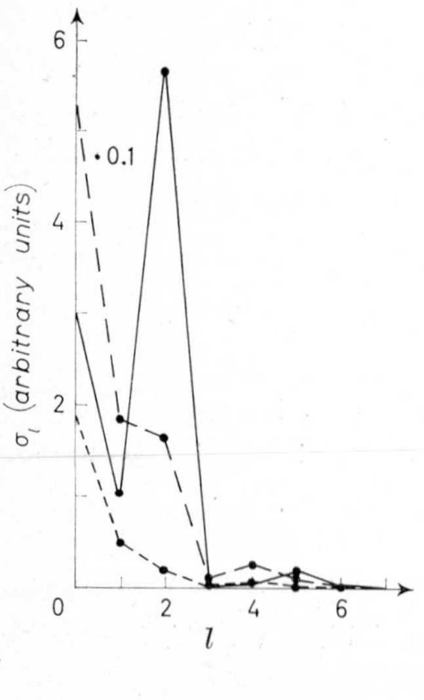

Fig. 1. – Partial cross-section σ_l *vs.* angular momentum l of the emitted particle for the hypothetical (n, n′) reaction described in Sect. **2**. See also Table I. ——— direct; – – – exchange; — — — zero-range.

this property of D amplitudes gives rise to a more rapidly fluctuating pattern than in the other two cases. When a partial wave is in resonance in the optical well, we expect that the corresponding D amplitude is strongly increased, due to the enhanced contribution from the nuclear surface, where the resonating wave function is large. One also expects that a large imaginary part of the optical potential, increasing the relative importance of the surface contribution, would amplify these effects; this agrees with the results of ref. [6].

TABLE I. – *Average angular momentum $\bar{l}$ of the emitted particle and its r.m.s. deviation $\overline{\Delta l}$ for the same reaction as in Fig.* 1.

	Direct	Zero-range	Exchange
$\bar{l}$	1.58	0.94	0.61
$\overline{\Delta l}$	1.25	1.27	1.09
$\bar{l}-\overline{\Delta l}$	0.33	-0.33	-0.48
$\bar{l}+\overline{\Delta l}$	2.83	2.21	1.70

An example is given in Table I and Fig. 1, for a hypothetical (n, n′) reaction involving a $1s \to 2s$ transition, with a Q-value $Q=0$, and a purely real optical potential, giving a resonance for $l=2$ and $E_n = 21$ MeV.

The effect of terms containing spin exchange in (2), *i.e.* B and H, are of some importance in (n, p) reactions, where they introduce a coherence between the spins of incident and emitted particles, increasing in this way the cross-section.

In (d, p) reactions the most important contribution comes often from the so-called stripping amplitude. Here the space-exchange term coincides with the ordinary one and the finite-range correction to the usual δ-force amplitude can be expected to be similar to the one of the D integral (3), but weaker. The argument is the following: E, D and stripping amplitudes can be written as an integral in momentum space

$$T_{fi}(\boldsymbol{k}_f, \boldsymbol{k}_i) = \int \langle \boldsymbol{k}_f^{(-)} | \boldsymbol{k}_2 \rangle B_{fi}(\boldsymbol{k}_2, \boldsymbol{k}_1) \langle \boldsymbol{k}_1 | \boldsymbol{k}_i^{(+)} \rangle \, \mathrm{d}^3 k_1 \, \mathrm{d}^3 k_2 \,, \tag{7}$$

where $B_{fi}(\boldsymbol{k}_2, \boldsymbol{k}_1)$ denotes the (plane-wave) Born approximation amplitude, which is, in the three cases,

$$B_{fi}^{(D)}(\boldsymbol{k}_2, \boldsymbol{k}_1) = \sqrt{\frac{\pi}{2}} \frac{\mu^3}{U_0} \tilde{U}(|\boldsymbol{k}_2 - \boldsymbol{k}_1|) B_{fi}^{(D0)}(\boldsymbol{k}_2 - \boldsymbol{k}_1) \,, \tag{8}$$

$$B_{fi}^{(D0)} = \frac{4\pi U_0}{\mu^3} \int \langle b_f | \boldsymbol{k} \rangle \langle \boldsymbol{k} + \boldsymbol{k}_2 - \boldsymbol{k}_1 | b_i \rangle \, \mathrm{d}^3 k \,; \tag{9}$$

$$(10)\qquad B^{(E)}_{fi}(\boldsymbol{k}_2, \boldsymbol{k}_1) = (2\pi)^{\frac{3}{2}}\int \langle b_f|\boldsymbol{k}_1+\boldsymbol{k}\rangle\, \widetilde{U}(k)\langle \boldsymbol{k}_2+\boldsymbol{k}|b_i\rangle\, \mathrm{d}^3k;$$

$$(11)\qquad B^{(S)}_{fi}(\boldsymbol{k}_2, \boldsymbol{k}_1) = (2\pi)^{\frac{3}{2}}\langle b_f|\boldsymbol{k}_1-\boldsymbol{k}_2\rangle \int \widetilde{U}(|\boldsymbol{k}_2-\tfrac{1}{2}\boldsymbol{k}_1+\boldsymbol{k}|)\langle \boldsymbol{k}|b_i\rangle\, \mathrm{d}^3k\,,$$

where $\widetilde{U}(k)$ is the Fourier transform of $U(r)$. The ket $|b_i\rangle$ is in (11) the deuteron internal state. Equation (9) represents the zero-range amplitude. Equation (11) can be written as

$$(12)\qquad B^{(S)}_{fi}(\boldsymbol{k}_2, \boldsymbol{k}_1) = \frac{\mu^3 F(p)}{4\pi U_0\langle r=0|b_i\rangle}\, B^{(S0)}_{fi}(\boldsymbol{q}), \qquad \boldsymbol{q} = \boldsymbol{k}_2 - \boldsymbol{k}_1,$$

where

$$B^{(S0)}_{fi}(\boldsymbol{q}) = 2(2\pi)^{\frac{5}{2}}(U_0/\mu^3)\langle r=0|b_i\rangle\langle b_f|\boldsymbol{q}\rangle$$

is the zero-range amplitude and the function

$$F(p) = \int \exp[i\boldsymbol{p}\cdot\boldsymbol{r}]\, U(r)\langle r|b_i\rangle\, \mathrm{d}^3r$$

depends only on the modulus of $\boldsymbol{p} = \boldsymbol{k}_2 - \frac{1}{2}\boldsymbol{k}_1$, provided that only central potentials and *s*-deuteron states are considered. The integral $F(p)$ can be easily evaluated exactly, assuming *e.g.* a Yukawa potential and a Hulthén deuteron wave function. However, by neglecting the variation of $\langle r|b_i\rangle$ inside the range of the potential $U(r)$ and calculating it at $r=0$, one can get a better insight on the properties of eq. (12); this approximation is justified because the range μ^{-1} is smaller than the deuteron radius. It is thus obtained

$$(13)\qquad B^{(S)}_{fi}(\boldsymbol{k}_2, \boldsymbol{k}_1) = \sqrt{\frac{\pi}{2}}\,\frac{\mu^3}{U_0}\,\widetilde{U}(p) B^{(S0)}_{fi}(\boldsymbol{q})\,.$$

This resembles eq. (8), except for the argument p instead of q in the function $\widetilde{U}$. Since, in the average, $p = (q^2 + \frac{1}{4}k_1^2 + k_1 q\cos\widehat{k_1 q})^{\frac{1}{2}}$ is a smoother function of q than q itself, it turns out that the finite-range corrections are more important for eqs. (7), (8) and (9) than for eqs. (7) and (13). The calculations of refs. [3, 4] seem to confirm this argument.

We remark finally that from eqs. (8) and (13) it is easily seen that the finite-range amplitude should be smaller than the zero-range one; this agrees with the arguments of ref. [5] and the numerical results of refs. [3, 4]. For the exchange amplitude (4) this effect is still stronger, due to the poorer overlap of the wave functions.

3. – Determination of the effective two-body interaction from (n, p) reactions on closed-shell nuclei.

In the theoretical expressions to be compared with the experimental data there are three sets of parameters, corresponding to *a*), *b*) and *c*) in Sect. **1**. The angular distributions are known to be very sensitive to the optical parameters, while this is not the case of the effective-interaction parameters, at least when a certain amount of space exchange is present. It seems therefore difficult to learn something about the effective interaction from angular distributions, unless we are able to consider a group of at least two transitions to different final states, corresponding to the same optical potential. This seems to be the case [7] of (n, p) reactions on closed-shell nuclei, where we have two or more residual states, deriving from the same particle-hole $T=1$ configuration and differing only in their spins J_f and slightly in their energies. The optical parameters can be determined in this case from elastic scattering, and, if necessary, from the unresolved (n, p) transitions to the group of residual states. The difference between resolved angular distributions is expected to be sensitive to the exchange mixture; in fact, let us consider the expression of the differential cross-section for a pure Heisenberg force:

$$\frac{\mathrm{d}\sigma}{\mathrm{d}\Omega}=\sum_L \begin{pmatrix}\lambda_i & \lambda_f & L\\ 0 & 0 & 0\end{pmatrix}^2 \begin{Bmatrix}\lambda_i & \lambda_f & L\\ j_f & j_i & \frac{1}{2}\end{Bmatrix}^2 \begin{Bmatrix}j_i & J_i & j_0\\ J_f & j_f & L\end{Bmatrix}^2 F_{\lambda_i\lambda_f L}(\theta)\,, \tag{14}$$

where j_i and j_f are the total angular momenta of the bound particles, j_0 the one of the core and J_i the target spin; the brackets denote, in the standard notation, the 3- and 6-j symbols. It is easily seen that expression (14) may vanish for certain J_f values, once all other angular momenta, except L appearing there, have been fixed. This happens, for instance, in the transitions to the 2^- and 0^- $T=1$ levels of ^{16}N, in the (n, p) reaction on ^{16}O. For the other exchange components the selection rules on angular momenta are not so severe. Thus, from the comparison of the theoretical curves with the experimental data it should be possible to determine the exchange parameters (2), at least in the more favourable cases. This comparison should be carried out preferably over an energy range, say between 14 and 20 MeV, in order to be sure that the approximations involved work well.

Some results of calculations with the interaction (2) have already been given [7]. Other details on the calculations are given in ref. [3, 8].

The (n, p) reactions are more suitable for our problem than, say, inelastic scattering, also for the simplified treatment of antisymmetrization in the formalism [3, 8].

Here two examples are shown in the figures for the reactions $^{16}O(n, p)^{16}N$ and $^{28}Si(n, p)^{28}Al$ at 14 MeV. Although the latter is not a closed-shell nucleus, the curves seem to fit well the data. The theoretical curves correspond to three exchange mixtures: *a*) is the Gillet [2] force, *b*) is the Rosenfeld force and *c*) is the nearest to the free n-p interaction. For ^{16}O, rather large values of U_0 have been found, and no appreciable compound nucleus contribution, in agreement with the experimental evidence [9]. It should be noted that in this case the optical parameters have not been determined from elastic scattering, but only guessed from the usual « average » interpolation formulae. Smaller values for the imaginary parts of the optical potentials, as well as many-particle

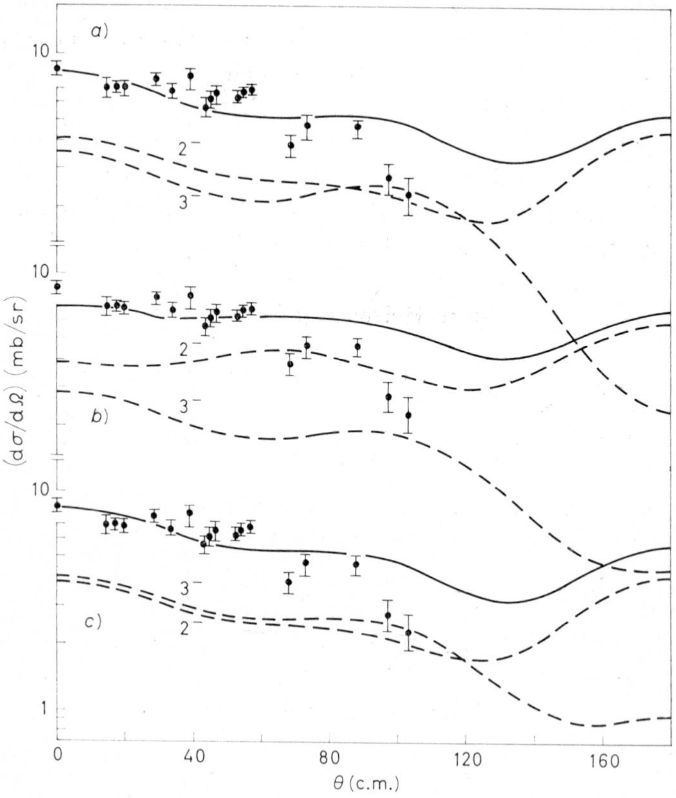

Fig. 2. – Angular distributions for the reaction $^{16}O(n, p)^{16}N$, $E_n = 14.4$ MeV. Experimental points [9] for unresolved transitions to the ground-state 2^-, 120 keV 0^-, 295 keV 3^- and 392 keV 1^- levels. Theoretical curves: DWBA with three different effective interactions. Full lines: 4 unresolved levels. Dashed lines: 2^- and 3^- levels. Optical parameters (Saxon-Woods central potential), in MeV or fermi: $V_n = 42.9$, $V_p = 49.4$, $W_n = 9.2$, $W_p = 5.3$, $a_n = a_p = 0.6$, $R_n = R_p = 3.35$. Effective interaction parameters: $\mu = 0.726$ fermi^{-1}; *a*) $U_0 = 152$ MeV, $W = M = 0.35$, $B = -0.1$, $H = 0.4$; *b*) $U_0 = 125$ MeV, $W = -0.13$, $M = 0.93$, $B = 0.46$, $H = -0.26$; *c*) $U_0 = 122$ MeV, $W = 0.46$, $M = 0.38$, $B = 0.36$, $H = -0.18$. No compound-nucleus contribution assumed.

effects [2,10], tend to increase the magnitude of the cross-section, leading to a smaller value of U_0. For another argument, see the seminar by Prof. AGODI. Clearly, this problem deserves further study.

In the case of ^{28}Si the parameters U_0 and μ correspond for the force *b*) to the triplet potential of the effective range theory for free n-p scattering. The compound nucleus contribution needed to fit the data for the forces *a*) and *b*) agrees with a recent calculation by PAPPALARDO [11] based on the theory of Hauser and Feshbach, using a set of parameters consistent with both ^{28}Si(n, p)^{28}Al and ^{27}Al(d, α)^{25}Mg reactions. The statistical angular distributions [11] are not exactly isotropic; this fact should be taken into account in a careful analysis. It is interesting to note how the spin-coherence effect described in Sect. 2 and a better value of the statistical cross-section have considerably reduced the large U_0 value found in ref. [3].

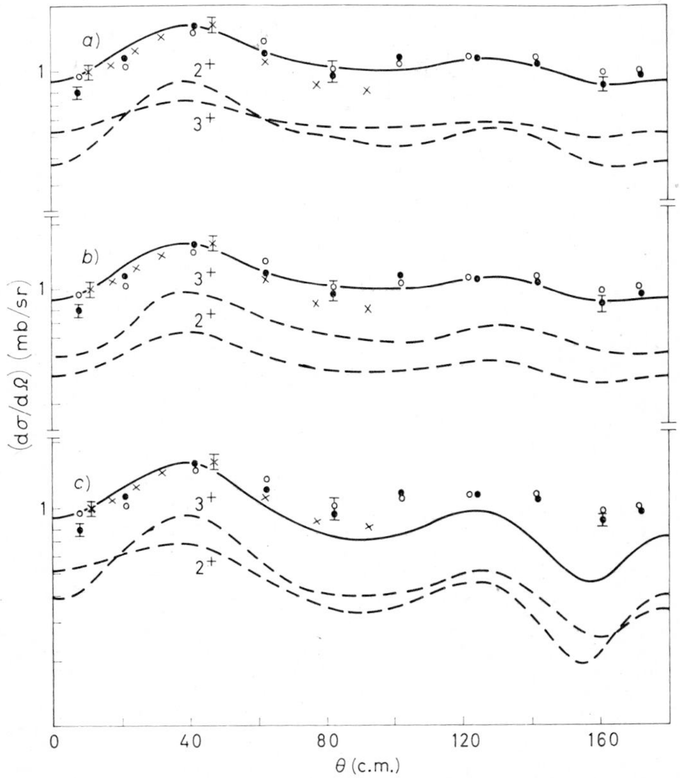

Fig. 3. – Angular distributions for the reaction ^{28}Si(n, p)^{28}Al, $E_n = 14$ MeV. Experimental points [12], [13], for unresolved ground-state 3^+ and 31 keV 2^+ levels: × COLLI *et al.*, ○ ● MAUSBERG *et al.* Theoretical curves: DWBA with optical parameters from Table I of ref. [3]. Full lines: 2 unresolved levels. Dashed lines: 3^+ and 2^+ levels. Effective interaction parameters: see Fig. 2, except for: *a*) $U_0 = 60.6$ MeV; *b*) $U_0 = 52$ MeV; *c*) $U_0 = 100$ MeV. Isotropic compound nucleus contribution assumed (in mb/sr for the unresolved levels): *a*) 0.83; *b*) 0.84; *c*) 0.37.

From the available data there is no conclusive evidence for a definite set of exchange parameters. Measurements of the resolved angular distributions, requiring in some cases a difficult (p, γ) coincidence detection, could be very useful for the determination of the effective interaction, allowing us to compare the effective interactions determined empirically from both (n, p) reactions and spectroscopic calculations.

* * *

The author is deeply indebted to Prof. A. AGODI for several useful discussions and critical remarks; to dr. R. PARISI for her collaboration in the numerical work; to dr. E. RÖSSLE, W. MAUSBERG and dr. G. PAPPALARDO for communication of unpublished results.

REFERENCES

[1] A. AGODI: to be published in *Suppl. Nuovo Cimento.*
[2] V. GILLET: this volume, p. 43.
[3] A. AGODI, R. GIORDANO and G. SCHIFFRER: *Phys. Lett.*, **4**, 253 (1963); A. AGODI and G. SCHIFFRER: *Nucl. Phys.*, **50**, 337 (1964).
[4] R. M. DRISKO and G. R. SATCHLER: *Phys. Lett.*, **9**, 342 (1964).
[5] N. AUSTERN, R. M. DRISKO, E. C. HALBERT and G. R. SATCHLER: *Phys. Rev.*, **133**, 3, (1964).
[6] A. AGODI and G. SCHIFFRER: *Comptes Rendus du Congrès Int. de Phys. Nucl.* (Paris, 1964), p. 952.
[7] G. SCHIFFRER: *Phys. Lett.*, **17**, 122 (1965).
[8] A. AGODI, R. GIORDANO and G. SCHIFFRER: *Nucl. Phys.*, **46**, 545 (1963).
[9] G. PAIĆ, I. ŠLAUS and P. TOMAŠ: *Phys. Lett.*, **9**, 147 (1964).
[10] L. S. RODBERG: *Ann. of Phys.*, **9**, 373 (1960); W. T. PINKSTON and G. R. SATCHLER: *Nucl. Phys.*, **27**, 270 (1961).
[11] G. PAPPALARDO: private communication.
[12] L. COLLI, M. G. MARCAZZAN, F. MERZARI, P. G. SONA and P. TOMAŠ: *Nuovo Cimento*, **20**, 928 (1961).
[13] W. MAUSBERG and E. RÖSSLE: private communication; W. MAUSBERG: IKF-14, Frankfurt/M (1965).

Some Aspects of the Photodisintegration of Light Nuclei.

E. HAYWARD

National Bureau of Standards - Washington, D. C.

1. – Introduction.

In this lecture two interesting aspects of the photodisintegration of light nuclei will be discussed. They are 1) isotopic spin mixing and 2) intermediate structure. First of all it is worth-while to review the main properties of the nuclear photodisintegration cross-section. Its main feature is, of course, the giant dipole resonance which occurs in all nuclei and may therefore be viewed as a general property of nuclear matter. For heavy nuclei, *i.e.*, those with $A > 100$, the magnitude of the photon absorption cross-section integrated over the giant resonance is at least as large as the dipole sum

$$\int \sigma \, \mathrm{d}E \geqslant \frac{2\pi^2 e^2 \hbar}{Mc} \cdot \frac{NZ}{A} = 60 \frac{NZ}{A} \text{ MeV mb} .$$

This resonance is located near 15 MeV; in fact, the resonance energy varies inversely as the nuclear radius and is given by the result of the hydrodynamic model, $80\,A^{-\frac{1}{3}}$ MeV. The giant resonance width varies from 3 to 8 MeV depending on the nuclear deformation. The giant resonances for these nuclei are smooth functions of energy except for the double peaking that results from the intrinsic deformation and the structure produced by the coupling of the dipole excitation with the quadrupole surface vibrations [1].

For light nuclei, $A < 40$, on the other hand, the situation is quite different. Here the giant resonance contains only $0.5 \div 0.8$ of the dipole strength. The resonance energy displays no systematic dependence on A and is approximately 20 MeV. Again the width varies between 3 and 8 MeV and depends on the deformation. The giant-resonance cross-sections for these nuclei contain a great deal of structure. It is extremely varied and depends on the individual nuclear properties.

These nuclei have been treated theoretically by various embellishments of the independent-particle model and GILLET has already described these in his lectures. These calculations succeed in placing the electric-dipole oscillator strength at its experimentally observed energy, but the cross-section magnitudes are always much too large. These theories are also much too simple to reproduce the complicated structure that occurs in nature.

These remarks are illustrated in Fig. 1 where the results of ELLIOTT and FLOWERS [2] are compared with the experimentally measured total

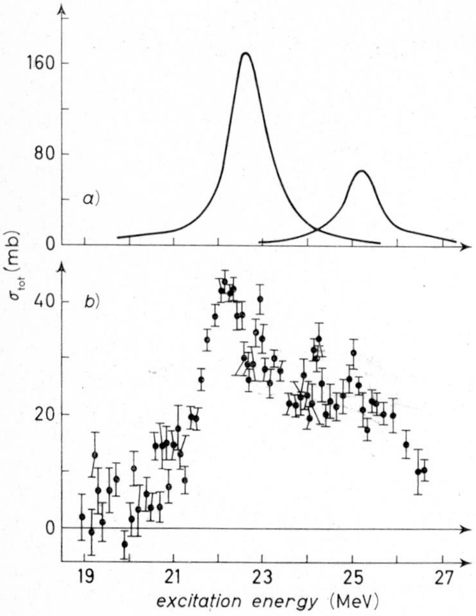

Fig. 1. – A comparison of the results of ELLIOTT and FLOWERS [2] with the measured [3] total absorption cross-section for ^{16}O. *a*) Elliot and Flowers' results, *b*) measured.

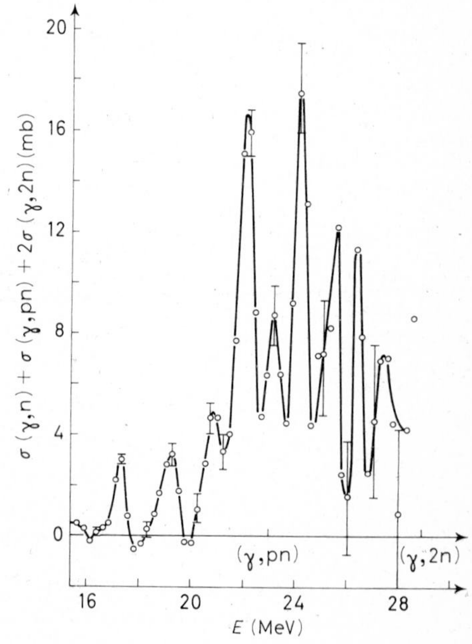

Fig. 2. – The (γ, n) cross-section for ^{16}O from ref. [4], $\Delta E = 0.5$ MeV.

photon absorption cross-section [3] for ^{16}O. Arbitrary widths of one MeV have been associated with the two predicted states in order to make them resemble as closely as possible the experimental data. Note the difference in the cross-section magnitudes indicated by the different ordinate scales. Also notice that the experimental cross-section contains many peaks. These are now well established and have been observed in many experiments where only partial cross-sections were measured. Figure 2 shows the (γ, n) cross-section as an example [4]. It is evident that the situation is more complex than that suggested by the current theories.

Figure 3 is meant to show how varied the structure can be in these light nuclei. It shows a comparison of the ground states, proton capture cross-sections [5, 6] for ^{11}B and ^{27}Al. These cross-sections are part of the giant resonance of ^{12}C and ^{28}Si, since the detailed balance theorem relates them to the ^{12}C and $^{28}Si(\gamma, p_0)$ cross-sections. For ^{12}C the only evidences for structure

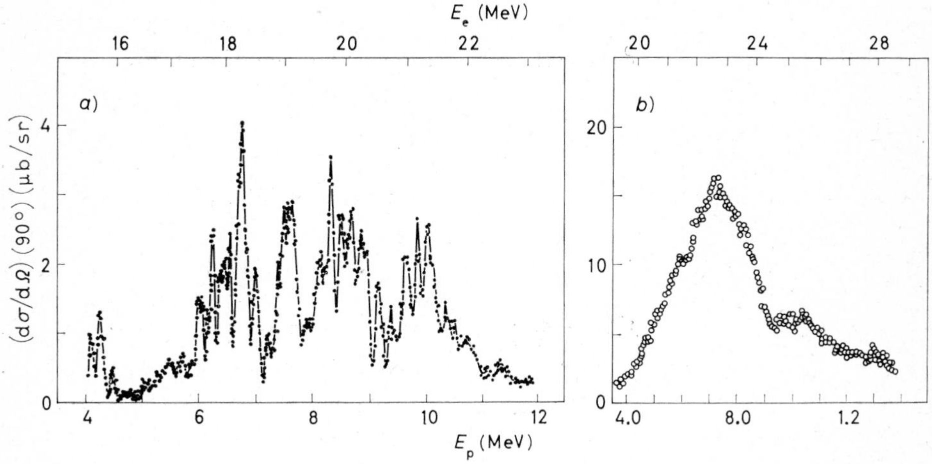

Fig. 3. – A comparison of the ground states, proton capture cross-sections [5, 6] for ^{11}B and ^{27}Al. There is an important qualitative difference between the amount of structure seen for these two nuclei. *a*) $^{11}B(p, \gamma_0)^{12}C$; *b*) $^{27}Al(p_0, \gamma)^{28}Si$.

are the slight undulations on the rising and falling sides of the giant resonance. For ^{28}Si we see that the main giant resonance is broken up into many sharp spikes having widths less than 100 keV.

2. – Mixing of $T=0$ and $T=1$ states in the giant resonance.

If we have perfect charge symmetry and electric-dipole interactions in which the excited particle comes directly out of the nucleus, then the (γ, p) and (γ, n) cross-sections should be identical in both magnitude and shape [7]. The (γ, p) thresholds are, in general, lower than the (γ, n) thresholds but by just such an amount as to compensate for the Coulomb barrier. For a given excitation energy, then, the outgoing protons do have slightly higher energies than the neutrons but only enough to make the (γ, p) cross-sections $\sim 20\%$ larger than the (γ, n) cross-sections. Experimentally [8], the ratio of the (γ, p) to (γ, n) cross-sections integrated over the giant resonance varies from 1 at helium to 5 at ^{40}Ca. This then is a gross indication of isotopic-spin mixing in the giant resonance.

The detailed partial cross-section shapes are only known for a few nuclei so that it is difficult to compare them. The (γ, p) and (γ, n) cross-sections [5, 9] for ^{12}C are rather well known in the giant resonance region and they do display a rather conspicuous difference. See Fig. 4. Here we see that the (γ, n) cross-section has a valley just where the (γ, p) cross-section peaks. In the corresponding cross-sections for ^{16}O there is no such obvious difference; the ground-state (γ, n) and (γ, p) cross-sections are apparently identical [10].

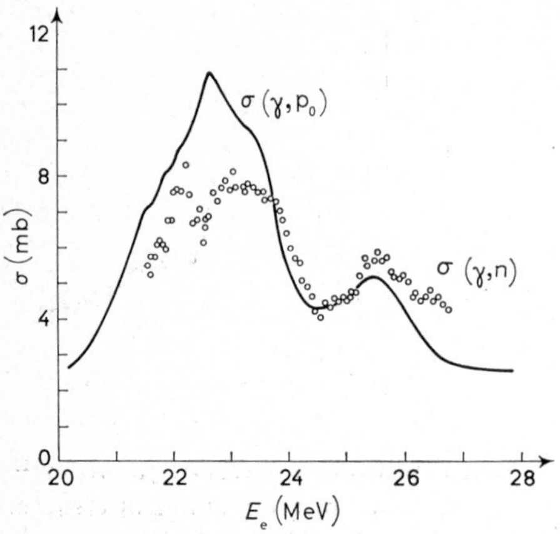

Fig. 4. – A comparison of the (γ, p_0) and (γ, n) cross-sections [5, 9] for ^{12}C. Note the important difference in shape near 22.5 MeV.

One reaction does take place that shows that there is at least a little isotopic-spin mixing in ^{16}O. It is the $^{14}N(d, \gamma_0)^{16}O$ reaction [11] which cannot occur at all through electric-dipole emission in the absence of isotopic-spin mixing. It does take place but the integrated cross-section is $< 10^{-3}$ of the dipole sum.

Alpha capture reactions may also be used to study the failure of charge symmetry in the giant resonance. These reactions are forbidden for electric-dipole transitions in the absence of mixing between $T = 1$ and $T = 0$ states. The cross-section for the reaction $^{24}Mg(\alpha, \gamma_0)^{28}Si$ has recently been studied and displays some rather remarkable features [12, 13]. In the first place, the cross-section shows a great deal of fine structure similar to that seen in the $^{27}Al(p, \gamma_0)^{28}Si$ cross-section of Fig. 3. If we use the detailed balance relationship to obtain $\sigma(\gamma, p_0)$ and $\sigma(\gamma, \alpha_0)$, we find that the integrals $\int \sigma(\gamma, p_0)\,dE$ and $\int \sigma(\gamma, \alpha_0)\,dE$ are respectively 13% and 1% of the dipole sum. More important, the angular distribution of the outgoing gamma-rays shows that the transitions take place through electric-dipole absorption. Since the spins of all the particles involved are zero, these distributions are completely unambiguous being $1 - \cos^2\theta$ for $E1$ and $\cos^2\theta - \cos^4\theta$ for $E2$. Since α-particles cannot excite $T = 1$ states when they bombard ^{24}Mg, the $T = 0$ states must be deexcited through their mixing with $T = 1$ states.

Now, how can we understand these phenomena? Looking at it from the point of view of a photonuclear reaction, the incoming photons interact with a nucleon producing 1 particle-1 hole $J = 1^-$, $T = 1$ states. At the excitation energy of the giant resonance the nucleus may also have 2 particle-2 hole, 3 particle-3 hole, etc. states coupled to 1^-. In addition there may also be $T = 0$ states with $J = 1^-$. The strong 1^- entrance channel can couple to all of these provided it lasts long enough. The angular-momentum barrier helps keep the excited nucleon inside the nucleus. As a result, the *d*-wave nucleons can emerge much more readily from ^{12}C than can *f*-wave particles from ^{28}Si. In the available time the 1p-1h excitation mixes with the higher configurations and the dipole strength may be fractured into many sharp peaks as in the case of ^{28}Si. In fact, the same sort of thing is seen in the giant resonances of the other *s*-*d* shell nuclei [14-16], ^{24}Mg, ^{32}S and ^{40}Ca. As we progress beyond ^{40}Ca two effects conspire to make this fine structure disappear. The most important is, of course, that the density of 2p-2h, 1^- states becomes much higher. These channel the energy from the 1p-1h state to the thermal state [16]. In addition, the angular momentum associated with the important dipole transitions increases so that the 1p-1h state survives long enough for these interactions to occur. As a result the fine structure simply dissolves into a continuum.

Returning once more to the $^{28}Si(\gamma, p_0)$ reaction, we see from the widths of the spikes that these complicated configurations last for a time $\sim \hbar/70$ MeV. This is a sufficiently long time for the Coulomb interaction, $H^C \sim 100$ keV to mix the $T=1$ and $T=0$ states so that α-particles may be emitted in electric-dipole transitions.

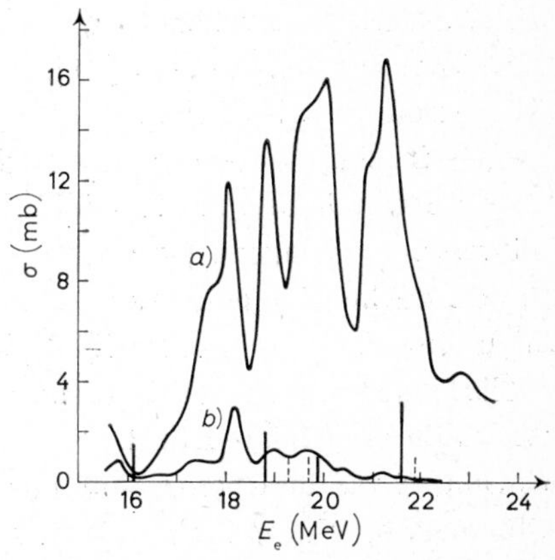

Fig. 5. – A comparison of the (γ, p_0) and (γ, α_0) cross-sections [6, 13] for ^{28}Si: *a*) $^{28}Si(\gamma, p_0)^{27}Al$; *b*) $^{28}Si(\gamma, \alpha_0)^{24}Mg$. The solid vertical lines at the bottom indicate the positions and relative strengths of the electric dipole transitions predicted by BOLEN and EISENBERG [17]. The dashed lines indicate the position of the $T=0$, 1^- states.

Figure 5 shows the $^{28}Si(\gamma, p_0)$ and $^{28}Si(\gamma, \alpha_0)$ cross-sections obtained by detailed balance from the experimental data on the inverse reactions. Here the data have been averaged with a $\Delta E = 0.5$ MeV so that the fine structure is not apparent. BOLEN and EISENBERG [18] have calculated the energies and strengths of the dipole transitions in ^{28}Si. These are indicated by the solid vertical lines in the figure. There are four important transitions, and these have been associated with the four peaks in the average cross-section. One of those peaks falls at too low an energy but this discrepancy probably results from the simplicity of the assumed ground state. They have also obtained the approximate position of the $T=0$, $J=1^-$ states; these are indicated by the dashed vertical lines. This shows that $T=0$ and $T=1$, $J=1^-$ states exist in the same energy region and close enough so that the Coulomb interaction can mix them.

3. – Intermediate structure.

What is intermediate structure? Intermediate structure and doorway states are two pairs of words [19, 20] invented at M.I.T. to label part of what has just been described. An incoming neutron is considered as interacting with a particle and a hole to form a three-quasi–particle state of angular momentum J and having a large amplitude. This is the doorway state. The intermediate structure in the cross-section is produced by the interaction of the doorway state with the 3 particle-2 hole, etc. states that exist at the same excitation energy and have the same angular momentum. This is completely analogous to the interaction of 1p-1h states with the 2p-2h states that we have in photonuclear reactions. The doorway state forms the envelope of the fine structure that reflects the density of the five quasi-particle states.

In a recent experiment [21], total neutron cross-sections were measured for neutron energies in the range $(4.5 \div 7.5)$ MeV corresponding to excitation energies in the giant-resonance region. These cross-sections showed a similar structure which became less important as the atomic number was increased and was not observed for any nucleus heavier than titanium ($Z = 22$). This appears to be the same range of excitation energy and atomic number for which the giant resonance displays structure.

This phenomenon needs to be distinguished from the Ericson fluctuations which are uncorrelated in different channels and which result from the superposition of random compound nucleus levels of unspecified spin. The giant resonance, on the other hand, results from the superposition of quasi-particle amplitudes associated with a well-defined angular momentum. The authors of the paper on the $^{27}Al(p, \gamma_0)^{28}Si$ reaction have tried very hard to show that the peaks in this cross-section result from Ericson fluctuations and have concluded that the cross-section is essentially a direct one.

To return once more to the $^{28}Si(\gamma, p_0)$ experiment, the angular distributions are nearly isotropic independent of excitation energy. If we take the composition of Bolen and Eisenberg's states and include the angular momentum and Coulomb barrier penetrabilities, we obtain angular distributions that are different for each of the four important states and considerably more anisotropic [22]. This is nature's way of telling us that the interaction of the dipole state with the higher configurations keeps the nucleus excited for a long enough time for the energy to be associated with a particle of low angular momentum ($l = 1$) which produces the observed angular distribution.

* * *

The author wishes to acknowledge a profitable coexistence with M. Danos with whom most of this material has been discussed. Thanks are also due to W. E. Stephens, J. Eisenberg, and L. Meyer-Schützmeister for sending unpublished results.

REFERENCES

[1] D. S. Fielder, J. Le Tourneux, K. Min and W. D. Whitehead: *Phys. Rev. Lett.*, **15**, 33 (1965).
[2] J. P. Elliott and B. H. Flowers: *Proc. Roy. Soc.* (*London*), Ser. A **242**, 57 (1957).
[3] N. A. Burgov, G. V. Danilyan, B. S. Bolbilkin, L. E. Lazareva and F. A. Nikolaev: *Žurn. Ėksp. Teor. Fiz.*, **43**, 70 (1962); *Sov. Phys. JETP.*, **16**, 50 (1963).
[4] E. Hayward and T. Stovall: *Nucl. Phys.*, **69**, 241 (1965).
[5] R. G. Allas, S. S. Hanna, L. Meyer-Schützmeister and R. E. Segel: *Nucl. Phys.*, **58**, 122 (1964).
[6] P. P. Singh, R. E. Segal, L. Meyer-Schützmeister, S. S. Hanna and R. G. Allas: *Nucl. Phys.*, **65**, 577 (1965).
[7] M. Gell-Mann and V. L. Telegdi: *Phys. Rev.*, **91**, 169 (1953).
[8] E. Hayward: *Nuclear Structure and Electromagnetic Interactions* (Scottish Universities' Summer School 1964), edited by N. MacDonald (Edinburgh, London, 1965).
[9] W. A. Lochstet and W. E. Stephens: *Phys. Rev.*, **141**, 1002 (1966).
[10] N. W. Tanner, G. C. Thomas and E. D. Earle: *Nucl. Phys.*, **52**, 45 (1964).
[11] M. Suffert, G. Costa and D. Magnac-Valette: *Journ. Phys. Rad.*, **24**, 1029 (1963).
[12] L. Meyer-Schützmeister, R. E. Segel and Z. Vagner: *Bull. Am. Phys. Soc.*, **9**, 666 (1964).
[13] L. Meyer-Schützmeister: *Bull. Am. Phys. Soc.*, **10**, 527 (1965).
[14] H. E. Gove: *Nucl. Phys.*, **49**, 279 (1963).
[15] G. Dearnaley, D. S. Gemmel, B. W. Hooton and G. A. Jones: *Nucl. Phys.*, **64**, 177 (1965).
[16] J. C. Hafele, F. W. Bingham and J. S. Allen: *Phys. Rev.*, **135**, B 365 (1964).
[17] M. Danos and W. Greiner: *Phys. Rev.*, **138**, B 876 (1965).
[18] L. N. Bolen and J. M. Eisenberg: *Phys. Lett.*, **9**, 52 (1964).
[19] B. Block and H. Feshbach: *Ann. of Phys.*, **23**, 47 (1963).
[20] A. K. Kerman, L. S. Rodberg and J. E. Young: *Phys. Rev. Lett.*, **11**, 422 (1963).
[21] A. D. Carlson, L. N. Rothenberg and S. M. Grimes: *Bull. Am. Phys. Soc.*, **10**, 498 (1965).
[22] J. B. Seaborn and J. M. Eisenberg: *Can. Journ. Phys.*, **42**, 2497 (1964).

Inelastic and Quasi-Free Proton Scattering on Medium-Weight Nuclei at 155 MeV.

R. A. Ricci

Istituto di Fisica Superiore dell'Università - Napoli
Istituto Nazionale di Fisica Nucleare - Sezione di Napoli

1. – Introduction.

The investigation of the nuclear structure with medium- and high-energy particles (*i.e.* above 100 MeV) has become very promising in recent years. The inelastic scattering of high-energy electrons is an example of a powerful tool in nuclear spectroscopy; the analysis of the experimental data is greatly simplified, in this case, by the knowledge of the electron-proton interaction and by the use of the Born and impulse approximations.

As far as protons are concerned, it is now quite well established that, in spite of the poor knowledge of the real nucleon-nucleon interaction inside the nucleus, the use of bombarding protons with energy above 100 MeV is of great interest, at least for two reasons:

a) protons interact equally well with both kinds of nucleons in a nucleus and they could give consequently information on the coupling rules characterizing the nucleon-nucleon interaction, at least in principle;

b) the analysis of the experimental data becomes less difficult as compared with the low-energy experiments because the very short wave-lenght (smaller than the mean distance between two nucleons) and the large mean free path (of the order of the nuclear radius) [1] would justify some lower approximations, among them the impulse approximation [2], like for electrons. Moreover, in comparison with the electron case there are two great experimental advantages: the larger interaction cross-section (some orders of magnitude) and the absence of radiative effects.

The experiments which can be performed with medium- and high-energy protons are:

1) *inelastic scattering* which gives information on excitation energies, multipolarities and transition probabilities concerning « excited states » of nuclei;

2) « *knock out* » (p, 2p) *or* « *pick-up* » (p, d) *reactions* which give information on the « hole states » in nuclear matter: the location of the inner shells and the momentum distribution of the individual nucleons (if distorsion effects are properly taken into account) [3].

Since the pioneer work of STRAUCH and TITUS [4], TYREN and MARIS [5] (inelastic scattering) and of TYREN, HILMANN and MARIS [6] (p, 2p reactions) several experiments have been performed, mostly restricted to light nuclei.

The results achieved in this case are now quite well established because from the experimental point of view, the resolution which can be obtained gives a reasonable separation energy (0.8 MeV for inelastic scattering and $(2 \div 4)$ MeV for quasi-free scattering at 155 MeV) which is enough for light nuclei and, from the theoretical point of view, the analysis of the inelastic scattering data with D.W.B.A. [7] and the fit of the experimental binding energies with some realistic shell-model potentials [8] seem to work quite well.

For heavier nuclei (around ^{40}Ca) owing to the experimental limitations due to the energy resolution and spurious effects which reduce the counting rates (especially for p, 2p reactions) and the lack of calculations of the distorsion effects, the situation would be less satisfactory. However one can make reliable experiments by choosing « good » criteria to extract the spectroscopic information to be compared with theories, as we will see later.

The results I would like to report here concern namely (p, p′) and (p, 2p) experiments on medium-weight nuclei recently performed at Orsay with the 155 MeV proton synchrocyclotron of the Laboratoire de Physique Nucléaire in collaboration with J. C. JACMART, M. LIU, M. RIOU, C. RUHLA, M. ARDITI, H. DOUBRE and L. VALENTIN.

2. – Inelastic scattering on *s-d* and $f_{\frac{7}{2}}$ nuclei.

2·1. *Experiment and analysis of the data.* – In inelastic-scattering experiments one measures, in general, the spectra of the scattered protons with magnetic spectrometers and multidetector devices [9]: this one-way energy measurement provides a good counting rate and a quite reasonable energy separation (about 0.7 MeV at 155 MeV for an over-all resolution of $\sim 0.5\,\%$). The decomposition of the measured spectra by a peeling method using the shape of the elastic peaks gives with reasonable accuracy (up to an energy separation of 0.4 MeV) the « centroid energies » [10] of the inelastic excitations of the target nucleus.

The angular distributions taken for laboratory angles corresponding to quite low momentum transfers should give the multipole order of the transitions involved if theoretical l-depending curves are available; these calculations are, in general, based on certain interaction model assumptions.

The « strenghts » [10] may also be evaluated from the experimental cross-sections and will depend on the model assumptions.

However one can use, in the case of high-energy experiments, a comparison method with the electron scattering data to avoid ambiguities due to the model approximations; this can be done, in the lowest approximation (*i.e.* P.W.B.A. and impulse approximation) by simply writing the inelastic proton scattering cross-section in the following way [9]:

$$\frac{d\sigma}{d\Omega} = \left(\frac{d\sigma}{d\Omega}\right)_{p\mathcal{N}} 4A^2 \left(\frac{A}{A+1}\right)^2 \frac{k_i}{k_f} F^2(q) , \tag{1}$$

where $(d\sigma/d\Omega)_{p\mathcal{N}}$ is the « appropriate » cross-section for the free-proton-nucleon scattering without isospin-flip (which is justified for low excitations) and without spin-flip (which is more arbitrary, but not very troublesome for electric transitions and in the $\Delta T = 0$ case [9]), for the same momentum transfer $\hbar\boldsymbol{q} = \hbar(\boldsymbol{k}_i - \boldsymbol{k}_f)$ (*i.e.* $\hbar q \simeq 2k \sin\theta$; $k_i \approx k_f = k$); $F(q)$ is a « nuclear form factor » given by

$$F(q) = \frac{\Gamma}{A} \sum_{j=1}^{A} \int \varphi_f^*(\boldsymbol{r}_1 \dots \boldsymbol{r}_A) \exp[i\boldsymbol{q}\boldsymbol{r}_j] \varphi_i(r_1 \dots r_A)\, dr_1 \dots dr_A \tag{2}$$

where φ_i and φ_f are the initial and final nuclear wave functions for the $i \to f$ nuclear transition. This form factor is similar to that used in the electron scattering case (where $A \to Z$ and $\Gamma \to 1$) [11] for electric transitions, where the differential cross-section is written

$$\left(\frac{d\sigma}{d\Omega}\right)_{el} = \left(\frac{d\sigma}{d\Omega}\right)_{Mott} \frac{k_i}{k_f} F_{el}^2(q) . \tag{3}$$

The comparison between the two form factors for the same electric transition $i \to f$ is quite general:

$$F^2(q) = \Gamma^2 F_{el}^2(q) \tag{4}$$

and should give an estimation of the « transmission factor » Γ^2 which includes any distortion effects. It is known that the use of D.W.B.A. instead of P.W.B.A. for high-energy proton-scattering results only in a reduction of the peak differential cross-section with little effect on the location or shape of the curve [7]; then the use of the Γ^2 factor to account for this reduction is quite justified at least for small momentum transfers, in our case. A plot of Γ^2, for $E2$ and $E3$ transitions, as given by the relation (4) for a set of comparisons is reported in Fig. 1, and can be used to extract other Γ^2 values of interest.

Then the location of the maximum in the experimental angular distribution is enough to give the multipolarity of the transition (at least for $l \leqslant 5$) and the reduced transition probabilities $B(El)$ (the « strenghts ») can be extracted by using the same formulas as in the electron case:

$$F^2(q) = \Gamma^2 F^2_{\text{el}}(q) = \Gamma^2 \beta_l j_l^2(qR) \exp[-q^2 g^2] , \tag{5}$$

with $R = 1.20 A^{\frac{1}{3}}$ fermi and $g = 0.95$ fermi, for $A > 12$ and

$$B(El)\uparrow = \frac{1}{4\pi} Z^2 R^{2l} C^{-2l} \beta_l , \tag{6}$$

where $C^{-2l} = (1 + 3Z\alpha/2qR)^{-2l}$ accounts for the change in the electron wavelenght in the nucleus [12].

Using Weisskopf units for single-particle transitions one has, for collective excitations, an enhancement factor G given by

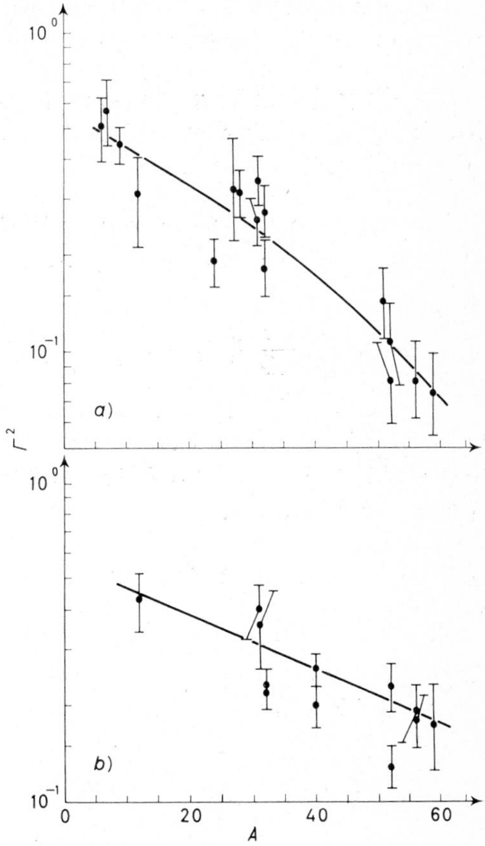

Fig. 1. – *a*) *E*2 transitions; *b*) *E*3 transitions.

$$G(El) = \frac{B(El)\uparrow}{B(El)\uparrow_{\text{s.p.}}} = \frac{2I_i + 1}{2I_f + 1} \frac{4\pi}{R^{2l}} \left(\frac{3+l}{3}\right) B(El, I_i \to I_f) . \tag{7}$$

2·2. *Results.* – Detailed investigations between ^{23}Na and ^{59}Co have been performed with 155 MeV protons, and some interesting results have been found, among them I would like to discuss the following

2·2.1. Core excitations in odd nuclei; the case of ^{39}K. Some « collective » excitations in odd-mass nuclei have been interpreted as due to an angular-momentum coupling between a collective (quadrupole or octupole) vibration of the even-even core, as deduced from the adjacent even-even nucleus, and the single-particle (hole) state available to the odd nucleon (hole) [13]. A consequence of this model is that, in inelastic scattering, one has to find in the odd nucleus a set of states ($2K+1$ where K is the minimum value between j, the single-particle angular momentum, and I, the core state angular momentum) with the following properties [14]:

i) they should have the same angular distribution as the core excitation (*i.e.* the corresponding transitions have the same multipolarity order as the core transition);

ii) the strength of the core excitation should be distributed among the set of states of the odd nucleus, *i.e.*

$$\frac{d\sigma}{d\Omega}(l, I_i \to I_f) = \frac{2I_f+1}{(2l+1)(2I_i+1)} \frac{d\sigma}{d\Omega}(0 \to l), \tag{8}$$

where $I_i = j$ and I_f are the angular momenta of the initial and final states in the odd nucleus and $l = I$ gives the transition multipolarity corresponding to the core excitation.

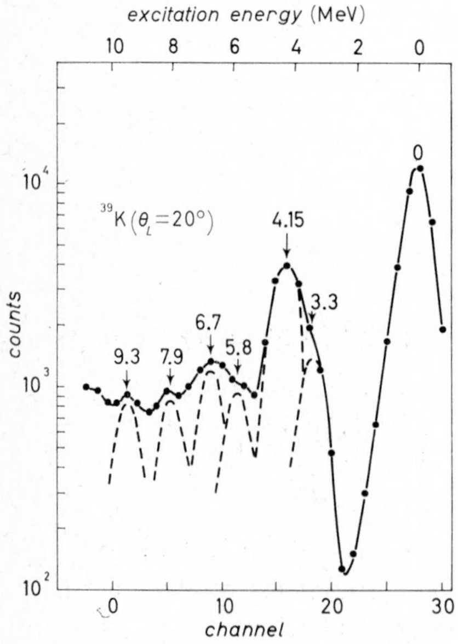

Fig. 2*a*.

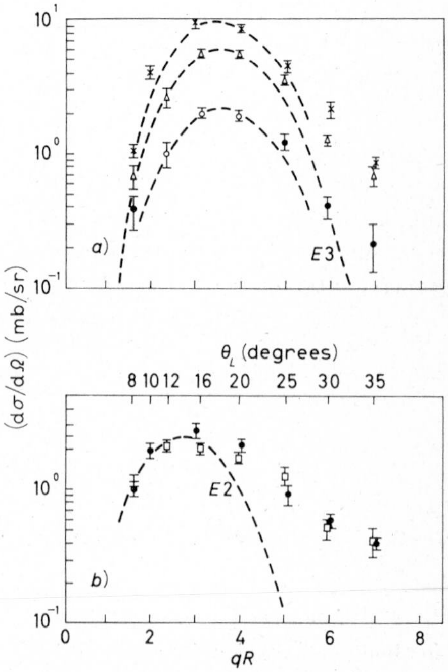

Fig. 2*b*. – *A*) × 3.7 MeV, ^{40}Ca; ○ 3.3 MeV, ^{39}K; △ 4.1 MeV, ^{33}K; *B*) • 6.8 MeV, ^{40}Ca, □ 6.8 MeV, ^{39}K.

The case of ^{39}K is a very good example to check this model for octupole excitations. Starting from the very-well-known 3^- state at 3.73 MeV in ^{40}Ca, one should expect in ^{39}K a set of negative-parity states, arising from the coupling of this octupole state of the ^{40}Ca core with the $d_{\frac{3}{2}}(\frac{3}{2}^+)$ hole state, having the properties mentioned above.

Figure 2 *a*) shows the experimental spectrum found for ^{39}K at 20°; the two strong peaks at 3.3 and 4.15 MeV have the same angular distributions as the 3.7 MeV level excited in ^{40}Ca; this can be easily seen in Fig. 2 *b*) where some angular distributions are reported: the dashed curves are theoretical $E3$ and $E2$ distributions calculated from expression (5). The distortion effects taken into account only by the empirical transmission factor Γ^2 give rise to a bad fit for $qR > 5$, but do not affect the multipolarity assignment.

Concerning the strengths, to a peak cross-section of (9 ± 1) mb/sr for the 3^- state in ^{40}Ca corresponds a total peak cross-section of (7.5 ± 0.7) mb/sr for the two corresponding levels in ^{39}K; the other levels belonging to the core excitation band have been probably missed, in our experiment, owing to our energy resolution.

2'2.2. Results on ^{40}Ca. Many inelastic-scattering experiments have been performed on this nucleus because of its theoretical interest [15]. Figure 3

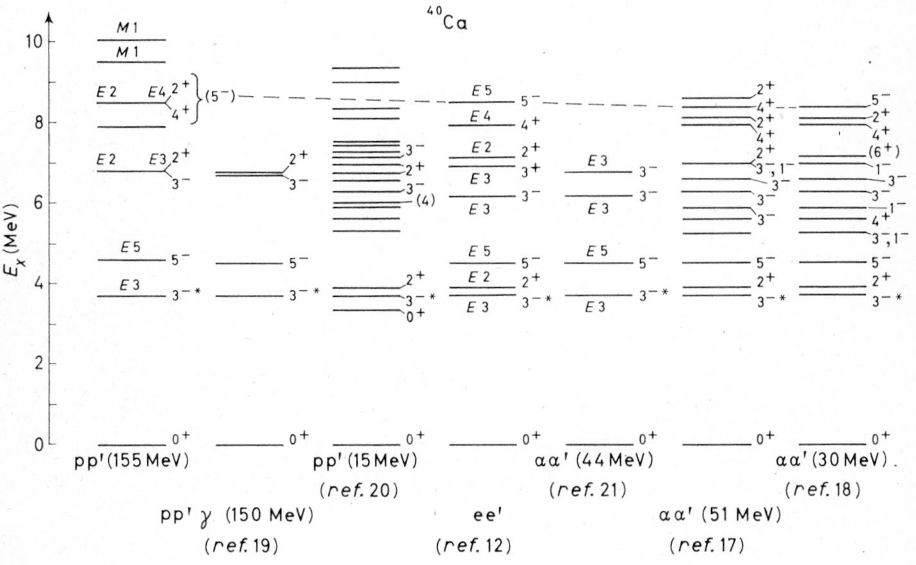

Fig. 3.

shows a review of the experimental spectra found so far. Of particular interest, apart from the well known 3^-, 5^- and 2^+ lowest excitations, are the states above 7 MeV, especially in the region of 8 to 9 MeV, where a 5^- level is expected from the particle-hole representation [16].

However the experimental evidence of such a state is far from being well established: our results are in favour of the presence of 2^+ and 4^+ levels at ~ 8.5 MeV (but do not exclude a 5^- interpretation) in agreement with the (α, α') experiment of SPRINGER and HARVEY [17], while other (α, α') investigations [18] and (e, e′) experiments [12] are interpreted in favour of a 5^- assignment (see Fig. 3). Owing to the difficulties in distinguishing between very close $E4$ and $E5$ angular distributions in these experiments, any interpretation is not very conclusive.

Additional high-energy states have been found, in the Orsay experiments (at 9 to 10 MeV), which may be interpreted as $M1$, $T=1$ excitations (the angular distributions are strongly forward peaked).

2˙2.3. Quadrupole and octupole states in s-d shell even-even nuclei. Figure 4 shows a schematic behavior of the 2^+ and 3^- lowest states (found in our and other experiments) following the s-d shell filling. The similar states of $1p$ nuclei have been also included for comparison. We have chosen, to avoid distinctions between neutron or proton filling only $Z=N$ nuclei. The figures in brackets are the enhancement factors (collective strengths) of the corresponding excitations in Weisskopf units.

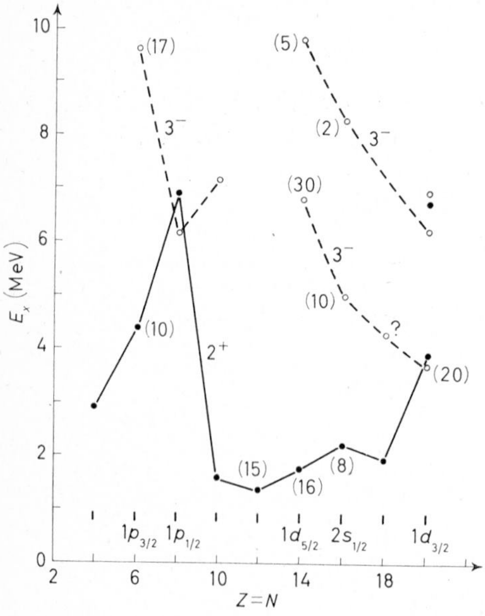

Fig. 4.

The strong coherent effects in the lowest 2^+ and 3^- states ($T=0$ vibrations) are properly accounted for by the R.P.A., as shown in Gillet's lectures for doubly closed-shell nuclei.

Concerning the excitation energy systematics, shell and subshell effects are quite evident for 2^+ states, while only major shell effects are present in the 3^- states, as expected [22].

2˙2.4. Quadrupole and octupole states in $f_{\frac{7}{2}}$ even-even nuclei. Figure 5 shows a representation of the 2^+ and 3^- states found in this interesting region.

Following the $f_{\frac{7}{2}}$ shell filling the quadrupole vibration is always well concentrated in the lowest 2^+ state ($B(E2)\simeq 10$ Weisskopf units), which is generally accounted for as a seniority 2 state [23], while the octupole strength is shared by more than one low-lying 3^- state (two in our case) which should arise from the structure of the unperturbed shell-model spectrum.

An interesting example is given by ^{50}Ti: The results of ^{51}V(p, 2p)^{50}Ti experiments, as we shall see later, give a single-hole excitation at about 6 MeV, which should correspond to a $(f_{\frac{7}{2}})(2s_{\frac{1}{2}})^{-1}$ particle-hole state at this energy in

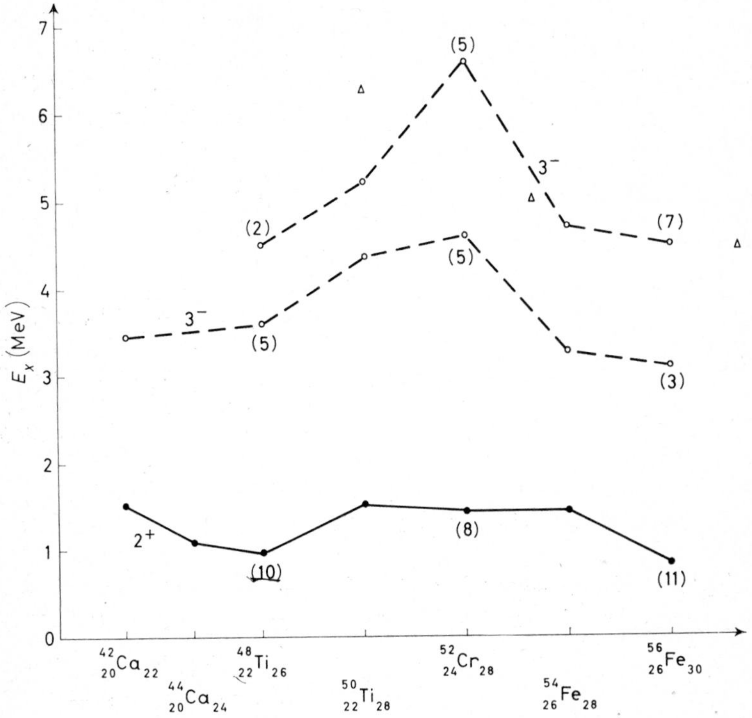

Fig. 5. – 2^+ and 3^- states in $f_{\frac{7}{2}}$ nuclei; △ $((f_{\frac{7}{2}})(2s_{\frac{1}{2}})^{-1})$.

the ^{50}Ti unperturbed spectrum. Actually a second 3^- level at 5.2 MeV has been found in a low-energy (p, p′) experiment [24].

To extract more information from (p, p′) experiments at 155 MeV we need more accurate theoretical form factors using D.W.B.A. and proper nuclear models. GILLET has given some examples of the remarkable agreement obtained in comparing R.P.A. predictions with the experiments in the case of ^{12}C, ^{16}O and ^{40}Ca [15]. Recently HAYBRON [25] has calculated the theoretical form factors for 155 MeV proton scattering using the collective model and fitting the parameters of the optical potential. He finds good agreement with our experiments with deformation parameters close to those obtained by other means, assuming that both the real and imaginary parts of the appropriate

« volume » absorbing potential are deformed (volume complex potential); a similar agreement is also found for the « surface » absorbing potential, but requires unreasonable large deformations. This situation is quite different from that found in low-energy experiments where surface and volume absorption fit equally well the data. As an example Fig. 6 shows the fits obtained for various choices in the case of the 3.73 MeV 3^- state of ^{40}Ca. Similar results are obtained for the 2^+ states in the $f_{\frac{7}{2}}$ nuclei.

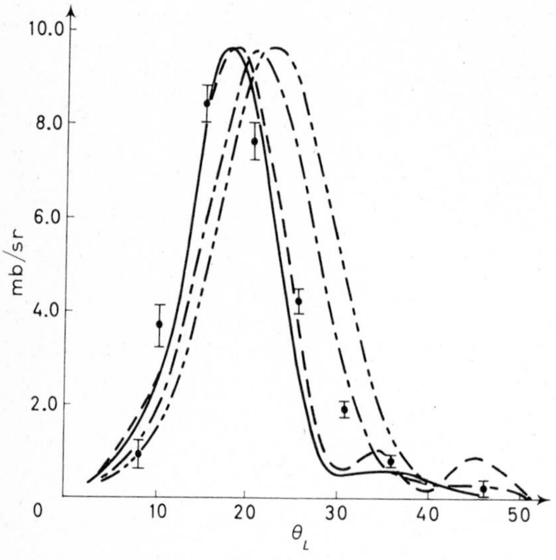

Fig. 6. – ^{40}Ca, 3^-, 3.7 MeV: ——— volume complex, $\beta = 0.307$; —·—·— volume real, $\beta = 0.881$; – – – surface complex, $\beta = 0.514$; —··—··— surface real, $\beta = 1.18$.

3. – (p, 2p) reactions on ^{40}Ca and $f_{\frac{7}{2}}$ nuclei.

3·1. *Experiment and analysis of the data.* – As pointed out before (p, 2p) reactions at energies higher than 100 MeV may be considered as direct interactions where the low momentum transfer justifies the « quasi free » scattering interpretation. In this kind of experiments one measures, in general, the energies E_1 and E_2 of the outgoing protons, which should give the binding energy E_L of the proton extracted from the target nucleus by the conservation equation

$$E_0 = E_1 + E_2 + E_L + E_R \, , \tag{9}$$

where E_0 is the energy of the incident proton and E_R the recoil energy of the nucleus, which can be minimized choosing a proper geometry for which the kinematics of the reaction, in the lowest approximation, becomes very simple. Looking in the vector momentum space (see Fig. 7) these conditions are:

a) all vectors are coplanar;

b) the scattering angles $(\boldsymbol{k}_0, \boldsymbol{k}_1) = \theta_1$ and $(\boldsymbol{k}_0, \boldsymbol{k}_2) = \theta_2$ are opposite: $\theta_1 = -\theta_2$;

c) $E_1 = E_2$; $k_1 = k_2$.

This is achieved by selecting an energy interval in one of the two detecting ways, so that $\boldsymbol{k}_R$ is parallel (or antiparallel) to $\boldsymbol{k}_0$ and has the value $k_R = k_0 - 2k\cos\theta$ (where $\theta = |\theta_1| = |\theta_2|$).

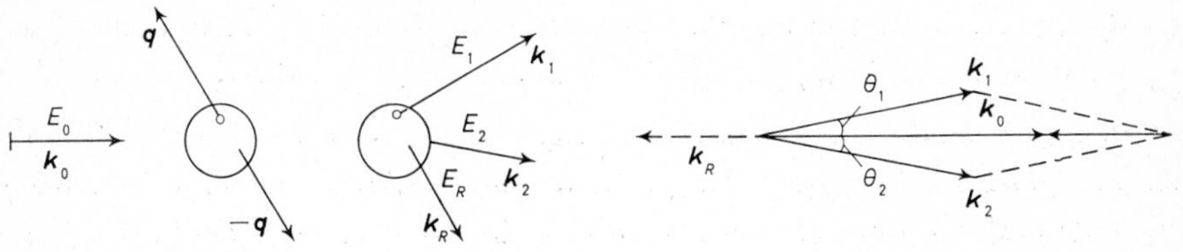

Fig. 7.

Then $k_R = 0$ for $\theta = \theta_0 = \arccos k_0/2k$, *i.e.* at 44° (laboratory angle) for $E_L = 0$, at 155 MeV.

Using the impulse approximation and neglecting distorsion effects, we have $\hbar\boldsymbol{k}_R = -\hbar\boldsymbol{q}$, $\hbar\boldsymbol{q}$ being the momentum of the proton in the nucleus.

The summed energy spectrum $(E_1 + E_2)$ which is measured by coincidence methods (with a final energy separation of ~ 2 MeV) would then give the E_L values $(E_L \simeq E_0 - (E_1 + E_2)$, neglecting E_R in the chosen kinematics$)$ for the various proton groups belonging to different l orbitals.

At $\theta = \theta_0$ (44° in our case) only s-protons should be observed $(q = 0)$.

At different θ values one has an angular correlation distribution which depends on the momentum distribution.

In the lowest approximation one has for the differential (p, 2p) cross-section

$$\frac{\mathrm{d}\sigma}{\mathrm{d}\Omega_1\,\mathrm{d}\Omega_2\,\mathrm{d}E_1} \propto \varrho(q)\cdot\left(\frac{\mathrm{d}\sigma}{\mathrm{d}\Omega}\right)_{\mathrm{p-p}}, \tag{10}$$

where $\varrho(q)$ is the proton density in the momentum space and $(\mathrm{d}\sigma/\mathrm{d}\Omega)_{\mathrm{p-p}}$ is the cross-section for free proton-proton scattering at $\theta = 90°$ in the center-of-mass, at an energy corresponding to $k_0 - q$.

In measuring the angular correlation distribution one should find, in general, a maximum near θ_0 for s-protons and a dip for $l \neq 0$ protons and therefore one can distinguish quite easily between s-states and $l \neq 0$ states; however it is rather difficult to distinguish between different $l \neq 0$ states; moreover higher l-states are more difficult to observe because of lower cross-sections due to the normalization factor in $\varrho(q)$.

In fact the distorted-wave calculations performed for light nuclei [26] show that:

a) the absolute cross-section decreases by a factor due to absorption;

b) the maxima and minima do not occur exactly at $\theta = \theta_0$, but at larger angles;

c) for $l \neq 0$, the dip is more and more steep going from light to heavier nuclei;

d) the shape of the angular correlation distributions is not affected by distorsion effects, except for low and large q-values.

The experiments carried out in Orsay for nuclei heavier than ^{40}Ca have been analysed in the lowest approximation, which is enough to give the correct 2*s* and 1*d* binding energies, whose systematics is of great interest for the theory of nuclear matter.

3·2. *Results on* ^{40}Ca; *the proton binding energies in the s-d shell.* – Figure 8 shows the experimental (p, 2p) summed energy spectra taken at $\theta = 40°$ and 58° in the case of ^{40}Ca, as found in the recent experiments at Orsay.

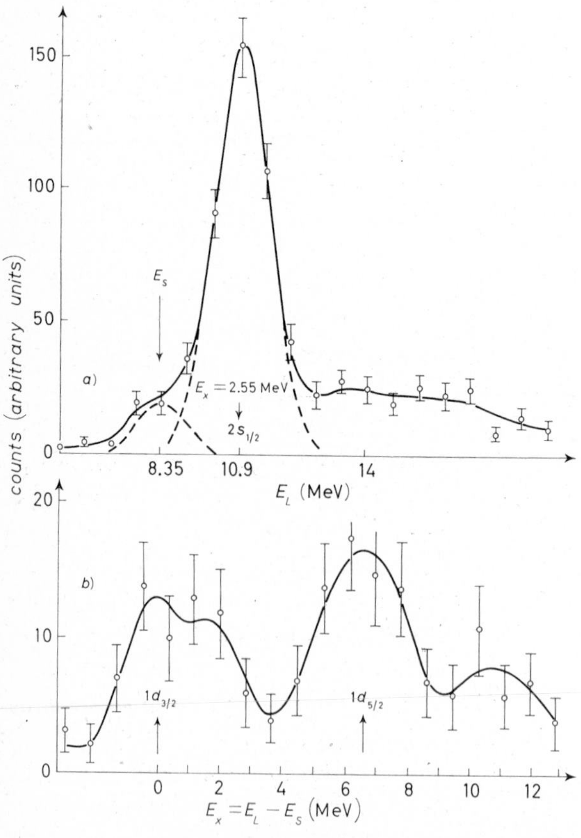

Fig. 8. – ^{40}Ca(p, 2p)^{39}K: *a*) $\theta = 40°$; *b*) $\theta = 58°$.

The strong peak at $E_L = (10.9 \pm 0.3)$ MeV, which goes down at higher angles is interpreted as due to 2*s* protons, while the peak at $E_L = (8.35 \pm \pm 0.20)$ MeV corresponds very well to the ^{39}K ground state (the proton separation energy deduced from mass difference is 8.336 MeV), so that it may be interpreted as a $1d_{\frac{3}{2}}$ state.

The corresponding angular correlation distributions are reported in Fig. 9, showing the expected behaviour for *s*-states (maximum at 44°) and for $l \neq 0$ states; a second peak with $l \neq 0$ distribution at a (6.6 ± 0.8) MeV of excitation energy (binding energy (14 ± 1) MeV) may be interpreted as given by $1d_{\frac{5}{2}}$ protons.

Our results obtained with a better energy-resolution confirm those found in previous work [27] and agree, in the limits of the experimental errors, with those reported in other (p, 2p) experiments [28, 29]; moreover the l assignment, in our recent experiment, can be considered quite well established from the experimental angular correlations.

Table I summarizes the experimental data concerning the $2s_{\frac{1}{2}}$, and $1d_{\frac{5}{2}}$ excitation energies (both for protons (^{39}K) and neutrons (^{39}Ca) (single-hole states in the s-d shell)); the levels known from the work of ENDT and VAN DER LEUN [30] are reported for comparison together with the theoretical predictions [31] on the basis of the Brueckner theory; this latter gives too low absolute values for binding energies, but correct values for the excitation energies.

All results seem to be consistent; the $2s_{\frac{1}{2}}$ single-hole state in ^{39}K should then corresponds to the first level found by ENDT

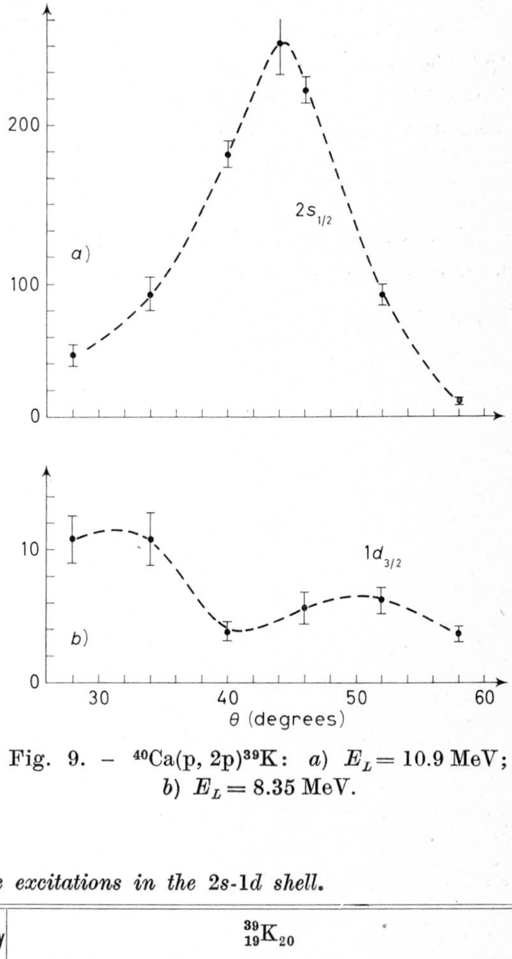

Fig. 9. – ^{40}Ca(p, 2p)^{39}K: *a*) $E_L = 10.9$ MeV; *b*) $E_L = 8.35$ MeV.

TABLE I. – *Single-hole excitations in the 2s-1d shell.*

	$^{39}_{20}Ca_{19}$				Theory	$^{39}_{19}K_{20}$				
	(p, d) ref. [32]	(p, d) ref. [33]	ref. [34]	ENDT ref. [30]	ref. [31]	(p, 2p) ref. [28]	(p, 2p) ref. [29]	(p, 2p) Orsay	(d, ^{3}He) ref. [35]	ENDT ref. [30]
$2s_{\frac{1}{2}}$	2.6±0.15	2.5±0.2		2.47 2.80 3.03	2.4	2.0±0.9	2.3±0.7	2.55±0.35	2.58±0.05	2.53
$1d_{\frac{5}{2}}$		5.1 6.1 7.4 8.3	6 8.3		6.6	6.4±1.8	7.2±0.9	6.6 ±0.8		

and VAN DER LEUN; a similar assignment seems to be correct for ^{39}Ca. However the situation may be not so simple. Another, though very weak, $l=0$ transition of 3.9 MeV has been observed in (p, d) work on ^{40}Ca [31, 32], so the $2s_{\frac{1}{2}}$ state could give more than one level.

Moreover the peak at (6.6 ± 0.8) MeV we have found certainly contains the $1d_{\frac{3}{2}}$ excitation in agreement with the Brueckner theory, but we cannot conclude that this assignment is unique; our experimental energy resolution does not exclude the presence in this peak of other levels found in (p, d) reactions.

3'3. *Results on $f_{\frac{7}{2}}$ nuclei; the 2s proton binding energy in the $1f_{\frac{7}{2}}$ shell.* – Some interesting results have been found for nuclei with protons in the $1f_{\frac{7}{2}}$ shell

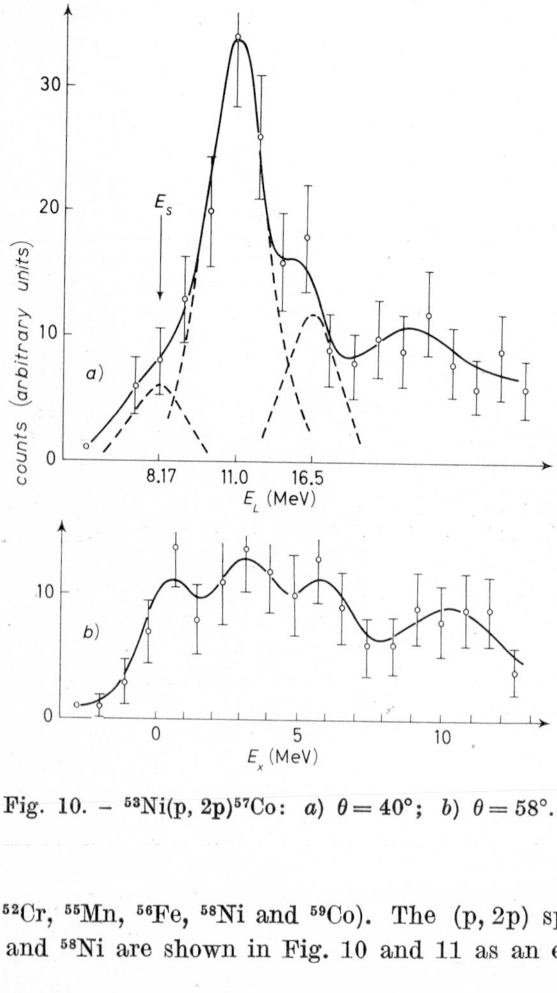

Fig. 10. – ^{58}Ni(p, 2p)^{57}Co: *a*) $\theta=40°$; *b*) $\theta=58°$.

(^{45}Sc, ^{48}Ti, ^{51}V, ^{52}Cr, ^{55}Mn, ^{56}Fe, ^{58}Ni and ^{59}Co). The (p, 2p) spectra found in the case of ^{51}V and ^{58}Ni are shown in Fig. 10 and 11 as an example.

Similar results have been found for the other nuclei and enable us to draw the following preliminary conclusions:

a) the 2*s*-state is very well characterized in all these nuclei with binding energies which do not vary very much with the mass number;

b) the 1*f* state (corresponding to the proton separation energy) is not observed in some cases and generally it cannot be distinguished from the $1d_{\frac{3}{2}}$ state; taking into account our energy resolution, it can be inferred that the separation between $1f_{\frac{7}{2}}$ and $1d_{\frac{3}{2}}$ binding energies is not greater than $(2 \div 3)$ MeV;

c) peaks which may be interpreted as $1d_{\frac{5}{2}}$ states are observed at a binding energy about 4 MeV higher than the 2*s* binding energy, as in ^{40}Ca;

d) it follows that ^{40}Ca can be considered as a core for heavier nuclei, characterizing the binding energies in the *s*-*d* shell, also for $f_{\frac{7}{2}}$ nuclei.

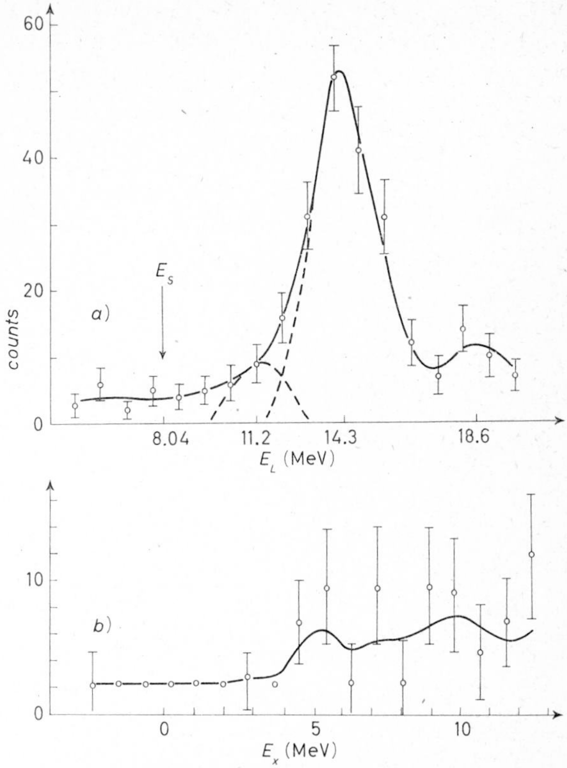

Fig. 11. – ^{51}V(p, 2p)^{50}Ti: *a*) $\theta = 40°$; *b*) $\theta = 58°$.

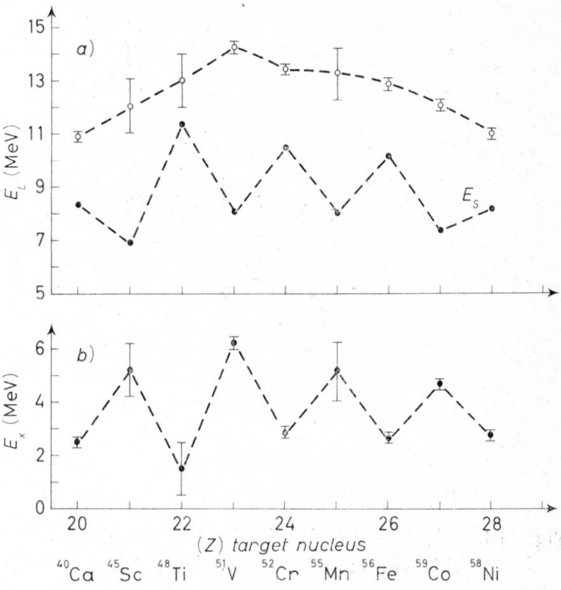

Fig. 12. – Binding energies (E_L) and excitation energies (E_x) for 2*s* states in $1f_{\frac{7}{2}}$ nuclei from (p, 2p) reactions.

Figure 12 gives the binding energies E_L and the corresponding excitation energies $E_L - E_S$ (E_S being the ground-state energy of the residual nucleus) for the 2*s*-state in 1*f* nuclei. It can be seen that for the binding energies no strong fluctuations are found in contrast with the situation for 2*s*-1*d* nuclei [3] and that the general behavior is characterized by a smooth rise up to ^{51}V fol-

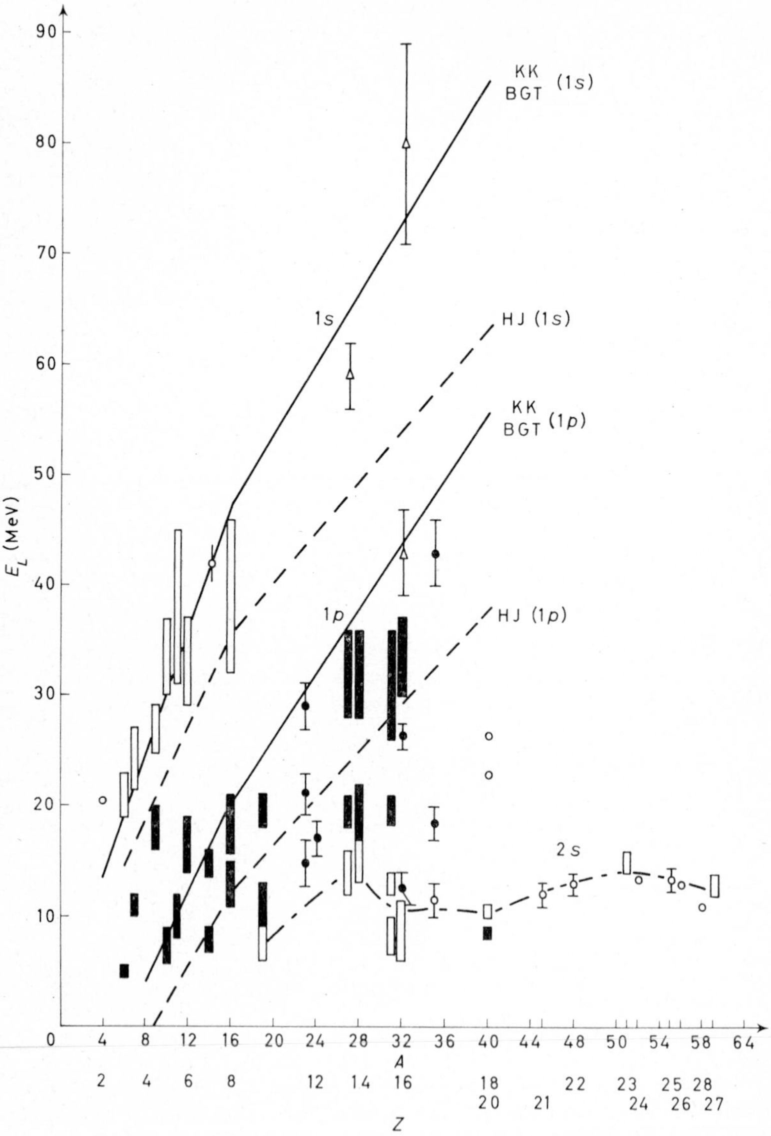

Fig. 13. – ——— KK, Kallio-Kolltveit; ——— BGT, Brueckner-Gammel-Thaler; – – – HJ, Hamada-Johnston; □ ○ $l = 0$ (p, 2p); ■ ● $l \neq 0$ (p, 2p); △ (e, e′, p).

lowed by a decreasing trend up to the end of the $f_{\frac{7}{2}}$ shell; the fluctuations in the excitation energies are due to pairing effects, as expected.

These results are different from those obtained for the $1s$ and $1p$ binding energies in $1s$ and $1p$ nuclei, where E_L rises monotonically as function of A.

Figure 13 shows the experimental binding energies as function of A.

The data are taken from the tables recently collected by RIOU [3], TIBELL *et al.* [28] and by the group of the Istituto Superiore di Sanità [35] including recent experiments with high-energy electrons [36] and our results on $1f_{\frac{7}{2}}$ nuclei.

The results on $1s$ and $1p$ binding energies in nuclei up to ^{32}S are well accounted for by calculations which take into account a nucleon-nucleon potential of the Kallio-Kollveit type (K.K.) [37] as found by BRINK and SHERMAN [8]; an interaction energy of the Brueckner-Gammel-Thaler type (B.G.T.) gives the same results, while the Hamada-Johnston (H.J.) potential gives the correct behaviour but does not fit the absolute experimental values [8].

The slope of the curve is about 2 MeV per nucleon between ^{4}He and ^{16}O ($1s$-$1p$ nuclei) and $\sim$1.4 MeV per nucleon between ^{16}O and ^{32}S ($2s$-$1d$ nuclei) for the $1s$-state and somewhat less for the $1p$-state.

This slope can be considered as the mean interaction energy between $1s$ (or $1p$) protons and external nucleons, assuming the interaction energy in the $1s$ ($1p$) shell is not affected. For the $2s$-state the situation is completely different as we have mentioned before; the corresponding binding energy shows strong fluctuations in the $2s$-$1d$ nuclei before ^{40}Ca and is quite constant in the $1f_{\frac{7}{2}}$ nuclei where ^{40}Ca seems to act as a stabilizing core.

It should be interesting to perform calculations for the $2s$ binding energies to explain these properties; on the other hand there is some hope to permit observation of the $1s$ and $1p$ states in heavier nuclei, which escape to the (p, 2p) experiments, with investigations using high-energy electrons ((e, e′p) reactions) [35, 36].

REFERENCES

[1] R. SERBER: *Phys. Rev.*, **72**, 1114 (1947); E. SEGRÈ and D. CHAMBERLAIN: *Phys. Rev.*, **87**, 81 (1952); J. M. WILCOX and B. J. MOYER: *Phys. Rev.*, **99**, 875 (1955); L. S. AZGHIREV, I. K. VZOROV, V. P. ZRELOV, M. G. MESCHERIAKOV and NEGANOV: *Sov. Phys. JETP*, **36**, 1162 (1959).

[2] G. F. CHEW and M. L. GOLDBERGER: *Phys. Rev.*, **87**, 778 (1952); A. K. KERMAN, H. MACMANUS and R. M. THALER: *Ann. of Phys.*, **8**, 551 (1959).

[3] Cfr. M. RIOU: *Rev. Mod. Phys.*, **37**, 375 (1965).

[4] K. STRAUCH and F. TITUS: *Phys. Rev.*, **95**, 854 (1954); **103**, 200 (1956); **104**, 191 (1956).

[5] H. TYREN and T. A. MARIS: *Nucl. Phys.*, **3**, 52 (1957); **4**, 637 (1957); **6**, 446 (1958).
[6] H. TYREN, P. HILLMANN and T. A. MARIS: *Nucl. Phys.*, **10**, 1 (1958).
[7] R. M. HAYBRON and H. MACMANUS: *Phys. Rev.*, **136**, B 1730 (1964).
[8] D. M. BRINK and M. SHERMAN: Reports of Laboratori di Fisica dell'Ist. Sup. di Sanità ISS64/36 (1964); cfr. ref. [36]; D. M. BRINK: private communication.
[9] J. C. JACMART: *Thèse*, Orsay 1964, *Cahiers de Physique*, **173**, (1965); J. C. JACMART, M. LIU, R. A. RICCI, M. RIOU and C. RUHLA: *Phys. Lett.*, **8**, 273 (1964); M. LIU, J. C. JACMART, R. A. RICCI, M. RIOU and C. RUHLA: *Nucl. Phys.*, **75**, 481 (1966).
[10] Cfr. J. B. FRENCH: this volume, p. 278.
[11] See for example R. H. HELM: *Phys. Rev.*, **104**, 1446 (1956); W. C. BARBER: *Ann. Rev. Nucl. Sci.*, **12**, 1 (1962); G. R. BISHOP: *Proc. of the Int. Conf. on Direct Interac. and Nuclear Reaction Mechanism* (Padua, 1963); *Proc. of the Conf. Nucl. Phys.* (Paris, 1964).
[12] D. BLUM, P. BARREAU and J. BELLICARD: *Phys. Lett.*, **4**, 109 (1963).
[13] R. D. LAWSON and J. URETSKY: *Phys. Rev.*, **108**, 1300 (1957); A. DE SHALIT: *Phys. Rev.*, **122**, 1530 (1961).
[14] Cfr. P. E. HODGSON: *Proc. of the NUFFIC Int. Summer Course in Nucl. Spectr. Nijenrode* (1963); see also ref. [22].
[15] V. GILLET: This volume, p. 43.
[16] V. GILLET: *Thesis*, Paris (1962); V. GILLET and E. A. SANDERSON: *Nucl. Phys.*, **54**, 472 (1964); H. P. JOLLY: *Nucl. Phys.*, **67**, 209 (1965).
[17] A. SPRINGER and B. G. HARVEY: *Phys. Lett.*, **14**, 116 (1965).
[18] R. W. BAUER, A. M. BERNSTEIN, G. HEYMANN, E. P. LIPPINCOTT and M. S. WALL: *Phys. Lett.*, **14**, 129 (1965).
[19] D. NEWTON, A. B. CLEGG and G. L. SALMON: to be published; private communication.
[20] J. J. KRAUSHAAR, W. S. GRAY and R. A. KENEFICK: *Proc. Int. Conf. Nucl. Phys. Paris*, 1964.
[21] J. SAUDINOS, R. BEURTY, P. CASTILLON, R. CHAMINADE, M. CRUT, H. FARAGGI, A. PAPINEAU and J. THIRION: *Compt. Rend.*, **252**, 260 (1961).
[22] O. NATHAN and S. G. NILSSON: *α, β, γ-Ray Spectroscopy*, edited by SIEGBAHN, Chap. X (1965).
[23] Cfr. I. TALMI: *Proc. of the NUFFIC Int. Summer Course in Nucl. Spectr. Nijenrode* (1963).
[24] W. S. GRAY, R. A. KENEFICK and J. J. KRAUSHAAR: *Nucl. Phys.*, **67**, 565 (1965).
[25] R. M. HAYBRON: preprint, private communication.
[26] T. BERGGREN and G. JACOB: *Phys. Lett.*, **1**, 258 (1962); *Nucl. Phys.*, **47**, 481 (1963); K. K. LIM and I. E. MAC CARTHY: *Phys. Rev.*, **133**, 13, 1006 (1964); I. E. MAC CARTHY: *Rev. Mod. Phys.*, **37**, 388 (1965).
[27] C. RUHLA, M. RIOU, R. A. RICCI, M. ARDITI, H. DOUBRE, J. C. JACMART, M. LIU and L. VALENTIN: *Phys. Lett.*, **1**, 326 (1964); *Proc. of the Int. Conf. on Nucl. Phys. Paris* (1964). cfr. also C. RUHLA: *Thèse*, Paris 1966.
[28] G. TIBELL, O. SUNDBERG and MIKLAVZIC: *Phys. Lett.*, **1**, 172 (1962); **2**, 100 (1962); G. TIBELL, O. SUNDBERG and P. U. RENBERG: *Ark. Fys.*, **25**, 433 (1963).
[29] H. TYREN, S. KULLANDER and R. RAMACHANDRAN: *Proc. of the Int. Conf. on Direct Interactions and Nuclear Reaction Mechanism* (Padua, 1962); H. TYREN, S. KULLANDER, R. RAMACHANDRAN and O. SUNDBERG: *Proc. of the Int. Conf. on Nuclear Physics Paris* (1964).
[30] P. M. ENDT and C. VAN DER LEUN: *Nucl. Phys.*, **34**, 1 (1962).

[31] K. A. BRUECKNER, A. M. LOCKETT and M. ROTENBERG: *Phys. Rev.*, **121**, 255 (1961).

[32] C. P. KAVALOSKI, G. BASSANI and M. M. HINTZ: *Phys. Rev.*, **132**, 813 (1963).

[33] D. BACHELIER, M. BERNS, C. DETRAZ and P. RADVANYI: *Journ. Phys.*, **24**, 1055 (1963); C. DETRAZ: *Thesis*, Paris (1964).

[34] P. E. CAVANAGH, C. F. COLEMAN, G. A. GARD, B. W. RIDLEY and J. F. TURNER: *Nucl. Phys.*, **50**, 49 (1964).

[55] G. CAMPOS VENUTI and P. SALVADORI: Reports of Laborat. di Fisica Istituto Superiore Sanità, ISS 65/3 (1965).

[36] U. AMALDI jr., G. CAMPOS VENUTI, G. CORTELLESSA, C. FRONTEROTTA, A. REALE and P. SALVADORI: *Phys. Rev. Lett.*, **13**, 341 (1964).

[37] A. KALLIO and K. KOLLTVEIT: *Nucl. Phys.*, **53**, 87 (1964).

$^7Li(d, \alpha)^5He$ Reaction and α-Clustering in Light Nuclei.

R. POTENZA
Istituto di Fisica dell'Università - Catania

I shall refer here about some experimental results we obtained in Catania laboratories. These results are in part contained in a paper that will be submitted to *Nuclear Physics* for publication as soon as possible [1].

The interaction of deuterons with ^7Li at E_d between 0.6 and 2.0 MeV can give rise to the following reactions:

$$(1)\quad \left| \begin{array}{l} ^7Li + d \to (^9Be^*) \to \\ \to {}^7Li + d\,, \\ \to {}^7Li^* + d'\,, \end{array} \right.$$

$$(2)\quad \left\{ \begin{array}{l} \to {}^8Li + p_0 \\ \to {}^8Li^* + p' \end{array} \right\} \; {}^8Li(\beta^-)\,{}^8Be^*; \quad {}^8Be^* \to 2\alpha\,, \quad Q_{d,p_0} = -0.192 \text{ MeV},$$

$$(3)\quad \left\{ \begin{array}{l} \to {}^8Be + n_0 \\ \to {}^8Be^* + n' \end{array} \right\} \; {}^8Be \to 2\alpha\,, \quad \begin{array}{l} Q_{d,n_0} = 15.026 \text{ MeV}, \\ Q'_{Be} = 0.094 \text{ MeV}, \end{array}$$

$$(4)\quad \left\{ \begin{array}{l} \to {}^5He + \alpha_0 \\ \to {}^5He^* + \alpha' \end{array} \right\} \; {}^5He \to \alpha + n\,, \quad \begin{array}{l} Q_{d,\alpha_0} = 14.15 \text{ MeV}, \\ Q'_{He} = 0.96 \text{ MeV}, \end{array}$$

$$(5)\quad \to 2\alpha + n\,, \quad \text{(three-body break-up)} \quad Q_{t.b.b.} = 15.11 \text{ MeV}\,,$$

where we have not considered γ emission from $^9Be^*$ and where the brackets around this latter nucleus mean that it may appear in the process as a compound nucleus or it may not.

Up to now experiments have shown no clear evidence of the three-body break-up (reaction (5)) of the ^9Be up to $E_x = 18$ MeV [2, 3].

This situation is to be compared with the very different one arising in the investigation of ^{12}C [4] and ^{13}C [5] where the three- and four-body break-ups seem to be preponderant.

In order to have more information about the three-body break-up of ^{9}Be and on the clustering of this nucleus:

i) We are performing measurements of the spectra and angular distributions of α-particles and neutrons that come from the listed reactions, in order to determine their mechanism.

ii) We are measuring, moreover, the angular correlations between two particles from reactions (3), (4) and (5) and two-dimensional spectra of two coincident α-particles in order to be able to separate the contributions of the various processes.

We will discuss these arguments separately:

i) Figure 1 shows a typical spectrum of the α-particles taken at $E_d = 0.8$ MeV and 90° in the laboratory system.

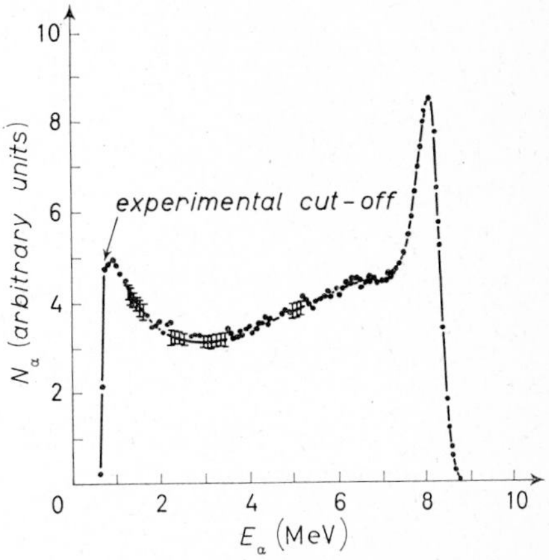

Fig. 1. – Typical α-spectrum from the ^{7}Li+d reactions, $\theta = 90°$, $E_d = 0.8$ MeV.

We attributed the high-energy peak to the first of the reactions (4), as done by other authors [3, 5]. We extracted the angular distributions of these α-particles taking into account only the part of the peak at the right of the maximum.

The first results we obtained show angular distributions completely symmetrical about 90° in the c.m. system. They can be well represented by

$$W(\theta, E_d) = a(E_d) + b(E_d) \cos^2 \Theta$$

in the range $0.8 < E_d < 1.6$ MeV in the laboratory system.

There are not appreciable contributions from higher powers of the cosine within the range of the experimental errors. These errors are of the order of 5 % and arise mainly from the uncertainty in fixing the position of the maximum of the experimental peak.

The values of the ratio b/a at various energies are reported in Table I.

This trend denotes a compound nucleus mechanism for the ^{7}Li(d, α_0)^{5}He reaction with interference of states of the same parity. The same conclusion can be reached for the reactions (3) by examining the angular distributions of the neutrons that leave ^{8}Be in the ground and first excited state [1].

The fact that these reactions proceed mainly by compound-nucleus formation can be understood if we consider that the momentum transfer in going

TABLE I. – *Anisotropy ratio of the angular distributions of the α-particles from the* ^{7}Li(d, α_0)^{5}He *reaction.*

E_d (MeV)	b/a
0.8	-0.38
1.2	-0.30
1.4	$+0.57$
1.6	$+0.85$

from the initial state to the final one is large compared to the internal momentum of the neutron in the deuteron or in ^{9}Be and to that of a ^{3}T cluster in ^{7}Li, so excluding appreciable contributions of stripping, heavy-particle stripping and pick-up mechanism.

(In reaction (2) there is not such a momentum transfer and it does in fact proceed by stripping mechanism [6].)

The fact that the angular distributions in reactions (3) and (4) show strong contributions of a $\cos^2\Theta$ term and no one of $\cos^4\Theta$, etc. terms indicates that the deuteron interacts in a *p*-state. Since ^{7}Li has odd parity in its ground state we can conclude that ^{9}Be* is formed in even parity levels, that is nonnormal parity levels, requiring a neutron in a *d*-state.

The angular distributions are moreover consistent with a choice $J \geqslant \frac{3}{2}$ for the angular momentum of at least one of the interfering levels.

These results are all in agreement with the almost complete absence of compound nucleus contribution to the ^{7}Li(d, p_0)^{8}Li reaction.

ii) As regards the contribution of the three-body break-up to the spectra it was estimated in ref. [3] to be of the order of 10% in the region of the peak due to reaction (4).

In order to check this result we did two-dimensional coincidences between α-particles fixing one of the detectors at 90° in the laboratory system with respect to the incident deuterons and varying the angle of the other detector as shown in Fig. 2.

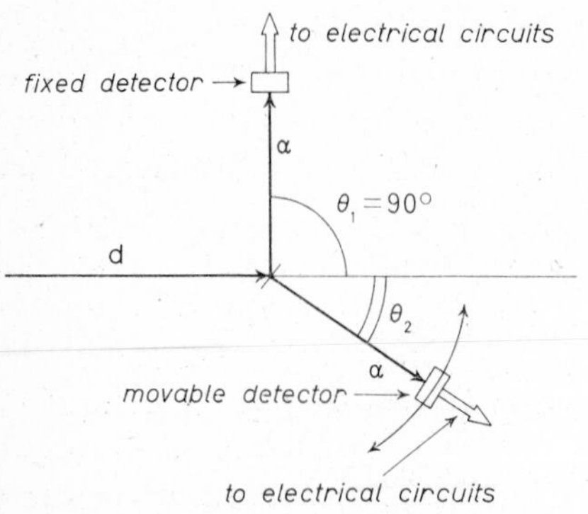

Fig. 2. – Experimental set-up.

In Fig. 3 is shown the bidimensional spectrum obtained by putting the movable detector at $\theta_2 = 77°$ that is the angle kinematically conjugated to 90° in the reaction ^{7}Li(d, α_0)^{5}He. In other words, if the decay of the ^{9}Be* proceeds by the two-stage process indicated in (4), then, if the α_0-particle that leaves

^{5}He in its ground state goes along the 90° direction, the recoiling ^{5}He is initially emitted at $\theta_2 = 77°$. About the same angle is that at which the α_0-particle is emitted when the ^{5}He is emitted at 90°, because of the very large momenta of the emitted particles with respect to the incident one.

The dashed curve reported in Fig. 3 is the kinematical one.

The α-particles due to the reactions (3), (4) and (5) must lie on it. The continuous curves are the lines of equal number of pulses per unit energy intervals. As we can see, the pulses are grouped around the intersections of the kinematical curve with the lines a) and b) drawn through the points at which the high-energy peaks appear in the spectra of the α-particles (see Fig. 1). This behavior is typical of a two-stage decay: so we can conclude that a ^{5}He cluster is very likely to be formed within ^{9}Be* at these excitation energies ($\sim$ 17 MeV), as it seems to be at 2.43 MeV excitation [2].

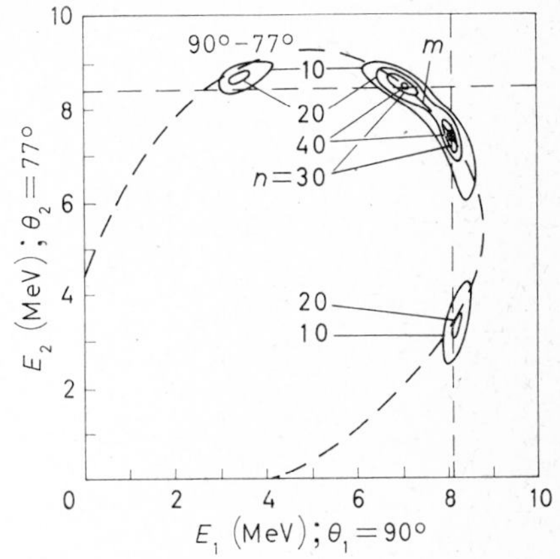

Fig. 3. – Two-dimensional display of the α-pulses from the ^{7}Li+d reactions when $\theta_1 = 90°$ and $\theta_2 = 77°$.

The three-body break-up is, on the contrary, very unlikely. Referring in fact to the c.m. system of the reaction (5) we can write for the probability per unit time that the two alphas are emitted at (θ_1, φ_1) and (θ_2, φ_2) with energies E_1 and E_2, respectively:

$$dP \,\tilde{\propto}\, |M|^2 E_1^{\frac{1}{2}} E_2^{\frac{1}{2}} \delta(E_2 - E_{20})\, dE_1\, dE_2\, d\Omega_1\, d\Omega_2 \,,$$

where $M = M(E_1, E_2, \theta_1, \varphi_1, \theta_2, \varphi_2)$ is the matrix element for the transition from the initial to the final states and E_{20} is the value of E_2 allowed by kinematics when $E_1, \theta_1, \varphi_1, \theta_2, \varphi_2$ are fixed.

In the very simple case that $M = \text{const}$ we must expect a maximum at $E_1 = E_2$ in the c.m. system, that is in the region indicated by m in Fig. 3.

However in every case we would expect that the alpha-particles produced in reaction (5) have energies such to cover the most part of the kinematical curve. On the contrary, the experimental data show that around this curve, with the exception of the region of the points due to reaction (4), the number of coincidences per unit energy intervals does not differ from that expected by chance. So the three-body break-up is perhaps even less probable than it was extimated.

Longer measurements are necessary to make precise conclusions about this point. However, we make the hypothesis that the peak in the spectrum of Fig. 1 is due almost entirely to $^7Li(d, \alpha_0)^5He$ reaction [3]. Under this hypothesis we can calculate the contribution to the spectrum of Fig. 1 of the α-particles from the two stages of reaction (4), taking into account the results of the angular correlation, reported in Fig. 4.

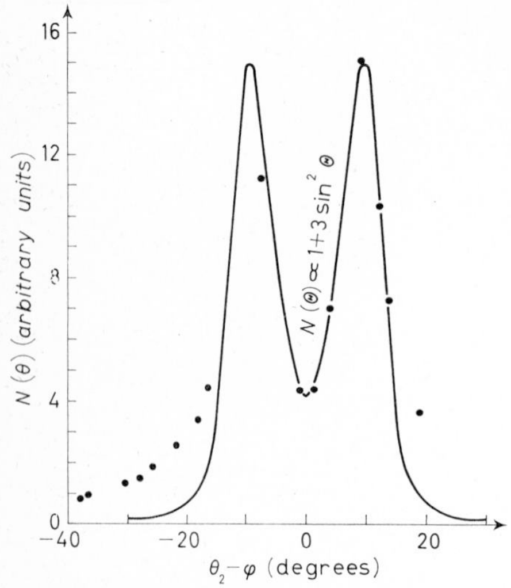

Fig. 4. – α-α correlation for the ^7Li+d reactions.

In this figure we report the number of coincidences between two particles emitted respectively at $\theta_1 = 90°$ and various θ_2 at $E_d = 0.8$ MeV. Calling φ the angle conjugated to 90° we have $\varphi = 77°$.

In Fig. 4 the points are the experimental ones and the curve is the calculated one under the hypothesis that ^5He decays in flight, emitting an α-particle with an angular distribution (in the system in which ^5He is at rest), given by

$$W(\Theta) \propto 1 + 3 \sin^2 \Theta .$$

As we see, this result also is consistent with the conclusion that the most part of the high-energy α-particles are emitted in a two-stage decay of $^9Be^*$ of the type (4). The points which do not fall on the calculated curve can be perhaps due to reactions (3) or to $^7Li(d, \alpha')^5He^*$ reaction.

Using now the information taken from the angular correlation, we can calculate the spectrum of the two alphas coming from reaction (4), which is reported in Fig. 5.

Curve *a*) in Fig. 5 represents the contribution of the α_0-particles, calculated as in ref. [3] and corrected for the finite resolving power of the experimental device.

Curve *b*) gives that of the α-particles emitted in the subsequent decay of ^5He and *c*) is the sum of the two contributions.

Curve *c*) contains about 50% of the experimental spectrum. The other part can

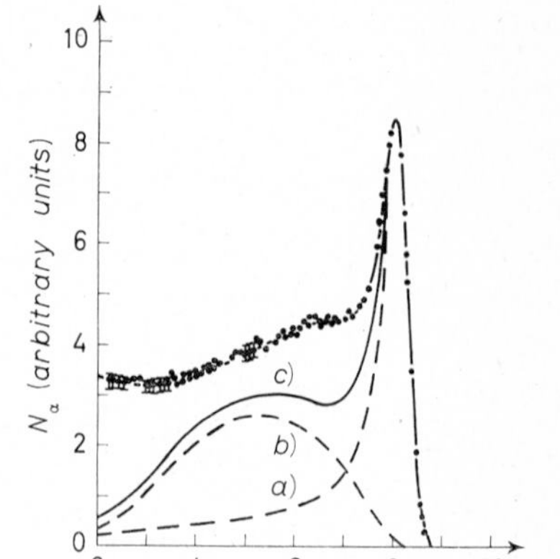

Fig. 5. – The α-spectrum from $^7Li(d, \alpha)$ reactions at $\theta = 90°$ analysed in its components (see text), $E_d = 0.8$ MeV.

be attributed to reactions (2, 3) at least at energies below 4 MeV. At higher energies there is some possibility of ^{7}Li(d, α')^{5}He* contribution.

iii) Concluding we may say that the ^{9}Be nucleus at these excitation energies is likely to be in cluster states of the form ^{8}Be-n or ^{4}He-^{5}He. The existence of ^{4}He-^{4}He-n states is not very clear and perhaps can be ruled out in this energy region. It seems as the neutron in the aspherical states *p* or *d* tends to bind itself to one of the α-clusters, so giving a strong probability to the ^{4}He-^{5}He clustering, at the expenses of the three-body break-up. The ^{12}C nucleus, on the contrary, seems to show a large probability of forming three-cluster states.

We may suppose that this behavior is perhaps due to the fact that the three α-particles in this case are in a spherical *s*-state. This is in agreement with the fact that the three-body break-up of ^{9}Be seems to be much more probable at higher excitation energies [7] where the 2*s* states of the neutron begin to be populated.

However some calculations based on a definite model are necessary to explain this point.

REFERENCES

[1] C. Milone and R. Potenza: *Nucl. Phys.* (1966) (in press).
[2] D. Bodansky, S. F. Eccles and I. Halpern: *Phys. Rev.*, **108**, 1019 (1957).
[3] G. Weber: *Phys. Rev.*, **110**, 529 (1958).
[4] W. E. Dorenbusch and C. P. Browne: *Phys. Rev.*, **132**, 1759 (1963).
[5] P. Paul and D. Kohler: *Phys. Rev.*, **129**, 2699 (1963).
[6] J. P. F. Sellschop: *Phys. Rev.*, **119**, 251 (1960).
[7] V. Gillet: (private communication).

PROCEEDINGS OF THE INTERNATIONAL SCHOOL OF PHYSICS
« ENRICO FERMI »

Course XIV
Ergodic Theories
edited by P. CALDIROLA

Course XV
Nuclear Spectroscopy
edited by G. RACAH

Course XVI
Physicomathematical Aspects of Biology
edited by N. RASHEVSKY

Course XVII
Topics of Radiofrequency Spectroscopy
edited by A. GOZZINI

Course XVIII
Physics of Solids (Radiation Damage in Solids)
edited by D. S. BILLINGTON

Course XIX
Cosmic Rays, Solar Particles and Space Research
edited by B. PETERS

Course XX
Evidence for Gravitational Theories
edited by C. MØLLER

Course XXI
Liquid Helium
edited by G. CARERI

Course XXII
Semiconductors
edited by R. A. SMITH

Course XXIII
Nuclear Physics
edited by V. F. WEISSKOPF

Course XXIV
Space Exploration and the Solar System
edited by B. ROSSI

Course XXV
Advanced Plasma Theory
edited by M. N. ROSENBLUTH

Course XXVI
Selected Topics on Elementary Particle Physics
edited by M. CONVERSI

Course XXVII
Dispersion and Absorption of Sound by Molecular Processes
edited by D. SETTE

Course XXVIII
Star Evolution
edited by L. GRATTON

Course XXIX
Dispersion Relations and Their Connection with Causality
edited by E. P. WIGNER

Course XXX
Radiation Dosimetry
edited by F. W. SPIERS and G. W. REED

Course XXXI
Quantum Electronics and Coherent Light
edited by C. H. TOWNES and P. A. MILES

Course XXXII
Weak Interactions and High-Energy Neutrino Physics
edited by T. D. LEE

Course XXXIII
Strong Interactions
edited by L. W. ALVAREZ

Course XXXIV
The Optical Properties of Solids
edited by J. TAUC

Course XXXV
High-Energy Astrophysics
edited by L. GRATTON

Information about Courses I-XIII may be obtained from the Italian Physical Society.

Tipografia Compositori - Bologna - Italy